C000030780

UNDERGRADUATE PHYSICS
[Vol. II]

*For the Undergraduate (General) students of Physics and Engineering
of all Indian Universities as also for GATE, SET and NET candidates*

UNDERGRADUATE PHYSICS

[Vol. II]

[Containing Electrostatics, Magnetostatics, Current Electricity,
Physical Optics, Electronics and Modern Physics]

Dr A. B. Bhattacharya MSc, PhD, FIETE

Professor, Department of Physics, University of Kalyani
Formerly in the Department of Physics, Serampore College, Serampore

Dr R. Bhattacharya MSc, PhD

Reader, Department of Environmental Science, University of Kalyani
Formerly in the Department of Physics, K. N. College, Berhampore, Murshidabad

New Central Book Agency (P) Ltd

8/1 Chintamoni Das Lane, Kolkata 700 009
INDIA

Front Cover : Simulation of a Depressed Collector
Back Cover : Surface Plot of Bose-Einstein Condensate

Undergraduate Physics
[Vol. II]

First Published : January 2008

Copyright reserved by the Authors

Publication, Distribution, and Promotion Rights reserved by
New Central Book Agency (P) Ltd

No part of this publication may be reproduced in any form
or by any means, without the written permission of the Publisher

ISBN : 81-7381-563-1

Publisher : New Central Book Agency (P) Ltd
            8/1 Chintamoni Das Lane, Kolkata 700 009

Typesetter : Anin
            BC 97, Sector I, Salt Lake, Kolkata 700 064

Printer : New Central Book Agency (P) Ltd
            Web-Offset Division, Dhulagarh, Sankrail, Howrah

Cover Designer : Soumen Paul

Cover Printer : Liba Graphics
            90C Christopher Road, Kolkata 700 046

Proof Checking : Pradip Kr. Chowdhury and Authors

Technical Editor : Dipan Roy

Project Team : Prabhat Jas and Somenath Ganguly

Price : [Rupees Three Hundred and Twenty-five only]

32.00

Contents

Magnetostatics

Current Electricity

Electronics

Modern Physics

Preface

Our 'Undergraduate Physics' Volume II, similar to the Volume I, is also written essentially on the basis of the syllabi of different Indian Universities; recently revised and modernised following the suggestions of the University Grants Commission (UGC). This volume includes 'Electrostatics', 'Magnetostatics', 'Current Electricity', 'Physical Optics', 'Electronics' and 'Modern Physics'.

Like our other presentations we have given highest priority to clarity of the subjects and conciseness. For a lucid presentation of the physical concepts and principles, the book has been well-illustrated with self-explanatory diagrams. A large number of typical worked-out problems have been given at the end of each chapter. Many essay-type, short answer-type questions and numerical problems including those of different university examinations have been given as exercise in each chapter. The readers of the text will thus be able to equip themselves with the modern trend of questions and their corresponding answers in the examinations. In addition, a large number of short questions with answers have been incorporated at the end of each section to make the text more useful for different competitive entrance examinations like GATE, SET and NET examinations.

We sincerely acknowledge our debt to the authors whose standard works we have freely consulted during the long preparation of our manuscript. We gratefully acknowledge the suggestions given by our colleagues of various degree colleges. We express our sincere thanks to Mr. Amitabha Sen, Director, New Central Book Agency (P) Ltd, for his personal interest and efforts at all stages of production. Our special thanks are due to Mr. Dipan Roy, Technical Editor, and Mr. Pradip Kumar Chowdhury for their careful and sincere editing and proof-reading throughout. Our thanks are also due to Mr. Prabhat Jas and Mr. Soumen Paul for their active role during the course of production and printing.

We hope to get suggestions and comments from the interested readers of this book so that we can improve the volume by incorporating those in the subsequent edition.

25 December, 2007   **Authors**
Kolkata

Syllabi

[For B.Sc. Three-year General Course]

Calcutta University

(Only SI units to be used.)

Physical Optics   20 lectures

1. **Light as an electromagnetic wave**, full electromagnetic spectrum, properties of electromagnetic waves. Huygens' principle—explanation of the laws of reflection and refraction.

2. **Interference of light** : Young's experiment, intensity distribution, conditions of interference. Interference in thin films—Newton's ring.

3. **Diffraction** : Fresnel and Fraunhofer class, Fresnel's half-period zones—zone plate.

4. **Fraunhofer diffraction** due to single slit and plane transmission grating (elementary theory)—resolving power.

5. **Polarization** : Different states of polarization, Brewster's law, double refraction, retardation plate, polaroid, optical activity.

Electrostatics   60 lectures

(Use of vector should be encouraged.)

1. **Electrostatics** : Quantization of charge—Millikan's oil-drop experiment, Coulomb's law, intensity and potential—example of point charge, Gauss' theorem—simple applications, potential and field due to an electric dipole, mechanical force on the surface of a charged conductor. Dielectric medium, Polarization, electric displacement.

2. **Capacitor** : Parallel plates and cylindrical, energy stored in parallel plate capacitor.

3. **Magnetic materials** : Intensity of magnetization, relation between $\vec{B}, \vec{H}$ and $\vec{M}$—illustration in the case of bar magnet, magnetic susceptibility dia-, para- and ferromagnetic materials—statement of Curie's law. Hysteresis in ferromagnetic material—hysteresis loss.

Electricity

1. **Steady current** : Network analysis—Kirchhoff's laws, Thevenin and Norton's theorem; Wheatstone bridge, potentiometer.

2. **Magnetic effect of current** : Biot and Savart's law, Ampere's circuital law (statement only), magnetic field due to straight conductor, circular coil, solenoid, endless solenoid; magnetic field due to a small current loop—concept of magnetic dipole, Ampere's equivalence theorem. Lorentz force, force on a current-carrying conductor in a magnetic field, torque on a rectangular current loop in a uniform magnetic field.

3. **Electromagnetic induction** : Self and mutual inductances in simple cases, energy stored in inductance.

4. **Varying currents :** Growth and decay of currents in LR circuit; charging and discharging of capacitor in CR circuit.

5. **Alternating current :** Mean and r.m.s. values of current and e.m.f. with sinusoidal waveform; LR, CR and series LCR circuits, reactance, impedance, phase-angle, power dissipation in a.c. circuit—power factor, vector diagram, resonance in a series LCR circuit, Q-factor, principle of ideal transformer.

6. **Thermoelectricity :** Seebeck, Peltier and Thomson effects, laws of thermoelectricity, thermoelectric curve—neutral and inversion temperature, thermoelectric power.

Electronics   15 lectures

1. **P-N junction diode**—bridge rectifier; capacitance input filter, Zener diode—voltage regulator. Transistors—α and β and their interrelations, output characteristics in CE mode, single-stage CE amplifier—approximate expressions of current and voltage gain with the help of 'Load Line'.

2. **Digital circuits :** Binary systems, binary numbers, decimal to binary and binary to decimal conversions, binary addition and subtraction.

3. **Logic gates :** OR, AND, NOT gates—truth tables. Statement of de Morgan's theorem, NOR and NAND as universal gates.

Modern Physics   30 lectures

1. **Postulates of special theory of relativity,** Formula (i) Length contraction, (ii) Time dilation, (iii) Velocity addition, (iv) Mass variation and (v) Mass-Energy equivalence.

2. **Quantum theory of radiation :** Planck's concept—radiation formula (statement only)—qualitative discussions of photoelectric effect and Compton effect in support of quantum theory, Raman effect.

3. **Wave nature of material particles,** wave-particle duality, wavelength of de Broglie wave, Heisenberg uncertainty principle, Schrödinger equation; particle in one-dimensional infinite well—energy eigenvalue, wave function and its probabilistic interpretation.

4. **Bohr's theory of hydrogen spectra :** Concept of quantum number, Pauli exclusion principle.

5. **Crystalline nature** of solid, diffraction of X-rays, Bragg's law; Mosley's law—explanation from Bohr's theory.

6. **Binding energy of nucleons :** Binding energy curve and stability, Radio-activity—successive disintegration—radioactive equilibrium, radioactive dating, radioisotopes and their uses, Nuclear transmutation—fission and fusion—nuclear reactor.

Total—125 lectures

Burdwan University

Electromagnetism

(SI units and modern symbols are to be used.)

[Electromagnetism is a single subject of electricity and magnetism. An electric charge appears to be static w.r.t. one observer and moving w.r.t. another. First observer finds only electric field E but the second detects simultaneous existence of both electric field E and magnetic field B. An electric current I (moving charge) transports electric charge q and sets up magnetic field B too. Then a suitable choice of unit for I will lead to consistent units of both q and B.]

Electrostatics (both q and E static) : Electric field, force on a charge q, Millikan's oil-drop experiment, idea of quantized charge and value of e, the electronic charge, conservation of electric charge; electric dipole placed in electric field; Gauss's law : $\epsilon_0 \int_S \vec{E} \cdot \vec{ds} = q_{\text{total}} \rightarrow \vec{\Delta} \cdot \vec{E} = \frac{\rho}{\epsilon_0}$ (Maxwell's 1st equation), $\epsilon_0 = 8.95 \times 10^{-12}$ $C^2 N^{-1}$ m^{-2} or, $\frac{1}{4\pi\epsilon_0} = 9 \times 10^9$ Nm^2 C^{-2} (experimentally determined from Coulomb's law) application of Gauss's law to simple cases (charged line, cylinder, sphere—hollow and solid, sheet and conductor); line integral of electric field, electric potential V, $\vec{E} = \vec{\Delta} V$, $\vec{\nabla} \times E = 0$ and electrostatic field conservative; potential and field at any point due to electric dipole.   8

Dielectric and capacitor : Polarization and three electric vectors $\vec{E}$, $\vec{F}$ and $\vec{D}$, polarizability, $\vec{D} = \epsilon_0 \vec{E} + \vec{P}$; Gauss's law in dielectric, dielectric constant, parallel plate and cylindrical capacitors with dielectric inside, energy density in electric field.   5

Magnetostatics (Magnetic field B static) : Defining equation of $\vec{B}$ (magnetic induction vector), the fundamental magnetic vector—$\vec{F} = q \cdot \vec{v} \times \vec{B}$ or, $\vec{F} = \vec{H} \times \vec{B}$, Lorentz force equation, Thomson experiment for $\frac{e}{m}$; Dempster's mass spectrometer; non-existence of magnetic monopole—$\vec{\nabla} \cdot \vec{B} = 0$ (Maxwell's 2nd equation), i.e., no source of magnetic field, causes of magnetic field B: electric current, electromagnet, permanent magnet, time-varying electric field, some atoms, molecules and some elementary particles.

Materials and magnetization : Three magnetic vectors—$\vec{B}$, $\vec{M}$, $\vec{H}$; $\vec{H} = \frac{\vec{B}}{\mu_0} - \vec{M}$ and illustration referred to a bar magnet; susceptibility and relative permeability; dia-, para- and ferromagnetic properties, idea of domain theory, statement of Curie's law; hysteresis and hysteresis loss.   5

Wave-optics and Laser

Huygens' principle : Idea of wavefronts—plane, spherical and cylindrical; secondary wavelets, construction and propagation of wavefront.

Interference : Young's experiment, intensity redistribution, condition of stable interference—pattern, coherent source, interference by division of amplitude and Newton's ring experiment, interference by division of wavefront and experiment with Fresnel's biprism; idea of coherence-time and coherence-length.   5

Diffraction : Fresnel and Fraunhofer classes, Fresnel's half-period zones, zone plate, explanation of rectilinear propagation of light and zone plate; Fraunhofer diffraction in single slit, double slit and plane diffraction grating (simple theory).

Resolving power and the Rayleigh criterion for resolution (statement), grating spectra versus prism spectra. 6

Polarization : Transverse nature of light (e.m.) wave, different states of polarization, plane polarized light, Brewster's law, double refraction, uniaxial crystal, polaroid and Nicol prism (qualitative functions); optical activity and rotation of plane of polarization. 6

Laser : Spontaneous and stimulated emission, Einstein's A and B coefficients; idea of population inversion, principle of laser, laser versus ordinary light. 3

Electricity

Unit of electric current : Ampere (A), the fundamental SI unit of electromagnetism. Definition of 1 A in terms of force between two long straight filamentary parallel currents; 1 coulomb = 1 A × 1 sec, the charge transported by 1 A in 1 second—derived SI unit of electric charge. 1

Direct current (steady) : Electric current density $\vec{J}, I = \int \vec{J} \cdot d\vec{S}$ and equation of continuity; voltage source and current source, linear passive circuit elements. Kirchhoff's laws and analysis of multiloop circuits; Thevenin and Norton theorems (statements and explanation) and reduction of two-terminal linear network, calculation of galvanometer current in an unbalanced Wheatstone bridge with ideal voltage source by Thevenin theorem; applications of Wheatstone bridge principle; potentiometer—principle and applications. 8

Biot-Savart law, Ampere's law in magnetostatics $\int \vec{B} \cdot d\vec{l} = \mu_0 I$ (enclosed) $\rightarrow \vec{\Delta} \times \vec{B} = \mu_0 \vec{J}$, B due to long straight filamentary current, force between two long parallel currents and $\mu_0 = 4\pi \times 10^{-7}$ NA^{-2} (assigned value); B on the axis of circular current, solenoidal current and toroidal current. Torque on a current loop in uniform B, magnetic moment of a magnetic dipole, equivalence of current loop with magnetic dipole. 10

Electromagnetic induction : Magnetic flux $\phi_S = \int_S \vec{B} \cdot \vec{ds}$, flux-linkage with a coil of N turns, Faraday's law and Lenz's law of electromagnetic induction, $e_{\text{ind}} = -\frac{\partial \varphi}{\partial t}$, for a single turn, integral form $\oint \vec{E} \cdot d\vec{l} = -\frac{\partial}{\partial t} \int_S \vec{B} \cdot \vec{ds}$, using Stokes' theorem; differential form $\vec{\Delta} \times \vec{E} = -\frac{\partial \vec{B}}{\partial t}$ (Maxwell's 3rd equation); self and mutual inductances and calculation of L for circular and solenoidal coils; energy stored in current-carrying inductor and energy density in magnetic field. 5

Direct current (varying) : Growth and decay of current in LR circuit, charging and discharging of a capacitor through a resistor using voltage source. 3

Alternating current (steady state) : Sinusoidal voltage and current, mean and effective (r.m.s.) values, steady-state solution (using complex quantity) for current in LR and CR series circuit excited by sinusoidal voltage; reactance, impedance, phase angle and phasor diagram; power analysis and power factor; resonance in series RLC and parallel RLC circuit (using complex quantity and phasor diagram), sharpness of resonance including Q-factor and bandwidth; basic idea about transformer. 8

Electromagnetic waves : Laws of electromagnetism before Maxwell : $\vec{\Delta} \cdot \vec{E} = \frac{\rho}{E_0}, \vec{\Delta} \cdot \vec{B} = 0, \vec{\Delta} \times \vec{E} = -\frac{\partial \vec{B}}{\partial t}$ and $\vec{\Delta} \times \vec{B} = \mu_0 \vec{J}$ (only expressions), introduction of displacement current density $\frac{\partial \vec{B}}{\partial t}$ and Maxwell's equations : $\vec{\Delta} \cdot \vec{E} = \frac{\rho}{\epsilon_0}$,

$\vec{\Delta} \cdot \vec{B} = 0$, $\vec{\Delta} \times \vec{E} = -\frac{\partial \vec{B}}{\partial t}$ and $\vec{\Delta} \times \vec{B} = \mu_0 \left(\vec{\delta} + \frac{\partial \vec{D}}{\partial t} \right)$ (electromagnetic wave equations in free space), wave-speed $= \frac{1}{\sqrt{\mu_0 \epsilon_0}} = 3 \times 10^8$ m-sec^{-1} = speed of light in free space and wave nature of light. $\qquad$ 2

Modern Physics

Special theory of relativity : Reference frames, postulates of special theory of relativity, Lorentz transformation formula (only explanation) and consequences such as length contraction and time dilatation; relativistic transformation of velocity and mass, mass-energy relation and total energy, zero and finite rest masses.

Experiments of quantum physics : Failure of classical physics to explain black-body radiation, photoelectric effect, Compton effect, Raman effect, etc., and success of quantum theory (qualitative discussion only); Bohr's theory of hydrogen spectra, principle quantum numbers, limitations, correspondence principle, qualitative introduction of four quantum numbers and Pauli's exclusion principle; wave-particle duality, de Broglie wavelength, Davison and Germer experiment. Superposition of two waves, wave packet and group velocity; Heisenberg's uncertainty relation (statement and explanation). Idea of wave function and Schrödinger equation (time-dependent and time-independent parts), interpretation of wave function in term of probability, just mention of the remarkable results of application of Schrödinger equation (A) particle in a box, (B) linear harmonic oscillator and (C) barrier penetration problem.

Crystal nature of solid, diffraction of X-rays, Bragg's law; Moseley's law and its importance.

Nuclear physics : Nuclear mass, size, nucleons and binding energy; binding energy—mass number curve and explanation of stability, fission and fusion of nuclei; radioactive disintegration, successive equilibrium, radio isotopes and uses; nuclear reactor, nuclear reaction, thermonuclear reaction and stellar energy; basic information about some elementary particles; principles of operations of G-M counter as detector and cyclotron as accelerator.

Solid State Devices and Electronics

Semiconductor physics : Qualitative ideas of energy bands at 0K, generation of hole-electron pairs at room temperature and intrinsic semiconductor, carrier density, doping and impurity semiconductor, majority and minority carriers, P-type and N-type semiconductor, advantage of silicon, germanium as semiconductor device material; P-N junction and properties (depletion region, barrier voltage, barrier width and junction capacitance).

Devices and circuits : Junction diode—forward and reverse characteristic diode equation (I-V expression only), a.c. and d.c. resistances of a diode; use of diode as rectifier, qualitative explanation of use of capacity filter properties and uses of Zener and light-emitting diodes, bipolar junction transistor (N-P-N and P-N-P), current components in a transistor under normal bias and current gain α, CE output characteristics and current gain β; use of transistor as CE amplifier, basic idea of feedback in amplifier and principles of oscillator.

Digital electronics : Binary numbers, binary-decimal interconversion, binary addition; OR, AND and NOT gates. de Morgan's theorem, NOR and NAND universal gates, XOR gates, half adder and full adder (using half adders).

[Problems related to physical theories to be covered.]

Kalyani University

Electricity and Magnetism

(3 questions to be set, 2 to be answered.)

1. **Electrostatics :** Electrostatic field and potentials; calculation of these quantities for point charges and simple charge distributions; lines of force and flux; Gauss's theorem and simple applications; Laplace's and Poisson's equations; applications to simple one-dimensional problems only; electrostatic field energy; dielectric medium; polarization; dielectric constant; capacitance and condensers—energy density in dielectrics; electric dipoles; principles of electrometers—attracted disc and quadrant electrometers. (10)

2. **Stationary currents :** Ohm's law and application to circuits; Kirchhoff's law and simple networks (including Wheatstone's bridge and potentiometers); ammeters, voltmeters. (3)

3. **Thermal and chemical effects of currents :** Faraday's laws of electrolysis; thermoelectric effects—Seebeck, Peltier and Thomson; thermoelectric curves and power. (3)

4. **Magnetic effects of currents :** Biot-Savart's law; Ampere's circuital law; application to simple geometries; solenoids; closed current loops; moving-coil galvanometer—ammeter and voltmeter. (4)

5. **Magnetism :** Magnetic moment; dipoles in external magnetic field; magnetic induction and magnetic field intensity; magnetic susceptibility; origin and comparative study of dia-, para- and ferromagnetisms; terrestrial magnetism, Lorentz force and applications. (5)

6. **Non-stationary current :** Faraday's laws of electromagnetic induction; elementary applications, self and mutual inductance; electromagnets; hysteresis loss; transients (L-R, C-R and L-C-R circuits). (5)

7. **Alternating currents and voltages :** R.M.S. values; impedances and phases; power factor; L-R, C-R and L-C-R circuits, power generation and transmission; working principle of generators, transformers and electrical motors. (5)

Optics

(3 questions to be set, 2 to be answered.)

1. **Wave theory of light :** Huygens' principle; and reflection and refraction plane surfaces from Huygens' principle.

2. **Interference :** Principle of superposition, Young's double-slit experiment; conditions of interference; division of wavefront—Fresnel's bi-prism and Lloyd's mirror, division of amplitude—thin films and Newton's rings. (4)

3. **Diffraction :** Qualitative discussion of half-period zones and rectilinear propagation of light, zone plate; Fraunhofer and Fresnel diffractions; Fraunhofer diffraction—single slit, double slit, plane grating, circular aperture (descriptive and qualitative); Rayleigh criterion and resolving power of optical instruments. (8)

4. **Polarization :** Production and detection of polarized light; polarization by reflection and refraction; Nicol's prism; polarization by selective absorption;

polarization by scattering; retardation plates, blue of the sky; circular and elliptic polarization; optical activity and polarimeter. (5)

5. **Optical effects :** Zeeman effect; Faraday effect (qualitative discussion). (3)

6. **Spectroscopy :** Emission and absorption spectra; prism spectroscopy in visible, ultraviolet and infrared regions; different types of spectrometers and interferometers. (4)

Modern Physics I
(3 questions to be set, 2 to be answered.)

1. **Electromagnetic theory :** Maxwell's equations in vacuum describing electromagnetic effects in terms of fields generated by free charges and currents using Ampere's circuital theorem, the displacement currents and the law of e.m. induction. Electromagnetic waves in vacuum, wave equation in one dimension, plane wave solution, transverse nature of e.m. waves, Hertz experiment, Poynting theorem and Poynting vector (one dimension). Momentum in e.m. waves (statement only), the pressure of light—Nicol's and Hull experiment. (6)

2. **Special theory of relativity :** Postulates of special relativity, Lorentz transformation equations (no derivation), length contraction. Mehelson-Morley experiment, time dilatation, simultaneity, relativistic expressions of total energy, rest energy, kinetic energy and momentum and relations between them, velocity addition theorem, mass-energy equivalence, relativistic Doppler effect. (5)

3. **Quantum theory and atoms :** (a) The photoelectric effect; line spectra and Bohr's theory of the hydrogen atom, Franck-Hertz experiment. (2)

(b) The X-ray spectrum, continuous and characteristic radiation, Moseley's law and its importance, diffraction of X-rays by a crystal lattice, Bragg's law; Compton effect. (3)

(c) Matter waves and de Broglie's relation between wavelength and momentum of a moving particle, wave and group velocity, experimental verification by electron diffraction (Davison and Germer expt.), Bohr's quantum condition in terms of de Broglie waves. (4)

(d) The Schrödinger wave equation in one dimension (time-independent and time-dependent; statement only); interpretation of wave function and concept of stationary states; the uncertainty principle, verification by thought expt. (Young's expt.). Particle moving in an one-dimensional box with infinitely high potential barrier; particle crossing a potential barrier, tunnelling. (6)

(e) Vector atom model; Stern-Gerlach exp., alkali spectra (qualitative discussion), periodic table and Pauli exclusion principle. (4)

Modern Physics II
(3 questions to be set, 2 to be answered.)

1. **Radioactivity :** Alpha, beta and gamma rays; nature of these rays; laws of radioactive decay; successive decay and radioactive equilibrium (secular). (3)

2. **Atoms :** Discovery of the electron; Thomson's experiment and Millikan's oil-drop experiment, positive rays; atomic weight and atomic number; (Aston's)

mass spectrograph (principles only) and measurement of atomic masses; isotopes. (4)

3. **Atomic nucleus :**

(a) Rutherford's experiment (no derivation of formula); constituents of nucleus; discovery of the neutron; properties of the proton and the neutron. (2)

(b) Nuclear gross properties; binding energy; nuclear energy levels; qualitative discussions about nuclear structure (liquid-drop and shell models). (3)

(c) Nuclear decays, disintegrations and reactions; alpha and beta decays—systematics and characteristics of nuclear reactions; fission and nuclear reactors; fusion; artificial disintegration. (3)

(d) Accelerators—linear and cyclic—cyclotron (basic principles). (2)

(e) Nuclear detectors. (2)

4. **Electronics :**

(a) Thermionic emission; diode, triode and other multielectrode valves. (2)

(b) Semiconductors, semiconductor junctions and bipolar transistors. (2)

(c) Valve and transistor characteristics—load lines. (2)

(d) Basic rectifier and amplifier circuits. (2)

(e) Feedback and basic oscillator circuits. (2)

(f) Simple ideas about modulation and demodulation—transmission and reception of radiowaves (block diagrams only). (2)

North Bengal University

Physical Optics :

1. **Wave theory of light :** Huygens' principle, explanation of reflection and refraction. Electromagnetic theory of light, propagation of electromagnetic waves, Maxwell's theory of wave propagation (physical interpretation).

2. **Interference of light :** Young's experiment, intensity distribution, conditions of interference; Fresnel's bi-prism; interference in thin films—Newton's ring.

3. **Diffraction of light :** Classes of diffraction, Fresnel's half-period zones, zone plate. Fraunhofer diffraction due to single slit, double slit and a plane diffraction grating (elementary theory). Resolving power of optical instruments.

4. **Polarization of light :** Different states of polarization, plane-polarized light by reflection, refraction and double refraction in crystals, Nicol prism, retardation plates, elliptically and circularly polarized light—production and analysis. Optical activity, elementary discussion of Faraday effect.

Electricity and Magnetism (40)

Electrostatics :

1. **Electrostatic field :** Quantization of charge, conservation of electric charge, Coulomb's law, intensity and potential, potential of a charge distribution, derivation of field from potential, energy of charge distribution. Gauss' theorem and its application in the determination of electric field due to line distribution of charge, surface distribution of charge and spherical distribution of charge; electric dipole—field and potential due to an electric dipole.

2. **Dielectric :** Polar and non-polar dielectrics, electric polarization, electric displacement, Gauss' law in the presence of dielectric.

3. **Conductors, capacity and capacitors :** Field near the surface of a charged conductor, mechanical force on the surface of a charged conductor. Capacity of parallel plate, spherical and cylindrical capacitors, energy stored in a capacitor. Force between two plates of a parallel plate capacitor—absolute electrometer and its use.

Current Electricity :

1. **Steady current :** Network analysis—Kirchhoff's laws, Thevenin and Norton's theorem, Wheatstone bridge, Carey-Foster bridge, Potentiometer.

2. **Magnetic effect of current :** Force on a moving charge; Lorentz force equation and definition of force on a straight conductor carrying current in a uniform magnetic field, torque on a current loop, magnetic dipole moment. Biot and Savart's law, Ampere's circuital law (statement only), magnetic field due to straight conductor, circular coil, solenoid, endless solenoid; Galvanometers—moving-coil galvanometer, ballistic galvanometer (moving-coil type).

3. **Electromagnetic induction and varying currents :** Faraday's laws of electromagnetic induction, self and mutual inductances, energy stored in inductance, growth and decay of currents in L-R circuit, charging and

discharging of capacitor in CR circuit, displacement current, Maxwell's electromagnetic field equations (only mention of the equations with qualitative discussion).

4. **Alternating current :** Mean and rms values of current and emf with sinusoidal waveform, L-R, C-R and L-C-R circuits, reactance, impedance, phase angle, power dissipation in AC circuits, power factor; vector diagram, resonance in series L-C-R circuit, Q-factor; principle of ideal transformer.

5. **Thermoelectricity :** Seebeck, Peltier and Thomson effects, laws of thermo-electricity, thermoelectric curve, neutral and inversion temperatures, thermoelectric power.

Electronics—I

1. **Semiconductor devices and application :** P-N junction diode, half-wave, full-wave and bridge rectifiers, L-type and p-type filters, Zener diode—voltage regulator. Transistor—a and b parameters and their interrelation, input and output characteristics in CB, CE and CC modes, single-stage CE amplifier—approximate expressions of current and voltage gain with the help of load line.

2. **Digital electronics :** Binary systems, binary numbers, decimal to binary and binary to decimal conversions, binary addition and subtraction. Logic Gates—OR, AND, NOT gates—truth tables; statement of de Morgan's theorem, NOR and NAND gates as universal gates.

Special Theory of Relativity and Atomic
and Nuclear Physics (35)

Special Theory of Relativity : (15)

1. Reference systems, inertial frames, Galilean invariance and conservation laws, Michelson-Morley experiment, postulates for the special theory of relativity, Lorentz transformation (deduction not required), length contraction, retardation of moving clocks; relativistic velocity addition, variation of mass with velocity, mass-energy equivalence.

Atomic and Nuclear Physics : (8 + 12)

1. **Atomic physics—e/m for electrons :** Thomson's method, determinations of electronic charge—Millikan's oil-drop method, positive rays, determination of e/m—Thomson's parabola method, isotopes. Structure of the atom—Bohr's hypothesis and description of the atom, Bohr's theory of hydrogen spectra, concept of quantum numbers, Pauli exclusion principle.

2. **Nuclear physics :** Constitution of atomic nuclei, general properties of nuclei, nuclear spin and magnetic moment, nuclear radius, nuclear mass, stability conditions of atomic nuclei, spontaneous nuclear disintegration, successive disintegration—radioactive equilibrium, radioactive dating, radio-isotopes and their uses, standard devices for the measurement of nuclear radiation—cloud chamber, G-M counter, cyclotron, nuclear reaction, Q-value of nuclear reaction, chain reaction, nuclear fussion, nuclear fusion, nuclear reactor.

Solid State Physics and Elementary
Quantum Mechanics (25)

Solid State Physics :

1. **Crystals :** Crystal lattice X-ray diffraction, Laue spots, Bragg's law; Miller indices and interplanar spacing.

2. **Magnetic properties of matter :** Intensity of magnetization, magnetic induction, permeability, susceptibility, relation between, dia-, para- and ferromagnetic materials, statement of Curie's law, Hysteresis in ferromagnetic materials, hysteresis loss.

3. **Semiconductors :** Intrinsic semiconductors, electrons and holes, Fermi level, temperature dependence of electron and hole concentration. Doping—impurity states, N and P-type semiconductors.

4. **Semiconductor devices :** P-N junction, majority and minority carriers, diode, Zener and tunnel diodes, light-emitting diode, transistor, solar cell.

Elementary Quantum Mechanics : (15)

1. **Quantum theory of radiation :** Failure of classical physics to explain the phenomena such as black-body spectrum, photoelectric effect. Planck's radiation law (statement only), and Einstein's explanation of photoelectric effect, Compton effect and Raman effect.

2. **Wave nature of material particles :** de Broglie hypothesis of matter waves, wave-particle duality; Heisenberg's uncertainty principle, gamma-ray microscope. Schrödinger equation, wave function and its interpretation, particle, in a one-dimensional infinite well, energy eigenvalue.

Vidyasagar University

Electricity and Magnetism   45 lectures

Electrostatics : Expression of potential and intensity due to a single charge and dipole. Normal induction. Gauss' theorem and its applications, e.g., intensity due to a charged sphere cylinder. Coulomb's theorem, electrostatics pressure, charged soap bubble energy density of electrostatic field. Capacitance of parallel plate, spherical and cylindrical condenser. Loss of energy due to sharing of charge between two conductors composite dielectric. Attracted disc-electrometer. Electrolytic condenser. Application of electrostatics (principle of xerox copying, etc.).

Electromagnetism : Magnetic field due to current. Laplace's equation. Ampere's circuital theorem. Magnetic field at an axial point of a circular coil and solenoid. Helmholtz double-coil galvanometer. Motor rule force due to magnetic field on a wire carrying current. Moving-coil galvanometer. Ammeters and voltmeters and other common instruments.

Magnetic Materials : Intensity of Magnetization. Permeability, Susceptibility dia-, para- and feromagnetism. Cycle of Magnetization.

Hysteresis. Calculation of hysteresis loss and its importance. d.c. circuits : Kirchhoff's laws and their application for determining currents in unbalanced Wheatstone's bridge. Potentiometer and its use. Platinum resistance thermometer.

Thermoelectricity : Thermoelectric effects, laws of thermoelectricity. Thermo-electric power. Inversion temperature, neutral temperature. Thermocouple and its application (for determining temperature). Application of thermodynamics to thermocouple circuit.

Electromagnetic induction : Self and mutual inductance in simple case. Varying currents, growth and decay of current, L-R circuit, charging an discharging of condenser in C.R. circuit. Time constant and log decrement. Moving-coil ballistic galvanometer and its use. Comparison between deadbeat and ballistic type of galvanometers.

Alternating current : R.M.S. and mean values of current and e.m.f. Reactance, impedance, power factor, form factor, choke power in a.c. circuits. L.R., C.R. and L.C.R. circuits, series and parallel resonant circuits, Q-factor, principle of ideal transformer. Watt-hour meter.

Electronics   40 lectures

(a) Electronics : Triode parameters and their relations, classification of amplifier according to operating point. Triode as an amplifier and oscillator, fundamental ideas on semiconductors. Crystal diode, Zener diode, junction diode as half-wave and full-wave rectification. Elementary idea about filter circuits. Characteristic curves of transistors. Transistor as amplifier and oscillator (Hartley's oscillator).

Digital electronics : Boolean algebra and logic gates (basic idea).

(b) Modern physics : Measurement of sp. charge of electron by J.J. Thomson method and charge of electron by Millikan's oil-drop method. Positive rays. Positive ray analysis by Thomson method. Isotopes, Atomic weight and Mass number.

Elements of quantum theory of radiation : Bohr's theory of hydrogen spectra. Quantum numbers. Pauli exclusion principle and distribution of electrons in different orbits.

Production of X-rays, continuous and characteristic of X-ray, X-ray spectra, Moseley's law and Bragg's law.

Qualitative discussion of dual aspects of matter and radiation. Uncertainty principles (statement only), Radioactive decay laws. Half-life, mean life, successive disintegration, secular and transient equilibrium. Age of rocks and Earth (qualitative discussion). Use of radioactive isotopes. GM counter, and related detecting devices. Properties of nuclear structure and nuclear reactions, cosmic rays. Accelerators. Cyclotron (VEC in Kolkata).

Basic idea on plasma.

Physical Optics   20 lectures

Nature of light : Electromagnetic character of light. Huygens' principle, explanation of reflection, refraction for plane surface. Interference of light; conditions of interference, measurement of wavelength of light by bi-prism and Lloyd's mirror, Interference in thin films, Newton's rings.

Diffraction : Half-period zone, Zone plate and rectilinear propagation of light. Fraunhofer diffraction; Single-slit Double-slit, plane transmission grating. Measurement of wave-length by grating. Resolving power of grating.

Polarisation : Double refraction, production of plane, circular and elliptically polarised light and identification. Nicol prism and its use. Optical activity, polarimeter, polaroids and their uses.

Selected topic : Element of scattering. Raman effect, Zeeman effect, Kerr effect, Faraday effect (qualitative treatment only for all effects).

Laser optics : Basic idea on laser emission.

Electrostatics

Electrostatics

Chapter 1

Electric Field and Potential : Gauss's Theorem : Dielectrics

1.1 Introduction

Some substances like glass, ebonite, etc., when rubbed with silk, flannel or other suitable materials, acquire the properties of attracting light bodies such as pieces of pith, bits of paper. Substances in such a state are known as *electrified* and the electricity so produced due to friction is called *frictional electricity*. When it does not move from one point to another within the substance, then it is called *statical electricity*. A study of the properties of such electrified bodies forms the subject matter of a branch called *electrostatics*. Du Fay was the scientist who enunciated first the fundamental law of electrostatics stating that, 'Two bodies with like charges repel and with unlike charges attract each other.' The charge generated on glass by rubbing it with silk is called positive while that generated on sealing-wax when rubbed with flannel is called negative. The kind of charge to be generated by rubbing depends on the nature of the two materials.

1.2 Theories of Electricity

In order to explain the known electrical phenomena, various theories have been put forward from time to time. Of those the two-fluid theory and the one-fluid theory came in succession. The latest of those known as the *electron theory* as discussed below is now universally accepted.

It is now well established that an atom contains as constituents tiny particles of which one kind is associated with negative charge. This sub-atomic particle is known as *electron* whose mass is about $\frac{1}{1840}$ of that of a hydrogen atom and is associated with the negative charge of value 4.803×10^{-10} e.s.u. An atom consists of a nucleus of positive electricity surrounded by a number of orbital electrons which revolve in definite orbits round the positive nucleus. The positive nucleus is constituted by the positively charged particles called *protons* and some uncharged particles known as *neutrons*. A proton or a neutron has nearly the same mass as that of a hydrogen atom. Proton has a positive charge equal in magnitude to that of an electron while the neutron is electrically neutral. The above three particles—electron, proton and neutron, are the fundamental particles of all matters. The difference of an atom of one type with other is due to the difference in the number of these particles.

1.3 The Law of Force between Electric Charges

The force of attraction or repulsion between two charges will depend on the magnitudes of the two charges, the nature of the medium separating the charges and the distance of separation between them. The above statement is expressed by the following law :

The force of attraction or repulsion between two charges at rest varies directly as the product of the charge and inversely as the square of the distance of separation

3

between them. The latter part of the law is known as the *Inverse Square Law*. It can be mathematically stated as

$$F = \frac{1}{4\pi\epsilon} \cdot \frac{q_1 q_2}{r^2}, \tag{1.1}$$

where q_1 and q_2 are the point charge, r is the distance between them and ϵ is a constant of the medium called *absolute permittivity* of the medium.

The force between two charges was first directly measured by Charles Augustin de Coulomb and the above law of force is known also as Coulomb's law of force.

Unit of charge : It is the quantity of electric charge which exerts a force of repulsion of one dyne on an equal and similar charge placed at a distance of 1 cm apart in vacuum or air. It is also known as a *stat coulomb*. The practical unit of electric charge in S.I. is coulomb.

1 coulomb = 3×10^9 e.s.u.

1.4   Potential due to a Point Charge

The potential at any point in an electric field is the amount of work done in bringing a unit positive charge from infinity to that point. The unit charge does not effect the distribution of charges of the field concerned. Suppose we have a point charge q at the point P (Fig. 1.1). Then the intensity at the point A will be $E = \frac{q}{r^2}$, where r is the distance of A from the point P. Now the work done by the field if a unit positive charge moves from B to A will be $-E\cos\theta \cdot ds$, where θ is the angle between AP and the tangent of the arc ds at A.

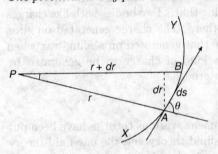

Fig. 1.1

$$\therefore\ E\cos\theta ds = \frac{q}{4\pi\epsilon r^2}\cos\theta ds$$

$$= \frac{q}{4\pi\epsilon r^2} \cdot \frac{dr}{ds} ds, \quad \text{where} \quad \cos\theta = \frac{dr}{ds}$$

$$= \frac{q}{4\pi\epsilon r^2} dr.$$

∴ work done by the field when the unit positive charge moves from B to A against the field will be

$$-E\cos\theta ds = -\frac{q}{4\pi\epsilon r^2} dr.$$

If the positive charge brings from infinity to A, the work done will be

$$-\int_{\infty}^{r} \frac{a}{4\pi\epsilon r^2} dr = \frac{q}{r\pi\epsilon r}.$$

Therefore, the potential at the point A due to the point charge q at P is

$$\phi = \frac{q}{4\pi\epsilon r}. \tag{1.2}$$

1.5   Potential and Field due to a Charged Spherical Conductor

Suppose we have a charged spherical conductor having radius a and surface density of charge σ. Consider a ring formed by AB about OP (Fig. 1.2).

The area of the ring $= 2\pi a^2 \sin\theta d\theta$.

Then the potential at P due to this charged ring will be

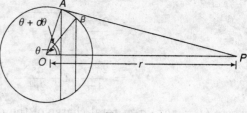

$$d\phi = \frac{2\pi a^2 \sin\theta d\theta \cdot \sigma}{4\pi\epsilon x}.$$

Now $x^2 = a^2 + r^2 - 2ar\cos\theta$

or, $xdx = ar\sin\theta d\theta$.

Fig. 1.2

$$\therefore \quad d\phi = \frac{2\pi a^2 \sigma x dx}{4\pi\epsilon x \cdot ar} = \frac{2\pi a\sigma dx}{4\pi\epsilon r}.$$

$$\therefore \quad \phi = \int_{r-a}^{r+a} \frac{2\pi a\sigma dx}{4\pi\epsilon r} = \frac{2\pi a\sigma}{4\pi\epsilon r} \cdot 2a = \frac{4\pi a^2 \sigma}{4\pi\epsilon r} = \frac{Q}{4\pi\epsilon r}, \tag{1.3}$$

where Q = total charge of the spherical conductor $= 4\pi a^2 \cdot \sigma$.

From Eq. (1.3) one can make the conclusion that the potential due to charged spherical conductor is the same as that obtained by assuming the whole charge Q to be confined at the centre of the conductor.

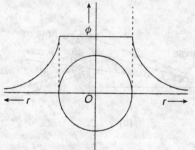

For an internal point,

$$\phi = \int_{a-r}^{a+r} \frac{2\pi a\sigma}{4\pi\epsilon r} \cdot dx = 4\pi a\sigma$$

$$= \frac{4\pi a^2 \sigma}{4\pi\epsilon a} = \frac{Q}{4\pi\epsilon a}. \tag{1.4}$$

The potential for an internal point will be constant. The potential is represented in Fig. 1.3.

Fig. 1.3

1.6 Potential and Field due to Charged Disc

Suppose we have a uniformly charged disc of radius a (Fig. 1.4) having surface density of charge σ. Now consider a ring of the disc between radii p and $p + dp$.

$\therefore$ the area of the ring $= 2\pi p dp$ and the amount of charge contained in this ring $= 2\pi p\sigma dp$.

The potential at P due to this charged element

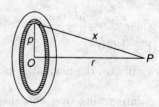

$$d\phi = \frac{2\pi\sigma p dp}{4\pi\epsilon x}.$$

Fig. 1.4

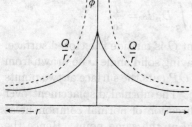

Now, $p^2 + r^2 = x^2$.

$$\therefore \quad \phi = \frac{2\pi\sigma}{4\pi\epsilon} \int_0^a \frac{p dp}{\sqrt{p^2 + r^2}}$$

$$= \frac{2\pi\sigma}{4\pi\epsilon} [\sqrt{a^2 + r^2} - r]$$

$$\therefore \quad E = -\frac{d\phi}{dr} = \frac{2\pi\sigma}{4\pi\epsilon} \left[1 - \frac{r}{\sqrt{r^2 + a^2}}\right].$$

Fig. 1.5

If the point P is situated at infinity, $r \gg a$. In that case,

$$\phi = \frac{2\pi\sigma r}{r\pi\epsilon}\left[\sqrt{\frac{a^2}{r^2}+1}-1\right]$$

$$= \frac{2\pi\sigma r}{4\pi\epsilon}\left[1+\frac{a^2}{2r^2}-1\right] = \frac{2\pi\sigma a^2}{4\pi\epsilon 2r} = \frac{Q}{4\pi\epsilon r},$$

where $Q = \pi a^2 \cdot \sigma = $ total charge of the disc. The potential variation with r is shown in Fig. 1.5.

1.7   Gauss's Theorem

This theorem states that, "The surface integral of the normal component of the electric displacement over a closed surface containing a total charge Q is $4\pi Q$."

Consider a point charge q at O within a closed surface as shown in Fig. 1.6. The medium has absolute permittivity ϵ_r. Suppose ds is an elementary area at P [Fig. 1.6(a)] on this closed surface.

∴ the electric field at P will be $E = \dfrac{q}{4\pi\epsilon r^2}$.

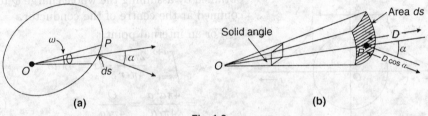

Fig. 1.6

Suppose, α is the angle between the normal to the surface ds and OP.

∴ normal displacement over the surface $ds = D\cos\alpha \cdot ds$

$$= \epsilon_r E \cos\alpha ds = \frac{q\cos\alpha ds}{4\pi\epsilon_0 r^2} = \frac{q}{4\pi\epsilon_0}\cdot d\omega,$$

where $d\omega = \dfrac{ds\cos\alpha}{r^2} = $ the solid angle subtended at the point O by the area ds [Fig. 1.6(b)].

Hence, the normal displacement over $ds = \dfrac{qd\omega}{4\pi\epsilon_0}$.

∴ integrating over the closed surface, the total normal displacement will be $\dfrac{q}{\epsilon_0}$, because the solid angle of closed surface is 4π.

The above result can be mathematically expressed

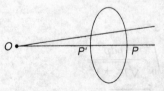

Fig. 1.7

as

$$\iint_S D_n ds = \frac{q}{\epsilon_0}.$$

Suppose the point O is outside the closed surface. A very small cone having solid angle ω be drawn from O such that the axis OP cuts the surface at two points P and P' (Fig. 1.7). The normal displacement over the area cut by the cone at P will be q^ω. The direction of normal component at P' will be opposite to the outward drawn normal at the same point. Hence the normal displacement over a small area at P' will be $-Q\omega$. So the total flux over the two surfaces at P and P' is zero. This is true for any cone that is drawn from O through the surface. Therefore, one may say that the total normal displacement or total flux over the surface is zero. The surface encloses no charge and so by Gauss's theorem this result is obvious.

If the charge is not a point charge, then we may assume that the total charge is concentrated at a point.

If the charge is distributed over the surface, we assume that the total charge is divided into a number of charges $q_1, q_2, q_3, q_4, \ldots$ at different points on the surface of the conductor. The total normal displacement over the surface

$$= 4\pi q_1 + 4\pi q_2 + 4\pi q_3 + \cdots$$
$$= 4\pi(q_1 + q_2 + q_3 + \cdots)$$
$$= 4\pi Q.$$

Suppose the surface is re-entrant [Fig. 1.8(a)] and the point O be inside the surface. Every cone from O cut the surface in an odd number of times. Hence extra cuts will be even in number. Half of these will represent cones passing out and half will be passing into the surface and so these will balance.

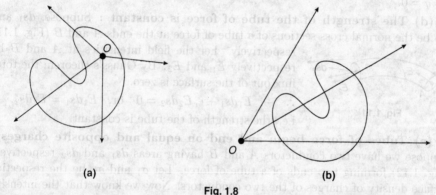

(a)   (b)

Fig. 1.8

If the point O lies outside the surface [Fig. 1.8(b)], the cone will cut the surface in even number of times. So the total normal flux over the surface is zero.

If there are both types (+ve and −ve) of charges, then the total charge will be the algebraic sum of the charges inside.

1.8   Applications of Gauss's Theorem

(a) Potential of long charged wire : Consider a charged wire having linear density of charge, i.e., charge per unit length is ρ. If E be the electric field at a distance r from the charged wire, then

$$\epsilon_r E \cdot 2\pi r = \frac{\rho}{\epsilon_0}$$

$$\therefore \ E = \frac{\rho}{2\pi\epsilon_r\epsilon_0 r}.$$

Now, the potential $\phi = -\int E dr = -\int \frac{2\rho}{r} dr$

$$= -2\rho \log_e r + \text{constant}.$$

(b) Field due to an infinite plane sheet of charge : Suppose, $PQRS$ be the portion of an infinite plane sheet of charge (Fig. 1.9) having surface density of

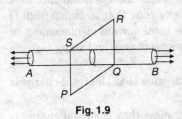

Fig. 1.9

charge σ. Draw a cylinder AB having end face surface area to be ds. The contribution towards outward flux by the sides will be zero because the intensity will be along the length of the cylinder. Then the total flux through the closed surface of the cylindrical element is $2Eds$.

$$\therefore \ 2\epsilon_r Eds = \frac{\sigma ds}{\epsilon_0}, \quad \therefore \ E = \frac{\sigma}{2\epsilon_0\epsilon_r}.$$

(c) **No charge at any point inside the conductor :** Suppose we have a conductor AB of any shape and P be a point within the conductor (Fig. 1.10). Draw a sphere about P so that the sphere encloses a charge q.

$$\therefore \ \int \epsilon_r Eds = \frac{q}{\epsilon_0}.$$

Now, $E = -\dfrac{\partial \phi}{\partial r} = 0$ because the potential inside the conductor is zero.

Fig. 1.10

$$\therefore \ q = 0.$$

(d) **The strength of the tube of force is constant :** Suppose, ds_1 and ds_2 be the normal cross-sections of a tube of force at the ends A and B (Fig. 1.11)

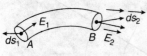

Fig. 1.11

respectively. Let the field intensities at A and B be respectively E_1 and E_2. By Gauss's theorem the total flux out of the surface is zero.

$$\therefore \ -\epsilon_r E_1 ds_1 + \epsilon_r E_2 ds_2 = 0 \quad \text{or,} \quad E_1 ds_1 = E_2 ds_2,$$

i.e., the strength of the tube is constant.

(e) **Tubes of force begin and end on equal and opposite charges :** Suppose we have two conductors A and B having areas ds_1 and ds_2 respectively (Fig. 1.12) forming two ends of a tube of force. Let σ_1 and σ_2 be the respective surface density of charges of the two conductors. Now we know that the intensity is everywhere parallel to the surface of the tube and the strength of the tube is constant.

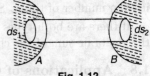

$\therefore \ E_1 ds_1 = -E_2 ds_2$ (minus sign indicates that the direction of E_2 is opposite to that of E_1).

From Coulomb's theorem we have $E_1 = 4\pi\sigma_1$ and $E_2 = 4\pi\sigma_2$.

Fig. 1.12

$$\therefore \ \sigma_1 ds_1 = -\sigma_2 ds_2.$$

So one can conclude that the charges at the start and termination of the tube are equal but opposite in nature.

(f) **Intensity near a charged conductor (Coulomb's theorem) :** Consider a cylinder with faces having area ds, one face just inside the conductor and the other is just outside the cylinder (Fig. 1.13). The surface density of charge is σ. Now the intensity of electric field inside the conductor is zero. Therefore, the flux through the area ds of the conductor will be zero. Again, the surface of the conductor is equipotential, so the intensity of electric field will be normal to the surface. Hence,

Fig. 1.13

$$\epsilon_r Eds = \frac{\sigma ds}{\epsilon_0}. \quad \therefore \ E = \frac{\sigma}{\epsilon_r \epsilon_0}.$$

(g) Stress acting on a charged conducting surface : Let PQ (Fig. 1.14) be a charged conductor having surface density of charge σ and XY be a unit area chosen on its surface. Consider two very close points A and B on the opposite sides of XY such that the intensities due to charges on the conductor will be almost identical at both the points. Let E_1 be the intensity at A and B due to the charge σ on XY and E_2 be the intensity due to the remaining charges on the conductor.

Now inside the conductor the intensity of electric field is zero.

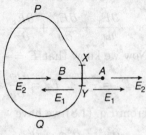

$\therefore$ $\qquad E_2 - E_1 = 0$, i.e., $E_1 = E_2$.

At the point A outside the conductor the electric intensity is given by

$$E_1 + E_2 = \frac{\sigma}{\epsilon_r \epsilon_0} \text{ (using Coulomb's theorem).}$$

Hence, $2E_2 = 2E_1 = \dfrac{\sigma}{\epsilon_r \epsilon_0}$, i.e., $E_1 = E_2 = \dfrac{\sigma}{2\epsilon_r \epsilon_0}$.

Fig. 1.14

$\therefore$ the force per unit area of the conductor $= \dfrac{\sigma}{2\epsilon_r \epsilon_0} \cdot \sigma = \dfrac{\sigma^2}{2\epsilon}$.

1.9   Laplace's and Poisson's Equations in Cartesian Coordinates

Poisson's equation is the local relation between charge density at some point and the corresponding potential function in the immediate neighbourhood.

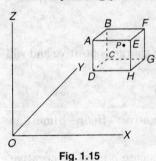

Fig. 1.15

Suppose there be a volume distribution of charge at any point $P(x, y, z)$ of which the volume density of charge is ρ. Consider an elementary rectangular parallelopiped of volume $dv = dx\,dy\,dz$ surrounding the point P (Fig. 1.15).

Let E_x be the x-component of intensity at P; then the component of intensity of $ABCD$ plane will be

$$E_x + \left(\frac{\partial E_x}{\partial x}\right)\left(-\frac{1}{2}dx\right).$$

$\therefore$ outward flux over the plane $ABCD$ is

$$\left\{E_x + \left(\frac{\partial E_x}{\partial x}\right)\left(-\frac{1}{2}dx\right)\right\}dy\,dz. \qquad (1.5)$$

Similarly, outward flux over the plane $EFGH$ is

$$\left\{E_x + \left(\frac{\partial E_x}{\partial x}\right)\left(\frac{1}{2}dx\right)\right\}dy\,dz. \qquad (1.6)$$

Therefore, combining Eqs. (1.5) and (1.6) we get the total outward flux through the parallelopiped along X-direction as

$$\frac{\partial E_x}{\partial x}dx\,dy\,xz.$$

In a similar way we have the total outward flux through the parallelopiped along Y and Z direction as

$$\frac{\partial E_y}{\partial y}dx\,dy\,dz \quad \text{and} \quad \frac{\partial E_z}{\partial z}dx\,dy\,dz.$$

Hence the total outward flux over the parallelopiped will be

$$\left(\frac{\partial E_z}{\partial x} + \frac{\partial E_y}{\partial y} + \frac{\partial E_z}{\partial z}\right) dx\,dy\,dz. \tag{1.7}$$

Now according to Gauss's theorem,

$$\left(\frac{\partial E_x}{\partial x} + \frac{\partial E_y}{\partial y} + \frac{\partial E_z}{\partial z}\right) dx\,dy\,dz = \frac{\rho}{\epsilon} dx\,dy\,dz$$

or, $\quad \dfrac{\partial E_x}{dx} + \dfrac{\partial E_y}{\partial y} + \dfrac{\partial E_z}{\partial z} = \dfrac{\rho}{\epsilon}. \tag{1.8}$

Now we know that $E = -\nabla\phi$.

$\therefore \; E_x = -\dfrac{\partial\phi}{\partial x}, \; E_y = \dfrac{\partial\phi}{\partial y}$ and $E_z = -\dfrac{\partial\phi}{\partial z}$, where ϕ is the potential at the point P.

From Eq. (1.8) we have

$$\frac{\partial^2\phi}{\partial x^2} + \frac{\partial^2\phi}{\partial y^2} + \frac{\partial^2\phi}{\partial z^2} = -\frac{\rho}{\epsilon}$$

or, $\quad \nabla^2\phi = -\dfrac{\rho}{\epsilon} \tag{1.9}$

If the parallelopiped contains no charge, then

$$\nabla^2\phi = 0 \tag{1.10}$$

Eqs. (1.9) and (1.10) are respectively known as Poisson's equation and Laplace's equation.

Some Important Results

(i) The potential at any point will be maximum if the charge is positive and will be minimum if the charge is negative.

From Poisson's equation, $\nabla^2\phi = -\dfrac{\rho}{\epsilon}$, we find that

if the potential ϕ is maximum, $\nabla^2\phi$ will be negative. Hence ρ must be positive.

Again ϕ is minimum when $\nabla^2\phi$ is positive. In this case ρ must be negative.

(ii) At any point in space, the potential cannot have a maximum or a minimum value if the space is not occupied by an electric charge.

If the space round the point does not contain any charge, then

$$\nabla^2\phi = 0.$$

Now the potential ϕ will be maximum or minimum according as $\nabla^2\phi$ is negative or positive. But if the space contains no charge, $\nabla^2\phi = 0$. Hence the potential will be neither positive nor negative if the space contains no charge.

1.10   Boundary Conditions for Lines of Force

The electric field in passing from one medium to the other obeys two boundary conditions. The boundary conditions are :

(a) *The normal component of the electric field across the boundary of separation between two media will be continuous or discontinuous according as the boundary contains charge or not.*

Suppose, AB is a pillbox at the interface between two media with end faces S_1 and S_2 (Fig. 1.16). The intercept on the interface being S_3. Unit normal vectors to the end faces and to the curved surfaces are respectively $\hat{n}_1$, $\hat{n}_2$ and $\hat{n}_3$.

Now according to integral form of Gauss's theorem we have

$$\int_S E \cdot ds = \frac{1}{\epsilon} \int \sigma ds \quad \text{or,} \quad \int_{S_1} E\hat{n}_1 ds + \int_{S_2} E\hat{n}_2 ds + \int_{S_3} E\hat{n}_3 ds = \frac{1}{\epsilon} \int \sigma ds.$$

If the pillbox is of small size, $\int_{S_3} E \cdot \hat{n}_3 ds$ can be neglected.

$$\therefore \int_{S_1} E_1\hat{n}_1 ds + \int_{S_2} E_2\hat{n}_2 ds = \frac{1}{\epsilon} \int \sigma ds$$

Suppose, $S_1 = S_2 = S$.

$$\therefore \int \left[(E_n)_1 - (E_n)_2 - \frac{\sigma}{\epsilon} \right] ds = 0.$$

The above equation holds good for any arbitrary value of ds.

$$\therefore \quad (E_n)_1 - (E_n)_2 = \frac{\sigma}{\epsilon},$$

where $(E_n)_1$ and $(E_n)_2$ refer to normal component of electric intensity in medium 1 and 2.

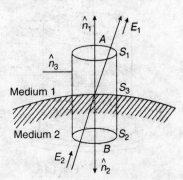

Fig. 1.16

Now, if the surface of separation contains no charge, $(E_n)_1 = (E_n)_2$, i.e., the normal component of electric intensity is continuous across the surface of separation of two media.

(b) *Tangential component of electric intensity is continuous across the boundary separating two media.*

Consider a small rectangular contour $ABDC$ (Fig. 1.17) whose sides AB and CD are parallel to the boundary and the sides AC and BD are normal to it. The work done in carrying unit charge round the contour must be zero because the charge gains energy due to work done by the field in one side of the contour and it loses energy due to work done against the field on the opposite side of the contour.

Now the work done, $\partial w = (E_1 \sin \theta_1 - E_2 \sin \theta_2)\partial l.$

The work done along the sides BD and CA are neglected.

$$\therefore \quad E_1 \sin \theta_1 - E_2 \sin \theta_2 = 0$$

or, $E_1 \sin \theta_1 = E_2 \sin \theta_2.$

$$\therefore \quad (E_t)_1 = (E_t)_2,$$

where $(E_t)_1$ and $(E_t)_2$ represent respectively the transverse components of electric field in medium 1 and 2 respectively. From the above equation, we find that the tangential component of electric intensity is continuous across the boundary.

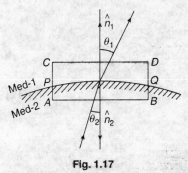

Fig. 1.17

1.11 Verification of Inverse Square Law

A direct verification of inverse square law in electrostatics was made by Coulomb using torsion balance. The apparatus is shown in Fig. 1.18. A metal-coated pith-ball A carried at one end of a pointer B is suspended by a quartz wire. The suspension wire is attached with a torsion head. The whole arrangement is enclosed in a glass cylinder. A pot containing pumice stone soaked in H_2SO_4 is placed inside the cylinder to absorb moisture. Another pith-ball C at the end of a glass rod is also placed in a manner as shown. The angular distance between these two balls is directly noted from the circular scale.

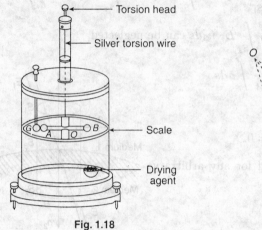

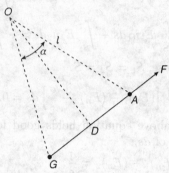

Fig. 1.18   Fig. 1.19

The ball A is first made to touch the ball G by means of the torsion head. Then B is charged by $2q$ units of charge and replaced in its first position. Then both the balls acquire q units of charge. Now due to like charges repulsion, the ball A rotates through an angle. The torsion head is now rotated through an angle β in opposite direction so that the angle of rotation is reduced to α (Fig. 1.19).

Suppose the force between the balls is F. The twist on the suspension wire is $(\alpha + \beta)$. Therefore, the torque exerted by the suspension wire $= C(\alpha + \beta)$, where C is the torque per unit twist.

Now the moment of the couples due to repulsive force $= F \times OD = Fl \cos \dfrac{\alpha}{2}$. At equilibrium position, $Fl \cos \dfrac{\alpha}{2} = C(\beta + \alpha)$

or, $F = C \dfrac{\beta + \alpha}{l \cos \frac{\alpha}{2}}.$ (1.11)

If the inverse square law is true,

$$F \propto \frac{1}{AG^2}, \quad \text{i.e., } F \propto \frac{1}{\left(2l \sin \frac{\alpha}{2}\right)^2}$$

or, $F \times 4l^2 \sin^2 \dfrac{\alpha}{2} = \text{constant} = K \text{ (say)}.$ (1.12)

From Eqs. (1.11) and (1.12) we get

$$C \cdot \frac{\beta + \alpha}{l \cos \frac{\alpha}{2}} \cdot 4l^2 \sin^2 \frac{\alpha}{2} = K$$

or, $(\beta + \alpha) \tan \dfrac{\alpha}{2} \sin \dfrac{\alpha}{2} = \dfrac{K}{4l^2 C} = \text{constant}$

or, $(\beta + \alpha) \cdot \dfrac{\alpha}{2} \cdot \dfrac{\alpha}{2} = \text{constant (provided } \alpha \text{ is small)}$

or, $(\beta + \alpha)\alpha^2 = \text{constant}.$ (1.13)

To verify inverse square law the experiment is repeated for different values of α and β, and it is found that $(\beta + \alpha)\alpha^2$ is approximately constant.

The above method has several disadvantages and so the method is not an accurate one. Some of which are :

(i) Point charges are not available.

(ii) Charge will induce on the neighbouring conductor, so the deflection is affected to some extent.

(iii) Leakage of charges from A and G occur.

(iv) The angle cannot be measured accurately.

Most of the errors may be reduced sufficiently with modified arrangements made by Cavendish. The apparatus used by him is shown in Fig. 1.20. Two spherical shells of conducting materials are fixed by means of two ebonite ring (Q, Q). B is a trap door made by a conducting wire MN. The two spheres are connected with each other by a wire passing through B of such a length that it just touches the inner shell when the door closes (Fig. 1.20).

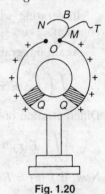

Suppose the outer sphere is positively charged and the door B is now closed. Then the door is opened out. The outer shell will begin to discharge and the inner shell is tested with an electrometer. It will be found that there is no charge on the inner sphere. We shall show that this will happen only when the inverse square law is valid.

Fig. 1.20

Let us now calculate the potential at any point P inside the sphere of having radius R (Fig. 1.21). The sphere contained a charge Q and the surface density of charge is σ.

$\therefore$ the charge contained in area $ds = \sigma ds = \sigma R^2 \sin\theta d\theta d\phi = \dfrac{Q}{4\pi R^2} \cdot R^2 \sin\theta d\theta d\phi$

$$= \frac{Q}{4\pi} \sin\theta d\theta d\phi.$$

Therefore, the potential at the point P will be

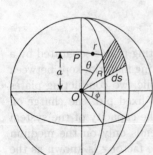

$$\phi_p = \frac{1}{4\pi\epsilon_0} \int_0^\pi \int_0^{2\pi} \frac{Q}{4\pi} \sin\theta d\theta d\phi \int_0^\infty F(r)dr,$$

where $F(r)$ is some function of r

$$= \frac{Q}{2} \int_0^\pi \left(\int_r^\infty F(r)dr \right) \sin\theta d\theta$$

Now, $r^2 = R^2 + a^2 - 2aR\cos\theta$.

$$\therefore \quad rdr = aR\sin\theta d\theta \quad \text{or,} \quad \sin\theta d\theta = \frac{rdr}{aR}.$$

Fig. 1.21

$\therefore \quad \phi_p = \dfrac{1}{8\pi} \dfrac{Q}{\epsilon_0} \displaystyle\int_{R-a}^{R+a} \left(\int_r^\infty F(r)dr \right) \dfrac{rdr}{aR} = \dfrac{Q}{8\pi\epsilon_0 aR} \int_{R-a}^{R+a} \left(\int_r^\infty F(r)dr \right) rdr.$

Let us put $\psi(r) = \displaystyle\int \left(\int_r^\infty F(r)dr \right) rdr.$

$$\therefore \quad \phi_p = \frac{Q}{8\pi\epsilon_0 aR}[\psi(R+a) - \psi(R-a)]. \tag{1.14}$$

Now ϕ_p must be independent of a, otherwise for different values of a we get different values of ϕ. In other words, potential of the two spheres cannot be different when the electric communication exists between them.

Differentiating Eq. (1.14) with respect to a we get

$$\frac{8\pi\epsilon_0 R}{Q}\phi_p = \psi'(R+a) - \psi'(R-a).$$

Further differentiation results

$$0 = \psi''(R+a) - \psi''(R-a) \quad \text{or,} \quad \psi''(R-a) = \psi''(R+a),$$

which shows that $\psi''(r) = $ constant,

i.e., $\psi''(r) = C$ (say).

Integrating with respect to r, we get $\psi'(r) = C_r + B$, where B is another constant.

Again integrating we get $\psi(r) = \frac{1}{2}Cr^2 + Br + D$.

$$\therefore \quad \int \left(\int_r^\infty F(r)dr \right) r dr = \frac{1}{2}Cr^2 + Br + D. \tag{1.15}$$

Differentiation of Eq. (1.15) results

$$\left[\int_r^\infty F(r)dr \right] r = Cr + B \quad \text{or,} \quad \int_r^\infty F(r)dr = C + \frac{B}{r}.$$

Now, if $f'(r) = F(r)$, then

$$f(r)\Big|_r^\infty = C + \frac{B}{r} \quad \text{or,} \quad f(\infty) - f(r) = C + \frac{B}{r}.$$

After differentiation we have

$$-f'(r) = -\frac{B}{r^2} \quad \text{or,} \quad F(r) = \frac{B}{r^2}.$$

Therefore, experiment can be done provided the law of force is of inverse square in nature.

1.12   Dielectric Constant

Cavendish first observed that the capacity of two conducting plates separated by a fixed distance depends on the characteristics of the insulating material kept between the plates. Faraday observed that if the space between the two conducting plates is filled with medium like glass, ebonite, etc., then for a fixed p.d. the charge on each increases when the space is vacuum. That means the capacity of the system increases. It is increased by a factor $\epsilon > 1$, which depends only on the medium and is independent of the size or shape of the plates. The factor ϵ is known as the dielectric constant of the medium whose value for air is 1.000588. So the capacity of two plates with air is nearly the same as that with vacuum.

1.13   Potential and Field due to a Dipole

Two equal and opposite charges separated by small fixed distances are said to constitue a dipole.

Suppose we have a dipole AB with $-q$ charge at A and $+q$ charge at B (Fig. 1.22). Now the potential at $P(r, \theta)$ due to the charge $-q$ at A will be $\frac{-q}{4\pi\epsilon r}$ and due to the charge $+q$ at B will be $\frac{q}{4\pi\epsilon(r+dr)}$.

Therefore, the potential at P,

$$\phi_p = \frac{1}{4\pi\epsilon}\left[-\frac{q}{r} + \frac{q}{r+dr}\right].$$

Now, $\dfrac{1}{r+dr} = (r+dr)^{-1} = \dfrac{1}{r}\left(1 + \dfrac{dr}{r}\right)^{-1}$

$$= \frac{1}{r}\left(1 - \frac{dr}{r}\right) = \frac{1}{r} - \frac{dr}{r^2},$$

neglecting the higher order terms like $\left(\dfrac{dr}{r}\right)^2$, etc., because dr is very small.

$$\therefore \quad \phi_p = \frac{1}{4\pi\epsilon}\left[-\frac{q}{r} + q\left(\frac{1}{r} - \frac{dr}{r^2}\right)\right] = -\frac{1}{r\pi\epsilon}\cdot\frac{qdr}{r^2}$$

$$= -\frac{1}{4\pi\epsilon}\frac{qdl}{r^2}\cdot\frac{dr}{dl}.$$

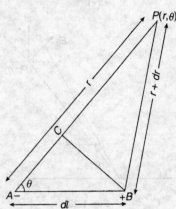

Fig. 1.22

Now from Fig. 1.22 we find that

$$\cos\theta = \frac{AC}{AB} = \frac{r - (r+dr)}{dl} = -\frac{dr}{dl}.$$

$$\therefore \quad \phi_p = \frac{1}{4\pi\epsilon}\frac{qdl}{r^2}\cos\theta = \frac{M\cos\theta}{4\pi\epsilon r^2},$$

where $M = qdl$ = moment of the dipole.

The dipole moment has a direction along $\overrightarrow{AB}$ and it has got a finite magnitude. Hence it is a vector.

Now, $\nabla_A\left(\dfrac{1}{r}\right) = \left(\hat{i}\dfrac{\partial}{\partial x} + \hat{j}\dfrac{\partial}{\partial y} + \hat{k}\dfrac{\partial}{\partial z}\right)\left(\dfrac{1}{\sqrt{x^2+y^2+z^2}}\right)$

$$= -\frac{\hat{i}x}{(x^2+y^2+z^2)^{3/2}} - \frac{\hat{j}y}{(x^2+y^2+z^2)^{3/2}} - \frac{\hat{k}z}{(x^2+y^2+z^2)^{3/2}}$$

$$= -\frac{\hat{i}x + \hat{j}y + \hat{k}z}{(x^2+y^2+z^2)^{3/2}} = -\frac{r}{r^3} = -\frac{1}{r^2}.$$

The potential at the point P can also be written as

$$\phi_p = \frac{M\cos\theta}{4\pi\epsilon r^2} = -\frac{M}{4\pi\epsilon}\nabla_A\left(\frac{1}{r}\right),$$

where ∇_A denotes differentiation with respect to the coordinate of the dipole, where $r = AP$.

If we take $AP = r$, then

$$\phi_p = \frac{M}{4\pi\epsilon}\nabla_A\left(\frac{1}{r}\right).$$

If the differentiation is taken with respect to the coordinate of the field point P, then

$$\phi_p = -\frac{M}{4\pi\epsilon}\nabla_P\left(\frac{1}{r}\right),$$

where ∇_P denotes the differentiation with respect to the coordinate of the field point and $AP = r$.

Intensity due to a Dipole

Suppose, E be the intensity at P (Fig. 1.23) making an angle ϕ with r, then the electric field components are given by

$$E_r = -\frac{\partial \phi_p}{\partial r} = -\frac{\partial}{\partial r}\left(\frac{M\cos\theta}{4\pi\epsilon r^2}\right)$$

$$= \frac{2M\cos\theta}{4\pi\epsilon r^3} \tag{1.16}$$

and $\quad E_\theta = -\frac{1}{r}\frac{\partial \phi_p}{\partial \theta} = -\frac{1}{r}\cdot\frac{\partial}{\partial \theta}\left(\frac{M\cos\theta}{4\pi\epsilon r^2}\right)$

$$= \frac{M\sin\theta}{4\pi\epsilon r^3}. \tag{1.17}$$

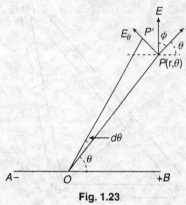

Fig. 1.23

Therefore, magnitude of the electric field

$$E = \sqrt{E_r^2 + E_\theta^2}$$

$$= \frac{1}{4\pi\epsilon}\sqrt{\left(\frac{2M}{r^3}\cos\theta\right)^2 + \left(\frac{M\sin\theta}{r^3}\right)^2}$$

$$= \frac{1}{4\pi\epsilon}\frac{M}{r^3}\sqrt{4\cos^2\theta + \sin^2\theta}$$

$$= \frac{1}{4\pi\epsilon}\frac{M}{r^3}\sqrt{1 + 3\cos^2\theta}$$

and $\quad \tan\phi = \frac{E_\theta}{E_r} = \frac{\sin\theta}{2\cos\theta} = \frac{1}{2}\tan\theta.$ (1.18)

1.14 Potential Energy of a Dipole in a Field

Here we have to calculate the work done required in bringing two charges $-q$ and $+q$ from infinity to the positions A and B respectively (Fig. 1.24). Let the potential at A is ϕ_A, then the potential at the point B will be

$$\phi_B = \phi_A + \frac{d\phi_A}{dl}\cdot dl$$

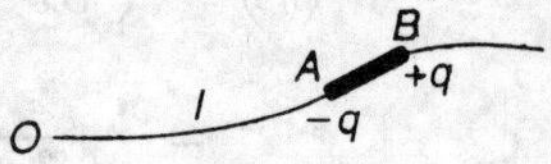

Fig. 1.24

$\therefore$ the work done to place the dipole in the above position will be

$$W = -q\phi_A + q\phi_B = -q\phi_A + q\phi_A + q\frac{d\phi_A}{dl}\cdot dl = q\cdot\frac{d\phi_A}{dl}\cdot dl$$

$$= M\frac{d\phi_A}{dl}, \quad \text{where } M = qdl = \text{moment of the dipole}$$

$$= -M\cdot E, \tag{1.19}$$

since $\quad E = -\frac{d\phi_A}{dl}.$

Eq. (1.19) gives the energy of the dipole of moment M in a field having intensity E.

Interaction between two dipoles

Considering Fig. 1.23, the electric intensity E can be written as

$$E = \hat{r}E_r + \hat{\theta}E_\theta,$$

where $\hat{r}$ and $\hat{\theta}$ are unit vectors along E_r and E_θ respectively.

Now, suppose, $\hat{x}$ is a unit vector along the dipole AB and $\hat{y}$ is a unit vector normal to $\hat{x}$. Therefore, from Fig. 1.23,

$$\hat{r} = \hat{x}\cos\theta + \hat{y}\sin\theta$$

$$\hat{\theta} = -\hat{x}\sin\theta + \hat{y}\cos\theta$$

$$\therefore \quad E = \frac{1}{4\pi\epsilon}\left[\frac{2M\cos\theta}{r^3}\hat{r} + \frac{M\sin\theta}{r^3}\hat{\theta}\right]$$

$$= \frac{1}{4\pi\epsilon}\left[\frac{2M\cos\theta}{r^3}(\hat{x}\cos\theta + \hat{y}\sin\theta) + \frac{M\sin\theta}{r^3}(-\hat{x}\sin\theta + \hat{y}\cos\theta)\right]$$

$$= \frac{1}{4\pi\epsilon}\left[\left(\frac{2M\cos^2\theta}{r^3} - \frac{M\sin^2\theta}{r^3}\right)\hat{x} + \left(\frac{3M\cos\theta\sin\theta}{r^3}\right)\hat{y}\right]$$

$$= \frac{1}{4\pi\epsilon}\left[\left(\frac{3M\cos^2\theta}{r^3} - \frac{M}{r^3}\right)\hat{x} + \frac{3M\sin\theta\cos\theta}{r^3}\cdot\hat{y}\right]$$

$$= \frac{1}{4\pi\epsilon}\left[-\frac{M}{r^3}\hat{x} + \frac{3M\cos^2\theta}{r^3}\hat{x} + \frac{3M\sin\theta\cos\theta}{r^3}\hat{y}\right]$$

$$= \frac{1}{4\pi\epsilon}\left[-\frac{M}{r^3} + \frac{3M\cos\theta}{r^3}(\hat{x}\cos\theta + \hat{y}\sin\theta)\right]$$

$$= \frac{1}{4\pi\epsilon}\left[-\frac{M}{r^3} + \frac{3M\cos\theta}{r^3}\cdot\hat{r}\right]$$

$$= \frac{1}{4\pi\epsilon}\left[-\frac{M}{r^3} + \frac{3(M\vec{r})\vec{r}}{r^5}\right]. \qquad (1.20)$$

Suppose, AB and CD are two dipoles oriented in a manner as shown in Fig. 1.25. The angle between the two dipoles be ψ. The potential energy of the dipole CD placed in the field of the dipole AB of moment M_1 (Fig. 1.25) can be expressed as

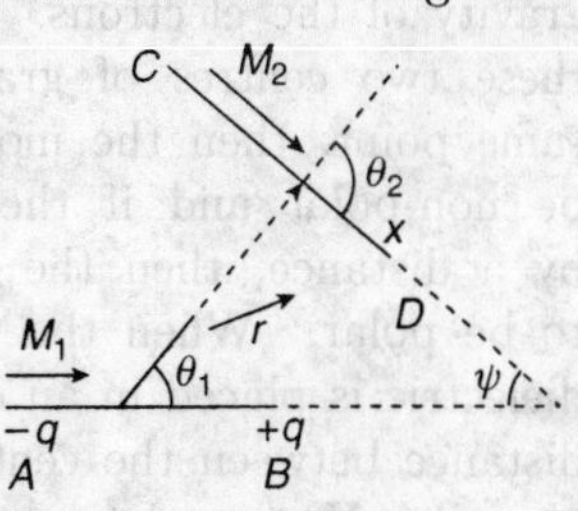

$$W = -M_2 \cdot E$$

$$= \frac{1}{4\pi\epsilon}\left[\frac{M_1 M_2}{r^3} - \frac{3(M_1 \cdot r)(M_2 \cdot r)}{r^5}\right].$$

Fig. 1.25

Now the angle between the dipole, $\psi = (\theta_2 - \theta_1)$

$$\therefore \quad W = \frac{1}{4\pi\epsilon}\left[\frac{M_1 M_2 \cos(\theta_2 - \theta_1)}{r^3} - \frac{3M_1 M_2 \cos\theta_1 \cos\theta_2}{r^3}\right]$$

$$= \frac{M_1 M_2}{4\pi\epsilon r^3}(\sin\theta_1 \sin\theta_2 - 2\cos\theta_1 \cos\theta_2). \qquad (1.21)$$

1.15 Force and Couple on the Dipole

Force on a Dipole

Suppose the dipole is placed in a non-uniform field $\vec{E}$. Consider a dipole AB of length ∂l and with charges $-q$ at A and $+q$ at B respectively (Fig. 1.26). Since the field is non-uniform, the field at A and at B will be different. Suppose the field at A is E, then the field at B will be $E + \frac{\partial E}{\partial l} \cdot \partial l$.

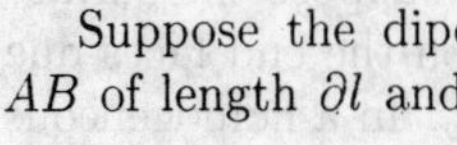

Fig. 1.26

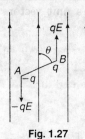

Fig. 1.27

Therefore, the force on the dipole will be

$$F = -qE + q\left(E + \frac{\partial E}{\partial l} \cdot \partial l\right) = q\frac{\partial E}{\partial l} \cdot \partial l.$$

Now, let l, m, n be the direction cosines of the direction along $\overrightarrow{AB}$. Hence,

$$\frac{\partial}{\partial l} = l\frac{\partial}{\partial x} + m\frac{\partial}{\partial y} + n\frac{\partial}{\partial z} \quad \text{or,} \quad \frac{\partial E}{\partial l} = l\frac{\partial E}{\partial x} + m\frac{\partial E}{\partial y} + n\frac{\partial E}{\partial z}.$$

Therefore, $F = q \cdot \partial l \left[l\dfrac{\partial E}{\partial x} + m\dfrac{\partial E}{\partial y} + n\dfrac{\partial E}{\partial z}\right] = M\left[l\dfrac{\partial E}{\partial x} + m\dfrac{\partial E}{\partial y} + n\dfrac{\partial E}{\partial z}\right]$

$$= (M \cdot \nabla)E. \tag{1.22}$$

Couple on a Dipole

Suppose the dipole AB is placed in a uniform field $\overrightarrow{E}$. Then two equal and opposite forces, qE and $-qE$, will act on the points A and B respectively (Fig. 1.27). Therefore, a couple will act on the dipole. The moment of the couple,

$$\tau = \partial l \times qE = q\partial l \times E = M \times E.$$

1.16   Polarisation of a Dielectric

In an insulator, the electrons are all tightly bounded to the nucleus of the atom so that a few numbers of free electrons are available. The insulators are known as *dielectrics*. If a molecule of an insulator is placed in an electrostatic field, the electrons in the orbits of the atom cannot overcome the binding force unless the field is very intense and hence they cannot move along the line of force of the field. In any molecule, the protons can be considered to be an equivalent positive charge situated at the centre of gravity of the protons. Similarly, there will be a centre of gravity of the electrons. If in a molecule these two centres of gravity are at the same point, then the molecule is said to be non-polar and if they are separated by a distance, then the molecule is said to be polar. When the molecules of the dielectric is placed in an electric field, the distance between the centres of gravity is altered. Hence, the non-polar molecules become induced dipole and polar molecules

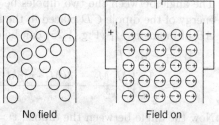

No field   Field on

Fig. 1.28

will be oriented by the field. The orientation will be such that the axis of the dipole lies along the line of force. Such a phenomenon is known as electric polarisation. This phenomenon may be illustrated as shown in Fig. 1.28.

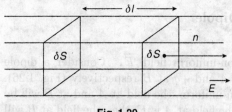

Fig. 1.29

Consider a small elementary volume of a polarised medium having length δl and surface of the end face to be δS (Fig. 1.29). Again, suppose the surface density of charges on the end faces due to polarisation is σ_p. In a homogeneous isotropic dielectric, the electric moment is proportional to the electric field applied provided the field is not very intense.

Hence, electric moment $P = \alpha E$, where α is a constant, known as the molecular polarisability of the medium. Suppose, there are x molecules per unit volume of the medium, then the electric moment per unit volume, $P = \alpha E \cdot x$, known as *polarisation*.

Now, $P = \sigma_p \cdot \delta S \cdot \delta l \cdot \hat{n}$, where $\hat{n}$ is the unit normal vector of the end faces.

$$\therefore \quad P = \frac{\sigma_p \delta S \cdot \delta l \cdot \hat{n}}{\delta S \cdot \delta l} = \sigma_p \hat{n}$$

i.e., $|P| = \sigma_p$. \hfill (1.23)

Eq. (1.23) shows that the surface density of charge gives the measure of the polarisation of the medium.

1.17   Electric Induction

Suppose we have a parallel plate condenser [Fig. 1.30(a)] with the plate A having surface density of charge σ. Therefore, the intensity of electric field within the plate is given by

$$E_1 = \frac{\sigma}{\epsilon_0}.$$

Let a dielectric medium is inserted between the plates [Fig. 1.30(b)]. The presence of dielectric body will affect the distribution of charges on the plates. Suppose, P is the polarisation due to the field E within it, then it will produce $-P$ and $+P$ very near to positive and negative plates. Therefore, the effective surface densities on the plates A and B become respectively $\sigma_1 = \sigma - P$ and $\sigma_2 = -\sigma + P$.

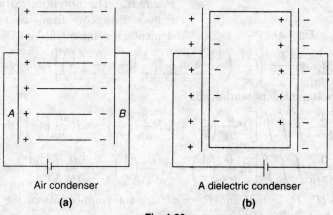

Air condenser

(a)

A dielectric condenser

(b)

Fig. 1.30

Again, the intensity in the dielectric, $E = \dfrac{E_1}{\epsilon_r}$, where ϵ_r is the dielectric constant.

Now we can write $E = (\sigma - P)/\epsilon_0$

or, $\quad E + \dfrac{P}{\epsilon_0} = \dfrac{\sigma}{\epsilon_0} = E_1 = \epsilon_r E \quad$ or, $\quad 1 + \dfrac{P}{\epsilon_0 E} = \epsilon_r$

or, $\quad 1 + \kappa = \epsilon_r$, \hfill (1.24)

where $\kappa \left(= \dfrac{1}{\epsilon} \dfrac{P}{E} \right)$ is called the *electric susceptibility* of the medium.

Again, $E_1 = E + \dfrac{P}{\epsilon_0}$

or, $\epsilon_r E = E + \dfrac{P}{\epsilon_0}$

or, $D = E + \dfrac{P}{\epsilon_0},$ (1.25)

where $D(= \epsilon_r E)$ is called the *dielectric displacement* or *electric induction*. With fields of low intensity, P is proportional to E.

Writing $P = \alpha E$ we have

$$D = E + \frac{\alpha E}{\epsilon_0} \quad \text{or,} \quad \epsilon_r E = E + \frac{\alpha E}{\epsilon_0}.$$

$\therefore \qquad \epsilon_r = 1 + \dfrac{\alpha}{\epsilon_0},$ (1.26)

where $\alpha \left(= \dfrac{P}{E} \right)$ is called the *polarisability* per unit volume.

1.18   Field due to a Polarised Medium

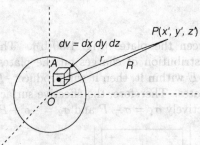

Fig. 1.31

In a polarised medium, there are many dipoles in alignment. The potential at a point P (Fig. 1.31) may be calculated as follows :

Consider a volume element dv at A of the material with sides dx, dy and dz. The electric moment of that volume will be $P dx dy dz$. The potential $d\phi$ at the point P at a distance r from the centre of the elementary volume will be

$$d\phi = \frac{P}{4\pi\epsilon_0} \left[l\frac{\partial}{\partial x}\left(\frac{1}{r}\right) + m\frac{\partial}{\partial y}\left(\frac{1}{r}\right) + n\frac{\partial}{\partial z}\left(\frac{1}{r}\right) \right] dx dy dz.$$

For a finite volume the potential will be

$$\phi = \frac{1}{4\pi\epsilon_0} \int\int\int \left[lP\frac{\partial}{\partial x}\left(\frac{1}{r}\right) + mP\frac{\partial}{\partial y}\left(\frac{1}{r}\right) + nP\frac{\partial}{\partial z}\left(\frac{1}{r}\right) \right] dx dy dz$$

$$= \frac{1}{4\pi\epsilon_0} \int\int\int \left[P_x\frac{\partial}{\partial x}\left(\frac{1}{r}\right) + P_y\frac{\partial}{\partial y}\left(\frac{1}{r}\right) + P_z\frac{\partial}{\partial z}\left(\frac{1}{r}\right) \right] dx dy dz, \quad (1.27)$$

where $P_x = lP$, $P_y = mP$ and $P_z = nP$ are the components of the polarisation along X, Y and Z directions respectively.

Now, $\dfrac{\partial}{\partial x}\left(\dfrac{P_x}{r}\right) = P_x \dfrac{\partial}{\partial x}\left(\dfrac{1}{r}\right) + \dfrac{1}{r}\left(\dfrac{\partial P_x}{\partial x}\right)$

$\therefore \quad P_x \dfrac{\partial}{\partial x}\left(\dfrac{1}{r}\right) = \dfrac{\partial}{\partial x}\left(\dfrac{P_x}{r}\right) - \dfrac{1}{r}\left(\dfrac{\partial P_x}{\partial x}\right).$

Similarly, we get

$$P_y \frac{\partial}{\partial y}\left(\frac{1}{r}\right) = \frac{\partial}{\partial y}\left(\frac{P_y}{r}\right) - \frac{1}{r}\left(\frac{\partial P_y}{\partial y}\right)$$

and $P_z \dfrac{\partial}{\partial z}\left(\dfrac{1}{r}\right) = \dfrac{\partial}{\partial z}\left(\dfrac{P_z}{r}\right) - \dfrac{1}{r}\left(\dfrac{\partial P_z}{\partial z}\right).$

Substituting in the expression (1.27) we get

$$\phi = \int\int\int \sum \left[\frac{\partial}{\partial x}\left(\frac{P_x}{r}\right) - \frac{1}{r}\left(\frac{\partial P_x}{\partial r}\right)\right] dx\,dy\,dz$$

$$= \int\int\int \left[\sum \frac{\partial}{\partial x}\left(\frac{P_x}{r}\right)\right] dx\,dy\,dz - \int\int\int \left[\frac{1}{r}\sum\frac{\partial P_x}{\partial x}\right] dx\,dy\,dz.$$

Now according to Gauss's divergence theorem, the first volume integral can be transformed into surface integral.

$$\therefore \quad \int\int\int \left[\sum \frac{\partial}{\partial x}\left(\frac{P_x}{r}\right)\right] dx\,dy\,dz = \int\int\left(l'\frac{P_x}{r} + m'\frac{P_y}{r} + n'\frac{P_z}{r}\right) ds,$$

where l', m' and n' are the direction cosines of an element having surface area ds.

$$\therefore \quad \phi = \frac{1}{r\pi\epsilon_0}\int\int\left(\frac{l'P_x}{r} + \frac{m'P_y}{r} + \frac{n'P_z}{r}\right) ds$$

$$= \frac{1}{4\pi\epsilon_0}\int\int\int \frac{1}{r}\left(\frac{\partial P_x}{\partial x} + \frac{\partial P_y}{\partial y} + \frac{\partial P_z}{\partial z}\right) dx\,dy\,dz \qquad (1.28)$$

Therefore, the potential at the point P due to a polarised medium may be considered to be due to two contributions :

(a) A surface distribution of charge P_n on the boundary surface of the dielectric where P_n is the normal component of P.

(b) A volume distribution of charge, $-\left(\dfrac{\partial P_x}{\partial x} + \dfrac{\partial P_y}{\partial y} + \dfrac{\partial P_z}{\partial z}\right) = -\mathrm{div}\ P.$

In a uniform polarisation, the volume distribution of charge is zero and so

$$\mathrm{div}\ P = 0.$$

Therefore, the potential is given by

$$\phi = \frac{1}{4\pi\epsilon_0}\int\int_S\left(l'\frac{P_x}{r} + m'\frac{P_y}{r} + n'\frac{P_z}{r}\right) ds. \qquad (1.29)$$

1.19   Potential due to a Uniformly Polarised Sphere

(i) At an External Point : Suppose we have a sphere of radius a, having polarisation P. Consider an elementary volume $dv = dx\,dy\,dz$ at a distant r from the field point P.

From Eq. (1.27), we can write

$$\phi_P = \frac{1}{4\pi\epsilon_0}\int\int\int P\nabla_A\left(\frac{1}{r}\right) dv,$$

where ∇_A denotes the differentiation with respect to the point $A(x, y, z)$.

Now, $r^2 = (x - x')^2 + (y - y')^2 + (z - z')^2$

or, $\quad r = \sqrt{(x - x')^2 + (y - y')^2 + (z - z')^2}$

$$\therefore \quad \frac{\partial}{\partial x}\left(\frac{1}{r}\right) = -\frac{1}{r^2}\frac{\partial r}{\partial x} = -\frac{x - x'}{r^3} \quad \text{and} \quad \frac{\partial}{\partial x'}\left(\frac{1}{r}\right) = -\frac{1}{r^2}\frac{\partial r}{\partial x'} = \frac{x - x'}{r^3}.$$

$$\therefore \quad \frac{\partial}{\partial x}\left(\frac{1}{r}\right) = -\frac{\partial}{\partial x'}\left(\frac{1}{r}\right).$$

Therefore, we find that $\nabla_A\left(\dfrac{1}{r}\right) = -\nabla_P\left(\dfrac{1}{r}\right).$

$$\therefore \quad \phi_P = -\frac{P}{4\pi\epsilon_0} \int\int\int \nabla_P \left(\frac{1}{r}\right) dv$$

$$= \frac{P}{4\pi\epsilon_0}(-\nabla_P \cdot V), \quad \text{where } V = \int\int\int \frac{dv}{r}.$$

Now let us substitute $N = -\nabla_P \cdot V$, where N is the electric field due to the potential V. Again, V is the potential due to uniform distribution of charges having surface density of charge unity. Hence we have to find out the field at the point P due to charged sphere of unit volume density.

$$\text{Thus, } N = \frac{\frac{4}{3}\pi a^3}{R^2} \cdot \hat{R} = \frac{4}{3}\pi a^3 \frac{R}{R^3}.$$

$$\therefore \qquad \phi_P = \frac{4}{3}\pi a^3 \frac{P \cdot R}{R^3}. \tag{1.30}$$

(ii) At an Internal Point : Suppose the sphere is polarised along X-direction.

$$\therefore \quad P = iP.$$

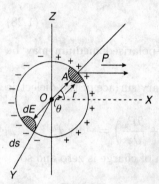

Fig. 1.32

Consider an elementary area ds at A (Fig. 1.32), the charge of the area is $Pds\cos\theta$.

The field at the centre O due to positive charge on ds and negative charge on the opposite area of ds will be $dE = 2\frac{Pds\cos\theta}{4\pi\epsilon_0 r^2}$ along $\overrightarrow{AO}$.

Now resolving dE along and normal to X-direction, we get

$$dE_\parallel = \frac{2Pds\cos^2\theta}{4\pi\epsilon_0 r^2} \quad \text{along } \overrightarrow{XO}$$

and $\quad dE_\perp = \frac{2Pds\sin\theta\cos\theta}{4\pi\epsilon_0 r^2} \quad$ along $\overrightarrow{ZO}$.

$$\therefore \quad E_\parallel = -\frac{2P}{4\pi\epsilon_0} \int \frac{\cos^2\theta}{r^2} ds \quad \text{along } \overrightarrow{OX}$$

$$= -\frac{2P}{4\pi\epsilon_0} \int_0^{\pi/2}\int_0^{2\pi} \cos^2\theta \sin\theta d\theta d\phi \quad [\because \ ds = r^2\sin\theta d\theta d\phi]$$

$$= -\frac{4\pi P}{3\cdot 4\pi\epsilon_0} = -\frac{P}{3\epsilon_0}. \tag{1.31}$$

Again, $E_\perp = -\dfrac{2P}{4\pi\epsilon_0} \displaystyle\int \frac{\sin\theta\cos\theta}{r^2} ds \quad$ along $\overrightarrow{OZ}$

$$= -\frac{2P}{4\pi\epsilon_0} \int_0^{\pi/2}\int_0^{2\pi} \cos\theta\sin^2\theta d\theta d\phi = 0.$$

So the field at the point O will be opposite to the direction of P, i.e.,

$$E = -\frac{P}{3\epsilon_0} \quad \text{or,} \quad \frac{\partial\phi}{\partial x} = \frac{4}{3}\pi P.$$

$$\therefore \qquad \phi = \frac{Px}{3\epsilon_0} + \phi_0. \tag{1.32}$$

1.20   Cavities in a Solid Dielectric

The idea of electric field inside a solid dielectric may be obtained by considering the force acting on a unit positive charge in free space within the dielectric. According to Kelvin's approach one may consider empty cavities within the dielectric and determine the field from the equivalent charge distribution. The results will, however, depend on the shape of the cavity. Here we shall discuss three types of cavity :

(a) **Needle-shaped Cavity** : Let AB (Fig. 1.33) be a cavity whose length is greater compared with its cross-section and it is placed along the direction of the lines of electric field in a homogeneous dielectric. In such a cavity the polarised bound charges on the surface of the cavity will appear on the end face surfaces A and B, and the surface density of charge will be $\sigma_P = P$. Since the cross-section of the cavity is small, the effect of charges at the end faces will be negligibly small at the point C (centre of the cavity). Therefore, the force on the charge at C will be due to only the surface charges on the conducting plates. According to boundary conditions, the tangential components of electric field are continuous across the boundary separating two dielectric media. So the field in the cavity will be same as the inner field within the dielectric.

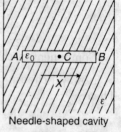

Needle-shaped cavity

Fig. 1.33

Thus the force on a unit positive charge placed at C will give the measure of the electric field E in the dielectric.

(b) **Disc-shaped Cavity** : Suppose, AB is a disc-shaped cavity (Fig. 1.34) whose diameter is greater compared with its thickness along the field E. A small unit positive charge placed at C will experience a force due to bound charge σ_P per unit area of the circular sides and to the charge σ_X per unit area of the conducting plate. The respective displacement

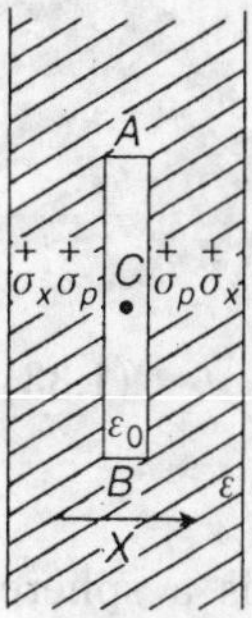

$$D_1 = \frac{\sigma_X}{\epsilon} \text{ due to } \sigma_X \text{ per unit area,}$$

$$D_2 = \frac{\sigma_P}{\epsilon} \text{ due to } \sigma_P \text{ per unit area.}$$

So the total displacement within the cavity is

$$D = [\sigma_X + \sigma_P]\frac{1}{\epsilon} = \epsilon E + P.$$

Disc-shaped cavity

Fig. 1.34

According to boundary condition the normal component of displacement at the boundary separating the two media must be continuous. So the force on unit positive charge placed at C will give a measure of electric displacement in the dielectric.

(c) **Spherical Cavity** : Consider a cavity of spherical shape having radius r and centre at C (Fig. 1.35).

Here we find out the force on a unit positive charge placed at C.

The force F acting on the unit positive charge will be due to

(i) charge σ per unit area on the parallel plates on either side of the dielectric. This force will be

$$E_1 = \frac{\sigma}{\epsilon}.$$

(ii) polarised dielectric surrounding the sphere. This force E_2 itself consists of two parts :

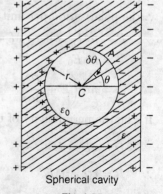

Spherical cavity

Fig. 1.35

(a) The force due to bound charges σ_P per unit area on the dielectric surface facing the parallel plates,

$$x_1 = -\frac{\sigma_P}{\epsilon}.$$

(b) The force by the charge on the surface of the cavity due to polarisation. To find out this force x_2 we consider an elementary area ds at $A(r, \theta)$. The component of polarisation normal to ds will be $P \cos \theta$. So the force on unit charge at C will be

$$\frac{P \cos \theta ds}{4\epsilon r^2} \quad \text{along } \overrightarrow{CA}.$$

Component of this force along X is $\frac{P \cos^2 \theta ds}{4\pi\epsilon r^2}$ and normal to X is $\frac{P \sin \theta \cos \theta ds}{4\pi\epsilon r^2}$.

Now we choose the area ds to be ring-shaped between angles θ and $(\theta + d\theta)$. Then

$$ds = 2\pi r^2 \sin \theta d\theta$$

The components of force normal to X due to this ring will vanish on account of symmetry. The component of force along X is

$$P \frac{2\pi r^2 \sin \theta \cos^2 \theta d\theta}{4\pi\epsilon r^2}.$$

$$\therefore \quad x_2 = 2 \int_0^{\pi/2} \frac{2\pi P r^2 \sin \theta \cos^2 \theta d\theta}{4\pi\epsilon r^2} = \frac{4\pi P}{4\pi\epsilon} \int_0^{\pi/2} \sin \theta \cos^2 \theta d\theta = \frac{P}{3\epsilon}.$$

Therefore, the resultant force on the unit charge at C is

$$E_0 = E_1 + E_2 = E_1 + x_1 + x_2$$

$$= \frac{\sigma}{\epsilon} - \frac{P}{\epsilon} + \frac{P}{3\epsilon} = \frac{1}{\epsilon}(\sigma - P) + \frac{P}{3\epsilon}$$

$$= E + \frac{P}{3\epsilon}. \tag{1.33}$$

1.21   Clausius-Mosotti Relation

Suppose we have n atoms per unit volume of the gas. Each atom is a sphere provided the gaseous dielectric is isotropic. Then the electric field within the atom according to Eq. (1.33) will be

$$E_0 = E + \frac{P}{3\epsilon}. \tag{1.34}$$

$\therefore$ the polarisation per unit volume is

$$P = nM, \quad \text{where } M = \text{moment of the atom} = \alpha X_0$$

$$= n\alpha E_0$$

$$= n\alpha \left(E + \frac{P}{3\epsilon} \right). \tag{1.35}$$

If ϵ be the permittivity of the medium, then the displacement

$$D = \epsilon E = E + \frac{P}{\epsilon}.$$

$$\therefore \quad P = \epsilon(\epsilon - 1)E.$$

$$\therefore \quad E = \frac{1}{\epsilon(\epsilon - 1)}P.$$

Substituting in Eq. (1.34), we get

$$E_0 = \frac{P}{\epsilon(\epsilon - 1)} + \frac{P}{3\epsilon} = \frac{\epsilon + 2}{3\epsilon(\epsilon - 1)}P$$

$$\therefore \quad P = \frac{3\epsilon(\epsilon - 1)}{\epsilon + 2}E_0. \tag{1.36}$$

From Eqs. (1.35) and (1.36), we have

$$\frac{3\epsilon(\epsilon - 1)}{\epsilon + 2} = n\alpha \quad \left[\because E_0 = E + \frac{P}{3\epsilon} \right]$$

or, $\quad \dfrac{\epsilon - 1}{\epsilon + 2} = \dfrac{n\alpha}{3\epsilon_0}. \tag{1.37}$

The molecular polarisability is constant; $\frac{\epsilon-1}{\epsilon+2}$ is proportional to the density. This equation has been examined for different gases. The Eq. (1.37) is known as *Clausius-Mosotti relation*.

If η be the refractive index of the medium, then $\epsilon \propto \eta^2$. Hence Eq. (1.37) may also be written as $\frac{\eta^2-1}{\eta^2+2}$ = constant and is known as *Lorentz-Lorentz formula*.

1.22   Stresses in Dielectric

Suppose a tube of induction starts from a charged conductor having dielectric constant k. Consider an elementary area ds (Fig. 1.36) having charge σ per unit area. Then the total number of tubes of unit strength will be σds. Therefore, the number of such tubes per unit area will be $N = \sigma$.

Now, $\quad E = \dfrac{\sigma}{\epsilon} = \dfrac{N}{\epsilon} \quad$ or, $\quad N = \epsilon E.$

The force on area ds is $\dfrac{2\pi\sigma^2 ds}{4\pi\epsilon} = \dfrac{2\pi N^2 ds}{4\pi\epsilon}$ towards the tubes.

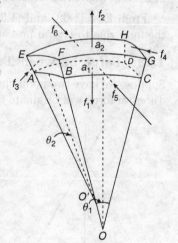

At equilibrium of the conductor the tension near the ends of the tube must be $\frac{N^2 ds}{2\epsilon}$ towards the conductor.

Consider a small section of the tube. $ABCD$ and $EFGH$ are two surfaces of the section. The downward force on $ABCD$ is

$$f_1 = \frac{N_1^2}{2\epsilon} \cdot a_1, \text{ where } a_1 = \text{area } ABCD.$$

Similarly, the upward force on $EFGH$ is

$$f_2 = \frac{N_2^2}{2\epsilon} \cdot a_2, \text{ where } a_2 = \text{area } EFGH.$$

$$\therefore \quad f_1 - f_2 = \frac{1}{2\epsilon}(N_1^2 a_1 - N_2^2 a_2)$$

Now unit tubes on the two sides must be equal.

$$\therefore \quad N_1 a_1 = N_2 a_2$$

Fig. 1.36

$$\therefore \quad f_1 - f_2 = \frac{1}{2\epsilon}(N_1 N_2 a_2 - N_1 N_2 a_1) = \frac{1}{2\epsilon}N^2(a_2 - a_1).$$

Again, suppose the lateral pressure due to tube on $AEFB$ is $\frac{N^2}{2\epsilon}$. Therefore, force on $AEFB$ is

$$f_3 = \frac{N^2}{2\epsilon} \cdot a_3, \text{ where } a_3 = \text{area } AEFB.$$

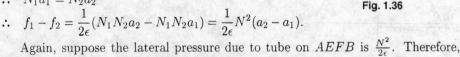

Component of f_3 along $f_2 = \dfrac{N^2}{2\epsilon} a_3 \sin\theta_1$

$$= \dfrac{N^2}{2\epsilon} a_3\theta_1, \text{ provided } \theta_1 \text{ is very small.}$$

In a similar way, component of force f_4 along $f_2 = \dfrac{N^2}{2\epsilon} a_4\theta_1$,

where a_4 = area $DHGC$.

Therefore, the resultant force along f_2 is

$$2 \times \dfrac{N^2}{2\epsilon} a_3\theta_1 = \dfrac{N^2}{\epsilon} a_3\theta_1 \quad (\because \; a_3 = a_4)$$

Similarly, the component of force along f_2 due to lateral pressure on the area $FGCB$ and $AEHD$ will be

$$2 \times \dfrac{N^2}{2\epsilon} a_5\theta_2 = \dfrac{N^2}{\epsilon} a_5\theta_2.$$

$\therefore$ total upward force $= \dfrac{N^2}{\epsilon}(a_3\theta_1 + a_5\theta_2) = \dfrac{N^2}{\epsilon}(dr \cdot r_2 \cdot \theta_2\theta_1 + dr \cdot r_1 \cdot \theta_1\theta_2)$

$$= \dfrac{N^2}{\epsilon}\theta_1\theta_2 dr(r_1 + r_2) \tag{1.38}$$

Again, total downward force $= \dfrac{N^2}{\epsilon}(a_2 - a_1)$

$$= \dfrac{N^2}{\epsilon}\{(r_1 + dr)\theta_1 \cdot (r_2 + dr)\theta_2 - (r_1 \cdot \theta_1 \cdot r_2 \cdot \theta_2)\}$$

$$= \dfrac{N^2}{\epsilon}\theta_1\theta_2 dr(r_1 + r_2) \tag{1.39}$$

neglecting high order terms of dr.

From Eqs. (1.38) and (1.39) we find that the force due to tension will balance the force due to lateral pressure.

1.23 Force between Two Point Charges in Air

Suppose we have two point charges (q, q) placed at A and B respectively (Fig. 1.37). Tubes of force will originate from A and B and will terminate at infinity.

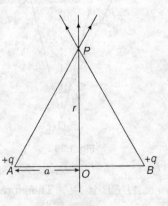

Fig. 1.37

Intensity at P,

$$E = \dfrac{1}{4\pi\epsilon_0} \dfrac{2q}{AP^2} \sin\theta \quad \text{along } OP.$$

Now, $\sec\theta = \dfrac{AP}{AO}, \quad \therefore \quad AP = a\sec\theta.$

$$\therefore \qquad E = \dfrac{1}{4\pi\epsilon_0} \dfrac{2q\sin\theta}{a^2\sec^2\theta}. \tag{1.40}$$

Total force due to lateral pressure will be

$$F = \dfrac{1}{4\pi\epsilon_0} \int_0^\infty 2\pi N^2 \cdot 2\pi r dr$$

$$= \dfrac{1}{2\epsilon_0} \int_0^\infty N^2 \cdot 2\pi r dr.$$

Now, $2\pi r dr = 2\pi a \tan\theta \cdot a\sec^2\theta \, d\theta = 2\pi a^2 \tan\theta \sec^2\theta \, d\theta.$

Again, $N = \epsilon_0 E = \dfrac{q \sin \theta}{2\pi a^2 \sec^2 \theta}$.

$$F = \frac{1}{2\epsilon_0} \int_0^{\pi/2} \frac{q^2 \sin^2 \theta}{4\pi^2 a^4 \sec^2 \theta} 2\pi a^2 \tan^2 \theta \sec^2 \theta d\theta$$

$$= \frac{1}{4\pi\epsilon_0} \int_0^{\pi/2} \frac{q^2}{a^2} \sin^3 \theta \cos \theta d\theta.$$

Let us put $\sin \theta = x$.

$$\therefore \qquad F = \int_0^1 \frac{1}{4\pi\epsilon_0} \frac{q^2}{a^2} \cdot x^3 dx = \frac{1}{4\pi\epsilon_0} \cdot \frac{q^2}{a^2} \cdot \frac{1}{4}$$

$$= \frac{q^2}{16\pi\epsilon_0 a^2}. \tag{1.41}$$

1.24 Dielectric Absorption

When a capacitor having solid or liquid dielectric is charged, it does not acquire full charge immediately though the circuit have practically zero resistance. After a finite interval of time the capacitor will be fully charged. Again, when the charged capacitor is made to discharge, it is found that the capacitor still retains a residual charge when the external short circuit is removed. These phenomena are due to dielectric absorption. After the application of external field induced dipoles are not all oriented immediately along the field unless the dielectric is perfectly homogeneous. The charges obtained after the discharge is known as residual discharge. The gases have no residual discharges. The explanation of the phenomena may be obtained from the idea of orientation of the dipoles. When the charged capacitor is short-circuited, the plates of the capacitor have same potential. If then the short circuit is removed, the charges on the surface of plates and the charges inside the dielectric will not be in equilibrium. The discharge of electricity is much weaker process than the re-orientation of the dipoles. As a result current is set up in dielectric. On short circuiting the capacitor again, a new discharge will occur due to residual discharge.

Examples

1. Six equal charges $+q$ are placed at the corners of the base of a hexagonal pyramid. If the slant edge of the pyramid is equal to the diagonal of its base, find the intensity of field at the apex due to the charges at the base.

   Solution : Let $ABCDEF$ be the base of the hexa-gonal pyramid (Fig. 1.38). Each side of the base is of length a and each base angle is $120°$. Length of each diagonal will be $2a$.

   Now, the intensity at the apex due to the charge q at A will be

   $$F_A = \frac{q}{4a^2} \text{ along } AR.$$

   Resolving the intensity along OS and perpendicular to OS, we find that the perpendicular components will cancel each other because the intensity due to each charge is the same.

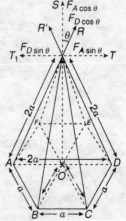

Fig. 1.38

Hence total intensity at the apex due to all charges

$$= \frac{6q}{4a^2}\cos\theta \text{ along } OS = \frac{6q}{4a^2}\cdot\frac{\sqrt{3}}{2}$$

$$= \frac{3\sqrt{3}q}{4a^2}.$$

2. Calculate the radius of a water drop which would just remain suspended in the earth's electric field of 3 volts/cm when charged with one electron ($e = 4.805 \times 10^{-10}$ e.s.u. and $g = 980$ cm/s^2).

Solution : According to the problem, the electric intensity,

$$E = 3 \text{ volts/cm} = \frac{3}{300} = \frac{1}{100} \text{ e.s.u./cm.}$$

Force experienced by the electron $= eE = 4.805 \times 10^{-10} \times \dfrac{1}{100}$

$$= 4.805 \times 10^{-12} \text{ dynes.}$$

At equilibrium this force must be balanced by the downward force due to gravity.

$$\therefore \quad 4.805 \times 10^{-12} = \frac{4}{3}\pi r^3 \rho g,$$

where r is the radius of water drop, and density of water, $\rho = 1$ g/cc.

$$\therefore \quad r^3 = \frac{3 \times 4.805 \times 10^{-12}}{4 \times 3.14 \times 1 \times 980}$$

$$r = \sqrt[3]{\frac{3 \times 4.805 \times 10^{-12}}{4 \times 3.14 \times 1 \times 980}} = 1.05 \times 10^{-5} \text{ cm.}$$

3. If the potential at a point outside a conducting sphere of radius a is $-F\cos\theta\left(r - \frac{a^3}{r^2}\right)$, where r is the distance measured from the centre, θ is the angular distance measured from a fixed diameter and F is a constant. Find the surface density at any point of the sphere and show that the total charge on the sphere is zero.

Solution : Potential at any point outside the sphere,

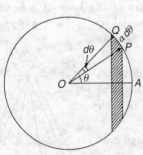

$$\phi = -F\cos\theta\left(r - \frac{a^3}{r^2}\right).$$

$$\therefore \quad -\frac{d\phi}{dr} = F\cos\theta\left(1 + \frac{2a^3}{r^3}\right) = E.$$

But on the surface of the sphere, $E = 4\pi\sigma$.

$$\therefore \quad 4\pi\sigma = E|_{r=a} = 3F\cos\theta \quad \text{or,} \quad \sigma = \frac{3F\cos\theta}{4\pi}.$$

Hence, the surface density of charge at any point of the sphere,

Fig. 1.39

$$\sigma = \frac{3}{4\pi}F\cos\theta.$$

Now charge on the elementary ring (Fig. 1.39)

$$= 2\pi a^2\sin\theta d\theta\cdot\sigma = \frac{3F}{2}a^2\sin\theta\cos\theta d\theta.$$

$\therefore$ total charge on the sphere, $Q = \int_0^{\pi} \dfrac{3F}{2} a^2 \sin\theta \cos\theta\, d\theta$

$$= \dfrac{3F}{4} a^2 \cdot \int_0^{\pi} \sin 2\theta\, d\theta = 0.$$

4. Suppose two dipoles are kept separated by a fixed distance. Show that if angles of the dipoles made with the line joining their centres are θ_1 and θ_2 respectively, then at equilibrium $\tan\theta_1 = -2\tan\theta_2$.

Solution : The position of the dipoles is shown in Fig. 1.40. Suppose, M_1 and M_2 are respectively the moment of the two dipoles A and B. We know that the mutual potential energy between the dipoles,

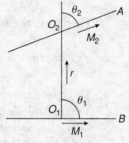

Fig. 1.40

$$W = \dfrac{M_1 M_2}{r^3} (\sin\theta_1 \sin\theta_2 - 2\cos\theta_1 \cos\theta_2).$$

If the angle θ_1 is kept fixed, then torque,

$$\Gamma = \dfrac{\partial W}{\partial \theta_2} = \dfrac{M_1 M_2}{r^3} (\sin\theta_1 \cos\theta_2 + 2\cos\theta_1 \sin\theta_2).$$

For equilibrium, $\Gamma = 0$;

$\therefore$ $\sin\theta_1 \cos\theta_2 = -2\cos\theta_1 \sin\theta_2$ or, $\dfrac{\sin\theta_1}{\cos\theta_1} = -2\dfrac{\sin\theta_2}{\cos\theta_2}$.

$\therefore$ $\tan\theta_1 = -2\tan\theta_2$ **(Proved)**.

5. Two large parallel plates at a distance d are maintained at potentials ϕ_1 and ϕ_2; find the force per unit area on either of them, and find the effect of interposing a slab of dielectric constant ϵ and thickness t between the plates.

Solution : Suppose, σ be the charge per unit area of the plate AB (Fig. 1.41).

$E = 4\pi\sigma$.

$\therefore$ $\phi_1 - \phi_2 = 4\pi\sigma \cdot d$.

$\therefore$ $\sigma = \dfrac{\phi_1 - \phi_2}{4\pi d}$.

Hence force per unit area on either of the plates,

$$E = 2\pi\sigma^2 = 2\pi \left(\dfrac{\phi_1 - \phi_2}{4\pi d} \right)^2 = \dfrac{(\phi_1 - \phi_2)^2}{8\pi d^2}.$$

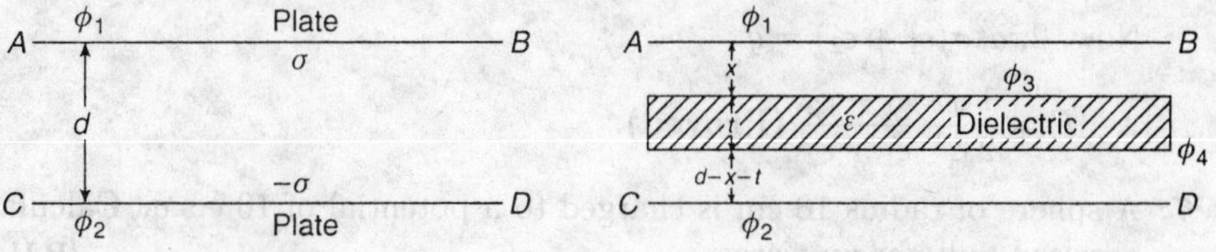

A — ϕ_1 — Plate — B		A — ϕ_1 — B

Fig. 1.41   **Fig. 1.42**

If A be the area of the plate, then total force,

$$F = \dfrac{(\phi_1 - \phi_2)^2}{8\pi d^2} \cdot A.$$

When there is a dielectric between the plates (Fig. 1.42),

$$\phi_1 - \phi_2 = (\phi_1 - \phi_3) + (\phi_3 - \phi_4) + (\phi_4 - \phi_2)$$

Now, $\phi_1 - \phi_3 = 4\pi\sigma x$,

$$\phi_3 - \phi_4 = \frac{4\pi\sigma}{\epsilon} \cdot t,$$

$$\phi_4 - \phi_2 = 4\pi\sigma(d - x - t).$$

$$\therefore \quad \phi_1 - \phi_2 = 4\pi\sigma\left(d - t + \frac{t}{\epsilon}\right).$$

$$\therefore \quad \sigma = \frac{\phi_1 - \phi_2}{4\pi\left(d - t + \frac{t}{\epsilon}\right)}.$$

Therefore, the force experienced by the plate

$$= 2\pi\sigma^2 \cdot A = 2\pi\frac{(\phi_1 - \phi_2)^2}{16\pi^2\left(d - t + \frac{t}{\epsilon}\right)^2} \cdot A = \frac{A}{8\pi}\left(\frac{\phi_1 - \phi_2}{d - t + \frac{t}{\epsilon}}\right)^2.$$

6. The space between two concentric conducting spheres is filled on one side of a diametral plane with a dielectric of dielectric constant ϵ_1 and on the other side, with a dielectric of dielectric constant ϵ_2. The inner sphere is of radius a and has a charge q; show that the force on it perpendicular to this diametral plane is $F = \dfrac{1}{2}\dfrac{\epsilon_1 - \epsilon_2}{(\epsilon_1 + \epsilon_2)^2} \cdot \dfrac{q^2}{a^2}.$

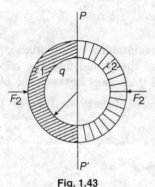

Fig. 1.43

Solution : Suppose σ_1 and σ_2 be the surface densities of charge on the left and the right of the diametral plane (Fig. 1.43) respectively.

$$\therefore \quad 2\pi a^2\sigma_1 + 2\pi a^2\sigma_2 = q.$$

If σ be the surface density of charge in the absence of dielectric, then

$$q = 2\pi a^2\sigma(\epsilon_1 + \epsilon_2).$$

Now, force per unit area of the dielectric $= \dfrac{2\pi\sigma^2}{\epsilon}.$

$$\therefore \quad F_2 = \int_0^{\frac{\pi}{2}} \frac{2\pi(\sigma\epsilon_2)^2}{\epsilon_2} 2\pi a \sin\theta \cos\theta\, a\, d\theta$$

$$= 2\pi^2\sigma^2 a^2\epsilon_2.$$

Similarly, $F_1 = 2\pi^2\sigma^2 a^2\epsilon_1.$

$\therefore$ resultant force $F = F_1 - F_2 = 2\pi^2\sigma^2 a^2(\epsilon_1 - \epsilon_2).$

Now, $2\pi a^2\sigma(\epsilon_1 + \epsilon_2) = q.$

$$\therefore \quad F = \frac{1}{2}\frac{q^2}{a^2}\frac{\epsilon_1 - \epsilon_2}{\epsilon_1 + \epsilon_2} \textbf{ (Proved)}.$$

7. A sphere of radius 10 cm is charged to a potential of 10 e.s.u. Calculate the outward pull per unit area.   **[P.U. 1957]**

Solution : Here, $V = 10$ e.s.u., $r = 10$ cm.

$$\because \quad V = \frac{q}{r},$$

$$\therefore \quad q = V \times r = 10 \times 10 = 100 \text{ e.s.u.}$$

The surface density of charge,

$$\sigma = \frac{q}{4\pi r^2} = \frac{100}{4\pi \times 100} = \frac{1}{4\pi}\text{e.s.u./cm}^2.$$

∴ outward force per unit area,

$$f = 2\pi\sigma^2 = 2\pi\left(\frac{1}{4\pi}\right)^2 = \frac{1}{8\pi} \text{ dyne/cm}^2.$$

8. A metal ball of radius 5 cm is given a charge of 100 e.s.u. Find the force acting on it per unit area.   [C.U. 1971]

   Solution : Here, charge, $q = 100$ e.s.u., radius of the ball, $r = 5$ cm.

   ∴ the surface area of the ball $= 4\pi r^2 = 4\pi \times 25$ sq. cm $= 100\pi$ sq. cm

   The surface density of charge, $\sigma = \dfrac{q}{4\pi r^2} = \dfrac{100}{100\pi} = \dfrac{1}{\pi}$ e.s.u./sq. cm.

   So the force per unit area of the charged surface,

   $$f = \frac{2\pi\sigma^2}{K} = 2\pi\sigma^2 \quad (\text{in air, } K = 1)$$
   $$= 2\pi\left(\frac{1}{\pi}\right)^2 = \frac{2}{\pi} = \frac{2}{3.14}$$
   $$= \mathbf{0.637 \text{ dyne/sq. cm.}}$$

9. Calculate the potential in e.s.u. to which a spherical conductor of unit radius has to be charged in order that the mechanical pressure may be equal to the normal atmospheric pressure, viz., 10^6 dynes/sq. cm.   [C.U. 1939]

   Solution : Here, mechanical pressure, $2\pi\sigma^2 = 10^6$ dynes/sq. cm.

   $$\therefore \qquad \sigma = \frac{10^3}{\sqrt{(2\pi)}}.$$

   Again, $\sigma = \dfrac{q}{4\pi r^2} = \dfrac{q}{4\pi (1)^2} \quad (\because r = 1)$

   $$= \frac{q}{4\pi}.$$

   $$\therefore \qquad q = 4\pi\sigma = \frac{4\pi \cdot 10^3}{\sqrt{(2\pi)}}.$$

   So the required potential, $V = \dfrac{q}{r} = \dfrac{4\pi \cdot 10^3}{\sqrt{(2\pi)} \cdot 1}$

   $$= \mathbf{5024 \text{ e.s.u.}}$$

10. Find the value of electrostatic pressure on a charged surface with a surface density of 10 e.s.u./cm². What will be its value expressed in mm of mercury? Given that density of mercury = 13.6 g/cc, acceleration due to gravity = 980 cm/second².   [B.U. 1969]

    Solution : Here, $\sigma = 10$ e.s.u./cm².

    ∴ electrostatic pressure, $f = 2\pi\sigma^2 = 2\pi \cdot (10)^2$
    $$= 200\pi \text{ dynes/cm}^2.$$

    Let the pressure of h mm of Hg column $= 200$ dynes/cm²,

    i.e., $\dfrac{h}{10}\rho g = 200\pi.$

    $$\therefore \quad h = \frac{200\pi \times 10}{\rho g} = \frac{2000 \times 3.14}{13.6 \times 980}$$

    $$= \mathbf{0.471 \text{ mm.}}$$

11. The pressure of air inside an electrically charged soap-bubble of radius 1.5 cm is the same as that of outside. If the surface tension of soap solution is 27 dynes/cm, find the electric potential of the bubble.   **[Bihar.U. 1952]**

   Solution : We know that the charge on the surface of the bubble,

   $$q = 4r\sqrt{(2\pi Tr)}.$$

   $\therefore$ the required potential, $V = \dfrac{q}{r} = 4\sqrt{(2\pi Tr)} = 4\sqrt{2 \times 3.14 \times 27 \times 1.5}$

   $$(\because\ T = 27 \text{ dynes/cm and } r = 1.5 \text{ cm})$$

   $$= 63.81 \text{ e.s.u.} = 63.81 \times 300 \text{ volts}$$

   $$= \ \mathbf{19143 \ volts.}$$

12. A soap-bubble has a radius of 1.2 cm when charged to a potential of 12000 volts. Calculate the excess pressure inside the bubble, the surface tension of soap-solution being 24×10^{-5} N/m.

   Solution : If Q coulomb be the charge of the soap-bubble, then

   $$Q = 4\pi\epsilon_0 r \times V.$$

   The excess pressure of the charged bubble,

   $$P = \frac{4T}{r} - \frac{Q^2}{32\epsilon_0\pi^2 r^4} = \frac{4T}{r} - \frac{16\pi^2\epsilon_0 r^2 \times V^2}{32\epsilon_0\pi^2 r^4} = \frac{4T}{r} - \frac{\epsilon_0 V^2}{2r^2}$$

   $$= \frac{4 \times 24 \times 10^{-3}}{1.2 \times 10^{-2}} - \frac{8.85 \times 10^{-12} \times (12000)^2}{2 \times (1.2 \times 10^{-2})}$$

   $$\doteq 8 - 4.42 = \ \mathbf{3.58 \ N/m^2}.$$

13. The pressure of air inside an electrically charged soap-bubble of radius 1.5 cm is the same as that of outside. If the surface tension of the soap solution is 27×10^{-3} N/m, find the electric potential of the bubble.

   Solution : When inner and outer pressure of a bubble are equal, then the potential of soap-bubble is

   $$V = 2\sqrt{2T \cdot r/\epsilon_0}.$$

   Given that $T = 27 \times 10^{-3}$ N/m, $r = 1.5$ cm $= 0.015$ m,

   $$\epsilon_0 = 8.85 \times 10^{12} \text{ C}^2/\text{ N-m}^2.$$

   $$\therefore\quad V = 2\sqrt{\frac{2 \times 27 \times 10^{-3} \times 0.015}{8.85 \times 10^{-12}}} = \ \mathbf{19.13 \times 10^3 \ volts.}$$

14. The diameter of a soap-bubble is 0.04 metre. To what potential must the bubble be raised so that the pressure inside the bubble is equal to the pressure outside? Surface tension of soap solution $= 24 \times 10^{-3}$ N/m. What will be the charge on the bubble at that time?

   Solution : When the pressure inside and outside are equal,

   $$V = 2\sqrt{\frac{2Tr}{\epsilon_0}}.$$

   Given that $T = 24 \times 10^{-3}$ N/m; $r = 0.02$ m; $\epsilon_0 = 8.85 \times 10^{-12}$ C^2/N-m^2.

   $$\therefore\quad V = 2 \times \sqrt{\frac{2 \times 24 \times 10^{-3} \times 0.02}{8.85 \times 10^{-12}}} = 20\,840 \text{ volts.}$$

Again, $Q = 8\pi r\sqrt{2\epsilon_0 T r}$

$$= 8 \times 3.14 \times 0.02\sqrt{2 \times 8.85 \times 10^{-12} \times 24 \times 10^{-3} \times 0.02}$$

$$= \mathbf{0.46 \times 10^{-7} \ coulomb}.$$

15. **A soap-bubble is blown at one end of a capillary glass tube inside an evacuated chamber, the source of air pressure then being cut off. The bubble is then charged to a potential of 6000 volts and the radius of the charged bubble is found to be 1 cm. If the surface tension of soap solution is 30×10^{-3} N/m, find the original radius of the bubble.**

Solution : Let the initial radius of the bubble $= r_0$ cm. If p_0 be the initial pressure inside the bubble, then the excess pressure will also be p_0.

$\therefore \quad p_0 = \dfrac{4T}{r_0}$, where T = surface tension of soap solution.

Let, after charging, the radius of the bubble increase to r cm and the internal air pressure reduce to p. Then according to Boyle's law,

$$p_0 v_0 = p \cdot v \quad \text{or,} \quad p_0 \times \frac{4}{3}\pi r_0^3 = p \times \frac{4}{3}\pi r^3.$$

$\therefore \quad p = \left(\dfrac{r_0}{r}\right)^3 \cdot p_0,$

i.e., $\quad p = \dfrac{r_0^3}{r^3} \times \dfrac{4T}{r_0} = \dfrac{4Tr_0^2}{r^3}.$

If q coulomb be the quantity of charge of the bubble, then

$$V = \frac{q}{4\pi\epsilon_0 r} \ \text{volt}.$$

Again, if the surface density of charge of the bubble be σ coulomb/m^2, then $q = 4\pi r^2 \cdot \sigma$.

$\therefore \quad V = \dfrac{4\pi r^2 \cdot \sigma}{4\pi\epsilon_0 \cdot r} \quad \text{or,} \quad \sigma = \dfrac{V\epsilon_0}{r}.$

At the steady condition,

$$p + \frac{\sigma^2}{2\epsilon_0} = \frac{4T}{r}, \quad \text{where} \quad \frac{\sigma^2}{2\epsilon_0} = \text{outward electrostatic pressure}.$$

$\therefore \quad \dfrac{4Tr_0^2}{r^3} + \dfrac{\epsilon_0^2 V^2}{2\epsilon_0 \cdot r^2} = \dfrac{4T}{r} \quad \text{or,} \quad \dfrac{r_0^2}{r^2} = 1 - \dfrac{V^2\epsilon_0}{8rT}$

$\therefore \quad \dfrac{r_0^2}{r^2} = 1 - \dfrac{36 \times 10^6 \times 8.85 \times 10^{-12}}{8 \times 30 \times 10^{-3} \times 10^{-2}} \quad (\because \ r = 1 \ \text{cm} = 10^{-2} \ \text{m})$

$$= 1 - 0.01275 = 0.98725.$$

So, $\quad \dfrac{r_0}{r} = 0.994$

or, $\quad r_0 = 0.994 \times 10^{-2} \ \text{m} = \mathbf{0.994 \ cm}.$

16. **Calculate the potential to which a spherical conductor of radius 1 m has to be raised in order that the electrostatic pressure may be equal to twice the normal atmospheric pressure which is 10^5 N/m^2.** **[C.U. 1993]**

Solution : If σ be the surface density of charge of the conductor, then electrostatic pressure $= \sigma^2/2\epsilon_0$.

$\therefore \quad \dfrac{\sigma^2}{2\epsilon_0} = 2 \times 10^5 \quad$ or, $\quad \sigma = 200\sqrt{10\epsilon_0}$.

If Q be the quantity of charge of the conductor, then

$$\sigma = \dfrac{Q}{4\pi r^2} = \dfrac{Q}{4\pi(1)^2} \quad \text{or,} \quad Q = 4\pi\sigma = 4\pi \times 200\sqrt{10\epsilon_0}$$

$\therefore \quad$ potential of the conductor, $V = \dfrac{Q}{4\pi\epsilon_0 \cdot r} = \dfrac{4\pi \times 200\sqrt{10\epsilon_0}}{4\pi\epsilon_0 \times 1}$

$$= \mathbf{212.2 \times 10^6 \ V} \ (\epsilon_0 = 8.85 \times 10^{-12}).$$

17. A conducting sphere of radius 5 cm is charged to a potential of 300 volts. Find the outward force exerted per unit area of the surface of the sphere due to its charge, the sphere being placed in air. **[C.U. 1984]**

Solution : We know, charge, $q = 4\pi\epsilon_0 \cdot r \cdot V = 4\pi\epsilon_0 \cdot 300 \times (0.05)$ coulomb.

$$(r = 5 \text{ cm} = 0.05 \text{ m})$$

So the surface density of charge,

$$\sigma = \dfrac{\text{charge}}{\text{surface area}} = \dfrac{4\pi\epsilon_0 \cdot 300 \times (0.05)}{4\pi(0.05)^2} = \dfrac{3\epsilon_0}{5} \times 10^4 \ \text{C/m}^2.$$

$\therefore \quad$ outward pressure per unit area $= \dfrac{\sigma^2}{2\epsilon_0} = \dfrac{9\epsilon_0^2 \times 10^8}{25 \times 2\epsilon_0} = 18 \times \epsilon_0 \times 10^6$

$$= 18 \times 8.85 \times 10^{-12} \times 10^6$$

$$= \mathbf{15.93 \times 10^{-5} \ N/m^2}.$$

18. The force of attraction between two charges of $+80$ e.s.u. and -70 e.s.u. separated by a distance of 25 cm is found to be 4 dynes. Find the dielectric constant of the medium. **[C.U. old reg. 1965]**

Solution : From coulomb's law we get, $F = \dfrac{q_1 q_2}{K r^2}$

or, $\quad K = \dfrac{q_1 q_2}{F r^2} \quad$ (K = dielectric constant)

$$= \dfrac{80 \times 70}{4 \times (25)^2} = \mathbf{2.24}.$$

19. A negatively charged pith ball, weighing 0.1 gram is held in equilibrium in space by a body at a distance of 2 cm above it. If the negative charge on the pith ball is -20 e.s.u., what should be the amount of charge on the other body? Assume $g = 980$ cm/second^2. **[C.U. 1963]**

Solution : As the other body is above the pith ball, so there will remain positive charge in that body. If $\pm q$ be the charge of that body, then

$$\text{attractive force} = \dfrac{20 \times q}{(2)^2} = 5q \text{ dynes upward}$$

and the downward weight of the pith ball, $mg = 0.1 \times 980$.

$\therefore \quad 5q = 0.1 \times 980 \quad$ or, $\quad q = \mathbf{19.6}$ **e.s.u.**

20. A conducting plate is charged to a potential of 4000 volts. A second metal plate, charged to a potential of 1000 volts, is brought near the first to a distance of 10 cm. What is the field intensity at any point between the plates? **[C.U. 1964]**

Solution : The potential of the first plate,

$$V_1 = 4000 \text{ volts} = \frac{4000}{300} \text{ e.s.u.} = \frac{40}{3} \text{ e.s.u.}$$

The potential of the second plate,

$$V_2 = \frac{1000}{300} = \frac{10}{3} \text{ e.s.u.}$$

We know, intensity, $E = \dfrac{dV}{dx} = \dfrac{V_1 - V_2}{x}$,

where the separation between the plates, $x = 10$ cm.

$$\therefore \quad E = \frac{\frac{40}{3} - \frac{10}{3}}{10} = \frac{10}{10} = \textbf{1 dyne/e.s.u. charge.}$$

21. A spherical conductor of radius 5 cm carries a charge of 20 e.s.u. and lies in its own field only. Find the potential at a point 10 cm from its centre.

[**C.U. Spl. 1973**]

Solution : Required potential $= \dfrac{q}{x} = \dfrac{\text{charge}}{\text{distance of the point from the centre}}$.

Here, $q = 20$ e.s.u. and $x = 10$ cm.

$$\therefore \quad \text{potential} = \frac{20}{10} = \textbf{2 e.s.u.}$$

22. What velocity will an electron at rest acquire in moving through a potential difference of 1 volt? Given, $e = 4.803 \times 10^{-10}$ e.s.u. and the mass of the electron $= 9.108 \times 10^{-28}$ g. [**C.U. 1964**]

Solution : We have, $\dfrac{1}{2}mv^2 = eV$.

$$\therefore \quad v = \sqrt{\frac{2eV}{m}}.$$

Here, $e = 4.803 \times 10^{-10}$ e.s.u., $V = 1$ volt $= \frac{1}{300}$ e.s.u., $m = 9.108 \times 10^{-28}$ g.

So, $v = \sqrt{\dfrac{2 \times 1 \times 4.803 \times 10^{-10}}{9.108 \times 10^{-28} \times 300}} = \textbf{0.6} \times \textbf{10}^8 \textbf{ cm/second.}$

23. Two spherical raindrops having equal diameters have been charged with equal quantities of positive electricity. They combine to form one large drop. Compare the potentials before and after union. [**C.U. 1990**]

Solution : $V = \dfrac{\text{charge}}{4\pi\epsilon_0 \times \text{radius of the drop}} = \dfrac{q}{4\pi\epsilon_0 r}$.

$\therefore$ total potential, $V_1 = 2V = \dfrac{2q}{4\pi\epsilon_0 r}$.

If R be the radius of the larger drop formed by two smaller drops, then

$$\frac{4}{3}\pi R^3 = 2 \times \frac{4}{3}\pi r^3.$$

$$\therefore \quad R = \sqrt[3]{2} \cdot r$$

The surface potential of the larger drop,

$$V_2 = \frac{\text{total charge}}{4\pi\epsilon_0 \times \text{radius of the drop}} = \frac{2q}{4\pi\epsilon_0 R} = \frac{2q}{4\pi\epsilon_0 \sqrt[3]{2} \cdot r}.$$

$$\therefore \quad \frac{V_1}{V_2} = \frac{2q}{r} \times \frac{\sqrt[3]{2} \cdot r}{2q} = \sqrt[3]{2} = 1.26.$$

Questions

Essay-type

1. Show that the total normal induction across a closed surface in an electrostatic field is equal to the total charge enclosed by the surface. Hence find the intensity due to an infinitely long charged cylinder of radius r, at a point distant $d(d > r)$ from the axis of the cylinder.

2. State and prove Gauss's theorem on total normal induction. Hence show that the charges on a sphere practically exert their influence at an external point in such a way that they may be supposed to be concentrated at its centre.

3. State and prove Gauss's theorem on electrostatics. Find the electric intensity at a point due to a charged cylinder.   [B.U. 1990]

4. State and prove Gauss's theorem of total normal induction over a closed surface. Apply the theorem to prove that electric intensity within a charged sphere is zero.   [C.U. 1983, '90]

5. Explain what is meant by total normal induction over a surface. State what relation this bears to the total electrostatic charge enclosed by the surface. Find the intensity at a point outside an isolated charged conducting sphere at a distance from the centre.

6. State and prove Gauss's theorem in electrostatics and use it to determine the electric intensity very near to the surface of a closed charged conductor.
                                                        [C.U. 1968, '80]

7. Apply Gauss's theorem to find the intensity of the electrostatic field near a charged plane conductor.

8. Deduce an expression for the electrostatic pressure developed on the surface of an insulated charged conductor.

9. Show that the energy stored up in a unit volume of an electric field is $\dfrac{\epsilon_r \epsilon_0 E^2}{2}$, where E is the electric intensity and ϵ_r, the dielectric constant of medium.

10. Define electric potential. Deduce its relation with the electric intensity at a point in an electric field. What is an equipotential surface? Prove that a line of force and an equipotential surface must be mutually at right angles to each other. Show, by drawing, the nature of the lines of force and equipotential surfaces around a charged spherical ball.

11. State and explain the inverse square law of force between two charged particles. Hence define unit of electric charge and also dielectric constant of a medium.

12. What do you mean by an electric dipole? Calculate the intensity of electric field due to a dipole at a point distant r from its centre and making an angle θ with its axis.

13. Show that the potential at any point distant r from a point charge Q is $\frac{Q}{4\pi\epsilon_0 r}$.

14. What do you mean by an electric dipole? What is dipole moment? Is it a scalar or a vector?   [Tripura 1998]

Short Answer-type

15. State Gauss theorem. Is it applicable to fields other than electrostatics?

16. What are normal induction and total normal induction? Do they depend on the medium?

17. How can you show from Gauss theorem that no electric field exists inside a charged sphere? [C.U. 1983]

18. A closed surface drawn entirely in a conducting medium may contain no net charge. Explain.

19. What is the total normal induction across a closed surface due to a charge kept outside the surface?

20. Why does a charged conductor experience a mechanical force? What will happen to a soap-bubble if it is charged?

21. Is Coulomb's law applicable to a point further away from a charged conductor?

22. A soap-bubble is electrified. Will the diameter **(i)** increase, **(ii)** decrease or **(iii)** remain unaltered? [C.U. 1989]

23. A small plane area is rotated in an electric field. In which orientation of the area is the normal induction through the area maximum? In which orientation is it zero?

24. **(i)** Define dielectric constant of a medium.

(ii) Define intensity of an electric field.

25. What is the relation between electric potential and intensity? Write down an expression for electric potential at a distance r from a point charge q placed in a medium of dielectric constant K.

26. What do you mean by electric lines and tubes of forces?

27. What do you mean by electric dipole? Mention the intensity of electric field due to a dipole at a point distant r from its centre and making an angle θ with its axis.

28. What is an equipotential surface? Show that a line of force and an equipotential surface must be mutually at right angle to each other. Show by drawing, the nature of lines of force and equipotential surfaces around a charged sphere.

29. What is the potential of the earth? In what direction will electrons flow when **(i)** a positively charged body is earth-connected and **(ii)** a negatively charged body is earth-connected? Draw figure in each case. [C.U. 1990]

30. Can two equipotential surfaces cut each other?

31. Two point charges q_1 and q_2 placed at a distance a are such that there is no point where the intensity of the field is zero. What can be concluded from this?

32. What is the magnitude of electric field inside a conductor placed in a uniform electric field?

33. Two conductors are at a very large difference of potential. What will happen if **(i)** the conductors are connected by a thin metallic wire, **(ii)** positive and negative ions are present in the air between the conductors, **(iii)** there is vacuum in the space between the conductors?

Numerical Problems

34. To what voltage must a soap-bubble be charged in order that the air pressure outside the bubble may be equal to that of inside? The radius of the charged bubble is 1.5 cm; the surface tension is 39×10^{-3} N/m. [**Ans.** 2.3×10^4 volts]

35. Find the value of electrostatic pressure on a charged surface with a surface density of 3.3×10^{-5} C/m^2. What will be its value expressed in mm of mercury. Density of mercury $= 13.6 \times 10^3$ kg/m^3 and acceleration due to gravity $= 9.8$ m/s^2. [**Ans.** 62.8 N/m^2; 0.47 mm]

36. A soap-bubble has a radius of 2 cm when the surface tension of soap solution is 24×10^{-3} N/m. To what potential the soap-bubble be raised in volts for the pressure inside the bubble to equal that of the surrounding atmosphere? [**Ans.** 2.1×10^4 volts]

37. If the intensity of the field near the earth's surface is 330 volts/metre, directed downwards, calculate the surface density of charge on the earth's surface. [**Ans.** 2.92×10^{-9} C/m^2]

38. 4 g of gold are beaten into a thin leaf of area 104 cm^2. A small piece is cut out of it and placed upon a conductor. Calculate the charge density required by the conductor so that the piece of gold is just lifted up. [**B.U. 1983**] [**Ans.** 8.5×10^{-6} C/m^2]

39. A soap-bubble of radius 0.5 cm is blown in vacuum. It is then charged with 7.2×10^{-8} coulomb of charge. If surface tension of soap solution be 27×10^{-3} N/m, calculate the present radius of the bubble. [**Ans.** 2.58 cm]

40. A particle of mass 5×10^{-6} g is kept over a large horizontal sheet of charge of density 4×10^{-6} C/m^2. What charge should be given to this particle so that if released, it will not fall down?

41. If the normal tension on the surface of an insulated sphere of radius 5 cm be 10 N/m^2, calculate its potential. [**Ans.** 1.5×10^6 volts]

42. Two equal and similar charges 0.03 m apart in air repel each other with a force of 4.5 kg-wt. Find the magnitude of each charge. [**Ans.** 21×10^{-7} C]

43. The force of attraction between two charges $+80$ μC and -70 μC separated by a distance of 25 cm is found to be 100 N. Find the dielectric constant of the medium. [**Ans.** 80]

44. Charges q, $2q$ and $3q$ are placed on three consecutive points a, b and c respectively, all lying on a straight line. If the resultant force on the charge $2q$ is zero, find the relative positions of a, b and c. [**Ans.** $ab : bc = 1 : \sqrt{3}$]

45. Suppose you have a large number of particles with identical charge. Any two of them at 10 cm separation repel with a force of 3×10^{-10} N. If one of them is repelled by a group of the particles which are at a distance of 10 cm and the force of repulsion is 6×10^{-6} N, how many particles are there in the group? [**Ans.** 20,000]

46. ABC is an equilateral triangle whose sides are 5 cm in length. Two point charges of $+100$ μC and -100 μC are placed at A and B respectively. Find the direction and magnitude of electric field at C. [**Ans.** 3.6×10^8 N; parallel to BC]

47. Find the electric field at the centre of a uniformly charged semicircular arc of radius a and charge per unit length q.   [**Ans.** $\frac{q}{2\pi\epsilon_0} \cdot a$]

48. Three charges, each equal to q, are placed at the three corners of a square of side a. Find the electric field at the fourth corner.   [**Ans.** $(2\sqrt{2}+1)\frac{q}{8\pi\epsilon_0 \cdot a^2}$]

49. Two charges $+10$ μC and $+20$ μC are placed at a separation of 2 cm. Find electric potential due to the pair at the middle point of the line joining the two charges.   [**Ans.** 27×10^6 V]

50. A vertical electric field is preventing a charged oil drop of values 1.3×10^{-4} cm from falling downwards. The electric field is produced by charging two horizontal plates, 1.6 cm apart, to 8340 volts of potential difference. If the density of oil is 920 kg-m^{-3}, find the charge on the drop. $g = 9.8$ m/s.^{2}
[**Ans.** 1.59×10^{-19} C]

51. Find the radius of a water drop which will just remain suspended with a charge of 1 electron in the earth's field of intensity 3 volts/cm. $e = 1.6 \times 10^{-19}$ coulomb.   [**Ans.** 1.1×10^{-7} metre]

52. Two charges 10 μC and -10 μC are placed at points A and B separated by a distance of 10 cm. Find the electric field at a point P on the perpendicular bisector of AB at a distance 12 cm from its middle point.

[**Ans.** 4.1×10^6 N; along $\overrightarrow{AB}$]

53. Two equally charged identical metal spheres A and B repel each other with a force 2×10^{-5} newton. Another identical uncharged sphere C is touched to A and then placed at the mid-point between A and B. What is the net electric

force on C?   [**Ans.** 2×10^{-5} N along $\overrightarrow{BC}$]

Chapter 2

Conductors and System of Conductors

2.1 Introduction

Every body has a capacity for receiving heat which is known as the thermal capacity of the body. The thermal capacity is the quantity of heat necessary for raising the temperature of the body through one degree. In a similar way, the electrical capacity of a conductor is a measure of the quantity of charge required for raising the potential of the conductor by one unit. The term capacitance indicates the capacity of a condenser or of a conductor. Thus the capacitance of a condenser may be defined as the charge on the positive plate of a condenser per unit potential difference between its plates. If charge q produces a potential difference ϕ between the plates, then the capacitance C can be written as

$$C = \frac{q}{\phi} \tag{2.1}$$

or, $\quad$ capacitance $= \dfrac{\text{quantity of charge}}{\text{rise of potential}}.$ $\tag{2.1a}$

2.2 Unit of Capacitance

In Eq. (2.1), if we put $q = 1$ and $\phi = 1$, then $C = 1$. Therefore, a conductor has a capacitance of one *electrostatic unit* (e.s.u.) or a *stat-farad* if one e.s.u. of charge raises its potential by unity. The practical unit of capacitance is called *farad*. A conductor is said to have a capacitance of 1 farad, when a charge of one coulomb of electricity raises its potential by 1 volt.

For all practical purposes, farad is a too large unit. So a small unit which is one-millionth of a farad is used. This is called a microfarad. We thus have

$$1 \text{ farad} = \frac{1 \text{ coulomb}}{1 \text{ volt}}$$

$$= \frac{3 \times 10^9 \text{ e.s.u. of charge}}{\frac{1}{300} \text{ e.s.u. of p.d.}}.$$

$$= 9 \times 10^{11} \text{ e.s.u. of capacitance}$$

and $\quad$ 1 microfarad(or μF) $= 10^{-6}$ farad $= 9 \times 10^5$ e.s.u. of capacitance.

2.3 Uses of Capacitors

Capacitors are used for various purposes, some of which are : (i) to conserve electrical energy and to use it at intervals; (ii) as an accumulator of electricity to use in rectifiers and electrostatic machines; (iii) to establish strong electric fields in a small space; (iv) to stop the flow of direct current but to allow an alternating current in a circuit; (v) for studying the behaviour of electric materials when placed in an electric field; (vi) to increase the efficiency of transmission of an alternating current; (vii) to eliminate sparking in electrical circuits, e.g., in ignition system of an automobile, induction coil, etc.; (viii) as a potential divider for measuring high potentials; (ix) to measure small current by using the relation, $i = C\frac{d\phi}{dt}$, where C is the capacitance; (x) in radio circuits for producing oscillations, for coupling in power supply units, for reducing voltage fluctuations and to provide time delays.

2.4   Forms of Condensers

(a) Electrolytic Condenser : It has two aluminium plates A and B, as shown in Fig 2.1, in which A is the anode and B is the cathode. The plates are placed in a solution of ammonium borate or a paste of borates. On passing direct current, a thin film (10^{-6}cm) of aluminium oxide is formed which serves as the dielectric between the two plates. With such a condenser we can obtain a large capacity.

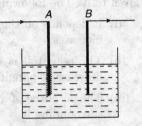

Fig. 2.1

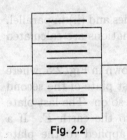

Fig. 2.2

(b) Fixed Condenser : It is made in the form of parallel plate condensers consisting of two thin layers of metal coated on the surface of mica or paper impregnated with paraffin. Such condensers, particularly when mica is used as the dielectric, are sometimes arranged in boxes. The condensers are then kept in parallel or in series by means of plugs. A fixed mica condenser is shown in Fig. 2.2. Ceramic materials are now also used as low loss dielectric.

(c) Variable Condenser : It is constructed by two sets of metal plates or vanes, alternate plates being connected together. One set remains fixed while the other is movable with air as the dielectric. This is shown in Fig. 2.3. With the rotation of the movable part, the overlapping area between the two sets changes bringing a change in the capacity of the condenser.

Fig. 2.3

(d) Guard-ring Standard Condenser : In order to overcome the end effect, Lord William Kelvin utilised a circular plate surrounded by a ring in the same plane as the inner plate. As shown in Fig. 2.4, A and B are two plates of equal area. B is connected to earth while A and G are maintained at the same potential by a conducting wire. The separation of the plates can be changed by a micrometer fixed to the lower plate B.

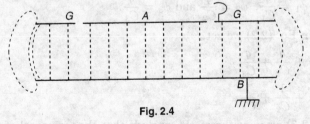

Fig. 2.4

2.5   Factors Determining the Capacitance and Potential of a Conductor

The capacitance of a conductor may be increased by means of the following ways :

(i) By increasing its area;

(ii) By decreasing the separation between the plates;

(iii) By introducing a dielectric between the plates;

(iv) By bringing near it an insulated conductor or an earth-connected conductor.

The potential of a conductor proportionately increases with the amount of charge given to it. The following factors also determine the potential :

(i) It depends on the size of the conductor. If the size diminishes, its potential increases.

(ii) The potential is diminished by bringing another conductor near it. The decrease of potential is maximum if the neighbouring conductor is earthed.

(iii) The potential of a charged conductor depends on the nature of the dielectric surrounding it.

2.6   Grouping of Condensers

Condensers may be connected in two different ways : (i) in series and (ii) in parallel. The value of the equivalent capacitance for these two combinations are calculated below :

(a) **Condensers in series :** The series arrangement is shown in Fig. 2.5, where the second plate of the first condenser is connected to the first plate of the second

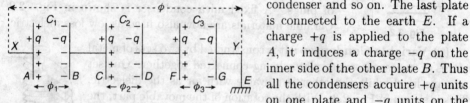

Fig. 2.5

condenser and so on. The last plate is connected to the earth E. If a charge $+q$ is applied to the plate A, it induces a charge $-q$ on the inner side of the other plate B. Thus all the condensers acquire $+q$ units on one plate and $-q$ units on the other.

If ϕ be the potential difference between the first plate A and the last plate G of the series combination and ϕ_1, ϕ_2, ϕ_3 be the potential differences between A and B, C and D, F and G respectively, then

$$\phi = \phi_1 + \phi_2 + \phi_3. \qquad (2.2)$$

If C_s be the equivalent capacitance of the combination and C_1, C_2, C_3 the individual capacitances, then

$$\phi = \frac{q}{C_s}, \ \phi_1 = \frac{q}{C_1}, \ \phi_2 = \frac{q}{C_2} \text{ and } \phi_3 = \frac{q}{C_3}.$$

Hence, from Eq. (2.2) we get,

$$\frac{q}{C_s} = \frac{q}{C_1} + \frac{q}{C_2} + \frac{q}{C_3}$$

or, $$\frac{1}{C_s} = \frac{1}{C_1} + \frac{1}{C_2} + \frac{1}{C_3}. \qquad (2.3)$$

From Eq. (2.3) we may, therefore, conclude that the reciprocal of the equivalent capacitance of a number of condensers connected in series is the sum of the reciprocals of the capacitances of the separate condensers.

(b) **Condensers in parallel :** The parallel arrangement is shown in Fig. 2.6 where the insulated plates are connected to a common terminal X which is joined to the source of potential while the other plates are connected to another common terminal Y which is earthed. In this combination all the condensers have the same potential difference ϕ. If a charge is applied at the point X, it will be distributed to the condensers depending on the capacitances.

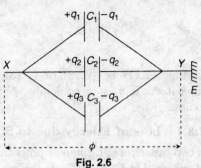

Fig. 2.6

Let q_1, q_2, q_3 are the charges of the capacitors. The total charge q can then be written as,

$$q = q_1 + q_2 + q_3. \qquad (2.4)$$

If C_p be the equivalent capacitance of the combination and C_1, C_2, C_3 are the individual capacitances, then

$$q = \phi C_p, \quad q_1 = \phi C_1, \quad q_2 = \phi C_2, \quad q_3 = \phi C_3.$$

Hence, we get

$$\phi C_p = \phi C_1 + \phi C_2 + \phi C_3$$

or, $C_p = C_1 + C_2 + C_3.$ $\qquad (2.5)$

Therefore, the equivalent capacitance of a number of condensers in parallel is equal to the sum of the separate capacitances.

2.7 Capacitance of a Sphere

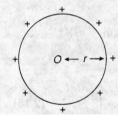

Fig. 2.7

Let us consider a sphere of radius r, as shown in Fig. 2.7. If the sphere is charged with q units of electricity, then according to Gauss's theorem the potential of the sphere

$$\phi = \frac{q}{4\pi\epsilon_0 r} \text{ (in air)} \qquad (2.6)$$

or, $\phi = \frac{1}{4\pi\epsilon} \cdot \frac{q}{r}$ (in a dielectric medium), $\qquad (2.7)$

where ϵ is the dielectric constant.

Therefore, the capacitance C can be obtained from,

$$\frac{1}{4\pi\epsilon} \frac{q}{r} = \frac{q}{C} \qquad (2.8)$$

or, $C = 4\pi\epsilon r.$ $\qquad (2.9)$

Eq. (2.8) above shows that the capacitance of a sphere is numerically equal to its radius if the surrounding medium is air.

2.8 Energy Stored in the Field of Charged Capacitor

The energy of a charged capacitor is equal to the work done in charging it. Let at any instant the p.d. between the plates is ϕ. The work done in bringing a small amount of charge dq to the condenser,

$$dW = \phi \cdot dq. \qquad (2.10)$$

So the total work done in charging it with a charge q,

$$W = \int_0^a \phi \cdot dq = \int_0^a \frac{q}{C} dq \quad \left(\because \phi = \frac{q}{C} \right)$$

$$= \frac{1}{2} \frac{q^2}{C}. \qquad (2.11)$$

The above equation can alternately be written as,

$$W = \frac{1}{2}q\phi \tag{2.12}$$

$$= \frac{1}{2}C\phi^2. \tag{2.13}$$

Eqs. (2.11) or (2.12) or (2.13) represents the energies stored in a charged capacitor. If q is in coulombs, C in farads and ϕ in volts, then W will be in joules.

2.8.1   Loss of Energy due to Sharing of Charges

If two capacitors at different potentials are joined together, then there will be a loss of energy. Let C_1 and C_2 are the capacitances of two capacitors. These are charged with q_1 and q_2 e.s.u. respectively. If ϕ_1 and ϕ_2 are their potentials respectively, then the common potential ϕ when joined can be written as

$$\phi = \frac{C_1\phi_1 + C_2\phi_2}{C_1 + C_2}$$

$$= \frac{q_1 + q_2}{C_1 + C_2}. \tag{2.14}$$

$$\text{Loss of energy} = \frac{1}{2}q_1\phi_1 + \frac{1}{2}q_2\phi_2 - \frac{1}{2}(q_1 + q_2) \cdot \frac{q_1 + q_2}{C_1 + C_2}$$

$$= \frac{1}{2(C_1 + C_2)}[q_1^2 + q_2^2 + C_2 q_1\phi_1 + C_1 q_2\phi_2 - (q_1 + q_2)^2]$$

$$= \frac{1}{2(C_1 + C_2)}(C_1 C_2\phi_1^2 + C_1 C_2\phi_2^2 - 2q_1 q_2)$$

$$= \frac{C_1 C_2}{2(C_1 + C_2)}(\phi_1 - \phi_2)^2 \quad [\because q_1 q_2 = C_1\phi_1 C_2\phi_2]. \tag{2.15}$$

Eq. (2.15) indicates that there will always be a loss of energy on connecting two condensers which are at different potentials. One may calculate the above loss of energy in terms of any two of the quantities q, ϕ and C.

2.9   Uniqueness Theorem

In the case of charged conductors we have the following two propositions :

(a) If the potentials of all the conductors are given, then there can be only one distribution of electric charge on the conductors.

(b) If the charge on each conductor is given, then there is one way only by which the charges can be distributed in equilibrium on the conductors.

The above two propositions are called as the uniqueness theorem.

Proof

In order to prove the first proposition, let us assume that σ be the surface density of charge at any point. Then the potential ϕ at a point P on a particular conductor is

$$\phi = \int\int \frac{\sigma ds}{r}, \tag{2.16}$$

where r is the distance of the point from an infinitesimal surface ds of any conductor. The above integration is taken over the surface of all the conductors.

Now, let us assume that there be any other distribution σ' so that the potential of each conductor remains unaltered. Then, again, the potential at P is

$$\phi = \int \int \frac{\sigma' ds}{r}. \tag{2.17}$$

The potential at P due to a distribution $(\sigma - \sigma')$ must be

$$\int \int \frac{(\sigma - \sigma')ds}{r} = \int \int \frac{\sigma ds}{r} - \int \int \frac{\sigma' ds}{r} = 0.$$

Hence, we have

$$\sigma = \sigma'. \tag{2.18}$$

Thus we find that if the potential of each conductor is given, then there is only one way of distribution of charge on the conductors.

Next, to prove the second proposition let us assume that two distributions of surface densities σ and σ' are possible. Since $\sigma \neq \sigma'$, so there are both positive and negative electrifications on each conductor but for a surface distribution $(\sigma - \sigma')$ the resulting charge on each conductor is zero. In this way the lines of force start from and terminate on each conductor. Therefore, there must be some point of maximum potential in space. But in empty space the potential can be neither maximum nor minimum. Hence σ must be equal to σ'. This proves the second proposition. It is, therefore, found that the distribution of electricity on conductors is specified fully if the charge and potential of each conductor are known.

2.10 Principle of Superposition

Let us assume that we have the following two equilibrium distributions :

  (i) A distribution of surface density σ at any point giving total charges $q_1, q_2, \ldots$, etc., and potentials $\phi_1, \phi_2, \ldots$, etc., on different conductors.

  (ii) A distribution of surface density σ' at any point giving total charges $q_1', q_2', \ldots$, etc., and potentials $\phi_1', \phi_2', \ldots$, etc., on different conductors.

Now we consider a distribution of surface density $(\sigma + \sigma')$. It is clear that the total charges on the conductors will be $q_1 + q_1'$, $q_2 + q_2'$, $\ldots$, etc., and if ϕ_p is the potential at any point P, then

$$\phi_p = \int \frac{\sigma + \sigma'}{r} ds \tag{2.19}$$

integrated over all the surfaces of the conductors.

or, $$\phi_p = \int \frac{\sigma ds}{r} + \int \frac{\sigma' ds}{r}. \tag{2.20}$$

If the point P is on the first conductor, then

$$\int \frac{\sigma ds}{r} = \phi_1 \quad \text{and} \quad \int \frac{\sigma' ds}{r} = \phi_1'.$$

$$\therefore \quad \phi_p = \phi_1 + \phi_1'. \tag{2.21}$$

Similar is true when P is present on the other conductor.

Thus we find that if charges $q_1, q_2, \ldots$ give rise to potentials $\phi_1, \phi_2, \ldots$, and $q_1', q_2', \ldots$ give rise to $\phi_1', \phi_2', \ldots$, then $q_1 + q_1', q_2 + q_2', \ldots$ will give rise to $\phi_1 + \phi_1', \phi_2 + \phi_2', \ldots$. Or in other words, if we superpose two systems of charges, the potentials produced are obtained by adding the potentials corresponding to the component systems.

2.11   Coefficients of Potential, Capacity and Induction

Let us imagine a system of n independent isolated conductors in a dielectric medium. If unit charge is placed on conductor no. 1, it will increase the potential of all the conductors. Let the potentials of the conductors are designated as follows :

Conductor	No. 1	No. 2	No. 3	$\cdots$	No. n
Potential	p_{11}	p_{12}	p_{13}	$\cdots$	p_{1n}

The first number of the suffix represents the conductor on which the charge is placed and the second number represents the conductor on which a resulting potential is produced. If instead of a unit charge on conductor no. 1, a charge q_1 is placed, then the resulting potentials of all the conductors will be multiplied by q_1. Then

Conductor	No. 1	No. 2	No. 3	$\cdots$	No. n
Potential	$p_{11}q_1$	$p_{12}q_1$	$p_{13}q_1$	$\cdots$	$p_{1n}q_1$

Taking the same set of conductors let us choose conductor no. 2, on which a unit charge is placed. Then with a similar nomenclature as before, the resulting potential can be written as

Conductor	No. 1	No. 2	No. 3	$\cdots$	No. n
Potential	p_{21}	p_{22}	p_{23}	$\cdots$	p_{2n}

If instead of a unit charge, charge q_2 is placed on conductor no. 2, then we have

Conductor	No. 1	No. 2	No. 3	$\cdots$	No. n
Potential	$p_{21}q_2$	$p_{22}q_2$	$p_{23}q_2$	$\cdots$	$p_{2n}q_2$

In a similar way if a charge q_3 is placed on conductor no. 3, only then the potentials become accordingly :

Conductor	No. 1	No. 2	No. 3	$\cdots$	No. n
Potential	$p_{31}q_3$	$p_{32}q_3$	$p_{33}q_3$	$\cdots$	$p_{3n}q_3$

This process is continued until all the n conductors are charged, one at a time.

Next, let us assume that all the conductors are charged all at the same time, then the potentials will be additive. Thus the final potential for conductor no. 1 is given by

$$\phi_1 = p_{11}q_1 + p_{21}q_2 + p_{31}q_3 + \cdots + p_{n1}q_n. \qquad (2.22)$$

Similarly,

$$\phi_2 = p_{12}q_1 + p_{22}q_2 + p_{32}q_3 + \cdots + p_{n2}q_n \quad \text{(for conductor no. 2)}$$
$$\phi_3 = p_{13}q_1 + p_{23}q_2 + p_{33}q_3 + \cdots + p_{n3}q_n \quad \text{(for conductor no. 3)}$$
$$\cdots \quad \cdots \quad \cdots \quad \cdots \quad \cdots$$
$$\phi_n = p_{1n}q_1 + p_{2n}q_2 + p_{3n}q_3 + \cdots + p_{nn}q_n \quad \text{(for conductor no. } n)$$

The ps are known as the coefficients of potential. These coefficients depend on the size, shape and position of the conductors.

Since ϕs are linear function of qs, we can write the solutions in the following form :

$$q_1 = Q_{11}\phi_1 + Q_{21}\phi_2 + Q_{31}\phi_3 + \cdots + Q_{n1}\phi_n$$
$$q_2 = Q_{12}\phi_1 + Q_{22}\phi_2 + Q_{32}\phi_3 + \cdots + Q_{n2}\phi_n$$
$$\cdots \quad \cdots \quad \cdots \quad \cdots \quad \cdots$$
$$q_n = Q_{1n}\phi_1 + Q_{2n}\phi_2 + Q_{3n}\phi_3 + \cdots + Q_{nn}\phi_n$$

When all the conductors other than the rth are earthed, then $q_r = Q_{rr}\phi_r$ and all other ϕ terms are zero. Thus, when all the conductors are connected to earth, the coefficient Q_{rr} becomes the capacitance of the body and so these forms of coefficients are called coefficients of capacitance. But coefficients like Q_{rs} is the ratio of charge on a body compared with the potential on another, when the rest of the bodies are earthed. This charge is brought about by the phenomenon of electrical induction and hence such coefficients are called *coefficients of induction*.

2.11.1 Some Properties of Coefficients

(i) Coefficients of capacitance are positive and those of induction are negative

Let us assume that the conductor no. 1 is insulated and charged to raise a potential ϕ_1 and let other conductors are earthed so that $\phi_2 = \phi_3 = \cdots = \phi_n = 0$. Then,

$$q_1 = Q_{11}\phi_1, \ q_2 = Q_{12}\phi_1, \ q_3 = Q_{13}\phi_1, \ \ldots, \ q_n = Q_{1n}\phi_1$$

Now, if q_1 is a charge of positive nature, then potential ϕ_1 is also positive for all the tubes of flux start from conductor no. 1 and proceed to places of lower potential (in the present case, zero).

$\therefore \ Q_{11}$ is positive.

But the induced charges on conductor nos. 2, 3, etc., are all negative in nature, being at the other ends of the tubes of flux. Hence, $Q_{12}, Q_{13}, \ldots, Q_{1n}$ are all negative.

Also, if the charges $q_2, q_3 \ldots, q_n$ are added, then the sum cannot numerically exceed q_1.

$\therefore \ Q_{12} + Q_{13} + \cdots + Q_{1n} \not> Q_{11}$.

(ii) Coefficients of potential are positive

Let us assume that the rth conductor is charged by unity and the others are uncharged. Then we have,

$\phi_1 = p_{r1} \ (\because q_1 = q_2 = \cdots = q_{n-1} = q_{r+1} = \cdots = q_n = 0 \text{ and } q_r = 1)$

Similarly, $\phi_2 = p_{r2}, \ \phi_3 = p_{r3}, \ \ldots, \ \phi_r = p_{rr}, \ \ldots, \ \phi_s = p_{rs}, \ \ldots, \ \phi_n = p_{rn}$.

Here $\phi_1, \phi_2, \phi_3, \ldots, \phi_n$ are all positive. Therefore, $p_{r1}, p_{r2}, p_{rs}, \ldots, p_{rn}$ will also be positive.

But p_{rr} is the maximum potential in the field and so $p_{rr} > p_{rs}$.

2.12 Green's Reciprocal Theorem

The theorem states that if charges and potentials of a set of n fixed conductors are changed from

$$q_1, \phi_1; q_2, \phi_2; \ldots; q_n, \phi_n$$

to $\quad q_1', \phi_1'; q_2', \phi_2'; \ldots; q_n', \phi_n',$

then $\quad q_1\phi_1' + q_2\phi_2' + q_3\phi_3' + \cdots + q_n\phi_n' = q_1'\phi_1 + q_2'\phi_2 + q_3'\phi_3 + \cdots + q_n'\phi_n$

or, $\quad \sum q\phi' = \sum q'\phi$.

Proof

Let at any instant each conductor have received an equal fraction x of its final increment of charge so that the charges now are

$$q_1 + x(q_1' - q_1), q_2 + x(q_2' - q_2), \ldots, q_n + x(q_n' - q_n).$$

Their potentials are respectively written as

$$\phi_1 + x(\phi_1' - \phi_1), \phi_2 + x(\phi_2' - \phi_2), \ldots, \phi_n + x(\phi_n' - \phi_n)$$

and the work necessary for a further small increments of charges,

$$dx(q_1' - q_1), dx(q_2' - q_2), \ldots, dx(q_n' - q_n),$$

respectively will be a summation of all the products of potential multiplied by the change in charge. Thus,

$$\text{work done} = \sum [\phi_r + x(\phi_r' - \phi_r)](q_r' - q_r)dx. \tag{2.22a}$$

In the above equation, the summation extends over the n terms formed by the suffixes $r = 1, 2, 3, \ldots, n$.

Hence, the total work done to change the state of the conductors will be obtained by summing for all values of x from 0 to 1. Thus we have

$$W = \sum \int_0^1 [\{\phi_r + x(\phi_r' - \phi_r)\}(q_r' - q_r)]dx$$

$$= \sum \frac{1}{2}(q_r' - q_r)[2\phi_r x + x^2(\phi_r' - \phi_r)]_0^1$$

$$= \sum \frac{1}{2}(q_r' - q_r)(\phi_r + \phi_r'). \tag{2.23}$$

But this work done must be equal to the difference of the initial and final energies of the system. So we can write,

$$\frac{1}{2}\sum(q_r' - q_r)(\phi_r + \phi_r') = \frac{1}{2}\sum(q_r'\phi_r') - \frac{1}{2}\sum(q_r\phi_r)$$

or, $$\frac{1}{2}\sum q_r'\phi_r - \frac{1}{2}\sum q_r\phi_r' = 0$$

or, $$\sum_{r=1}^n q_r'\phi_r = \sum_{r=1}^n q_r\phi_r' \tag{2.24}$$

Eq. (2.24) represents the famous Green's reciprocal or reciprocation theorem.

2.13   Energy of a System of Conductors

Let there be n conductors which are charged from their uncharged state. We assume that the charges on the conductors are $q_1, q_2, q_3, \ldots, q_n$ and the corresponding potentials are $\phi_1, \phi_2, \phi_3, \ldots, \phi_n$.

Now, let the n conductors be charged simultaneously such that at any instant in the process each conductor has received an equal fraction x of its final charge. So the charges are $xq_1, xq_2, xq_3, \ldots, xq_n$ and the corresponding potentials are $x\phi_1, x\phi_2, x\phi_3, \ldots, x\phi_n$. If additional charges $q_1dx, q_2dx, \ldots, q_ndx$ are brought to the conductors, then

$$\text{work done} = (x\phi_1)(q_1dx) + (x\phi_2)(q_2dx) + \cdots + (x\phi_n)(q_ndx)$$

$$= xdx\sum_{r=1}^n q_r\phi_r.$$

Therefore, the total work done in bringing the final charges $q_1, q_2, \ldots, q_n$, etc. to the conductors is

$$W = \int_0^1 x\,dx \sum_{r=1}^n q_r \phi_r$$

$$= \frac{1}{2} \sum_{r=1}^n q_r \phi_r. \tag{2.25}$$

This gives the energy of the conductors.

2.13.1   Force on a Conductor

Let all the conductors be fixed in position except the first one which is free to move. If it moves through an elementary distance ds impelled by a force F, then we can write,

$$-dW = F \cdot ds$$

or,

$$F = -\frac{dW}{ds}$$

$$= -\frac{d}{ds}\left(\frac{1}{2} \sum_{r=1}^n q_r \phi_r\right). \tag{2.26}$$

2.14   The Screening Theorem

If an electric system is surrounded by a conductor at zero potential, then it is said to be screened electrically from the influence of other charged bodies outside the conductor. This is the so-called screening theorem in electrostatics.

Let us consider three conductors A, B and C as shown in Fig. 2.8. The conductor B is at zero potential and it surrounds the conductor A while C is a third conductor at outside.

The equations which determine the charges in the conductor can be written as

$$q_1 = Q_{11}\phi_1 + Q_{21}\phi_2 + Q_{31}\phi_3$$
$$q_2 = Q_{12}\phi_1 + Q_{22}\phi_2 + Q_{32}\phi_3$$
$$q_3 = Q_{13}\phi_1 + Q_{23}\phi_2 + Q_{33}\phi_3.$$

If B is earthed and A is without any charge, then potential inside B is everywhere zero. Thus we can write,

$$0 = Q_{11}(0) + Q_{21}(0) + Q_{31}\phi_3$$

or, $Q_{31} = 0$.

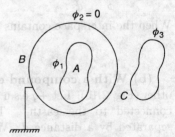

Fig. 2.8

We can, therefore, conclude that the charge on C does not affect the conductor A if B is connected to the earth. In this way, the conductor A becomes electrically screened from external charges.

2.15   Calculations of Capacitances of Condensers

In order to calculate the capacitances of various types of condensers, the general procedure can be divided in three distinct stages : (i) to have one of the plates charged with q units of electricity, (ii) to work out the p.d. ϕ or $(\phi_1 - \phi_2)$ between the plates by a suitable relation and (iii) to calculate the capacitance from the relation $C = \frac{q}{\phi}$.

It may be noted that the capacitances of simple types of condensers are easily obtained from the fundamental principles but to calculate the capacitances of rather complicated types of condensers one should follow the general procedure.

Case 1. Parallel Plate Condensers

(a) **With a single isotropic dielectric :** Let P and Q be two parallel plates separated by a distance d. The plate P of area A is charged with $+q$ e.s.u. of electricity but the plate Q is earthed as shown in Fig. 2.9.

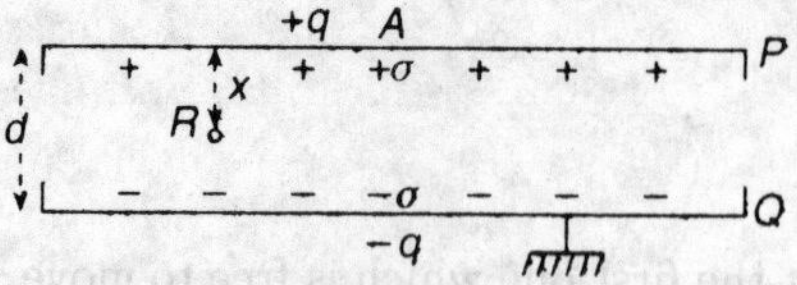

Fig. 2.9

The surface density of charge on P is

$$\sigma = \frac{q}{A} \tag{2.27}$$

By induction $-\alpha$ e.s.u. of charge will be developed per unit area of Q. If the separation d is small, all the lines of force from P will terminate on Q and those will be fairly parallel. Thus the field in the interspace of the plates will be uniform.

$\therefore$ the intensity at any point R at a distance x from P is

$$E = -\frac{d\phi}{dx} = \frac{\sigma}{\epsilon} \text{ (by Coulomb's therorem),}$$

where ϕ is the p.d. between P and Q; ϵ is the dielectric constant.

or, $\quad \phi = -\frac{\sigma}{\epsilon} \int_d^0 dx$ (by definition of potential)

$$= \frac{\sigma}{\epsilon} d$$

$$= \frac{q}{\epsilon A} d \quad \left[\because \ \sigma = \frac{q}{A} \right] \tag{2.28}$$

$$\therefore \quad C = \frac{q}{\phi} = \frac{\epsilon A}{d}. \tag{2.29}$$

When the interspace contains air, $\epsilon = 1$ and then

$$C = \frac{A}{d}. \tag{2.29a}$$

(b) **With a compound dielectric :** P and Q are two plates parallel to each other (Fig. 2.10). Let $+q$ e.s.u. of charge be given to the plate P of area A and ϕ be connected to the earth. The plates are separated by a distance d. We assume that in the interspace there is a dielectric medium of permittivity ϵ_1. A parallel slab of thickness t and permittivity ϵ_2 is inserted between the plates of the condenser.

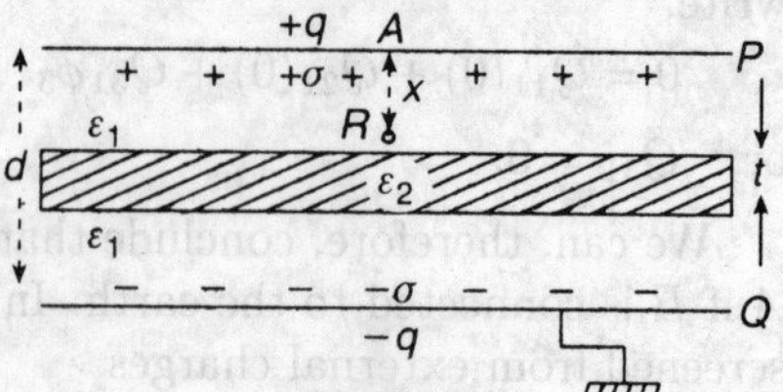

Fig. 2.10

The intensity at any point R at a distance x from the charged plate is given by

$$E = -\frac{d\phi}{dx} = \frac{\sigma}{\epsilon}, \text{ where } \sigma \text{ is the surface density of charge on } P \tag{2.30}$$

or, $\quad d\phi = -\frac{\sigma}{\epsilon} dx.$ \hfill (2.31)

Now, integrating Eq. (2.31) with proper limits and taking the appropriate values for ϵ, we have

$$\phi = \sigma \left[\frac{1}{\epsilon_1} \int_{(d-t)}^{0} -dx + \frac{1}{\epsilon_2} \int_{t}^{0} -dx \right]$$

$$= \sigma \left[\frac{d-t}{\epsilon_1} + \frac{t}{\epsilon_2} \right]. \tag{2.32}$$

In Eq. (2.32) the first term indicates the work done to transfer positive charge through the medium ϵ_1 and the second term that through the medium ϵ_2. The above equation can alternately be written as

$$\phi = \sigma \left[\frac{d}{\epsilon_1} - t \left(\frac{1}{\epsilon_1} - \frac{1}{\epsilon_2} \right) \right] = \frac{q}{A} \left[\frac{d}{\epsilon_1} - t \left(\frac{\epsilon_2 - \epsilon_1}{\epsilon_1 \epsilon_2} \right) \right]$$

or, $\quad C = \dfrac{q}{\phi} = \dfrac{A \epsilon_1 \epsilon_2}{[\epsilon_2 d - (\epsilon_2 - \epsilon_1)t]}.$

If, $\epsilon_1 = 1$ and $\epsilon_2 = \epsilon$, then

$$C = \frac{\epsilon A}{[\epsilon d - (\epsilon - 1)t]} \text{ e.s.u.} = \frac{A}{\left[d - \left(1 - \frac{1}{\epsilon}\right) t \right]} \text{e.s.u.}$$

$$= \frac{A}{\left[d - \left(1 - \frac{1}{\epsilon}\right) t \right] \times 9 \times 10^5} \ \mu\text{F}. \tag{2.33}$$

If there is no dielectric slab, $t = 0$.

$$\therefore \quad C = \frac{A}{d}, \tag{2.34}$$

which is the capacitance of a parallel plate air condenser.

(c) **With a variable dielectric :** Let P and Q be two parallel plates of a condenser. A charge $+q$ e.s.u. is applied to plate P, and Q is connected to the earth. Let A be the area of the plate P and d the separation between P and Q. The space between P and Q is filled with a dielectric whose permittivity uniformly varies from one plate to another.

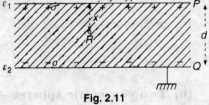

Fig. 2.11

If ϵ_1 and ϵ_2 be the permittivities of the contact layers of the media at P and Q, then supposing ϵ to be increasing from P to Q we have the space rate of variation of ϵ as $\frac{\epsilon_2 - \epsilon_1}{d}$. So the permittivity at a distance x from $P = \left(\epsilon_1 + \dfrac{\epsilon_2 - \epsilon_1}{d} x \right).$

$\therefore \quad$ the intensity at R at a distance x from P,

$$E = -\frac{d\phi}{dx} = \frac{\sigma}{\epsilon_1 + \frac{\epsilon_2 - \epsilon_1}{d} x}, \text{ where } \sigma = \frac{+q}{A} \tag{2.35}$$

or, $\quad \phi = -\displaystyle\int \frac{\sigma}{\epsilon_1 + \frac{\epsilon_2 - \epsilon_1}{d} x} \cdot dx = \sigma \int_{0}^{d} \frac{\frac{d}{\epsilon_2 - \epsilon_1} \cdot \frac{\epsilon_2 - \epsilon_1}{d} dx}{\epsilon_1 + \frac{\epsilon_2 - \epsilon_1}{d} x}$

$$= \frac{d \cdot q}{A(\epsilon_2 - \epsilon_1)} \left[\log \left(\epsilon_1 + \frac{\epsilon_2 - \epsilon_1}{d} x \right) \right]_{0}^{d}.$$

$$= \frac{d \cdot q}{A(\epsilon_2 - \epsilon_1)}[\log(\epsilon_1 + \epsilon_2 - \epsilon_1) - \log \epsilon_1]$$

$$= \frac{d \cdot q}{A(\epsilon_2 - \epsilon_1)} \log_e \frac{\epsilon_2}{\epsilon_1}$$

$$\therefore \quad C = \frac{q}{\phi} = \frac{A(\epsilon_2 - \epsilon_1)}{d \log_e \frac{\epsilon_2}{\epsilon_1}}. \tag{2.36}$$

Case II. Spherical Condensers

(a) **Two concentric spheres—the inner charged and the outer earthed :**
Let A and B be two spheres of radii a and b respectively (Fig. 2.12). A charge of $+q$ e.s.u. is applied to the inner sphere A with the outer one B connected to the earth. For calculating the capacitance of the spherical condenser so formed let us assume that the intervening space between the spheres is filled with a dielectric of permittivity ϵ. Consider a point P in this space at a distance r from the common centre O.

The intensity at P is given by

$$E = -\frac{d\phi}{dr} = \frac{q}{4\pi\epsilon_0\epsilon_r r^2}, \tag{2.37}$$

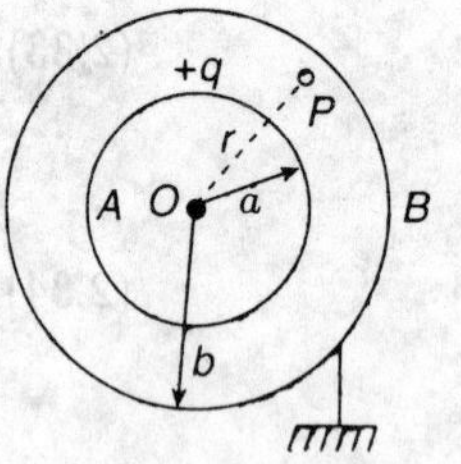

where ϕ is the p.d. between A and B

or, $\quad d\phi = -\dfrac{q}{4\pi\epsilon_0\epsilon_r r^2}dr.$

$$\therefore \quad \phi = -\int_b^a \frac{q}{4\pi\epsilon_0\epsilon_r r^2}dr = \frac{q}{4\pi\epsilon_0\epsilon_r}\left[\frac{1}{r}\right]_b^a$$

$$= \frac{q}{4\pi\epsilon_0\epsilon_r}\left(\frac{1}{a} - \frac{1}{b}\right) = \frac{q(b - a)}{4\pi\epsilon_0\epsilon_r ab}.$$

Fig. 2.12   Hence, the capacitance of the system,

$$C = \frac{q}{\phi} = \frac{4\pi\epsilon_0\epsilon_r ab}{b - a}. \tag{2.38}$$

For air medium, $\epsilon = 1$ and then

$$C = \frac{4\pi\epsilon_0 ab}{b - a}. \tag{2.38a}$$

(b) **Two concentric spheres—inner earthed and the outer charged :**
Let the inner sphere A of radius a be earthed while the outer spherical shell B be charged with $+q$ e.s.u. Let the inner surface of the outer shell be of radius b and the outer surface D be of radius d. The space between A and B is filled with a dielectric of permittivity ϵ.

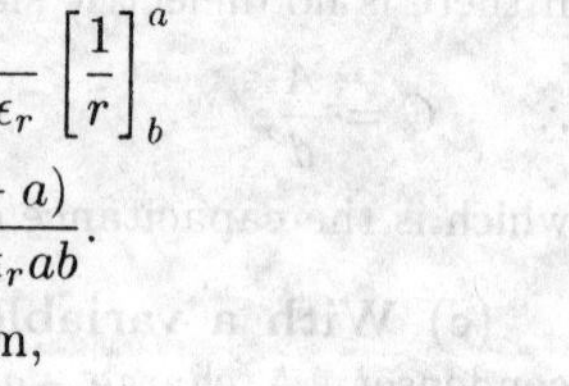

In this case due to the presence of the earthed sphere inside, a part of the total charge $+q$ will be transferred to the inner surface of the outer sphere. Let on the inner surface the amount of charge be $+q_2$ and on the outer one the charge be $+q_1$ so that the total charge becomes equal to q, i.e., $q = q_1 + q_2$. The charge $+q_2$ induces $-q_2$ on the inner sphere A, which is kept at zero potential. We may thus write,

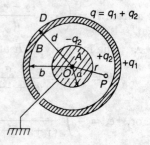

Fig. 2.13

$$\phi = 0 = \frac{1}{4\pi}\left[-\frac{q_2}{\epsilon a} + \frac{q_2}{\epsilon b} + \frac{q_1}{\epsilon d}\right]$$

or, $\quad \dfrac{q_2}{\epsilon}\left(\dfrac{1}{a} - \dfrac{1}{b}\right) = \dfrac{q_1}{\epsilon d}$

or, $\quad q_1 = \dfrac{q_2}{\epsilon} \cdot \dfrac{\epsilon d(b-a)}{ab}.$ \hfill (2.39)

So the total charge on the spherical shell,

$$q = q_1 + q_2 = q_2 \cdot \frac{d(b-a)}{ab} + q_2$$

$$= q_2\left[\frac{d(b-a)}{ab} + 1\right] \hfill (2.40)$$

Since the surfaces B and D are of same potential, the p.d. between A and B is also the p.d. between the spheres. Let P be a point inside the dielectric medium in the interspace between A and B at a distance r from O. Here the charges $+q_1$ and $+q_2$ contribute nothing to the field at the point P. Therefore, the intensity at P is solely due to $-q_2$ on A. We thus have

$$E = -\frac{d\phi}{dr} = -\frac{q_2}{4\pi\epsilon r^2},$$

where ϕ is the p.d. between the spheres

or, $\quad d\phi = \dfrac{q_2}{4\pi\epsilon r^2}dr.$ \hfill (2.41)

Integrating Eq. (2.41), we get

$$\phi = \frac{q_2}{4\pi\epsilon}\int_a^b \frac{dr}{r^2} = \frac{q_2}{4\pi\epsilon}\left[-\frac{1}{r}\right]_a^b$$

$$= \frac{q_2}{4\pi\epsilon}\left(\frac{1}{a} - \frac{1}{b}\right)$$

$$= \frac{q_2(b-a)}{4\pi\epsilon ab}. \hfill (2.42)$$

Here we have integrated in the limit from a to b since A being earthed, the potential of B is the work done in transferring unit charge from A onto B.

Now, the capacitance is given by,

$$C = \frac{q}{\phi} = \frac{q_2\left[\frac{d(b-a)}{ab} + 1\right]}{q_2\frac{(b-a)}{4\pi\epsilon ab}}$$

$$= 4\pi\epsilon\left[d + \frac{ab}{b-a}\right] \hfill (2.43)$$

If the medium is air, then

$$C = 4\pi\epsilon_0\left[d + \frac{ab}{b-a}\right]. \hfill (2.44)$$

Further, if the thickness of the outer shell is negligibly small, then, $d = b$.

$$\therefore \quad C = 4\pi\epsilon\left[b + \frac{ab}{b-a}\right]$$

$$= \frac{4\pi\epsilon b^2}{b-a} \hfill (2.45)$$

(c) Two concentric spheres—inner charged and the outer earthed, the intervening space is filled with a compound dielectric : Let a charge of $+q$ e.s.u. be given to the sphere A of radius a and the surrounding spherical shell B of radius b be earthed. The interspace is filled with concentric layers of two different dielectrics of permittivities ϵ_1 and ϵ_2 (Fig. 2.14). Let the separating spherical surface of the two dielectrics be of radius r.

In order to calculate the p.d. between A and B we choose a point P in the interspace at a distance x from O. The intensity at P is given by

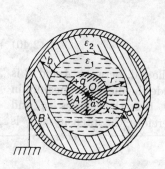

$$E = -\frac{d\phi}{dx} = \frac{q}{4\pi\epsilon x^2} \quad \text{or,} \quad d\phi = -\frac{q}{4\pi\epsilon x^2}dx$$

$$\therefore \quad \phi = \frac{q}{4\pi}\left[\frac{1}{\epsilon_1}\int_r^a -\frac{dx}{x^2} + \frac{1}{\epsilon_2}\int_b^r -\frac{dx}{x^2}\right]$$

$$= \frac{q}{4\pi}\left\{\frac{1}{\epsilon_1}\left[\frac{1}{x}\right]_r^a + \frac{1}{\epsilon_2}\left[\frac{1}{x}\right]_b^r\right\}$$

$$= \frac{q}{4\pi}\left\{\frac{1}{\epsilon_1}\frac{r-a}{ra} + \frac{1}{\epsilon_2}\frac{b-r}{rb}\right\}$$

Fig. 2.14

$$= \frac{q}{4\pi}\left\{\frac{r(\epsilon_2 b - \epsilon_1 a) - ab\epsilon_2 + ab\epsilon_1}{\epsilon_1\epsilon_2 abr}\right\}$$

So the capacitance, $C = \dfrac{q}{\phi} = \dfrac{4\pi\epsilon_1\epsilon_2 abr}{r(\epsilon_2 b - \epsilon_1 a) - ab\epsilon_2 + ab\epsilon_1}.$ \hfill (2.46)

Case III. Cylindrical Condenser

In this condenser a charged solid metallic cylinder is surrounded by a hallow metallic cylinder connected to earth (Fig. 2.15). Let a and b be respectively the radii of the inner and the outer cylinders, and ϵ is the permittivity of the intervening space. Let us, for the time being, consider a unit length of the condenser and suppose $+q$ e.s.u. of charge is given to this unit length of the inner cylinder.

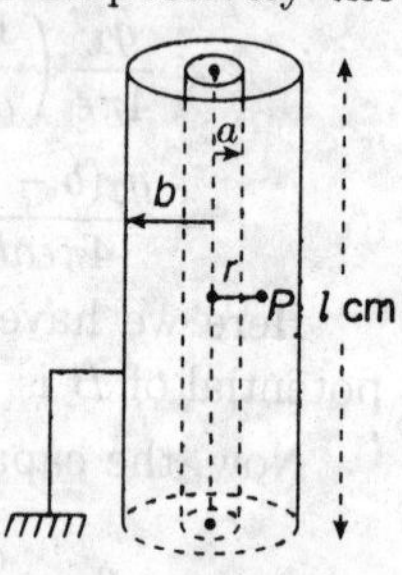

Now, consider a point P in the interspace at a distance r from the common axis. The intensity at P is given by

$$E = -\frac{d\phi}{dr} = \frac{2q}{4\pi\epsilon r}$$

or, $\quad \phi = -\displaystyle\int_b^a \frac{2q}{4\pi\epsilon r}dr = \frac{q}{2\pi\epsilon}\log_e\frac{b}{a}$

Fig. 2.15

Therefore, the capacitance per unit length is given by

$$C = \frac{q}{\phi} = \frac{2\pi\epsilon}{\log_e\frac{b}{a}} \hfill (2.47)$$

Hence, the capacitance of a condenser, l cm length $= \dfrac{2\pi\epsilon l}{\log_e\frac{b}{a}}.$ \hfill (2.48)

2.16 Calculation of Capacitances using Laplace's Equation

(a) Parallel Plate Condenser : Let the X-axis be represented by OX, A and B be the two parallel plates whose potentials are ϕ_A and ϕ_B respectively (Fig. 2.16).

At any point, the potential will depend on x only. Applying Laplace's equation we have

$$\frac{d^2\phi}{dx^2} = 0 \qquad (2.49)$$

Integrating the above equation twice,

$$\frac{d\phi}{dx} = K_1$$

or, $\quad \phi = K_1 x + K_2, \qquad (2.50)$

where K_1 and K_2 are two constants.

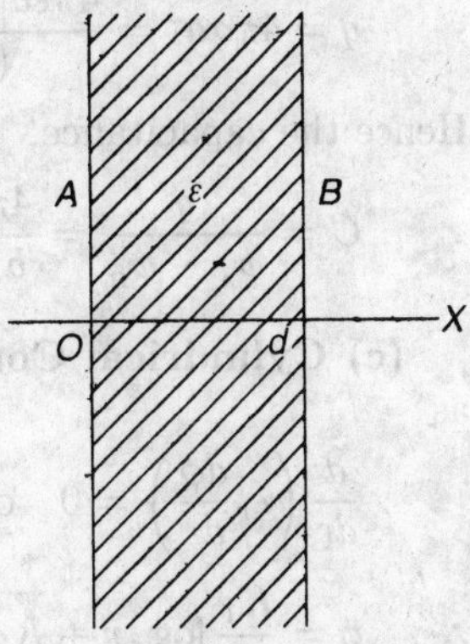

Now, by Coulomb's theorem we can write,

$$\frac{d\phi}{dx} = -\frac{\sigma}{\epsilon}.$$

$$\therefore \quad K_1 = -\frac{\sigma}{\epsilon}.$$

Fig. 2.16

Further at $x = 0$, $\phi = \phi_0 = K_2$

and also, at $x = d$, $\phi = 0 = -\dfrac{\sigma d}{\epsilon} + \phi_0.$

$\therefore$ the potential of the insulated plate is $\phi_0 = \dfrac{\sigma d}{\epsilon}.$

Hence, the capacitance per unit area $= \dfrac{\sigma}{\phi_0} = \dfrac{\epsilon}{d}. \qquad (2.51)$

(b) Spherical Condenser : In this case, Laplace's equation can be expressed as

$$\frac{d}{dr}\left(r^2 \frac{d\phi}{dr}\right) = 0 \quad \text{or,} \quad \frac{d\phi}{dr} = \frac{K_1}{r^2}$$

or, $\quad \phi = -\dfrac{K_1}{r} + K_2. \qquad (2.52)$

Now, at $r = a$, $\phi = \phi_A$

and at $r = b$, $\phi = \phi_B.$

Putting these values, we have

$$\phi_A - \phi_B = K_1\left(\frac{1}{b} - \frac{1}{a}\right)$$

or, $\quad K_1 = \dfrac{ab(\phi_A - \phi_B)}{(a-b)}. \qquad (2.53)$

Taking this value of K_1, we obtain

$$K_2 = \frac{b\phi_B - a\phi_A}{(b-a)} \qquad (2.54)$$

Putting the values of K_1 and K_2 from Eqs. (2.53) and (2.54) in Eq. (2.52) we get,

$$\phi = -\frac{ab(\phi_A - \phi_B)}{(a-b)} \cdot \frac{1}{r} + \frac{b\phi_B - a\phi_A}{(b-a)}. \qquad (2.55)$$

Again, by Coulomb's law,

$$E = -\left(\frac{d\phi}{dr}\right)_{r=a} = -\frac{ab(\phi_A - \phi_B)}{(a-b)}\frac{1}{a^2} = \frac{\sigma}{\epsilon}.$$

So, the total charge on the sphere of radius a is

$$q = 4\pi\sigma a^2 = \frac{4\pi\epsilon ab(\phi_A - \phi_B)}{(b - a)}.$$

Hence the capacitance,

$$C = \frac{q}{\phi_A - \phi_B} = \frac{4\pi\epsilon ab}{b - a}. \tag{2.56}$$

   (c) Cylindrical Condenser : In this case, Laplace's equation can be written as

$$\frac{d}{dr}\left(\epsilon_r \frac{d\phi}{dr}\right) = 0 \quad \text{or,} \quad d\phi = \frac{K_1}{\epsilon_r}dr$$

$$\therefore \quad \phi = \frac{K_1}{\epsilon} \log_e r + K_2 \tag{2.57}$$

Now, at $r = a$, $\phi = \phi_A$

and   at $r = b$, $\phi = \phi_B$.

$$\therefore \quad \phi_A - \phi_B = \frac{K_1}{\epsilon} (\log_e a - \log_e b)$$

or, $\quad K_1 = \dfrac{\epsilon(\phi_A - \phi_B)}{\log_e \frac{a}{b}}.$ \hfill (2.58)

Taking this value of K_1, we obtain

$$K_2 = \frac{\phi_B \log_e a - \phi_A \log_e b}{\log_e \frac{a}{b}} \tag{2.59}$$

Putting the values of K_1 and K_2 in Eq. (2.57), we get

$$\phi = \frac{\phi_A - \phi_B}{\log_e \frac{a}{b}} \log_e r + \frac{\phi_B \log_e a - \phi_A \log_e b}{\log_e \frac{a}{b}}$$

Again, by Coulomb's law the intensity E is given by

$$E = -\left(\frac{d\phi}{dr}\right)_{r=a} = \frac{\sigma}{\epsilon} \quad \text{or,} \quad \left.\frac{\phi_A - \phi_B}{\log_e \frac{b}{a}}\right|_{r=a} = \frac{\sigma}{\epsilon}$$

or, $\quad \dfrac{\sigma}{\epsilon} = \dfrac{\phi_A - \phi_B}{\log_e \frac{b}{a}} \cdot \dfrac{1}{a}.$

So, the total surface charge per length of the inner cylinder,

$$q = 2\pi a\sigma = \frac{2\pi\epsilon(\phi_A - \phi_B)}{\log_e \frac{b}{a}} = \frac{2\pi\epsilon(\phi_A - \phi_B)}{\log_e \frac{b}{a}}$$

Hence, the capacitance,

$$C = \frac{q}{\phi_A - \phi_B} = \frac{2\pi\epsilon}{\log_e \frac{b}{a}}.$$

2.17   Calculation of Capacitance by Coefficient of Potential

Let us consider two spheres A and B of radii a and b respectively (Fig. 2.17). We assume that q_1 and q_2 are the charges of the inner and the outer spheres, and ϕ_1

and ϕ_2 are their potentials. For this system, considering the coefficient of potential we can write,

$$\phi_1 = p_{11}q_1 + p_{21}q_2, \quad \phi_2 = p_{12}q_1 + p_{22}q_2.$$

If $q_1 = 1$ and $q_2 = 0$, then we get

$$\phi_1 = p_{11} = \frac{1}{a} \quad \text{and} \quad \phi_2 = p_{12} = \frac{1}{b}.$$

Substituting these values of the coefficients,

$$\phi_1 = \frac{q_1}{a} + \frac{q_2}{b}, \quad \phi_2 = \frac{q_1}{b} + \frac{q_2}{b}.$$

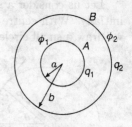

Fig. 2.17

Let B be earthed, then $\phi_2 = 0$ and so

$$q_1 = -q_2.$$

$$\therefore \quad \phi_1 = \frac{q_1}{a} - \frac{q_1}{b} = q_1\left(\frac{b-a}{ab}\right).$$

So, the capacitance of the inner sphere,

$$C_1 = \frac{q_1}{\phi_1} = \frac{ab}{b-a}.$$

Again, if the inner sphere is earthed, then $\phi_1 = 0$.

$$\therefore \quad \frac{q_1}{a} + \frac{q_2}{b} = 0 \quad \text{or,} \quad q_1 = -\frac{a}{b}q_2.$$

So,

$$\phi_2 = \frac{q_1}{b} + \frac{q_2}{b} = -\frac{a}{b^2}q_2 + \frac{q_2}{b} = q_2\left(\frac{b-a}{b^2}\right)$$

$$C_2 = \frac{q_2}{\phi_2} = \frac{b^2}{b-a} = \frac{ab}{b-a} + b. \tag{2.60}$$

2.18 Force between Two Plates of a Parallel Plate Condenser

Let one of the plates of a parallel plate condenser be charged. If σ be the surface density of charge, then the electric intensity between the plates is

$$E = \frac{\sigma}{\epsilon}. \tag{2.61}$$

From Eq. (2.61), we have

$$\sigma = \epsilon E. \tag{2.62}$$

Now, the mechanical force per unit area on the charged conductor is given by

$$dF = \frac{2\pi\sigma^2}{4\pi\epsilon} = \frac{1}{2\epsilon} \cdot \epsilon^2 E^2$$

$$= \frac{\epsilon E^2}{2}. \tag{2.63}$$

So the force on a plate of area A is

$$F = \frac{\epsilon E^2}{2} \cdot A = \frac{A}{2}\epsilon E^2. \tag{2.64}$$

2.19 Electrified Soap-Bubble

When a soap-bubble is electrified, the charge residing on the surface of the bubble will change the condition of equilibrium for an uncharged bubble. As a result, the radius of the bubble will change so as to obtain a condition of equilibrium again for a charged bubble.

Let us consider a spherical soap-bubble of radius r in the uncharged condition initially. With centre O' on the line OX passing though the centre of the bubble we draw a small circle on the spherical surface of the bubble (Fig. 2.18).

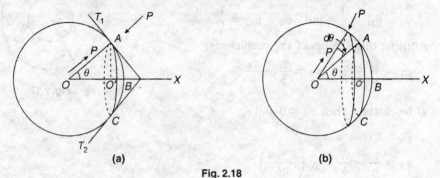

Fig. 2.18

Let P be the external atmospheric pressure. Then the component along XO of the force acting normally on the surface ABC is

$$\int_0^\theta 2\pi r \sin\theta r d\theta P \cos\theta = \pi r^2 P \int_0^\theta \sin 2\theta d\theta$$
$$= P\pi r^2 \sin^2\theta.$$

If p be the pressure of the gas inside the bubble, then according to Boyle's law at constant temperature, we have

$$p = \frac{\alpha}{r^3}, \text{ where } \alpha \text{ is a constant.}$$

Again, the resultant component of force along OX owing to the internal pressure acting normally on the area of the surface of the bubble enclosed by the small circle is $p\pi r^2 \sin^2\theta$.

In addition to above forces, there is another force due to the surface tension forming the membrane of the bubble which acts tangentially to the surface at the boundary of the small circle on the bubble. The component of this force along OX is

$$T \cdot 2\pi r \sin\theta \cdot \sin\theta = 2\pi r \cdot T \sin^2\theta,$$

where T = surface tension of the liquid.

If both the surfaces of the membrane is taken into consideration, then the force will be

$$4\pi r T \sin^2\theta.$$

If we now consider the equilibrium of the portion of the membrane, we can write,

$$P\pi r^2 \sin^2\theta + 4\pi r T \sin^2\theta = p\pi r^2 \sin^2\theta$$

or, $p - P = \dfrac{4T}{r}$ (2.65)

or, $\dfrac{\alpha}{r^3} - P = \dfrac{4T}{r}$.   (2.66)

Let us assume that a charge q is now applied to the soap-bubble. Since the soap solution is a conductor, so when it is given some charge to electrify, the charge will be distributed on the external surface. The electrical pressure amounting to $2\pi\sigma^2$ per unit area acts normally outwards. Since electrification causes a change of the radius, let the radius change to r' from initial radius r of the uncharged bubble.

Now, considering the equilibrium of the portion of the membrane bounded by a small circle, we have

$$P\pi r'^2 \sin^2\theta + 4\pi r'T\sin^2\theta = \frac{\alpha}{r'^3}\pi r'^2\sin^2\theta + \frac{\sigma^2}{2\epsilon}\pi r'^2\sin^2\theta$$

or,
$$\frac{4T}{r'} = \frac{\alpha}{r'^3} + \frac{\sigma^2}{2\epsilon} - P \tag{2.67}$$

$$= \frac{\alpha}{r'^3} + \frac{1}{2\epsilon}\left(\frac{q}{4\pi r'^2}\right)^2 - P \quad \left[\because \sigma = \frac{q}{4\pi r'^2}\right]$$

$$= \frac{\alpha}{r'^3} + \frac{q^2}{32\pi^2\epsilon r'^2} - P$$

or,
$$P - \frac{\alpha}{r'^3} + \frac{4T}{r'} - \frac{q^2}{32\pi^2\epsilon r'^2} = 0. \tag{2.68}$$

Eq. (2.68) gives the condition of equilibrium for a bubble of radius r'.
From Eq. (2.68) eliminating T we have

$$P(r'-r) - \alpha\left(\frac{1}{r'^2} - \frac{1}{r^2}\right) = \frac{q^2}{32\pi^2\epsilon r'^3}. \tag{2.69}$$

This gives a relation between the radii in uncharged and charged conditions. If the bubble is connected to a potential ϕ, then $\phi = \dfrac{q}{4\pi\epsilon r}$ and so we get

$$P(r'-r) - \alpha\left(\frac{1}{r'^2} - \frac{1}{r^2}\right) = \frac{\epsilon\phi^2}{2r}. \tag{2.70}$$

Examples

1. A capacitor of 1 μF is charged to 10 000 volts and suddenly discharged through a fine copper wire. If all the energy went to heating the wire, how many calories would be adiabatically liberated?

   Solution : Here, $C = 1$ μF $= 10^{-6}$ farad $= 9 \times 10^5$ e.s.u. of capacity

   $$\phi = 10\,000 \text{ volts} = \frac{10^4}{300} \text{ e.s.u. of potential} = \frac{10^2}{3} \text{ e.s.u.}$$

   We have, $W = \dfrac{1}{2}C\phi^2 = \dfrac{1}{2}\cdot 9\cdot 10^5\cdot\dfrac{10^4}{9} = 0.5 \times 10^9$ ergs.

   $$\therefore \qquad H = \frac{W}{J} = \frac{0.5\times 10^9}{4.2\times 10^7} \text{ cal} = \textbf{12 cal (approx.).}$$

2. A parallel plate condenser of 1 μF capacity is to be constructed using paper sheets of 0.05 mm thickness as the dielectric. Find how many sheets of circular metal foils of diameter 20.0 cm will be needed for the purpose. Dielectric constant of paper = 4.0.

Solution : If the required number of metal sheets be n, then the number of condensers formed by them will be $(n-1)$. When these condensers are connected in parallel, the total capacitance will be

$$C = \frac{(n-1)\epsilon A}{4\pi d}.$$

Here, $\epsilon = 4$, $A = \pi \times 10^2$ ($\because$ diameter=20 cm)

$$d = 0.005 \text{ cm}, C = 1 \ \mu F = 9 \times 10^5 \text{ e.s.u.}$$

$$\therefore \qquad 9 \times 10^5 = \frac{(n-1) \times 4 \times \pi \times 10^2}{4 \times \pi \times 5 \times 10^{-3}} \quad \text{or,} \quad (n-1) = 45.$$

$$\therefore \qquad n = 46.$$

3. A slab of dielectric is inserted in the air-gap of a parallel plate condenser. Show that the capacity per unit area of the condenser is doubled if the dielectric constant is

$$\epsilon = \frac{2b}{2b-a},$$

where a is the air-gap thickness before the insertion of the slab and b is the thickness of the dielectric.

Solution : Before insertion of the dielectric, the capacity per unit area is

$$C_1 = \frac{1}{4\pi a}.$$

After insertion of the dielectric, the capacity per unit area is

$$C_2 = \frac{1}{4\pi \left[a - b\left(1 - \frac{1}{\epsilon}\right)\right]}.$$

From the condition of the problem, we can write,

$$\frac{2}{4\pi a} = \frac{1}{4\pi \left[a - b\left(1 - \frac{1}{\epsilon}\right)\right]} \quad \text{or,} \quad a = 2a - 2b\left(1 - \frac{1}{\epsilon}\right)$$

or, $\quad 1 - \dfrac{1}{\epsilon} = \dfrac{a}{2b}$ or, $\dfrac{1}{\epsilon} = 1 - \dfrac{a}{2b} = \dfrac{2b-a}{2b}.$

$$\therefore \qquad \epsilon = \frac{2b}{2b-a} \quad \textbf{(Proved)}.$$

4. Two spheres of radii 5 and 10 cm respectively have equal charges of 50 units each. They are then joined by a thin wire so as to be able to share the charge between them. Calculate the total energy of the conductors before and after sharing.

Solution : Let C_1, q_1, ϕ_1 and C_2, q_2, ϕ_2 respectively denote the capacitance, charge and potential of the two spheres in e.s.u. respectively. Then we have

$$C_1 = 5, \ q = 50, \ \phi_1 = \frac{50}{5} = 10$$

and $\quad C_2 = 10, \ q_2 = 50, \ \phi_2 = \dfrac{50}{10} = 5.$

The energy before sharing,

$$W_i = \frac{1}{2}C_1\phi_1^2 + \frac{1}{2}C_2\phi_2^2 = \frac{1}{2} \cdot 5 \cdot (10)^2 + \frac{1}{2} \cdot 10 \cdot (5)^2$$

$$= 250 + 125 = 375 \text{ ergs.}$$

After sharing,

total charge $= q_1 + q_2 = 100 = q$ (say)

total capacitance $= C_1 + C_2 = 10 + 5 = 15 = C$ (say).

Hence, the energy after sharing

$$= \frac{1}{2}\frac{q^2}{C} = \frac{1}{2}\frac{(100)^2}{15}$$

$$= \textbf{333.33 ergs.}$$

5. Calculate the capacity per centimeter of a condenser formed by two long co-axial cylinders of radii 5 cm and 5.2 cm field with a dielectric of permittivity 1.2.

Solution : Here, $a = 5$ cm, $b = 5.2$ cm, $\epsilon = 1.2$

We have, $C = \dfrac{\epsilon}{2 \log_e \frac{b}{a}} = \dfrac{1.2}{2 \log_e \frac{5.2}{5}} = \dfrac{1.2}{2 \times 2.3026 \log_{10} \frac{5.2}{5}}$

$$= \frac{1.2}{2 \times 2.3026 \times 0.0170}$$

$$= \textbf{15.33 e.s.u./cm.}$$

6. Two cylindrical condensers are of equal length and same dielectric. The radii of the inner and outer cylinders of one are 8 cm and 10 cm, respectively and those of other are 7 cm and 9 cm. Find the ratio of their capacities.

Solution : The capacity of the first condenser,

$$C_1 = \frac{\epsilon l}{2 \log_e \frac{b}{a}} = \frac{\epsilon l}{2 \log_e \frac{10}{8}} \qquad (\because b = 10 \text{ cm}, a = 8 \text{ cm})$$

$$= \frac{\epsilon l}{2 \times 2.3026 \log_{10} \frac{5}{4}}.$$

Similarly, the capacity of the second condenser,

$$C_2 = \frac{\epsilon l}{2 \times 2.3026 \log_{10} \frac{9}{7}} \qquad (\because a = 7 \text{ cm}, b = 9 \text{ cm})$$

Hence we get,

$$\frac{C_1}{C_2} = \frac{\log_{10} \frac{9}{7}}{\log_{10} \frac{5}{4}} = \frac{0.1091}{0.0969} = \textbf{1.126.}$$

7. If the radii of two concentric spheres be a, b $(b > a)$ and each sphere is electrified with a positive charge q, show that the energy of the system will be

$$\frac{q^2(b + 3a)}{2ab}.$$

Solution : The general relation between the potentials and charges can be written as

$$\phi_1 = p_{11}q_1 + p_{21}q_2, \quad \phi_2 = p_{12}q_1 + p_{22}q_2.$$

Here, $q_1 = q_2 = q$.

$\therefore$ $\phi_1 = (p_{11} + p_{12})q$ $(\because p_{21} = p_{12})$

and $\phi_2 = (p_{12} + p_{22})q.$

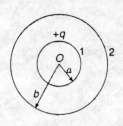

Fig. 2.19

The energy of the system

$$= \frac{1}{2}q\phi_1 + \frac{1}{2}q\phi_2 = \frac{1}{2}q(\phi_1 + \phi_2)$$

$$= \frac{q}{2}[q(p_{11} + p_{12}) + q(p_{12} + p_{22})]$$

$$= \frac{q^2}{2}[p_{11} + 2p_{12} + p_{22}]$$

Considering Fig. 2.19 we have

$$\text{energy} = \frac{q^2}{2}\left(\frac{1}{a} + \frac{2}{b} + \frac{1}{b}\right) = \frac{q^2}{2}\left(\frac{1}{a} + \frac{3}{b}\right)$$

$$= \frac{q^2}{2ab}(b + 3a) \quad \textbf{(Proved)}.$$

8. A soap-bubble has a radius of 2 cm. Assuming the surface tension to be 24 dynes/cm, calculate the potential to which it must be raised so that the pressure inside and outside is the same.

Solution : The equation for equilibrium of a charged bubble of radius r is

$$P - \frac{\alpha}{r'^3} + \frac{4T}{r'} - 2\pi\sigma^2 = 0.$$

Here, $P = \dfrac{\alpha}{r'^3}$.

$$\therefore \quad \frac{4T}{r'} = 2\pi\sigma^2 \quad \text{or,} \quad T = \frac{1}{2}\pi r'\sigma^2.$$

Let ϕ be the required potential. Then,

$$4\pi r'^2\sigma = q = C\phi = r'\phi \quad \text{or,} \quad \phi = 4\pi r'\sigma.$$

$$\therefore \quad \phi^2 = 16\pi^2 r'^2\sigma^2 = 16\pi^2 r'^2 \cdot \frac{2T}{r'\pi} = 32\pi r'T$$

or, $\quad \phi = \sqrt{32\pi r'T}$

$$= \sqrt{32 \times 3.14 \times 2 \times 24} \quad (\because \; r' = 2 \text{ cm}, \; T = 24 \text{ dynes/cm})$$

$$= 69.44 \text{ e.s.u.} = 69.44 \times 300 \text{ volts} = \textbf{20\,832 volts.}$$

9. A spherical soap-bubble is blown at the end of a thin metal tube and given a charge q. Show that when the pressure inside the bubble is equal to that of the surrounding atmosphere, its radius r is determined by the equation $q^2 = 32\pi r'^3T$, T being the surface tension.

Solution : We have $\dfrac{4T}{r'} = 2\pi\sigma^2$.

Now the charge, $q = 4\pi r'^2\sigma \quad$ or, $\quad q^2 = 16\pi^2 r'^4\sigma^2$.

$$\therefore \quad \frac{4T}{r'} = 2\pi \cdot \frac{q^2}{16\pi^2 r'^4} \quad \text{or,} \quad q^2 = 32\pi r'^3T \quad \textbf{(Proved)}.$$

10. A conductor is charged to a potential of 1000 volts. If the capacitance of the conductor be 10 μF, determine the energy stored in the conductor.

Solution : Here, $V = 1000$ volts $= \dfrac{1000}{300}$

$$= \frac{10}{3} \text{ e.s.u.} \quad (\because \; 1 \text{ e.s.u.} = 300 \text{ volts})$$

and $C = 10\ \mu F = 10 \times 10^{-6}$ F

$\qquad = 10^{-5} \times 9 \times 10^{11}$ e.s.u. $\quad (\because\ 1\ F = 9 \times 10^{11}$ e.s.u.$)$

$\qquad = 9 \times 10^6$ e.s.u.

$\therefore$ energy stored $= \dfrac{1}{2}CV^2 = \dfrac{1}{2} \times 9 \times 10^6 \times \dfrac{10^2}{9}$

$\qquad\qquad\qquad = 5 \times 10^7$ ergs $= \textbf{5 joules.}$

11. A sphere of radius 5 cm and charged to 50 e.s.u. is connected by a wire of negligible capacitance with another sphere with the same charge but double the radius. Calculate the loss of energy. **[C.U. 1944, '65]**

Solution : $r_1 = 5$ cm

$\therefore \qquad C_1 = 5$ e.s.u. and $q_1 = 50$ e.s.u.

$\therefore \qquad V_1 = \dfrac{q_1}{C_1} = \dfrac{50}{5} = 10$ e.s.u.

Again, $r_2 = 2r_1$ (according to the condition)

$\qquad\qquad = 2 \times 5 = 10$ cm.

$\therefore \qquad C_2 = 10$ e.s.u. and $q_2 = 50$ e.s.u.

$\therefore \qquad V_2 = \dfrac{q_2}{C_2} = \dfrac{50}{10} = 5$ e.s.u.

$\therefore$ loss of energy $= \dfrac{C_1 C_2}{2(C_1 + C_2)}(V_1 - V_2)^2 = \dfrac{5 \times 10}{2(5 + 10)}(10 - 5)^2 = \textbf{41.66 ergs.}$

12. Find the capacity of two circular parallel metal plates, each of radius 10 cm separated by an air-distance of 1 mm. Express the result in microfarads. **[C.U. 1971]**

Solution : Here, $r = 10$ cm and $d = 1$ mm $= 0.1$ cm.

$\therefore \quad A = \pi r^2 = \pi \cdot 100$ sq. cm.

Capacitance of the parallel plate capacitor, $C = \dfrac{A}{4\pi d} \quad (\because\ K = 1)$

$\qquad\qquad\qquad\qquad\qquad\qquad = \dfrac{\pi \cdot 100}{4\pi \times 0.1} = 250$ e.s.u.

$\qquad\qquad\qquad\qquad\qquad\qquad = \dfrac{250}{9 \times 10^5}\ \mu F$

$\qquad\qquad\qquad\qquad\qquad\qquad = \textbf{2.78} \times \textbf{10}^{-4}\ \boldsymbol{\mu} \textbf{F.}$

13. A parallel plate condenser consists of two plates of area 100 sq. cm each and separated by a distance of 1 cm. A square glass slab of thickness 1 cm and side 5 cm is placed between the plates. Calculate the capacity of the condenser. The S.I.C. of glass is 10. **[P.U. 1942; Agra U. 1964]**

Solution : Here, area of the metal plate $= 100$ sq. cm, area of the glass slab $= 5 \times 5 = 25$ sq. cm, distance between metal plates, $d =$ distance of glass slab, $t = 1$ cm and $K = 10$.

So it is seen that the glass slab covers 25 sq.cm of the metal plate. On the remaining 75 sq.cm of the surface of the metal plate, air is present.

So capacitor, $C = \dfrac{A_1}{4\pi d} + \dfrac{A_2}{4\pi \left(d - t + \frac{t}{K}\right)}$

$\qquad = \dfrac{A_1}{4\pi d} + \dfrac{KA_2}{4\pi} \quad (\because \; d = t = 1 \text{ cm})$

$\qquad = \dfrac{75}{4\pi \times 1} + \dfrac{10 \times 25}{4\pi}$

$\qquad\qquad$ (putting $A_1 = 75$ sq. cm and $A_2 = 25$ sq. cm)

$\qquad = \mathbf{25.85. \; e.s.u.}$

14. The plates of a parallel plate condenser are 2 cm apart. A slab of dielectric of S.I.C. = 5 and thickness 1 cm is placed between the plates and the distance between the plates is altered so as to keep the capacity of the condenser unchanged. What is the new distance between the plates?   [C.U. 1946]

Solution : Before placing the dielectric slab the capacitance,

$$C = \frac{A}{4\pi d}$$

After placing the dielectric slab the capacitance increases. But since the capacitance remains same by changing d to d', we can write

$$\frac{A'}{4\pi \left(d' - t + \frac{t}{K}\right)} = \frac{A}{4\pi d} \quad \text{or,} \quad d' - t + \frac{t}{K} = d$$

$\therefore \quad d' = d + t - \dfrac{t}{K}.$

Here, $d = 2$ cm, $t = 1$ cm and $K = 5$.

$\therefore \quad d' = 2 + 1 - \dfrac{1}{5} = \dfrac{14}{5} = \mathbf{2.8 \; cm}.$

15. A metal wire 1 mm in diameter is stretched along the axis of a conducting cylinder whose internal radius is 1 cm. Calculate the capacity of the structure per unit length in micro-farad.   [C.U. 1970]

Solution : Here, $K = 1$, $d = 1$ mm.

$\therefore \quad r_1 = 0.05$ cm   and $r_2 = 1$ cm

$\therefore$ capacitance, $C = \dfrac{K}{2 \times 2.3026 \log_{10}\left(\frac{r_2}{r_1}\right)} = \dfrac{1}{4.6052 \log_{10}\left(\frac{1}{0.05}\right)}$

$\qquad = \dfrac{1}{5.9911} \text{ e.s.u.} = \dfrac{1}{5.9911 \times 9 \times 10^5} \; \mu\text{F}$

$\qquad = \mathbf{1.85 \times 10^{-7} \; \mu F \; (approx.).}$

16. Calculate the capacity of a spherical condenser if the diameter of the inner-sphere is 20 cm and that of the outer-sphere is 30 cm, the space between them being filled with liquid having a specific inductive capacity 2.   [C.U. Spl. Exam. 1967]

Solution : If the outer-sphere is taken as earthed,

$\qquad$ capacitor, $C = \dfrac{K r_1 r_2}{r_2 - r_1}.$

Here, $r_1 = \dfrac{20}{2} = 10$ cm, $r_2 = \dfrac{30}{2} = 15$ cm and $K = 2$.

$$\therefore \quad C = \frac{2 \times 10 \times 15}{15 - 10} = 60 \text{ e.s.u.} = \frac{60}{9 \times 10^5}\ \mu F$$

$$= 6.6 \times 10^{-5}\ \mu F.$$

17. When a slab of insulating material 4 mm thick is introduced between the plates of a parallel plate capacitor, it is found that the distance between the plates has to be increased by 3.5 mm to restore the capacitance to its original value. Calculate the dielectric constant of the material.

Solution : Increase of distance between the two plates, $x = \dfrac{t}{\epsilon_r}(\epsilon_r - 1)$.

Here, $x = 3.5$ mm $= 3.5 \times 10^{-3}$ m; $t = 4$ mm $= 4 \times 10^{-3}$ m.

Therefore, $3.5 \times 10^{-3} = \dfrac{4 \times 10^{-3}}{\epsilon_r} \times (\epsilon_r - 1)$

or,· $\qquad \dfrac{3.5}{4} = \left(1 - \dfrac{1}{\epsilon_r}\right)$

$\therefore \qquad\qquad \epsilon_r = 8.$

18. A parallel plate capacitor consists of two plates of area 100 cm² each and separated by a distance of 1 cm. A square glass slab of thickness 1 cm and sides 5 cm each is placed between the plates. Calculate the capacitance of the capacitor. The specific inductive capacity of glass = 10.

Solution : Since the glass slab does not acquire the total area, therefore, capacitance,

$$C = \frac{\epsilon_0 \alpha_1}{d} + \frac{\epsilon_0 \alpha_2}{d - t + \frac{t}{\epsilon_r}} = \frac{\epsilon_0 \alpha_1}{d} + \frac{\epsilon_0 \epsilon_r \alpha_2}{d} = \frac{\epsilon_0}{d}(\alpha_1 + \epsilon_r \cdot \alpha_2).$$

(Here, $t = d = 1$ cm)

Here, $\alpha_1 = 100 - (5 \times 5) = 75$ cm² $= 75 \times 10^{-4}$ m²; $d = 1$ cm $= 10^{-2}$ m; $\alpha_2 = 25$ cm² $= 25 \times 10^{-4}$ m²; $\epsilon_r = 10$ and $\epsilon_0 = 885 \times 10^{-12}$.

$$\therefore \quad C = \frac{8.85 \times 10^{-12}}{10^{-2}}(75 \times 10^{-4} + 25 \times 10^{-4} \times 10)$$

$$= \frac{8.85 \times 10^{-12} \times 10^{-4}}{10^{-2}} \times 325 = 2876.25 \times 10^{-14}\ F$$

$$= 2.87 \times 10^{-5}\ \mu F.$$

19. A capacitor is composed of two plates separated by a sheet of insulating material 3 mm thick and of permittivity 4. The distance between the plates is increased to allow the insertion of a second sheet of insulating material 5 mm thick and of permittivity ϵ_{r_1}. If the capacitance of the capacitor so formed is $\frac{1}{3}$ of the original capacitance, find ϵ_{r_1}.

Solution : In the first case, $C_1 = \dfrac{\epsilon_r \cdot \epsilon_0 \alpha}{d} = \dfrac{4\epsilon_0 \alpha}{3 \times 10^{-3}}$

and in the second case, $C_2 = \dfrac{\epsilon_0 \alpha}{\left[\frac{d}{\epsilon_r} + \frac{d_1}{\epsilon_{r_1}}\right]} = \dfrac{\epsilon_0 \alpha}{\left[\frac{3}{4} + \frac{5}{\epsilon_{r_1}}\right] \times 10^{-3}}.$

According to the question, $C_2 = \dfrac{1}{3}C_1$ or, $3C_2 = C_1.$

$$\therefore \quad \frac{3\alpha \cdot \epsilon_0}{10^{-3} \left[\frac{3}{4} + \frac{5}{\epsilon_{r_1}}\right]} = \frac{4\alpha \cdot \epsilon_0}{3 \times 10^{-3}} \quad \text{or,} \quad \frac{3}{4} = \frac{1}{3}\left(\frac{3}{4} + \frac{5}{\epsilon_r}\right)$$

$$\therefore \quad \epsilon_{r_1} = \mathbf{3.33}.$$

20. The thickness of the air layer between the two coatings of a spherical air capacitor is 2 cm. The capacitor has the same capacitance as that of a sphere of diameter 1.2 m. Find the radii of the surfaces of the air capacitor.

Solution : Capacitance of the spherical air capacitor, $C = \dfrac{4\pi\epsilon_0 ab}{b - a}$.

Here, $b - a = $ thickness of air layer $= 2$ cm $= 2 \times 10^{-2}$ m

and $\quad C = 4\pi\epsilon_0 \times \dfrac{1.2}{2} = 4\pi\epsilon_0 \times 0.6.$

So, $\quad 4\pi\epsilon_0 \times 0.6 = \dfrac{4\pi\epsilon_0 ab}{2 \times 10^{-2}}$

or, $\quad a \cdot b = 1.2$ m $= 120$ cm

Now, $\quad (b + a)^2 = (b - a)^2 + 4ab = 4 + 4 \times 120 = 484$

$\therefore \quad a + b = 22$ cm

Also, $\quad b - a = 2$ cm

Therefore, $b = 12$ cm and $a = \mathbf{10}$ **cm.**

21. A submarine cable consists of a copper wire of diameter 4 mm surrounded by gutta-percha of thickness 6 mm. If the S.I.C. of gutta-percha be 4.2, find capacitance of 30 kilometres of the cable.

Solution : $C = \dfrac{2\pi\epsilon_r \cdot \epsilon_0 \cdot l}{2.3026 \log_{10}\left(\frac{b}{a}\right)}$ farad.

Here $\epsilon_r = 4.2$; $\epsilon_0 = 8.85 \times 10^{-12}$; $l = 30$ km $= 30 \times 10^3$ m;

$\quad a = 2$ mm $= 2 \times 10^{-3}$ m; $b = 2 + 6 = 8$ mm $= 8 \times 10^{-3}$ m.

$$\therefore \quad C = \frac{2\pi \times 4.2 \times 8.85 \times 10^{-12} \times 30 \times 10^3}{2.3026 \log_{10}\left(\frac{8}{2}\right)} \text{ F}$$

$$= \frac{2\pi \times 4.2 \times 8.85 \times 3 \times 10^{-8}}{2.3026 \times 0.6} = 50.75 \times 10^{-7} \text{ F}$$

$$= \mathbf{5.075} \ \boldsymbol{\mu}\mathbf{F}.$$

22. A metal wire 1 mm in diameter is stretched along the axis of a conducting cylinder whose internal radius is 1 cm. Calculate the capacitance of the structure per unit length in microfarad.

Solution : Capacitance of the cylindrical capacitor per unit length,

$$C = \frac{2\pi\epsilon_0}{2.3026 \log_{10}\left(\frac{b}{a}\right)}.$$

Here, $b = 1$ cm $= 10^{-2}$ m and $a = 0.05$ cm $= 0.05 \times 10^{-2}$ m.

$$\therefore \quad C = \frac{2\pi\epsilon_0}{2.3026 \log_{10}\left(\frac{1}{0.05}\right)} = \frac{2\pi\epsilon_0}{2.3026 \times \log_{10} 20}$$

$$= \frac{2\pi \times 8.85 \times 10^{-12}}{2.3026 \times 1.3} \, \text{F} = 18.59 \times 10^{-12} \, \text{F}$$

$$= 18.59 \times 10^{-6} \, \mu\text{F}.$$

23. Two metal plates, each of area 20 cm^2 are maintained difference of potential of 1200 volts. If the distance between the plates be 0.5 cm, find the force of attraction between them. **[B.U. 1996]**

Solution : $F = \dfrac{\alpha}{2} \dfrac{(V_A - V_B)^2}{d^2} \epsilon_0.$

Here, $\alpha = 20 \, \text{cm}^2 = 20 \times 10^{-4} \, \text{m}^2$; $V_A - V_B = 1200$ volts; $\epsilon_0 = 8.85 \times 10^{-12}$

and $d = 0.5 \, \text{cm} = 0.5 \times 10^{-2} \, \text{m}.$

$$\therefore \quad F = \frac{(20 \times 10^{-4}) \times (1200)^2 \times 8.85 \times 10^{-12}}{2 \times (0.5 \times 10^{-2})^2}$$

$$= 50.9 \times 10^{-5} \, \text{N}.$$

Questions

Essay-type

1. Define capacity and explain the principle of a condenser. **[B.U. 1983]**

2. Show that when two different conductors charged to different potentials are connected to each other, there is always a loss of energy. Where does this energy go?

3. Show that the energy W of a charged capacitor is given by $W = \frac{1}{2}CV^2$, where C and V are capacitance and potential respectively.

4. Calculate the capacitance of a parallel plate capacitor. How will the capacitance be altered if the space between the plates be partially filled with a slab of thickness d and of dielectric constant ϵ_r?

5. Deduce an expression for the capacitance of a parallel plate capacitor with two-component dielectric.

6. Deduce an expression for the capacitance of a parallel plate capacitor with a dielectric medium.

7. Calculate the capacitance of a spherical conductor of radius a in a medium of dielectric constant ϵ_r. How will the capacitance change if an earth-connected hollow spherical conductor of radius $b(b > a)$ is placed concentrically with the first? **[C.U. 1980]**

8. Find the capacitance of a capacitor consisting of two concentric metallic spheres the inner of which is charged and the outer earthed.

[C.U. '83, '89; B.U. 1996]

9. Find the capacitance of two concentric spheres when the outer sphere is connected to the earth and the inner sphere is maintained at a given potential. What will happen if the inner sphere is earthed and the outer sphere is maintained at the above potential?

10. Find the capacitance per unit length of a cylindrical capacitor, the outer cylinder being earthed. **[B.U. 1983]**

11. Show that the capacity of a sphere is numerically equal to $4\pi\epsilon_0\epsilon_r$ times its radius, ϵ_r being the S.L.C. of the dielectric in which the sphere is embedded.

[B.U. 1983]

12. Derive an expression for the energy of a capacitor C charged to potential V. Two capacitors of capacitances C_1 and C_2 are charged to potentials V_1 and V_2. Then they are connected together. Calculate the loss of energy for sharing charges.

13. Find an expression for the capacitance per unit length of two co-axial cylinders in air. Investigate the effect of inserting between the cylinders a co-axial cylinder of dielectric substance of thickness less than that of the layer of air.

Short Answer-type

14. Will there be any loss of energy when two charged conductors of same potential are connected together?   [C.U. 1989]

15. What is capacitance? What is farad?

16. Define specific inductive capacity. 'The specific inductive capacity of glass is 8.5'—explain the statement fully.

17. What effect does a dielectric medium have on the action of a capacitor?

18. 'When an insulated sphere is charged, it may be regarded as a spherical capacitor with its outer coating at infinity.' Explain the statement fully.

19. What would be the change in the capacitance of a spherical capacitor if its outer coating is insulated while the inner coating is given a charge?

20. What will be the effect of the following on the capacitance of a parallel plate capacitor—(i) a slab of insulating material is inserted between the plates, (ii) distance between the plates is doubled, the space being occupied by air, (iii) one plate is insulated and charged while the other plate is not earth-connected?

21. Distinguish between the terms 'polar dielectrics' and 'non-polar dielectrics'.

Numerical Problems

22. A parallel plate capacitor consists of two plates of area 500 cm^2 each separated by a sheet of mica 0.075 cm thick. Find its capacitance in microfarads, if dielectric constant for mica is 6.5.   [Ans. 0.0038 μF]

23. Two isolated spherical conductors of diameters 6 cm and 10 cm are charged to 3000 volts and 4500 volts of potential respectively and are then connected together by a wire. Find the common potential and the loss of energy on sharing the charge.   [Ans. 3937 volts; 2.36×10^{-7} J]

24. A capacitor consists of 200 circular sheets of tin foils separated by mica of S.I.C. 6 and thickness 0.5 mm, alternate plates being connected together. If the capacitance of the capacitor be 0.4 microfarad, find the radius of the tin foils.   [C.U. 1990]

[Ans. 7.7 cm]

25. The plates of a parallel plate capacitor are 2 cm apart. A slab of dielectric of S.I.C. = 5 and thickness 1 cm is placed between the plates and the distance between the plates is altered so as to keep the capacitances of the capacitor unchanged. What is the new distance between the plates?   [Ans. 2.8 cm]

26. Two spherical rain drops of radii 1 mm and 2 mm come in contact under a potential of 500 volts and then coalesce. Find the potential of the resulting drop and the loss or gain of energy due to coalescence.

    [**Ans.** 721 volts; 1.8×10^{-8} J gain]

27. A slab of dielectric is inserted in the air-gap of a parallel plate capacitor. Show that the capacitance per unit area of the capacitor is doubled if the dielectric constant $K = \frac{2x}{2x-d}$, where d = air-thickness before insertion of dielectric and x = thickness of dielectric.

28. Calculate the capacitance of a spherical capacitor if the diameter of the inner sphere is 20 cm and that of the outer sphere is 30 cm, the space between them being filled with a liquid having a specific inductive capacity of 2.

    [**Ans.** 6.6×10^{-5} μF]

29. A cylindrical cable is made up of an inner conductor of diameter 0.5 cm surrounded by a co-axial conductor of internal diameter 1 cm, with a substance of dielectric constant 8 filling the space between them. What is its capacitance per metre? If the cable is 1 km long, calculate the charge required to raise the potential of the inner conductor to 300 volts above that of the outer.

    [**Ans.** 644.35×10^{-6} μF/m; 193.3 μC]

30. Three capacitors, each of capacitance 6 microfarads are connected in series and a battery of 100 volts applied across the combination. Calculate the charge taken from the battery and the energy stored in the capacitors.

    [**Ans.** 2×10^{-4} coulomb; 10^{-9} joule]

31. The diameter of the copper conductor of a submarine cable is 4 cm and that of gutta-percha covering 9 cm. Calculate the capacitance of one kilometre of the cable. Dielectric constant of gutta-percha = 4.   [**B.U. 1990**]

    [**Ans.** 0.213 μF]

32. A potential difference of 400 volts is applied between the ends of two capacitors of capacitances 10 microfarads and 30 microfarads connected in series. Find the P.D. across each condenser and the energy of each.

    [**Ans.** $V = 300$ volts, $V = 100$ volts; 0.45 J, 0.15 J]

33. Calculate the force of attraction, neglecting end effects between two parallel plates each of area 200 cm^2 and 4 mm apart in air charged to a potential difference of 3000 volts.   [**Ans.** 4.98×10^{-2} N]

34. Two brass plates of area 1 metre^2 are placed parallel at a distance of 10 cm from each other. Calculate the capacitance. Find also the change in capacitance when a slab of glass of thickness 5 cm is placed parallel between the two plates. S.I.C. of glass = 8.   [**Ans.** 8.84×10^{-5} μF, 6.8×10^{-5} μF]

35. Two spheres of diameters 6 cm and 10 cm respectively placed at a distance from each other, are charged with 8 units and 12 units of positive electricity respectively. They are connected by a fine wire. Does any spark pass? How much energy is dissipated?   [**Ans.** No spark passes; $\frac{1}{15}$ erg]

36. Show that when two condensers of equal capacitances are connected in parallel, the system has 4 times the capacity of that obtained by connecting the same condensers in series.

37. Three capacitors, each of capacitance 6 μF are connected in series and a battery of 100 volts applied across the combination. Calculate the charge taken from the battery and the energy stored in the capacitors.

[**Ans.** 2×10^{-4} coulomb; 0.01 joule]

38. Two plane sheets of metal and a sheet of mica of thickness 0.002 cm and dielectric constant 6 are supplied for making a condenser of capacitance 0.02 μF. What area of sheet should be cut from the sheets supplied for the purpose?

[**Ans.** 75.43 sq. cm]

39. A parallel plate condenser is made of 26 metal plates of area 44 sq. cm each and mica foils of thickness 0.1 mm. If the dielectric constant of mica be 6, what is the capacity in μF of the condenser formed?   [**Ans.** 0.0583 μF]

40. A parallel plate slab of insulating material 5 mm thick, is introduced between the plates of a parallel plate air condenser. To restore its capacity to its original value it is found necessary to increase the separation between the plates by 2.5 mm. Find the dielectric constant of the material of the slab.

[C.U. 1963]

[**Ans.** 2]

Chapter 3

Electrostatic Instruments and Measurements

3.1   Introduction

For performing experiments with static charges we have to find out some means so that we can measure the potential and their variations accurately. In electrostatic measurements good insulation is essential to avoid any leakage either from the body or from the measuring instruments. For measuring the static potential Faraday used the gold-leaf electroscopes. But the uncertainty of their readings and the low sensitivity restricted their use. Recently, electroscopes have been made more accurate with a greater sensitivity and are now being used as detector of charges. In fact, various instruments have been designed from time to time for the measurement of charge and potential with a high degree of accuracy and also for their absolute determination. Such instruments are called *electrometers*.

3.2   Attracted Disc Electrometer

This is an absolute electrometer of Kelvin type. Essentially, the electrometer is a parallel plate air condenser provided with a guard-ring arrangement.

The diagram of an attracted disc electrometer is shown in Fig. 3.1. In the figure, A is the attracted disc situated in the plane of the guard-ring G. The disc is carried by a small coach spring S. B is another plate parallel to A. A constant potential is maintained at A. B is brought in contact with the bodies. It can be lowered or raised by a micrometer screw M.

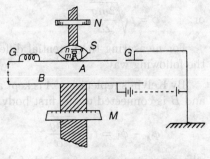

Fig. 3.1

In order to measure the potential of a body, A, G and B are first earthed. A small weight m is now kept upon A. As a result, it will be lowered. By an adjusting screw N, A is brought in the plane of G again which is to be ensured optically. Sometimes a pointer is provided whose tip lies against a mark n on the fixed casing when A and G are in the same plane. Removing the weight m, the disc A is now raised from the plane of G. B is now disconnected from the earth and it is connected to the body whose potential is to be measured. Adjusting the position of B by M the distance t is made such that due to the attraction between A and B, the disc A again comes in the plane of G.

If g is the acceleration due to gravity, then the attractive force $= mg$.

Again, if α is the area of the plate and t the separation, then the capacitance of the air condenser,

$$C = \frac{\epsilon \alpha}{t}. \tag{3.1}$$

71

Therefore, potential energy,

$$W = \frac{1}{2}C\phi^2 \quad [\phi = \text{potential of } B]$$

$$= \frac{\epsilon\alpha\phi^2}{2t}. \tag{3.2}$$

As the field between the plates is uniform, hence the force of attraction (F) between them will also be so.

Now, $\quad F = -\dfrac{dW}{dx} \quad$ or, $\quad F \cdot dx = -dW$.

Integrating we have

$$F \int_0^t dx = -\int_W^0 dW$$

or, $\quad Ft = W$

$$= \frac{\epsilon\alpha\phi^2}{2t} \quad [\text{By Eq. (3.2)}] \tag{3.3}$$

From Eq. (3.3), we get

$$F = \frac{\epsilon\alpha\phi^2}{2t^2}. \tag{3.4}$$

We then have,

$$\frac{\epsilon\alpha\phi^2}{2t^2} = mg \quad \text{or,} \quad \phi^2 = \frac{2t^2}{\epsilon\alpha}mg$$

or, $\quad \phi = t\sqrt{\dfrac{2mg}{\epsilon\alpha}}. \tag{3.5}$

For measuring the potential difference between two bodies we may proceed in the following way :

By Kelvin's replenisher A is kept at a constant potential instead of being earthed and B is connected to the first body. Then,

$$\phi_A - \phi_1 = t_1\sqrt{\frac{2mg}{\epsilon\alpha}}, \tag{3.6}$$

where ϕ_A = constant potential of A, ϕ_1 = potential of the first body, t_1 = distance of separation between the plates in the first part of the experiment.

Next, the plate B is connected to the second body. Then we have,

$$\phi_A - \phi_2 = t_2\sqrt{\frac{2mg}{\epsilon\alpha}}, \tag{3.7}$$

where ϕ_2 = potential of the second body, t_2 = distance of separation between the plates in the second part of the experiment.

Subtracting Eq. (3.7) from Eq. (3.6),

$$\phi_2 - \phi_1 = (t_1 - t_2)\sqrt{\frac{2mg}{\epsilon\alpha}}. \tag{3.8}$$

Knowing $(t_1 - t_2)$ from micrometer screw readings and mg and α from actual measurements we can find the absolute value of the potential difference. It is to be noted that exact knowledge of ϕ_A, t_1 and t_2 is not required in this arrangement; only ϕ_A is to be maintained constant.

3.3   Quadrant Electrometer

This electrometer is more sensitive than the absolute electrometer but it needs calibration for measuring the potential difference. In that sense it is not an absolute instrument.

The Dolezalek type of the electrometer has four metallic hollow quadrants A, A', B, B' separated from each other as shown in Fig. 3.2. The instrument is supported on insulating pillars in a manner as shown in Fig. 3.3. The needle C is made either by a light paper frame coated with a metal to make it conducting or by a very thin aluminium sheet.

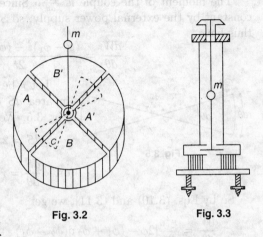

Fig. 3.2   **Fig. 3.3**

Two of the quadrants are mounted on a pivot and may be swung aside to introduce the needle C. The opposite quadrants are joined together to terminals under the base plate of the electrometer. The needle is connected to a light rod which carries a mirror m. This is supported by a thin phosphor-bronze strip or by a quartz fibre from a torsion head.

When the instrument is used, the four quadrants including the needle are first earthed. The needle kept symmetrically between the quadrants and the zero position of the spot of light reflected from m is noted. This is called the *mechanical zero*. Next, disconnecting the needle from the earth a small charge is applied and again the zero position of the light spot is noted. This is known as the *electrical zero*. The instrument is to be carefully levelled so that the mechanical zero coincides with the electrical zero. After disconnecting from the earth the quadrants AA' and BB' are connected to the points whose potential difference is to be measured and the needle is connected to a source of constant high potential. The needle is now deflected so that a part of the needle is transferred from A to B quadrant till the deflecting couple is in equilibrium with the torsional couple. The deflecting angle of the needle will be proportional to the potential difference between the pairs of quadrants.

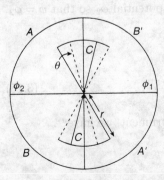

Fig. 3.4

Theory : Let us assume that when the needle rotates at an angle θ, the total area α of the needle is placed so that an area S is within the pair of quadrants at a potential ϕ_1 and an area $(\alpha - S)$ is within the quadrant pair at potential ϕ_2 (Fig. 3.4). Let ϕ be the potential of the needle and t be the thickness of the air space between the quadrants and the needle. Hence the needle forms two parallel plate air condensers of area S with a potential difference $(\phi - \phi_1)$ and area $(\alpha - S)$ with a potential difference $(\phi - \phi_2)$. Since these condensers have two faces, the electrical energy W of the system is given by

$$W = 2\left(\frac{1}{2}C_s\phi_s^2\right) + 2\left(\frac{1}{2}C_{\alpha-S}\phi_{\alpha-S}^2\right)$$

$$= \frac{S(\phi-\phi_1)^2}{2t}\epsilon + \frac{(\alpha-S)(\phi-\phi_2)^2}{2t}\epsilon. \tag{3.9}$$

The moment of the couple is $\frac{dW}{d\theta}$. Since α is constant; ϕ, ϕ_1 and ϕ_2 are kept constant by the external power supply; so S is the only variable in Eq. (3.9). We thus have

$$\frac{dW}{d\theta} = \frac{(\phi-\phi_1)^2 - (\phi-\phi_2)^2}{2t}\epsilon \cdot \frac{dS}{d\theta}. \tag{3.10}$$

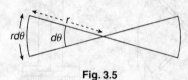

Fig. 3.5

Let r be the radius of the needle. The change in area dS can then be obtained by considering Fig. 3.5. We have

$$dS = 2 \cdot \frac{1}{2}r \cdot r d\theta = r^2 d\theta$$

or, $\quad \dfrac{dS}{d\theta} = r^2. \tag{3.11}$

So by Eqs. (3.10) and (3.11), we get

$$\frac{dW}{d\theta} = \frac{r^2\epsilon}{2t}[2\phi - (\phi_1 + \phi_2)](\phi_2 - \phi_1)$$

$$= \frac{r^2\epsilon}{t}\left[\phi - \frac{\phi_1 + \phi_2}{2}\right](\phi_2 - \phi_1). \tag{3.12}$$

This couple in equilibrium is balanced by the torsional couple of the fibre $k\theta$, k being the mean couple per unit twist. So the equation of equilibrium can be written as

$$k\theta = \frac{r^2\epsilon}{t}\left[\phi - \frac{\phi_1 + \phi_2}{2}\right](\phi_2 - \phi_1). \tag{3.13}$$

Since $\phi \gg \phi_2 > \phi_1$, we can write from Eq. (3.13),

$$\theta = \frac{\phi r^2\epsilon}{kt}(\phi_2 - \phi_1). \text{ [considering } \tfrac{\phi_1+\phi_2}{2} \text{ very negligible compared to } \phi] \tag{3.14}$$

Eq. (3.14) indicates that when ϕ and r are constants,

$$\theta \propto (\phi_2 - \phi_1).$$

In the above arrangement the conductors A, B and C are kept at different potentials. The instrument is then said to be used *heterostatically*. If C is joined to one of the pairs of the quadrants, then the instrument is said to be used *idiostatically*. Let C be connected to the quadrants at potential ϕ_2 so that $\phi = \phi_2$. Then Eq. (3.13) becomes

$$k\theta = \frac{r^2\epsilon}{2t}(\phi_2 - \phi_1)^2$$

or, $\quad \theta = \dfrac{r^2\epsilon}{2kt}(\phi_2 - \phi_1)^2. \tag{3.15}$

Putting $\dfrac{r^2}{2kt} = c$, where c is the constant of the instrument, we have

$$\theta = c\phi(\phi_2 - \phi_1) \text{ for heterostatic use}$$

and $\quad \theta = \dfrac{1}{2}c(\phi_2 - \phi_1)^2 \text{ for idiostatic use.}$

Considering Eq. (3.14) and (3.15) we find that for idiostatic use only the deflection θ is proportional to $(\phi_2 - \phi_1)^2$. Hence for measuring potential difference in alternating circuits the electrometer may be used idiostatically.

3.3.1 Alternative Theory of Quadrant Electrometer

An evaluation using the coefficients of capacitance and induction may be undertaken by considering the needle and the pairs of quadrants as conductor nos. 1, 2 and 3. Let the charges of 1, 2 and 3 are Q_1, Q_2, Q_3, while the corresponding potentials are ϕ_1, ϕ_2 and ϕ_3 respectively. Then for any position θ of the needle we can write,

$$\left. \begin{array}{l} Q_1 = q_{11}\phi_1 + q_{21}\phi_2 + q_{31}\phi_3 \\ Q_2 = q_{12}\phi_1 + q_{22}\phi_2 + q_{32}\phi_3 \\ Q_3 = q_{13}\phi_1 + q_{23}\phi_2 + q_{33}\phi_3 \end{array} \right\} \tag{3.16}$$

The electrical energy W of the system is given by,

$$\begin{aligned} W &= \frac{1}{2}Q_1\phi_1 + \frac{1}{2}Q_2\phi_2 + \frac{1}{2}Q_3\phi_3 \\ &= \frac{1}{2}[q_{11}\phi_1 + q_{21}\phi_2 + q_{31}\phi_3]\phi_1 + \frac{1}{2}[q_{12}\phi_1 + q_{22}\phi_2 + q_{32}\phi_3]\phi_2 \\ &\qquad\qquad\qquad\qquad + \frac{1}{2}[q_{13}\phi_1 + q_{23}\phi_2 + q_{33}\phi_3]\phi_3 \end{aligned} \tag{3.17}$$

Since, $q_{12} = q_{21}$, $q_{13} = q_{31}$, etc., we get

$$W = \frac{1}{2}[q_{11}\phi_1^2 + q_{22}\phi_2^2 + q_{33}\phi_3^2 + 2q_{13}\phi_1\phi_3 + 2q_{12}\phi_1\phi_2 + 2q_{23}\phi_2\phi_3]. \tag{3.18}$$

The deflecting torque τ on the needle at the position θ is

$$\tau = \frac{dW}{d\theta} = \frac{1}{2}\left[\frac{dq_{11}}{d\theta}\phi_1^2 + \frac{dq_{22}}{d\theta}\phi_2^2 + \frac{dq_{33}}{d\theta}\phi_3^2 + 2\frac{dq_{13}}{d\theta}\phi_1\phi_3 \right.$$

$$\left. + 2\frac{dq_{12}}{d\theta}\phi_1\phi_2 + 2\frac{dq_{23}}{d\theta}\phi_2\phi_3 \right]. \tag{3.19}$$

If the change of capacitance within a quadrant is proportional to θ, then the number of lines of electric displacement which leave the conductor 2 per unit potential is

$$\frac{q_{22}}{\epsilon} = \epsilon(q_{2\infty} - q_{21} - q_{32}),$$

where $q_{2\infty}$ = number of lines going to infinity.

Similarly, for conductor no. 3 we can write,

$$\frac{q_{33}}{\epsilon} = (q_{3\infty} - q_{31} - q_{32})/\epsilon.$$

Now, for given charges $q_{2\infty}$ and $q_{3\infty}$ are constant and depending on the fixed charges on the fixed quadrants q_{23} is also constant.

$$\therefore \qquad \frac{dq_{23}}{d\theta} = 0. \tag{3.20}$$

Also, $\left. \begin{array}{l} \dfrac{dq_{22}}{d\theta} = -\dfrac{dq_{21}}{d\theta} \\[2mm] \dfrac{dq_{33}}{d\theta} = -\dfrac{dq_{31}}{d\theta} \end{array} \right\}. \tag{3.21}$

and

When the quadrants and the needle are symmetrical, then the number of lines of displacement gained by a pair of quadrants is identical to the number lost by the other. Thus we have,

$$\frac{dq_{21}}{d\theta} = -\frac{dq_{31}}{d\theta} = C \text{ (say)},\tag{3.22}$$

where C represents the change of quadrant-needle capacitance per unit angle of rotation of the needle.

Further, $\phi_2 - \phi_3 = 0$, when $\theta = 0$ for all values of ϕ_1. Therefore, if q_{11} is not a function of θ, we have

$$\frac{dq_{11}}{d\theta} = 0.\tag{3.23}$$

Hence using Eqs. (3.19), (3.22) and (3.23), we get

$$\tau = \frac{1}{2}[-C\phi_2^2 + C\phi_3^2 - 2C\phi_1\phi_2 + 2C\phi_1\phi_2]$$

$$= \frac{C}{2}[(\phi_1 - \phi_3)^2 - (\phi_1 - \phi_2)^2]$$

$$= C\left[\phi_1 - \frac{\phi_2 + \phi_3}{2}\right](\phi_2 - \phi_3).\tag{3.24}$$

Now, the equilibrium is attained when the opposing torque due to the twist of the suspension fibre balances the deflecting torque. If c is the couple per unit twist of the wire and θ is the steady deflection, then

$$c\theta = C\left[\phi_1 - \frac{\phi_2 + \phi_3}{2}\right](\phi_2 - \phi_3).\tag{3.25}$$

For all practical purposes one pair of quadrants is earthed. Let $\phi_3 = 0$. Then we have

$$\theta = \frac{C}{c}\left[\phi_1 - \frac{\phi_2}{2}\right]\phi_2.\tag{3.26}$$

This is the working equation for the quadrant electrometer.

In the case of idiostatic connection, the needle and the one pair of quadrants are connected together. Then we have

$$\phi_1 = \phi_2$$

and so Eq. (3.25) becomes,

$$\theta = \frac{C}{c}\left[\phi_2 - \frac{\phi_2 + \phi_3}{2}\right](\phi_2 - \phi_3)$$

$$= \frac{C}{2c}(\phi_2 - \phi_3)^2.\tag{3.27}$$

Thus the deflection θ in this case becomes proportional to the square of the potential difference $(\phi_2 - \phi_3)$ across the pair of quadrants.

3.3.2 Sensitiveness of Quadrant Electrometer

When $\phi_3 = 0$, the sensitivity of the quadrant electrometer,

$$S = \frac{\delta\theta}{\delta\phi_2}.\tag{3.28}$$

Then from Eq. (3.26), we have

$$\frac{\delta\theta}{\delta\phi_2} = \frac{C\phi_1}{c} - \frac{C\phi_2}{c}.$$ (3.29)

For heterostatic connection, $\phi_1 \gg \phi_2$. Hence, one may expect that the sensitivity increases regularly with ϕ_1. But for a close consideration the change of capacitance depends on the first power of the angle of deflection θ. Then Eq. (3.23) becomes

$$\frac{dq_{11}}{d\theta} = (m+n)\theta$$ (3.30)

and Eq. (3.22) becomes

$$\frac{dq_{21}}{d\theta} = -\frac{dq_{31}}{d\theta} = (r+s\theta),$$ (3.31)

where m, n, r and s are constants.

If we consider,

$$\frac{dq_{22}}{d\theta} = -\frac{dq_{21}}{d\theta}, \quad \frac{dq_{23}}{d\theta} = 0 \quad \text{and} \quad \phi_3 = 0$$

then from Eq. (3.19), we have

$$c\theta = \frac{1}{2}[(m+n\theta)\phi_1^2 - (r+s\theta)\phi_2^2 + 2(r+s\theta)\phi_1\phi_2]$$

or, $$\theta = \frac{m\phi_1^2 - r\phi_2^2 + 2r\phi_1\phi_2}{2c - n\phi_1^2 + s\phi_2^2 - 2s\phi_1\phi_2}.$$ (3.32)

Now, when $\phi_2 = 0$, then

$$\theta = 0 \text{ (for all values of } \phi_1).$$

$$\therefore \quad m = 0.$$

Again, since $\phi_1 \gg \phi_2$, we can ignore $r\phi_2^2$, $s\phi_2^2$ and $2s\phi_1\phi_2$, then

$$\theta \simeq \frac{2r\phi_1\phi_2}{2c - n\phi_1^2}.$$ (3.33)

$\therefore$ the sensitivity, $$S = \frac{\delta\theta}{\delta\phi_2} = \frac{2r\phi_1}{2c - n\phi_1^2}.$$ (3.34)

For the sensitivity to be a maximum,

$$\frac{\delta}{\delta\phi_1}\left(\frac{\delta\theta}{\delta\phi_2}\right) = 0$$

$$\frac{(2c - n\phi_1^2)2r - 2r\phi_1(-2n\phi_1)}{(2c - n\phi_1^2)^2} = 0$$

or, $$4cr - 2nr\phi_1^2 + 4nr\phi_1^2 = 0$$

or, $$\phi_1^2 = -\frac{2c}{n}$$

or, $$\phi_1 = \sqrt{-\frac{2c}{n}}.$$ (3.35)

Eq. (3.35) represents the potential of the needle at which the maximum sensitivity is attained.

3.4   Uses of Quadrant Electrometer

Quadrant electrometer is used for different purposes. Some of which are :

  (i) Measurement of ionisation current of the order of 10^{-13} to 10^{-15} ampere and of low potential differences;

 (ii) Determination of dielectric constants of solids, liquids and gases;

(iii) Determination and comparison of capacitances;

 (iv) Comparison of e.m.fs. of cells;

  (v) Measurement of alternating potential difference when used idiostatically.

3.4.1   Measurement of Ionisation Current

In order to measure the ionisation current of the order of 10^{-13} ampere by an electrometer first of all its capacitance is found with a standard condenser of known capacity. Let the capacity of the electrometer is C.

Now, to find the ionisation current one pair of quadrants of the electrometer is connected to earth while the other pair is connected to one collecting plate of the ionisation chamber. The second collecting plate is kept at a potential difference with respect to the first and the needle is kept at a constant potential by a H.T. battery.

Let ϕ be the potential acquired by the quadrant in t seconds. Then,

$$i = \frac{Q}{t} \ [\text{where } i = \text{ionisation current})$$

$$= \frac{C\phi}{t}. \tag{3.36}$$

In e.s.u. the ionisation current i can be written as

$$i = \frac{1}{300} \cdot \frac{C\phi}{t} \ \text{e.s.u.} = \frac{10}{300 \times 3 \times 10^{10}} \frac{C\phi}{t} \ \text{ampere}$$

$$= 1.11 \times 10^{-12} \frac{C\phi}{t} \ \text{ampere}. \tag{3.37}$$

3.4.2   Comparison of Capacitances

Kelvin's bridge method of comparison of capacitances is shown in Fig. 3.6. Four condensers C_1, C_2, C_3 and C_4 are connected in the form of a Wheatstone bridge. A battery B is connected between A and D through a key K while the quadrant electrometer is connected between E and F.

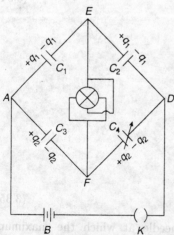

Fig. 3.6

Ordinarily due to charging there will be a deflection in the electrometer. Adjusting the capacitor C_4 this deflection is made zero. Then the junctions E and F will be at the same potential. Thus we have,

  (i) p.d. between A and E = p.d. between A and F;

 (ii) p.d. between E and D = p.d. between F and D.

Now considering the figure, we get

from condition (i),

$$\frac{q_1}{C_1} = \frac{q_2}{C_3}$$

or, $\quad \dfrac{C_1}{C_3} = \dfrac{q_1}{q_2}.$ $\hfill (3.38)$

from condition (ii),

$$\frac{q_1}{C_2} = \frac{q_2}{C_4}$$

or, $\quad \dfrac{C_2}{C_4} = \dfrac{q_1}{q_2}.$ $\hfill (3.39)$

Hence we have,

$$\frac{C_1}{C_3} = \frac{C_2}{C_4}$$

or, $\quad \dfrac{C_1}{C_2} = \dfrac{C_3}{C_4}$ [by Eqs. (3.38) and (3.39)] $\hfill (3.40)$

Thus from a knowledge of C_3 and C_4, one can compare C_1 and C_2.

3.4.3 Measurement of Dielectric Constants for Solids, Liquids and Gases

(i) For Solids : Faraday in his experiment of determining the dielectric constant of solids took two similar spherical condensers each of which had its outer metallic shell made of two separable hemispheres. The inner sphere was connected by a metallic collar to the knob K. The collar was insulated by a sulphur plug C (Fig. 3.7).

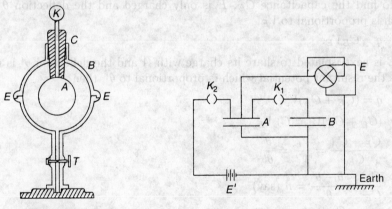

| Fig. 3.7 | Fig. 3.8 |

The circuit diagram of the experiment is shown in Fig. 3.8. A and B are two spherical condensers, E is the quadrant electrometer, K_1 and K_2 are two keys and E' is the battery (Fig. 3.8). Since one pair of the quadrants of electrometer are earthed while the other pair are connected to one plate of the capacitor A, the deflection of the electrometer will be proportional to the potential of the plate.

During experiment the capacitor B is filled with the dielectric to be measured while the capacitor A has air between the spheres. The key K_2 is now closed with K_1 open and in the electrometer the deflection θ_1 which is proportional to V_A, the potential of A, is noted.

The charge on the capacitor A is

$$q = (C_A + C_E)V_A, \tag{3.41}$$

where C_A = capacitance of A and C_E = capacitance of E.

Next, the key K_1 is closed and K_2 is disconnected. The deflection θ_2 of the electrometer is again noted. Since the charge q is now distributed over A, B and E, we have

$$q = (C_A + C_B + C_E)V \tag{3.42}$$

(where C_B = capacitance of B, V = resultant potential).

By Eqs. (3.41) and (3.42), we have

$$(C_A + C_B + C_E)V = (C_A + C_E)V_A$$

or, $$1 + \frac{C_B}{C_A + C_E} = \frac{V_A}{V} \tag{3.43}$$

If the resultant potential V of A, B and E after the redistribution of charges is proportional to θ_2, then we can write,

$$\frac{V_A}{V} = \frac{\theta_1}{\theta_2}. \tag{3.44}$$

Thus, we have

$$1 + \frac{C_B}{C_A + C_E} = \frac{\theta_1}{\theta_2}$$

or, $$\frac{C_B}{C_A + C_E} = \frac{\theta_1 - \theta_2}{\theta_2}. \tag{3.45}$$

To find the capacitance C_E, E is only charged and the deflection θ is noted which is proportional to V_E.

$$\therefore \quad q = C_E V_E. \tag{3.46}$$

E is next isolated to share its charge with A and the deflection θ' is noted. If V' is the resultant potential which is proportional to θ', then

$$q = (C_E + C_A)V'$$

$$\therefore \quad (C_E + C_A)V' = C_E V_E$$

or, $$\frac{C_E + C_A}{C_E} = \frac{V_E}{V'} = \frac{\theta}{\theta'}$$

or, $$\frac{C_A}{C_E} = \frac{\theta - \theta'}{\theta'} = n \text{ (say)}$$

or, $$C_E = \frac{C_A}{n}, \tag{3.47}$$

where n is known.

Hence by Eqs. (3.45) and (3.47), we get

$$\frac{C_B}{C_A \left(1 + \frac{1}{n}\right)} = \frac{\theta_1 - \theta_2}{\theta_2}$$

or, $$\frac{C_B}{C_A} = \left(1 + \frac{1}{n}\right)\left(\frac{\theta_1 - \theta_2}{\theta_2}\right) = K. \tag{3.48}$$

Using Eq. (3.48), the dielectric constant K can be determined.

(ii) For Liquids : Silow's method can be applied for determining the dielectric constant of the liquid. It is a cylindrical quadrant electrometer, A, A, B, B are fixed four metal strips and C is a cylindrical vane. The instrument is used idiostatically and the connection is made in a manner as shown in Fig. 3.9. A is connected to a constant potential source when the deflection will be proportional to the square of the potential difference.

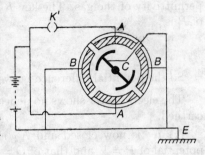

Fig. 3.9

If with air in the cylinder θ_1 be the deflection noted by pressing the key K', then

$$\theta_1 = aV^2, \tag{3.49}$$

where a is a constant and V is the constant potential difference between A and B.

Next, the dielectric liquid is introduced in the cylinder so as to cover up the vane. Let now θ_2 be the deflection noted. Since the capacitance of the system has increased by K times, we can write,

$$\theta_2 = KaV^2 \tag{3.50}$$

By Eqs. (3.49) and (3.50),

$$\frac{\theta_2}{\theta_1} = K. \tag{3.51}$$

Thus knowing θ_1 and θ_2, one can determine K. The same method can also be employed for measuring K of gas under pressure. Then the cylindrical vessel must be perfectly air-tight.

(iii) For Gases : The experimental arrangement for determining the conductivity of gases by Boltzmann's method is shown in Fig. 3.10. In the figure, P and Q are two parallel plates of a condenser supported inside an earthed metal chamber C through two non-conducting plugs. The plates and the chamber are enclosed further in a glass chamber G. The glass chamber can be evacuated through O. E is the quadrant electrometer; K_1, K_2 are two keys and B is a battery.

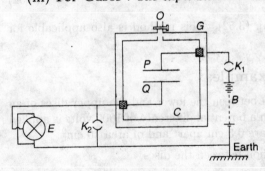

Fig. 3.10

The experiment can be operated in four different steps :

(a) G is evacuated by closing K_1 first and then by closing K_2; electrometer will not show any deflection. Then,

potential of P is $V = ne$,

where n = number of Daniell cells used, e = e.m.f. of a Daniell cell.

Potential of $Q = 0$ (since it is earthed through K_2).

(b) K_1 is disconnected and the dry experimental gas is introduced at a known high pressure. The capacity of the condenser increases k times, where k is the permittivity of the gas. The key K_2 being closed, the potential of $Q = 0$ and that of P is

$$V_k = \frac{V}{k}.$$

So the potential difference between P and $Q = \frac{V}{k}$.

The electrometer shows no deflection during the insertion of the gas as Q is still earthed.

(c) K_1 is now closed and K_2 is disconnected. P being connected to B, the potential of $P = V$ and that of $Q = V - \frac{V}{k}$. The electrometer will give a deflection θ, which is proportional to the potential of Q.

$$\therefore \qquad \theta \propto V - \frac{V}{k}$$

$$\propto V\left(\frac{k-1}{k}\right)$$

$$\propto ne\left(\frac{k-1}{k}\right).$$

(d) Next, with K_1 closed and K_2 open one more Daniell cell is introduced in the battery and the deflection θ' is noted.

Let $(\theta' - \theta) = \beta$, where β is directly proportional to the e.m.f. of the extra cell introduced in the battery, i.e.,

$$\beta \propto e.$$

Hence, we have

$$\frac{\theta}{\beta} = n\left(\frac{k-1}{k}\right)$$

or, $\qquad k = \dfrac{n\beta}{n\beta - \theta}.$ $\hfill (3.52)$

Thus k can be found by using Eq. (3.52). This method is also applicable for finding the k of liquids.

Examples

1. Calculate the force of attraction between the lower and the upper discs of an attracted disc electrometer when a potential difference of 1000 volts is applied between them, given that they are 0.5 cm apart and of area 10 cm^2.

   Solution : The force of attraction between the discs,

   $$F = \frac{\alpha \phi^2}{8\pi t^2}.$$

   Here, $\quad \alpha = 10$ cm^2, $\phi = 1000$ volts $= \dfrac{1000}{300} = \dfrac{10}{3}$ e.s.u., $t = 0.5$ cm.

   $$\therefore \qquad F = \frac{10 \times (10)^2}{8 \times 3.14 \times (0.5)^2 \times 9} = \mathbf{17.69 \ dynes.}$$

2. A small current flows through a resistance of 10^{10} ohms, the ends of which are connected to opposite quadrants of an electrometer. The deflection is 120 scale divisions. When a Daniell cell of 1.08 volts e.m.f. is connected across these quadrants, the deflection is 54 scale divisions. What is the magnitude of the current?

Solution : If i ampere be the current flowing through the resistance, then the potential difference across the resistance $= i \times 10^{10}$ volts.

Since the deflection of the quadrant electrometer is proportional to the potential difference applied to the adjacent quadrants, we can write,

120 divisions $\propto i \times 10^{10}$ volts.

In a similar way,

54 divisions $\propto 1.08$ volts.

Taking the ratio, we get

$$\frac{120}{54} = \frac{i \times 10^{10}}{1.08}$$

or, $\quad i = \dfrac{120}{54} \cdot \dfrac{1.08}{10^{10}} = \mathbf{2.4 \times 10^{-10}}$ **amperes.**

3. A quadrant electrometer is set up for heterostatic use and one pair of quadrants are given a charge by connecting them momentarily to a battery. A deflection of 100 divisions is obtained. The quadrants are then connected in parallel with an uncharged condenser of capacitance 80 e.s.u. and the deflection is observed to decrease 60 divisions. Calculate the capacity of the electrometer.

Solution : Let C be the capacity of the electrometer and C_1 the uncharged capacitance. We assume that the charge q given by the battery makes the potential ϕ_1. We then have

$$q = C\phi_1.$$

When the uncharged condenser is connected in parallel, the total capacity becomes $(C + C_1)$ for a potential ϕ_2. Hence,

$q = (C + C_1)\phi_2$

$\therefore \quad C\phi_1 = (C + C_1)\phi_2$

or, $\quad \dfrac{\phi_1}{\phi_2} = \dfrac{C + C_1}{C} = 1 + \dfrac{C_1}{C}.$

But $\frac{\phi_1}{\phi_2} = \frac{\theta_1}{\theta_2}$, where θ_1 and θ_2 are the deflections for potentials ϕ_1 and ϕ_2 respectively. Thus we get,

$$1 + \frac{C_1}{C} = \frac{\theta_1}{\theta_2}$$

or, $\quad \dfrac{C_1}{C} = \dfrac{\theta_1}{\theta_2} - 1 = \dfrac{\theta_1 - \theta_2}{\theta_2}$

or, $\quad C = \dfrac{\theta_2}{\theta_1 - \theta_2} \cdot C_1.$

Here, $\theta_1 = 100$ div., $\theta_2 = 60$ div., $C_1 = 80$ e.s.u.

$\therefore \quad C = \dfrac{60}{100 - 60} \cdot 80 = \dfrac{60}{40} \cdot 80 = \mathbf{120}$ **e.s.u.**

4. If the moving element is 20 cm in diameter and the plates are 5 cm apart, what weight will be required to balance the force of attraction between them when their potential difference is 10 kilovolts? **[C.U.(Hons.) 1950]**

Solution : Here, $\alpha = \pi \cdot 10^2 = 100\pi$ sq. cm, $d = 5$ cm

and   potential difference, $V_A - V_B = 10\,000$ volts $= \dfrac{10\,000}{300} = \dfrac{100}{3}$ e.s.u.

So the attractive force between the disc,

$$F = \frac{(V_A - V_B)^2 \alpha}{8\pi d^2} = \frac{\left(\frac{100}{3}\right)^2 \cdot 100\pi}{8\pi \cdot 25}$$

$$= 555.55 \text{ dynes.}$$

If the required opposing force be m gram-wt, then

$$m = \frac{F}{g} = \frac{555.55}{981} = 0.566 \text{ gram-wt.}$$

5. Two metal plates, each of area 20 sq. cm are maintained at a difference of potential of 1200 volts. If the distance between the plates be 0.5 cm, find the force of attraction between them.

Solution : Here, $\alpha = 20$ sq. cm, $V_A - V_B = 1200$ volts $= \dfrac{1200}{300} = 4$ e.s.u., $d = 0.5$ cm.

$$\therefore \quad F = \frac{\alpha}{8\pi} \cdot \frac{(V_A - V_B)^2}{d^2} = \frac{20 \times 7 \times (4)^2}{8 \times 22 \times (0.5)^2}$$

$$= 50.9 \text{ dynes.}$$

Questions

Essay-type

1. Describe an attracted disc electrometer. Deduce the necessary working formula.

2. Give an account of the attracted disc electrometer pointing out the advantages which it may have over other forms of electrometer.

3. Describe a quadrant electrometer and give the theory of its action when it is used heterostatically and when idiostatically.

4. Give the construction and method of using a quadrant electrometer. How will you measure feeble currents with it? Discuss its sensitivity.

5. Describe a method for determining the dielectric constants for (i) solid, (ii) liquid and (iii) gas.

Numerical Problems

6. An insulated plate, 10 cm in diameter is charged with electricity and supported horizontally at a distance of 1 mm below a similar plate suspended from a balance and connected to the earth. If the attraction is balanced by the weight of one decigram, find the charge on the plate.   [**Ans.** 35 e.s.u.]

7. Circular insulated plate 10 cm in diameter is charged with electricity and supported horizontally at a distance of 1 mm below a similar plate suspended from a balance and connected to earth. If the attraction is balanced by a weight of 0.1 g, find the charge and the potential of the plate.

[**Ans.** 34.91 e.s.u., 168 volts]

8. A quadrant electrometer whose capacity is 5 cm is connected to a charged condenser of unknown capacity and it indicates 200 millivolts. A known capacity of 15 cm is connected in parallel to the unknown capacity and the indication is 150 millivolts. What is the value of the unknown capacity?

[**Ans.** 40 cm]

9. The plates of a parallel plate condenser are separated by a distance of 1 mm in air and are charged to a potential difference of 400 volts. Find the force of attraction between the plates per unit area. [**B.U. 1965**]

[**Ans.** 7.07 dynes/cm^2]

10. The plates of an attracted disc electrometer have radii 7 cm and are 0.4 cm apart. Calculate the mass required to give them a force equal to the force of attraction between the plates when they have a potential difference of 200 volts. [**Ans.** 0.4 gram]

Chapter 4
Electrical Images

4.1 Introduction

The method of images consists itself with the problem of one or more point charges in presence of boundary surfaces (such as conductors either grounded or held at fixed potential). It is possible to obtain from the geometrical situation of a suitably placed charges of appropriate magnitude which can satisfy the required boundary conditions. This charges are called *image charges*.

The electrical image can be defined as a point charge or a system of point charges on one side of a boundary which produces the same electric field on the other side of the boundary.

The replacement of the actual problem with the image charges is known as the *method of images*. A simple example is a point charge located in front of an infinite earthed conductor. An equal and opposite charge at the mirror image point behind the conductor will produce the same electric field. In this method we want to find a distribution of the charge system which together with the original charges will satisfy the following boundary conditions :

(i) $\iint D \cdot ds = \dfrac{q}{\epsilon}$, when the surface enclosed the charge q.

$\qquad = 0$, when the surface does not enclose the charge q.

(ii) The conductor may have potential either zero or infinite according to the problem arises.

(iii) $\phi = 0$, when the point of observation is at an infinite distance.

All these three boundary conditions satisfied by any distribution of charge will be the unique solution of the problem.

4.2 Point Charge in front of an Infinite Earthed Plane Conductor

Suppose a point charge q is placed at the point A at a distance a from an infinite plane conductor XOY (Fig. 4.1). By using the method of images we have to find our the distribution of induced charge σ on the right-hand surface of the conductor and the field in the space due to $+q$ and the induced charge in equilibrium on the same side of the conductor.

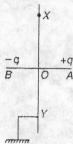

Fig. 4.1

Now we place a point charge $-q$ on the point B which is the mirror image point of A. Therefore, the potential at the point X due to $+q$ at A and $-q$ at B will be

$$\frac{q}{AX} - \frac{q}{BX} = \frac{q}{a} - \frac{q}{a} = 0.$$

So the charges $+q$ at A and $-q$ at B and both the charges $+q$ at $A

86

and induced charge on the conducting plane will satisfy the boundary conditions

    (i) $\phi = 0$ on the infinite conductor and at infinity;

    (ii) $\nabla^2 \phi = 0$ except at the point A.

Thus the effect of $+q$ at A and $-q$ at B on the plane is the same as the effect of q at A and the induced distribution on the plane. The charge $-q$ at B is called the electrical image of the charge $+q$ at A.

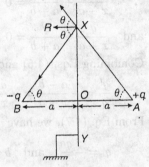

The intensity at the point X (Fig. 4.2) due to $+q$ at A is

$$\frac{q}{4\pi\epsilon AX^2} \quad \text{along } AX$$

and due to $-q$ at B is

$$\frac{q}{4\pi\epsilon BX^2} \quad \text{along } BX.$$

Taking the components we find that the components tangential to the plane cancel out and so the resultant intensity along XR is equal to

$$\frac{2q}{4\pi\epsilon AX^2}\cos\theta = \frac{2qa}{4\pi\epsilon AX^3}.$$

Fig. 4.2

Suppose E_n is the intensity at the point X along the outward drawn normal to the charged surface.

$$\therefore \quad E_n = -\frac{2qa}{AX^3}\cdot\frac{1}{4\pi\epsilon} = -\frac{qa}{2\pi\epsilon AX^3}. \tag{4.1}$$

If σ be the surface density of charge, then by using Coulomb's theorem we get

$$E_n = \sigma/\epsilon.$$

$$\therefore \quad \sigma = \frac{qa}{2\pi AX^3}. \tag{4.2}$$

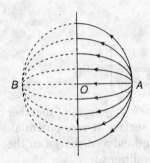

The force of attraction between $+q$ at A and $-q$ at B is equal to

$$\frac{q^2}{4\pi\epsilon(2a)^2} = \frac{q^2}{16\pi\epsilon a^2},$$

which must be equal to the attraction between the point charge q and the induced charge on the plane. The distribution of field lines is shown in Fig. 4.3.

Fig. 4.3

4.3   A Point Charge Outside an Earthed Spherical Conductor

Suppose a point charge q is placed at the point A in front of a spherical earthed conductor of radius a, having its centre at O (Fig. 4.4). We have to find out an image charge which together with q at A will make the external surface of the spherical conductor at zero potential.

Let us now place a point charge q' at D on the line joining A and O; q' will be the image charge if q' at D and q at A will make the surface a zero potential surface. Suppose, $OD = b$.

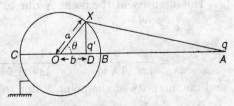

Fig. 4.4

Potential at B is $\dfrac{1}{4\pi\epsilon}\left[\dfrac{q}{x-a}+\dfrac{q'}{a-b}\right]$, where $OA=x$ \hfill (4.3)

and the potential at C is $\dfrac{1}{4\pi\epsilon}\left[\dfrac{q}{x+a}+\dfrac{q'}{a+b}\right]$. \hfill (4.4)

If q' is the image charge, then the potential at B and the potential at C will be zero.

$\therefore\qquad \dfrac{q}{x-a}+\dfrac{q'}{a-b}=0$ \hfill (4.5)

and $\qquad \dfrac{q}{x+a}+\dfrac{q'}{a+b}=0.$ \hfill (4.6)

Combining Eqs. (4.5) and (4.6), we get

$$\frac{q'}{q}=-\frac{a-b}{x-a}=-\frac{a+b}{x+a}.$$ \hfill (4.7)

From Eq. (4.7), we have

$$q'=-\frac{qa}{x}\quad\text{and}\quad b=\frac{a^2}{x}.$$

Let X be any point on the surface of the sphere and $\angle XOB=\theta$. Potential ϕ at X is

$$\phi=\frac{1}{4\pi\epsilon}\left[\frac{q}{AX}+\frac{q'}{DX}\right]$$

$$=\frac{1}{4\pi\epsilon}\left[\frac{q}{\sqrt{OA^2+OX^2-2OA\cdot OX\cos\theta}}\right]$$

$$=\frac{1}{4\pi\epsilon}\left[\frac{q\cdot\frac{a}{x}}{\sqrt{OX^2+OD^2-2OX\cdot OD\cos\theta}}\right]$$

$$=\frac{1}{4\pi\epsilon}\left[\frac{q}{\sqrt{x^2+a^2-2ax\cos\theta}}-\frac{q\cdot\frac{a}{x}}{\sqrt{a^2+\frac{a^4}{x^2}-2a\frac{a^2}{x}\cos\theta}}\right]=0.$$

Therefore, a point charge $q'=-\frac{qa}{x}$ placed at a distance $b=\frac{a^2}{x}$ from O together with the point charge q at a distance x from O makes the surface at zero potential. Thus q at A and $-\frac{qa}{x}$ at D and both the charges q at A and induced charge on the spherical conductor will satisfy the following boundary conditions :

(i) $\phi=0$ on the surface of the conductor and at infinity;

(ii) $\nabla^2\phi=0$ except on the point A.

Let us now find out the resultant intensity at the point X due to q at A and q' at D.

The intensity at the point X due to q at A is

$$E_A=\frac{q}{AX^2}\text{ along }AX$$

$$=\frac{1}{4\pi\epsilon}\frac{q}{AX^3}\cdot\overrightarrow{AX}=\frac{1}{4\pi\epsilon}\frac{q}{AX^3}[\overrightarrow{AO}+\overrightarrow{OX}]$$ \hfill (4.8)

and the intensity at the point X due to $-\frac{qa}{x}$ at D is

$$E_D=\frac{1}{4\pi\epsilon}\left[\frac{qa}{x\cdot XD^2}\right]\text{ along }XD$$

$$= \frac{1}{4\pi\epsilon} \frac{qa}{x \cdot XD^3}[\overrightarrow{XD}] = \frac{1}{4\pi\epsilon} \frac{qa}{x \cdot XD^3}[\overrightarrow{XO} + \overrightarrow{OD}]. \tag{4.9}$$

Combining components of intensity along OA and OX from Eqs. (4.8) and (4.9), we get

the sum of components along OA

$$= \frac{1}{4\pi\epsilon} \frac{q}{AX^3} \left[\overrightarrow{AO} + \frac{a}{x} \cdot \frac{AX^3}{XD^3} \cdot \overrightarrow{OD}\right]$$

$$= \frac{1}{4\pi\epsilon} \frac{q}{AX^3} \left[-x + \frac{a}{x} \cdot \frac{x^3}{a^3} \cdot \frac{a^2}{x}\right] = 0 \tag{4.10}$$

and the sum of components along $\overrightarrow{OX}$

$$= \frac{1}{4\pi\epsilon} \left[\frac{a}{AX^3} \cdot \overrightarrow{OX} + \frac{qa}{x \cdot XD^3} \cdot \overrightarrow{XO}\right]$$

$$= \frac{1}{4\pi\epsilon} \frac{q}{AX^3} \left[\overrightarrow{OX} + \frac{a}{x} \cdot \frac{AX^3}{XD^3} \cdot \overrightarrow{XO}\right]$$

$$= \frac{1}{4\pi\epsilon} \frac{q}{AX^3} \left[\overrightarrow{OX} + \frac{a}{x} \cdot \frac{x^3}{a^3} \cdot \overrightarrow{XO}\right]$$

$$= \frac{1}{4\pi\epsilon} \frac{qa}{AX^3} \left[1 - \frac{x^2}{a^2}\right]$$

$$= -\frac{1}{4\pi\epsilon} \frac{q}{a \cdot AX^3}(x^2 - a^2). \tag{4.11}$$

Therefore, the resultant intensity will be in the direction of the radius or in other words one can say that the sphere is an equipotential surface.

By using Coulomb's theorem, we have

$$E_n = \frac{\sigma}{\epsilon} = -\frac{1}{4\pi\epsilon} \frac{q}{a \cdot AX^3}(x^2 - a^2),$$

where σ is the surface density of induced charge.

$$\therefore \quad \sigma = -\frac{q}{4\pi a} \cdot \frac{1}{AX^3}(x^2 - a^2). \tag{4.12}$$

From Eq. (4.12) we find that surface density of charge is negative at all points on the sphere. The field lines are shown in Fig. 4.5.

We know that the field at any point external to the sphere due to the charge q and induced charge is same as the field due to q and its image charge $-\frac{qa}{x}$. Therefore, the force of attraction between the point charge q and the induced charge will be equal to

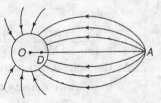

Fig. 4.5

$$F = \frac{1}{4\pi\epsilon} \frac{q \cdot \frac{qa}{x}}{\left(x - \frac{a^2}{x}\right)^2} = \frac{1}{4\pi\epsilon} \frac{q^2 ax}{(x^2 - a^2)^2}. \tag{4.13}$$

4.4 Point Charge in front of an Insulated Conducting Sphere

Let us assume that a point charge q is placed at the point A (Fig. 4.6) in front of an insulated conducting sphere. The potential of the spherical surface will be $\frac{q}{x}$ and the induced charge must be zero.

The boundary conditions to be satisfied are :

(i) Potential on the spherical surface is $\frac{q}{x}$;

(ii) $\nabla^2\phi = 0$ at all points except at the point A;

(iii) Total induced charge is zero;

(iv) $\phi = 0$ at infinity.

In order to take into account the condition (iii) we must place a charge $\frac{qa}{x}$ at the centre O of the sphere which together with the image charge $-\frac{qa}{x}$ will make the resultant charge on the sphere to be zero. Now the potential at any point on the

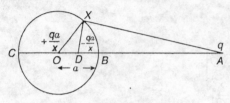

Fig. 4.6

surface of the sphere due to q at A and $-\frac{qa}{x}$ at D will be zero. Hence the potential at any point on the surface will be solely due to the charge $+\frac{qa}{x}$ at the centre O and is equal to $\frac{qa}{x} \cdot \frac{1}{a} = \frac{q}{x}$, which satisfies the condition (i). The positions of the charges which help us to solve the present problem are shown in Fig. 4.6.

Now we have to find out the surface density of induced charge. The surface density of charge due to q at A and $-\frac{qa}{x}$ at D will be

$$\sigma_1 = -\frac{q(x^2 - a^2)}{4\pi a \cdot AX^3} \quad \text{[from Eq. (4.12)]} \tag{4.14}$$

Again, the intensity at X due to the charge $+\frac{qa}{x}$ at O will be

$$\frac{1}{4\pi\epsilon} \frac{qa}{x} \cdot \frac{1}{OX^2} \quad \text{along } OX$$

$$= \frac{1}{4\pi\epsilon} \frac{qa}{x} \cdot \frac{1}{a^2} = \frac{1}{4\pi\epsilon} \frac{q}{ax}.$$

By Coulomb's theorem,

$$\frac{1}{4\pi\epsilon} \frac{q}{ax} = \frac{\sigma_2}{\epsilon}.$$

$$\therefore \quad \sigma_2 = \frac{q}{4\pi ax}. \tag{4.15}$$

Therefore, total surface density at X will be

$$\sigma = \sigma_1 + \sigma_2$$

$$= \frac{q(x^2 - a^2)}{4\pi a \cdot AX^3} + \frac{q}{4\pi a \cdot x}. \tag{4.16}$$

At the point nearest to q, i.e., at B, $AX = x - a$.

So the surface density at B will be

$$-\frac{q(x^2 - a^2)}{4\pi a(x - a)^3} + \frac{q}{4\pi ax} = -\frac{q}{4\pi a}\left[\frac{x + a}{(x - a)^2} - \frac{1}{x}\right]$$

$$= -\frac{q}{4\pi a}\left[\frac{x^2 + ax - x^2 - a^2 + 2ax}{x(x - a)^2}\right]$$

$$= -\frac{q}{4\pi a}\frac{a(3x - a)}{x(x - a)^2}$$

$$= -\frac{q(3x - a)}{4\pi x(x - a)^2}. \tag{4.17}$$

At the point C, $AX = x + a$.

$$\therefore \quad \sigma = -\frac{q}{4\pi a} \cdot \frac{x^2 - a^2}{(x+a)^3} + \frac{q}{4\pi a \cdot x}$$

$$= \frac{q}{4\pi a} \left\{ \frac{1}{x} - \frac{x-a}{(x+a)^2} \right\}$$

$$= \frac{q}{4\pi a} \cdot \frac{a(3x+a)}{x(x+a)^2}$$

$$= \frac{q(3x+a)}{4\pi x(x+a)^2}. \tag{4.18}$$

From Eqs. (4.17) and (4.18) we find that the surface density is positive at the point B and negative at the point C. It means that there must be some points where $\sigma = 0$. For such points $AX^3 = x(x^2 - a^2)$. The circle with radius $AX = \sqrt[3]{x(x^2 - a^2)}$ defines a circle on the sphere which separates positive and negative electrification and known as the circle of no electrification.

Now the force of attraction between the conducting sphere and the point charge q must be the resultant of those forces between q and $-\frac{qa}{x}$ at D and q and $+\frac{qa}{x}$ at O.

Therefore, the force of attraction,

$$F = \frac{1}{4\pi\epsilon} \left[\frac{q \cdot \frac{qa}{x}}{\left(x - \frac{a^2}{x}\right)^2} - \frac{q \cdot \frac{qa}{x}}{x^2} \right]$$

$$= \frac{1}{4\pi\epsilon} \left[\frac{q^2 a x}{(x^2 - a^2)^2} - \frac{q^2 a}{x^3} \right]$$

$$= \frac{1}{4\pi\epsilon} q^2 a x \left[\frac{1}{(x^2 - a^2)^2} - \frac{1}{x^4} \right]$$

$$= \frac{1}{4\pi\epsilon} \frac{q^2 a x \cdot a^2 (a^2 - 2x^2)}{x^4 (x^2 - a^2)^2}$$

$$= \frac{1}{4\pi\epsilon} \frac{q^2 a^3 (a^2 - 2x^2)}{x^3 (x^2 - a^2)^2}. \tag{4.19}$$

4.5 Point Charge in front of an Insulated Sphere Carrying a Charge Q

Let us assume that a point charge q is placed at the point A (Fig. 4.6) in front of an insulated conducting sphere carrying a charge Q. The potential of the spherical surface will be $\frac{q}{x} + \frac{Q}{a}$. The boundary conditions to be satisfied are:

(i) Potential on the spherical surface is $\frac{q}{x} + \frac{Q}{a}$;

(ii) $\nabla^2 \phi = 0$ at all points except at the point A;

(iii) Total charge on the conductor is Q;

(iv) $\phi = 0$ at infinity.

Now in order to satisfy the boundary conditions we have to place an additional charge Q at the centre in addition to the charge arrangement in Fig. 4.6. Therefore, the field must be due to charges q at A, $-\frac{qa}{x}$ at D, $\frac{qa}{x} + Q$ at O.

Therefore, at the point X on the sphere the surface density of charge will be

$$\sigma = -\frac{q}{4\pi a} \cdot \frac{(x^2 - a^2)}{AX^3} + \frac{\frac{qa}{x} + q}{4\pi a^2}. \tag{4.20}$$

Now at the nearest point B, $AX = (x - a)$. The surface density at the point B will be

$$\sigma_1 = -\frac{q(3x - a)}{4\pi x(x - a)^2} + \frac{Q}{4\pi a^2} \tag{4.21}$$

and at the point C the surface density will be

$$\sigma_2 = -\frac{q(3x + a)}{4\pi x(x + a)^2} + \frac{Q}{4\pi a^2}. \tag{4.22}$$

From Eqs. (4.22) and (4.21) we find that σ_2 is always positive but the sign of σ_1 will depend on Q.

Now the force between the insulated conducting sphere and the point q will be

$$F = \frac{1}{4\pi\epsilon} \left[-\frac{q \cdot \frac{qa}{x}}{\left(x - \frac{a^2}{x}\right)^2} + \frac{q\left(Q + \frac{aq}{x}\right)}{x^2} \right]$$

$$= \frac{1}{4\pi\epsilon} \left[-\frac{q^2 a^3 (2x^2 - a^2)}{x^3 (x^2 - a^2)^2} + \frac{qQ}{x^2} \right]. \tag{4.23}$$

The force may be attractive or repulsive according to the magnitude of the two terms of the Eq. (4.23).

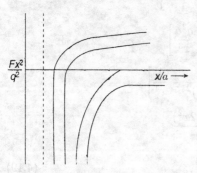

Fig. 4.7

Eq. (4.23) may be written as

$$F = \frac{1}{4\pi\epsilon} \frac{q^2}{x^2} \left[\frac{Q}{q} - \frac{a^3(2x^2 - a^2)}{(x^2 - a^2)^2} \right]. \tag{4.24}$$

· In Fig. 4.7 we have plotted $\frac{Fx^2}{q^2}$ against $\frac{x}{a}$ for different values of $\frac{Q}{q}$. From the figure it is evident that the force is attractive at close distances but repulsive for large distances. Again, the force will be zero when

$$\frac{Q}{q} = \frac{a^3(2x^2 - a^2)}{(x^2 - a^2)^2}. \tag{4.25}$$

4.6   Point Charge inside a Spherical Conductor at Zero Potential

In this case the field at any point outside the sphere will be zero because the charge lies inside the sphere.

Now place a point charge $-\frac{qa}{x}$ at D such that $OD = \frac{a^2}{x}$ (Fig. 4.8). Then the potential at any point X on the sphere will be

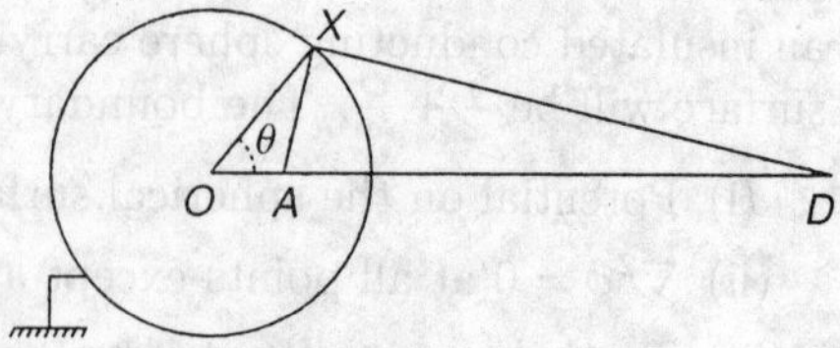

$$\phi = \frac{1}{4\pi\epsilon} \left[\frac{q}{AX} - \frac{\frac{qa}{x}}{XD} \right]$$

Fig. 4.8

$$= \frac{1}{4\pi\epsilon} \left[\frac{q}{\sqrt{x^2 + a^2 - 2ax\cos\theta}} - \frac{qa}{\sqrt{\left(\frac{a^2}{x}\right)^2 + a^2 - \frac{2a^2}{x} \cdot a\cos\theta}} \right] \tag{4.26}$$

$$= 0.$$

Therefore, $-\dfrac{qa}{x}$ will be the image charge.

Now the radial component of intensity at X due to the charge q will be

$$\frac{1}{4\pi\epsilon}\,\frac{q}{AX^3}\cdot\overrightarrow{OX}.$$

In a similar way, the radial component of intensity at X due to $-\frac{qa}{x}$ will be

$$\frac{1}{4\pi\epsilon}\left[-\frac{qa}{x\cdot XD^3}\cdot\overrightarrow{OX}\right].$$

Therefore, resultant intensity along the normal to the surface of the sphere

$$E_n=\frac{1}{4\pi\epsilon}\left(-\frac{q}{AX^3}+\frac{qa}{x\cdot XD^3}\right)\cdot OX.$$

Now from Eq. (4.26), we get

$$\frac{q}{Ax}=\frac{qa}{x\cdot XD}.$$

$$\therefore\quad E_n=\frac{1}{4\pi\epsilon}\left[-\frac{qa}{AX^3}\left(1-\frac{a}{x}\cdot\frac{AX^3}{XD^3}\right)\right]$$

$$=-\frac{1}{4\pi\epsilon}\frac{qa}{AX^3}\left(1-\frac{x^2}{a^2}\right)=-\frac{1}{4\pi\epsilon}\frac{q}{a\cdot AX^3}(a^2-x^2). \tag{4.27}$$

Using Coulomb's theorem, we get

$$\frac{1}{4\pi\epsilon}\left[-\frac{q}{a\cdot AX^3}(a^2-x^2)\right]=\frac{\sigma}{\epsilon}$$

$$\therefore\quad \sigma=-\frac{q}{4\pi a}\cdot\frac{a^2-x^2}{AX^3}. \tag{4.28}$$

The force between the sphere and the charge q will be

$$F=\frac{1}{4\pi\epsilon}\left[\frac{q\cdot\frac{qa}{x}}{\left(\frac{a^2}{x}-x\right)^2}\right]=\frac{1}{4\pi\epsilon}\left[\frac{q^2ax}{(a^2-x^2)^2}\right]. \tag{4.29}$$

From Eq. (4.29) we find that the force is attractive.

4.7 Insulated Conducting Sphere in a Uniform Field

A uniform field having intensity $E=\frac{1}{4\pi\epsilon}\frac{2q}{x^2}$ parallel to the X-axis may be supposed to be due to two charges $\pm q$ at $X=\pm x$ where both q and Qx are infinite.

Now, if an insulated conducting sphere is placed in a uniform field of the above type, then the charge $+q$ will give rise to an image charge $-\frac{qa}{x}$ at a distance $\frac{a^2}{x}$ from the centre O of the sphere (a being the radius of the sphere) and the charge $-q$ will give rise to an image charge $\frac{qa}{x}$ at a distance $-\frac{a^2}{x}$ from the centre O. These two images will form a doublet provided x is very large.

$$\text{The moment of doublet}=\frac{1}{4\pi\epsilon}\frac{qa}{x}\times\frac{2a^2}{x}$$

$$=\frac{1}{4\pi\epsilon}\frac{2qa^3}{x^2}=Ea^3. \tag{4.30}$$

Therefore, the induced charge on the sphere will produce the same field at an external point as that due to a doublet of moment Ea^3 placed at the centre.

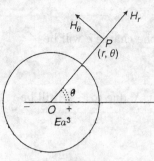

Fig. 4.9

Now the potential at any point P due to this doublet will be

$$\frac{Ea^3 \cos\theta}{r^2}.$$

Hence, if a sphere is placed in a uniform field of intensity E, the potential is increased by $\frac{Ea^3 \cos\theta}{r^2}$.

But $E = -\dfrac{\partial \phi_0}{\partial x}$.

$$\therefore \quad \phi_0 = -Ex + C = -Er\cos\theta + C.$$

[C is any constant of integration.]

Therefore, the total potential $= \phi_0 + \dfrac{Ea^3\cos\theta}{r^2} = -Er\cos\theta + \dfrac{Ea^3\cos\theta}{r^2} + C$

$$= -E\cos\theta \left(r - \frac{a^3}{r^2} \right) + C.$$

$$\therefore \quad -\frac{\partial\phi}{\partial r} = H_r = E\cos\theta\left(1 + \frac{2a^3}{r^3}\right)$$

and $\quad -\dfrac{1}{r}\left(\dfrac{\partial\phi}{\partial\theta}\right) = H_\theta = -E\sin\theta\left(1 - \dfrac{a^3}{r^3}\right).$

Therefore, at the point on the surface of the sphere

$$r = a, \quad -\frac{\partial\phi}{\partial r} = 3E\cos\theta \quad \text{and} \quad -\frac{1}{r}\left(\frac{\partial\phi}{\partial r}\right) = 0,$$

i.e., the force is directed radially.

Now, $3E\cos\theta = \dfrac{\sigma}{\epsilon}$ (from Coulomb's law).

$$\therefore \quad \sigma = 3\epsilon E\cos\theta. \tag{4.31}$$

The surface density is positive over one half of the sphere and negative over the other half. The circle $\theta = \frac{1}{2}\pi$ is the line of no electrification.

The total induced positive charge on the hemisphere (right to O)

$$= \int_0^{\pi/2} 2\pi a\sin\theta \cdot ad\theta \cdot \sigma$$

$$= \frac{3}{4}Ea^2 = 3\epsilon\pi Ea^2. \tag{4.32}$$

Similarly, the total induced charge on the hemisphere (left to O).

$$= \int_{\pi/2}^{\pi} 2\pi a\sin\theta \cdot ad\theta \cdot \sigma = 3\epsilon\pi Ea^2. \tag{4.33}$$

4.8 Point Charge in front of a Semi-infinite Dielectric

Suppose a point charge q is placed in a medium having dielectric constant K_1, in front of another medium having dielectric constant K_2, infinite in extent both to the left and along OY (Fig. 4.10). To evaluate the image charge, we shall have to take the following boundary conditions into considerations :

(i) The potential in the medium having dielectric constant K_1 will satisfy the Laplace's equation $\nabla^2\phi = 0$ except the point A where the point charge q is located.

(ii) The potential in the medium having dielectric constant K_2 will satisfy the Laplace's equation $\nabla^2\phi = 0$ at all points.

(iii) $\phi = 0$ as the field point approaches to infinity.

(iv) Normal components of intensity must be continuous across the boundary.

(v) The tangential component of intensity must be continuous across the surface of separation.

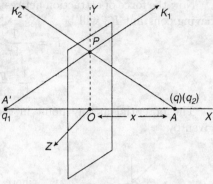

Fig. 4.10

Now in order to find the field at any point in the medium (K_1), we have to place an image charge q_1 at A' so that $OA = OA' \cdot a$, and again to find out the field at any point in the medium (K_2), we have to place an image charge q_2 at A. These two image charges q_1 and q_2 must satisfy the above boundary conditions.

The intensity at P due to q at A and q_1 at A' will be

$$\vec{E}_1 = \frac{1}{4\pi}\left[\frac{q}{K_1 AP^3}\cdot\overrightarrow{AP} + \frac{q_1}{K_2 A'P^3}\cdot\overrightarrow{A'P}\right]$$

$$= \frac{1}{4\pi}\left[\frac{q}{K_1 AP^3}(\overrightarrow{AO}+\overrightarrow{OP}) + \frac{q_1}{K_1 A'P^3}(\overrightarrow{BO}+\overrightarrow{OP})\right]. \tag{4.34}$$

The intensity at P due to q_2 at A' will be

$$\vec{E}_2 = \frac{1}{4\pi}\left[\frac{q_2}{K_2 AP^3}\cdot\overrightarrow{AP}\right]$$

$$= \frac{1}{4\pi}\left[\frac{q_2}{K_2 AP^3}(\overrightarrow{AO}+\overrightarrow{OP})\right]. \tag{4.35}$$

Now according to the boundary condition (iv) total normal component of intensity across the boundary must be continuous.

$$\therefore \quad K_1\left(\frac{q}{K_1 AP^3}\overrightarrow{AO} + \frac{q_1}{K_1 A'P^3}\overrightarrow{BO}\right) = K_2\frac{q_2}{K_2 AP^3}\cdot\overrightarrow{AO}$$

or, $\quad \dfrac{q}{AP^3}\cdot\overrightarrow{AO} - \dfrac{q_1}{A'P^3}\overrightarrow{OB} = \dfrac{q}{AP^3}\cdot\overrightarrow{AO}$

or, $\quad (q - q_1) = q_2. \tag{4.36}$

Again, to satisfy the boundary condition (v) we have

$$\frac{q}{K_1 AP^3}\overrightarrow{OP} + \frac{q_1}{K_1 A'P^3}\cdot\overrightarrow{OP} = \frac{q_2}{K_2 AP^3}\cdot\overrightarrow{OP}$$

or, $\quad \dfrac{q + q_1}{K_1} = \dfrac{q_2}{K_2}. \tag{4.37}$

After solving Eqs. (4.36) and (4.37) we get

$$q_1 = q\,\frac{K_1 - K_2}{K_1 + K_2} \tag{4.38}$$

and $\quad q_2 = 2q\,\dfrac{K_2}{K_1 + K_2}. \tag{4.39}$

Now the force of attraction between the point charge q and the dielectric medium having constant K_2 will be

$$F = -\frac{1}{4\pi} \frac{qq_1}{K_1 \cdot 4a^2}$$

$$= \frac{1}{4\pi} \frac{q}{4a^2} \cdot \frac{q(K_2 - K_1)}{K_1(K_1 + K_2)}. \tag{4.40}$$

The potential at any point in the dielectric medium of constant K_1 will be given by

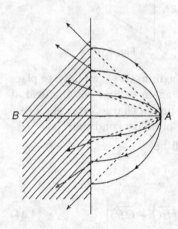

Fig. 4.11

$$\phi_1 = \frac{1}{4\pi} \left[\frac{q}{K_1 x_1} + \frac{q_1}{K_1 x_2} \right],$$

where x_1 and x_2 are the distances of the field point from the charges q and q_1 respectively.

Again, the potential at any point in the dielectric medium of constant K_2 will be given by

$$\phi_2 = \frac{1}{4\pi} \frac{q_2}{K_2 x},$$

where x is the distance of the field point from the charge q_2.

Hence the lines of force in this medium will be straight and appear to originate from A. The distribution of the lines of force are shown in Fig. 4.11.

4.9   Dielectric Sphere Placed in a Uniform Field

Suppose a sphere of a material having dielectric constant K_1 and radius a is placed in a medium of dielectric constant K_2 (Fig. 4.12). There exists a uniform field of intensity E_0 along the positive X-direction. We have to find out the effect on the field due to introduction of the dielectric sphere and the field within the sphere. The problem must satisfy the following boundary conditions :

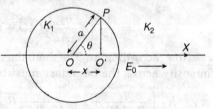

Fig. 4.12

(i) The potential at any point will satisfy the Laplace's equation $\nabla^2 \phi = 0$.

(ii) Normal component of intensity must be continuous at the bounding surface.

(iii) The tangential component of intensity must be continuous across the boundary.

(iv) At a very large distance from the sphere the intensity will be E_0.

Let ϕ_1 and ϕ_2 be the potential inside and outside the sphere; then we can write,

$$\phi_1 = -Ex \tag{4.41}$$

$$\phi_2 = -E_0 x + \frac{E_0 A \cos \theta}{r^2}$$

$$= -E_0 x + \frac{E_0 A x}{r^3}. \tag{4.42}$$

where A is some constant.

Now according to the boundary conditions,

$$\left.\begin{array}{c} \phi_1 = \phi_2 \\[2mm] \text{and} \quad K_1 \dfrac{\partial \phi_1}{\partial r} = K_2 \dfrac{\partial \phi_2}{\partial r} \end{array}\right\} \text{ at } r = a.$$

$$\therefore \quad -Ea = -E_0 a + \frac{E_0 A a}{a^3}$$

$$\text{or,} \quad E = E_0 - \frac{E_0 A}{a^3}. \tag{4.43}$$

Again, $\phi_1 = -Ex = -Er \cos \theta$

$$\phi_2 = -E_0 r \cos \theta + \frac{E_0 A \cos \theta}{r^2}.$$

The condition, $K_1 \left.\dfrac{\partial \phi_1}{\partial r}\right|_{r=a} = K_2 \left.\dfrac{\partial \phi_2}{\partial r}\right|_{r=a}$ gives,

$$-E K_1 \cos \theta = -K_2 E_0 \cos \theta - \frac{2E_0 A K_2 \cos \theta}{a^3}$$

$$\text{or,} \quad K_1 E = K_2 E_0 + K_2 \frac{2E_0 A}{a^3}$$

$$\text{or,} \quad K_1 \left(E_0 - \frac{E_0 A}{a^3} \right) = K_2 E_0 + K_2 \frac{2E_0 A}{a^3} \quad \text{[from Eq. (4.43)]}$$

$$\text{or,} \quad K_1 E_0 - K_2 E_0 = \left(K_2 \frac{2E_0}{a^3} + \frac{K_1 E_0}{a^3} \right) A$$

$$\text{or,} \quad (K_1 - K_2) E_0 = \frac{E_0}{a^3} (2K_2 + K_1) A.$$

$$\therefore \quad A = a^3 \frac{K_1 - K_2}{2K_2 + K_1}. \tag{4.44}$$

Substituting the value of A in Eq. (4.43), we get

$$E = E_0 \frac{3K}{K_1 + 2K_2}. \tag{4.45}$$

If the dielectric sphere is placed in air, $K_2 = 1$ and $K_1 = K$ (say).

$$\therefore \quad E = E_0 \frac{3}{K + 2}$$

$$\therefore \quad A = a^3 \frac{K - 1}{K + 2}.$$

The electric moment of the dielectric sphere will be

$$= E_0 A = E_0 a^3 \frac{K - 1}{K + 2}.$$

Thus the effect produced by the sphere will be the same as produced by a doublet of moment $E_0 A$ at its centre. The field is uniform and $\frac{3}{K+2}$ times of the field which would be present in the

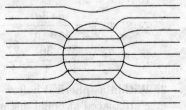

Fig. 4.13

absence of the dielectric. The number of unit tubes of forces which crosses a plane normal to the field in the dielectric will be $\frac{3K}{K+2}$ times of that which would be present in the absence of the dielectric.

As K increases, the factor $\frac{3K}{K+2}$ approaches to 3.

Examples

1. A charge q placed on small conducting sphere of radius a has its centre at a distance x from an infinite earthed plane. Show that the capacity is approximately $a + \frac{a^2}{2x}$, where $\frac{a}{x}$ is negligibly small.

Solution : The potential of the sphere in the absence of the earthed plane

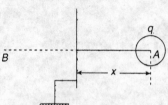

will be $\phi = \frac{q}{a}$. The induced image charge is located at the point B such that $AB = 2x$ (Fig. 4.14). Hence the potential of the sphere due to q at A and $-q$ at B will be

$$\phi = \frac{q}{a} - \frac{q}{(2x - a)} = \frac{q}{a}\left[1 - \frac{a}{2x\left(1 - \frac{a}{2x}\right)}\right]$$

Fig. 4.14

$$= \frac{q}{a}\left(1 - \frac{a}{2x}\right) \quad [\because \frac{a}{x} \text{ is negligibly small}]$$

$\therefore$ capacity, $C = \dfrac{q}{\phi} = \dfrac{a}{\left(1 - \frac{a}{2x}\right)}$

$$= a\left(1 + \frac{a}{2x}\right), \quad \text{neglecting higher order terms of } \frac{a}{x}$$

$$= a + \frac{a^2}{2x} \quad \textbf{(Proved)}.$$

2. Show that if the inducing charge is at a distance from the centre of a sphere at zero potential equal to double the radius, the surface densities at the nearest and the most remote points of the sphere are in the ratio $27 : 1$.

Solution : We know that the surface density of induced charge is given by

$$\sigma = -\frac{q(x^2 - a^2)}{4\pi a A P^3}.$$

At the point B nearest to the point charge (Fig. 4.15), surface density is given by

$$\sigma_B = -\frac{q(x + a)}{4\pi a(x - a)^2}.$$

At the point C farthest from the point charge, surface density is given by

$$\sigma_C = -\frac{q(x - a)}{4\pi a(x + a)^2}.$$

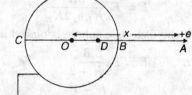

Here, $x = 2a$.

Fig. 4.15

$\therefore \quad \sigma_B = -\dfrac{q \cdot 3a}{4\pi a \cdot a^2} = -\dfrac{3q}{4\pi a^2}$ and $\sigma_C = -\dfrac{q \cdot a}{4\pi a \cdot 9a^2} = -\dfrac{q}{36\pi a^2}$.

$\therefore \quad \dfrac{\sigma_B}{\sigma_C} = \dfrac{3}{4} \times \dfrac{36}{1} = \dfrac{27}{1}$.

3. Within a spherical hollow conductor connected to earth, equal point charges e are placed at equal distances f from the centre on the same diameter. Show that each is acted on by a force equal to

$$e^2\left[\left\{\frac{4a^3 f^3}{(a^4 - f^4)^2}\right\} + \frac{1}{4f^2}\right].$$

Solution : The charges e, e at A, B and $-\frac{eq}{f}, -\frac{ea}{f}$ at A', B' will make the sphere at zero potential (Fig. 4.16).

Force on the charge e at A along AA',

$$F = \frac{e^2}{(BA)^2} - \frac{e \cdot \frac{ea}{f}}{(B'A)^2} + \frac{e \cdot \frac{ea}{f}}{(AA')^2}$$

$$= \frac{e^2}{4f^2} - \frac{e^2 a}{f \left(\frac{a^2}{f} + f\right)^2} + \frac{e^2 a}{f \left(\frac{a^2}{f} - f\right)^2}$$

$$= \frac{e^2}{4f^2} - \frac{e^2 af}{(a^2 + f^2)^2} + \frac{e^2 af}{(a^2 - f^2)^2}$$

$$= e^2 \left[\frac{4a^3 f^3}{(a^4 - f^4)^2} + \frac{1}{4f^2} \right] \quad \textbf{(Proved)}.$$

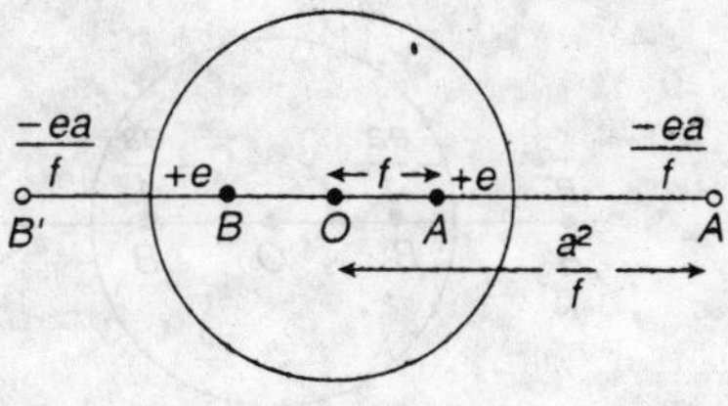

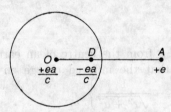

Fig. 4.16

4. A charge e is situated at a distance c from the centre of a conducting sphere of radius a. If the sphere is insulated and uncharged, find the rise in its potential due to the pressure of the charge and show that there is an attractive force between the sphere and the charge equal to $qe^2 \dfrac{a^3 (2c^2 - a^2)}{c^3 (c^2 - a^2)^2}$.

Solution : Here the distribution of the charges is shown in Fig. 4.17. The charges e at A and $-\frac{ea}{c}$ at D will make the surface of the sphere at zero potential. But the presence of the charge $+\frac{ea}{c}$ at O will raise its potential from zero to that value which is given by

$$\phi = \frac{\frac{ea}{c}}{a} = \frac{e}{c}.$$

Fig. 4.17

Now the force on e at A due to the charges $-\frac{ea}{c}$ at D and $+\frac{ea}{c}$ at O will be

$$F = \frac{e^2 ac}{(c^2 - a^2)^2} - \frac{e^2 a}{c^3} = \frac{e^2 a \{ c^4 - (c^2 - a^2)^2 \}}{c^3 (c^2 - a^2)^2}$$

$$= \frac{e^2 a^3}{c^3 (c^2 - a^2)^2} (2c^2 - a^2) \quad \textbf{(Proved)}.$$

5. Two identical point charges are at a distance $2f$ apart in air, and an insulated uncharged conducting sphere of radius a is placed mid-way between them. If $a \ll f$, show that the introduction of the sphere reduces the force experienced by either point charge to $\left(1 - B\frac{a^5}{f^5}\right)$ of its original value and find B.

Solution : The distribution of charges are shown in Fig. 4.18. The force on e at A along OA is given by

$$F = -\frac{e^2 a}{f} \cdot \frac{1}{\left(f - \frac{a^2}{f}\right)^2} + \frac{2e^2 a}{f} \cdot \frac{1}{f^2} - \frac{e^2 a}{f} \cdot \frac{1}{\left(f + \frac{a^2}{f}\right)^2} + \frac{e^2}{4f^2}$$

$$= \frac{e^2 a}{f^3} \left[-\left(1 - \frac{a^2}{f^2}\right)^{-2} + 2 - \left(1 + \frac{a^2}{f^2}\right)^{-2} + \frac{f}{4a} \right]$$

$$= \frac{e^2 a}{f^3} \left[-\left(1 + \frac{2a^2}{f^2} + 3\frac{a^4}{f^4}\right) + 2 - \left(1 - \frac{2a^2}{f^2} + \frac{3a^4}{f^4}\right) + \frac{f}{4a} \right]$$

$$= \frac{e^2 a}{f^3} \left[\frac{f}{4a} - 6\frac{a^4}{f^4} \right].$$

In absence of the sphere the force on the charge e at A,

Fig. 4.18

$$F_0 = \frac{e^2}{4f^2}.$$

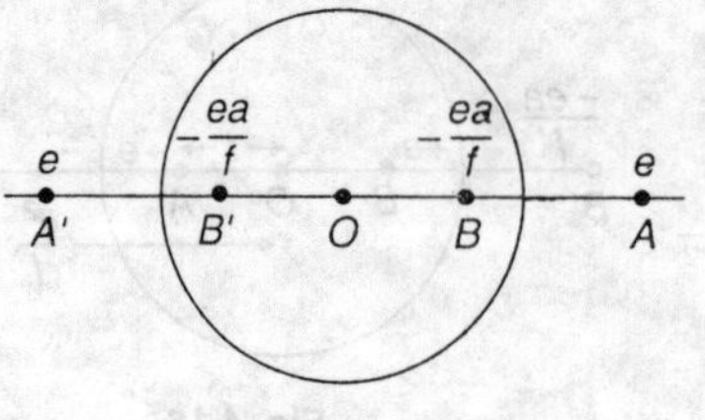

$$\therefore \quad \frac{F_0}{F} = \frac{\frac{q^2}{4f^2}}{\frac{q^2 a}{f^3}\left(\frac{f}{4a} - \frac{6a^4}{f^4}\right)} = \frac{1}{\frac{4a}{f}\left(\frac{f}{4a} - \frac{6a^4}{f^4}\right)}$$

$$= \frac{1}{\left(1 - \frac{24a^5}{f^5}\right)}.$$

$$\therefore \quad F = \left(1 - \frac{24a^5}{f^5}\right)F_0.$$

Now, $\left(1 - B\dfrac{a^5}{f^5}\right) = \left(1 - \dfrac{24a^5}{f^5}\right)$

$$\therefore \quad B = 24.$$

Questions

Essay-type

1. A point charge is placed at a distance of x from the centre of an earthed spherical conductor of radius a. Show that the induced charge on the hemisphere facing q is $-\dfrac{q(x^2 - a^2)}{2x}\left\{\dfrac{1}{x-a} - \dfrac{1}{\sqrt{x^2 + a^2}}\right\}$.

2. Show that the field within a homogeneous dielectric sphere when introduced in a uniform field is independent of the radius of the sphere.

   How is the dipole moment altered when the dielectric sphere is replaced by an insulated conducting sphere?

3. A point charge is placed at a distance x from the centre of an earthed conducting sphere of radius $a(< x)$. Show that density of charge induced on the sphere is inversely proportional to the cube of distance from the point charge. Show also that, if the sphere is insulated and uncharged, then the part of the sphere on which the induced charge density has the same sign as the point charge has area $\dfrac{\pi a}{x}[(x+a)^2 - \{x(x^2 - a^2)\}^{2/3}]$.

4. Show that the capacity of a spherical conductor of radius a is increased in the ratio $1 : 1 + \left[\dfrac{a(K-1)}{2b(K+1)}\right]$ by the presence of a large mass of dielectric with a plane face, at a distance b from the centre of the sphere, if $\frac{a}{b}$ is so small that its square may be neglected.

Numerical Problems

5. A point charge $+20$ e.s.u. is placed at a distance of 50 cm from the centre of an insulated spherical conductor of radius 30 cm charged with q e.s.u. What is the minimum value of q so that the surface density of charge on the sphere is nowhere negative?   [**Ans.** $q = 108$ e.s.u.]

6. If a sphere of radius a be earthed and positive charges e and e' are placed on opposite sides of the sphere, at distances $2a, 4a$ respectively from the centre

and in a straight line with it, show that the charge e' is repelled from the sphere, if $e' < \dfrac{25e}{144}$.

7. A charge e is placed mid-way between two equal spherical conductors which are kept at zero potential. Show that the charge induced on each is $-e\left(m - \dfrac{m^2}{2} + \dfrac{m^3}{4} - \dfrac{3m^4}{8}\right)$, neglecting higher powers of m, which is the ratio of the radius of a conductor to half the distance between their centres.

8. A field is produced by a point charge e in presence of an uninsulated spherical conductor of radius a whose centre is at a distance c from the charge. Find the force with which the charge e is attracted to the sphere and show that the force is changed to a repulsion by insulating the sphere and connecting it to a large distant conductor at potential ϕ, provided that $\phi > \dfrac{ec^3}{(c^2 - a^2)^2}$.

[**Ans.** Force of attraction $\dfrac{e^2 ac}{(c^2-a^2)^2}$]

9. An insulated conducting sphere of radius a is under the influence of a point charge e at a distance $f(> a)$ from its centre. What is the least positive charge that must be given to the sphere in order that the surface density may be everywhere positive? [**Ans.** $Q = \dfrac{ea^2(3f-a)}{f(f-a)^2}$]

10. A point charge e is held at a distance f from the centre of an insulated spherical conductor of radius a, which carries a charge Q. Prove that the surface density at the point of the sphere most remote from the charge e will be zero, if $Q = -\dfrac{ea^2(3f + a)}{f(f + a)^2}$.

Review Short Questions on *Electrostatics*
(with Answers)

Electric Force : Field : Potential

1. *What is the law of force between two electric charges? State the inverse square law.*

Ans. The relationship between two electric charges placed in a medium can be expressed by the following law :

"The force of attraction or repulsion between two charged bodies is directly proportional to the product of the charges and inversely proportional to the square of the distance between them."

The second part of the law is called the inverse square law.

2. *Write down the mathematical form of the law of force.*

Ans. If q_1 and q_2 are two charged bodies, and r the distance between them, then the force F can be written as

$$F \propto q_1 q_2 \quad \text{and} \quad F \propto \frac{1}{r^2}.$$

$$\therefore \quad F \propto \frac{q_1 q_2}{r^2} \quad \text{or,} \quad F = K \frac{q_1 q_2}{r^2},$$

where K is a constant whose value depends on the nature of the medium. K is called the dielectric constant or the permittivity or the specific induction capacity of the medium.

If the medium is air, then for $q_1 = q_2 = 1$, $r = 1$ cm and $F = 1$ dyne, we get $K = 1$.

3. *Define electrostatic unit of charge.*

Ans. The electrostatic unit of charge (e.s.u.) may be defined as the amount of charge which exerts a force of repulsion of one dyne on a similar and equal charge situated at a distance of one centimetre in air.

4. *What is the practical unit of charge? How is it related to e.s.u. ?*

Ans. The practical unit of charge is coulomb. It is equal to 3×10^9 e.s.u.

5. *Define electrical intensity at a point.*

Ans. The electrical intensity at a point in an electric field may be defined as the force experienced by a unit positive charge placed at that point. In c.g.s. system the unit of intensity is dynes per unit e.s.u. of charge.

6. *Define the term 'lines of force'.*

Ans. The lines of force may be defined as the path of an infinitely small positive charge allowed to move freely in the field and is such that the tangent at any point of this path gives the direction of the electric intensity at that point.

7. *What are the important properties of lines of force?*

Ans. (i) They repel one another.

(ii) They are in a state of tension.

(iii) They start from a positively charged body and end on a negatively charged body.

(iv) They do not pass through the interior of a conductor.

(v) They never intersect one another.

8. *Define electric field.*

Ans. The space surrounding a charged body where the electrical attraction or repulsion can be noticed is known as the electric field.

9. *Define the term potential at a point.*

Ans. The potential at a point in an electric field is defined as the work done by or against electric forces to bring a unit positive charge from infinity to that point.

10. *How is the potential of a conductor be measured?*

Ans. The potential of a conductor can be measured by the work done to bring a unit positive charge from an infinite distance, i.e., from a point of zero potential to a point close upon the conductor.

11. *Write down the unit of potential.*

Ans. In c.g.s. system, the unit of time difference of potential is erg per unit charge while the practical unit is one volt.

12. *Find the relation between volt and erg per e.s.u. of charge.*

Ans. Volt is the unit of p.d. between two points in an electric field so that the transfer of one coulomb of charge from one point to other involves an expenditure of one joule of work. Thus we can write

$$1 \text{ volt} = \frac{1 \text{ joule}}{1 \text{ coulomb}} = \frac{10^7 \text{ ergs}}{3 \times 10^9 \text{ e.s.u. of charge}}$$

$$= \frac{1}{300} \text{ ergs per e.s.u. of charge.}$$

13. *What will be the potential at a point due to a charge?*

Ans. Let us consider a charge q producing an electric field. At a distance r from q, let P be any point in the field and let at an infinitesimally small distance dr from it there be another point P_1. The p.d. between these two points P and P_1 is given by

$$dV = -E \cdot dr,$$

where the intensity at P is

$$E = \frac{q}{Kr^2} \quad (K = \text{dielectric constant}).$$

$$\therefore \quad dV = -\frac{q}{Kr^2} \cdot dr.$$

By definition, the absolute potential at P is equal to the difference of potential between P and infinity.

$$\therefore \quad V_p = \int_\infty^r dV = -\int_\infty^r \frac{q}{Kr^2} \cdot dr = \left[\frac{q}{Kr}\right]_\infty^r = \frac{q}{Kr} \text{ ergs/unit charge. When the}$$

medium is air,

$$V_p = \frac{q}{r}.$$

14. *What will be the p.d. between two points due to a charge?*

Ans. The p.d. between two points placed at distances r_1 and r_2 from charge q is given by

$$V_1 - V_2 = \frac{q}{K}\left(\frac{1}{r_1} - \frac{1}{r_2}\right) \text{ ergs/unit charge,}$$

where K is the dielectric constant of the medium.

15. *What will be the potential at a point due to a number of charges?*

Ans. If $q_1, q_2, q_3, \ldots, q_n$ be the charges in a field and if the point P be at distances $r_1, r_2, r_3, \ldots, r_n$, then the potential at P will be

$$V_p = \frac{q_1}{Kr_1} + \frac{q_2}{Kr_2} + \frac{q_3}{Kr_3} + \cdots + \frac{q_n}{Kr_n}$$

$$= \sum_1^n \frac{q}{Kr} \text{ ergs/unit charge.}$$

16. *What is the relation between electric intensity and potential?*

Ans. Let A and B are two points separated by a distance x. If V_1 and V_2 are the potentials at the points A and B respectively, then the p.d. between them is $(V_1 - V_2)$ which is equal to the amount of work done in transfering unit positive charge from B to A. If E represents the electric intensity which is by definition equal to the force in dynes per unit charge, then,

work done = intensity × displacement

or, $(V_1 - V_2) = -E \cdot x$ ($\because$ the displacement is from B to A)

or, $E = -\dfrac{V_1 - V_2}{x}$

or, by Calculus we can write,

$E = -\dfrac{dV}{dx}$.

So we can say that the negative space-rate of variation of the potential is equal to intensity.

17. *State Gauss's theorem.*

Ans. Gauss's theorem may be stated as follows : "The total normal induction over a closed surface is either equal to 4π times the charge or zero according as the charge is covered by the surface or not."

Capacitance : Dielectrics

18. *Define the term capacitance of a conductor.*

Ans. The capacitance or the capacity of a conductor is measured by the quantity of charge required to have its potential raised by one unit. Thus,

$$\text{capacitance } (C) = \frac{\text{quantity of charge } (Q)}{\text{rise of potential } (V)}.$$

19. *What is the unit of capacitance?*

Ans. The capacitance is measured in e.s.u. when both the charge and the potential are expressed in e.s.u. The practical unit of capacitance is farad.

20. *What is a 'farad?'*

Ans. 'farad' is the practical unit of capacitance. A conductor is said to have a capacitance of 1 farad when a charge of 1 coulomb of electricity raises its potential by 1 volt.

$$1 \text{ farad} = 10^6 \text{ microfarads} = 10^{12} \text{ picofarads.}$$

21. *What is the relation between 1 farad and 1 e.s.u. of capacity?*

Ans. $1 \text{ farad} = \dfrac{1 \text{ coulomb}}{1 \text{ volt}} = \dfrac{3 \times 10^9 \text{ e.s.u. of charge}}{\frac{1}{300} \text{ e.s.u. of charge}}$

$= 9 \times 10^{11}$ e.s.u. of capacity.

22. *How is the capacitance of a sphere related to its radius?*

Ans. If r be the radius of a sphere, then its potential is given by

$$V = \frac{Q}{r} \text{ (in air)} \quad \text{or,} \quad V = \frac{Q}{Kr} \text{ (in dielectric medium)}$$

$\therefore$ capacitance, $C = \frac{Q}{V} = \frac{Q}{Q/r} = r$ (in air).

When the surrounding medium is air, the capacitance of a sphere thus becomes equal to its radius.

23. *What factors control the capacity of a conductor?*

Ans. (i) The capacity of a conductor depends upon the dimension of the conductor. The greater the surface area, the greater will be the capacitance.

(ii) It also depends upon the presence of neighbouring conductors.

24. *What is a condenser?*

Ans. A condenser, in its simplest form, consists of two close parallel metal plates with an insulating medium in between them. It is used to collect a large quantity of electricity on a comparatively small surface.

If an earth-connected plate is kept close to a charged plate, its potential decreases and thereby rises its capacity. Such arrangement by which the capacitance of a charged conductor is artificially increased is called a capacitor or a condenser.

25. *Distinguish between potential and potential energy of a charged conductor.*

Ans. The potential of a charged conductor may be defined as the work done in bringing a unit positive charge from infinity to a point close to the conductor while the potential energy of the charged conductor is the total electrical work done in charging the conductor.

26. *What will be the potential energy of a charged conductor?*

Ans. Let us consider a condenser of capacitance C, and Q and V are respectively the final charge and potential. At any instant of charging let the charge and potential be q and v respectively. Now if a small quantity of charge dq be added to the conductor at a potential v, then the work done dw is given by

$$dw = v \cdot dq \text{ ergs.} \tag{i}$$

Again $v = \dfrac{q}{C}$, $\therefore$ $C\,dv = dq$. $\tag{ii}$

By Eqs. (i) and (ii),

$$dw = Cv\,dv.$$

$\therefore$ total work done from the initial uncharged state to the final potential V is

$$W = C \int_0^V v\,dv = \frac{1}{2}CV^2 \text{ ergs.}$$

Now, since $V = \dfrac{Q}{C}$, $\therefore$ $W = \dfrac{1}{2}\dfrac{Q^2}{C}$.

The work done is stored up as the potential energy of the charge.

27. *How is the value of the capacitance related to the specific inductive capacity of the material used?*

Ans. It is seen that mica, paraffin, ebonite, glass, etc., when used as dielectrics instead of air, the capacitance increases and so they have a higher specific inductive capacity (S.I.C.) which may be defined as, S.I.C. of any dielectric x

$$= K = \frac{\text{capacitance of any condenser with dielectric } x}{\text{capacitance of the same condenser with air as dilectric}}.$$

Capacitance of a condenser is thus proportional to the S.I.C. of the material used.

28. *What will be the value of the capacitance if (i) the distance between the plates is increased, (ii) a dielectric is introduced between the plates?*

Ans. (i) The capacitance will be decreased.

(ii) The capacitance will be increased.

29. *What factors determine the potential of a conductor?*

Ans. The potential of a conductor depends upon : **(i)** the amount of charge given to it, **(ii)** the nature of the dielectric and **(iii)** the size of the conductor.

30. *How condensers can be joined (i) in series and (ii) in parallel?*

Ans. (i) *In series*—In series arrangement, the first plate of the second condenser is connected with the second plate of the first and so on. If a charge $+Q$ is applied to the first plate of the first condenser, it induces a charge $-Q$ on the inner side of the second plate and thereby $+Q$ to the first plate of the second condenser, and this is repeated in a similar fashion. If V be the p.d. between the first plate of the first condenser and the last plate of the third condenser and V_1, V_2, V_3 are the p.d. between the plates of the three condensers respectively, then

$$V = V_1 + V_2 + V_3.$$

(ii) *In parallel*—In parallel arrangement, the insulated plates of all the condensers are joined to a common terminal connected with a source of potential and the other plates are connected to another common terminal with the earth. Thus, all the condensers have the same p.d., V, say. As a result when a charge is applied to a common terminal, it is distributed to the condensers depending on their capacitances. If Q_1, Q_2, Q_3 are the charges of the capacitors, the total charge Q will be

$$Q = Q_1 + Q_2 + Q_3.$$

31. *What will be the value of the combined capacitance of three condensers when connected (i) in series and (ii) in parallel?*

Ans. (i) *In series*—We have $V = V_1 + V_2 + V_3$. Let C be the combined capacitance and C_1, C_2, C_3 are the individual capacitances of the three capacitors. Then,

$$V = \frac{Q}{C}, \quad V_1 = \frac{Q}{C_1}, \quad V_2 = \frac{Q}{C_2} \quad \text{and} \quad V_3 = \frac{Q}{C_3}.$$

$$\therefore \quad \frac{Q}{C} = \frac{Q}{C_1} + \frac{Q}{C_2} + \frac{Q}{C_3} \quad \text{or,} \quad \frac{1}{C} = \frac{1}{C_1} + \frac{1}{C_2} + \frac{1}{C_3}.$$

∴ reciprocal of combined capacitance = sum of the reciprocal of the separate capacitances.

(ii) *In parallel*—We have, $Q = Q_1 + Q_2 + Q_3$.

Here, $Q = VC$, $Q_1 = VC_1$, $Q_2 = VC_2$ and $Q_3 = VC_3$.

$$\therefore \quad VC = VC_1 + VC_2 + VC_3 = V(C_1 + C_2 + C_3)$$

or, $\quad C = C_1 + C_2 + C_3$.

∴ combined capacitance = sum of separate capacitances.

32. *How charges can be distributed between two conductors at the same potential?*

Ans. Let q_1 and q_2 are the charges of two conductors, and V be the common potential. Each of the spheres may be considered as a condenser whose positive plate is the sphere itself and the negative plate is earth-connected. By such connections, since the spheres are in parallel, we have the combined capacitance as $(C_1 + C_2)$.

$$V = \frac{q_1}{C_1} = \frac{q_2}{C_2} = \frac{q_1 + q_2}{C_1 + C_2} = \frac{Q}{C_1 + C_2} \quad (\because \text{total charge, } Q = q_1 + q_2)$$

or, $q_1 = Q\dfrac{C_1}{C_1 + C_2}$ and $q_2 = Q\dfrac{C_2}{C_1 + C_2}$.

33. *What will be the loss of energy due to sharing of charge?*

Ans. When two conductors carrying charges at different potentials are joined together, a readjustment of charge occurs till the potentials are equalised. The process involves some expenditure of work and the system loses some amount of energy.

Let two condensers of capacitances, C_1 and C_2, have charges Q_1 and Q_2 and initial potentials V_1 and V_2 respectively. So the energy of the system before sharing of charges is

$$W_i = \frac{1}{2}(C_1 V_1^2 + C_2 V_2^2).$$

Since in this case the total charge $Q = Q_1 + Q_2 = C_1 V_1 + C_2 V_2$ and the combined capacitance (in parallel) $C = C_1 + C_2$, so after sharing, the final potential becomes $V = (C_1 V_1 + C_2 V_2)/(C_1 + C_2)$. Therefore, the final energy of the system W_f is given by,

$$W_f = \frac{1}{2}(C_1 + C_2)V^2 = \frac{1}{2}\frac{(C_1 V_1 + C_2 V_2)^2}{C_1 + C_2}.$$

$$\therefore \quad W_i - W_f = \frac{1}{2}\left[C_1 V_1^2 + C_2 V_2^2 - \frac{C_1^2 V_1^2 + C_2^2 V_2^2 + 2 C_1 C_2 V_1 V_2}{C_1 + C_2}\right]$$

$$= \frac{1}{2}\frac{C_1 C_2}{C_1 + C_2}(V_1 - V_2)^2. \tag{1}$$

Since C_1 and C_2 are positive, the r.h.s. of Eq. (1) is always positive.

$$\therefore \quad W_i > W_f.$$

Thus by sharing of charges there is always a loss of energy except for $V_1 = V_2$ when no redistribution of charges occur.

34. *Give names of some practical and standard condensers.*

Ans. *Practical condensers*—**(i)** Mica condenser, **(ii)** Paper condenser, **(iii)** Variable air condenser, **(iv)** Electrolytic condenser, etc.

Standard condensers—**(i)** Spherical condenser, **(ii)** Cylindrical condenser, **(iii)** Guard-ring parallel plate condenser, etc.

35. *What will be the value of the capacitance for a simple parallel plate air condenser in c.g.s. System?*

Ans. The value of the capacitance for a parallel plate air condenser is obtained from the relation,

$$C = \frac{A}{4\pi d},$$

where A is the area of the plate and d is the separation between the two plates.

If the medium has a dielectric constant K, then the capacity becomes

$$C = \frac{KA}{4\pi d}.$$

Electrostatic Instruments

36. *What are electrometers?*

Ans. Electrometers are instruments used to measure the electric potential and potential difference.

37. *Give two names of electrometers used for exact measurement of potentials.*

Ans. The names are : **(i)** Kelvin's attracted disc absolute electrometer and **(ii)** Thomson's quadrant electrometer.

38. *Mention the important advantages of electrostatic voltmeters.*

Ans. **(i)** These are used either with alternating or direct pressure. **(ii)** They neither take any current nor waste any energy. **(iii)** As the action of electrostatic voltmeters are independent of the passage of current, there are no errors due to variation in temperature and magnetic field.

39. *What are electrostatic machines?*

Ans. Electrostatic machines are mechanical devices used for the rapid production of electrical charges.

40. *What are the different classes of electrostatic machines?*

Ans. Electrostatic machines are divided into two classes. These are : **(i)** the Frictional machines and **(ii)** the Induction or Influence machines.

41. *Give the name of an induction machine.*

Ans. The electrophorus is the name of an induction machine since with the help of this machine a series of charges are obtained from an initial single charge by the process of induction.

42. *How the charge obtained in each operation in an electrophorus can be increased?*

Ans. By increasing the area of the electrophorus the charge obtained can be proportionately increased in each operation.

43. *What is Van de Graaff generator?*

Ans. It is an electrostatic generator used to produce very high voltages. In the construction of this machine there is a vertical endless belt which transfers charge to a large insulating metal dome, where a high voltage is produced.

44. *What is the order of voltage usually derived from Van de Graaff generator?*

Ans. By this machine voltage of the order of 10^6 volts can be developed.

45. *What happens when two bodies are charged by rubbing each other?*

Ans. We know that each atom has the same number of electrons and protons, and as a whole it becomes electrically neutral. When an ebonite rod is rubbed with flannel, some electrons are removed from the flannel by the rod. In fact, this left the flannel with an excess of protons, i.e., with a negative charge. Thus the transfer of electrons takes place by rubbing.

46. *A metal sphere of diameter about 5 cm placed on an insulating stand is given a strong positive charge.*

(i) If it is brought near an uncharged pith-ball suspended by a silk thread, it is at first attracted and then after touching the ball repelled away. Briefly explain the reason of this behaviour.

(ii) Will the pith-ball still experience a force exerted by the metal sphere if an earthed thin metal plate be interposed in between the pith-ball and the metal sphere without touching either of them?

Ans. (i) If the positively charged metal sphere is brought close to an uncharged freely suspended pith-ball, attraction takes place. There will be an attraction between unlike charges and repulsion between like charges but as the unlike charges are nearer than the like charges, so attraction will be predominant. When the charged metal sphere touches the pith-ball, the latter shares similar charge with the sphere and consequently there will be repulsion.

(ii) The pith-ball will not experience any force since the earthed metal plate has lost induced free charge on the side facing the pith-ball.

47. *A hollow sphere of radius a is charged to a potential v and charge q. What is the field intensity at a point (i) outside the sphere, (ii) inside the sphere?*

Mention also the charge density on the internal surface of the sphere and the potential at a point distant r from the centre where r < a, i.e., the point is inside the sphere.

Ans. *1st Part*—**(i)** The electric field intensity at a point outside the sphere $= \frac{q}{ka^2}$ (k = dielectric const.).

(ii) Since the charge q inside the sphere is zero, so the intensity inside a hollow charged sphere is zero.

2nd Part—As the charge reside on the outer surface of a charged conductor, the charge density on the inner surface is zero.

All the points on the surface of a conductor and also at the interior points are at the same potential v.

48. *Find the relations between (i)* coulomb *and e.s.u. of charge, (ii)* volt *and e.s.u. of potential.*

Ans. (i) 1 coulomb $= 3 \times 10^9$ e.s.u. of charge

(ii) 1 volt $= \dfrac{1 \text{ joule}}{1 \text{ coulomb}} = \dfrac{10^7 \text{ erg}}{3 \times 10^9 \text{ e.s.u. of charge}} = \dfrac{1}{300}$ e.s.u. of potential.

49. *If the distance between the electron and the nucleus of a hydrogen atom is 5.3×10^{-9} cm, find in C.G.S. system the magnitude of electric force between them.*

Ans. We know that the charge of an electron is 4.8×10^{-10} e.s.u. Since hydrogen nucleus is formed by 1 proton only, so it has a positive charge of value 4.8×10^{-10} e.s.u.

Hence the magnitude of force,

$$F = \frac{q_p q_e}{r^2} = \frac{4.8 \times 10^{-10} \times 4.8 \times 10^{-10}}{(5.3 \times 10^{-9})^2}$$

$$= 82 \times 10^{-4} \text{ dyne.}$$

50. *A metal plate is charged to 12 kV of potential. It is placed 4 cm above the ground. Calculate the electric intensity at any point of the field produced.*

Ans. We have the intensity,

$$E = \frac{V_2 - V_1}{x}.$$

Here, $V_2 = 12$ kV, $V_1 = 0$, $x = 4$ cm.

$$\therefore \qquad E = \frac{12 - 0}{4} = 3 \text{ kV/cm}.$$

51. *If in an electric field the potential at any point be V and if a charge $+q$ be situated at that point, then what is the amount of potential energy on the charge?*

Ans. The work done in bringing a charge $+q$ from infinity to the point $= Vq$ which is stored as potential energy.

Therefore, the required PE $= Vq$.

52. *Explain why the electric potential at any point due to positive charge decreases with distance but due to negative charge increases.*

Ans. Due to $+q$ charge, the potential $V = +\frac{q}{r}$ while due to $-q$ charge, the potential $V = -\frac{q}{r}$, where r is the distance.

Considering the positive and the negative sign respectively, we find that if r increases, $+\frac{q}{r}$ decreases, i.e., V decreases. But for negative charge there is an increase of V with r.

53. *What will be the work done on a unit positive charge to move it from one point to another on an equipotential surface?—Explain.*

Ans. If a charge q is moved from a point of potential V_2 to a point of potential V_1, then the work done

$$W = (V_2 - V_1)q.$$

On an equipotential surface since the potential at all points are same, so $V_2 - V_1 = 0$.

$$\therefore \quad W = 0,$$

i.e., the work done will be zero.

54. *Explain why no neutral point exists in an electric field due to two equal unlike charges.*

Ans. In an electric field with two equal unlike charges there exists no point where the magnitudes and directions of intensities due to two charges satisfy the condition of producing the neutral point. Hence no neutral point exists in such case.

55. *Explain why the electric intensity at the pointed part of a charged conductor is very large.*

Ans. By Coulomb's theorem, we have,

$$\text{the electric intensity, } E = \frac{4\pi\sigma}{K}$$

where σ is the surface density of charge and K the dielectric constant.

At the pointed part of the charged conductor the surface density of charge (σ) is very large. So the intensity E is also very large.

56. *Explain why the volume of a soap-water bubble increases when it is charged.*

Ans. When the soap-water bubble is charged, an outward pressure is developed. So its volume increases.

57. *The radius of the earth is 6400 km. Find its capacitance in e.s.u. and μF.*

Ans. We have, capacitance of a sphere, (C) = its radius (r)

Considering the earth as a spherical conductor we get its capacitance,

$$C = 6400 \times 10^5 \text{ e.s.u. } [\because r = 6400 \text{ km } = 6400 \times 10^5 \text{ cm}]$$

Again, we know that

1 μF = 9×10^5 e.s.u. of capacitance

$\therefore \quad C = \dfrac{6400 \times 10^5}{9 \times 10^5} \ \mu$F = 711.1 μF (approx.).

58. *What will be the effect of introducing a dielectric slab between the plates of a condenser and why?*

Ans. The capacitance of the condenser will increase when a dielectric slab is introduced between the plates. This is because the dielectric constant (K) of the material of the slab is always greater than unity. For a parallel plate air condenser, the capacitance, $C = \frac{A}{4\pi d}$ while with the dielectric slab the capacitance, $C_1 = \frac{KA}{4\pi d}$.

Hence, $\dfrac{C_1}{C} = K > 1$

$\therefore \qquad C_1 > C.$

59. *After sharing of charges between two charged conductors connected by a wire a deficit of energy is always found—why?*

Ans. During the sharing of charge some energy is always lost in the form of heat, so there is a deficit.

Magnetostatics

Chapter 5
Fundamental Laws of Magnetostatics : Theories

5.1 Introduction

A dark-coloured ore called magnetite which consists of an oxide of iron (Fe_3O_4), was first discovered in Magnesia in Asia Minor. Subsequently, it was noted that natural magnets occur in nature as an ore and possess both attractive and directive properties. These two properties are weak in natural magnets which, however, are very strongly developed in some metals or alloys. Magnets so prepared are called artificial magnets such as bar magnet, horse-shoe magnet, etc. Many alloys like tungsten steel, cobalt steel, alnico, etc., have been prepared in recent years. These possess the quality of a magnetic substance to a far greater degree than iron, nickel, etc.

5.2 Law of Force between Magnetic Poles

Coulomb showed that the force between two magnetic poles varies directly to the product of the strengths of two magnets and inversely as the square of the distance between the poles. The direction of the force will be along the line joining the two poles. This law is valid, provided the distance between the poles are very long. Mathematically, the law is expressed as

$$F = K\frac{m_1 m_2}{r^2}, \qquad (5.1)$$

where m_1 and m_2 are the strengths of the two poles and r is the distance between them. K is a constant whose magnitude will depend on the nature of the medium and the unit in which the force is measured.

In S.I. unit, $K = \dfrac{\mu}{4\pi}$

In general, for an isotropic medium the above law may be written as

$$F = \frac{\mu_0 \mu_r m_1 m_2}{4\pi r^2}, \qquad (5.2)$$

where μ_0 is the permeability of the free space, μ_r is relative permeability of the medium on which the poles are situated. $\mu = \mu_0 \mu_r$ is called the absolute permeability of the medium.

5.3 Magnetic Field, Lines and Tubes of Force

A magnetic pole placed anywhere in a space around a magnet will experience a force and the pole is said to be situated in the magnetic field. The force experienced by a unit north pole in a magnetic field is called the strength or intensity of the field at that point.

So the intensity is the force per unit pole. In S.I. units, it is expressed in $\dfrac{\text{newton}}{\text{weber}}$.

The path along which a free N-pole placed in a magnetic field is directed is called a *line of force*. The paths are, in general, curved and continuous. A line of

115

force may be defined as the curve such that the tangent at any point on this curve gives the direction of the intensity at the point. In a magnet each line of force emerges from the north pole and enters into the south pole externally and S-pole to N-pole internally.

A unit pole is supposed to give one-unit tubes of force per unit area of the surface of a sphere of unit radius.

5.4 Magnetic Flux and Flux Density

Magnetic lines of force lie in all planes around a magnet or a magnetic pole. These lines are known as flux and usually represented by ϕ. The unit of flux is weber.

$$1 \text{ weber} = 10^8 \text{ maxwells}.$$

The flux per unit area on a plane perpendicular to the flux is called *flux density*. It is denoted by B. B is also known as magnetic induction. Flux density will depend on the magnetic field H and on the nature of the medium and is expressed as

$$B = \mu H, \tag{5.3}$$

where μ is the permeability of the medium.

5.5 Magnetic Moment

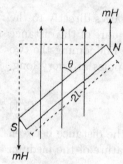

Fig. 5.1

Let SN is a bar magnet having magnetic length $2l$ which is the length between the two poles of the magnet. Here we assume that the poles are situated at the ends of the magnet (Fig. 5.1). Under the action of the external uniform field H it makes an angle θ with the direction of the field at equilibrium. The forces acting on the ends are respectively mH and $-mH$. So the magnet will experience a couple or torque of moment,

$$\tau = -mH \times 2l \sin\theta$$
$$= -2ml\, H \sin\theta$$
$$= -MH \sin\theta. \tag{5.4}$$

$M = 2ml$ is the magnetic moment of the magnet. Minus sign indicates that the torque tends to decrease θ.

Now, if $\theta = \frac{1}{2}\pi$ and $H = 1$, then $\tau = -M$. Thus we may define the magnetic moment as the couple required to place a magnet at right angle to the external field.

The unit of magnetic moment in the SI system is ampere-metre^2 (A-m^2).

5.6 Field due to a Magnet

(i) Point P lies on the line joining the two poles (end-on position).

Let O be the centre of the bar magnet SN (Fig. 5.2) having magnetic length $2l$.

Fig. 5.2

Field at P due to the pole $+m = \dfrac{\mu_0}{4\pi} \dfrac{m}{(x - l)^2}$ along OP

and field at P due to the pole $-m = -\dfrac{\mu_0}{4\pi}\dfrac{m}{(x+l)^2}$ along PO.

Therefore, the resultant intensity at P,

$$F = \frac{\mu_0}{4\pi}\left[\frac{m}{(x-l)^2} - \frac{m}{(x+l)^2}\right] \text{ along } OP$$

$$= \frac{\mu_0}{4\pi}\frac{4mlx}{(x^2-l^2)^2} \tag{5.5}$$

$$= \frac{\mu_0}{4\pi}\frac{2Mx}{(x^2-l^2)^2}, \text{ where } M = 2ml = \text{magnetic moment.}$$

For the short magnet $x \gg l$

$$F = \frac{\mu_0}{4\pi}\cdot\frac{2M}{x^3} = \frac{\mu_0 M}{2\pi x^3}. \tag{5.6}$$

(ii) Point P lies on the line perpendicular to the axis of the magnet (broadside-on position).

Field intensity at P due to $+m = \dfrac{\mu_0}{4\pi}\dfrac{m}{x^2+l^2}$ along NP

and field intensity at P due to $-m = -\dfrac{\mu_0}{4\pi}\dfrac{m}{x^2+l^2}$ along PS.

Now resolve the intensities in the directions parallel and normal to the magnetic axis SN (Fig. 5.3). Components along OP will cancel each other. So the resultant field intensity will be

$$F = \frac{\mu_0}{4\pi}\frac{2m\cos\theta}{x^2+l^2}.$$

Now, $\cos\theta = \dfrac{l}{(x^2+l^2)^{1/2}}.$

$\therefore$ resultant intensity at P,

$$F = \frac{\mu_0}{4\pi}\frac{2m}{x^2+l^2}\cdot\frac{l}{(x^2+l^2)^{1/2}}$$

$$= \frac{\mu_0}{4\pi}\frac{M}{(x^2+l^2)^{3/2}} \text{ along } PR. \tag{5.7}$$

If $x \gg l$, i.e., for a short magnet,

$$F = \frac{\mu_0}{4\pi}\frac{M}{x^3}. \tag{5.8}$$

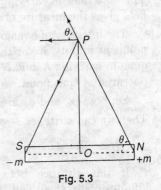

Fig. 5.3

5.7 Intensity at Any Point due to a Short Magnet or Magnetic Dipole

Suppose the point P is at a large distance r (Fig. 5.4) from the centre of a small magnet having magnetic moment M and effective length $2l$.

We resolve the magnetic moment M along OP and perpendicular to OP.

The point P is at end-on position with respect to $M\cos\theta$. So the intensity at P due to $M\cos\theta$ will be

$$F_1 = \frac{\mu_0}{4\pi}\frac{2M\cos\theta}{r^3} \text{ along } PS.$$

In a similar way the point P is at broadside-on position with respect to $M\sin\theta$.

So the intensity at P due to $M \sin \theta$ component will be

$$F_2 = \frac{\mu_0}{4\pi} \frac{M \sin \theta}{r^3} \text{ along } PQ.$$

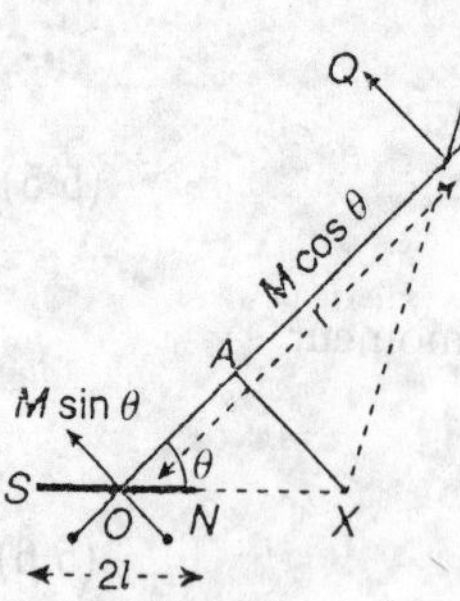

Therefore, the resultant intensity at P is

$$F = \frac{\mu_0}{4\pi} \sqrt{\left(\frac{2M \cos \theta}{r^3}\right)^2 + \left(\frac{M \sin \theta}{r^3}\right)^2} \text{ along } PR$$

$$= \frac{\mu_0}{4\pi} \frac{M}{r^3} \sqrt{1 + 3\cos^2 \theta} \qquad (5.9)$$

Fig. 5.4

and $\quad \tan \alpha = \dfrac{F_2}{F_1} = \dfrac{1}{2} \tan \theta$

or, $\quad \alpha = \tan^{-1}\left(\dfrac{1}{2} \tan \theta\right).$ $\qquad (5.10)$

Now, $\tan \alpha = \dfrac{AX}{AP}$ and $\tan \theta = \dfrac{AX}{AO}.$

$\therefore \quad \dfrac{AX}{AP} = \dfrac{1}{2}\dfrac{AX}{AO}$

$\therefore \quad AP = 2AO.$ $\qquad (5.11)$

Hence the direction of the resultant intensity is such that it cuts the axis at X, the perpendicular XA drawn from X on OP dividing it in the ratio $AO : OP = 1 : 2$.

5.8   Magnetic Potential

The work done in carrying a unit pole from one point to another point in a magnetic field gives the measure of potential difference between these two points.

The intensity of a magnetic field at an infinite distance from a pole is zero. So all points at infinity are at the same potential and it is taken as zero. Hence the work done in carrying a unit N-pole from infinity to a point is defined as the magnetic potential at that point.

Suppose ϕ_a and ϕ_b are respectively the potentials at the points A and B.

Then we can write, $\phi_a - \phi_b = H \times AB$, where H is the intensity of magnetic field.

$\therefore \quad H = \dfrac{\phi_a - \phi_b}{AB}$ $\qquad (5.12)$

If the distance between A and B (Fig. 5.5) is infinitesimally small and the field is non-uniform, then

$$H = -\frac{d\phi}{dx} \quad \text{or,} \quad d\phi = -H\,dx, \qquad (5.13)$$

Fig. 5.5

where $d\phi$ is the potential difference across AB and dx is the distance between two points A and B. Negative sign indicates that the work is done against the field.

From Eq. (5.13) we may define the intensity of magnetic field as the rate of change of magnetic potential at that point.

5.9   Potential at Any Point due to a Small Magnet (or Magnetic Dipole)

Suppose we have a small magnet NS (Fig. 5.6) having length $2l$ which is small compared with the distance of the point $P(r, \theta)$. We have to calculate the potential at the point P.

Let us draw normals from the point N and S on OP. Since $l \ll r$, we have $PN = PQ$ and $PS = PR$.

Now, the potential at P,

$$\phi = \frac{\mu_0}{4\pi}\left[\frac{m}{PQ} - \frac{m}{PR}\right]$$

$$= m\frac{\mu_0}{4\pi}\left[\frac{1}{OP - OQ} - \frac{1}{OP + OQ}\right]$$

$$= m\frac{\mu_0}{4\pi}\frac{2 \cdot OQ}{OP^2 - OQ^2}$$

$$= m\frac{\mu_0}{4\pi}\frac{2l\cos\theta}{r^2} \quad [\text{since } OQ \ll OP]$$

$$= \frac{\mu_0}{4\pi}\frac{M\cos\theta}{r^2}, \tag{5.14}$$

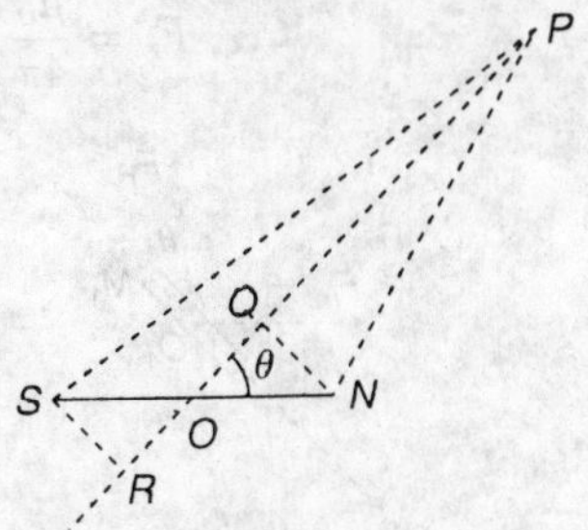

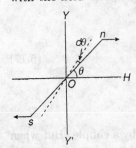

Fig. 5.6

where $M = 2ml = $ moment of the magnet.

Eq. (5.14) gives the potential of the magnet at any point.

5.10 Work Done in Rotating a Magnet

The couple acting on a magnet ns having moment M when it makes an angle θ with the field direction H will be $MH\sin\theta$.

Therefore, the work done in turning the magnet through an angle $d\theta$ (Fig. 5.7) along the field is

$$dW = MH\sin\theta d\theta$$

So the total work done in displacing the magnet from its initial position through an angle θ will be

$$W = \int_0^\theta MH\sin\theta d\theta$$

$$= MH(1 - \cos\theta). \tag{5.15}$$

Fig. 5.7

The work done is stored in the system in the form of potential energy.

If YY' represents the zero energy position of the magnet, then the work done in rotating the magnet through an angle θ with the field direction will be

$$W = \int_{\frac{\pi}{2}}^\theta MH\sin\theta d\theta = -MH\cos\theta. \tag{5.16}$$

In case of non-uniform field H, the magnet will subject to a couple as well as a translational force.

5.11 Mutual Potential Energy of Two Coplanar Short Magnets (or Magnetic Dipoles)

Mutual potential energy between the dipoles is the energy of one of the dipoles placed in the field of the other. So here we find out the mutual potential energy between the dipoles by calculating the potential energy of the dipole 1 having moment M_1, when it is placed in the field of the dipole 2 having moment M_2.

Let r is the distance O_1O_2 between the dipoles, and θ_1 and θ_2 are respectively the angles made by M_1 and M_2 with the line O_1O_2 (Fig. 5.8).

Now the radial and transverse components of the field due to the dipole 2 at the position of the dipole 1 are respectively

$$F_r = \frac{\mu_0}{4\pi} \frac{2M_2 \cos\theta_2}{r^3} \quad \text{and} \quad F_\theta = \frac{\mu_0}{4\pi} \frac{M \sin\theta_2}{r^3}.$$

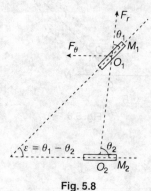

Now the potential energy of a dipole of moment M_1 placed at an angle θ_1 with F_r,

$$W_r = -M_1 F_r \cos\theta_1$$

$$= -\frac{\mu_0}{4\pi} \frac{2M_1 M_2 \cos\theta_1 \cos\theta_2}{r^3}.$$

Similarly, the potential energy of the dipole placed at an angle $\left(\frac{\pi}{2} + \theta_1\right)$ with F_θ is given by

$$W_\theta = -M_1 F_\theta \cos\left(\frac{\pi}{2} + \theta_1\right) = M_1 F_\theta \sin\theta_1$$

$$= \frac{\mu_0}{4\pi} \frac{M_1 M_2 \sin\theta_1 \sin\theta_2}{r^3}.$$

Fig. 5.8

Therefore, total mutual potential energy between the dipoles is

$$N = W_r + W_\theta$$

$$= \frac{\mu_0}{4\pi} \frac{M_1 M_2}{r^3} (\sin\theta_1\theta_2 - 2\cos\theta_1\cos\theta_2)$$

$$= \frac{\mu_0}{4\pi} \frac{M_1 M_2}{r^3} [\cos(\theta_1 - \theta_2) - 3\cos\theta_1\cos\theta_2]$$

$$= \frac{\mu_0}{4\pi} \frac{M_1 M_2}{r^3} [\cos\epsilon - 3\cos\theta_1\cos\theta_2], \tag{5.17}$$

where ϵ is the angle between the two magnetic dipoles.

5.12   Forces and Couples on Short Magnets

When a magnet is placed in a uniform field, it is acted upon by a couple. But when a magnet is placed near another magnet, the former is acted upon by a couple and by a force.

Suppose $N_1 S_1$ and $N_2 S_2$ are two magnets having magnetic moments M_1 and M_2 respectively. The magnets have pole strength m_1 and m_2 respectively and each have length $2l$. Let d be the distance between the centres of the magnet, i.e., $O_1 O_2 = d$.

Case I : The axes of the two magnets lie in the same line (Fig. 5.9).

(a) Forces : Intensity of the magnetic field at S_2

due to $N_1 S_1 = -\dfrac{\mu_0}{4\pi} \dfrac{2M_1}{(d-l)^3}$ along $S_2 N_2$.

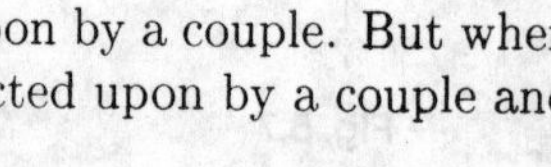

Force on m_2 at $S_2 = -\dfrac{\mu_0}{4\pi} \dfrac{2M_1 m_2}{(d-l)^3}$ along $S_2 N_2$.

Fig. 5.9

Similarly, force on m_2 at $N_2 = +\dfrac{\mu_0}{4\pi} \dfrac{2M_1 m_2}{(d+l)^3}$ along $S_2 N_2$.

So the resultant force on $N_2 S_2$,

$$F = \frac{\mu_0}{4\pi} 2M_1 m_2 \left[\frac{1}{(d+l)^3} - \frac{1}{(d-l)^3}\right] = \frac{\mu_0}{4\pi} 2M_1 m_2 \left[\frac{-6d^2 l - 2l^3}{(d^2 - l^2)^3}\right].$$

Now $d \gg l$, so the terms having higher power of l can be neglected.

$$\therefore \quad F = -\frac{\mu_0}{4\pi} 2M_1 m_2 \cdot \frac{6d^2 l}{d^6} = -\frac{\mu_0}{4\pi} \frac{6M_1 M_2}{d^4}$$

$$= -\frac{3\mu_0 M_1 M_2}{2\pi d^4}. \tag{5.18}$$

The negative sign in the expression for the force acting between two magnets indicates that it is directed along $N_2 S_2$. Or in other words, it is attractive in nature.

(b) Couples : As the forces are all directed along the common axes of the magnets $S_1 N_1 S_2 N_2$, they exert no torque on the magnet. Hence the couples are zero.

Case II : The axes of the magnets are at right angles.

(a) Forces : The intensity of the magnetic field at S_1 due to $S_2 N_2$

$$= \frac{\mu_0}{4\pi} \frac{M_2}{(d-l)^3} \text{ along } S_1 P_1.$$

So the force on $-m_1$ at $S_1 = -\frac{\mu_0}{4\pi} \frac{M_2 m_1}{(d-l)^3}$ along $S_1 P_1$.

Similarly, the force on $+m_1$ at $N_1 = \frac{\mu_0}{4\pi} \frac{M_2 m_1}{(d+l)^3}$ along $N_1 P_2$.

Therefore, the resultant force on $N_1 S_1$

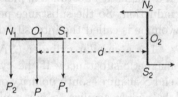

Fig. 5.10

$$= \frac{\mu_0}{4\pi} M_2 m_1 \left[\frac{1}{(d+l)^3} - \frac{1}{(d-l)^3} \right]$$

$$= -\frac{\mu_0}{4\pi} \frac{M_2 m_1 \times 6d^2 l}{d^6},$$

higher powers of l are neglected because $d \gg l$

$$= -\frac{\mu_0}{4\pi} \frac{3M_1 M_2}{d^4} = -\frac{3\mu_0 M_1 M_2}{4\pi d^4}. \tag{5.19}$$

If the magnets are free to move, one will move upward and the other will move downward.

(b) Couples : Since the magnets are small, we may neglect their lengths compared to the distance d.

Now the magnet $N_1 S_1$ is on the broadside-on position with respect to $N_2 S_2$. So the force on each of the poles of $N_1 S_1$ due to $N_2 S_2$ is $\frac{M_2 m_1}{d^3}$. They are opposite and parallel forces. So they form a couple with arm $2l$.

Therefore, moment of the couple will be

$$= \frac{M_2 m_1}{d^3} \times 2l = \frac{M_1 M_2}{d^3} \text{ (anti-clockwise).}$$

Again, the magnet $N_2 S_2$ is on the end-on position with respect to $N_1 S_1$. So the force on each of the poles of $N_2 S_2$ due to $N_1 S_1$ is $\frac{2M_1 m_2}{d^3}$. They are parallel and oppositely directed, so they also form a couple of moment

$$= \frac{2M_1 m_2}{d^3} \times 2l = \frac{2M_1 M_2}{d^3} \text{ (anti-clockwise).}$$

The Paradox

Both of the above couples are in the anti-clockwise direction. Hence the total couple in the anti-clockwise direction is $\frac{3M_1 M_2}{d^3}$. It may, therefore, appear that if the two magnets are placed on a board floating on water, the system will rotate continuously without any supply of energy. So it seems to go against the principle of conservation of energy. The fallacy consists in neglecting the finite length of the magnet, i.e., neglecting the forces $\frac{3M_1M_2}{d^4}$ acting on N_1S_1 and N_2S_2 in the opposite direction. They are equivalent to a couple of moment $\frac{3M_1M_2}{d^4} \times d = \frac{3M_1M_2}{d^3}$ in the clockwise direction. So the resultant couple on the system vanishes and the paradox disappears.

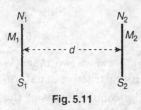

Fig. 5.11

(c) **Magnets parallel to each other :** Here the couples vanish, but the force acting along the line joining the centre is $\frac{3M_1M_2}{d^4}$.

From the above calculation we find that the couple varies inversely as the cube of the distance between the magnets and the force varies as the fourth power of the distance between the magnets. The couple vanishes less rapidly than the forces as the distance increases. That is why a pivoted magnetic needle is sensitive to a feeble magnetic field.

5.13   Intensity of Magnetization

If a magnetic substance is placed in a magnetic field, it acquires magnetism due to induction. So the substance possesses a magnetic moment. This moment per unit volume is called the intensity of magnetization.

Let a circular cylinder (SN) of length $2l$ and of cross-section A is made by a magnetic substance. If the cylinder is placed in a magnetic field (Fig. 5.12) the end S acquires south polarity of strength $-m$ and the end N acquires a north polarity of strength $+m$. So the moment of the magnet will be

$$M = 2ml$$

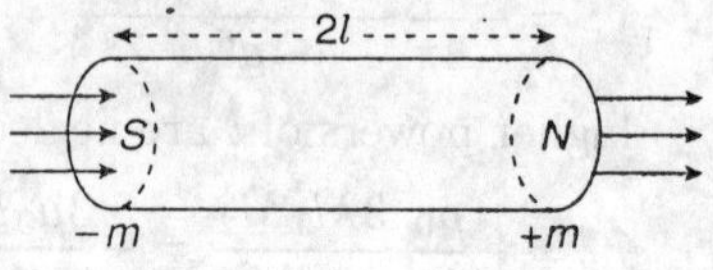

and intensity of magnetization,

$$I = \frac{\text{magnetic moment}}{\text{volume}} = \frac{2ml}{2l \times A} = \frac{m}{A}. \tag{5.20}$$

Fig. 5.12

Therefore, the intensity of magnetization may also be defined as the pole strength acquired by the magnetic substance per unit area.

5.14   Magnetic Potential and Field due to a Magnetized Sphere

Suppose the sphere is magnetized in the direction of the arrow. So the right surface of the sphere will exhibit the north polarity and the left, the south polarity as shown in Fig. 5.13.

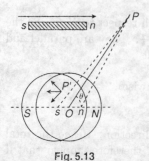

Fig. 5.13

Let the sphere be made up of a large number of dipoles each of magnetic moment ml, where m is the pole strength of each dipole and l is the effective length. All dipoles are lying parallel to the direction of magnetization. Here we assume that all N-poles (or S-poles) of the dipoles are distributed uniformly throughout a sphere whose centre is at n (or s).

Let there are x dipoles per unit volume of the sphere each of pole strength m. So the amount of north (or south) magnetism per unit volume $= mx$.

Therefore, total amount of north (or south) magnetism $= \frac{4}{3}\pi R^3 \cdot mx$.

Let a sphere of magnetism act as if the whole magnetism is concentrated at its centre. So the effect of the sphere at an external point is the same as if the magnetism is concentrated at n and s, the two poles of a dipole each of strength $\frac{4}{3}\pi R^3 mx$.

Now we have to calculate the potential and field at the point $P(r, \theta)$.

(a) **Potential :** The potential at P due to the uniformly magnetized sphere will be

$$\phi = \frac{4}{3}\pi R^3 mx \frac{\mu_0}{4\pi} \left(\frac{1}{nP} - \frac{1}{sP} \right)$$

$$= \frac{4}{3}\pi R^3 mx \frac{\mu_0}{4\pi} \frac{sP - nP}{nP \cdot sP}$$

$$= \frac{4}{3}\pi R^3 mx \frac{\mu_0}{4\pi} \frac{l\cos\theta}{r^2},$$

in case of a dipole we assume that $nP = sP = OP = r$.

If I_m be the intensity of magnetization of the sphere, then

$$I_m = mlx. \tag{5.21}$$

$$\therefore \quad \phi = \frac{4}{3}\pi R^3 I_m \frac{\mu_0}{4\pi} \frac{\cos\theta}{r^2}$$

$$= \frac{\mu_0}{4\pi} \frac{M\cos\theta}{r^2}, \tag{5.22}$$

where M is the magnetic moment of the sphere.

Therefore, a uniformly magnetized sphere will produce the same potential at an external point as that produced by a magnetic dipole placed along the direction of magnetization and having magnetic moment which is equal to the magnetic moment of the sphere.

(b) **Field :**

(i) **Point lies outside the sphere :** The components of magnetic field at P will be

$$F_r = -\frac{d\phi}{dr} = -\frac{d}{dr}\left(\frac{\mu_0}{4\pi}\frac{M\cos\theta}{r^2}\right) = \frac{\mu_0}{4\pi}\frac{2M\cos\theta}{r^3}$$

and $F_\theta = -\frac{1}{r}\left(\frac{d\phi}{dr}\right) = -\frac{1}{r}\frac{\mu_0}{4\pi}\frac{d}{dr}\left(\frac{M\cos\theta}{r^2}\right) = \frac{\mu_0}{4\pi}\frac{M\sin\theta}{r^3}.$

Therefore, the resultant intensity at P will be

$$F = \frac{\mu_0}{4\pi}\frac{M}{r^3}\sqrt{1 + 3\cos^2\theta}. \tag{5.23}$$

We find that the intensity of magnetic field will be the same as that produced by a magnetic dipole placed at the centre of the sphere.

(ii) **Point lies inside the sphere :** Suppose we have to calculate the field at any point P' inside the sphere. In this case according to Gauss's theorem the field at P' will be due to magnetized sphere of radii nP' (sP'); the portion outside this sphere will produce no effect at P'.

Now the force at P' due to north magnetism concentrated at n is

$$= \frac{4}{3}\pi(nP')^3 mx\frac{\mu_0}{4\pi}\frac{1}{(nP')^2} \text{ along } nP'$$

$$= \frac{4}{3}\pi\frac{\mu_0}{4\pi}(nP')mx.$$

Similarly, the force at P' due to south magnetism concentrated at s is

$$= \frac{4}{3}\pi(sP')^3 mx\frac{\mu_0}{4\pi}\frac{1}{(sP')^2} \text{ along } sP'$$

$$= \frac{4}{3}\pi\frac{\mu_0}{4\pi}(sP')mx.$$

Therefore, the resultant intensity at P' will be

$$= \frac{4}{3}\pi\frac{\mu_0}{4\pi}(ns)\cdot mx \text{ along } ns \text{ (by triangular law of forces)}$$

$$= \frac{\mu_0}{4\pi}\frac{4}{3}\pi mxl = \frac{\mu_0}{4\pi}\frac{4}{3}\pi I_m$$

$$= \frac{\mu_0 I_m}{3}. \tag{5.24}$$

So the intensity of magnetic field inside the sphere is constant but its direction is opposite to that of magnetization.

5.15   Magnetic Shell

A magnetic shell is a thin sheet of ferromagnetic material of uniform thickness and magnetized so that the direction of magnetization is everywhere normal to the surface of the sheet. Here the distribution of magnetization is uniform. The

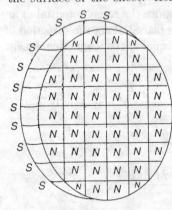

magnetic shell may be regarded as made up of a large number of magnetic dipoles situated in such a way that the materials have opposite polarities on the two faces (Fig. 5.14). The magnetic moment of the shell will be the vector sum of the magnetic moments of the constituent dipoles. The strength of the shell is equal to the magnetic moment per unit area.

Let I_m = intensity of magnetization of the shell, t = thickness of the shell, A = surface area of the shell, V = volume of the shell, m = pole strength of the shell.

Fig. 5.14

$$\therefore \quad I_m = \frac{\text{magnetic moment}}{\text{volume}} = \frac{M}{V} = \frac{m \times t}{A \times t} = \frac{m}{A}.$$

Now magnetic moment of the shell = pole strength × length = $m \times t = I_m A \cdot t$

Hence, strength of the shell, $\Omega = \dfrac{\text{magnetic moment}}{\text{area}} = \dfrac{I_m At}{A} = I_m t.$ \hfill (5.25)

5.16   Potential at a Point due to a Magnetic Shell

Suppose XY is a magnetic shell whose right-hand face has south polarity and left-hand face has north polarity. The point P lies on the left-hand side of this shell. The shell may be considered as made up of a large number of dipoles placed side by side and each has length t which is equal to the thickness of the shell.

Let us now consider a dipole AB having cross-sectional area ds. The strength of the shell, $\Omega = \sigma t$, where $\sigma =$ the surface density of magnetism = intensity of magnetization.

The magnetic moment of the elementary dipole is equal to Ωds directed along the normal NON' of the surface.

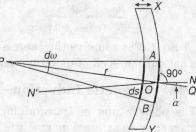

Now the potential at P (Fig. 5.15) due to the elementary magnet,

$$d\phi = \frac{\mu_0}{4\pi} \frac{\Omega ds \cos\theta}{r^2} = \frac{\mu_0}{4\pi} \Omega d\omega,$$

where $d\omega =$ solid angle subtended by ds at P.

Fig. 5.15

Therefore, the potential at P due to whole shell,

$$\phi = \frac{\mu_0}{4\pi} \int \Omega d\omega = \frac{\mu_0}{4\pi} \Omega\omega, \tag{5.26}$$

where ω is the solid angle subtended by the contour of the shell at P. ϕ is positive if the point P lies on the positive pole side and it is negative if the point P lies on the negative pole side. From Eq. (5.26) we find that the potential at an external point will depend on the periphery of the shell. So all shells having same strength and same contour line will give rise to equal potential at the point under consideration.

5.17 Intensity of Magnetic Field on the Axis of a Flat Circular Shell of Uniform Strength

Suppose ABC be a uniform circular shell (Fig. 5.16) of uniform strength. Let $ADEC$ be an annular strip of the shell. The area of the strip $= 2\pi y \cdot ds = 2\pi r \sin\theta r d\theta$.

Therefore, area of the shell $= \displaystyle\int_0^\theta 2\pi r^2 \sin\theta d\theta = 2\pi r^2(1 - \cos\theta)$.

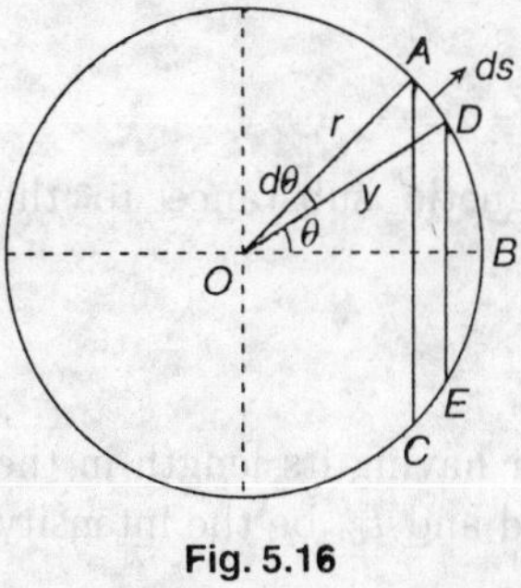

Now the solid angle subtended on the axis of the shell is

$$\omega = 2\pi(1 - \cos\theta).$$

So the potential at the point O,

$$\phi = \frac{\mu_0}{4\pi} \Omega\omega, \quad \text{where } \Omega \text{ is the strength of the shell}$$

$$= \frac{\mu_0}{4\pi} 2\pi\Omega(1 - \cos\theta)$$

$$= \frac{\mu_0\Omega}{2}(1 - \cos\theta).$$

Fig. 5.16

Now, $\cos\theta = \dfrac{x}{(a^2 + x^2)^{\frac{1}{2}}}$ [from Fig. 5.17]

$\therefore \qquad \phi = \dfrac{\mu_0}{2}\Omega \left[1 - \dfrac{x}{(a^2 + x^2)^{\frac{1}{2}}} \right].$ \qquad (5.27)

Therefore, intensity of field at O,

$$F = -\frac{d\phi}{dx}$$

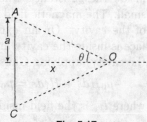

Fig. 5.17

$$= \frac{\mu_0 \Omega}{2} \left[-x \cdot \frac{1}{2} \cdot \frac{2x}{(a^2 + x^2)^{\frac{3}{2}}} + \frac{1}{(a^2 + x^2)^{\frac{1}{2}}} \right] = \frac{\mu_0 \Omega}{2} \frac{-x^2 + a^2 + x^2}{(a^2 + x^2)^{\frac{3}{2}}}$$

$$= \frac{\mu_0}{2} \frac{\Omega a^2}{(a^2 + x^2)^{\frac{3}{2}}}. \tag{5.28}$$

Eq. (5.28) will give the expression for intensity of magnetic field on the axis of a flat circular shell of uniform strength.

5.18 Magnetic Induction—Permeability—Susceptibility

The phenomenon of transforming an unmagnetized magnetic substance into a magnet by an external magnetic field or another magnet itself is known as magnetic induction. When magnetic substance is placed in a magnetic field, then two sets of lines of force may be taken into consideration, (i) due to magnetizing field and (ii) due to magnetization of the substance.

Suppose a cylindrical bar having cross-sectional area S is placed in a magnetic field H. In case of non-magnetic substance the lines of force crossing the cylinder will be SH. But in case of magnetic substance, the substance itself will be magnetized

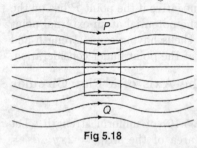

Fig 5.18

by induction. So in addition to original lines, a certain number of lines of force due to magnetization of the substance will enter into the cylinder (Fig. 5.18). The lines of force are more concentrated inside the cylinder. The degree to which the lines can penetrate into a magnetic substance is called *permeability*. The permeability of the substance will depend on its nature.

The total lines of force crossing normally to the surface is called *magnetic flux*. Magnetic flux per unit area is called magnetic induction B.

The ratio of magnetic induction B produced in a magnetic substance to the magnetising field H is called *permeability* of the medium.

$$\therefore \quad \mu = \frac{B}{H}$$

The ratio of intensity of magnetization of a magnetic substance to the magnetizing field is called *susceptibility* of the medium.

$$\therefore \quad \chi = \frac{I_m}{H}.$$

Let us take a magnetic substance in the form of a bar having its length in the direction of magnetization. Let H be the magnetizing field and I_m be the intensity of magnetization. Now consider a cylindrical cavity inside the substance whose length dl is extremely small. The magnetic field is normal to the plane face of the cavity. On an extremely small area ds (one face is inside the cavity and the other face is outside the cavity) applying Gauss's theorem we get

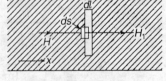

Fig. 5.19

$$-\mu_0 H ds + H_1 ds = \mu_0 I_m ds,$$

where H_1 is the field inside the cavity and is supposed to be uniform.

$$\therefore \quad H_1 ds = \mu_0 [H ds + I_m ds]. \tag{5.29}$$

The lines of force per unit area inside a magnetic substance is known as magnetic induction B. Hence H_1 can be identified as B. Here the contribution from the sides of the cavity is zero because magnetic field H is along the length of the cavity.

Therefore, Eq. (5.29) becomes

$$B = \mu_0(H + I_m).$$

Now we know that $B = \mu H$ and $I_m = \chi H$. Substituting the value of B and I_m in the above expression we get

$$\mu H = \mu_0(H + I_m) = \mu_0(H + \chi H)$$

$$= \mu_0 H(1 + \chi) \tag{5.30}$$

$$\therefore \quad \mu = \mu_0(1 + \chi).$$

Eq. (5.30) gives the relation between permeability and susceptibility of a substance.

5.19 Gauss's Theorem in Magnetism

This theorem states that the total normal magnetic induction over a closed surface is equal to μ_0 times the total magnetism inside the surface.

Suppose S is a closed surface (Fig. 5.20) of a medium of permeability μ. AB is an elementary area ds on the surface at a distance r from the point O, where an N-pole of strength m is placed. Let H be the intensity of magnetic field at P making in angle θ with the normal of the surface ds at P.

Therefore, normal induction over ds

$$= H\cos\theta ds$$

$$= \frac{\mu_0}{4\pi} \cdot \frac{m}{r^2} \cdot r^2 \frac{ds\cos\theta}{r^2}$$

$$= \frac{\mu_0}{4\pi} \cdot md\omega.$$

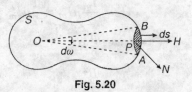

Fig. 5.20

where $d\omega$ is the solid angle subtended at O by ds and m is the pole strength of N-pole and $H = \frac{\mu_0}{4\pi}\frac{m}{r^2}$.

Therefore, total normal induction over the surface S

$$= \int \frac{\mu_0}{4\pi} md\omega = \frac{\mu_0}{4\pi}m \int d\omega = \frac{\mu_0}{4\pi}m \cdot 4\pi$$

[solid angle subtended at O by the closed surface is 4π].

$$= \mu_0 m \tag{5.31}$$

If the pole lies outside the closed surface, total normal induction over the surface is zero because the flux entering the closed surface and the outgoing flux are equal.

5.20 Applications of Gauss's Theorem

(i) Intensity of magnetic field due to a plane polar sheet : Suppose I_m be the intensity of magnetization (Fig. 5.21) of a plane polar sheet AB. We have to calculate the intensity of the field at P due to this sheet. Consider a rectangular box PQ having end face area to be unity cuts the plane sheet at R also in unit area and distance PR = distance RQ.

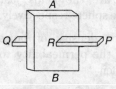

Fig. 5.21

According to Gauss's theorem total normal induction on both sides of the sheet passing out of R is μI_m. Since the magnetic field is normal to the sheet, induction passing through unit area at $P =$ induction passing through unit area at Q. So the induction at $P = \mu I_m$.

Therefore, intensity of magnetic field at $P = \mu I_m / \mu = I_m$.   (5.32)

(ii) Strength of magnetic field at a point between two poles : Suppose N and S are two poles, each having intensity of magnetization I_m (Fig. 5.22). The poles are placed at a very close distance. Consider a point P between N- and S-poles and let the medium N and S have a permeability μ.

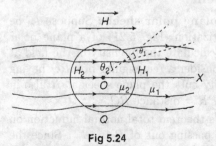

Fig. 5.22

Now the strength of magnetizing field at P due to N-pole $= I_m$ along NP and the strength of magnetizing field at P due to S-pole $= I_m$ along PS.

Therefore, total field strength $= 2I_m$ along NP.

(iii) Force between two opposite poles very close to each other : The field strength at a point very close to a plane pole is I_m.

$\therefore \quad H = I_m$.   (5.33)

Now, suppose N and S are two parallel pole faces (Fig. 5.23) having pole strength I_m per unit area. The poles on S are in the field of the magnetism of N. So the field in between is the sum of the equal contributions coming from induced magnetism on N and S. So the field on S due to N-pole will be $\frac{I_m}{2}$.

Therefore, the force per unit area on S will be

$$F = \frac{I_m}{2}\mu I_m = \frac{1}{2}\mu I_m^2 = \frac{1}{2}\mu H^2 \quad \text{[using Eq. (5.33)]}$$

$$= \frac{\mu}{2}H^2$$

$$= \frac{B^2}{2\mu}.$$ (5.34)

Fig. 5.23

Again, if N-pole is displaced through a distance dx, then the work done per unit area,

$$dW = F dx = \frac{\mu H^2}{2}dx.$$

Therefore, energy density or energy of the field per unit volume $= \frac{\mu H^2}{2}$.   (5.35)

5.21   A Magnetic Sphere in a Homogeneous Field

We consider a magnetic sphere placed in a uniform field H and it is directed along X-direction. Before the introduction of magnetic sphere the field was H. But when the sphere of permeability μ_2 is placed in a medium (Fig. 5.24) having permeability μ_1, the following boundary conditions have to be satisfied :

(i) $\mu_1 H_1 \cos\theta_1 = \mu_2 H_2 \cos\theta_2$,   (5.36)

where H_1 and H_2 are the fields just outside and inside the sphere respectively.

(ii) If σ be the surface density of poles produced, assuming the permeability to be μ_1 everywhere, then

$$\mu_1 H_1 \cos\theta_1 - \mu_1 H_2 \cos\theta_2 = \mu_1 \sigma. \quad (5.37)$$

Fig 5.24

From Eqs. (5.36) and (5.37), we get

$$\mu_2 H_2 \cos\theta_2 - \mu_1 H_2 \cos\theta_2 = \mu_1 \sigma$$

or, $\quad \sigma = \dfrac{(\mu_2 - \mu_1) H_2 \cos\theta_2}{\mu_1}.$ \hfill (5.38)

The field outside the sphere will be H plus that due to the surface density σ.

Now we have to calculate the surface density σ. Let us now assume that the sphere is demagnetized before applying the field H. This is explained by the method adopted by Poisson who assumed that two spheres having volume densities of poles ρ and $-\rho$ respectively remain in coincident position. After the application of field H, the centres of the two spheres will be relatively displaced. Let the distance between the spheres is OO' (Fig. 5.25). Consider a cylinder with end faces (on the surface of each

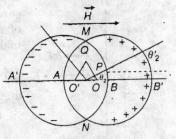

Fig. 5.25

sphere) having area ds. The volume of the cylinder will be $ds \times OO' \cos\theta_2$ (Fig. 5.26).

So the density of poles per unit area at $P = \rho \times O'O \cos\theta_2.$ \hfill (5.39)

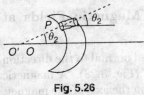

Fig. 5.26

Now the field at an internal point Q due to the positive charge will be

$$F_1 = \frac{\frac{\mu_1}{4\pi} \cdot \frac{4\pi}{3} OQ^3 \cdot \rho}{OQ^2}$$

$$= \frac{\mu_1}{3}\rho \cdot OQ. \hfill (5.40)$$

Again, the field at an internal point Q due to the negative charge will be

$$F_2 = \frac{\mu_1 \rho}{3}\overrightarrow{QO'} \hfill (5.41)$$

So the resultant field at Q,

$$F = \frac{\mu_1 \rho}{3}(\overrightarrow{OQ} + \overrightarrow{QO'}) = \frac{\mu_1 \rho}{3}\overrightarrow{OO'}. \hfill (5.42)$$

So the field inside the sphere at all points is uniform and parallel but opposite to the original field H.

The surface density given by the Eqs. (5.38) and (5.39) must be identical.

$$\therefore \quad \rho OO' \cos\theta_2 = \frac{(\mu_2 - \mu_1) H_2 \cos\theta_2}{\mu_1}$$

or, $\quad \rho OO' = \dfrac{(\mu_2 - \mu_1)}{\mu_1} H_2.$ \hfill (5.43)

Substituting the value of $\rho OO'$ in Eq. (5.43) we get

$$F = \frac{(\mu_2 - \mu_1)}{3} H_2. \hfill (5.44)$$

Therefore, the field inside the sphere is

$$H_2 = H - F = H - \frac{(\mu_2 - \mu_1)}{3} H_2.$$

$$\therefore \quad H_2 = \frac{3\mu_1}{\mu_2 + 2\mu_1} H. \hfill (5.45)$$

The field outside the sphere will be the resultant of H and that due to dipoles placed at O and O' respectively.

5.22 Two Magnetic Fields Perpendicular to Each Other

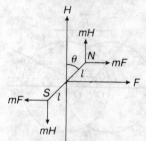

Fig. 5.27

Suppose a magnetic needle NS (Fig. 5.27) is acted upon by two cross magnetic fields; one being due to horizontal component of the earth's magnetic field H and other being due to field F of another magnet. The needle will be in equilibrium making an angle θ with the direction of H.

The moment of the couple due to the force $mF = mF \times 2l \cos\theta = 2mlF \cos\theta$ and the moment of the couple due to the force $mH = mH \times 2l \sin\theta = 2mlH \sin\theta$.

At equilibrium these two couples are equal. Therefore,

$$2mlF \cos\theta = 2mlH \sin\theta$$

$$\therefore \quad F = H \tan\theta. \tag{5.46}$$

From Eq. (5.46) we can say that the tangent of the angle of deflection is equal to the ratio of F and H. This is known as tangent law.

5.23 Action of a Magnetic Needle in Two Magnetic Fields at Right Angles

(a) tan-A position of Gauss : A bar magnet NS is placed normal to the direction of the horizontal component of the earth's magnetic field (Fig. 5.28). A magnetic needle $N'S'$ is suspended in such a way that its centre lies on the axis of the magnet. The couples acting on the needle are shown in the figure. The needle will be in equilibrium position making an angle θ with H and for such a position the two couples will balance each other.

The moment of the couple due to the force mH (known as restoring couple) $= 2mlH \sin\theta$ and the moment of the couple due to the force $mF = 2mlF \cos\theta$.

At equilibrium,

$$2mlH \sin\theta = 2mlF \cos\theta$$

or, $F = H \tan\theta$.

But $F = \dfrac{2Md}{(d^2 - l^2)^2}$.

$\therefore \quad \dfrac{2Md}{(d^2 - l^2)^2} = H \tan\theta$

or, $\dfrac{M}{H} = \dfrac{(d^2 - l^2)^2}{2d} \tan\theta$.

If $l \ll d$, then $\dfrac{M}{H} = \dfrac{d^3}{2} \tan\theta$.

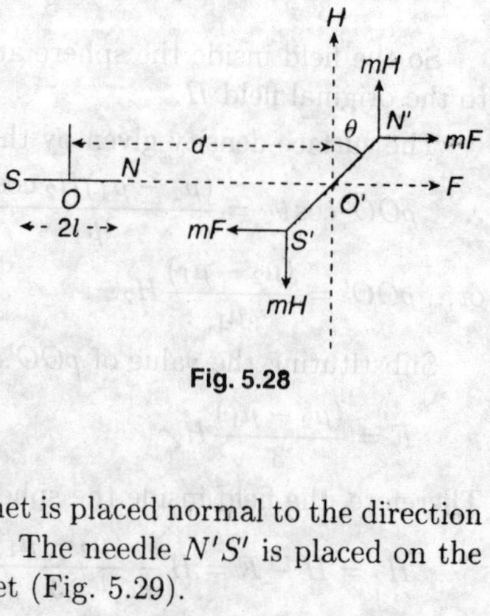

Fig. 5.28

(b) tan-B position of Gauss : A bar magnet is placed normal to the direction of the horizontal component of the earth's field. The needle $N'S'$ is placed on the broadside-on position with respect to the magnet (Fig. 5.29).

The moment of the couple due to the force mH (restoring couple) $= 2mlH \sin\theta$ and the moment of the couple due to the force mF (deflecting couple) $= 2mlF \cos\theta$.

At equilibrium,

$$2mlH\sin\theta = 2mlF\cos\theta.$$

$\therefore \quad H\sin\theta = F\cos\theta.$

$\therefore \quad F = H\tan\theta.$

But $F = \dfrac{M}{(d^2+l^2)^{\frac{3}{2}}}.$

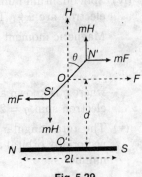

Fig. 5.29

$\therefore \quad \dfrac{M}{(d^2+l^2)^{\frac{3}{2}}} = H\tan\theta$

or, $\quad \dfrac{M}{H} = (d^2+l^2)^{\frac{3}{2}}\tan\theta.$

If $l \ll d$, then $\dfrac{M}{H} = d^3\tan\theta.$

5.24   Theories of Magnetism

The magnetic properties of solids are classified as follows :

(a) diamagnetism, (b) paramagnetism, (c) ferromagnetism, antiferromagnetism.

Suppose a substance is placed in a magnetic field H. If the magnetic moment per unit volume is M, then M is called the *magnetization*. For isotropic substances, M and H are parallel and related by

$$M = \chi H, \tag{5.47}$$

where χ is called the *magnetic susceptibility*. In diamagnetic substance the induced moment produces negative susceptibility. In paramagnetic substances the susceptibility is positive and it depends on temperature.

The magnetic induction B can be written as

$$B = \mu_0(H + M) = \mu H, \tag{5.48}$$

where μ is known as *permeability* of the substance. For diamagnetic and paramagnetic substances the permeability is a constant but for ferromagnetic substance the relation between B and H is much complicated.

From Eqs. (5.47) and (5.48) we find that

$$\mu = \mu_0(1 + \chi). \tag{5.49}$$

This relation is the analogue of the expression for dielectric constant.

5.25   Quantum Numbers

(i) Principal quantum number (n) will determine the orbital energy. The principal quantum number has only integer values.

$n = 1, 2, 3, 4, \ldots$ which represents the $K, L, M, N, \ldots$ shells respectively.

(ii) Angular momentum quantum number (l) determines the angular momentum of the orbit and it takes the set of values $l = 0, 1, 2, \ldots, (n-1)$ which represent respectively $s, p, d, \ldots, f$ states of the electron.

Orbital angular momentum $= \dfrac{n}{2\pi}[l(l+1)]^{1/2}.$

(iii) Magnetic quantum number (m_l) determine the possible components of angular momentum along the direction of external field. It takes the values

$$m_l = l, (l-1), \ldots, 0, \ldots, -l$$

(iv) Spin quantum number (S) : The possible angular momentum components of electron are $\pm\frac{\hbar}{2}$. This has led to the spin quantum number $S = \pm\frac{1}{2}$.

Magnetic moment of the spin along the external field is given by

$$\mu_s = g\left(\frac{e}{2me}\right)\frac{\hbar}{2},$$

where g is known as spectroscopic splitting factor or gyromagnetic ratio. For electron spin $g = 2.0023$.

(v) The total angular momentum quantum number j is obtained by adding vectorially orbital angular momentum quantum number l and spin quantum number s.

$$\therefore \quad j = l \pm s.$$

If an atom has a number of electrons, the l vectors are combined to form a resultant L and the spin vectors are combined to form a resultant S. This coupling is known as *Russell-Saunders coupling*. L and S combine to give total angular momentum J. For such an atom the gyromagnetic ratio,

$$g = 1 + \frac{J(J+1) + S(S+1) - L(L+1)}{2J(J+1)}. \tag{5.50}$$

To find out the magnetic moment of the dipole for a given atom the above coupling must be according to Pauli principle and Hund's rule. According to physicist Wolfgang Pauli only one electron can occupy a state defined by the quantum numbers n, l, m and s. Filled electron shell does not contribute to the magnetic moment of the atom. Incomplete electron shell will contribute to the magnetic moment of the atom. Hund's rule states that for ground state of an atom,

(a) spins add to give maximum possible value for S;

(b) orbital momenta will combine to give maximum value for L consistent with (a);

(c) for an incomplete filled shell;

  $J = L - S$ for a shell less than half occupied,

  $J = L + S$ for a shell more than half occupied.

The orbital motion and spin of the electrons will contribute to the magnetic moment of the atoms. Another contribution results from nuclear spin.

5.26 Langevin's Theory of Diamagnetism

The basic principle of diamagnetic behaviour may be explained readily with the help of electron theory.

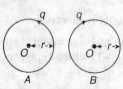

Fig. 5.30

Suppose an electron having mass m and charge e is rotating in a circular orbit of radius r with an angular velocity ω. Then $F = m\omega^2 r$, where F is the force of attraction towards the centre. The moving charge e will be equivalent to a circular current $i = \frac{\omega e}{2\pi}$ and from Ampere's law the magnetic moment associated with it will be $M = \pi r \cdot i = \frac{\omega e r^r}{2}$ and directed normal to the plane of the Fig. 5.30.

Now, let a magnetic field H is applied perpendicular to the plane. The force on the electron will be $Hev = He\omega r$ towards the centre. Therefore, the force towards the centre will be $F + He\omega r$. At the same time, suppose, the angular velocity is increased by $d\omega$. Therefore,

$$F + He\omega r = m\omega^2 r + 2m\omega r d\omega$$

or, $2m\omega r d\omega = He\omega r$

$$\therefore \quad d\omega = \frac{He}{2m}.$$

The corresponding magnetic moment of the shell will be

$$M + dM = \frac{r^2 e}{2}(\omega + d\omega)$$

$$\therefore \quad dM = \frac{r^2 e}{2}d\omega = \frac{r^2 e}{2} \cdot \frac{He}{2m}$$

$$= \frac{He^2 r^2}{4m}. \tag{5.51}$$

The magnetic moment due to the field is opposite to the direction of the field and hence equal to

$$-\frac{He^2 r^2}{4m}.$$

If the angle between the normal on the orbit and the direction of H be θ, then

$$dM = -\frac{e^2 r^2}{4m} H \cos\theta. \tag{5.52}$$

Therefore, magnetic moment opposite to the direction of the field will be

$$\frac{e^2 r^2}{4m} H \cos^2\theta.$$

Therefore, intensity of magnetization $= \dfrac{e^2 H}{4m} \sum r^2 \cos^2\theta.$

Therefore, susceptibility, $\chi = -\dfrac{e^2}{4m} \sum r^2 \cos^2\theta.$ \hfill (5.53)

The diamagnetic susceptibility is negative and independent of temperature.

Larmor Precession

The precession of an orbit of an electron under the influence of an applied magnetic field is called Larmor precession.

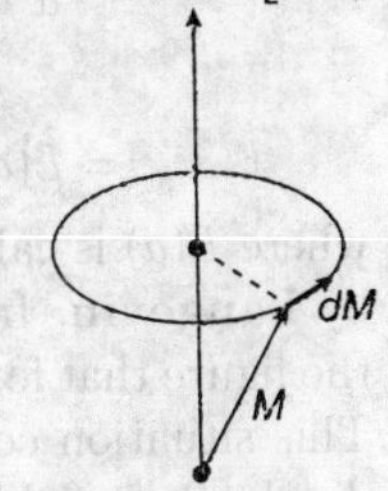

With reference to the Fig. 5.31 we take any arbitrary direction or the angular momenta M relative to the magnetic field H. The magnetic dipole moment will be

$$m_d = -\left(\frac{e}{2mc}\right) M. \tag{5.54}$$

Hence the torque on the dipole

$$\tau = m_d \times H = -\left(\frac{e}{2mc}\right) M \times H \tag{5.55}$$

Fig. 5.31

The Eq. (5.55) represents the equation of motion of M having angular velocity ω_L, precessing about H, where

$$\omega_L = \left(\frac{e}{2mc}\right) H. \tag{5.56}$$

ω_L is known as *Larmor frequency*.

Now we know that $\left(\frac{e}{2me}\right) = 1.40 \times 10^6/\text{second/gauss}$. But even for a field having intensity 10^6 gauss, Larmor frequency ω_L is much smaller than the angular frequency of the electron. The deviation is due to the assumption that M is independent of H. In other words, in the above expression we have assumed that the orbit remains unchanged under the influence of the magnetic field.

5.27 Paramagnetic Susceptibility

(a) The Classical Theory : Consider a medium having N magnetic dipole per unit volume. Here we assume that the interaction between the dipoles is weak so that each dipole is subjected to a magnetic field H and the dipoles are assumed to be rotating freely.

In the absence of the magnetic field H the orientation of the dipoles are random.

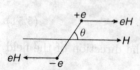

Fig. 5.32

As a result the medium has no resultant dipole moment. The application of the field H will produce a torque on each dipole and the dipole wants to rotate in the direction of the field as shown in Fig. 5.32.

In this problem we have taken the potential energy to be zero for a dipole making an angle $\frac{\pi}{2}$ with the field H. Hence potential energy for a dipole making an angle θ with H will be $-m_d H \cos\theta$.

Therefore, according to statistical mechanics the probability for a dipole making an angle between θ and $\theta + d\theta$ with H is proportional to

$$2\pi \sin\theta d\theta e^{(\mu H \cos\theta/KT)}.$$

The average component of dipole moment along the field will be

$$m_d\langle\cos\theta\rangle = \frac{\displaystyle\int_0^\pi m_d \cos\theta 2\pi \sin\theta d\theta e^{(\mu H \cos\theta/KT)}}{\displaystyle\int_0^\pi 2\pi \sin\theta d\theta e^{(\mu H \cos\theta/KT)}}.$$

Let us now put $\dfrac{\mu H \cos\theta}{KT} = x$ and $\dfrac{\mu H}{KT} = a$.

$$\therefore \quad \langle\cos\theta\rangle = \frac{1}{a}\frac{\displaystyle\int_{-a}^a x e^x dx}{\displaystyle\int_{-a}^a e^x dx} = \frac{e^a + e^{-a}}{e^a - e^{-a}} - \frac{1}{a}$$

$$= L(a). \tag{5.57}$$

where $L(a)$ is called the **Langevin** function. The expression (5.57) was formulated by **Langevin**. In Fig. 5.33 we have plotted $L(a)$ against a. One can conclude from the figure that for large value of a the function $L(a)$ approaches to a saturated value. This situation correspond to the complete alignment of the dipole along field direction.

When the intensity of field and the temperature are not too high we take the approximation

$$a \ll 1 \quad \text{or,} \quad \frac{\mu H}{KT} \ll 1,$$

i.e., $\mu H \ll KT$. In this case $L(a) = \dfrac{a}{3}$.

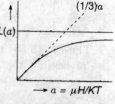

Fig. 5.33

Therefore, $m_d\langle\cos\theta\rangle = \dfrac{md^2}{3KT}H$.

Since the medium contains N dipole per unit volume, we have

$$M = N\frac{md^2 H}{3KT}.$$

$$\therefore \quad \chi = \frac{Nmd^2}{3KT}. \tag{5.58}$$

The susceptibility of paramagnetic substance depends on temperature. At room temperature the expression (5.58) is satisfied except for a very low temperature.

From the expression (5.58) we find that

$$\chi = \frac{\text{const.}}{T},$$

i.e., it is inversely proportional to absolute temperature T. This relation is also known as Curie's law and the constant is called Curie's constant.

(b) **Quantum Theory :** Consider a medium having N atoms per unit volume subjected to an external field of intensity H. According to quantum theory the permanent magnetic moment of an atom is restricted to a finite set of orientations. Suppose the total angular momentum quantum number of each atom is J. Corresponding possible components of the magnetic moment will be $M_J g\mu_B$, where M_J is the magnetic quantum number and μ_B is the Bohr magneton. Hence, the potential energy of a dipole along the applied field H will be

$$-M_J g\mu_B H.$$

Therefore, the magnetization, $M = N\dfrac{\displaystyle\sum_{-J}^{J} M_J g\mu_B \exp\left(\dfrac{M_J g\mu_B H}{KT}\right)}{\displaystyle\sum_{-J}^{J} \exp\left(\dfrac{M_J g\mu_B H}{KT}\right)},$ \hfill (5.59)

where M_J have values $+J, (J-1), \ldots, -(J-1), -J$.

The expression (5.59) is obtained from Maxwell-Boltzmann statics.

(a) Suppose $\dfrac{M_J g\mu_B H}{KT} \ll 1$.

Under this condition the exponential term of the expression (5.59) reduces to $(1 + M_J g\mu_B H/KT)$. Again, $\sum M_J g\mu_B = 0$, because

$$\sum_{-J}^{J} M_J = J + (J+1) + \ldots - (J-1) - J = 0$$

and $\displaystyle\sum_{-J}^{+J} M_J^2 = J^2 + (J-1)^2 + \ldots \{-(J-1)\}^2 + (-J)^2 = \dfrac{2J(J+1)(2J+1)}{6}.$

Therefore, the expression (5.59) comes out to be

$$M = \frac{Ng^2\mu_B^2 J(J+1)(2J+1)}{3KT(2J+1)}H$$

$$= \frac{NJ(J+1)g^2\mu_B^2}{3KT}H. \tag{5.60}$$

The total magnetic moment μ_J corresponding to the total angular momentum quantum number J will be

$$\mu_J = g\sqrt{J(J+1)} \cdot \mu_B.$$

$$\therefore \quad \mu_J^2 = J(J+1)g^2\mu_B^2. \tag{5.61}$$

$$\therefore \quad M = \frac{N\mu_J^2 H}{3KT}.$$

Therefore, susceptibility, $\chi = \dfrac{M}{H} = N\dfrac{\mu_J^2}{3KT}. \tag{5.62}$

(b) At low temperatures and strong magnetic field, the condition (a) imposed on the expression (5.59) is not valid. After simplification one gets the following expression for magnetization :

$$M = NgJ\mu_B B_J(x), \tag{5.63}$$

where $B_J(x)$ is the Brillouin function and $x = \dfrac{gJ\mu_B H}{KT}$. Physically one gets saturation at low temperature.

The paramagnetic susceptibility is calculated from Eq. (5.62).

Paramagnetism requires the existence of incompletely filled electronic shell. Thus transition group elements are paramagnetic substances. Out of these, the rare earth group have incomplete $4f$ shell and iron group have incomplete $3d$ shell shows extensive paramagnetic effect.

5.28   Ferromagnetism

In case of ferromagnetic materials the magnetization and magnetic field will exhibit hysteresis. Above a critical temperature θ_f (Curie ferromagnetic temperature) the magnetization is zero. Above the Curie temperature the susceptibility satisfies Curie-Weiss law,

$$\chi = \frac{C}{T-\theta},$$

where C is the Curie constant and θ is the paramagnetic Curie temperature.

This law explains the ferromagnetic property of the solid by assuming :

(i) A macroscopic dimension of ferromagnetic material containing a large number of small regions or domains, each of which are spontaneously magnetized. The amount of magnetization is obtained from the sum of magnetic moments of each domain.

(ii) Within each domain, there exists a molecular field. So the dipoles are in parallel orientation and the specimen is spontaneously magnetized.

Weiss assumed that the molecular field H_m can be given by the relation

$$H_m = H + \gamma M,$$

where H is the intensity of the applied magnetic field, γ is the molecular field (Weiss constant) and M is the magnetization.

Suppose the solid contains N atoms per unit volume, each of which has total angular momentum quantum number J. According to the expression (5.63), the magnetization will be

$$M = Ng\mu_B JB_J(x), \tag{5.64}$$

where $x = g\mu_B HJ/KT$. But here H is replaced by H_m.

$$\therefore \quad x = \frac{g\mu_B J(H + \gamma M)}{KT}. \tag{5.65}$$

In case of spontaneous magnetization, $H = 0$.

$$\therefore \quad x = \frac{g\mu_B J\gamma M}{KT}.$$

So, $M = \dfrac{xKT}{g\mu_B J\gamma}.$ $\tag{5.66}$

Now M must satisfy both the Eqs. (5.64) and (5.66). In Fig. 5.34, M is plotted against χ taking into account both the equations. The value of M at a given temperature will be obtained from the interaction of two curves. For $T \geq \theta_f$ spontaneous magnetization is zero. Only for $T < \theta_f$, spontaneous magnetization occurs.

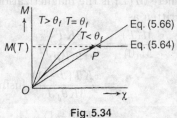

Fig. 5.34

The relation between the ferromagnetic Curie temperature θ_f and Weiss constant γ is obtained in region $x \ll 1$. In this case,

$$B_J(x) \simeq \frac{(J+1)x}{3J}. \tag{5.67}$$

So the tangent of the curve related to Eq. (5.64) will have a slope $Ng\mu_B(J+1)/3$, and the slope of the curve of Eq. (5.66) is $\frac{K\theta_f}{g\mu_B J\gamma}$.

$$\therefore \quad \frac{Ng\mu_B(J+1)}{3} = \frac{K\theta_f}{g\mu_B J\gamma}$$

or, $\dfrac{3K\theta_f}{\gamma} = Ng^2\mu_B^2 J(J+1) = N\mu_J^2.$ $\tag{5.68}$

From the above equation one gets the result that θ_f is proportional to the Weiss constant γ.

For $T > \theta_f$, the magnetization occurs only after the application of applied magnetic field. For low fields we may use the approximation of Eq. (5.67).

$$\therefore \quad M = \frac{Ng\mu_B(J+1)x}{3} = \frac{Ng\mu_B(J+1)g\mu_B(H+\gamma M)J}{3KT}$$

$$= \frac{Ng^2\mu_B^2 J(J+1)(H+\gamma M)}{3KT}$$

or, $M[3KT - Ng^2\mu_B^2 J(J+1)\gamma] = Ng^2\mu_B^2 J(J+1)H$

or, $M[3KT - N\mu_J^2\gamma] = N\mu_J^2 H$

or, $\dfrac{M}{H} = \dfrac{N\mu_J^2}{3KT - N\mu_J^2\gamma} = \dfrac{N\mu_J^2/3K}{T - \frac{\gamma N\mu_J^2}{3K}}$

$$= \frac{C}{T - \theta}, \tag{5.69}$$

where $C = \dfrac{N\mu_J^2}{3K}$ and $\theta = \dfrac{\gamma N\mu_J^2}{3K}.$

Eq. (5.69) is the well-known Curie-Weiss law.

Now maximum value of spontaneous magnetization is $Ng\mu_B J$ because for $x \to \infty$, $B_J(x) \to 1$. Again, from Fig. 5.34, we find that maximum magnetization occurs for $T = 0$.

So we write, $M(0) = Ng\mu_B J$.

Eq. (5.64) now becomes

$$M(T) = M(0)B_J(x)$$

or, $\quad \dfrac{M(T)}{M(0)} = B_J(x).$ \hfill (5.70)

where $M(T)$ is the magnetization at the temperature T. Again, Eq. (5.64) may be written as

$$\frac{M(T)}{M(0)} = \frac{xKT}{\gamma Ng^2\mu_B^2 J^2}$$

$$= \frac{xKT(J+1)}{3K\theta_f J} \text{ [using Eq. (5.68)]}$$

$$= \frac{xT(J+1)}{3\theta_f J}.$$ \hfill (5.71)

From the plotting of $\frac{M(T)}{M(0)}$ against $\left(\frac{T}{\theta_f}\right)$ for different values of J (Fig. 5.35), it is found that the curve for $J = \frac{1}{2}$ fits the experimental data best which in turn indicates that the magnetization is due to the spin of the electrons.

From saturation of magnetization we can calculate the effective number of Bohr magnetons per atom. It is found that the effective number is non-integral. This discrepancy is due to the fact that the atomic levels of a solid are broadened into bands. So the simple atomic structure is not valid.

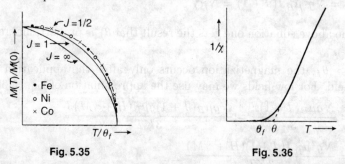

Fig. 5.35   Fig. 5.36

According to Curie-Weiss law [Eq. (5.69)], a plot of $\frac{1}{\chi}$ against T will be a straight line (Fig. 5.36) and this line cuts the T-axis at $T = \theta$. The experiment is carried out by Sucksmith and Pearce for Fe, Co and Ni. The result shows that the law is valid except in region about Curie point.

However, the molecular field used by Weiss satisfies the experimental result satisfactorily.

5.29   Domain Theory to Explain Ferromagnetism

We know that ferromagnetic substances can remain in a non-magnetized state and a weak magnetic field can produce saturated magnetization of the ferromagnetic substance. In order to explain it Weiss gave the domain hypothesis. A macroscopic dimension of the specimen contains a large number of domains, each of which are spontaneously magnetized. The amount of magnetization will depend on temperature. The total magnetization is the sum of the domain vector. So the magnetization is zero in case of Fig. 5.37(a). Magnetization is produced due to motion of the domain wall [Fig. 5.37(b)] or due to the rotation of domains [Fig. 5.37(c)].

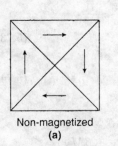
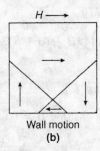
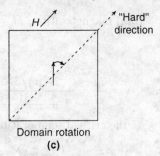

| Non-magnetized | Wall motion | Domain rotation |
| (a) | (b) | (c) |

Fig. 5.37

The magnetization curve given in Fig. 5.38 represents the processes in different regions. The portion of the curve OP is obtained due to reversible wall displacement of the domains. PQ is due to irreversible wall displacement of the domains and the portion QR is obtained from the rotation of the domain.

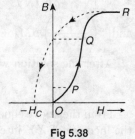

Fig 5.38

The number of domains and their structure will depend on the shape and size of the specimen we have taken. For a given domain structure, the size of each domain may be calculated from the principle of minimum energy. The volume of domains usually lies between 10^{-2} to 10^{-6} cm^3.

5.30   Antiferromagnetism

The susceptibility of an antiferromagnetic substance shows maxima when χ is plotted against the temperature T (Fig. 5.39). This can be explained by two sublattice model. According to this model two types of

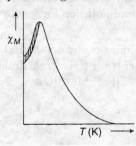

Fig. 5.39

atoms, say X and Y, are distributed over two interlocking lattices. If X atoms lie at the corner of a cubic lattice, the Y atoms will lie at the centre of these cubes. The interaction between two types of atoms is such that the X spin is antiparallel to Y spin. At low temperature the interaction is more pronounced and as the temperature increases, the effect will be less pronounced and the susceptibility increases. At a critical temperature, known as Neel temperature, the susceptibility is maximum. As the temperature increases further, all the spins become free and the substance becomes paramagnetic. The susceptibility now decreases as shown in Fig. 5.39.

Let in the lattice there be XY interaction, XX interaction and YY interaction. Again, suppose the molecular fields at X and Y site are given by

$$\left. \begin{array}{l} H_{mX} = H - \alpha M_X - \beta M_Y \\ H_{mY} = H - \beta M_X - \alpha M_Y \end{array} \right\}, \tag{5.72}$$

where M_X and M_Y are respectively the magnetization of X and Y lattices, and α and β are corresponding Weiss constants.

When the temperature is above the critical temperature, the magnetizations of A and B lattice are given by

$$M_X = \frac{N\mu_J^2}{3KT} H_{mX}, \quad M_Y = \frac{N\mu_J^2}{3KT} H_{mY}.$$

Total magnetization, $M = M_X + M_Y$

$$= \left(\frac{N\mu_J^2}{3KT}\right) [2H - (\alpha + \beta)M]. \tag{5.73}$$

$$\therefore \quad \chi = \frac{M}{H} = \frac{2N\mu_J^2/3K}{T + \frac{N\mu_J^2(\alpha+\beta)}{3K}} = \frac{C}{T + \theta}. \tag{5.74}$$

At the critical temperature T_N, we assume $H = 0$.

$$\therefore \quad M_X = -\frac{N\mu_J^2}{3KT_N}(\alpha M_X + \beta M_Y), \quad M_Y = -\frac{N\mu_J^2}{3KT_N}(\alpha M_Y + \beta M_X)$$

or, $$\left[\left(1 + \frac{N\mu_J^2}{3KT_N}\right)\alpha\right] M_a + \left(\frac{N\mu_J^2}{3KT_N}\right)\beta M_b = 0$$

and $$\left(\frac{N\mu_J^2}{3KT_N}\right)\beta M_a + \left[\left(1 + \frac{N\mu_J^2}{3KT_N}\right)\alpha\right] M_b = 0.$$

After the solution we have

$$T_N = \frac{C(\beta - \alpha)}{2}. \tag{5.75}$$

From the above equation one can conclude that Neel temperature increases with the increase of XY interaction (β).

5.31   Structure of Ferrites

The distributions of metal ions of these materials are given below :

(a) In the normal structure, the 8 divalent metal ions occupy tetrahedral; the 16 trivalent iron ions occupy octahedral positions. The usual notation for ferrite is $Me^{2+}(Fe_2^{3+})O_4$.

(b) In the inverse structure of a ferrite, the divalent Me^{2+} ions occupy octahedral sites Q and the Fe^{2+} ions are distributed in equal numbers over the tetrahedral and octahedral sites. The usual notation for this is $Fe^{3+}[Fe^{3+}Me^{2+}]Q_4$.

(c) The structure in general may be written as

$$Fe_x^{3+}Me_{1-x}^{2+}[Fe_{2-x}^{3+}Me_x^{2+}]O_4.$$

5.32   Differences between Ferro-, Para- and Diamagnets

Ferromagnets	Paramagnets	Diamagnets
1. Ferromagnets are solid and have definite crystalline structure.	Paramagnets may be solid, liquid or gas.	Diamagnets may also be solid, liquid or gas.
2. Ferromagnetic bar sets itself parallel to the direction of the magnetic field.	Paramagnetic bar also sets itself parallel to the direction of magnetic field.	Diamagnetic bar sets itself normal to the direction of magnetic field.

Contd.

Ferromagnets	Paramagnets	Diamagnets
3. Susceptibility is positive and greater than unity.	Susceptibility is less than unity and positive.	Susceptibility is very small and negative.
4. Permeability is greater than unity.	Permeability is slightly greater than unity.	Permeability is less than unity.
5. Ferromagnets exhibit hysteresis	They exhibit no hysteresis.	No hysteresis is exhibited.
6. Ferromagnets have definite Curie temperature. Above this temperature they become paramagnet.	No Curie point.	No Curie point.
7. Variation of B and I with H is not linear.	Variation of B and I with H is linear. At low temperature and high field, saturation is obtained.	Variation of B and I with H is linear.

Examples

1. A magnet 10 cm long with poles of unit strength is freely suspended in a horizontal uniform field of intensity 0.18 unit. Find the moment of the couple tending to restore the magnet to its original position of rest when it is deflected in a horizontal plane 30° from that position.

   Solution : At equilibrium, moment of the deflecting couple = moment of the restoring couple = $2mlH \sin \theta$.

   Here, $m = 1$ c.g.s. unit, $2l = 10$ cm, $H = 0.18$ unit, $\theta = 30°$.

   ∴ restoring couple $= 1 \times 10 \times 0.18 \times \sin 30° = \textbf{0.9 dyne-cm.}$

2. Two short bar magnets of moments 108 and 192 units are placed along two lines drawn on the table at right angles to each other. Find the intensity of field at the point of intersection of the lines, the centres of the magnets being respectively 30 and 40 cm from the point.

   Solution : The positions of the magnets are shown in Fig. 5.40.

   Intensity at P due to the magnet $N_1 S_1$

   $$= \frac{2Md}{(2d^2 - l^2)^2} = \frac{2M_1}{d^3}, \text{ since } l \text{ is small}$$

   $$= \frac{2 \times 192}{(40)^3} = \frac{3}{500} \text{ dynes along } PQ.$$

   Similarly, intensity at P due to the magnet $N_2 S_2$

   $$= \frac{2M_2}{d^3} = \frac{2 \times 108}{(30)^3}$$

   $$= \frac{1}{125} \text{ dynes along } PS.$$

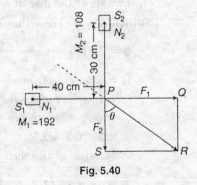

Fig. 5.40

Therefore, resultant intensity at $P = \sqrt{\left(\dfrac{3}{500}\right)^2 + \left(\dfrac{1}{125}\right)^2} = \mathbf{0.01\ dyne.}$

$$\tan\theta = \frac{F_1}{F_2} = \frac{3}{500} \times 125 = \frac{3}{4}.$$

$\therefore \quad \theta = \tan^{-1}\dfrac{3}{4}.$

3. Find the force of attraction or repulsion between two small magnets of moments 10 c.g.s. units and 20 c.g.s. units with their centres 20 cm apart and their axes in the same direction along the same line.

Solution : We know that the force of attraction or repulsion,

$$F = \frac{6M_1 M_2}{d^4} \text{ (approx.)}$$

Here, $M_1 = 10$ c.g.s. unit, $M_2 = 20$ c.g.s. unit and $d = 20$ cm.

$\therefore \qquad F = \dfrac{6 \times 10 \times 20}{20^4} = \mathbf{0.0075\ dynes.}$

4. A small bar magnet is placed at a point O with its axis horizontal and normal to the magnetic meridian. If P is the neutral point, show that the angle between OP and the axis of the magnet is $\tan^{-1}\sqrt{2}$.

Solution : The position of the point P with respect to SN is shown in Fig. 5.41.

We know that the total intensity at $P = \dfrac{M}{r^3}\sqrt{1 + 3\cos^2\theta}$ and $\tan\alpha = \dfrac{1}{2}\tan\theta$.

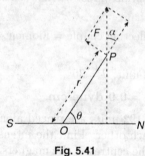

Since P is the neutral point, $F = H$, horizontal component of the earth's magnetic field and H is perpendicular to the magnet NS.

$\therefore \qquad \alpha = 90° - \theta.$

$\therefore \qquad \tan(90 - \theta) = \dfrac{1}{2}\tan\theta$

or, $\quad \tan^2\theta = 2$

$\therefore \qquad \tan\theta = \sqrt{2},$

i.e., $\quad \theta = \tan^{-1}\sqrt{2}$ **(Proved).**

Fig. 5.41

5. A magnetic shell is in the form of a disc of radius 5 cm, pole strength per unit area is 5 units/cm^2 and of thickness 5 mm. Calculate the magnetic potential on the axis of the disc at a distance of 10 cm from the centre.

Solution : We know that the magnetic potential due to a magnetic shell

$$\phi = 2\pi\Omega\left[1 - \frac{x}{(a^2 + x^2)^{1/2}}\right]$$

Ω = strength of the shell

   = intensity of magnetization × thickness

   = pole-strength per unit area × thickness

   = $5 \times 0.5 = 2.5$

a = radius of the shell = 5 cm, $x = 10$ cm

$\therefore \quad \phi = 2\pi \times 2.5\left[1 - \dfrac{10}{\sqrt{25 + 100}}\right] = \mathbf{1.658}$ **c.g.s. unit.**

6. A magnet is suspended horizontally in the magnetic meridian by a vertical wire which remains untwisted. In order to deflect the magnet through 45° from the meridian, the upper end of the wire has to be turned half-round. Show how much the upper end has to be twisted in order to deflect the magnet through 60° from the meridian.

Solution : Two couples will act on the magnet; (a) deflecting couple due to torsion of the wire and (b) restoring couple due to the earth's magnetic field.

Now angle of torsion = 180° − 45°

Moment of the restoring couple = $MH \sin 45°$

∴ $MH \sin 45° \propto (180° - 45°)$.

Again, $MH \sin 60° \propto (\phi - 60°)$, where ϕ is the angle through which the upper end has to be twisted.

∴ $\dfrac{MH \sin 45°}{MH \sin 60°} = \dfrac{180° - 45°}{\phi - 60°}$

or, $\dfrac{1/\sqrt{2}}{\sqrt{3}/2} = \dfrac{135°}{\phi - 60°}$.

∴ $(\phi - 60°) = 135° \times \dfrac{\sqrt{3}}{\sqrt{2}} = 165.36°$

∴ $\phi = (225.36)°$.

7. Two identical magnets having moments M and $2M$ are mounted in a cross position. The system is suspended at the centre with a fibre. Find the direction in which it will set in the earth's magnetic field. Calculate the intensity of the field at a distance d from the centre of the cross on the prolongation of one of the arms.

Solution : The combination of the magnet is shown in Fig. 5.42.

Suppose AB be the magnetic meridian.

Couple on the magnet $N_1 S_1$ having moment $2M = 2MH \sin \theta_1$ and couple on the magnet $N_2 S_2$ having moment $M = MH \sin \theta_2$.

At equilibrium, $2MH \sin \theta_1 = MH \sin \theta_2$

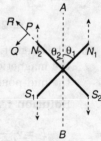

Fig. 5.42

∴ $2 \sin \theta_1 = \sin \theta_2$.

The angle between the magnets is 90°.

∴ $\theta_2 = 90° - \theta_1$.

∴ $\sin \theta_2 = \cos \theta_1$.

∴ $2 \sin \theta_1 = \cos \theta_1$.

or, $\tan \theta_1 = \dfrac{1}{2}$,

∴ $\theta_1 = \tan^{-1} \dfrac{1}{2}$.

Therefore, the system sets with the magnet of moment $2M$ to an angle $\tan^{-1} \frac{1}{2}$ with the meridian.

(a) Suppose the point P lies on axis of $N_2 S_2$. Intensity at P due to $N_2 S_2 = \frac{2M}{d^3}$ along PR and intensity at P due to $N_1 S_1 = \frac{2M}{d^3}$ along PQ.

Therefore, the resultant intensity at $P = \sqrt{\left(\dfrac{2M}{d^3}\right)^2 + \left(\dfrac{2M}{d^3}\right)^2} = \dfrac{2\sqrt{2}M}{d^3}$.

(b) Suppose the point P lies on the axis of $N_1 S_1$.

The intensity at P due to $N_1 S_1 = \frac{4M}{d^3}$ along $N_1 P_1$ and the intensity at P due to $N_2 S_2 = \frac{M}{d^3}$ parallel to $N_2 S_2$.

Therefore, the resultant intensity $= \sqrt{\left(\dfrac{4M}{d^3}\right)^2 + \left(\dfrac{M}{d^3}\right)^2} = \dfrac{\sqrt{17}M}{d^3}$.

8. What is the force of attraction between a point N-pole of strength 0.5×10^{-3} A-m and a point S-pole of strength 0.4×10^{-3} A-m placed in air 10 cm apart?

Solution : Here, $m_1 = 0.5 \times 10^{-3}$ A-m; $m_2 = 0.4 \times 10^{-3}$ A-m; $\mu_0 = 4\pi \times 10^{-7}$; $r = 10$ cm $= 0.1$ m.

$$\therefore \quad F = \frac{0.5 \times 10^{-3} \times 0.4 \times 10^{-3}}{4\pi \times 4\pi \times 10^{-7} \times (0.1)^2} = \mathbf{1.268 \ N}.$$

9. Calculate the magnitude and direction of the magnetic field due to a short bar magnet of magnetic moment 10^{-6} Wb-m at a point 20 cm from its mid-point measured along a line inclined at 45° to its magnetic axis.

Solution : Given that $M = 10^{-5}$ Wb-m; $d = 20$ cm $= 0.2$ m and $\theta = 45°$.

$$\therefore \quad F = \frac{M}{4\pi\mu_r\mu_0(d)^3} \times \sqrt{3\cos^2\theta + 1}$$

$$= \frac{10^{-6} \times \sqrt{3\left(\frac{1}{\sqrt{2}}\right)^2 + 1}}{4\pi \times 4\pi \times 10^{-7} \times (0.2)^3} \quad [\because \ \mu_r = 1]$$

$$= \frac{10^{-6} \times \sqrt{2.5}}{16\pi^2 \times 10^{-7} \times (0.2)^3} = \mathbf{1.25 \ A\text{-}m^{-1}}$$

and $\quad \tan\beta = \dfrac{1}{2}\tan\theta = \dfrac{1}{2}\tan 45° = \dfrac{1}{2}$

$$\therefore \quad \beta = \mathbf{26°30'}.$$

10. The magnetic moment of a short bar magnet is $16\pi^2 \times 10^{-4}$ Wb/m. Calculate the magnetic intensity at a point on the axial line at a distance 50 cm from the mid-point of the bar.

Solution : Magnetic intensity at a point along the axial line,

$$F = \frac{2M}{4\pi\mu_r\mu_0 d^3}.$$

Given that, $M = 16\pi^2 \times 10^{-4}$ Wb/m; $\mu_r = 1$ (Air); $\mu_0 = 4\pi \times 10^{-7}$; $d = 50$ cm $= 0.5$ m.

$$\therefore \quad F = \frac{2 \times 16\pi^2 \times 10^{-4}}{4\pi(4\pi \times 10^{-7}) \times (0.5)^3} = \mathbf{16 \times 10^3 \ A\text{-}m^{-1}}.$$

11. Magnetic poles of strength 10, 20, 30 and −40 c.g.s. units are placed at the corners of a square of side $2\sqrt{2}$ cm. Calculate the potential at the centre of the square.   [C.U. 1989]

Solution : Distance of O from any corner

$$= \frac{1}{2}\sqrt{(2\sqrt{2})^2 + (2\sqrt{2})^2} = 2 \text{ cm}$$

The potential at a distance r due to pole m in c.g.s. unit $= \dfrac{m}{r}$.

So the potential at O is

$$V = \frac{10}{2} + \frac{20}{2} + \frac{30}{2} - \frac{40}{2}$$

$$= \textbf{10 c.g.s. unit}.$$

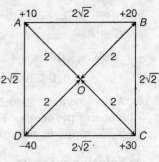

Fig. 5.43

12. The pole strength of a short bar magnet of length 0.05 metre is $64 \times 10^{-3}\pi^2$ weber. Find the magnitudes of the intensity and the potential at a point 0.5 metre on the perpendicular bisector of the bar.

Solution : Magnetic intensity, $F = \dfrac{M}{4\pi\mu_r\mu_0} \times \dfrac{1}{r^3}$.

Here, $M = 2ml = 64 \times 10^{-3}\pi^2 \times 0.05 = 3.2 \times 10^{-3}\pi^2$ Wb/m; $\mu_r = 1$, $\mu_0 = 4\pi \times 10^{-7}$ henry/m; $r = 0.5$ m.

$$\therefore \quad F = \frac{3.2 \times 10^{-3}\pi^2}{4\pi(4\pi \times 10^{-7})} \times \frac{1}{(0.5)^3} = \textbf{1.6} \times \textbf{10}^4 \text{ A-m}^{-1}.$$

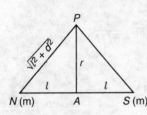

Fig. 5.44

The potential at P due to N-pole,

$$V_1 = \frac{m}{4\pi\mu_r\mu_0} \times \frac{1}{PN} = \frac{m}{4\pi\mu_r\mu_0} \times \frac{1}{\sqrt{l^2 + r^2}}.$$

Similarly, potential at P due to S-pole,

$$V_2 = -\frac{m}{4\pi\mu_r\mu_0} \times \frac{1}{PS} = -\frac{m}{4\pi\mu_r\mu_0} \times \frac{1}{\sqrt{l^2 + r^2}}.$$

As these two potentials are equal and opposite, the potential will be **zero at P**.

13. Find the value of the potential at a point situated on a line passing through the middle point of a magnet of moment $16\pi^2 \times 10^{-4}$ Wb/m at an angle of $60°$ with its axis, the point being 0.05 m away from the mid-point of the magnet.

Solution : We know, $V = \dfrac{M\cos\theta}{4\pi\mu_r\mu_0 r^2}$.

Here, $M = 16\pi^2 \times 10^{-4}$ Wb/m; $\theta = 60°$; $r = 0.05$ m.

$$\therefore \quad V = \frac{16\pi^2 \times 10^{-4} \times \cos 60°}{4\pi \times (4\pi \times 10^{-7}) \times (0.05)^2} = \frac{16\pi^2 \times 10^{-4} \times 0.5}{4\pi \times (4\pi \times 10^{-7}) \times (0.05)^2}$$

$$= \textbf{2} \times \textbf{10}^5 \text{ joules/Wb}.$$

14. Calculate the work done in rotating a magnet of pole strength 10^{-2} weber and magnetic length 0.4 m through an angle of $30°$ from its position along the magnetic meridian. $H = 200$ A-m^{-1}.

Solution : Work done, $W = MH(\cos\theta_1 - \cos\theta_2)$

$$= 2mlH(\cos\theta_1 - \cos\theta_2) \quad [\because M = 2ml]$$

Given that, $m = 10^{-2}$ weber, $2l = 0.4$ m, $H = 200$ A-m^{-1}, $\theta_1 = 0°$ and $\theta_2 = 30°$.

$$\therefore \quad W = 10^{-2} \times 0.4 \times 200(\cos 0° - \cos 30°) = 0.8(1 - \sqrt{3}/2) = \frac{0.8 \times 0.268}{2}$$

$$= \textbf{0.1 joule.}$$

15. A bar magnet makes 10 oscillations in 90 s at a place where H is equal to 200 amperes per metre. Find the time of swing at a place where the value of H is 250 amperes per m.

Solution : $T = 2\pi\sqrt{\dfrac{I}{MH}}$.

In the first case, time period $T = \dfrac{90}{10} = 9$ s.

$$\therefore \quad 9 = 2\pi\sqrt{\frac{I}{200M}}.$$

In the second case, if T be the time period, $T = 2\pi\sqrt{\dfrac{I}{250M}}$.

$$\therefore \quad \frac{T}{9} = \sqrt{\frac{200}{250}} = \frac{2}{\sqrt{5}} \quad \text{or,} \quad T = \textbf{8 s.}$$

16. The period of oscillation of a magnet swinging in a horizontal plane at a given place is 31.4 s. If the moment of inertia is 50 SI unit and its magnetic moment is 10 SI unit, calculate the horizontal component of the earth's magnetic field at the place.

Solution : $T = 2\pi\sqrt{\dfrac{I}{MH}}$; squaring, $T^2 = 4\pi^2 \cdot \dfrac{I}{MH}$.

$$\therefore \quad H = 4\pi^2 \cdot \frac{I}{MT^2}.$$

Here, $I = 50$ SI unit, $M = 10$ SI unit, $T = 31.4$ s.

$$\therefore \quad H = \frac{4(3.14)^2 \times 50}{10 \times (31.4)^2} = \textbf{0.2 A-m}^{-1}.$$

17. A small magnet A oscillates with a frequency of 15 per minute when in the earth's field alone. A bar magnet B is placed horizontally with its centre vertically below that of A and with its north pole pointing north. In this position, A still has its north pole directed northwards but when disturbed oscillates with a frequency of 10 per minute. What would be its frequency if B were turned in the horizontal plane through (a) 180° and (b) 90°?

Solution : Let the moment of inertia be I and magnetic moment M. Then,

$$T = 2\pi\sqrt{\frac{I}{MH}} \quad \text{or,} \quad \frac{1}{15} = 2\pi\sqrt{\frac{I}{MH}}. \tag{i}$$

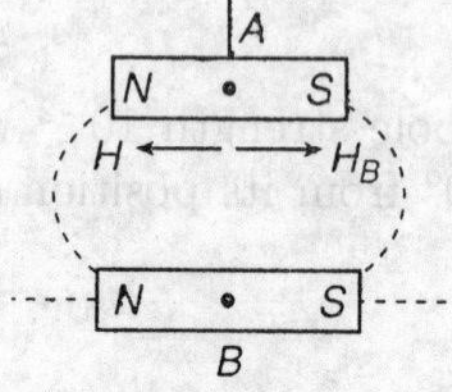

Again, $T_1 = \dfrac{1}{10} = 2\pi\sqrt{\dfrac{I}{M(H - H_B)}}.$ \hfill (ii)

Fig. 5.45

Squaring (i) and (ii) and taking ratio,

$$\frac{100}{225} = \frac{H - H_B}{H} = 1 - \frac{H_B}{H}.$$

$$\therefore \quad H_B = \frac{125}{225} \cdot H = \frac{5}{9} \cdot H.$$

Further, when the bar magnet B is rotated by $180°$,

$$T_2 = 2\pi\sqrt{\frac{I}{M(H + H_B)}} = 2\pi\sqrt{\frac{I}{MH(1 + 5/9)}} = 2\pi\sqrt{\frac{I}{\frac{14}{9} \cdot MH}}. \qquad \text{(iii)}$$

Dividing (iii) by (i),

$$15T_2 = \sqrt{\frac{9}{14}} \quad \text{or} \quad T_2 = \frac{1}{15}\sqrt{\frac{9}{14}}.$$

$$\therefore \quad n_2 = \frac{1}{T_2} = 15\sqrt{\frac{14}{9}} = \mathbf{18.71}.$$

When the bar magnet B is rotated by $90°$,

$$T_3 = 2\pi\sqrt{\frac{I}{M\sqrt{H^2 + H_B^2}}} = 2\pi\sqrt{\frac{I}{MH\sqrt{1 + (5/9)^2}}}. \qquad \text{(iv)}$$

Dividing (iv) by (i),

$$15T_3 = \frac{1}{\sqrt[4]{1 + (5/9)^2}}.$$

$$\therefore \quad n_3 = \frac{1}{T_3} = 15 \times \sqrt[4]{1 + \left(\frac{5}{9}\right)^2} = \frac{15}{3}\sqrt[4]{106} = \mathbf{16.05}.$$

18. A uniform magnetic shell of strength ϕ is bounded by a circle of radius a. A small magnet of moment M is placed along the axis of the shell at a distance x from its centre. If I be the moment of inertia of the magnet, find its period of oscillation.

   Solution : At a distance x on the axis intensity due to magnetic shell,

   $$F = \frac{a^2\phi}{2\mu_0\mu_r(a^2 + x^2)^{3/2}}.$$

   So the time period of the magnet,

   $$T = 2\pi\sqrt{\frac{I}{MF}} = 2\pi\sqrt{\frac{I}{M} \times \frac{2\mu_0\mu_r(a^2 + x^2)^{3/2}}{a^2\phi}}$$

   $$= \frac{2\pi}{a} \cdot (a^2 + x^2)^{\frac{3}{4}}\sqrt{\frac{2I\mu_0\mu_r}{M \cdot \phi}}.$$

19. A magnetic shell is in the form of a disc of radius 0.06 m. Its intensity of magnetisation is $56\pi \times 10^{-4}$ Wb/m^2 and its thickness is 0.002 m. Calculate the potential and intensity on the axis of the disc at a distance of 0.08 m from the centre.

   Solution : Here, $I = 56\pi \times 10^{-4}$ Wb/m^2 and $t = 0.002$ m.

   $$\therefore \quad \phi = I \times t = 56\pi \times 10^{-4} \times 0.002 = 112\pi \times 10^{-7},$$

   $$\mu_0 = 4\pi \times 10^{-7} \text{ henry/metre}, \mu_r = 1.$$

   $$\therefore \quad V = \frac{\phi}{2\mu_0}\left[1 - \frac{x}{(a^2 + x^2)^{\frac{1}{2}}}\right] = \frac{112\pi \times 10^{-7}}{2 \times 4\pi \times 10^{-7}}\left[1 - \frac{0.08}{\sqrt{(0.06)^2 + (0.08)^2}}\right]$$

   $$= 14 \times \frac{1}{5} = \mathbf{2.8 \text{ joules/Wb}}$$

and intensity, $F = \dfrac{a^2\phi}{2\mu_0(a^2+x^2)^{\frac{3}{2}}} = \dfrac{(0.06)^2 \times 112\pi \times 10^{-7}}{2 \times 4\pi \times 10^{-7}\{(0.06)^2+(0.08)^2\}^{\frac{3}{2}}}$

$= \dfrac{14 \times (0.06)^2 \times 1000}{1} = \textbf{50.4 A-m}^{-1}.$

20. The radius of a circular magnetic shell is 50 cm and its intensity of magnetisation is 5 poles/cm^2. Its thickness is 5 mm. Calculate the potential and intensity on the axis of the shell at a distance 10 cm from the centre.

Solution : At a distance x from the magnetic shell, the potential

$$V = \frac{\phi}{2\mu_0}\left[1 - \frac{x}{(a^2+x^2)^{1/2}}\right] \quad \text{(in air, } \mu_r = 1\text{).}$$

Now, $\phi = I \times t$.

Here, $I = 5$ poles/cm$^2 = 5 \times \dfrac{4\pi}{10^8} \times 10^4$

$= 2\pi/10^3$ Wb/m^2 $\left(1 \text{ pole} = \dfrac{4\pi}{10^8} \text{ Wb, } 1 \text{ cm} = 10^{-2} \text{ m}\right)$

and $\quad t = 5$ mm $= 5 \times 10^{-3}$ m.

$\therefore \quad \phi = \dfrac{2\pi}{10^3} \times 5 \times 10^{-3} = \pi \times 10^{-5}$ Wb-m^{-1}

$\therefore \quad V = \dfrac{\pi \times 10^{-5}}{2 \times 12.56 \times 10^{-7}}\left[1 - \dfrac{0.1}{\{(0.5)^2+(0.1)^2\}^{1/2}}\right]$

$$(\mu_0 = 12.56 \times 10^{-7} \text{ H-m}^{-1})$$

$= \textbf{10 J-Wb}^{-1}.$

Again, the intensity at a distance x from the centre of the magnetic shell,

$$F = \frac{a^2\phi}{2\mu_0(a^2+x^2)^{3/2}}$$

Here, $a = 0.5$ m, $\phi = \pi \times 10^{-5}$ Wb-m^{-1}, $\mu_0 = 12.56 \times 10^{-7}$ and $x = 0.1$ m.

$\therefore \quad F = \dfrac{(0.5)^2 \times \pi \times 10^{-5}}{2 \times 12.56 \times 10^{-7}[(0.5)^2+(0.1)^2]^{3/2}} = \textbf{23.67 A-m}^{-1}.$

21. If M is the magnetic moment of a short magnet, show that the potential at any point at a distance r is $V = \dfrac{\mu_r\mu_0}{4\pi}\dfrac{M\cos\theta}{r^2}$.

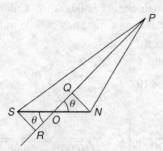

Fig. 5.46

Solution : If the length of the magnet is small compared to the length OP,

$$PN = PQ \quad \text{and} \quad PS = PR.$$

Potential at P due to N-pole

$$= \frac{\mu_r\mu_0}{4\pi}\frac{m}{PN} = \frac{\mu_r\mu_0}{4\pi}\frac{m}{PQ}$$

(where m = pole strength)

and potential at P due to S-pole

$$= \frac{\mu_r\mu_0}{4\pi}\left(\frac{-m}{PS}\right) = \frac{\mu_r\mu_0}{4\pi}\left(-\frac{m}{PR}\right).$$

So the resulting magnetic moment at the point P,

$$V = \frac{\mu_r \mu_0}{4\pi} \left(\frac{m}{PQ} - \frac{m}{PR} \right)$$

$$= \frac{\mu_r \mu_0}{4\pi} \left[\frac{m}{OP - OQ} - \frac{m}{OP + OQ} \right] \quad (\because OQ = OR)$$

$$= \frac{\mu_r \mu_0}{4\pi} \left[\frac{2m \cdot OQ}{(OP)^2 - (OQ)^2} \right]$$

$$= \frac{\mu_r \mu_0}{4\pi} \left[\frac{2ml \cos\theta}{(OP)^2} \right] \quad (\because OQ \ll OP)$$

But $2ml = M$ and $OP = r$.

$\therefore$ $V = \dfrac{\mu_r \mu_0}{4\pi} \dfrac{M \cos\theta}{r^2}$ **(Proved)**.

22. Find the value of the potential at a point situated on a line passing through the middle point of a magnet of moment 30, at an angle of 60° with its axis, the point being 5 cm away from the midpoint of the magnet. [**C.U. 1951, '55**]

Solution : We know, $V = \dfrac{M \cos\theta}{r^2}$.

Here, $M = 30$, $\theta = 60°$ and $r = 5$ cm.

$\therefore$ $V = \dfrac{30 \cos 60°}{(5)^2} = \dfrac{30 \times 0.5}{(5)^2} = \mathbf{0.6\ ergs}$.

23. The intensities of magnetic field at two points on the axis of a bar magnet at a distance 10 cm and 20 cm respectively from its centre are in the ratio 12.5 : 1.0. Find the distance between the poles of the magnet.

                                             [**C.U. 1966 (Spl. Old Reg.)**]

Solution : The intensity at the points A and B,

$$F_A = \frac{2Mr_1}{(r_1^2 - l^2)^2} \quad \text{and} \quad F_B = \frac{2Mr_2}{(r_2^2 - l^2)^2},$$

where M = magnetic moment and l = half of the magnetic length.

Here, $r_1 = 10$ cm and $r_2 = 20$ cm.

$\therefore$ $F_A = \dfrac{2M \times 10}{(10^2 - l^2)^2}$ and $F_B = \dfrac{2M \times 20}{(20^2 - l^2)^2}$.

$\therefore$ $\dfrac{F_A}{F_B} = \dfrac{(20^2 - l^2)^2}{2(10^2 - l^2)^2}$

But $\dfrac{F_A}{F_B} = \dfrac{12.5}{1.0}$

So, $\dfrac{12.5}{1.0} = \dfrac{(20^2 - l^2)^2}{2(10^2 - l^2)^2}$ or, $\dfrac{20^2 - l^2}{10^2 - l^2} = 5$ or, $l^2 = 25$.

$\therefore$ $l = 5$.

$\therefore$ distance between the two poles $(2l) = 2 \times 5 = \mathbf{10\ cm}$.

24. Two magnets of same dimension and mass are caused to oscillate separately in the earth's magnetic field. The first one performs 15 vibrations per minute

and the second one 10 vibrations per minute. Compare the magnetic moments of the two magnets.

Solution : Time-period for the first case, $T_1 = 2\pi\sqrt{I/M_1H}$.

But $T_1 = \dfrac{60}{15} = 4$ seconds.

$\therefore \quad 4 = 2\pi\sqrt{I/M_1H}$.

Similarly, time-period for the second case, $T_2 = 2\pi\sqrt{I/M_2H}$.

But $T_2 = \dfrac{60}{10} = 6$ seconds.

$\therefore \quad 6 = 2\pi\sqrt{I/M_2H}$.

So, $\dfrac{M_1}{M_2} = \dfrac{36}{16} = \dfrac{9}{4}$.

25. If a small magnet makes 12 oscillations per minute in the earth's field at a place, what additional field will be necessary for it to make 20 oscillations per minute at the same point? $H = 0.37$ Oe.   [C.U. 1942]

Solution : Let the value of the additional field $= F$.

For the first case, $T_1 = 2\pi\sqrt{I/MH}$

and for the second case, $T_2 = 2\pi\sqrt{I/M(F+H)}$.

So, $\dfrac{T_1}{T_2} = \sqrt{\dfrac{H+F}{H}}$ or, $\dfrac{T_1^2}{T_2^2} = \dfrac{H+F}{H}$

or, $\dfrac{n_2^2}{n_1^2} = \dfrac{F}{H} + 1$ or, $\dfrac{n_2^2 - n_1^2}{n_1^2} = \dfrac{F}{H}$

$\therefore \quad F = \dfrac{n_2^2 - n_1^2}{n_1^2} \cdot H = \dfrac{400 - 144}{144} \times 0.37 = \mathbf{0.658 \ Oe \ (approx.).}$

26. A steel bar magnet has a magnetic moment of $2\pi \times 10^{-7}$ Wb-m and a mass of 6.6×10^{-3} kg. If the density of steel is 7.9×10^3 kg/m^3, find the intensity of magnetisation of the bar.

Solution : Volume of the bar magnet $= \dfrac{\text{mass}}{\text{density}} = \dfrac{6.6 \times 10^{-3}}{7.9 \times 10^3}$

$$= 8.3 \times 10^{-7} \text{ m}^3.$$

Again, intensity of magnetisation, $I = \dfrac{M}{V} = \dfrac{2\pi \times 10^{-7}}{8.3 \times 10^{-7}(\text{m}^3)}$

$$= 0.75 \text{ Wb/m}^2.$$

27. A magnetic field of 20 e.m.u. produces a flux of 24 e.m.u. in a bar of iron of cross-section 0.2 cm^2. Calculate the susceptibility and permeability of iron.

                                                                    [C.U. 1992]

Solution : Magnetic field, $H = 20$ e.m.u.

Magnetic induction, $B = \dfrac{2400}{0.2} = 12000$ e.m.u.

$\therefore \quad$ Permeability, $\mu = \dfrac{B}{H} = \dfrac{12000}{20} = 600.$

Again, $\mu = 1 + 4\pi K$; so, $600 = 1 + 4\pi K$.

$$\therefore \quad K = \frac{599}{4\pi} = 47.7.$$

28. The magnetic susceptibility of a material is 25.14×10^{-11} henry/m. Calculate the relative permeability and absolute permeability of the material.

Solution : In SI unit, $K = \mu_0(\mu_r - 1)$

$$\therefore \quad 25.14 \times 10^{-11} = 4\pi \times 10^{-7}(\mu_r - 1)$$

or, $\quad \mu_r = 1 + \dfrac{25.14 \times 10^{-11}}{4\pi \times 10^{-7}} = 1.0002$

Absolute permeability, $\mu = \mu_r \mu_0 = 4\pi \times 10^{-7} \times 1.0002$

$$= \mathbf{12.562 \times 10^{-7} \ H\text{-}m^{-1}}.$$

29. An iron rod (density $= 7.7 \times 10^3$ kg/m^3 and sp. heat $= 470$ J/kg) is subjected to cycles of magnetisation having frequency 60 cycles/s. If the area enclosed by I-H curve for the specimen is 5×10^3 J, calculate the rise of temperature per minute, assuming no loss of heat by radiation.

Solution : Loss of energy per cycle per unit volume per second

$$= \text{Area of } (I\text{-}H) \text{ loop} = 5 \times 10^3 \text{ J}.$$

$\therefore$ loss of energy per unit volume per minute due to 60 cycles

$$= 5 \times 10^3 \times 60 \times 60 \text{ J} = 18 \times 10^6 \text{ J}.$$

Mass of the rod per unit volume $= 7.7 \times 10^3$ kg.

If the rise of temperature of the rod per minute is $\theta\,^\circ$C,

$$7.7 \times 10^3 \times 470 \times \theta = 18 \times 10^6$$

$$\therefore \quad \theta = \frac{18 \times 10^6}{7.7 \times 10^3 \times 470} = \mathbf{4.97\,^\circ C}.$$

30. A magnetic field of 20 e.m.u. produces a magnetic flux of 2400 e.m.u. in a bar of iron of cross-section 0.2 sq. cm. Calculate the intensity of magnetisation, magnetic permeability and magnetic susceptibility of it.

Solution : Here magnetic field, $H = 20$ e.m.u.; magnetic flux $N = 2400$ e.m.u. and cross-section, $\alpha = 0.2$ sq. cm.

Now we know, magnetic flux = magnetic flux density $\times$ cross-section,

i.e., $\quad N = B \times \alpha$

or, $\quad B = \dfrac{N}{\alpha} = \dfrac{2400}{0.2} = 12000$ e.m.u.

But, $\quad B = H + 4\pi I$

or, $\quad I = \dfrac{B - H}{4\pi} = \dfrac{12000 - 20}{4\pi} = \mathbf{954 \ e.m.u.}$

$\therefore \quad$ Permeability, $\mu = \dfrac{B}{H} = \dfrac{12000}{20} = \mathbf{600}$

and   magnetic susceptibility, $K = \dfrac{I}{H} = \dfrac{954}{20} = \mathbf{47.7}.$

31. An iron rod (density 7.7 g/cc and sp. heat = 0.11) is subjected to cycles of magnetisation having frequency 60 cycles/second. If the area enclosed by the I-H curve for the specimen is 50 000 ergs, calculate the rise of temperature per minute, assuming no loss of heat by radiation. $J = 4.2 \times 10^7$ ergs/cal.

Solution : Energy loss per unit volume per cycle per second

$$= \text{area of the } I\text{-}H \text{ loop} = 50\,000 \text{ ergs}$$

So the loss of energy per unit volume per minute $= 50\,000 \times 60 \times 60$ ergs

$$\therefore \quad \text{heat produced per minute} = \frac{50\,000 \times 60 \times 60}{4.2 \times 10^7} = \frac{30}{7} \text{ cal.}$$

Mass of the rod per unit volume = 7.7 grams.

If $\theta\,°C$ be the rise in temperature of the rod per minute,

$$7.7 \times 0.11 \times \theta = \frac{30}{7}$$

$$\therefore \quad \theta = \frac{30}{7.7 \times 0.11 \times 7} = \mathbf{5.06\,°C.}$$

32. An iron rod of length 25 cm and cross-section 4 sq. mm is introduced into a solenoid having 25 turns/cm. If the solenoid carries a current of 2 amperes for which μ of iron is 400, find the magnetic moment of iron.

Solution : We know, $H = \dfrac{4\pi n i}{10}$,

where no. of turns $n = 25$; current $i = 2$ amperes.

$$\therefore \quad H = \frac{4 \times 3.14 \times 25 \times 2}{10} = 62.80 \text{ oersted.}$$

Again, $B = H + 4\pi I$

or, $\quad \mu H = H + 4\pi I \quad (\because B = \mu H).$

$$\therefore \quad I = \frac{\mu H - H}{4\pi} = \frac{\mu - 1}{4\pi} \cdot H = \frac{400 - 1}{4 \times 3.14} \cdot 62.80$$

$$= 1995 \text{ c.g.s. unit.}$$

We know, $I = \dfrac{M}{V}$

or, $\quad M = I \times V = 1995 \times 1 = 1995$ c.g.s. unit.

So the magnetic moment of the bar magnet = **1995 c.g.s. unit**.

Questions

Essay-type

1. Define magnetic potential and magnetic intensity at a point. Derive an expression for the magnetic potential at any point in the field due to a short bar magnet. Hence determine the magnetic intensity at the point.

2. Find an expression for the magnetic potential at a point due to a short magnet; hence deduce the values of radial and transverse intensities at that point.

3. Obtain expressions for magnitude and direction of the magnetic intensity at any position in the magnetic field due to a short bar magnet.

4. (a) What is called a magnetic shell?

   (b) What is meant by strength of a magnetic shell?

   (c) Derive an expression for the magnetic potential due to a uniform magnetic shell at a point near it.

   (d) Find also an expression for magnetic intensity at that point.

5. Deduce an expression for the couple acting on a magnet freely suspended in a uniform magnetic field. **[C.U. 1982]**

6. Prove that the intensity of magnetic field due to a small bar magnet 'end-on' position is twice that due to the same magnet 'broadside-on' position at the same distance.

7. Find the magnitude and direction of the magnetic field at a point distant r from the centre of a short magnet of moment M in a direction making an angle θ with the magnetic axis. **[B.U. 1983, '96]**

8. Derive an expression for the strength of the magnetic field due to a short bar magnet at the boardside-on (tangent-B) position. **[C.U. 1980]**

9. Define magnetic potential. Derive an expression for the potential at any point due to a short magnet. Hence, calculate the radial and transverse field intensities. **[C.U. 1989; B.U. 1989, '90]**

10. Starting from the expression of magnetic potential at a point due to a short bar magnet, find the magnitude and direction of the field intensity at that point.

11. Find an expression for the work done in deflecting a magnet from its position of rest in a uniform magnetic field. **[C.U. 1983]**

12. Calculate the potential energy of a magnet in a uniform magnetic field.
    [B.U. 1983]

13. Show that the oscillations of a bar magnet in a uniform magnetic field are simple harmonic in nature and deduce an expression for its time-period.
    [B.U. 1996]

14. What is a magnetic shell? Derive an expression for the potential due to a uniform magnetic shell at a point near it. Hence determine the potential due to a circular magnetic shell at any point on its axis. **[C.U. 1983; B.U. 1966]**

15. Starting from the expression for the potential at a point due to a uniform magnetic shell, find the potential at any point on the plane of the diameter of a hemispherical shell.

16. Define magnetic shell and the strength of the magnetic shell. Obtain an expression for the potential at a point due to a magnetic shell. Calculate the work done in carrying a unit north pole from one face to the other of an infinitely extended magnetic shell.

17. Derive the relation connecting permeability and susceptibility of a magnetic substance.

18. Define the terms : magnetic induction (B), intensity of magnetisation (I), permeability (μ) and susceptibility (K). Show that $\mu = 1 + 4\pi K$. What is hysteresis loop?

19. Show the general nature of B-H loop. Prove that the energy dissipated per unit volume of a material during a complete hysteresis cycle is $\frac{1}{4}\pi$ times the area enclosed by the B-H curve.

20. Illustrate the nature of the hysteresis loop of a sample of steel and that of a soft iron piece. Indicate from these how the two materials differ in their magnetic behaviours.

21. Briefly state how you can distinguish between a ferromagnetic, paramagnetic and diamagnetic material.

Short Answer-type

22. Define magnetic field intensity. What is its unit?

23. Define magnetic moment of a bar magnet. Does it depend upon the pole strength of the magnet? A magnet of moment M is kept inclined at an angle θ with the direction of a uniform magnetic field H. Write down moment of the couple acting on the magnet. What is the maximum value of this moment?

24. A magnetised steel wire of length l has a magnetic moment M. It is then bent into a semi-circular arc. What is the new magnetic moment?   [C.U. 1980]

25. What is the relation between the intensity and potential at a point in a magnetic field?

26. The intensity at a point on the tangent-A position due to a short bar magnet is F. What will be the intensity at the same distance on the tangent-B position due to the same magnet?   [C.U. 1980]

27. Write down the tangent law in magnetism.

28. Write down the equation for the vibration of a magnet in a magnetic field.

29. What do you mean by equipotential lines and surfaces?

30. Explain what you understand by (a) hysteresis, (b) retentivity, (c) coercivity of a magnetic material.

31. Define and explain the following terms : (i) Intensity of magnetisation, (ii) Magnetic induction, (iii) Permeability, (iv) Susceptibility.

32. What is the difference between the I-H and B-H curves of a magnetic substance?   [C.U. 1990]

33. In which category of magnetic material would you place the following substances : (a) water, (b) nickel, (c) permalloy, (d) mercury?

34. Which properties of a magnetic material would you particularly enquire into for using it as the core of an electromagnet, and why?   [C.U. 1989]

35. Distinguish between lines of force, lines of magnetisation and lines of induction.

36. How would you test a small rod to find if it is diamagnetic, paramagnetic or ferromagnetic?

37. Show by means of a graph how the intensity of magnetisation of soft iron varies with the intensity of magnetising field (a) as the field is increased from the initial value zero, (b) for a cycle of magnetisation. Discuss the importance of the shape of graph in selecting materials for (i) permanent magnets and (ii) transformer cores.

38. What are the three basic forms of magnetic material? Write, in brief, their properties.

39. Derive a relation connecting permeability and susceptibility of a magnetic substance.

40. Define magnetic permeability and susceptibility, and show how these are related to each other.

41. Show that for a magnetic substance $B = H + 4\pi I$, the symbols being usual.

[C.U. 1990]

42. Describe an experimental method for determining the magnetic permeability and susceptibility of a specimen in the form of a thin rod.

43. Show the general nature of a B-H loop and explain the terms retentivity, coercivity and hysteresis with reference to it. Compare the B-H loops for iron and steel. Prove that the energy dissipated per unit volume of a material during a complete hysteresis is $\frac{1}{4}\pi$ times the area enclosed by the B-H curve.

[C.U. 1992]

44. Briefly state how you can distinguish between ferromagnetic, paramagnetic and diamagnetic materials.

45. Illustrate the nature of the hysteresis loop of a sample of steel and that of a soft iron piece. Indicate from these how the two materials differ in their magnetic behaviours.

46. Prove that when a sample of magnetic material is subjected to a periodic magnetising field, an amount of energy proportional to the area of the hysteresis loop is lost per cycle.

47. Draw curves showing the manner in which the magnetisation varies in a sample of soft iron and in a sample of steel as each is taken through a complete cycle of the magnetising force. With reference to the above curves, compare the properties of the two samples in respect to residual magnetism, coercive force and hysteresis loss. Discuss fully why soft iron is suitable for use as the core of a transformer while steel is preferred for making permanent magnets. What is 'Alnico'?

Numerical Problems

48. Two short bar magnets of moment 108 units and 192 units are placed along two lines drawn on the table at right angles to each other. Find the intensity of the field at the point of intersection of the lines, the centres of the magnets being 30 cm and 40 cm respectively from this point. [**Ans.** 0.01 Oe]

49. Magnetic poles of strength 10, 20, 30 and -40 c.g.s. units are placed at the corners of a square of side $2\sqrt{2}$ cm. Calculate the potential at the centre of the square. [**Ans.** 10 c.g.s. unit]

50. A magnetic shell is in the form of a disc of radius 5 cm. Its surface density is 5 poles per cm^2 and its thickness is 5 mm. Calculate the potential and intensity in c.g.s. unit on the axis of the disc at a distance of 10 cm from the centre. [**Ans.** 1.657 ergs, 0.281 oersted]

51. A rectangular thin magnet has a period of oscillation 6 seconds. If the magnet is divided into two equal halves, then show that the period of oscillation of each half will be equal to 3 seconds.

52. A small magnet free to oscillate horizontally makes 10 oscillations per minute. If the moment of inertia of the magnet about the axis of rotation concerned be 2500 gm-cm^2 and the earth's horizontal field at the place be 0.4 oersted, find the value of the magnetic moment of the magnet.

[**Ans.** 6847.2 c.g.s. units]

53. Calculate the work done in deflecting a freely suspended magnet of pole strength 100 units and magnetic length 8 cm through an angle 60° from the position of rest. $H = 0.36$ oersted. [**Tripura 1998**]

[**Ans.** 144 ergs]

54. Calculate the magnetic intensity due to a short magnet of magnetic moment $16\pi^2 \times 10^{-6}$ Wb/metre, at a point 0.5 metre from the centre of the magnet. The line joining the point with the centre of the magnet makes an angle of 60° with the axis of the magnet. [**Ans.** 1.06×10^2 A-m^{-1}]

55. Calculate the amount of work done in deflecting a magnet of moment 100 units and making an angle 30° with the meridian through a further angle of 30°. $H = 0.34$ Oe. [**Ans.** 12.44 ergs]

56. A bar magnet is suspended by a wire so as to hang horizontally. A twist of 120° at the top of the wire is necessary to deflect the magnet through 30°. By how much must the wire be twisted to deflect the magnet through 90° from the magnetic meridian? [**Ans.** 270°]

57. If a magnet is of magnetic length 8 cm, find the percentage error caused by neglecting the magnetic length of the magnet in calculating the magnetic field strength due to the magnet at a point on its axis 32 cm from its centre.

[**Ans.** 3.1%]

58. Calculate the work done in rotating a magnet of pole strength 2×10^{-2} Wb and magnetic length 0.5 m through an angle of 60° from its position of magnetic meridian. $H = 200$ ampere-m^{-1}. [**Ans.** 1 joule]

59. Calculate the magnitude and direction of the magnetic field due to a bar magnet which is 10 cm long and has a magnetic moment 10^{-6} Wb-m, at a point 20 cm from its mid-point measured along a line inclined at 45° to its magnetic axis. [**Ans.** 154 A-m^{-1}; 62°48′ to axis]

60. Two magnets of the same type but of moments M and $\sqrt{3}M$ are mounted on a frame so as to form a cross. If the combination is suspended at the centre with a vertical fibre, find out and indicate in a diagram the direction in which it will set in the earth's magnetic field. [**C.U. 1990**]

[**Ans.** The magnet of magnetic moment M will rotate by 60°]

61. A cylindrical bar of length 4 cm and diameter 2 mm is placed horizontally in the magnetic meridian. It is then found that a neutral point is situated 8.5 cm from each end of the bar. Find the magnetic susceptibility of the bar, assuming that it is uniformly magnetised by the earth's field.

[**Ans.** 4885 c.g.s. units]

62. A magnetic field of 50 e.m.u. generates a flux of 2500 e.m.u. in a long bar of steel. Calculate the permeability and the intensity of magnetization of iron which has a cross-section of 0.25 cm^2. [**Ans.** $\mu = 200$; $I = 792.3$]

63. An iron rod 20 cm long, 1 cm in diameter and of permeability 1000, is placed inside a long solenoid, wound with 5 turns per cm. If 0.5 A current passes through the solenoid, find the magnetic moment of the rod.   [**Ans.** 3926]

64. The hysteresis loop for a specimen of iron weighing 12 kg is equivalent in area to 300 joules/m^3. Find the loss of energy per hour at 25 Hz. Density of iron = 7.5 g-cm^{-3}.   [**Ans.** 720 J]

65. A specimen of iron of density 7.7 g/cm^3 and specific heat 0.11 is magnetized by alternating field of frequency 100 cycles/s. Assuming no loss of heat, calculate the rise in temperature of the iron per minute if the hysteresis loss is 50 000 ergs per cycle.   [**C.U. (Hons.) 1942, (Pass) 1990**]

[**Ans.** 8.4 °C]

Chapter 6
Magnetic Measurements

6.1 Introduction

From the consideration of magnetic properties English physicist Michael Faraday in 1845 divided the materials into three classes, known as ferromagnetic, paramagnetic and diamagnetic substances. The intensity of magnetization of the ferromagnetic materials is not directly proportional to the magnetizing field but it also depends on the previous history. In other words, we can say that ferromagnetics have hysteresis and retentivity. But for paramagnetic or diamagnetic substances, their intensity of magnetization is linearly related to the applied field. A choice of the ferromagnetic substance is decided by its behaviour when subjected to hysteresis cycle.

6.2 Magnetometers

The measurements of the magnetic moment M and the field H are the two important parameters which can be determined by the following two instruments : (i) Vibration magnetometer and (ii) Deflection magnetometer.

6.2.1 Vibration Magnetometer

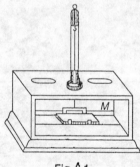

Fig. 6.1

The instrument is shown in Fig. 6.1. It consists of a short magnet M closed in a wooden box with glass windows. The magnet is horizontally kept in a double-loop frame which is suspended by a silk thread. There is a torsion head at the top of the tube. Any air current is prevented by the glass case.

At the time of the experiment, the magnet is placed in the magnetic meridian and is made to oscillate in the earth's field of intensity H. Let us assume that the magnet oscillates in the field H and E. During its oscillations it makes an angle θ with the direction of H.

The restoring couple acting on it $= MH \sin \theta$ (M = moment of the magnet)

$$= MH\theta \quad (\theta \text{ being small}).$$

If I denotes the moment of inertia of the magnet, then the deflecting couple is $I \frac{d^2\theta}{dt^2}$.

In the equilibrium condition of oscillation,

$$I\frac{d^2\theta}{dt^2} = -MH\theta \quad \text{or,} \quad \frac{d^2\theta}{dt^2} + \frac{MH}{I}\theta = 0$$

or, $$\frac{d^2\theta}{dt^2} + \omega^2\theta = 0, \tag{6.1}$$

where $\omega = \sqrt{\dfrac{MH}{I}}$.

Eq. (6.1) gives the equation of simple harmonic motion with angular velocity ω. If T is the time-period, then we have

$$\omega = \frac{2\pi}{T}. \tag{6.2}$$

So we can write,

$$\frac{2\pi}{T} = \sqrt{\frac{MH}{I}}$$

or, $\quad T = 2\pi\sqrt{\dfrac{I}{MH}}. \tag{6.3}$

Eq. (6.3) represents the time-period of oscillation of a magnet in the earth's field.

Uses

(i) **Comparison of magnetic moments :** If T_1 and T_2 be the time period obtained by performing experiments with the two magnets separately, then we can write,

$$T_1 = 2\pi\sqrt{\frac{I_1}{M_1 H}} \tag{6.4}$$

and $\quad T_2 = 2\pi\sqrt{\dfrac{I_2}{M_2 H}}. \tag{6.5}$

$$\therefore \quad \frac{M_1}{M_2} = \frac{T_2^2}{T_1^2} \cdot \frac{I_1}{I_2}. \tag{6.6}$$

In Eq. (6.6), I_1 and I_2 can be found from the geometry of the magnets and hence the moments of two magnets can be compared.

(ii) **Comparison of field strengths :** Let H_1 and H_2 be two fields where a vibration magnetometer is separately placed. Then we have

$$T_1 = 2\pi\sqrt{\frac{I}{MH_1}} \tag{6.7}$$

and $\quad T_2 = 2\pi\sqrt{\dfrac{I}{MH_2}}. \tag{6.8}$

Squaring the above two equations and taking the ratio, we get

$$\frac{H_1}{H_2} = \frac{T_2^2}{T_1^2}. \tag{6.9}$$

Searles Magnetometer : Verification of the inverse square law

It is a vibration type magnetometer. In Fig. 6.2, ns is a small magnet fixed to a brass cylinder B suspended by an unspun silk thread. P is a long aluminium pointer fixed below the magnet. It enables the oscillations to be counted. Since B is a massive cylinder, it increases the inertia and hence the time-period of oscillation. Thus the period of vibration may be large enough to be measured accurately.

If T is the time-period obtained experimentally, then

$$T = 2\pi\sqrt{\frac{I}{MH}}$$

or, $\quad \dfrac{1}{n} = 2\pi\sqrt{\dfrac{I}{MH}},\quad$ where n is the frequency. $\tag{6.10}$

From Eq. (6.10) we can write,

$$n^2 \propto H.$$

If a ball-ended long magnet NS is placed vertically in a manner as shown, then the field at the small magnet may be considered to be due to the N-pole only. Thus the magnet oscillates under the joint action of the earth's field and the field due to the north pole. We may thus write,

$$n_1^2 \propto (F_1 + H).$$

We thus have

$$\frac{n^2}{n_1^2} = \frac{H}{F_1 + H}. \tag{6.11}$$

If now the ball-ended magnet is displaced from d_1 to d_2, then

$$\frac{n^2}{n_2^2} = \frac{H}{F_2 + H}. \tag{6.12}$$

Eq. (6.11) can be rewritten as

$$\frac{n^2}{n_1^2 - n^2} = \frac{H}{F_1}$$

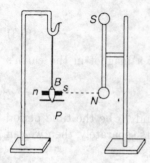

Fig. 6.2

and from Eq. (6.12),

$$\frac{n^2}{n_2^2 - n^2} = \frac{H}{F_2}.$$

Hence,
$$\frac{n_1^2 - n^2}{n_2^2 - n^2} = \frac{F_1}{F_2}. \tag{6.13}$$

From experimental observation it is seen that

$$\frac{n_1^2 - n^2}{n_2^2 - n^2} = \frac{d_2^2}{d_1^2}. \tag{6.14}$$

Thus, we get

$$\frac{F_1}{F_2} = \frac{d_2^2}{d_1^2}. \tag{6.15}$$

$$\therefore \qquad F \propto \frac{1}{d^2}$$

This verifies the inverse square law.

6.2.2 Deflection Magnetometer

In a deflection magnetometer, a given magnet is used to deflect a needle from the magnetic meridian. A magnetometer of this type is shown in Fig. 6.3. In the figure, PQ and RS are the two arms of the magnetometer. A magnetic needle is pivoted at the centre of a graduated circular scale. AB is a given magnet which is kept at a suitable distance from the centre of the circular scale.

Fig. 6.3

At the time of the experiment, the magnetometer is first adjusted so that the pointer shows 0-0. The given magnet is now placed at a suitable distance for getting a deflection of the needle by an angle of about 45°. The magnet is kept on the other arm at an equal distance and the deflection is noted to find the mean deflection θ. In the second part of the experiment, the given magnet is placed in the cradle of a vibration magnetometer and the time-period of oscillation is found out. From this experiment one can calculate the value of M and H.

If r is the distance of the centre of the circular scale where the needle is placed and $2l$ is the effective length of the magnet, then we have

$$\frac{M}{H} = \frac{(r^2 - l^2)^2}{2r} \tan \theta. \tag{6.16}$$

Again, the time-period of oscillation T is given by

$$T = 2\pi \sqrt{\frac{I}{MH}}$$

or, $\quad MH = \dfrac{4\pi^2 I}{T^2}.$ $\hspace{6cm}$ (6.17)

The moment of inertia I of the magnet is obtained from

$$I = \frac{m}{H}(l_1^2 + b^2), \tag{6.18}$$

where m is the mass of the magnet, l_1 and b are respectively the geometric length and breadth of the magnet.

Using Eqs. (6.16) and (6.17), we get

$$M^2 = \frac{(r^2 - l^2)^2}{2r} \tan \theta \times \frac{4\pi^2 I}{T^2} \tag{6.19}$$

and $\quad H^2 = \dfrac{4\pi^2 I}{T^2} \cdot \dfrac{2r}{(r^2 - l^2)^2 \tan \theta}.$ $\hspace{4cm}$ (6.20)

6.3   Force on a Para- or Ferromagnetic Body Placed in a Magnetic Field

When a para- or ferromagnetic substance is kept in a non-uniform magnetic field, the constituent molecular magnets align themselves in the direction of the field and as a matter of fact the specimen becomes magnetised. To calculate the magnetic force on the specimen let us calculate the same for an elementary dipole aligned in the direction of the field and then sum up for all constituent dipoles for getting the total force on the specimen.

Let AB be a dipole of length dl (Fig. 6.4); $-m$ and $+m$ be the pole-strengths at A and B respectively. Let at A the field strength is H and that at B is $\left(H + \frac{\delta H}{\delta l} dl\right)$, where $\frac{\delta H}{\delta l}$ is the space rate of variation of H within the specimen.

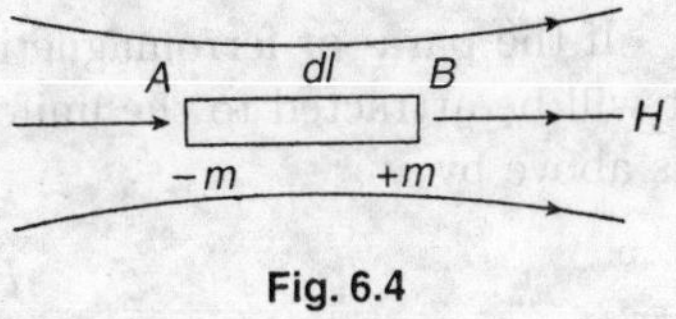

Fig. 6.4

Hence, the force on $+m$ is $m\left(H + \dfrac{\delta H}{\delta l} dl\right)$ and the force on $-m$ is $-mH$.

Therefore, the resultant force on the dipole $= m\left(H + \dfrac{\delta H}{\delta l} dl\right) - mH = m\dfrac{\delta H}{\delta l} dl$

$$= M_1 \frac{\delta H}{\delta l} \quad \text{(where } M_1 = mdl\text{)}.$$

M_1 is called the moment of the dipole.

Summing up for all the constituent dipoles one may get the total force on the specimen which can be written as,

$$F = + \sum M_1 \frac{\delta H}{\delta l}$$

$$= M \frac{\delta H}{\delta l} \qquad (6.21)$$

In Eq. (6.21), M is the magnetic moment of the specimen.

Again, if I be the intensity of magnetization and v be the volume of the substance, then

$$M = Iv$$

$$= KvH, \qquad (6.22)$$

where K is the susceptibility of the specimen. Thus, we have

$$F = KvH \frac{\delta H}{\delta l}$$

$$= \frac{1}{2} Kv \frac{\delta H^2}{\delta l}. \qquad (6.23)$$

Eq. (6.23) can be conveniently used for determining the susceptibility of a specimen relative to air.

If in a medium of susceptibility K_1, a paramagnetic or ferromagnetic substance of susceptibility K_2 is placed, then due to the relative susceptibility $(K_2 - K_1)$ the force F on the specimen can be expressed as

$$F = \frac{1}{2} v(K_2 - K_1) \frac{\delta H^2}{\delta l}. \qquad (6.24)$$

Again, if μ is the permeability, then

$$\mu = \mu_0 (1 + K)$$

or, $(\mu_2 - \mu_1) = \mu_0 (K_2 - K_1)$. $\qquad (6.25)$

So from Eq. (6.24), we get

$$F = \frac{1}{2} v(\mu_2 - \mu_1) \frac{\delta H^2}{\delta l}. \qquad (6.26)$$

Eq. (6.26) can also be deduced from the energy considerations. Eqs. (6.23), (6.24) or (6.26) can be used for finding the values of K and μ by applying various methods.

If the para- or ferromagnetic specimen is brought close to a uniform field, then it will be attracted to the uniform region of the field. Then the force will be given as above by

$$F = \frac{1}{2} v(\mu_2 - \mu_1) \frac{\delta H^2}{\delta l}.$$

But since here the field has a constant maximum value of H, it can be integrated from O to H. If l is the length of the specimen, then we can write,

$$F \int_0^l dl = \frac{v(\mu_2 - \mu_1)}{2} \int_0^H \delta(H)^2$$

or, $F \cdot l = \dfrac{v(\mu_2 - \mu_1)}{2} H^2$

or, $\quad F = \dfrac{(\mu_2 - \mu_1)}{2} H^2 \dfrac{v}{l}$

$\qquad = \dfrac{(\mu_2 - \mu_1)}{2} H^2 S,$ \hfill (6.27)

where S is the cross-sectional area of the specimen.

From Eq. (6.27) it is seen that due to the magnetic field the specimen gets a pressure p per unit area of its section at right angle to the field direction. The pressure p can thus be expressed as

$$p = \frac{F}{S} = \frac{(\mu_2 - \mu_1)}{2} H^2. \qquad (6.28)$$

6.4　Measurement of Susceptibility

(i) Curie's Method (in a non-uniform field) : The magnetic susceptibility of a large number of substances was carefully examined by physicist Pierre Curie over a wide range of temperature. In order to produce a non-homogeneous field he used an electromagnet with inclined pole pieces as shown in Fig. 6.5. The specimen temperature was changed by keeping it in a porcelain tube surrounded by a platinum coil and a water jacket. By controlling the current in the coil the temperature could be accurately measured by a calibrated thermocouple.

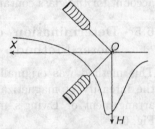

Fig. 6.5

We know that in a non-uniform magnetic field the force experienced by a substance along the X-axis is given by

$F_x = KvH\dfrac{\delta H}{\delta x}$

or, $\quad K = \dfrac{F_x}{vH\frac{\delta H}{\delta x}},$ \hfill (6.29)

where $\frac{\delta H}{\delta x}$ is the space rate of variation of H, v the volume of the specimen and H is the field where the specimen is placed. Knowing all the quantities on the right-hand side the value of K is determined. The above equation can be more accurately written as

$$(K_2 - K_1) = \frac{F_x}{vH\frac{\delta H}{\delta x}}. \qquad (6.30)$$

In an actual experiment F is measured directly by the method of deflection with a sensitive balance, v is calculated from its dimensions and H by an exploring coil with the help of a fluxmeter. Further measuring H at different positions along the X-axis an H-x curve can be drawn whose nature is shown in Fig. 6.5. From the curve one may get the value of $\frac{\delta H}{\delta x}$.

(ii) Quincke's Capillary Ascension Method (for liquids, in a uniform field) : This method is widely used for measuring the susceptibility of liquids. This is homogeneous field method.

The experimental arrangement is shown in Fig. 6.6. It is essentially a U-tube, one side of which is wider and the other narrow. Up to a certain height the U-tube is filled with the experimental liquid. The narrow portion of the tube passes between the two poles of a magnet as shown. The apparatus is arranged in such a way that the field at the liquid surface of the wider limb can be neglected.

Let with the application of the field, the liquid experience a pressure p due to which the liquid rises or falls depending on the magnetic nature of the liquid. If h denotes this height, then we have

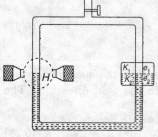

$$p = h\rho g \quad (\rho = \text{density of the liquid})$$

$$= \frac{F}{A}$$

$$= \frac{1}{2}(K_2 - K_1)H^2 \tag{6.31}$$

Fig. 6.6   or, $K_2 = K_1 + \dfrac{2p}{H^2} = K_1 + \dfrac{2h\rho g}{H^2}.$ \hfill (6.32)

If K_1 is known, then K_2 can be calculated by Eq. (6.32). The advantage of this method is that the presence of dust particles of higher susceptibility does not affect the result. So in this method no blank experiment is required to be performed to account for the glass container.

6.5 Determination of Intensity and Susceptibility (Magnetometer Method)

This method was originally applied by Ewing for determining the variation of the intensity of magnetization with the magnetising field strength. A modified arrangement of Ewing's magnetometer is shown in Fig. 6.7.

In the figure, m is a deflection magnetometer with its arms along the east-west direction and ab is a magnetic material in the form of a straight wire. C is a movable coil joined in series with the solenoid S. The circuit is completed through a commutator K, battery B, rheostat rh and an ammeter A.

The experimental wire is placed with its axis east-west so that the earth's magnetic field does not induce

Fig. 6.7

any magnetism in the sample. To start the experiment, the specimen is not inserted within the solenoid but a current is made to pass through S and C to get a deflection in the magnetometer. By a suitable adjustment of the position and the direction of current flow in C, the deflection in m is made equal to zero. In this position C is kept fixed so that the field due to solenoid is not affected for different observations. The specimen is subjected to a number of cyclic operations with a sufficient current in the magnetizing field.

If i be the current and n be the number of turns per unit length of the solenoid, then the magnetizing field is

$$H = ni. \tag{6.33}$$

Due to the above field the sample acquires an intensity of magnetization. If M be the magnetic moment acquired and V be the volume of the specimen, then the intensity of magnetization I can be expressed as

$$I = \frac{M}{V},$$

where $V = l \times \pi r^2.$ \hfill (6.34)

Again, due to the magnetism acquired by ab it exerts an end-on field at m. This field is $\frac{\mu_0}{4\pi}\frac{2Md}{(d^2-l^2)^2}$. Due to this field and the horizontal field H_0 of the earth acting at right angle, the magnetometer reveals a deflection θ following the tangent law. Hence, we can write,

$$\frac{\mu_0}{4\pi}\frac{2Md}{(d^2-l^2)^2} = H_0\tan\theta \quad \text{or,} \quad M = \frac{(d^2-l^2)^2 H_0\tan\theta}{2d}\cdot\frac{4\pi}{\mu_0}.$$

$$\therefore \quad I = \frac{M}{V} = \frac{(d^2-l^2)^2 H_0\tan\theta}{2Vd}\cdot\frac{4\pi}{\mu_0}. \tag{6.35}$$

Knowing H_0 from an auxiliary experiment, I can be calculated. From a knowledge of I and H, the susceptibility $K(= I/H)$ is obtained. Also the permeability μ is found from the relation,

$$\mu = \mu_0(1 + K). \tag{6.36}$$

Magnetization Curves

A plot of the different values of I against H gives the magnetization curve (I-H) as shown in Fig. 6.8(a). For a low value of H, the slope of the curve is also small but with an increase of H it steepens and finally reaches the point S after which I remains almost constant with a further increase of H. At S the magnet is said to have attained magnetic saturation. Similarly, one can draw a B-H curve since $B = \mu_0(H + I)$. The nature is shown in Fig. 6.8(b) where the magnetic saturation is reached at the point S.

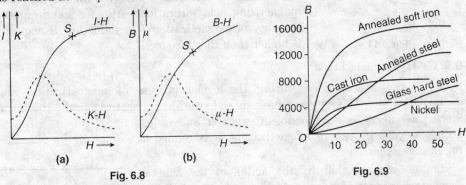

(a)   (b)

Fig. 6.8   **Fig. 6.9**

Since $K = \frac{I}{H}$ and $\mu = \frac{B}{H}$, one can also draw the (K-H) and (μ-H) curve as shown by the dotted lines. A number of magnetization curves for various magnetic materials have been shown in Fig. 6.9.

6.6 Cycle of Magnetization : Hysteresis

If a magnetic material is subjected to a number of cyclic operations of magnetization and demagnetization, the specimen takes up a steady state. Starting from the zero value the specimen is subjected to a gradually increasing magnetizing field until the saturation is attained at S (Fig. 6.10). The field is then decreased gradually to zero value when the intensity of magnetization retained in the sample is Oa and the curve is traced as Sa.

The field is now reversed when the curve ab is obtained. I is reduced to zero at b. The reverse field is

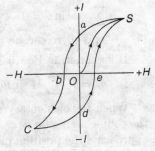

Fig. 6.10

now further increased till in the reverse direction the saturation is obtained at C. With the fall of the negative field to zero the curve Cd is obtained. Next by applying the field in the positive direction again, the saturation point S is restored and thus the complete cyclic operation describes a closed loop $SabCdeS$.

The above loop is characteristic of the material of the specimen and is called the *hysteresis loop*. The ascending and the descending portions of the loop are exactly symmetrical. It is also seen that when H reduces to zero, the intensity of magnetization has a definite value Oa. Thus I lags behind H in a cycle of magnetization and demagnetization. Such lagging of I behind H is known as the phenomenon of hysteresis and the characteristic loop is called the hysteresis loop. The magnetization retained in the sample when H is reduced to zero is a measure of the *retentivity* or *remanence* of the material as represented by Oa in Fig. 6.10 while the negative magnetizing field Ob is required to demagnetize the sample completely and is measure of the *coercivity* of the material.

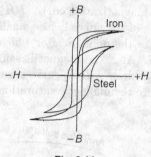

Fig. 6.11

The B-H loop, which can be drawn in a similar way as the I-H, is a more commonly known hysteresis loop. The B-H curve is also a characteristic of the material. As shown in Fig. 6.11, the area of the B-H loop of steel is much greater than that of the soft iron. The coercivity of steel is also much greater. That is why for permanent magnets steel is preferred. However, for electromagnets soft iron is preferred due to the small magnetizing field saturation. Also for soft iron, the intensity of magnetization I or induction B acquired is higher than that for steel.

6.6.1   Hysteresis Loss

Some energy is expanded during the cyclic process of magnetization and demagnetization. This energy exhibits itself in the form of heat within the specimen. Since this energy is not possible to recover and is lost during a cyclic process of magnetization, it is termed as the *hysteresis loss*.

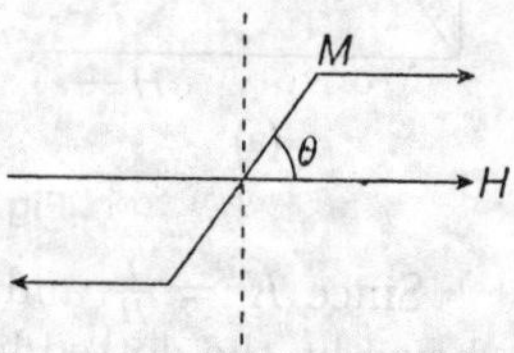

Let us suppose that by the action of the field an elementary magnet of moment M is set at an angle θ with the direction of the field (Fig. 6.12). The component of M along H is $M\cos\theta$ and that at perpendicular to H is $M\sin\theta$. If summed up for unit volume of the specimen,

Fig. 6.12

$$\sum M\cos\theta = I \quad (I = \text{intensity of magnetization}) \tag{6.37}$$

$$\sum M\sin\theta = 0 \tag{6.38}$$

(as there can be no magnetization perpendicular to the magnetizing field)

Differentiating Eq. (6.37), we get

$$dI = -\sum M\sin\theta d\theta. \tag{6.39}$$

When the elementary magnet is inclined at an angle θ with H, the moment of the couple acting on it $= MH\sin\theta$. To displace it through an angle $-d\theta$ so that it approaches the position of perfect alignment along H, the work done on it is

$$d\omega = -\mu_0 MH\sin\theta d\theta.$$

So the work done per unit volume of the specimen,

$$\sum d\omega = dW = -\mu_0 \sum MH \sin\theta d\theta = H \cdot dI,$$

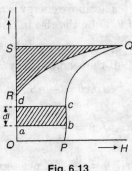

where $H \cdot dI$ represents the elementary shaded area *abcd* of the *I-H* loop (Fig. 6.13).

During the process of magnetization from P to Q the work done is the sum of all such elementary areas taken from P to Q, i.e., by the area $OPQSRO$. Further, during demagnetization of the specimen as represented by QR, the work recovered is represented by the shaded area QSR.

Fig. 6.13

Therefore, the total work expended = area $OPQSRO$ − area QSR

$$= \text{area } OPQRO.$$

Similarly, it can be shown that for a complete *I-H* loop when a single cyclic operation is taken into consideration the work done is

$$\oint H dI = \text{ area of the } I\text{-}H \text{ loop},$$

where $\oint$ represents the integral extending for the whole cyclic process.

Therefore, the work expended (i.e., the energy loss due to hysteresis) for unit volume of the material per cycle of magnetization,

$$W = \oint H \cdot dI = \text{ area of the } I\text{-}H \text{ loop}.$$

Let us now consider the case of B-H loop. For this we start with the equation,

$$B = \mu_0(H + I). \tag{6.40}$$

Differentiating, we get

$$dB = \mu_0(dH + dI). \tag{6.41}$$

Multiplying both sides by H and integrating over the whole cycle, we get

$$\oint H dB = \mu_0 \oint H dH + \mu_0 \oint H dI.$$

But $\quad \oint H dH = 0 \quad [\because H\text{-}H \text{ curve is a straight line}]$

$\therefore \quad \oint H dB = \mu_0 \oint H dI$

or, $\quad \oint H dI = \dfrac{1}{\mu_0} \oint H dB. \tag{6.42}$

From Eq. (6.42) we can conclude that the hysteresis loss of cycle per unit volume of the material is $\frac{1}{\mu_0}$ times the area of the B-H loop.

If S denotes the area of the I-H loop, then the energy loss per cycle per unit volume of the material $= S$ ergs (when I and H are in c.g.s. units).

Let n = frequency of the cyclic operation per second, m = mass of the specimen, ρ = density of the specimen, then,

$$\text{energy loss per second} = \frac{m}{\rho} nS \text{ ergs}.$$

The above energy is converted to heat and raises the temperature of the material. If $\theta\,°C$ be the rise in temperature, then

$$\text{heat generated} = mc\theta \text{ cal } (c = \text{specific heat}).$$

If the whole energy is utilised in heating up the specimen, we can write,

$$Jmc\theta = \frac{m}{\rho}nS$$

or, $$Jc\theta = \frac{nS}{\rho} \tag{6.43}$$

or, $$\theta = \frac{nS}{Jc\rho}\,°C \text{ per second,} \tag{6.44}$$

where J is the mechanical equivalent of heat.

6.6.2 *B–H* Curve by Ballistic Method

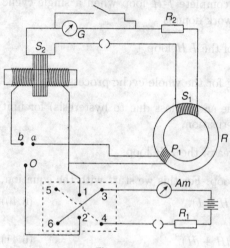

Fig. 6.14

The nature of the magnetization curve can be drawn by a ballistic galvanometer. The circuit diagram of the experiment is shown in Fig. 6.14. The sample is taken in the form of a ring of circular or square cross-section so that there are no free poles and hence the demagnetizing field becomes zero. The magnetizing force in the specimen can, therefore, be calculated from the dimensions and the current in the toroidal winding.

Theory

If a current of I ampere flows through the primary P_1 on an anchor ring, then the magnetizing field of the anchor ring is given by

$$H = 0.4\pi n_p I \quad (n_p = \text{number of turns/cm of the ring})$$

$$= m_1 I, \tag{6.45}$$

where $m_1 = 0.4\pi n_p$.

If B denotes the induction within the specimen, then the magnetic flux embraced by the secondary S_1 of the ring is

$$\psi = BA_1 n_s, \tag{6.46}$$

where A_1 is the mean cross-sectional area of the anchor ring and n_s is the number of turns/cm of the secondary S_1. When this flux is suddenly changed in S_1, the charge passing through the galvanometer circuit is given by

$$q = \frac{BA_1 n_s}{R_t \times 10^8} \text{ coulombs,} \tag{6.47}$$

where R_t = total resistance of the galvanometer circuit. The above charge flowing through the galvanometer produces first throw of d of the light spot. Hence we can write,

$$q = \frac{BA_1 n_s}{R_t \times 10^8} = kd\left(1 + \frac{\lambda}{2}\right), \tag{6.48}$$

where k is a constant.

To find k, a current of C ampere is passed through the primary of the standard solenoid so that the flux embraced by the secondary S_2 is

$$\phi = 0.4\pi n_1 n_2 C A_2, \qquad (6.49)$$

where n_1 is the number of turns/cm of the primary and n_2 is that of the secondary; A_2 is the area of cross-section of the secondary S_2.

If the sudden linking up of this flux in the secondary causes a charge q_1 to move in the galvanometer circuit, then we can write,

$$q_1 = \frac{0.4\pi n_1 n_2 C A_2}{R_t \times 10^8} = k d_1 \left(1 + \frac{\lambda}{2}\right), \qquad (6.50)$$

where d_1 is the first throw of the light spot.

Dividing Eq. (6.48) by Eq. (6.50),

$$\frac{q}{q_1} = \frac{B A_1 n_s}{0.4\pi n_1 n_2 C A_2} = \frac{d}{d_1} \quad \text{or,} \quad B = \frac{0.4\pi n_1 n_2 C A_2}{n_s A_1} \left(\frac{d}{d_1}\right) = m_2 d,$$

where $\quad m_2 = \dfrac{0.4\pi n_1 n_2 A_2}{n_s A_1} \left(\dfrac{C}{d_1}\right).$ $\qquad (6.51)$

Knowing the constants of the apparatus and finding the value of $\left(\frac{C}{d_1}\right)$, one can calculate H and B.

Procedure

After the proper circuit connection, closing the two-way key between O and a the residual magnetism is destroyed. Putting a resistance of value greater than the critical damping resistance in the galvanometer circuit, the resistance of the battery circuit is changed until the current at which the magnetization curve is to be found is attained.

To get the curve for saturation current, the current in the battery circuit is gradually increased and for each case the first throw after reversing the current I is noted. With the increase of the primary current in the ring if the throw shows a constant value, then the magnetization of the iron of the ring attains saturation.

When the saturation current is attained, the maximum current in the primary of the anchor ring is reversed for several times so that the iron attains the steady condition. Now completing the galvanometer circuit, the saturation current is reversed and the throw d' is noted. The rocker is next moved from right to left when the throw d'' is noted again from which $d[= (d' + d'')/2]$ is obtained. From the ammeter the current I is noted and hence H is obtained. Thus we may get a point (H, B) of the curve. By decreasing the primary current different values of B and H can be found.

With the help of a standard solenoid (C/d_1) is determined and thereby m_2 can be calculated.

6.7 Magnetostriction and Villari Effect

If an iron is subjected to an external magnetic field, a small change in length occurs. This was observed by the physicist James P. Joule in 1842. For all ferromagnetic materials such mechanical deformation is observed. This phenomenon can be determined by optical and mechanical levers, and is known as *magnetostriction*.

A converse of this effect was demonstrated by Villari. He showed from suitable experimental arrangement that in iron and steel longitudinal tension increases magnetization for a weak field but there is a definite fall in magnetization when the field is strong. This is known as the *Villari effect*. It can be explained by assuming changes in domains due to the strain developed by the applied tension.

6.8 Steinmetz's Law

A relation between the hysteresis loss W per cc of iron per cycle and the maximum induction B_m was established by Steinmetz. This can be expressed as

$$W = \eta B_m^n, \tag{6.52}$$

where n is a constant whose value lies between 1.6 and 1.7.

Eq. (6.52) gives the famous Steinmetz's law. For hardened steel, $\eta = 0.025$ and for annealed iron, $\eta = 0.0015$ only. Thus W and hence the shape of the hysteresis loop depends on the numerical value of η.

6.9 Magnetic Circuit

By the term magnetic circuit we mean the path or route followed by the lines of flux. Let us consider a toroidal iron ring of magnetic path length l cm and cross-sectional

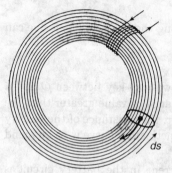

Fig. 6.15

area A (Fig. 6.15). At any point over the ring a coil of n turns per cm carrying a current of I ampere is wound. The strength of the magnetic field H is then written as

$$H = nI. \tag{6.53}$$

Therefore, the magnetic induction in the ring material is

$$B = \mu H \quad (\mu \text{ is the permeability})$$

and the total *flux* passing through the ring is

$$\phi = B \cdot S = \mu H \cdot S$$
$$= \mu S n I. \tag{6.54}$$

If N is the total number of the turns in the coil of the electromagnet, then the above equation can be rewritten as

$$\phi = \frac{N I \mu S}{l}, \tag{6.55}$$

where NI = ampere-turns.

Again, since the intensity inside the ring material is $4\pi nI/10$, it also represents the force per unit N-pole placed inside the material. In order to carry this unit N-pole by a distance dl, the work done is

$$Hdl = nIdl.$$

Therefore, the work done in carrying unit N-pole once round the magnetic circuit of length l is

$$\int_0^l Hdl = nI \cdot l = NI. \tag{6.56}$$

This work done is called the *magnetomotive force*. If it is represented by M, then Eq. (6.55) becomes

$$\phi = \frac{M}{l} \cdot \mu S = \frac{M}{\frac{l}{\mu S}}, \tag{6.56a}$$

where $\frac{l}{\mu S}$ is called the *magnetic reluctance* and $\frac{1}{\mu}$ is referred to as *reluctivity*.

We may now define the above quantities in the following way :

(a) Magnetic flux : Magnetic flux (or magnetic lines of force) is the total number of lines of induction in a magnetic circuit.

(b) Magnetomotive force : It drives or tends to drive flux through a magnetic circuit and is measured by the work done in carrying unit N-pole once round the magnetic circuit.

(c) Reluctance : It is the property of a magnetic material to set up opposition to the creation of magnetic flux in it. The reciprocal of reluctance is called *permeance*.

(d) Reluctivity : It is the specific reluctance of a magnetic circuit.

6.9.1   Comparison of Magnetic and Electric Circuits

(a) Similarities :

Magnetic Circuit	Electric Circuit
(i) Flux = $\dfrac{\text{m.m.f.}}{\text{reluctance}}$	(i) Current = $\dfrac{\text{e.m.f.}}{\text{resistance}}$
(ii) m.m.f. is measured in ampere-turns.	(ii) e.m.f. is measured in volts.
(iii) Reluctance = $\dfrac{1}{\mu A}$	(iii) Resistance, $R = \rho\dfrac{l}{A}$
(iv) Permeance = $\dfrac{1}{\text{reluctance}}$	(iv) Conductance = $\dfrac{1}{\text{resistance}}$
(v) Reluctivity	(v) Resistivity
(vi) Permeability (μ)	(vi) Conductivity (σ)

(b) Dissimilarities :

Magnetic Circuit	Electric Circuit
(i) Magnetic reluctance varies with the flux.	(i) Resistance of a conductor does not depend on the current strength.
(ii) In a magnetic circuit energy is required only to set up the flux initially. Once it is established no energy is expended for its maintenance.	(ii) In an electric circuit energy is required to maintain the current in a circuit.
(iii) μ changes with ϕ.	(iii) σ is independent of the current strength.

6.9.2   Reluctances in Series and Parallel

Since Ohm's law is valid in a magnetic circuit, so the law of series and parallel resistances may be modified in the form of laws of series and parallel reluctances.

(i) Series Reluctances :

$$R = \frac{l_1}{\mu_1 S_1} + \frac{l_2}{\mu_2 S_2} + \frac{l_3}{\mu_3 S_3} + \cdots = \sum_1^n \frac{l_n}{\mu_n S_n}. \tag{6.57}$$

(ii) Parallel Reluctances :

$$\frac{1}{R} = \frac{\mu_1 S_1}{l_1} + \frac{\mu_2 S_2}{l_2} + \frac{\mu_3 S_3}{l_3} + \cdots = \sum_1^n \frac{\mu_n S_n}{l_n}. \tag{6.58}$$

6.9.3 Magnetic Reluctance due to Air Gap

In a.c. machines like motors, dynamos, etc., the iron paths through the core in addition to the air gaps complete the circuit. The effect of an air gap is to increase the total reluctance of the circuit.

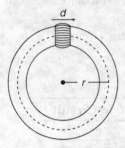

We consider a ring-shaped electromagnet of mean radius r as shown in Fig. 6.16. In it an air gap of width d is made, then the air gap and the iron path being in series, the total reluctance R is given by

$$R = \frac{'d}{1 \times S} + \frac{\text{iron path}}{\mu S}$$

$$= \frac{d}{S} + \frac{2\pi r - d}{\mu S}, \tag{6.59}$$

Fig. 6.16   where S is the sectional area and μ is the permeability.

Eq. (6.59) can be rewritten as

$$R = \frac{2\pi r + (\mu - 1)d}{\mu S}. \tag{6.60}$$

When there is no air gap, the reluctance become $\dfrac{2\pi r}{\mu S}$.

If in the above magnetic circuit with air gap, N be the total number of turns on the core and I ampere be the current flowing through these turns, then

$$\text{m.m.f.} = NI. \tag{6.61}$$

Therefore, the total flux $= \dfrac{NI}{R} = \dfrac{NI \cdot \mu S}{2\pi r + (\mu - 1)d}$

$$= B_a S = \mu H_a S, \tag{6.62}$$

where B_a and H refer to the magnet with air gap.

From Eq. (6.62) we get

$$H_a = \frac{NI}{2\pi r + (\mu - 1)d}. \tag{6.63}$$

Eq. (6.63) gives us the value of the magnetizing field with air gap. If there is no air gap in the ring magnet, the magnetizing field is

$$H = \frac{NI}{2\pi r}. \tag{6.64}$$

Dividing Eq. (6.64) by Eq. (6.63),

$$\frac{H}{H_a} = \frac{NI}{2\pi r} \times \frac{2\pi r + (\mu - 1)d}{NI} = \frac{2\pi r + (\mu - 1)d}{2\pi r}$$

$$= 1 + \frac{(\mu - 1)d}{2\pi r}. \tag{6.65}$$

This provides us a relative measure of H and H_a. Since $H_a < H$, the effect of air gap decreases the magnetic field of the ring magnet, i.e., the air gap has a demagnetizing effect.

6.9.4 Units

The units of flux (ϕ), flux density or induction (B), magnetomotive force (M) and reluctance (R) are usually expressed in c.g.s. electromagnetic units.

According to the above system of units, maxwell is the unit of total magnetic flux. It may be defined as the amount of flux induced through an area of one square centimetre by a perpendicular magnetic field of one gauss. gauss is the SI unit of magnetic induction or magnetic flux density which is equal to one ten-thousandth of a tesla. The unit of m.m.f. is called gilbert which corresponds to 1 erg of work done to take a unit magnetic pole once round the circuit. The unit of reluctance is also known as the reluctance. A magnetic circuit possesses one unit reluctance if one unit m.m.f. is necessary to establish a flux of one maxwell.

6.10 Production of Intense Magnetic Field : Electromagnet

Usually magnetic fields are produced by solenoids, electromagnets or permanent magnets. In order to produce an intense magnetic field, however, electromagnets are preferred in most of the cases.

The conditions to be satisfied in an electromagnet are :

 (i) The core and the pole-pieces must be of proper shape.

 (ii) The core, pole-pieces and the yoke should be made from a material of high permeability.

 (iii) There should be a large number of turns in the coil and it will be capable of standing a large current.

 (iv) There must be a cooling device connected to the coil.

The construction of an electromagnet is shown in Fig. 6.17. Here the total reluctance is the sum of the reluctance of the yoke Y, the pole-pieces P and the air-gap between the pole-pieces. If s_1, s_2 and s_3 represent cross-sections of yoke Y, pole-pieces P and air-gap respectively, then the total reluctance is

$$R = \frac{l_1}{\mu_1 s_1} + \frac{2l_2}{\mu_2 s_2} + \frac{l}{s_3}. \qquad (6.66)$$

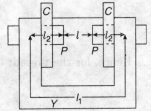

Fig. 6.17

In general, the yoke is a forging of dead mild carbon steel which is magnetically soft. The pole-pieces are also constructed from the same material or by soft iron. The coils C of the electromagnet are excited by 10 to 20 amperes current from a 220 volt d.c. source. For high current, the coils are of bare copper strips of tubings cooled by forcing oil or air.

The electromagnet due to Weiss gave a field strength of 40 000 oersteds approximately.

6.11 Hall Effect

When a magnetic field be applied to a system in which a current is flowing, then there is a tendency for the charge carriers to be deflected laterally. Let an external electric field E be applied along the axis of the specimen, then the electrons will drift in the opposite direction. If a magnetic field is applied perpendicular to the axis of the specimen, then the carriers will be deflected to one side. At the surface of

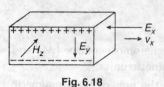

Fig. 6.18

the crystal a surface charge will be developed which will give rise to a transverse electric field. This field is known as the *Hall field*. The *Hall effect* is thus observed when a magnetic field is applied at right angles to a conductor carrying a current. This is shown in Fig. 6.18.

The electric field E which can produce a current I, causes a force of magnitude eE on the electrons. As soon as a magnetic field is applied, a magnetic force proportional to the magnetic field strength H and the average velocity v of the electron also acts on it. Since this force is at right angles to the directions of H and v, so each electron is deflected towards one side of the conductor. Let us consider a slab where an external electric field E_x is applied along the X-axis and a magnetic field H_z along the Z-axis as shown in Fig. 6.18. Due to the application of the electric field a current density I_x will flow in the E_x-direction.

For the time being, we assume that the current is carried by electrons of charge $-e$. By the influence of the magnetic field the electrons will be subjected to a Lorentz force such that the lower surface collects a negative charge and the upper one a positive charge. Finally, a stationary state is attained when the current along y-direction disappears and a field E_y is set up. Now, if the charge carriers were considered positive, then the upper surface would become negative and the lower surface positive, i.e., E_y would be reversed. A measurement of the Hall voltage provides the information about the sign of charge carriers.

The electric force on an electron of charge $-e$ is $-eE$.

Force due to the magnetic field,

$$\vec{H} = -\left(\frac{e}{C}\right)\vec{V} \times \vec{H}.$$

So the total force on an electron,

$$\vec{F} = -e\left[\vec{E} + \frac{1}{C}(\vec{V} \times \vec{H})\right]. \tag{6.67}$$

Hence, for the present case, we can write,

$$F_y = -e\left[E_y - \frac{1}{C}v_x H_z\right]. \tag{6.68}$$

6.11.1 Hall Voltage and Hall Coefficient

In the steady state, the flow of electrons stops, i.e., $F_y = 0$. Therefore, from Eq. (6.68) we have

$$0 = -e\left[E_y - \frac{1}{C}v_x H_z\right]$$

or, $E_y = \dfrac{1}{C}v_x H_z,$ $\tag{6.69}$

where v_x is the average drift velocity.

E_y in Eq. (6.69) is known as the *Hall voltage*.

Again, the current density I can be expressed as

$$I_x = -nev_x \quad \text{(where } n = \text{number of electrons per unit volume)}$$

or, $\quad v_x = -\dfrac{I_x}{ne}.$ \hfill (6.70)

Hence by Eq. (6.69),

$$E_y = \frac{1}{C}\left(-\frac{I_x}{ne}\right)H_z \hfill (6.71)$$

or, $\quad \dfrac{E_y}{I_x \cdot H_z} = -\dfrac{1}{neC} = R_H,$ \hfill (6.72)

where R_H is the Hall coefficient. In the above equation R_H is obtained in e.m.u. If it is considered in e.s.u., then we can write,

$$R_H = -\frac{1}{ne}. \hfill (6.73)$$

6.11.2 Mobility and Hall Angle

If the current-carrying particles acquire a velocity per unit electric field, then the velocity is termed as the mobility which can be expressed as

$$\mu = \frac{v_x}{E_x} \quad \text{or,} \quad v_x = \mu E_x. \hfill (6.74)$$

Putting this value of v_x in Eq. (6.69), we get

$$E_y = \frac{1}{C}\mu E_x H_z. \hfill (6.75)$$

But by Eq. (6.72), we have

$$E_y = R_H I_x H_z. \hfill (6.76)$$

Hence by Eqs. (6.75) and (6.76) we can write,

$$R_H I_x H_z = \frac{1}{C}\mu E_x H_z$$

or, $\quad \mu = \dfrac{R_H I_x}{E_x} \cdot C.$ \hfill (6.77)

Let us put, $\frac{I_x}{E_x} = \sigma$, the electrical conductivity.

$\therefore \quad \mu = R_H \sigma C \quad \text{(in e.s.u.)}$ \hfill (6.78)

or, $\quad \mu = R_H \sigma \quad \text{(in e.m.u.)}.$ \hfill (6.79)

Using Eqs. (6.72) and (6.79), we have

$$\mu = R_H \sigma = \frac{E_y}{I_x H_z}\sigma$$

$$= \frac{E_y}{\sigma E_x H_z}\sigma \quad [\because I_x = \sigma E_x]$$

$$= \frac{E_y}{E_x} \cdot \frac{1}{H_z} = \phi\frac{1}{H_z}, \hfill (6.80)$$

where $\phi = \dfrac{E_y}{E_x}$ is known as the *Hall angle*.

By Eq. (6.80), we get

$$\phi = \mu H_z. \hfill (6.81)$$

6.11.3   Determination of Hall Coefficient

The Hall voltage E_y can be expressed as

$$E_y = -\frac{1}{C} \cdot \frac{I_x}{ne} H_z.$$

If i denotes the total current, then

$$I_x = \frac{i}{b \times d}, \tag{6.82}$$

where b and d are respectively the breadth and thickness of the specimen. Then we have

$$E_y = -\frac{1}{C} \cdot \frac{i}{nebd} H_z$$

or, $E_y d = -\frac{1}{C} \cdot \frac{i}{neb} . H_z = V_H$ (say) [V_H is the Hall voltage] $\tag{6.83}$

Or we can write,

$$V_H = R_H \frac{i}{b} H_z \quad \left[\because R_H = -\frac{1}{neC} \right]$$

or, $R_H = \frac{b}{i} \cdot \frac{V_H}{H_z}.$ $\tag{6.84}$

Knowing i and H_z we may calculate the value of Hall coefficient if the Hall

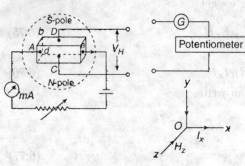

Fig. 6.19

voltage V_H is measured experimentally. The experimental arrangement for the determination of Hall voltage is shown in Fig. 6.19. The Hall voltage V_H developed across C and D can be measured by means of a sensitive galvanometer or by a calibrated potentiometer. In order to increase the accuracy of the measurement, the length of the specimen should be sufficiently large in comparison to its thickness.

Sources of error

(i) It is seen that even in the absence of a magnetic field there exists a potential difference between C and D, in general. This is due to their imperfect alignment. The error can be eliminated by reversing the magnetic field and noting the potential difference again between C and D.

(ii) If a temperature gradient is present, then also some errors may be introduced which can be eliminated by reversing the current and noting another pair of readings with the magnetic field normal and reversed.

6.11.4   Importance of Hall Effect

(i) From the Hall coefficient R_H, the number of charge carriers per unit volume can be calculated.

(ii) The sign of the current-carrying charges can be determined.

(iii) It can be used to find the electronic structure of a substance, i.e., to determine whether the substance is a metal, a semiconductor or an insulator.

(iv) If the Hall constant of a slab is known, then the knowledge of Hall voltage helps to measure high unknown magnetic field.

(v) It provides us the concept of negative mass as explained by Bleaney.

(vi) The mobility can be measured directly.

Examples

1. Two magnets A and B are caused to oscillate in the same magnetic field. A performs 15 vib/min and B 10 vib/min. The magnet A is then caused to oscillate in one magnetic field and B in another. If then A performs 5 vib/min and B 20 vib/min, compare the intensities of the fields in which A and B oscillate and also compare the magnetic moments of the magnets.

Solution : Let the intensity of the first field in which A and B oscillate be H_1, the intensity of the second field in which only A oscillates be H_2 and that in which only B oscillates be H_3. Then

$$\text{for } A,\ H_1 \propto 15^2 \quad \text{and} \quad H_2 \propto 5^2$$

and for B, $H_1 \propto 10^2$ and $H_3 \propto 20^2$.

$$\therefore \quad \frac{H_2}{H_1} = \frac{5^2}{15^2} = \frac{1}{9} \quad \text{and} \quad \frac{H_3}{H_1} = \frac{20^2}{10^2} = \frac{4}{1}.$$

$$\therefore \quad \frac{H_2}{H_3} = \frac{\frac{1}{9}}{\frac{4}{1}} = \frac{1}{36} \quad \text{or,} \quad H_2 : H_3 = \mathbf{1 : 36}.$$

Again, for A, $T_1 = 2\pi\sqrt{\dfrac{I}{M_1 H}}$ and for B, $T_2 = 2\pi\sqrt{\dfrac{I}{M_2 H}}$.

$$\therefore \quad \frac{M_1}{M_2} = \frac{T_2^2}{T_1^2} = \frac{n_1^2}{n_2^2},$$

where n_1 and n_2 are the numbers of vibrations performed in one minute by A and B, respectively.

Hence, $\dfrac{M_1}{M_2} = \dfrac{15^2}{10^2} = \dfrac{9}{4}$.

2. A specimen of iron of density 7.7 g/cc and specific heat 0.11 is magnetized by an alternating field of frequency 100 cycles/second. Assuming no loss of heat, calculate the rise in temperature of the iron per min, if the hysteresis loss is 50 000 ergs per cc per cycle.

Solution : If θ be the rise in temperature, then we have

$$\theta = \frac{nS}{Jc\rho} \times 60 = \frac{100 \times 50\,000 \times 60}{4.2 \times 10^7 \times 0.11 \times 7.7} = \mathbf{8.4\,°C.}$$

3. Calculate the loss of energy caused by hysteresis in one hour in 50 kg of iron when subjected to cyclic magnetic changes. The frequency is 25 and the area of the hysteresis loop represents 24 000 ergs per cc and the density of iron is 7.8.

Solution : The energy loss/second $= \dfrac{m}{\rho}nS.$

Here, $m = 50 \times 10^3$ g, $n = 25$, $S = 24\,000$ ergs/cc and time $= 3\,600$ seconds,

Therefore, energy loss $= \dfrac{50 \times 10^3}{7.8} \times 25 \times 24\,000 \times 3\,600$

$$= \mathbf{1.38 \times 10^{13}\ ergs.}$$

4. The magnetic moment of a steel bar magnet weighing 66 g is 2 500. If the density of steel is 7.9 g/cc, find the intensity of magnetization.

Solution : Volume of the magnet, $V = \dfrac{\text{mass}}{\text{density}} = \dfrac{66}{7.9}$ cc

Therefore, intensity, $I = \dfrac{M}{V} = \dfrac{2500}{66/7.9} = \dfrac{2500 \times 7.9}{66} = \mathbf{299.24.}$

5. A magnetic field of 50 e.m.u. generates a flux of 2 500 e.m.u. in a long bar of steel. Calculate the permeability and intensity of magnetization of the bar, its cross-section being 0.25 sq. cm.

Solution : Magnetic induction or flux density, $B = \dfrac{N}{S}$,

where $N = 2\,500$ cm units and $S = 0.25$ sq. cm.

$\therefore \qquad B = \dfrac{2500}{0.25} = 10^4$ e.m.u.

Now, permeability, $\mu = \dfrac{B}{H} = \dfrac{10^4}{50}$ $[\because H = 50$ e.m.u.$]$

$$= 200.$$

Since $B = H + 4\pi I$ or, $10^4 = 50 + 4\pi I$

or, $\quad I = \dfrac{10^4 - 50}{4\pi} = \mathbf{791.47\ e.m.u.}$

6. An anchor ring of mean diameter 30 cm is wound with 200 turns of wire carrying a current of 2 amperes. The cross-section of the magnetic material of the ring is 12 sq. cm., and its permeability is 1 000. What is the flux through it?

Solution : We have, m.m.f. $= \dfrac{4\pi N I}{10}$ and reluctance $= \dfrac{l}{\mu S}$.

Here, $N = 200$, $I = 2$ A, $l = 2\pi r = 2\pi \cdot \frac{30}{2} = 30\pi$ cm, $\mu = 1000$, $S = 12$ cm^2.

Therefore, flux through the ring $= \dfrac{\text{m.m.f.}}{\text{reluctance}} = \dfrac{\frac{4\pi \times 200 \times 2}{10}}{\frac{30\pi}{1000 \times 12}}$

$$= \mathbf{64\,000\ maxwells.}$$

7. A coil of 200 turns is wound on a circular iron ring of circumference 100 cm and of cross-section 2 sq. cm and carries a current of 3 amperes. Calculate (a) magnetomotive force, (b) reluctance and (c) flux density within the iron, assuming that its permeability is 500 c.g.s. units.

Solution : (a) m.m.f. $= \dfrac{4\pi N I}{10} = \dfrac{4\pi \times 200 \times 3}{10} = \mathbf{753.6\ gilberts.}$

(b) Reluctance $= \dfrac{l}{\mu S} = \dfrac{100}{500 \times 2} = \mathbf{0.1.}$

(c) Flux, $\phi = \mu S \cdot H$ $\left[\because H = \dfrac{\phi}{\mu S} \right]$

$$= \mu S \cdot \frac{4\pi NI}{10l} = \frac{500 \times 2 \times 4\pi \times 200 \times 3}{10 \times 100}$$

$$= 2\,400\pi \text{ maxwells.}$$

Therefore, flux density $= \dfrac{\phi}{S} = \dfrac{2400\pi}{2} = 1\,200\pi$

$$= 3\,768 \text{ maxwells/sq. cm.}$$

8. In an experiment to determine M/H, using deflection magnetometer in the end-on position, the centre of the bar magnet was placed 20 cm from the magnetometer compass. The deflection was $18°$ and the length of the magnet is 10 cm. If $H = 0.18$ c.g.s. unit, calculate the moment of the bar magnet.

   [C.U. 1966]

   Solution : We know, $\dfrac{M}{H} = \dfrac{(r^2 - l^2)^2}{2r} \tan \theta.$

   Here, $r = 20$ cm, $\theta = 18°$, $l = 5$ cm and $H = 0.18$ c.g.s. unit.

   $\therefore \quad \dfrac{M}{0.18} = \dfrac{(400 - 25)^2}{2 \times 20} \tan 18°$

   or, $\quad M = \dfrac{(375)^2}{40} \times 0.3249 \times 0.18$

   $$= \textbf{205.6 units (approx.).}$$

9. In an experiment to determine M/H using a deflection magnetometer in the 'end-on' position, the centre of the bar magnet was placed 20 cm from the magentometer compass. The defelction was $18°$ and the length of the magnet was 10 cm. If $H = 0.18$ Oe, calculate the moment of the bar magnet. Given that $\tan 18° = 0.3249.$

   Solution : Here, $\dfrac{M}{H} = \dfrac{4\pi \mu_0 (d^2 - l^2)^2}{2d} \tan \theta.$

   Given that $d = 20$ cm $= 0.2$ m; $l = 5$ cm $= 0.5$ m; $H = 0.18 \times \frac{10^3}{4\pi}$ A-m^{-1}; $\mu_0 = 12.56 \times 10^{-7}$ and $\theta = 18°$.

   $\therefore \quad \dfrac{M \times 4\pi}{0.18 \times 10^3} = \dfrac{4\pi \mu_0 (0.04 - 0.0025)^2 \tan 18°}{2 \times 0.2} = \dfrac{4\pi \mu_0 \times 0.00141 \times 0.3249}{0.4}$

   $\therefore \quad M = \dfrac{\mu_0 \times 0.00141 \times 0.3249 \times 0.18 \times 10^3}{0.4} = \mu_0 \times 0.2$

   $$= 12.56 \times 0.2 \times 10^{-7} = \textbf{2.512} \times \textbf{10}^{-7} \textbf{ Wb-m.}$$

10. A short bar magnet of moment $2\pi \times 10^{-7}$ Wb-m placed on a horizontal table with its north pole pointing $30°$ east of magnetic north. In what direction will a small compass needle set if it is placed on the table 20 cm magnetic north of the bar magnet. $H = 14$ A-m^{-1}

    Solution : Let NS be a bar magnet. The component of magnetic moment along the magnetic axis $M_1 = M \cos 30° = \frac{\sqrt{3}}{2} \cdot M$ and its perpendicular component $M_2 = M \sin 30° = \frac{M}{2}.$ Intensity at the point P,

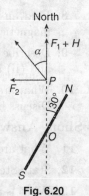

Fig. 6.20

$$F_1 = \frac{2M_1}{4\pi \mu_r \mu_0 \cdot r^3} = \frac{2M(\sqrt{3}/2)}{4\pi \mu_r \mu_0 r^3}$$

Here, $\mu_r = 1$, $r = 0.2$ m, $\mu_0 = 4\pi \times 10^{-7}$, $M = 2\pi \times 10^{-7}$ Wb-m.

$$\therefore \quad F_1 = \frac{2 \times 2\pi \times 10^{-7} \times (\sqrt{3}/2)}{4\pi(4\pi \times 10^{-7}) \times (0.2)^3} = 8.62 \text{ A-m}^{-1}.$$

11. If two bar magnets of same mass and size are set to oscillate in the earth's magnetic field, one of it makes 12 oscillations per minute while the other 15 oscillations. Compare their magnetic moments.

Solution : We have $M_1 H = \dfrac{4\pi^2 I}{T_1^2}$ and $M_2 H = \dfrac{4\pi^2 I}{T_2^2}$.

$$\therefore \quad \frac{M_1}{M_2} = \frac{T_2^2}{T_1^2}.$$

Here, $T_1 = \dfrac{60 \text{ seconds}}{12} = 5$ seconds and $T_2 = \dfrac{60 \text{ seconds}}{15} = 4$ seconds.

$$\therefore \quad \frac{M_1}{M_2} = \frac{4^2}{5^2} = \frac{16}{25}.$$

Questions

Essay-type

1. Describe the deflection and vibration magnetometers. How would you use them to determine the horizontal component of the earth's magnetic field? Deduce the necessary formulae.

2. Describe a deflection magnetometer.

3. Describe a method of determining the horizontal component of the earth's magnetic field with the help of two suitable magnetometers.

4. What is inverse square law of magnetic force? Verify the law.

5. Define magnetic moment and describe a method by which you can compare the magnetic moments of two magnets. Derive expression you would use in your experiment.

6. What is a magnetometer? Describe with suitable theory a vibration magnetometer. How is this magnetometer used for (i) comparison of magnetic moments and (ii) comparison of field strengths?

7. What is Searles magnetometer? Explain how the inverse square law can be verified. Describe a deflection magnetometer.

8. Find an expression for force on a para- or ferromagnetic body placed in a magnetic field.

9. Describe briefly how you can measure (i) susceptibility by Quincke's method and (ii) intensity by magnetometer method.

10. What are magnetization curves and hysteresis? Calculate the hysteresis loss. Discuss how the B-H curve can be obtained by ballistic method.

Short Answer-type

11. What are magnetostriction and Villari effect?

12. State Steinmetz's law.

13. What is a magnetic circuit?

14. What do you mean by the terms magnetic flux, magnetomotive force and reluctance.

15. Make a comparative study of magnetic and electric circuits.

16. Write down expression for magnetic reluctance due to air-gap.

17. Define the units: maxwell, gauss, gilbert and reluctance.

18. What is an electromagnet?

19. What is Hall effect?

Numerical Problems

20. Two short bar magnets produce the same deflection in a magnetometer needle when their centres are respectively 30 cm and 40 cm from the needle. What is the ratio of the magnetic moments? **[Ans. 5 : 3]**

21. A magnetic field of 20 cm unit produces a flux of 2400 e.m.u. in a bar of iron of cross-section 0.2 sq. cm. Calculate the permeability and intensity of magnetization. **[Ans. 600; 953.2 cm unit]**

22. If the intensity due to a bar magnet at a point on its axis 30 cm from its centre is 0.2 gauss and if the length and cross-sectional area of the bar are 5 cm and 2 sq. cm respectively, find approximately its mean intensity of magnetization. **[Ans. 266.3]**

23. It is required to produce a magnetic flux of 2000 in the air gap in a uniform ring of soft iron of diameter 24 cm. Calculate the ampere-turns required if the cross-section of the iron in the ring is 4 sq. cm, the length of the air-gap is 2 cm and the permeability of iron is 800. **[Ans. 825.9]**

24. Two bar magnets, the moment of one being double than that of the other but otherwise similar, are arranged in parallel, one above the other, first with their like poles in contact and then with their unlike poles in contact. Find the ratio of the periods of vibration of the combination in the same magnetic field. **[Ans. $1 : \sqrt{3}$]**

25. The period of oscillation of a vibration magnetometer is T under the earth's field alone. When a bar magnet of magnetic length 16 cm is placed with its centre 20 cm east of the magnetometer and with its axis parallel to the magnetic meridian, the only change observed is a diminution of the period to $T/2$. If $H = 0.2$ oersted, then determine the pole strength of the magnet.

Ans. 375 units]

26. In an experiment to find M/H with a deflection magnetometer at tan A position, the centre of the bar magnet is at a distance of 25 cm from the compass-needle and the length of this magnet is 10 cm, the deflection of the compass-needle being 21°. If the magnetic moment of the bar magnet be 1000 c.g.s. unit, what is the horizontal intensity of the earth's magnetic field?

[Ans. 0.3616 oersted]

27. In an experiment with a magnetometer, a small magnet A produces a deflection of 30° when it is placed at a distance of 40 cm from the centre of the magnetometer needle in a tan A position; another small magnet B produces a deflection of 20° when it is in the tan B position and at a distance of 30 cm. Compare the moments of the two magnets. **[Ans. $\frac{M_A}{M_B} = \frac{1.88}{1.00}$]**

Review Short Questions on *Magnetostatics*
(with Answers)

Natural and Artificial Magnets

1. *What are natural and artificial magnets?*

Ans. A natural magnet is defined as a substance which occurs in nature as an ore and have weak attractive and directive properties.

The attractive and directive properties can be developed strongly in some metals or alloys. Magnets so prepared are called artificial magnets.

2. *Define the terms 'Pole', 'Magnetic Axis' and 'Neutral Region'.*

Ans. *Pole*—When a magnet is dipped into iron filings, attraction appears to be strongest near the two ends of the magnet. These two regions of the magnet are called poles.

Magnetic Axis—If the two poles of a magnet are joined by a straight line, then that line is called magnetic axis.

Neutral Region—It is the central part of the magnet where the magnet has no attracting power.

3. *What is the magnetic length and how is it related to the actual length?*

Ans. The distance joining the two poles of a magnet is the magnetic length and it is about 0.85 times the actual length.

4. *Distinguish between the magnetic meridian and geographical meridian.*

Ans. Magnetic meridian is an imaginary vertical plane passing through the magnetic axis of a freely suspended magnet at a place. Geographical meridian on the other hand, is an imaginary vertical plane passing through the given place on the earth's surface and the geographical north and south poles of the earth.

5. *What are the different ways of magnetization?*

Ans. An iron piece can be magnetized by striking it with magnets in three different ways. These are : **(i)** method of single touch, **(ii)** method of separate or divided touch and **(iii)** method of double touch.

6. *What is meant by magnetic saturation and magnetic induction?*

Ans. When the intensity of the magnetizing field becomes greater than a certain value, the degree of magnetization cannot be increased further. The bar, at this stage, is said to have acquired magnetic saturation.

A phenomenon by which temporary magnetism is developed in a magnetic substance due to the influence of another magnet is called magnetic induction.

7. *How the magnetism of any magnet may be destroyed?*

Ans. The magnetism of a magnet may be destroyed **(i)** by rough handling, **(ii)** by heating the magnet and **(iii)** by induction.

Magnetic Field : Potential

8. *What are the laws of magnetic force?*

Ans. The following are the two laws of magnetic force : **(i)** Similar poles repel while the dissimilar poles attract each other. **(ii)** The force of attraction or repulsion between two magnetic poles varies directly as the product of their pole strengths and inversely as the square of the distance between them.

182

If two poles of strengths m_1 and m_2, are separated by a distance d, then the force F is given by

$$F \propto m_1 m_2 \quad \text{and} \quad F \propto \frac{1}{d^2},$$

i.e., $\quad F \propto \dfrac{m_1 m_2}{d^2} \quad$ or, $\quad F = \dfrac{m_1 m_2}{\mu d^2},$

where the constant μ is known as the permeability of the medium.

9. *What is inverse square law?*

Ans. The force between two magnetic poles is inversely proportional to the square of the distance between them. Mathematically, $F \propto \frac{1}{d^2}$, when m_1 and m_2 are constants. This law is known as the inverse square law.

10. *Explain the term 'unit magnetic pole'.*

Ans. Let us consider that two like poles are placed in air medium. If $m_1 = m_2 = 1$ and $d = 1$ cm, then $F = 1$ dyne.

The unit magnetic pole is defined as a pole of such strength that it exerts in air a repulsive force of 1 dyne on an exactly similar pole placed at a distance of 1 cm.

11. *Define intensity of a magnetic field.*

Ans. When a magnetic pole is kept at any point in the space round a pole or a magnet, it experiences a force. If a unit north pole is taken particularly, the force exerted on it is called the magnetic intensity or the strength of the magnetic field.

12. *What is the unit of intensity?*

Ans. The unit of intensity in the c.g.s. system is called an oersted. The intensity of the field at a point becomes 1 oersted when a unit north pole is acted on with a force of 1 dyne at that point.

13. *Define magnetic lines of force.*

Ans. The magnetic lines of force may be defined as follows : "A line of force is a continuous curve drawn in a magnetic field such that the tangent at any point on it shows the direction of the resultant force at that point."

14. *Write down the important properties of lines of force.*

Ans. (i) They are closed curves.

(ii) They start from a N-pole and terminate on a S-pole, being continuous through the body of the magnet.

(iii) They can never intersect one another.

(iv) They are always in a state of longitudinal tension.

15. *What are neutral points?*

Ans. Depending on the axis of a magnet, there are two fixed points in a magnetic field where the intensity due to the magnet becomes equal and opposite to the intensity of the earth's magnetism. These fixed points are known as neutral points.

16. *What do you mean by magnetic potential and magnetic moment of a magnet?*

Ans. Magnetic potential may be defined as the amount of work done in bringing a unit N-pole from infinity up to that point against the magnetic intensity.

Magnetic moment may be defined as the product of the strength of one of its poles and the distance between them.

If m = strength of the pole,

and $2l$ = length of the magnet,

then magnetic moment,

$$M = m \times 2l.$$

17. *What will be the resultant magnetic moments of two magnets?*

Ans. If M_1 and M_2 are the magnetic moments of two magnets fixed on a common support with angle α, then the resultant magnetic moment M is given by,

$$M = \sqrt{M_1^2 + M_2^2 + 2M_1 M_2 \cos \alpha}.$$

18. *What is the relation between intensity and potential of a magnet?*

Ans. If H represents the field intensity and dv represents the potential difference between two points for a distance dx, then we can write,

$$H = -\frac{dv}{dx}.$$

Thus the magnetic intensity at a point is the negative gradient of the magnetic potential at that point.

19. *What will be the magnetic potential at a distance r due to a magnetic pole m?*

Ans. The potential V can be represented by the equation,

$$V = \frac{m}{r}.$$

20. *Define the term 'magnetic moment'.*

Ans. The product of the effective length of the magnet and its pole strength is called the magnetic moment.

21. *What will be the moment of the mechanical couple acting on a magnet?*

Ans. The moment of the mechanical couple G acting on a magnet is given by

$$G = 2l \sin \theta \times mH = MH \sin \theta,$$

where $M = 2l \times m$ is the magnetic moment.

22. *What will be the work done in rotating a magnet?*

Ans. The total work done by the magnet in rotating through an angle θ is

$$W = MH(1 - \cos \theta).$$

This energy is stored up in the form of potential energy.

23. *How the value of magnetic moment differs with temperature?*

Ans. The value of magnetic moment undergoes a change with temperature by the relation,

$$M = M_0(1 - \alpha\theta),$$

where α is a constant.

24. *What is a magnetic shell?*

Ans. A magnetic shell is a very thin sheet made by ferro-magnetic material and whose polarities are opposite in the two faces.

25. *What will be the value of the moment of the magnetic shell?*

Ans. The moment of the magnetic shell is equal to the product of its strength and surface area. Mathematically, we can write the moment M by the relation,

$$M = \phi A,$$

where ϕ is the strength and A the surface area.

26. *What will be the potential at a point due to a magnetic shell?*

Ans. The potential at a point due to a magnetic shell is given by

$$V = \phi \Omega,$$

where ϕ is the strength and Ω is the solid angle subtended by the contour of the shell at the point.

27. *What is meant by the intensity of magnetization?*

Ans. The intensity of magnetization may be defined as the pole strength acquired by the end faces of the sample per unit area of cross-section.

Magnetic Measurements

28. *What is meant by uniform magnetic field?*

Ans. If a magnetic field is everywhere same in both magnitude and direction, then the field is said to be uniform. The action of a uniform field is only directive and not translatory in nature.

29. *"The two poles of a magnet are of equal strength." Justify the statement.*

Ans. Let m and m' be the pole strengths of the north and south poles of a magnet placed in a uniform field of strength H. Then the force acting on the poles are mH and $m'H$. Now if the magnet is suspended freely at its c.g., the magnet will not move as a whole along the direction of the field. In the equilibrium position the forces acting on the needle by the earth's magnetic field neutralise one another, i.e., they are equal in magnitude but opposite in direction. So we have

$$mH = -m'H \quad \text{or,} \quad m = -m'.$$

Thus we can conclude that the two poles of a magnet are of equal strength but of opposite in kind.

30. *State tangent law.*

Ans. If F represents the field strength and H the magnetic intensity, then we have

$$F = H \tan \theta.$$

The tangent of the angle of reflection is, therefore, equal to the ratio of F to H. If H is a constant field, then

$$F \propto \tan \theta.$$

This is known as the tangent law.

31. *What are tangent A and B positions of gauss?*

Ans. When the magnetic axis of the deflecting magnet is placed perpendicular to the magnetic meridian, two distinct positions of the deflected magnetic needle are found. The magnetic needle in A-position is kept on the axial line while the needle in B-position is kept on the equatorial line of the deflecting magnet.

32. *What are the uses of a magnetometer?*

Ans. Magnetometers are used for **(i)** verifying the inverse square law, **(ii)** comparing magnetic moments and **(iii)** comparing magnetic field strengths.

33. *What relation can be utilised for determining the period of oscillation of a magnet?*

Ans. The period of oscillation of a magnet is obtained by using the relation,

$$T = 2\pi\sqrt{\frac{I}{MH}},$$

where M and H are the magnetic moment of the needle and the horizontal component of the earth's magnetic field respectively, and I represents the moment of inertia of the needle.

34. *What factors control the periodic time?*

Ans. The periodic time depends on : **(i)** the moment of inertia of the needle, **(ii)** the moment of the needle, and **(iii)** the earth's horizontal intensity.

35. *Will the values of MH and M/H remain same when you perform the experiment at different places of the world?*

Ans. The variation of H at different places are different. As a result the values of MH and M/H will also differ.

36. *Why do you keep the deflections of the needle small?*

Ans. If the deflection of the needle is small, then the error in the measurement of M/H would be minimum.

37. *Can you find the pole strength of the deflecting magnet by finding the magnetic moment?*

Ans. By dividing the magnetic moment (M) with the magnetic length $(2l)$ the pole strength (m) can be obtained.

Magnetic Properties of Substances

38. *Define the terms 'total induction', 'magnetizing force' and 'intensity of magnetization'.*

Ans. Total induction is defined as the total number of lines of force passing through unit area of the medium. **Magnetizing force** is defined as the magnetic force to which magnetic substance is subjected. **Intensity of magnetization** is defined as the pole strength per unit area or the magnetic moment per unit volume.

In the mathematical relation $B = H + 4\pi I$, B represents the total induction, H the magnetizing force and I the intensity of magnetization.

39. *Find the difference between (a) permeability and susceptibility, (b) retentivity and coercivity.*

Ans. (a) Permeability (μ) is defined as the ratio of total induction (B) to the magnetising force (H). Mathematically,

$$\mu = \frac{B}{H}.$$

Susceptibility (K), on the other hand, is defined as the ratio of intensity of magnetization (I) to the magnetizing force (H). Mathematically,

$$K = \frac{I}{H}.$$

(b) Retentivity is the property of a magnetic substance due to which it retains a major portion of magnetism when subjected to a magnetizing force.

Coercivity, on the other hand, is the property of a magnetic substance due to which it retains magnetism in spite of any demagnetizing influence or heating, rough handling, etc.

40. *Make a comparative study of dia-, para- and ferro-magnetic substances.*

Ans.

Dia-magnets	Para-magnets	Ferro-magnets
These may be solid, liquid or gas.	These may be solid, liquid or gas.	These are solid in nature with a definite crystalline structure.
Feebly repelled by a magnetic field.	Feebly attracted towards a magnetic field.	Strongly attracted towards a magnetic field.
Permeability is less than unity.	μ is slightly greater than unity.	μ is greater than unity.
A dia-magnetic bar tends to set itself perpendicular to the direction of the magnetic field.	A para-magnetic bar sets itself parallel to the field.	A ferro-magnetic bar sets itself parallel to the field.
Susceptibility is small and negative.	K is small and positive.	K is positive and greater than unity.
Susceptibility does not vary with temperature.	K falls with temperature.	K falls with temperature.
No hysteresis is exhibited.	No hysteresis is exhibited.	Hysteresis is exhibited.
They possess no retentivity.	They possess no retentivity.	They possess retentivity.
They have no Curie-point.	They have no Curie-point.	They have definite Curie-points.
B and I vary linearly but no saturation is attained.	B and I vary linearly with H and tend towards saturation.	B and I vary with H but not linearly and finally attain saturation.

41. *How the hysteresis loss is related to the area of the B-H loop for the substance?*

Ans. The hysteresis loss per cycle per unit volume of the substance is found to be $\frac{1}{4}\pi$ times the area of the B-H loop for the substance.

Terrestrial Magnetism

42. *What is meant by the magnetic equator?*

Ans. The magnetic equator is an irregular imaginary line passing round the earth near the equator, on which a magnetic needle has no dip.

43. *How is the magnetic field of the earth specified at any place?*

Ans. The magnetic field of the earth at any place can be specified by considering three factors. These are : **(i)** the **dip, (ii)** the **declination** and **(iii)** the **horizontal intensity**.

44. *What are the magnetic elements of the earth at a place?*

Ans. The dip (or inclination), declination (or variation) and the horizontal intensity are known as the magnetic elements of the earth at a place.

45. *Define the terms : (i) Dip, (ii) Declination and (iii) Horizontal intensity.*

Ans. (i) *Dip*—is the angle which the earth's resultant magnetic intensity makes at a place with the horizontal direction.

(ii) *Declination*—is the angle at a given place between the magnetic meridian and the geographical meridian.

(iii) *Horizontal intensity* is the resolved part of the earth's resultant magnetic intensity at a place in the horizontal direction along the magnetic meridian.

46. *How can you determine the total intensity of the earth's magnetic field?*

Ans. If I represents the total intensity of the earth's magnetic field, then we have

$$I = \frac{H}{\cos \delta} \quad \text{and} \quad I = \frac{V}{\sin \delta},$$

where H and V are the horizontal and vertical components of the earth's magnetic field respectively and δ is the dip.

From the equations we get

$$I^2 = H^2 + V^2 \quad \text{or,} \quad I = \sqrt{H^2 + V^2}$$

and $\dfrac{V}{H} = \tan \delta.$

Measuring H by oscillation and deflection experiments and δ by dip circle, I is found out.

The horizontal and vertical components can also be found out by using the earth inductor and a ballistic galvanometer.

47. *Are the magnetic elements constant at all places?*

Ans. No; the values are different at different places of the world.

48. *How does the earth's magnetic field run?*

Ans. The earth's magnetic field is running from south to north along a vertical plane known as the magnetic meridian.

49. *Why is it impossible to isolate a single magnetic pole?*

Ans. Each electron behaves like a tiny magnet. This arises out of a spinning motion of the electron about some axis through it, referred to as 'electron spin'. Further, electrons move in orbits round the nucleus. This orbital motion also gives rise to magnetism. We may thus say that the magnetism is a property of electric charges in motion.

50. *What is meant by the statement that the pole strength of a magnet is 50 units?*

Ans. Pole strength of a magnet is 50 units means that this pole will exert a force of 50 units on a unit pole situated at a unit distance.

51. *What do you mean by the following two statements : (i) dip of earth's magnetic field at Kolkata is 22° N, (ii) declination of earth's magnetic field at a place is 30° E?*

Ans. (i) 'Dip of the earth's magnetic field at Kolkata is 22°N' means that the angle between the direction of the earth's magnetic field and the horizontal measured in the plane of the magnetic meridian is 22° and the north pole of the magnetic needle sinks down.

(ii) 'Declination of the earth's magnetic field at a place is 30°E' means that the angle between the magnetic meridian and the true geographical north at the place under consideration is 30° and the compass needle points to the east of true north.

52. *State the name of the magnetic intensity in c.g.s. electromagnetic unit.*

Ans. The c.g.s. electromagnetic unit of magnetic intensity is called 'oersted'.

53. *The dip at Kolkata is 30°. Find the total intensity and vertical intensity of the earth's magnetic field at Kolkata.*

Ans. We have, angle of dip at Kolkata, $\theta = 30°$,

horizontal component, $H = 0.36$ Oe.

$\therefore$ total intensity, $I = \dfrac{H}{\cos\theta} = \dfrac{0.36}{\cos 30°} = \dfrac{36 \times 2}{\sqrt{3}} = 0.416$ Oe

Vertical intensity, $V = I \sin\theta = 0.416 \cdot \dfrac{1}{2} = 0.208$ Oe.

54. *A vertical pillar introduced partly in earth is seen to be magnetized after a few years. What will be the nature of polarity at the top of the pillar at the northern hemisphere of the earth.*

Ans. The earth's magnetic intensity at the northern hemisphere is in the downward direction. Hence the vertical component of the earth's magnetic intensity will be directed towards the centre of the earth and this vertical component will induce magnetism to the pillar. Hence at the top of the pillar south pole will be induced.

55. *Permanent magnets gradually lose strength even when left undisturbed— why? How is it possible to maintain their strength longer?*

Ans. Due to self-demagnetisation, magnets often lose strength. In order to minimise this effect, a piece of soft iron is placed across the poles of a horse-shoe magnet and the bar magnets are kept in pairs with opposite poles side by side having a soft-iron piece placed across the poles at each end. The soft-iron piece is known as the magnetic keepers.

56. *Two iron bars A and B are given to you; one of which is magnetized. Without using any aid, how will you determine which one is magnetized?*

Ans. *A* and *B* are the two iron bars given, one of which is magnet. Let us keep *B* on the table and run one end of the bar *A* from one end of *B* to the other, keeping all the time the end of *A* in contact with *B*. If a force of attraction is felt on points away from the middle of *B* but no attraction is felt at the middle of *B*, then *B* is the magnetised bar while *A* is not. If, on the other hand, attraction is felt at all points along the bar *B*, then *A* is the magnetised bar while *B* is not.

57. *Why are lines of force shown straight and parallel for indicating a uniform magnetic field?*

Ans. The straight and parallel lines indicate that equal number of lines of force can pass normally through unit area at any point of the field. It means the same intensity at any point and hence a uniform magnetic field.

58. *Do (i) magnetic length, (ii) pole-strength and (iii) magnetic moment change if a magnetized wire of 5 cm length is bent to bring its ends 1 cm apart?*

Ans. (i) Since the magnetic length is the distance between the two poles of the magnet, so it is 5 cm before bending and 1 cm after bending.

(ii) Pole-strength does not change.

(iii) We know that the magnetic moment is equal to the product of the pole-strength (m) and the magnetic length. So,

magnetic moment before bending, $M = m \times 5$

and magnetic moment after bending, $M' = m \times 1$.

Thus due to bending the initial moment M reduces to $\frac{1}{5}M$.

59. *A magnetized steel wire of length l has a magnetic moment M. It is then bent into a semicircular arc. What is the new magnetic moment?*

Ans. If m be the pole-strength and l be the length of the magnet, then magnetic moment, $M = ml$ (before bending).

The magnetized wire is bent into a semicircular arc when the distance between the poles is equal to the diameter of the circle d.

So after bending, the magnetic length $= d$.

$\therefore$ the magnetic moment, $M' = m \times d$.

Now, the length of the wire l = half the circumference, $\frac{\pi d}{2}$

or, $d = \frac{2l}{\pi}$.

$\therefore \quad M' = m\frac{2l}{\pi} = \frac{2lm}{\pi} = \frac{2M}{\pi}$.

Thus due to bending M reduces to $\frac{2M}{\pi}$.

60. *"A permanent magnet is kept on a table. It is seen to be gradually demagnetised." Explain why.*

Ans. The magnet is gradually demagnetised by its own magnetic field. The field at the sides of the magnet is directed from N-pole to S-pole and as a result the slow and gradual demagnetisation occurs.

61. *The intensity at a point on the tan-A position due to a short bar magnet is F. What will be the intensity at the same distance on the tan-B position due to the same magnet?*

Ans. If M be the magnetic moment of a short bar magnet and d is the distance from its centre, then

intensity at tan-A position, $F = \frac{2M}{d^3}$

and intensity at tan-B position, $F' = \frac{M}{d^3}$.

$\therefore \quad \frac{F'}{F} = \frac{1}{2}$ or, $F' = \frac{1}{2}F$.

62. *Calculate the amount of work done when a unit north pole is moved from an axial position to an equatorial position of a short bar magnet.*

Ans. At an axial position the magnetic potential is $V_1 = \frac{M}{r^2}$, where r is any distance and M is the magnetic moment.

At an equatorial position, the magnetic potential, $V_2 = 0$.

Therefore, the required work done $= V_1 - V_2 = \dfrac{M}{r^2}$.

63. *What is the amount of work done when a unit N-pole is moved along the equatorial line of a bar magnet?*

Ans. We know that the equatorial line of a bar magnet is zero potential line. So the amount of work done along this line is zero.

64. *Find the amount of work done when a unit N-pole is moved from one face to the other of an infinitely extended magnetic shell.*

Ans. Magnetic potential at a point near to the north pole face,

$$V_1 = \phi\omega = 2\pi\phi$$

and the magnetic potential at a point near to the south pole face,

$$V_2 = -\phi\omega = -2\pi\phi.$$

So the work done $= V_1 - V_2 = 2\pi\phi - (-2\pi\phi) = 4\pi\phi$.

65. *What is the magnetic potential (i) inside and (ii) outside a spherical magnetic shell?*

Ans. (i) At any point inside a sphere the solid angle, $\omega = 4\pi$.

∴ magnetic potential inside the sphere $= \phi\omega = 4\pi\phi$.

(ii) Solid angle at any point outside the sphere, $\omega = 0$.

∴ magnetic potential outside the sphere $= \phi\omega = 0$.

66. *What is the magnetic potential at the centre of a hemispherical magnetic shell?*

Ans. Solid angle subtended by a hemispherical magnetic shell at the centre, $\omega = 2\pi$.

∴ the required magnetic potential at its centre, $V = \phi\omega = 2\pi\phi$.

67. *A magnet suspended freely in a uniform magnetic field H is deflected by 30° from its direction. Find the magnitude of the restoring torque that acts on it.*

Ans. If M is the magnetic moment of the magnet, then

the restoring torque $= MH \sin\theta = MH \sin 30°$ $[\because \theta = 30°]$

$$= \frac{MH}{2}.$$

68. *A magnet is deflected by an angle θ from the direction of a uniform field H in which it is suspended freely. What is the amount of potential energy of the magnet?*

Ans. The potential energy of the deflected magnet $= MH(1 - \cos\theta)$, where M is the magnetic moment.

69. *A magnet is suspended freely in a uniform field H. If W be the amount of work done to rotate the magnet by 60°, what is the amount of work done to rotate it by 90°?*

Ans. We have, the work done $= MH(1 - \cos\theta)$.

For, $\theta = 60°$, $W = MH(1 - \cos 60°) = \dfrac{MH}{2}$.

For, $\theta = 90°$, $W' = MH(1 - \cos 90°) = MH = 2W$.

So the work done is double for 90° rotation.

70. *A thin rectangular magnet is cut into two halves. What will be the period of oscillation of each half?*

Ans. Let I be the initial moment of inertia of the magnet, M the magnetic moment and T the period of oscillation. In this case,

$$I = \frac{\omega l^2}{12} \quad [\omega = \text{mass of the bar magnet, } l = \text{its length}]$$

$$M = m \times l \quad \text{and} \quad T = 2\pi\sqrt{I/MH}.$$

For each half, $I_1 = \dfrac{\left(\frac{\omega}{2}\right)\left(\frac{l}{2}\right)^2}{12} = \dfrac{\omega l^2}{8 \times 12} = \dfrac{I}{8}$.

Now, $M_1 = \dfrac{ml}{2} = \dfrac{M}{2}$.

$$\therefore \quad T_1 = 2\pi\sqrt{\frac{I_1}{M_1 H}} = 2\pi\sqrt{\left(\frac{I}{8}\right)\bigg/\left(\frac{MH}{2}\right)}$$

$$= \frac{T}{2}.$$

So the period of each half becomes equal to half of the previous period.

71. *I-H loop of a ferro-magnetic substance covered an area of* 10000 cm^2. *Find the area of its B-H loop.*

Ans. The area of the B-H loop

$$= 4\pi \times \text{ area of } I\text{-}H \text{ loop}$$

$$= 4 \times 3.14 \times 10000 = 125600 \text{ cm}^2.$$

72. *For permanent magnets what type of magnetic material is preferred? Give two examples.*

Ans. For making permanent magnets a magnetic material with high coercivity and large retentivity is preferred. Besides it should have a large area of hysteresis loop.

Cobalt-steel, tungsten-steel, etc. have such properties and so selected for permanent magnets.

Current Electricity

Chapter 7

D.C. Circuits

7.1 Introduction

For the continuous movement of charges, constituting electric current, the necessary conditions are as follows : (i) the medium should contain free charges capable of movement and (ii) an electric field should be there to drive the charges in a particular direction. In fact, to flow a current through a conductor, an electric field must be maintained inside it. A source which maintains an electric field and supplies energy is called a seat of electromotive force. The electromotive force converts some other forms of energy into electrical energy while the potential difference causes conversion of electrical energy to some other form. Thus one can conclude that the electromotive force is the cause and the potential difference is its effect.

7.2 Flow of Electric Current in Metal

In absence of any electric field the free electrons move at random in all possible directions. But when an external field is applied the free electrons are urged to move in one definite direction and this constitutes electric current.

Let an electron of mass m move forward by the electric field with an average velocity u. If n represents the number of free electrons per unit length of the conductor, then the total momentum in unit length $= nmu$. Again, if e be the charge of an electron and E is the intensity of the electric field, then the total force acting on n electrons is nEe.

Now, we know that the collisions among the electrons cause a diminution in momentum which may be considered to be a factor of number of electrons and hence their velocity is proportional to nu. If β represents the constant of this proportionality, then

the rate of decrease of momentum $= \beta nu$.

Thus, the equation for the rate of increase of momentum can be written as

$$\frac{d}{dt}(nmu) = nEe - \beta nu. \tag{7.1}$$

But the current strength i may be defined mathematically as

$$i = nue \quad \text{or,} \quad nu = \frac{i}{e}$$

or, $$nmu = \frac{im}{e}. \tag{7.2}$$

Differentiating with respect to t, we get

$$\frac{d}{dt}(nmu) = \frac{m}{e}\frac{di}{dt}$$

or, $$\frac{di}{dt} = \frac{e}{m} \cdot \frac{d}{dt}(nmu)$$

or, $\dfrac{di}{dt} = \dfrac{e}{m}(nEe - \beta nu)$ [by Eq. (7.1)]

$\qquad = \dfrac{e}{m}\left(nEe - \beta\dfrac{i}{e}\right)$

$\qquad = \dfrac{ne^2}{m}\left(E - \dfrac{\beta}{ne^2}i\right).$ (7.3)

From Eq. (7.3), we find that

if $i = \dfrac{ne^2 E}{\beta}$,   then, $\dfrac{di}{dt} = 0.$

The above condition can be written as

$E = \dfrac{i\beta}{ne^2}.$ (7.4)

If the rate of fall of potential (ϕ) along the conductor is considered, then

the electric intensity, $E = -\dfrac{d\phi}{dx} = \dfrac{\beta}{ne^2}i$

or, $d\phi = -\dfrac{\beta}{ne^2}idx.$ (7.5)

Integrating Eq. (7.5), between two points separated by a finite length l, we get

$\phi = \dfrac{Bl}{ne^2}i$

$\quad = Ri,$ (7.6)

where $R = \dfrac{\beta l}{ne^2}.$

The constant of proportionality R in Eq. (7.6) is called the resistance of the conductor.

7.3   Equation of Continuity

We know that the current passing through unit area of a conductor is termed as current density. If i represents the current density, then the total current through an area ds may be written as

$$i = \iint \mathbf{j} \cdot ds.$$ (7.7)

If ds be an area enclosing an arbitrary volume dv and σ is the volume density of charge inside the element dv, then

$i = \iint \mathbf{j} \cdot ds$

$\quad = -\dfrac{\delta}{\delta t}\iint \sigma \cdot dv.$ (7.8)

But according to Gauss's theorem,

$$\iint \mathbf{j} \cdot ds = \iiint \text{div } \mathbf{j} \cdot dv$$ (7.9)

Hence, we have

$$\iiint \left[\text{div } \mathbf{j} + \dfrac{\delta\sigma}{\delta t}\right] dv = 0$$

or, $\text{div } \mathbf{j} + \dfrac{\delta \sigma}{\delta t} = 0.$ (7.10)

This is the equation of continuity.

If there is no change in volume density of charge, $\dfrac{\delta \sigma}{\delta t} = 0$ and then

$$\text{div } \mathbf{j} = 0. \tag{7.11}$$

7.4   Ohm's Law

If a steady current is made to pass through a conductor, the potential difference between its ends is directly proportional to the current, provided that the physical conditions of the conductor remain unchanged. This is Ohm's law.

Let us consider a conductor of length l and cross-sectional area A through which a current is passing. If ϕ_1 and ϕ_2 be the potentials of the two points where current enters and leaves the conductor, then

$$E = \frac{\phi_1 - \phi_2}{l}. \tag{7.12}$$

$\therefore \qquad i = jA = \sigma E A$

$$= \sigma A \frac{\phi_1 - \phi_2}{l} \quad [\text{by Eq. (7.12)}] \tag{7.13}$$

$$= \frac{\phi_1 - \phi_2}{R}, \tag{7.14}$$

where $R = \dfrac{l}{\sigma A}.$ (7.14a)

Eq. (7.14) shows that the current flowing through a conductor is directly proportional to the potential difference across its ends. The constant $R = \frac{l}{\sigma A}$ is called the resistance of the conductor.

If we put $\rho = \dfrac{1}{\sigma}$ in Eq. (7.14a), we get

$$R = \frac{\rho l}{A}. \tag{7.14b}$$

ρ is called the specific resistance of the material of the wire.

7.4.1   Practical Units

The current is measured in ampere, e.m.f. in volt and resistance in ohm. A conductor is said to have a resistance of one ohm if one ampere current flows through it causing a potential difference of one volt at its ends.

Each of the units can be defined by two different means. The units obtained from theoretical laws are known as *true units* while those obtained from practical agreed methods are called *international units*.

International ampere is defined as that unvarying current which when passed through an aqueous solution of silver nitrate deposits silver at a rate of 0.00111800 gram per second. International coulomb is the amount of charge carried by one international ampere current in one second. *International volt* is defined as the potential difference which drives a current of one international ampere when applied across a resistance of one international ohm. In practice, it is realised in terms of e.m.f. at 20 °C of standard cadmium cell taken to be 1.0183 volts. *International ohm* is the resistance of a column of mercury at the temperature of melting ice (0 °C) 14.4521 g in mass of uniform cross-sectional area comprising a length of 106.300 cm. It is little more than the true ohm.

7.4.2   Factors Affecting Resistance

Resistivity of any substance depends on the material used and also on its physical conditions like temperature, tension and on the environments such as light and magnetic fields.

(i) **Effects of temperature :** Resistance of a substance changes with temperature by the equation,

$$R_t = R_0(1 + \alpha t + \beta t^2), \tag{7.15}$$

where R_t and R_0 are the resistances at $t\,°C$ and $0\,°C$ respectively, and α, β are two constants for a particular material.

(ii) **Effect of tension and pressure :** Tension increases the resistance but pressure has a very poor effect.

(iii) **Effect of light :** For most of the metals incident light has no effect on resistance. But selenium is an exception. Its resistivity decreases with the intensity of light.

(iv) **Effect of magnetic field :** Magnetic field slightly affects the resistance, in general. However, it is much pronounced for bismuth. If a strong magnetic field is applied at right angles to the direction of current the resistance of a bismuth resistor becomes double than its original value.

7.5   Grouping of Resistors

(i) **Resistors in series :** When several resistors are connected in such a way that the same current flows through all of them, then those are said to be in series. Let in Fig. 7.1 three resistors R_1, R_2 and R_3 be joined in series so that the same current i flows through each of them. By applying Ohm's law we can write,

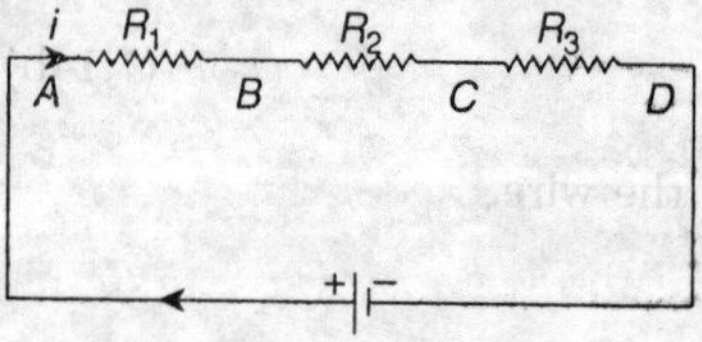

Fig. 7.1

$$\phi_A - \phi_B = iR_1, \tag{7.16}$$

$$\phi_B - \phi_C = iR_2 \tag{7.17}$$

and $\phi_C - \phi_D = iR_3.$ (7.18)

Adding we get

$$\phi_A - \phi_D = i(R_1 + R_2 + R_3). \tag{7.19}$$

If the same amount of current i is made to pass through a resistance R across which the potential difference is $\phi_A - \phi_D$, then,

$$\phi_A - \phi_D = iR. \tag{7.20}$$

By Eqs. (7.19) and (7.20),

$$iR = i(R_1 + R_2 + R_3)$$

or, $R = R_1 + R_2 + R_3.$ (7.21)

For n resistances,

$$R = R_1 + R_2 + R_3 + \cdots + R_n. \tag{7.21a}$$

(ii) **Resistors in parallel :** Let several resistors be arranged in such a way that each of them becomes an independent path for a part of the current obtained from the source for which those are connected independent of one another. The total current flowing through such a combination is the sum of the currents in the alternative paths. Let i_1, i_2 and i_3 be the currents in the respective branches having resistances R_1, R_2 and R_3 as shown in Fig. 7.2.

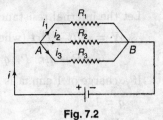

Fig. 7.2

Applying Ohm's law, we get

$$\phi_A - \phi_B = \phi = i_1 R_1 = i_2 R_1 = i_3 R_3. \tag{7.22}$$

$$\therefore \quad i_1 = \frac{\phi}{R_1}, \quad i_2 = \frac{\phi}{R_2} \quad \text{and} \quad i_3 = \frac{\phi}{R_3}.$$

Adding, $i = i_1 + i_2 + i_3$

$$= \phi \left(\frac{1}{R_1} + \frac{1}{R_2} + \frac{1}{R_3} \right), \tag{7.23}$$

where i is the total current.

If through a resistance R, current i passes at the same potential difference ϕ at its ends, then

$$i = \frac{\phi}{R}. \tag{7.24}$$

By Eqs. (7.23) and (7.24), we get

$$\frac{\phi}{R} = \phi \left(\frac{1}{R_1} + \frac{1}{R_2} + \frac{1}{R_3} \right)$$

or, $$\frac{1}{R} = \frac{1}{R_1} + \frac{1}{R_2} + \frac{1}{R_3}. \tag{7.25}$$

For n resistances,

$$\frac{1}{R} = \frac{1}{R_1} + \frac{1}{R_2} + \frac{1}{R_3} + \cdots + \frac{1}{R_n}. \tag{7.25a}$$

7.6 Production of Heat in a Conductor

If i e.m.u. current passes through a resistance of R e.m.u., then the potential difference developed across the resistance R can be written as

$$\phi = iR \text{ e.m.u.} \tag{7.26}$$

When q e.m.u. of charge flows down a potential gradient from ϕ_1 and ϕ_2, then the dissipation of energy W can be expressed as

$$W = q\phi \text{ ergs}, \tag{7.27}$$

where $\quad \phi = \phi_1 - \phi_2$.

Again, if t represents the time, then

$$q = it.$$

$$\therefore \quad W = it\phi$$

$$= i^2 Rt \quad \text{[by Eq. (7.26)]} \tag{7.28}$$

The energy W in Eq. (7.27) will appear as heat in the conductor.

7.7 The e.m.f. of the Cell

If several resistances R_1, R_2, R_3, etc., are connected in series, then the heat produced in t seconds is given by

$$W = i^2 R_1 t + i^2 R_2 t + i^2 R_3 t + \cdots \tag{7.29}$$

Let the internal resistance of the cell is r. The heat produced in t seconds is

$W = i^2 Rt + i^2 rt$ (where R = external resistance)

$$= qiR + qir \quad (\because q = it). \tag{7.30}$$

If a charge of 1 e.m.u. is made to pass, then

$q = 1.$

$\therefore \quad W = iR + ir. \tag{7.31}$

Now, the e.m.f. of a cell may be defined as the work **done** by a cell when a unit charge is delivered by it. If it is denoted by E, then

$$E = iR + ir. \tag{7.32}$$

If the external resistance, $R \gg r$, then

$$E = iR. \tag{7.32a}$$

That means the e.m.f. of the cell then becomes equal to the potential difference across the external resistance.

We can now calculate the power dissipated in an external resistance R. The rate of generation of heat W can be written as

$$W = i^2 R = \frac{E}{(R+r)^2} \cdot R.$$

$$\therefore \quad \frac{\delta W}{\delta R} = \frac{E^2}{(R+r)^2} - \frac{2E^2 R}{(R+r)^3} = \frac{E^2}{(R+r)^2}\left(1 - \frac{2R}{R+r}\right).$$

For a maximum heat generation, $\dfrac{\delta W}{\delta R} = 0$.

$$\therefore \quad 1 - \frac{2R}{R+r} = 0$$

or, $R = r.$ \hfill (7.33)

Therefore, we can conclude that the power developed **or** the rate of heat generation in the external resistance becomes maximum when the value of the internal resistance equals the external resistance.

7.8 Current Distribution in Network Circuit

Problems concerning the flow of current in a network may be solved by two famous laws enunciated by Kirchhoff. These are known as Kirchhoff's laws. The laws are given below :

Law I. The algebraic sum of the currents meeting at a point is zero. Or, in other words, the sum of the currents entering a junction is equal to sum of the currents leaving the junction. Note that the currents towards a junction are considered positive and those away from the same junction are considered negative.

Law II. The algebraic sum of the potential differences around a closed circuit is zero. Or, in other words, the sum of the rises of potential around any closed circuit equals the sum of drops of potential in that circuit.

The first law is illustrated in Fig. 7.3. Let i_1, i_2, i_3, i_4 and i_5 be the currents flowing through conductors connected at a junction point O. From the figure, we have

$$\sum \text{current entering} = \sum \text{current leaving}.$$

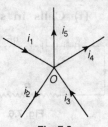

Fig. 7.3

$$\therefore \quad i_1 + i_3 = i_2 + i_4 + i_5$$

$$\text{or,} \quad i_1 + i_3 - i_2 - i_4 - i_5 = 0$$

$$\text{or,} \quad \sum i = 0. \qquad (7.34)$$

As in the steady state, there is no accumulation of charge so the sum of the currents towards O becomes equal to the sum of those leaving it. The result is thus obvious.

The second law is illustrated in Fig. 7.4. Let us consider the mesh $PQRSTP$ having no source of e.m.f. in the mesh. By applying Ohm's law, we can get

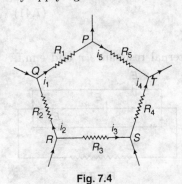

Fig. 7.4

$$\phi_Q - \phi_P = i_1 R_1$$

$$\text{or,} \quad \phi_P - \phi_Q = -i_1 R_1 \qquad (7.35a)$$

$$\phi_R - \phi_Q = i_2 R_2$$

$$\text{or,} \quad \phi_Q - \phi_R = -i_2 R_2 \qquad (7.35b)$$

$$\phi_R - \phi_S = i_3 R_3 \qquad (7.35c)$$

$$\phi_S - \phi_T = i_4 R_4 \qquad (7.35d)$$

$$\phi_P - \phi_T = i_5 R_5$$

$$\text{or,} \quad \phi_T - \phi_P = -i_5 R_5. \qquad (7.35e)$$

Adding Eqs. (7.35a) to (7.35e), we have

$$-i_1 R_1 - i_2 R_2 + i_3 R_3 + i_4 R_4 - i_5 R_5 = 0.$$

Starting from the point P, if we go along the mesh $PQRSTP$, then if the currents in the direction of the path is positive, those against it will be considered as negative. Thus, we have

$$\sum iR = 0. \qquad (7.36)$$

Now, in the portion RS of the circuit, if a cell of e.m.f. E is present, as shown in Fig. 7.5, then we can write,

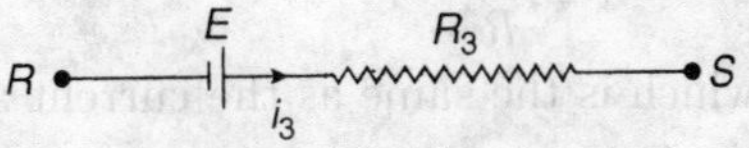

Fig. 7.5

$$\phi_R - \phi_S = -E + i_3 R_3. \qquad (7.37)$$

Adding up all the potential differences, we get

$$0 = -E + \sum iR$$

$$\text{or,} \quad E - \sum iR = 0. \qquad (7.38)$$

The second law may thus be briefly expressed in the form $\sum(E - iR) = 0$. Since this law can be expressed in the form,

$$\sum(Ei - i^2 R) = 0, \qquad (7.39)$$

it implies that the energy supplied by the sources of e.m.f. is equal to the energy dissipated by the current.

7.9 Setting up of a Battery

If more than one cell are combined to send a current through a circuit, then that combination is called battery of cells. This grouping is done by three different means.

(i) Cells in series : Let n number of cells each of internal resistance r and e.m.f. E be connected in such a way that the positive pole of one is connected to the negative pole of the next. Then the cells are said to be in series. A series combination of the cells is shown in Fig. 7.6. If the combination sends a current through an external resistance R, then the current i is given by

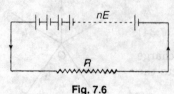

Fig. 7.6

$$i = \frac{nE}{R + nr}. \tag{7.40}$$

When $r \to 0$,

$$i = \frac{nE}{R}, \tag{7.41}$$

which is n times the current available in a single cell.

(ii) Cells in parallel : Let n cells each of internal resistance r and e.m.f. E be connected in such a way that all the positive poles are joined at one point to form one terminal and all the negative poles to other point to form another terminal. Then the cells are said to be in parallel. A parallel combination of the cells is shown in Fig. 7.7. If the combination sends a current through an external resistance R, then the current i can be expressed as

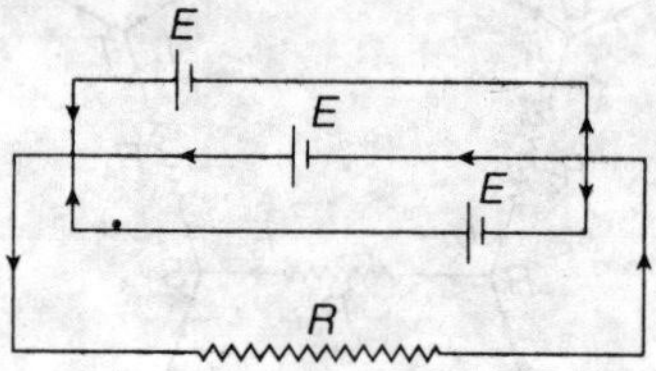

Fig. 7.7

$$i = \frac{E}{R + \frac{r}{n}}$$

$$= \frac{nE}{nR + r} \tag{7.42}$$

When $r \to 0$,

$$i = \frac{E}{R}, \tag{7.43}$$

which is the same as the current available in a single cell.

(iii) Mixed circuit : Let $(m \times n)$ number of cells are grouped in such a way that m rows of cells each containing n cells in series are joined in parallel. Such a combination of the cells is shown in Fig. 7.8. If the combination sends a current i through an external resistance R, then

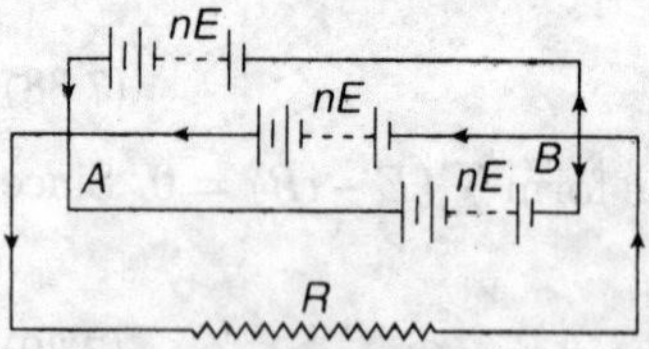

Fig. 7.8

$$i = \frac{nE}{R + \frac{nr}{m}} \quad \text{(where } r = \text{internal resistance)}$$

$$= \frac{mnE}{mR + nr}$$

$$= \frac{mnE}{[\sqrt{mR} - \sqrt{nr}]^2 + 2\sqrt{mRnr}}. \tag{7.44}$$

For maximum value of i,

$$\sqrt{mR} = \sqrt{nr}$$

and so, $R = \dfrac{nr}{m}$. \hfill (7.45)

Therefore, for maximum current, the external resistance should be equal to the total internal resistance of all cells.

7.9.1   Lost Voltage in a Battery

When a battery is joined to send a current through an external resistance called the load, the potential difference across it becomes less than the e.m.f. of the battery as found in an open circuit. This is due to the drop of voltage in the internal resistance of the battery.

If a battery of internal resistance r and e.m.f. E delivers a current i, then the voltage drop ϕ across the load is written as

$$\phi = E - ir \tag{7.46}$$

and $i = \dfrac{\phi}{R}.$ $\hspace{6cm}$ (7.47)

$\therefore$ $\phi = E - \dfrac{\phi}{R}r$ or, $\phi\left(1 + \dfrac{r}{R}\right) = E$

or, $\phi = \dfrac{E}{1 + \frac{r}{R}}.$ $\hspace{6cm}$ (7.48)

When $r \to 0$,

$$\phi = E. \tag{7.48a}$$

7.10   Wheatstone Bridge Network

In Fig. 7.9, four resistances r_1, r_2, r_3 and r_4 are connected in a manner as shown so that it forms a bridge. Let E be the e.m.f. of the cell and r its internal resistance. Let us also assume that r_g represents the resistance in the galvanometer circuit including the resistance of the galvanometer.

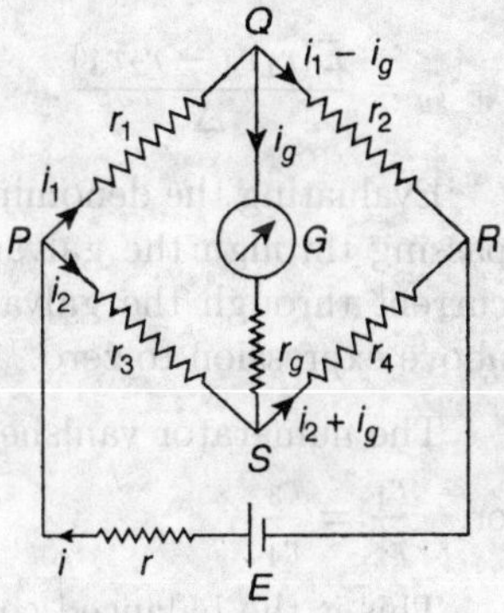

Fig. 7.9

The current i from the battery is divided into two parts i_1 and i_2 passing through the resistances r_1 and r_3 respectively. If in the direction Q to S, the galvanometer current is represented by i_g, then from Q to R the current will be $(i_1 - i_g)$ and from S to R it will be $(i_2 + i_g)$.

Now, for the closed circuit $PQSP$, we have

$$i_1 r_1 + i_g r_g - i_2 r_3 = 0. \tag{7.49}$$

For the mesh $QRSQ$,

$(i_1 - i_g)r_2 - (i_2 + i_g)r_4 - i_g r_g = 0$

or, $i_1 r_2 - i_g(r_2 + r_4 + r_g) - i_2 r_4 = 0.$ $\hspace{3cm}$ (7.50)

For the mesh $EPQRE$,

$ir + i_1 r_1 + (i_1 - i_g)r_2 = E$

or, $(i_1 + i_2)r + i_1 r_1 + (i_1 - i_g)r_2 = E$ $(\because i = i_1 + i_2)$

or, $i_1(r + r_1 + r_2) - i_g r_2 + i_2 r - E = 0.$ $\hspace{2.5cm}$ (7.51)

Eqs. (7.49), (7.50) and (7.51) can be rewritten as

$i_1 r_1 + i_g r_g - i_2 r_3 + E \times 0 = 0$

$i_1 r_2 - i_g(r_2 + r_4 + r_g) - i_2 r_4 + E \times 0 = 0$

$i_1(r + r_1 + r_2) - i_g r_2 + i_2 r - E = 0.$

Considering the above equations, we get

$$\frac{i_1}{\begin{vmatrix} r_g & -r_3 & 0 \\ -(r_2+r_4+r_g) & -r_4 & 0 \\ -r_2 & r & -1 \end{vmatrix}} = \frac{-i_g}{\begin{vmatrix} r_1 & -r_3 & 0 \\ r_2 & -r_4 & 0 \\ (r+r_1+r_2) & r & -1 \end{vmatrix}}$$

$$= \frac{i_2}{\begin{vmatrix} r_1 & r_g & 0 \\ r_2 & -(r_2+r_4+r_g) & 0 \\ (r+r_1+r_2) & -r_2 & -1 \end{vmatrix}}$$

$$= \frac{-E}{\begin{vmatrix} r_1 & r_g & -r_3 \\ r_2 & -(r_2+r_4+r_g) & -r_4 \\ (r+r_1+r_2) & -r_2 & r \end{vmatrix}}$$

$$= \frac{-E}{\Delta} \text{ (say).}$$

Solving for i_g, we get

$$i_g = \frac{E(r_1 r_4 - r_2 r_3)}{\Delta}. \tag{7.52}$$

Evaluating the denominator of Eq. (7.52) we can get the value of i_g, the current passing through the galvanometer under any arrangement. The condition for no current through the galvanometer is obtained by equating the numerator of the above expression to zero.

The numerator vanishes if $r_1 r_4 = r_2 r_3$

or, $$\frac{r_1}{r_2} = \frac{r_3}{r_4}. \tag{7.53}$$

This is the balanced condition of the bridge.

If the four resistances are so chosen so as to make the galvanometer current zero, then we have, $r_4 = \frac{r_2 r_3}{r_1}$. This indicates that if three resistances r_1, r_2 and r_3 are known, the unknown resistance r_4 can be obtained.

It is to be noted that if either the pair of resistances r_1-r_2 or the pair r_3-r_4 be extremely small, the numerator will be a small quantity and the arrangement will be insensitive under all conditions. The bridge is thus unsuitable for comparison of low resistances.

Wheatstone bridge is also unsuitable for comparison of high resistances as the high resistances put in one pair of arms would cause a very small current to pass through the galvanometer making the arrangement insensitive.

It would be advantageous to make the battery and the galvanometer resistances as low as possible as this would make the denominator small. In the Wheatstone bridge the branches comprising r_1 and r_2 are called ratio arms while the branch representing r_3 is the third arm. The unknown resistance is placed in the branch containing r_4, known as the fourth arm of the bridge.

7.10.1 Sensitivity of the Wheatstone Bridge

Sensitivity of the bridge implies that for a slight deviation from the balanced condition the current passing through the galvanometer should be appreciable. Or, in other words, for good sensitiveness the galvanometer must be capable of detecting a very small current. The sensitivity of the bridge will be given by the ratio of galvanometer current to the fourth arm current.

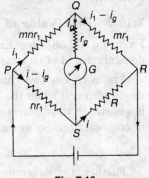

Fig. 7.10

Let i be the current passing through the resistance R to be measured and i_g be the galvanometer current (Fig. 7.10). The distribution of current is shown in the figure.

When the bidge is unbalanced, applying Kirchhoff's second law to the mesh $PQSP$, we get

$$mnr_1 i_1 + r_g i_g - nr_1(i - i_g) = 0 \tag{7.54}$$

and for the mesh $QRSQ$,

$$mr_1(i_1 - i_g) - Ri - r_g i_g = 0. \tag{7.55}$$

From Eq. (7.54), we have

$$i_1 = \frac{nr_1(i - i_g) - r_g i_g}{mnr_1}. \tag{7.56}$$

From Eq. (7.55) we have,

$$i_1 = \frac{r_g i_g + Ri + mr_1 i_g}{mr_1}. \tag{7.57}$$

By Eqs. (7.56) and (7.57) we can write,

$$nr_1(i - i_g) - r_g i_g = nr_g i_g + nRi + mnr_1 i_g$$

$$\text{or,} \quad ni(r_1 - R) = nr_g i_g + nr_1 i_g + r_g i_g + mnr_1 i_g$$

$$= i_g[r_g(n + 1) + r_1 n(m + 1)]$$

$$\therefore \quad \frac{i_g}{i} = \frac{n(r_1 - R)}{r_g(n + 1) + r_1 n(m + 1)}$$

$$= \frac{\Delta r}{r_g \left(1 + \frac{1}{n}\right) + r_1(m + 1)}, \tag{7.58}$$

where $\Delta r = r_1 - R$.

The ratio i_g/i is a measure of the sensitivity. We may consider the two limiting cases :

(i) When $m = n = 1$,

$$\frac{i_g}{i} = \frac{1}{2} \frac{\Delta r}{r_g + r_1}. \tag{7.59}$$

(ii) When $n \to \infty$, $m \to 0$,

$$\frac{i_g}{i} = \frac{\Delta r}{r_g + r_1}. \tag{7.60}$$

Again, if m is very large and n is very small, the sensitiveness i_g/i is much reduced. Hence, for all practical purposes n should not be very small or m very large because in that case the sensitivity will be considerably reduced. For a small defect of balance measured as Δr, the ratio i_g/i should be maximum for better sensitivity.

7.10.2   Best Value of Galvanometer Resistance

From Eq. (7.58), we find that the galvanometer resistance r_g occurs in the denominator. Let us consider what value of r_g should give the best advantage.

Let us choose two galvanometers with coils of same size and mass; one being a single turn coil while the number of turns in the other being p causing an increase in resistance to p^2 times due to p times increase in length and $(1/p)$th dimunition in cross-section. So we can write,

$$r_g \propto p^2 \quad \text{or,} \quad p \propto \sqrt{r_g}.$$

Further, the deflection θ of the coil for a given current is proportional to the number of turns and to the current strength, i.e.,

$$\theta \propto i_g \cdot p \quad \text{or,} \quad \theta \propto i_g \sqrt{r_g}.$$

But we know,

$$i_g = \frac{i(r_1 - R)}{r_g \left(1 + \frac{1}{n}\right) + r_1(m + 1)}.$$

So when i and $(r_1 - R)$ are not changed,

$$\theta \propto \frac{\sqrt{r_g}}{r_g \left(1 + \frac{1}{n}\right) + r_1(m + 1)}$$

or, $$\theta = \frac{k\sqrt{r_g}}{r_g \left(1 + \frac{1}{n}\right) + r_1(m + 1)} \tag{7.61}$$

or, $$\frac{d\theta}{dr_g} = \frac{\frac{1}{2}k}{\sqrt{r_g}\left[r_g \left(1 + \frac{1}{n}\right) + r_1(m + 1)\right]} - \frac{\left(1 + \frac{1}{n}\right)\sqrt{r_g} \cdot k}{\left[r_g \left(1 + \frac{1}{n}\right) + r_1(m + 1)\right]^2}.$$

For a maximum deflection,

$$\frac{d\theta}{dr_g} = 0.$$

So, $$\frac{1}{2\sqrt{r_g}} - \frac{\left(1 + \frac{1}{n}\right)\sqrt{r_g}}{r_g \left(1 + \frac{1}{n}\right) + r_1(m + 1)} = 0$$

or, $$r_g = \frac{1 + m}{1 + \frac{1}{n}} r_1. \tag{7.62}$$

Eq. (7.62) shows that r_g should be of the same order of magnitude as r_1.

When $m = 1$ and $n = \infty$,

$$r_g = 2r_1,$$

and when $m = 0$ and $n = 1$,

$$r_g = 0.5r_1.$$

7.11   Kelvin's Double Bridge

Low resistances of the order of 0.1 ohm and less cannot be measured by using the Wheatstone bridge because of (i) insensitiveness of the bridge, and (ii) errors due to inclusion of resistances of the junctions and connecting wires in the bridge arms. These errors are eliminated in Kelvin's double bridge.

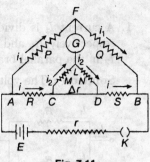

The essential parts of the Kelvin's double bridge are shown in Fig. 7.11. R is a standard resistance and S is an unknown resistance both having extra potential leads. These two resistors are joined by a metal bar CD having small resistance (Δr). Four known resistances P, Q, M, N are connected through a low resistance galvanometer to form the bridge. The distribution of currents through different resistances are shown in the figure.

Fig. 7.11

Applying Kirchhoff's law to the meshes $ACGF$ and $BDGF$, we get

$$Pi_1 - Mi_2 - Ri = 0 \tag{7.63}$$

$$Qi_1 - Si - Ni_2 = 0. \tag{7.64}$$

Eqs. (7.63) and (7.64) can be rewritten as

$$Ri + Mi_2 = Pi_1 \tag{7.65}$$

and $Si + Ni_2 = Qi_1.$ $\tag{7.66}$

Taking the ratio of Eqs. (7.65) and (7.66), we get

$$\frac{Ri + Mi_2}{Si + Ni_2} = \frac{P}{Q}$$

or, $i(QR - PS) = i_2(MQ - NP)$ $\tag{7.67}$

If $\dfrac{M}{N} = \dfrac{P}{Q}$, then $MQ - NP = 0$

Hence, from Eq. (7.67) we can write,

$$QR - PS = 0 \quad \text{or,} \quad \frac{P}{Q} = \frac{R}{S},$$

The condition for balance becomes

$$\frac{M}{N} = \frac{P}{Q} = \frac{R}{S}.$$

$\therefore \quad S = \dfrac{QR}{P}.$ $\tag{7.68}$

For balanced conditions, the resistor S between the two connecting points at D and B is equal to the value of R, a standard resistor.

In comparison experiment, the final adjustment is made by shunting S with a resistance box. If the balance is found with a resistance S_1 in parallel with S, then,

$$\frac{S \cdot S_1}{S + S_1} = \frac{Q}{P}R. \tag{7.69}$$

Using Eq. (7.69), S can be calculated.

In practice, for the construction of standard low resistances and determination of specific resistance P-Q and M-N are obtained from two pieces of resistance wires whose electric mid-points are connected with the galvanometer terminals. As such the ratio P/Q becomes equal to M/N. The resistances P, Q, M and N are to be placed near to each other to ensure similar temperature variation.

Examples

1. A current I_t is divided between two parallel branches whose resistances are respectively R_1 and R_2 as shown in Fig. 7.12. Calculate the currents I_1 and I_2 in the parallel branches.

Solution : The voltage drop is same in both the branches,

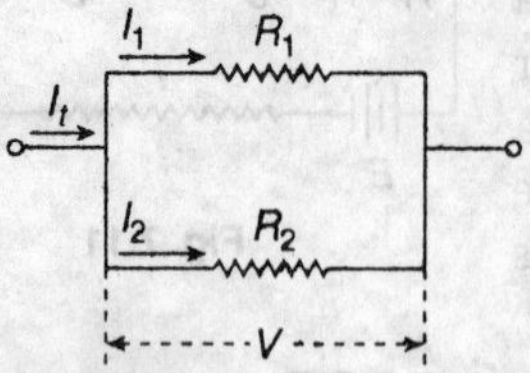

i.e., $\quad I_1 R_1 = I_2 R_2 = V$

or, $\quad I_1 = \dfrac{V}{R_1}$ and $I_2 = \dfrac{V}{R_2}$

Now, $\quad I_t = I_1 + I_2 = \dfrac{V}{R_1} + \dfrac{V}{R_2} = V\left(\dfrac{1}{R_1} + \dfrac{1}{R_2}\right)$

$$= I_1 R_1 \left(\dfrac{R_2 + R_1}{R_1 R_2}\right) = I_1 \left(\dfrac{R_2 + R_1}{R_2}\right).$$

Fig. 7.12

$$\therefore \qquad I_1 = I_t \left(\dfrac{R_2}{R_1 + R_2}\right).$$

Similarly, one can calculate

$$I_2 = I_t \left(\dfrac{R_1}{R_1 + R_2}\right).$$

2. If three resistances R_1, R_2 and R_3 are joined in parallel, what will be the value of the equivalent resistance?

Solution : As shown in Fig. 7.13, assume a voltage M to N of v and let in R_1, R_2 and R_3 the currents be respectively i_1, i_2 and i_3. The current through the equivalent resistance R_e must be equal to the total current i_t, i.e.,

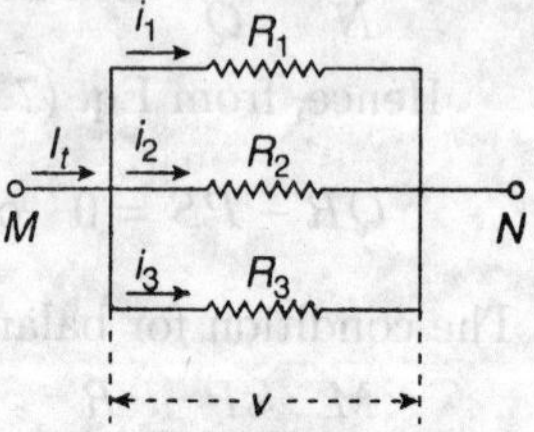

$$i_t = i_1 + i_2 + i_3.$$

Now, since $v = R_1 i_1 = R_2 i_2 = R_3 i_3$,

$$\therefore \qquad \dfrac{v}{R_e} = \dfrac{v}{R_1} + \dfrac{v}{R_2} + \dfrac{v}{R_3}$$

or, $\qquad \dfrac{1}{R_e} = \dfrac{1}{R_1} + \dfrac{1}{R_2} + \dfrac{1}{R_3}.$

Fig. 7.13

$\therefore$ the value of the equivalent resistance $(R_e) = \dfrac{R_1 R_2 R_3}{R_1 R_2 + R_2 R_3 + R_3 R_1}.$

3. If the applied constant voltage in the circuit of Fig. 7.14 is $V = 45$ volts, calculate (i) the current flowing, (ii) the voltage drop across each resistor and (iii) the power in each resistor.

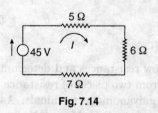

Fig. 7.14

Solution : (i) We know that around any closed loop,

   sum of the voltage rises

        = sum of the voltage drops

$$\therefore \quad V = I \times 5 + I \times 6 + I \times 7$$

or, $\quad 45 = I(5 + 6 + 7) = 18I$

$$\therefore \quad I = \dfrac{45}{18} = \textbf{2.5 amperes.}$$

(ii) Voltage drop across 5Ω resistor $= I \times 5 = 2.5 \times 5 = $ **12.5 volts**

„　　„　　„　6Ω　„　$= I \times 6 = 2.5 \times 6 = $ **15.0 volts**

„　　„　　„　7Ω　„　$= I \times 7 = 2.5 \times 7 = $ **17.5 volts**.

(iii) Power in the 5Ω resistor $= 2.5 \times 12.5 = $ **31.25 watts**

„　　„　„　6Ω　„　$= 2.5 \times 15.0 = $ **37.5 watts**

„　　„　„　7Ω　„　$= 2.5 \times 17.5 = $ **43.75 watts**.

4. Two constant voltage sources V_A and V_B act in the same circuit in a manner as shown in Fig. 7.15. What power does each deliver?

Solution : We know that around a closed circuit,

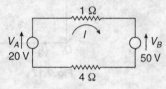

sum of the potential rises
$\qquad$ = sum of the potential drops

$\therefore \quad 20 - 50 = I \times 1 + I \times 4 \quad$ or, $\quad -30 = 5I$

Fig. 7.15

or, $\quad I = -6$ amperes.

$\therefore$ power delivered by $V_A = V_A I = 20(-6) = -120$ watts

and　„　　　„　　„　$V_B = V_B I = (-50)(-6) = 300$ watts.

5. Three cells of e.m.f. 2 volts, 1 volt and 4 volts and the corresponding resistances 4 ohms, 3 ohms and 2 ohms are in parallel with similar poles connected together. Determine the current flowing through each cell.

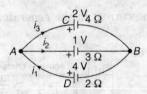

Fig. 7.16

Solution : Let i_1, i_2 and i_3 be the currents passing through the cells as shown in Fig. 7.16. From Kirchhoff's first law, at the point A, we have

$$i_1 = i_2 + i_3.$$

Next, applying Kirchhoff's second law in the mesh $ACBD$, we get

$$4 - 2 = 2i_1 + 4i_3 = 2(i_2 + i_3) + 4i_3 \quad (\because \ i_1 = i_2 + i_3)$$
$$= 2i_2 + 6i_3$$

or, $\quad 2 = 2i_2 + 6i_3.$ $\qquad\qquad$ (i)

Again, applying the same law to the mesh ABD,

$$4 - 1 = 2i_1 + 3i_2 = 2(i_2 + i_3) + 3i_2 = 5i_2 + 2i_3$$

or, $\quad 3 = 5i_2 + 2i_3.$ $\qquad\qquad$ (ii)

From Eqs. (i) and (ii), we get

$$10 = 10i_2 + 30i_3 \quad \text{and} \quad 6 = 10i_2 + 4i_3.$$

From above eliminating i_2 we get, $i_3 = \dfrac{2}{13}$ ampere.

Hence, from Eq. (i), we get

$$2 = 2i_2 + 6\frac{2}{13} \quad \text{or,} \quad i_2 = \frac{7}{13} \text{ ampere.}$$

Now, since $i_1 = i_2 + i_3$,

$$\therefore \quad i_1 = \frac{7}{13} + \frac{2}{13} = \frac{9}{13} \text{ ampere.}$$

6. Twelve identical wires, each of resistance r, are connected in the form of a cube. Determine the equivalent resistance of the cube when current enters the cube at one end and goes out from the diagonally opposite end.

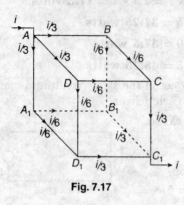

Fig. 7.17

Solution : The current i entering at A is divided into three parts along AB, AD and AA_1, each equal to $i/3$. Each part is again divided along the corresponding two wires as shown in Fig. 7.17.

The p.d. between A and C_1 is given by,

$$V_A - V_{C_1} = (V_A - V_{A_1}) + (V_{A_1} - V_{D_1})$$
$$+ (V_{D_1} - V_{C_1})$$
$$= \frac{1}{3}i \cdot r + \frac{1}{6}i \cdot r + \frac{1}{3}i \cdot r$$
$$= \frac{5}{6}i \cdot r.$$

If the cube is replaced by a single wire of resistance R between A and C_1 so that for the same current i, the p.d. between A and C_1 remains the same, then

$$V_A - V_{C_1} = iR$$
$$\therefore \quad iR = \frac{5}{6}i \cdot r \quad \text{or,} \quad R = \frac{5}{6}r.$$

7. Referring to the circuit of Fig. 7.18, calculate the current in the generator V_3 if $V_1 = 4$ volts, $V_2 = 1$ volt and $V_3 = 6$ volts.

Solution : The three loop equations can be written as

$$+V_2 + 2I_1 - V_1 + 6(I_1 - I_2) = 0,$$
$$6(I_2 - I_1) + 3I_2 + 7(I_2 - I_3) = 0$$

and $\quad 7(I_3 - I_2) + 4I_3 - V_3 = 0.$

Putting the values for the generators and rearranging,

$$8I_1 - 6I_2 \qquad = 3$$
$$-6I_1 + 16I_2 - 7I_3 = 0$$
$$- 7I_2 + 11I_3 = 6.$$

Using Cramer's rule, we get

$$I_3 = \frac{\begin{vmatrix} 8 & -6 & 3 \\ -6 & 16 & 0 \\ 0 & -7 & 6 \end{vmatrix}}{\begin{vmatrix} 8 & -6 & 0 \\ -6 & 16 & -7 \\ 0 & -7 & 11 \end{vmatrix}} = \frac{678}{620} = \mathbf{1.094 \ amperes.}$$

8. The positive poles of two cells of e.m.f. 2 V and 1.5 V and each of internal resistance 1 ohm are connected by a uniform wire of resistance 10 ohms and the negative poles are connected by a wire of resistance 6 ohms. If the middle

points of these two wires are connected by a resistance of 2 ohms, calculate the current flowing through this wire and also the p.d. developed between these two mid-points.   [C.U. 1963]

Solution : According to Kirchhoff's first law, at the points A and B,

$$i = i_1 + i_2. \tag{i}$$

Now applying second law in the loop E_1ABE_1, we get

$5i_1 + 2i + 3i_1 + i_1 = 2$

or, $9i_1 + 2(i_1 + i_2) = 2 \quad [\because \ i = i_1 + i_2]$

or, $11i_1 + 2i_2 = 2. \tag{ii}$

Again, at the loop, E_2ABE_2, applying the second law,

$5i_2 + 2i + 3i_2 + i_2 = 1.5$

or, $9i_2 + 2(i_1 + i_2) = 1.5$

or, $11i_2 + 2i_1 = 1.5. \tag{iii}$

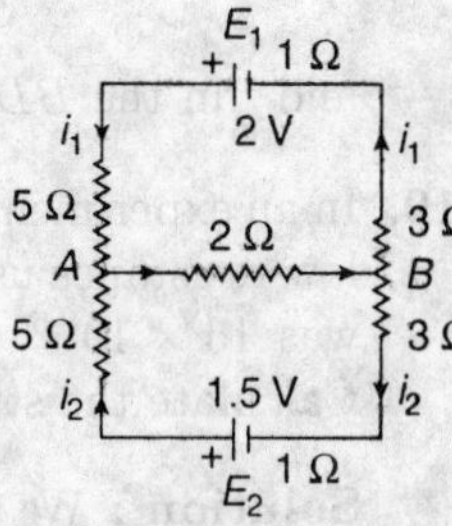

By Eqs. (ii) and (iii), we get

$$i_1 = \frac{19}{117} \text{ ampere} \quad \text{and} \quad i_2 = \frac{25}{234} \text{ ampere}$$

or, $\quad i = i_1 + i_2 = \dfrac{19}{117} + \dfrac{25}{234} = \mathbf{0.269\ ampere}$

and p.d., $V = 2i = \mathbf{0.538\ ampere}$.

Fig. 7.19

9. In a Wheatstone bridge network $ABCD$, the resistances in ohms are : $AB = 10$, $BC = 15$, $AD = 20$, $DC = 25$ and $BD = 10$. If the potential difference between A and C is 20 volts, find the current distribution in the network, neglecting the internal resistance of the battery.   [C.U. 1966]

Solution : Applying Kirchhoff's second law in the loop $ABCD$, we get

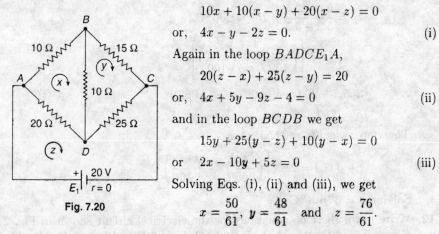

Fig. 7.20

$$10x + 10(x - y) + 20(x - z) = 0$$

or, $4x - y - 2z = 0. \tag{i}$

Again in the loop $BADCE_1A$,

$20(z - x) + 25(z - y) = 20$

or, $4x + 5y - 9z - 4 = 0 \tag{ii}$

and in the loop $BCDB$ we get

$15y + 25(y - z) + 10(y - x) = 0$

or $2x - 10y + 5z = 0 \tag{iii}$

Solving Eqs. (i), (ii) and (iii), we get

$$x = \frac{50}{61}, \ y = \frac{48}{61} \quad \text{and} \quad z = \frac{76}{61}.$$

Therefore, the distribution of currents are

in the AB path $\dfrac{50}{61}$ ampere,

in the BC path $\dfrac{48}{61}$ ampere,

in the CE_1A path $\dfrac{76}{61}$ ampere,

in the AD path $\left(\dfrac{76}{61} - \dfrac{50}{61}\right) = \dfrac{26}{61}$ ampere,

in the DC path $\left(\dfrac{76}{61} - \dfrac{48}{61}\right) = \dfrac{28}{61}$ ampere,

and in the BD path $\left(\dfrac{50}{61} - \dfrac{48}{61}\right) = \dfrac{2}{61}$ ampere.

10. In an experiment for measurement of current by a potentiometer, the standard low resistance used was 0.001 ohm. The drop of potential per centimetre wire was 13×10^{-6} volt. The balance point was at 760 cm of the bridge wire. Calculate the strength of current flowing through the given line. [C.U. 1970]

Solution : We know, $i = \dfrac{l \times e}{r}$,

where, i = current, l = balancing length = 760 cm,

e = p.d. per cm = 13×10^{-6} volt,

r = resistance = 0.001 Ω.

$\therefore \qquad i = \dfrac{760 \times 13 \times 10^{-6}}{0.001} =$ **9.88 amperes**.

11. The resistances of a platinum thermometer at $0\,°C$, $100\,°C$ and $206.2\,°C$ are found to be 3.5 ohms, 5.2 ohms and 6.9 ohms respectively. Find the temperature of the bath in which the resistance of the thermometer is 9.4 ohms.

Solution : We know, $t_p = \dfrac{R_t - R_0}{R_{100} - R_0} \times 100 = \dfrac{9.4 - 3.5}{5.2 - 3.5} \times 100 = 347.1\,°C.$

Now at the temperature $20\,°C$,

$$t_p = \dfrac{6.9 - 3.5}{5.2 - 3.5} \times 100 = 200\,°C.$$

$\because \qquad t - t_p = \delta\left[\left(\dfrac{t}{100}\right)^2 - \left(\dfrac{t}{100}\right)\right]$

$\therefore \qquad 206.2 - 200 = \delta[(2.062)^2 - (2.062)]$

$\therefore \qquad \delta = 2.83.$

Therefore, when $t_p = 347.1$, then

$$t - 347.1 = 2.83\left[\left(\dfrac{t}{100}\right)^2 - \left(\dfrac{t}{100}\right)\right]$$

Solving, $t =$ **376.8 °C**.

12. Write down the loop equations for the electrical circuit shown in Fig. 2.21. Given $R_1 = 2\,\Omega$, $R_2 = 1\,\Omega$, $R_3 = 10\,\Omega$, $V_1 = 6$ V and $V_2 = 5$ V. Considering the values given, calculate the current from each source and also find the current through R_3. [B.U. 2002]

Solution : In the first loop, $I_1R_1 + (I_1 - I_2)R_2 = V_1 - V_2$

In the second loop, $\qquad\qquad I_2R_3 + (I_2 - I_1)R_2 = V_2.$

Putting the values from the equation of the first loop,

$$2 \times I_1 + (I_1 - I_2) \times 1 = 6 - 5$$

or, $3I_1 - I_2 = 1.$

From the equation of the second loop,

$$I_2 \times 10 + (I_2 - I_1) \times 1 = 5$$

or, $11I_2 - I_1 = 5.$

Solving, $I_1 = I_2 = \mathbf{0.5 \ A}$

and the current through R_3 resistance, $I_2 = \mathbf{0.5 \ A}.$

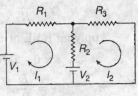

Fig. 7.21

13. A battery of 12 volts e.m.f. and 6 Ω internal resistance is connected in parallel to another battery of 8 volts e.m.f. and 4 Ω internal resistance. At the two ends of this combination a wire of 12 Ω resistance is connected. Calculate the current in the wire and also through the two batteries.

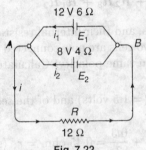

Fig. 7.22

Solution : Applying Kirchhoff's first law at A,

$$i = i_1 + i_2. \tag{i}$$

Applying the second law at the loop, $ARBE_2A$,

$$12i + 4i_2 = 8. \tag{ii}$$

Similarly, for the loop, $ARBE_1A$,

$$12i + 6i_1 = 12. \tag{iii}$$

From Eqs. (ii) and (iii), we get

$$3i + i_2 = 2 \quad \text{and} \quad 2i + i_1 = 2.$$

Adding, $5i + (i_1 + i_2) = 4$

or, $5i + i = 4$ [using equation (i)]

$$\therefore \qquad i = \frac{4}{6} = \mathbf{0.67 \ A}$$

Putting the value of i in (ii), $i_2 = 0.01$ A

and from (i), $i_1 = 0.66$ A.

14. Between the points A and B three resistors R_1, R_2 and R_3 are in parallel. A cell of e.m.f. E and of negligible resistance is connected between the points A and B. Applying Kirchhoff's laws prove that the equivalent resistance between the points A and B is

$$R = \frac{R_1 R_2 R_3}{R_1 R_2 + R_2 R_3 + R_1 R_3} \qquad \text{[B. U. 2000]}$$

Solution : Applying the KVL in the loop AR_1BE, we get

$$i \times 0 + i_1 R_1 = E \quad (r = 0)$$

or, $i_1 = \dfrac{E}{R_1}.$ (i)

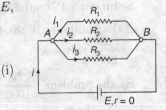

Fig. 7.23

Applying KVL at the loop AR_2BE, we get

$$i \times 0 + i_2 R_2 = E$$

or, $i_2 = \dfrac{E}{R_2}$.   (ii)

Applying KVL at the loop AR_3BE, we get

$$i \times 0 + i_3 R_3 = E$$

or, $i_3 = \dfrac{E}{R_3}$.   (iii)

Adding, $i_1 + i_2 + i_3 = E\left[\dfrac{1}{R_1} + \dfrac{1}{R_2} + \dfrac{1}{R_3}\right]$.

But applying KCL at the point A,

$$i = i_1 + i_2 + i_3 = E\left(\dfrac{1}{R_1} + \dfrac{1}{R_2} + \dfrac{1}{R_3}\right).$$

If the equivalent resistance be R between the points A and B,

$$R = \dfrac{E}{i} = \dfrac{1}{\frac{1}{R_1} + \frac{1}{R_2} + \frac{1}{R_3}} = \dfrac{R_1 R_2 R_3}{R_1 R_2 + R_2 R_3 + R_1 R_2}.$$

15. The e.m.f. of two cells are 1.5 volts and 1.1 volts, and their internal resistances are 0.1 ohm and 0.2 ohm respectively. These two cells are now connected with two wires of resistances 0.3 ohm and 0.4 ohm in same polarity. Calculate the e.m.f. of the combination.

    Solution : Let the e.m.f. of the first cell be $e_1 (= 1.5$ volts) and of the second cell be $e_2 (= 1.1$ volts).

    The total resistance of the first cell $= 0.1 + \dfrac{0.4}{2} + \dfrac{0.3}{2} = 0.45$ ohm $= r_1$ (say).

    The total resistance of the second cell $= 0.2 + \dfrac{0.4}{2} + \dfrac{0.3}{2} = 0.55$ ohm $= r_2$ (say).

    If the combination sends current I at the external circuit and since $e_1 > e_2$,

    $$e_1 = E + I \cdot r_1 \quad \text{and} \quad e_2 = E - I \cdot r_2.$$

    Solving the two equations,

    $$E = \dfrac{e_1 r_2 + e_2 r_1}{r_1 + r_2} = \dfrac{1.5 \times 0.55 + 1.1 \times 0.45}{0.45 + 0.55} = 1.32 \text{ volts.}$$

    ∴ the e.m.f. of the combination = **1.32 volts.**

16. A 10-wire potentiometer, each wire being 1 metre long and having uniform resistance, is driven by an accumulator of e.m.f. 2 volts and of negligible resistance. A cell of e.m.f. 1.5 volts is to be balanced on the potentiometer. Find the length of the wire at which the null point will be obtained.

    Solution : Potential drop per cm of the potentiometer wire $= \dfrac{2}{1000}$ volt.

    If the null point is obtained at l cm, then the fall of potential for that length $= \dfrac{2l}{1000}$ volt.

    By the problem, $\dfrac{2l}{1000} = 1.5$.

    ∴ $l = \mathbf{750}$ **cm.**

Questions

Essay-type

1. Discuss the flow of electric current through a metal. Establish the equation of continuity.

2. State and explain, with suitable diagram, Kirchhoff's laws concerning the current distribution in network circuit.

3. Discuss the setting up of cells (i) in series circuit, (ii) in parallel circuit and (iii) in mixed circuit. What is meant by lost voltage in a battery?

4. Establish the balanced condition of the Wheatstone bridge. Find the value of the current passing through the galvanometer in a Wheatstone bridge network under any arrangement.

5. Explain why the Wheatstone bridge is unsuitable for comparison of either low or high resistances.

6. Explain what you mean by the sensitivity of the Wheatstone bridge. Discuss theoretically the best value of the galvanometer resistance.

7. Give the theory of the Wheatstone bridge and discuss its sensitivity.

8. What are the advantages of Kelvin double bridge? Give the theory underlying the working of the bridge.

9. State and explain Kirchhoff's laws for the distribution of currents in a network of conductors.   [C.U. 1983, '89; B.U. 1991]

10. State Kirchhoff's laws for the distribution of currents in a network of conductors. Use these laws to find the current through the galvanometer when a Wheatstone bridge is out of balance. Hence, find the condition for balance.

11. Explain briefly how Kirchhoff's laws are applied in a Wheatstone network of conductors.

Short Answer-type

12. Describe how a potentiometer can be used to measure the resistance of a resistor. Draw a neat diagram of the circuit.

13. Describe the laboratory type potentiometer and explain the principle of its working with a suitable diagram. How can two e.m.f.s be compared with it?

14. What is the effect of light on the resistance of a conductor?

15. Explain the method of measuring the current flowing in a line with the help of a potentiometer.

16. How will the resistance of a metallic conductor increase with the increase of temperature? Will the resistance of an electrolyte increase or decrease when the temperature is raised?   [C.U. 1982]

17. When will a Wheatstone bridge be called 'balanced'? What is the condition for such a balance?

18. What are the different factors affecting the resistance of a substance? What is called temperature coefficient of resistance?

19. What laws do these symbols indicate : $\Sigma i = 0$; $\Sigma ir = \Sigma E$?   [C.U. 1990]

20. "The e.m.f. of a cell can be measured accurately by a potentiometer."—Justify the statement.   **[C.U. 1982]**

Numerical Problems

21. Two resistances R_1 and R_2 in parallel have an equivalent resistance of 10/3 ohms. When a current enters the parallel circuit, it divides between the two resistors in the ratio 2 : 1. Calculate the value of R_1 and R_2.

                               [Ans. $R_1 = 5$ ohms, $R_2 = 10$ ohms**]**

22. A 10-ohm resistor is in series with a parallel combination of two resistors of values 15 ohms and 5 ohms. If the constant current in the 5-ohm resistor is 6 amperes, what total power is dissipated in the three resistors?

                                       [Ans. 880 watts]

23. A battery of 6 volts e.m.f. and 0.5 ohm internal resistance is joined in parallel with another battery of 10 volts e.m.f. and internal resistance 1.0 ohm, and the combination is used to send current through an external resistance of 12 ohms. Calculate the current through the resistance.   **[Ans.** $\frac{22}{37}$ **A]**

24. You have a circular loop of wire of resistance 20 ohms and at two points at a quarter of the circumference apart, a battery of internal resistance 0.5 ohm and of e.m.f. 4 volts is connected by two wires of resistances 1 ohm each. Find the current at different parts of the circuit.   **[Ans.** $\frac{16}{25}$ A, $\frac{12}{25}$ A, $\frac{4}{25}$ A**]**

25. In a Wheatstone bridge, each of its four arms has 1 ohm resistance and the cell in its position has e.m.f. 1 volt and internal resistance 0.1 ohm. If the galvanometer is replaced by another cell of 1 volt e.m.f. and 0.1 ohm internal resistance, calculate the current in the different branches.

              [Ans. $BA = CD = 0$, $CA = BC = AD = \frac{10}{11}$ A**]**

26. Two cells of e.m.f. 1.5 volts and 1.1 volts and of internal resistances 0.1 ohm and 0.2 ohm respectively are joined in opposition by two wires of resistances 0.3 ohm and 0.4 ohm. Find the p.d. between the middle points of the wires.

                                   [Ans. 1.32 volts]

27. In a Wheatstone bridge network $ABCD$, the resistances in ohms are : $AB = 10$, $BC = 15$, $AD = 20$, $DC = 25$ and $BD = 10$. If the potential difference between A and C is 20 volts, find the current distribution in the network, neglecting the internal resistance of the battery.

                        [Ans. $AB = \frac{50}{61}$ A, $BC = \frac{48}{61}$ A, $BD = \frac{2}{61}$ A,

                                 $AD = \frac{26}{61}$ A, $DC = \frac{28}{61}$ A**]**

28. Twelve wires, each of resistance r, are joined to form a cube. Find its equivalent resistance if the current enters and leaves through adjacent corners of a face.   **[Ans.** $\frac{7}{12} \cdot r$**]**

29. A battery of 6 volts and internal resistance 0.6 ohm is connected in parallel with another battery of 10 volts and internal resistance 1 ohm by two resistances of 6 ohms each. Find the potential difference between the mid-points of the two connecting resistances.   **[Ans.** $\frac{107}{13.5}$ volts**]**

30. In Wheatstone bridge the four resistances in the arms of the bridge are : $AB = 2$ ohms, $BC = 4$ ohms, $AD = 1$ ohm and $DC = 3$ ohms. The terminals of a cell of e.m.f. 2 volts and negligible resistance are connected by wires of negligible resistance to A and C. If a galvanometer of resistance 10 ohms is connected between B and D, find the current in the galvanometer.

[**Ans.** $\frac{2}{145}$ A]

31. Three cells are connected in parallel. If the e.m.f.s of the cells be respectively 2 volts, 1 volt, 4 volts and if the corresponding resistances be 4 ohms, 3 ohms and 2 ohms, find the current through each cell. [**Ans.** $\frac{9}{13}$ A, $\frac{7}{13}$ A, $\frac{2}{13}$ A]

32. Twelve identical wires each of resistance r are connected to form a cube. Calculate the equivalent resistance of the cube if the current enters and leaves through the opposite corners of a face of the cube. [**Ans.** $R = \frac{3}{4}r$]

33. A cell of e.m.f. 6 volts and internal resistance 5 ohms is connected in parallel with another cell of e.m.f. 10 volts and internal resistance 1 ohm. The combination is used to send a current through an external resistance 12 ohms. Calculate the current through each cell. [**Ans.** 1.2 A and 0.46 A]

34. Two cells of e.m.f.s 1.5 V and 2.0 V having internal resistances of 1 ohm and 2 ohms respectively are connected in parallel and a resistance of 5 ohms is connected across the combination. Find the current through the 5 Ω resistance. [**B.U. 1998**]

[**Ans.** 0.284 A]

35. The positive and negative poles of a battery of 2 Grove cells are connected respectively to the positive and negative poles of a battery of 2 Daniel cells by wires of resistances 10 ohms and 6 ohms. The middle of the wires are connected by another wire of resistance 4 ohms. Calculate the current flowing through each of the batteries. e.m.f. and the internal resistance of a Grove cell are respectively 1.9 volts and 1 ohm; those of a Daniel cell are 1.1 volts and 2 ohms. [**Ans.** 0.25 A; 0.075 A]

36. You have a circular loop of wire of resistance 20 ohms and at two points at a quarter of the circumference apart, a battery of internal resistance 0.5 ohm and of e.m.f. 4 volts is connected by two wires of resistance 1 ohm each. Find the current at different parts of the circuit.

37. Two cells of e.m.f. 1.5 volts and 2 volts and internal resistances 2 ohms and 1 ohm respectively have their negative terminals joined by a wire of 6 ohms and positive terminals by another wire of 4 ohms. A third resistance of 8 ohms connects the mid-points of these wires. Find the p.d. at the ends of this third wire. [**Ans.** 1.26 volts]

38. A cube is formed with 12 equal resistances of 6 ohms each. Find the equivalent resistance along the diagonal of the cube. [**C.U. 1989**]

[**Ans.** 3.5 ohms]

39. In a Wheatstone bridge, the resistance in the arm AB is 2 ohms, BC 4 ohms, AD 1 ohm and DC 3 ohms. The terminals of a cell of e.m.f. 2 volts and negligible resistance are connected by wires of negligible resistance to A and C. If a galvanometer of resistance 10 ohms is connected between B and D, find the current in the galvanometer. [**Ans.** 0.011 A]

40. In a Wheatstone bridge, a battery of 2 volts and of resistance 2 ohms is used. Find the current through the galvanometer in the unbalanced condition of the bridge when $P = 1$ ohm; $Q = 2$ ohms; $R = 2$ ohms and $G = 4$ ohms.

[**Ans.** 0.011 A]

41. One of the gaps of a metre bridge is closed by a resistance of 2 ohms and the other by 3 ohms. Where will the null point be? What resistance should be placed in parallel with the 3 ohms coil so that null point may be at the middle of the wire?   [**Ans.** 40 cm; 6 ohms]

42. In a Wheatstone bridge, the resistance of the arm AB is 2 ohms, of BC 2 ohms, of AD 1 ohm and DC 1 ohm. A cell of e.m.f. 2 volts and internal resistance 1 ohm is connected between A and C, whereas another cell of e.m.f. 1 volt and internal resistance 2 ohms is connected between B and D. Find the current through the last cell.   [**Ans.** 0.29 A from D to B]

43. The resistances of the four arms of a Wheatstone bridge are 5 ohms, 15 ohms, 20 ohms and 60 ohms, so that bridge is balanced and no current passes through the galvanometer. The e.m.f. of the battery is 2 volts and its resistance is 4 ohms. What current passes through the battery?   [**Ans.** 0.1 A]

44. A 10-wire potentiometer, each of 1 metre length, has a resistance of 20 ohms. A cell of e.m.f. 2 volts and negligible resistance together with a resistance box is connected to it. How much resistance is to be put in the box so as to produce a p.d. of 1 microvolt per 2 mm of the wire? If an unknown p.d. produces a null point at 750 cm of the wire, find the value of the p.d.

[**Ans.** 7980 ohms; 3750 microvolts]

Chapter 8
Electrical Appliances and Applications

8.1 Introduction

Some useful accessories necessary for electrical experiments and their applications are discussed in this chapter.

8.2 Connectors and Binding Screws

For connecting two separate wires, connectors or binding screws are used. These are obtained in various shapes. A connector and a binding screw are shown in Figs. 8.1(a) and (b) respectively.

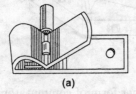

(a)   **(b)**

Fig. 8.1

These are made usually by brass or copper material and as such are of negligible resistance.

8.3 Keys

Keys are used for closing or opening an electrical circuit. These are also obtained in various types and shapes. The two types, very commonly used, are shown in Figs. 8.2(a) and (b).

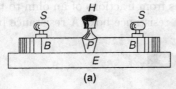 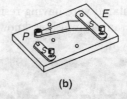

(a)   **(b)**

Fig. 8.2

Plug key : Fig. 8.2(a) shows a plug key. Two metallic bars B, B are fixed on an ebonite base E. The metallic bars are separated by a small gap which can be bridged by a brass plug P with an ebonite handle H. S, S in the figure are two binding screws.

Tapping key : It consists of an ebonite base E on which two binding screws S, S are fixed. One of the screws S is attached to a metal spring T having an ebonite tapping button P. Below this a metal stud is connected by means of a metal strip with the other binding screw. When P is pressed down on the stud a contact is made while when the finger is withdrawn, the metal spring springs up and as a result the circuit becomes out of contact.

If the current is required for a longer time we use a plug key while if the current is required for a short time we use a tapping key.

8.4   Commutator

Commutator is an arrangement for reversing the direction of current flowing through any portion of the circuit.

Different forms of commutator are there. In Fig. 8.3 two such forms are shown.

Plug commutator : Fig. 8.3(a) shows a four-terminal plug which is used as a commutator. Four thick metal plates $1, 2, 3, 4$ are separated from each other by gaps. The plates are fixed on an ebonite base E and provided with respective binding screws. When the metal plugs P, P inserted between the gaps, a contact is established.

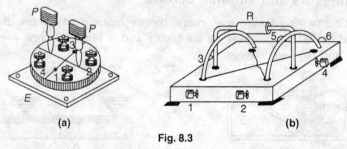

Fig. 8.3

Phol commutator : Fig. 8.3(b) shows another form of commutator known as pohl commutator. This is used, in general, for rapidly reversing the direction of current.

The commutator consists of six mercury cups on an insulating base. Each cup is provided with its own binding screws. One diametrically opposite pair of cups is connected by a piece of thick copper wire as shown. A second such pair is also connected by another wire which is bent to avoid any contact with the first.

8.5   Resistance Boxes and Coils

Coils of insulated wire having resistances from fractions of an ohm to thousands of ohms are arranged in a box, known as a resistance box. A resistance box is shown in Fig. 8.4.

Fig. 8.4

Fig. 8.5

Coils of standard resistance are sometimes sold and used for the purpose. In Fig. 8.5 an insulated wire $PQRS$ in the form of a coil is doubled on itself as PQ and

RS. This eliminates the effects of self-induction as the currents in the neighbouring two halves of the wire are in opposite directions. This type of winding is known as non-inductive winding.

8.6 Rheostat

The current flowing in a circuit can be changed by changing the resistance. When the value of such resistance is not required to know, an adjustable resistance can be used. Such a variable resistance is called a rheostat. A rheostat generally consists of a coil of uncovered wire with a high specific resistance and wound on a slate or porcelain cylinder such that the neighbouring turns do not touch one another. A rheostat is shown in Fig. 8.6. The two ends of the wire are connected to the two binding screws S, S. A jockey J is there which moves along the metal rod R.

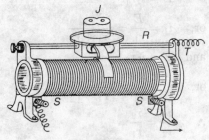

Fig. 8.6

The rheostat is placed in a circuit by the binding screw T at the top and one of the binding screws (S, S), as shown.

8.7 Regulator

It consists of a variable resistance generally fitted with electric motors or fans.

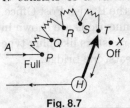

Fig. 8.7

Several resistances, PQ, QR, RS, ST, etc., are connected in series for regulating the current according to requirement (Fig. 8.7). There are several studs P, Q, etc., the last of which X is not in the circuit. A metal handle is so arranged that it moves over the studs and the current entering at A is completed through the end P. From Ohm's law we can say that the current will be maximum when the end of the handle (H) is over the stud P and will be off when shifted to X.

8.8 Shunt

A part of a current flowing through a resistor can be diverted by joining a second resistor in parallel. Such a combination of two resistances in parallel acts as shunt to each other. If the resistance of the shunt chosen is of relatively lower value, then a greater part of main current passes through it.

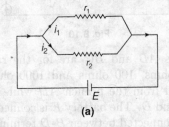

(a)

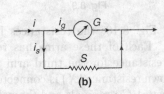

(b)

Fig. 8.8

Let r_1 and r_2 are two resistances connected in parallel through an e.m.f. E, as shown in Fig. 8.8. The equivalent resistance of the combination can be written as

$$R = \frac{r_1 r_2}{r_1 + r_2}.$$

$$(8.1)$$

∴ the current supplied by the cell is

$$i = E \cdot \frac{r_1 + r_2}{r_1 r_2}. \tag{8.2}$$

Let the current passing in the two branches be denoted as i_1 and i_2 respectively. Then we can write,

$$E = i_1 r_1$$

or, $$i_1 = \frac{E}{r_1} = i \frac{r_2}{r_1 + r_2} \tag{8.3}$$

and $$E = i_2 r_2$$

or, $$i_2 = \frac{E}{r_2} = i \frac{r_1}{r_1 + r_2} \tag{8.4}$$

∴ $$\frac{i_1}{i_2} = \frac{r_2}{r_1}. \tag{8.5}$$

Eq. (8.5) shows that the currents in the two branches are inversely proportional to the respective resistances. Or in other words, we can conclude that greater the resistance, the smaller is the current flowing through it.

8.9   Post Office Box

This is a compact form of the Wheatstone bridge, so named as it was originally intended for measuring resistances of telegraph wires, etc., in the British Post Office. A P.O. Box is shown in Fig. 8.9 while its inside electrical connections are shown in Fig. 8.10. In the box there is an assembly of different sets of resistors like plug type arranged in three branches forming the three arms of a Wheatstone bridge.

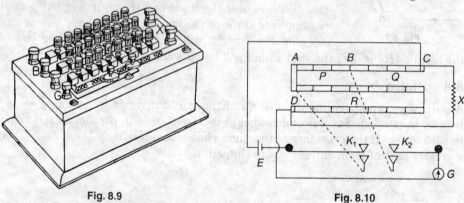

Fig. 8.9   Fig. 8.10

In Fig. 8.10, the resistances in the branches AB and BC are for the ratio arms. Each of these arms has resistances 10 ohms, 100 ohms and 1000 ohms. The resistance for the third arm (R) is obtained from the branch AD while the unknown resistance (X) is connected between C and D. The battery E is connected between A-C terminals and the galvanometer is connected between B-D terminals. Connections are closed through the tapping keys K_1 and K_2 respectively to avoid unnecessary heating of the coils.

In order to get the value of the unknown resistance, the third arm resistance (R) which gives the balance is to be multiplied by the ratio of resistances (Q/P) placed in the ratio arms.

8.10 Meter Bridge

In order to measure an unknown resistance by applying the principle of Wheatstone bridge the meter bridge can be used suitably with a greater precision than the P.O. Box.

A meter bridge is shown in Fig. 8.11. It consists of a fine wire A_1C_1 of one meter long, stretches along a meter scale upon a wooden board. The two extreme ends of the wire are soldered at the points A_1 and C_1. In the figure, A_1A, AL, ML_1, M_1C and CC_1 are copper plates of negligible resistance. At the points $A_1, A, L, M, B, L_1, M_1, C$ and C_1 binding screws are provided for necessary connections. There is a slider

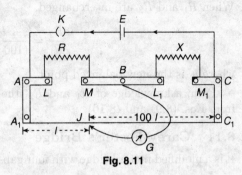

Fig. 8.11

J called the jockey. By pressing the jockey J contact can be made with the galvanometer G at any position of the wire. LM and L_1M_1 are the two gaps of the bridge where a known resistance (R) and an unknown resistance (X) are inserted.

Since the bridge wire used is uniform, the resistance of any portion of it will be proportional to its length. Thus, if ρ be the resistance per unit length of A_1C_1, the resistance of the length l is ρl and the resistance of the length $(100 - l)$ is $\rho(100 - l)$. Hence by applying Wheatstone's principle, we can write,

$$\frac{R}{X} = \frac{l}{(100 - l)}$$

or, $\quad X = \dfrac{R \times (100 - l)}{l}.$ \hfill (8.6)

Using Eq. (8.6) the unknown resistance X can be determined.

For a greater accuracy, readings are taken by adjusting R near the mid-point of the wire. If we choose a little higher resistance $(X + \delta X)$, then for a constant R the balance point will be shifted slightly by a length δl so that

$$\delta X = \frac{100R \cdot \delta l}{(100 - l)^2} \tag{8.7}$$

$$\therefore \quad \frac{\delta X}{X} = \frac{100\delta l}{l(100 - l)}. \tag{8.8}$$

If for finding the null point the error involved is δl, then the error in X is δX. So the proportional error $\frac{\delta X}{X}$ will be minimum when $l(100 - l)$ is maximum.

$\therefore$ for the greatest accuracy,

$$\frac{\delta}{\delta l}[l(100 - l)] = 0 \quad \text{or,} \quad 100 - 2l = 0 \quad \text{or,} \quad l = 50 \text{ cm.}$$

This implies that for maximum accuracy the null point should be near the mid-point of the wire. This is achieved when R and X are of equal values.

8.10.1 End Corrections

The wire in the meter bridge is either soldered or screwed with the copper strips and therefore some contact resistances must be there at the two ends. Such errors are corrected by a method due to Ferguson. If α_1 and α_2 represent the errors at the two ends respectively expressed in cm of length, then with two unequal resistances R_1 and R_2 in the left gap and the right gap respectively, the balance point is written as

$$\frac{R_1}{R_2} = \frac{l_1 + \alpha_1}{(100 - l_1) + \alpha_2}. \tag{8.9}$$

When R_1 and R_2 are interchanged,

$$\frac{R_2}{R_1} = \frac{l_2 + \alpha_1}{(100 - l_2) + \alpha_2}, \tag{8.10}$$

where l_2 is the new balanced point.

From a knowledge of R_1 and R_2, the end errors α_1 and α_2 can be calculated from Eqs. (8.9) and (8.10).

8.11 Carey-Foster's Bridge

It is a modified meter bridge with four gaps instead of two. This can be suitably used

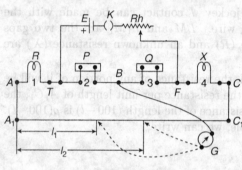

Fig. 8.12

for determining the resistance per cm of the bridge wire, i.e., to calibrate the bridge wire. The Carey-Foster's bridge is shown in Fig. 8.12. In the figure, P and Q are two nearly equal resistances placed in the inner gaps 2 and 3 and these form the ratio arms of Wheatstone bridge while R and X in gap 1 and gap 4 are the resistances to be compared.

For a balanced bridge, we can write,

$$\frac{P}{Q} = \frac{R + (l_1 + \alpha_1)\rho}{X + (100 - l_1 + \alpha_2)\rho}, \tag{8.11}$$

where l_1 is the length of the wire from the end to which R is connected. α_1 and α_2 are the end corrections at the respective ends and ρ is the resistance per unit length of the bridge wire.

When R and X are interchanged, we have

$$\frac{P}{Q} = \frac{X + (l_2 + \alpha_1)\rho}{R + (100 - l_2 + \alpha_2)\rho}. \tag{8.12}$$

From Eqs. (8.11) and (8.12), we have

$$\frac{R + X + (\alpha_1 + \alpha_2 + 100)\rho}{R + (100 - l_2 + \alpha_2)\rho} = \frac{R + X + (\alpha_1 + \alpha_2 + 100)\rho}{X + (100 - l_1 + \alpha_2)\rho}$$

or, $R + (100 - l_2 + \alpha_2)\rho = X + (100 - l_1 + \alpha_2)\rho$

or, $R - X = (l_2 - l_1)\rho. \tag{8.13}$

Eq. (8.13) can be employed to find ρ and to calibrate the bridge wire.

8.12 Callendar and Griffith's Bridge

It is used for the measurement of the change of resistance of a platinum wire due to change in temperature. The connections of the bridge are shown in Fig. 8.13.

P and Q are two equal resistances of value, usually 10 ohms. These are the ratio arms of the bridge. The platinum wire is connected by copper leads in the gap X. It is wound non-inductively on a mica sheet and enclosed in a glass or silica tube. An equivalent pair of leads is joined in the gap C. The two pairs of leads are kept very close to each other and their resistances are made equal. By a resistance R of a resistance box the bridge is balanced on a uniform wire of manganin of about 50 cm in length.

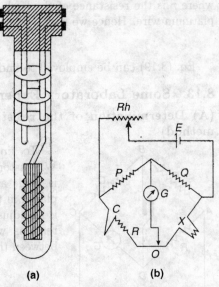

Fig. 8.13

For a pure platinum wire the resistance R_t at $t°C$ can be written as

$$R_t = R_0(1 + \alpha t + \beta t^2), \qquad (8.14)$$

where α and β are two constants for the metal.

The temperature t_p of the resistance wire at $t°C$ in the platinum scale can be obtained from

$$\frac{t_p}{100} = \frac{R_t - R_0}{R_{100} - R_0}. \qquad (8.15)$$

The actual temperature t is then calculated from

$$t - t_p = \delta \left(\frac{t}{100} - 1 \right) \frac{t}{100}, \qquad (8.16)$$

where δ is a constant involving α and β. For pure platinum the value of δ is 1.5. The value of δ in terms of α and β can be obtained by the following way :

We know that,

$$t_p = \frac{R_t - R_0}{R_{100} - R_0} \times 100 = \frac{\frac{R_t}{R_0} - 1}{\frac{R_{100}}{R_0} - 1} \times 100 = \frac{\alpha t + \beta t^2}{\alpha \cdot 100 + \beta \cdot 100^2} \times 100$$

or, $$t - t_p = t - \frac{\alpha t + \beta t^2}{\alpha + \beta \cdot 100} = \frac{-\beta t(t - 100)}{\alpha + 100\beta} = -\frac{100^2 \beta \frac{t}{100} \left(\frac{t}{100} - 1 \right)}{\alpha + 100\beta}$$

$$\therefore \quad \delta = -\frac{100^2 \beta}{\alpha + 100\beta}. \qquad (8.17)$$

The temperature t_p is calculated by putting R_0, R_{100} and R_t in Eq. (8.15). This value of t_p is substituted in Eq. (8.16) to get an approximate value of t. This is again substituted for t in the r.h.s. of Eq. (8.16) to get a more correct value of $(t - t_p)$ and hence t is found. The procedure is repeated several times when the final value of t is obtained.

In Fig. 8.13, let by shorting the pairs of leads at the gaps and making R zero, the electric mid-point be obtained at O. Next by removing the shorts if the balance point is found at a length l cm to the right from O, then since resistances P and Q are of equal values,

$$R + r + (50 + l)\rho = X + r + (50 - l)\rho, \qquad (8.18)$$

where r is the resistance of the leads in either gap and X is the resistance of the platinum wire. Hence we have,

$$X = R + 2l\rho \qquad (8.19)$$

Eq. (8.19) can be employed to find X.

8.13   Some Laboratory Experiments

(A) Determination of the resistance of the galvanometer (Thomson's method)

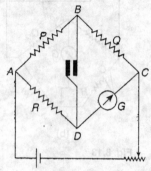

Fig. 8.14

To find the resistance of the galvanometer by Wheatstone bridge principle the circuit arrangement is made as shown in Fig. 8.14. The galvanometer is placed in the fourth arm of the P.O. Box. The current is so adjusted that the deflection of the galvanometer remains within the scale. The potential difference between the points B and D will be zero when

$$\frac{P}{Q} = \frac{R}{G}, \qquad (8.20)$$

where G is the galvanometer resistance.

(B) Determination of the internal resistance of the cell (Mance's method)

To find the internal resistance of the cell by Wheatstone bridge principle the circuit arrangement is made as shown in Fig. 8.15. The resistances P, Q and R in the first, second and third arms of the bridge are so adjusted that pressing a key between A and C does not change the galvanometer current. Therefore, in this condition,

$$\frac{P}{Q} = \frac{R}{r}$$

must hold, where r is the internal resistance of the cell.

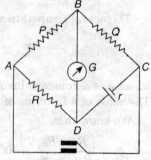

Fig. 8.15

Mance's method for the measurement of internal resistance is not good enough since the current in the cell on which the internal resistance depends is not known.

8.14   Mathiessen and Hockin's Method

The errors due to contact resistances can be eliminated by using this method. It is suitable specially for comparing two low resistances in the form of rod.

The experimental arrangement is shown in Fig. 8.16. XY is a uniform wire. R_1 and R_2 are two resistances connected by thick copper strips. The galvanometer G is connected with any of the potential terminals through a four-way key and also with the slide wire by a jockey.

For zero galvanometer current if A, B, C and D are the positions of the jockey on the slide wire, the other end of the galvanometer being connected to the potential terminals one after another, we can write,

$$i_1 R_1 = i_2 \cdot AB \cdot \rho \qquad (8.21)$$

and $i_1 R_2 = i_2 \cdot CD \cdot \rho, \qquad (8.22)$

where i_1 and i_2 are the currents through the branches R_1 and R_2 and the slide wire respectively; ρ is the resistance per unit length of the slide wire.

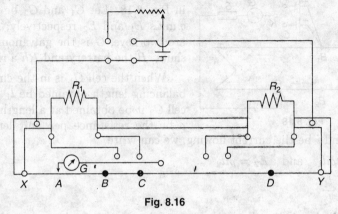

Fig. 8.16

Taking the ratio of Eq. (8.21) to Eq. (8.22), we get

$$\frac{R_1}{R_2} = \frac{AB}{CD}. \tag{8.23}$$

For comparing low resistances by this method, constancy of the battery current is not required.

8.15 Potentiometer

It has a unique importance for its universal application in electrical measurements. Fig. 8.17 shows an ordinary potentiometer. On a wooden board a number of uniform conducting wires (usually ten) each of length 1 metre are stretched and fixed parallel to one another. These are joined in series by thick copper strips. The combination of the wires acts as a single wire of length equal to the lengths of all the wires.

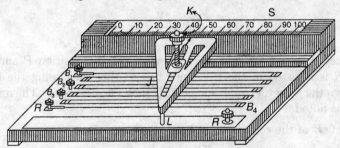

Fig. 8.17

B_1 and B_2 are two binding screws fixed to the free ends of the first and the last wire. RR is a brass strip provided with binding screws B_3 and B_4. J is a three-legged jockey-bridge made by brass, its one leg L always sliding on the strip RR. By pressing a metal push-key K of the jockey any one of the wires can be contacted. By an index mark I, the point of contact of the wire can be noted from the meter scale S.

8.15.1 Experiments Using a Potentiometer

Some important experiments with a potentiometer are described below indicating its wide scope of application.

(A) Comparison of the e.m.f.s of two cells

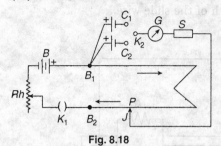

Fig. 8.18

The experimental arrangement is shown in Fig. 8.18. Let C_1 and C_2 be two cells of e.m.f.s E_1 and E_2 respectively; K_1 and K_2 are two keys, G is the galvanometer, S the shunt, B the battery and Rh a rheostat.

When the cell C_1 is in the circuit let the balancing length obtained be l_1 and for the cell C_2 it be obtained at a length l_2. Then if ρ be the resistance per unit length of the slide wire and i be the current flowing, we can write,

$$E_1 = \rho i l_1 \quad \text{and} \quad E_2 = \rho i l_2$$

$$\therefore \quad \frac{E_1}{E_2} = \frac{l_1}{l_2}. \tag{8.24}$$

Eq. (8.24) shows that the comparison of the two e.m.f.s depends only on the two balancing lengths.

(B) Measurement of the e.m.f. of a cell

The e.m.f. of a cell can be measured by using a milliammeter (mA) and a resistance box (R) as shown in Fig. 8.19.

Before connecting the circuit, the total resistance (X) of the potentiometer wire between the two binding screws B_1 and B_2 is measured with the help of P.O. Box. If L be the total length of the wire, then the resistance in ohms per unit length (ρ) of it is given by

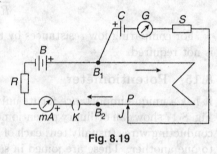

Fig. 8.19

$$\rho = \frac{X}{L}. \tag{8.25}$$

The jockey J is now brought on the last wire at the position P and a suitable resistance R is inserted in the resistance box so that on closing the key K and pressing down the jockey, the galvanometer G shows no defection. The milliammeter reading (i) is noted.

The e.m.f. E of the cell C = p.d. between B_1 and P

$$= \frac{Xi}{1000} \times l \text{ volts}, \tag{8.26}$$

where l is the length of the slide wire between B_1 and P.

(C) Measurement of current by potentiometer

The experimental arrangement is shown in Fig. 8.20. If E be the e.m.f. of the cell C and e be the p.d. across the low resistance r,

then $\quad E = \rho i l_1$ \hfill (8.27)

and $\quad e = \rho i l_2$, \hfill (8.28)

where ρ is the resistance of the potentiometer slide-wire per unit length, i is the constant slide-wire current to remain constant between the two balancings.

Taking the ratio of Eqs. (8.27) and (8.28), we get

$$\frac{E}{e} = \frac{l_1}{l_2}$$

or, $e = E\dfrac{l_2}{l_1}$ (8.29)

If i_x represents the unknown current, then,

$$e = r \times i_x \quad \therefore \quad r \times i_x = E\frac{l_2}{l_1}$$

or, $i_x = \dfrac{E}{r}\dfrac{l_2}{l_1}$ (8.30)

Knowing the quantities on the r.h.s., the unknown current can be determined by Eq. (8.30).

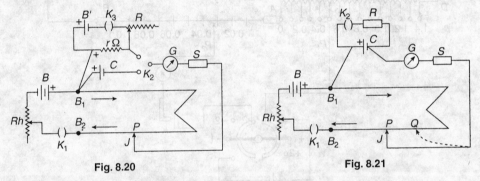

Fig. 8.20   Fig. 8.21

(D) Measurement of the internal resistance of a cell

The experimental arrangement is shown in Fig. 8.21. Let C be the cell whose internal resistance r is to be determined. The e.m.f. of the cell C is balanced at P by regulating the slide-wire current by the rheostat Rh. This balancing length is equal to l (say).

Next, by closing the key K_2 the test cell is shunted by a resistance R whereupon a current i_1 continuously flows through the cell. Let now the balance be obtained at the point Q. The length B_1Q which is equal to l_1 is less than its previous length l.

If E = e.m.f. of the cell, e = p.d. of the shunted cell, we have

$$\frac{E}{e} = \frac{l}{l_1}.$$ (8.31)

Now, $e = i_1 R = \dfrac{E}{R+r} \cdot R = \dfrac{E}{1 + \frac{r}{R}}$

or, $\dfrac{E}{e} = 1 + \dfrac{r}{R} = \dfrac{l}{l_1}.$

$\therefore \quad \dfrac{r}{R} = \dfrac{l - l_1}{l_1}$

$$r = \left(\frac{l - l_1}{l_1}\right) R.$$ (8.32)

From Eq. (8.32) we can calculate the value of the internal resistance of the cell.

8.15.2 Modern Potentiometer

It is highly precise and accurate. Crompton first modified the laboratory potentiometer to make it compact and suitable for direct reading. The arrangement of the potentiometer is shown in Fig. 8.22.

It has fourteen resistance coils each of value equal to that of AB in the figure. C is the supply battery and R_1, R_2 are two regulating resistances while P_1, P_2 are two movable contacts. The galvanometer G is connected through a key K to a multiple-circuit switch in series between P_1 and P_2.

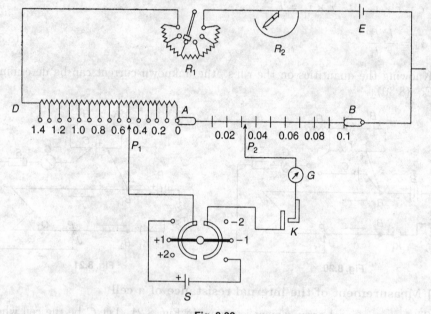

Fig. 8.22

The potentiometer is standardised by adjusting the potentiometric current supplied by C with the help of regulating resistances R_1 and R_2.

Questions

Essay-type

1. Describe the following accessories necessary for electrical experiments :
   (i) Key, **(ii)** Commutator, **(iii)** Rheostat, **(iv)** Regulator, **(v)** Shunt, **(vi)** P.O. Box, **(vii)** Meter bridge, **(viii)** Potentiometer.

2. Describe a meter bridge. For what purpose it is used? What is meant by the end correction of a metre bridge?

3. Describe with necessary mathematical theory : **(i)** Carey-Foster's bridge and **(ii)** Callender and Griffith's bridge.

4. Explain with necessary circuit diagram how you can determine : **(i)** the resistance of a galvanometer, **(ii)** the internal resistance of a cell.

5. How are the e.m.f.s of two cells compared by using a potentiometer?

6. Discuss how you can measure by using a potentiometer : **(i)** the current and **(ii)** the e.m.f. of a cell.

7. Describe briefly with suitable diagram any modern form of potentiometer.

Chapter 9
Thermoelectricity

9.1 Introduction

Thermoelectricity is a phenomenon where electricity is produced by thermal means. Studies on the thermoelectric phenomenon started in the year 1821. Thermoelectric effects have wide practical applications in constructing many sensitive instruments like thermo-milliammeter, thermoelectric thermometer, radio balance, etc.

9.2 Seebeck Effect

In 1821 Seebeck discovered that a current flows in a circuit consisting of two different metals when a temperature difference is maintained between the two junctions.

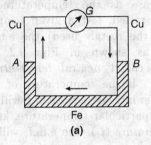

Fig. 9.1

A simple circuit is shown in Fig. 9.1. A and B are two junctions of copper and iron strips. A low resistance deadbeat galvanometer is connected in series in a manner as shown. Both the junctions are kept initially at the same temperature and then the temperature of the junction B is gradually increased by heating. As a result a current will flows from copper to iron across the junction B [Fig. 9.1(a)]. The strength of the current will increase as the temperature of the junction B is increased. Depending on the metals used, at a certain temperature the current strength will be maximum. If the temperature of the junction B is further increased, the strength of the current gradually decreases and ultimately falls to zero. On further increase of temperature the direction of the current will be reversed [Fig. 9.1(b)].

The current produced during the heating of a junction is called *thermoelectric current* and the above effect is known as *Seebeck effect*. Two dissimilar metals joined as above is called a *thermocouple*.

When a difference of temperature exists between the junctions of the thermocouple, an e.m.f., known as *thermo-e.m.f.*, is generated between the two junctions.

9.3 Thermoelectric Series

Seebeck arranged several metals and alloys in a series, known as the *thermoelectric series*. If a thermocouple is formed of any two of the metals in the series, the thermoelectric current will flow across the hot junction (below the inversion

231

temperature) from the metal which occurs earlier to that which occurs later in the series. Seebeck arranged 35 metals and alloys in the thermoelectric series,

	Bi	Ni	Co	Pd	Pt	U
Thermoelectric series	Cu	Mn	Ti	Hg	Pb	Sn
	Cr	Mo	Rh	Ir	Au	Ag
	Zn	W	Cd	Fe	As	Sb

The thermo-e.m.f. at given temperatures of the junction will be greater for a couple made from the metals which are more separated in the series. So a thermocouple bismuth-antimony pair will give the maximum thermo-e.m.f. In this thermocouple across the hot junction, the current will flow from bismuth to antimony.

9.4   Dependence of Thermo-e.m.f. with Temperature

Suppose one junction of the thermocouple is kept at $0\,^\circ$C and the temperature of the other junction is gradually increased. When the temperatures of both the

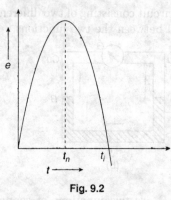

Fig. 9.2

junctions are same, the magnitude of the e.m.f. generated will be zero. But the e.m.f. will gradually increase as the temperature of the hot junction is raised. At a given temperature (depending on the metals used) the e.m.f. will be maximum as shown in Fig. 9.2. This temperature is called *neutral temperature* (t_n) of that couple. If the temperature of the hot junction is further increased, the e.m.f. will fall and ultimately at a particular temperature, known as *inversion temperature* (t_i), the e.m.f. will reduce to zero. Below the temperature of inversion, the direction of the e.m.f. is reversed. The plot of

e.m.f. (e) against the temperature will be parabolic. For a particular couple the neutral temperature is fixed while the inversion temperature depends on the temperature of the cold junction. For a thermocouple the neutral temperature (t_n)

$$= \frac{\text{temp. of cold junction} + \text{inversion temp.}}{2}.$$

For Fe-Cu couple having the cold junction at $0\,^\circ$C, the neutral temperature is $285\,^\circ$C and the inversion temperature is $570\,^\circ$C.

9.5   Peltier Effect

If a current is sent through a thermocouple by any external source connected in that thermocouple circuit, heat is evolved in one junction and absorbed in the other junction provided both the junctions are kept at the same temperature. If the direction of current is reversed, the junction which was previously heated up will now cooled down while the other will be heated. The above reversible effect was discovered by Jean C. A. Peltier in 1834 and known as Peltier effect.

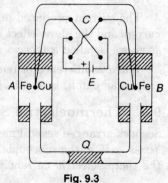

Fig. 9.3

The Peltier effect may be demonstrated by an arrangement as shown in Fig. 9.3. A current can be sent by a battery E through a Fe-Cu couple.

The two junctions of the Fe-Cu couple are placed in two identical glass tubes A and B. The tubes are connected by a capillary tube containing a thread Q of Hg. When a current is made to flow through the couple, the Hg thread will move one side indicating the expansion of air in one tube due to heating. By reversing the direction of current with the help of the commutator C, the direction of movement of the thread will be reversed.

9.6 Explanation of Peltier Effect

The Peltier effect may be explained if it is assumed that an e.m.f. does exist at the junction of two dissimilar metals. The direction of the e.m.f. will depend on the metals.

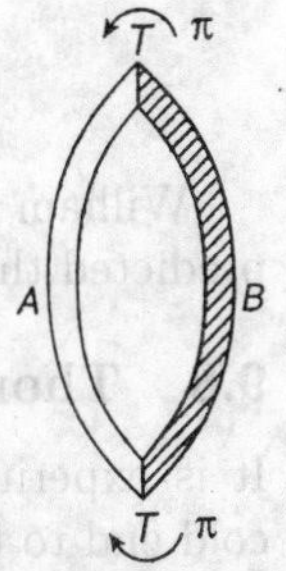

Suppose both the junctions of a couple A-B kept at the same temperature (T) and there exists an e.m.f. π at the junctions in the direction from B to A (Fig. 9.4). So the resultant e.m.f. in the circuit will be zero and there will be no current. Now by introducing a cell a current is sent from B to A for a small interval of time dt. The work done at the junction where the current flows in the direction of current will be $\pi i dt = \pi dq$. Here the energy must be supplied. So heat is absorbed from this junction. As a result, this end will be cooled down. On the other hand, the direction of charge flow is opposite to the direction of e.m.f. at the other junction. So heat is evolved at this junction and this end will be heated up. This effect will be reversed by reversal of the direction of current.

Fig. 9.4

Peltier coefficient is defined as the e.m.f. at the junction of a thermocouple. The heat absorbed or liberated at the junction when unit charge flows through it is a measure of the Peltier coefficient. It is usually denoted by π.

9.7 Application of Thermodynamics and Prediction of Thomson Effect

The Peltier effect is a reversible effect. So a thermocouple may be imagined as a Carnot engine which produces work by absorbing heat at higher temperature and giving back a part of it at lower temperature. The difference being equal to the amount of useful work.

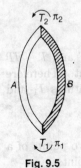

Suppose the temperatures of the junctions are T_2 and $T_1 (T_2 > T_1)$, and π_2 and π_1 are the Peltier coefficients at the temperatures T_2 and T_1 respectively (Fig. 9.5). If a charge q flows for a time t through the circuit, heat absorbed at the hot junction, $H_2 = \pi_2 q$ and heat evolved at the cold junction, $H_1 = \pi_1 q$.

By applying Carnot's principle, we get

$$\frac{\pi_2 q}{\pi_1 q} = \frac{T_2}{T_1} \quad \text{or,} \quad \frac{\pi_2}{\pi_1} = \frac{T_2}{T_1} \quad \text{or,} \quad \frac{\pi_2 - \pi_1}{\pi_1} = \frac{T_2 - T_1}{T_1}$$

$$\text{or,} \quad \pi_2 - \pi_1 = \frac{\pi_1}{T_1}(T_2 - T_1) \quad \text{or,} \quad e = \frac{\pi_1}{T_1}(T_2 - T_1). \tag{9.1}$$

Fig. 9.5

From the above equation it follows that if one junction is kept at constant temperature (T_1), the plot of e against $(T_2 - T_1)$ will be a straight line (Fig. 9.6). But from experimental result it is found that the nature of the curve will be parabolic (Fig. 9.7).

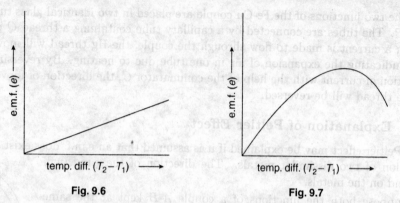

| Fig. 9.6 | Fig. 9.7 |

William Thomson concluded that the Peltier e.m.f. is not the only e.m.f. He predicted the existence of another e.m.f. due to gradient of temperature.

9.8 Thomson Effect

It is experimentally found that heat is absorbed when a current flows from the cold end to the hot end of an unequally heated metal bar and heat is evolved after reversing the direction of current. So a potential gradient must exist along the bar. The number of free electrons in metal depends upon the temperature. Hence a potential gradient should be accompanied with a temperature gradient. This effect is known as Thomson effect.

In Fig. 9.8 the ordinates represent temperature $(T_2 > T_1)$ and the arrows represent the direction of Thomson e.m.f. Thomson effect is said to be positive when the e.m.f. is directed from lower to higher temperatures and negative when directed from higher to lower temperatures. Fig. 9.8(a) and Fig. 9.8(b) represent respectively the positive and negative Thomson effect.

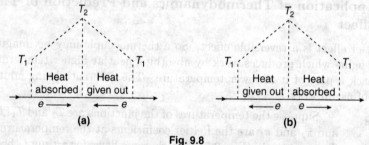

Fig. 9.8

The e.m.f. between two points of a metal bar at temperatures T and $T + dT$ respectively is σdT. The coefficient σ is called Thomson coefficient. Therefore the resultant e.m.f. of a metal bar whose ends are kept at temperatures T_1 and $T_2(T_2 > T_1)$ will be $\int_{T_1}^{T_2} \sigma dT$.

Thomson Coefficient

Thomson coefficient is defined as the e.m.f. developed between two points of a metal when unit temperature difference is maintained between the points.

Experimental Demonstration

Experimental arrangement to demonstrate Thomson effect is shown in Fig. 9.9. ABC is a U-shaped iron rod. The end B is heated by a Bunsen burner to red heat. The other two ends A and C are kept in a constant low temperature mercury baths.

S_1 and S_2 are two identical coils and they are connected to the 3rd and 4th arms of a Wheatstone bridge. The Wheatstone bridge remains in balanced condition when

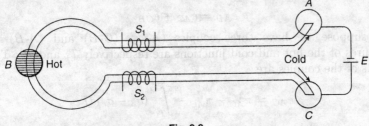

Fig. 9.9

there is no flow of current through the rod. Now a current is made to flow through the bar by using mercury baths at the terminals. The Wheatstone bridge becomes unbalanced due to the change of resistances of the coils S_1 and S_2. This is because of the liberation of heat at one end and absorption of heat at the other. This effect will be reversed on reversal of the direction of current.

9.9   e.m.f. of a Thermocouple

Let us consider a thermocouple with junctions (Fig. 9.10) at temperatures T_1 and T_2 $(T_2 > T_1)$. Then the e.m.f. due to Peltier effect is $\pi_2 - \pi_1$. The Thomson e.m.f. of the two metals

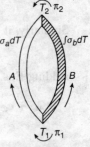

Fig. 9.10

are $-\int_{T_1}^{T_2} \sigma_a dT$ and $\int_{T_1}^{T_2} \sigma_b dT$ respectively.

Therefore, the resultant e.m.f. in the circuit will be

$$e = \pi_2 - \pi_1 - \int_{T_1}^{T_2} (\sigma_a - \sigma_b)dT. \qquad (9.2)$$

9.10   Thermoelectric Laws

(i) Law of intermediate metals : The introduction of a third metal in a thermoelectric circuit does not alter the resultant e.m.f. of the circuit provided the ends of the third metal are exactly at the temperatures of the points of the circuit in which it is introduced.

Consider a thermocouple $(A\text{-}B)$ whose junctions are at temperatures T_2 and $T_1(T_2 > T_1)$ respectively (Fig. 9.11). Now a third metal C is introduced in such a way that the junction of B and C and that of A and C are both at the temperature

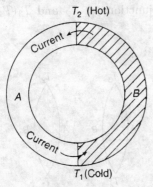

Fig. 9.11

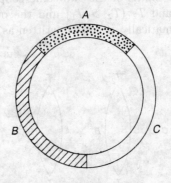

Fig. 9.12

T_1 (Fig. 9.12). According to the law of intermediate metals the e.m.f. of the circuit $(A\text{-}B\text{-}C)$ will be same as the circuit $(A\text{-}B)$. Mathematically, it can be written as

$$e_{AB} = e_{AC} + e_{CB}. \tag{9.3}$$

Now suppose we have three couples $(A\text{-}C)$, $(C\text{-}B)$ and $(A\text{-}B)$ and the temperatures of the hot and cold junctions are respectively T_1 and T_2. Therefore, the e.m.f.s of the couples are

$$e_{AC} = \pi_{AC}^2 - \pi_{AC}^1 - \int_{T_1}^{T_2} (\sigma_a - \sigma_c)dT \tag{9.4}$$

$$e_{CB} = \pi_{CB}^2 - \pi_{CB}^1 - \int_{T_1}^{T_2} (\sigma_c - \sigma_b)dT \tag{9.5}$$

$$e_{AB} = \pi_{AB}^2 - \pi_{AB}^1 - \int_{T_1}^{T_2} (\sigma_a - \sigma b)dT \tag{9.6}$$

Now if the three metals (Fig. 9.13) are at constant temperature T_1, we have

$$\pi_{AC}^1 + \pi_{CB}^1 + \pi_{BA}^1 = 0. \tag{9.7}$$

Similarly, if they are kept at constant temperature T_2, we have

$$\pi_{AC}^2 + \pi_{CB}^2 + \pi_{BA}^2 = 0. \tag{9.8}$$

Adding Eqs. (9.4) and (9.5) we get

$$e_{AC} + e_{CB} = (\pi_{AC}^2 - \pi_{AC}^1) + (\pi_{CB}^2 - \pi_{CB}^1) - \int_{T_1}^{T_2} (\sigma_a - \sigma_b)dT$$

$$= (\pi_{AC}^2 + \pi_{CB}^2) - (\pi_{AC}^1 + \pi_{CB}^1) - \int_{T_1}^{T_2} (\sigma_a - \sigma_b)dT$$

$$= -\pi_{BA}^2 + \pi_{BA}^1 - \int_{T_1}^{T_2} (\sigma_a - \sigma_b)dT$$

$$= \pi_{AB}^2 - \pi_{AB}^1 - \int_{T_1}^{T_2} (\sigma_a - \sigma_b)dT$$

$$= e_{AB}. \tag{9.9}$$

(ii) Law of intermediated temperatures : The thermo-e.m.f. of any couple with junctions at temperatures T_1 and $T_3(T_3 > T_1)$ is the algebraic sum of the thermo-e.m.f.s of the two same couples (Fig. 9.13, Fig. 9.14); one with junctions at T_1 and T_2 $(T_2 > T_1)$ and the other with junctions at T_2 and $T_3(T_3 > T_2)$. Mathematically, it can be written as

$$e_{13} = e_{12} + e_{23}.$$

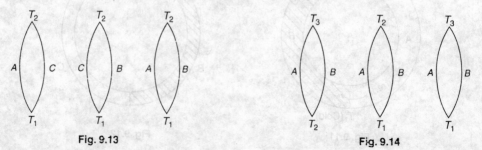

Fig. 9.13   Fig. 9.14

Now the e.m.f.s of the three couples are

$$e_{13} = \pi_3 - \pi_1 - \int_{T_1}^{T_3} (\sigma_a - \sigma_b)dT \qquad (9.10)$$

$$e_{12} = \pi_2 - \pi_1 - \int_{T_1}^{T_2} (\sigma_a - \sigma_b)dT \qquad (9.11)$$

$$e_{23} = \pi_3 - \pi_2 - \int_{T_2}^{T_3} (\sigma_a - \sigma_b)dT \qquad (9.12)$$

$$\therefore \quad e_{12} + 2_{23} = (\pi_2 - \pi_1) + (\pi_3 - \pi_2) - \int_{T_1}^{T_2} (\sigma_a - \sigma_b)dT - \int_{T_2}^{T_3} (\sigma_a - \sigma_b)dT$$

$$= (\pi_3 - \pi_1) - \int_{T_1}^{T_3} (\sigma_a - \sigma_b)dT = e_{13}.$$

9.11   Thermodynamics of a Thermocouple

Second law of thermodynamics can be used to a thermoelectric circuit, because the thermoelectric effects are reversible.

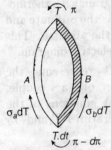

Suppose the junctions of the couple (A-B) are kept at temperatures T and $(T - dT)$ respectively. Peltier e.m.f.'s π and $(\pi - d\pi)$ are directed from the metal B to A at the junctions (Fig. 9.15). The metals A and B have Thomson coefficients σ_a and σ_b respectively and the Thomson e.m.f.s are directed from low to high temperatures. Therefore, the resultant e.m.f. of the circuit will be

$$de = d\pi - (\sigma_a - \sigma_b)dT \qquad (9.13)$$

$$\text{or,} \quad \frac{de}{dT} = \frac{d\pi}{dT} - (\sigma_a - \sigma_b). \qquad (9.14)$$

Fig. 9.15

Let a current i flow through the circuit for time dt. Since the process is a reversible one, the total change of entropy will be zero.

$$\therefore \quad \frac{\pi i dT}{T} - \frac{\pi i dT(\pi - d\pi)}{T - dT} - \frac{idt \cdot \sigma_a dT}{T} + \frac{idt \cdot \sigma_b dT}{T} = 0$$

$$\text{or,} \quad \frac{\pi}{T} - \frac{\pi - d\pi}{T - dT} - (\sigma_a - \sigma_b)\frac{dT}{T} = 0$$

$$\text{or,} \quad \frac{\pi}{T}\left[1 - \frac{1 - \frac{d\pi}{\pi}}{1 - \frac{dT}{T}}\right] - (\sigma_a - \sigma_b)\frac{dT}{T} = 0$$

$$\text{or,} \quad \frac{\pi}{T}\left[1 - \left(1 - \frac{d\pi}{\pi}\right)\left(1 + \frac{dT}{T}\right)\right] - (\sigma_a - \sigma_b)\frac{dT}{T} = 0$$

(neglecting smaller quantities)

$$\text{or,} \quad \frac{\pi}{T}\left[1 - 1 + \frac{d\pi}{\pi} - \frac{dT}{T}\right] - (\sigma_a - \sigma_b)\frac{dT}{T} = 0$$

$$\text{or,} \quad \pi\left[\frac{d\pi}{\pi} - \frac{dT}{T}\right] - (\sigma_a - \sigma_b)dT = 0$$

$$\text{or,} \quad d\pi - \frac{\pi}{T}dT - (\sigma_a - \sigma_b)dT = 0$$

$$\text{or,} \quad \frac{d\pi}{dT} = \frac{\pi}{T} + (\sigma_a - \sigma_b) = \frac{\pi}{T} + \frac{d\pi}{dT} - \frac{de}{dT}$$

[Substituting the value $(\sigma_a - \sigma_b)$ from Eq. (9.14)] or, $\dfrac{de}{dT} = \dfrac{\pi}{T}$

or, $\pi = T\dfrac{de}{dT}.$ (9.15)

Here $\dfrac{de}{dT} = P$ is called the thermoelectric power of the circuit. It is defined as the rate of change of e.m.f. with temperature of the thermocouple.

Now from Eqs. (9.14) and (9.15), we have

$$\frac{de}{dT} = \frac{d}{dT}\left(T\frac{de}{dT}\right) - (\sigma_a - \sigma_b) = \frac{de}{dT} + T\frac{d^2e}{dT^2} - (\sigma_a - \sigma_b).$$

$\therefore \quad (\sigma_a - \sigma_b) = T\dfrac{d^2e}{dT^2}.$ (9.16)

The Peltier coefficient and Thomson coefficient are obtained from Eqs. (9.15) and (9.16) respectively.

9.12   Thermoelectric Diagram

The thermoelectric effects in a couple can be represented by a diagram with thermo-electric power $P\left(=\dfrac{de}{dT}\right)$ as the ordinate and absolute temperature as the abscissa. This diagram is called thermoelectric diagram.

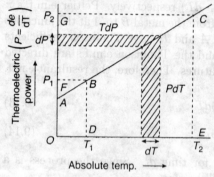

Fig. 9.16

In Fig. 9.16, ABC represents the thermoelectric diagram of a couple. Suppose the cold and hot junctions of the couple are at the temperatures T_1 and T_2 respectively.

Now the Peltier coefficient for the couple at temperature T_1 is

$$\pi_1 = T_1\left(\frac{de}{dT}\right)_1 = T_1 P_1 = \square\, ODBF$$

Similarly, $\pi_2 = T_2\left(\dfrac{de}{dT}\right)_2 = T_2 P_2 = \square\, OECG.$

$\therefore \qquad \pi_2 - \pi_1 = \square\, OECG - \square\, ODBF.$ (9.17)

Again, $\quad \sigma_a - \sigma_b = T\dfrac{d}{dT}\left(\dfrac{\pi}{T}\right),$

$\therefore \qquad \sigma_a - \sigma_b = T\dfrac{dP}{dT}\quad\left[\because\ \dfrac{de}{dT} = P = \dfrac{\pi}{T}\right].$

$\therefore \qquad \displaystyle\int_{T_1}^{T_2}(\sigma_a - \sigma_b)dT = \int_{T_1}^{T_2} T\,dP = \square\, BCGF.$

Putting the values of all the terms of the thermoelectric effect in the e.m.f. equation, we get

$$e = \pi_2 - \pi_1 - \int_{T_1}^{T_2}(\sigma_a - \sigma_b)dT$$

$$= \square\, OECG - \square\, ODBF - \square\, BCGF$$ (9.18)

$$= \square\, BDEC.$$

Thus the e.m.f. is given by the area between the thermoelectric diagram and the abscissa limited between the junction temperature of the couple.

In the above evaluation of e.m.f., one metal of the couple has been taken as the standard metal and the thermoelectric power of the other has been plotted. The standard metal which is usually used be lead for which the Thomson coefficient is zero. If the thermoelectric line for a couple slopes down, then σ is considered to be negative and it is considered positive when the line slopes up.

Suppose $A_1A_2A_3$ and $B_1B_2B_3$ are respectively the thermoelectric lines of the two metals A and B which have drawn with respect to lead (Fig. 9.17). Now consider a couple (A-B) with junctions at the temperatures T_1 and T_2. The thermoelectric power at the above temperatures are respectively A_1B_1 and A_2B_2 and the thermo-e.m.f. of the couple is given by the area $A_1A_2B_2B_1$. The point of intersection (N) of the two lines will be the neutral temperature for the couple.

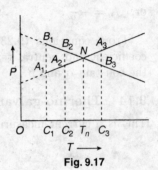

Fig. 9.17

If the junctions are kept at T_1 and T_3, the resultant e.m.f. is given by

$$e = \square\, B_1B_3C_3C_1 - \square\, A_1A_3C_3C_1$$

$$= \Delta B_1NA_1 - \Delta A_3NB_3. \tag{9.19}$$

If the area of the two triangles are equal, the e.m.f. will be zero. In this case, T_3 is the temperature of the inversion.

$$\therefore \quad T_n - T_1 = T_i - T_n$$

$$\text{or,} \quad T_n = \frac{T_1 + T_i}{2}. \tag{9.20}$$

9.13 Thermoelectric Constants

The thermo-e.m.f. of a couple is given by

$$e = \alpha(T - T_1) + \frac{1}{2}\beta(T - T_1)^2 \tag{9.21}$$

$$\text{or,} \quad \frac{de}{dT} = \alpha + \beta(T - T_1), \tag{9.22}$$

where $T_1 = 273\text{K} =$ temperature of the cold junction.

Now Peltier coefficient at TK is

$$\pi = T\frac{de}{dT} = \alpha T + \beta T(T - T_1)$$

$$= (\alpha - \beta T_1)T + \beta T^2 \tag{9.23}$$

and the Thomson coefficient, $(\sigma_a - \sigma_b) = T\dfrac{d^2e}{dT^2}$.

Now, $\dfrac{de}{dT} = \alpha + \beta(T - T_1)$,

$$\therefore \quad \frac{d^2e}{dT^2} = \beta.$$

Hence, $(\sigma_a - \sigma_b) = \beta T$. $\tag{9.24}$

Neutral temperature :

At neutral temperature, $\dfrac{de}{dt} = 0$.

We know that $\dfrac{de}{dt} = \alpha + \beta(T - T_1)$.

At neutral temperature $T = T_n$;

$\therefore \quad \alpha + \beta(T_n - T_1) = 0$

or, $\quad \alpha + \beta(t_n + 273 - 273) = 0 \quad [\because T_1 = 273\text{K and } T_n = t_n + 273]$

$\therefore \quad \alpha + \beta t_n = 0$

or, $\quad t_n = -\dfrac{\alpha}{\beta}.$ \hfill (9.25)

From equations (9.23), (9.24) and (9.25) the Peltier coefficient, Thomson coefficient and neutral temperature can be determined by knowing the value of the constant α and β.

9.14　Thermo-galvanometer

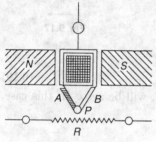

Fig. 9.18

This is a current measuring device which is based on thermal effects. A and B are two bars of antimony and bismuth respectively. A loop of silver wire whose ends are joined at A and B respectively, hangs between the pole piece of a magnet (Fig. 9.18). The bars A and B are joined at the point P so that they form a couple. Below the point P, a resistance wire R is kept through which the current to be measured is passed. The wire gets heated and the radiation from it causes the flow of a thermoelectric current through the couple (A-B). The current is measured from the deflection of the loop.

Examples

1. The e.m.f. of a thermocouple, one junction of which is at $0\,^\circ$C and the other junction at $t\,^\circ$C, is given by $E = at + bt^2$. Determine the Peltier and Thomson coefficient and also the neutral temperature and temperature of inversion of the thermocouple. **[C.U. 1969]**

Solution : $E = at + bt^2 = a(T - 273) + b(T - 273)^2.$

$\therefore \quad \dfrac{dE}{dT} = a + 2b(T - 273) \quad$ and $\quad \dfrac{d^2E}{dT^2} = 2b.$

Therefore, Peltier coefficient, $\pi = T\dfrac{dE}{dT} = (273 + t)[a + 2bt].$

Thomson coefficient, $\sigma = T\dfrac{d^2E}{dT^2} = 2bT = 2b(t + 273).$

At neutral temperature $\dfrac{dE}{dT} = 0.$

$\therefore \quad a + 2b(T_n - 273) = 0.$

$\therefore \quad T_n - 273 = -\left(\dfrac{a}{2b}\right) \quad$ or, $\quad t_n = -\left(\dfrac{a}{2b}\right)\,^\circ$C.

Again, at $t = t_i$, the temperature of inversion, $E = 0.$

$\therefore \quad at_i + bt_i^2 = 0 \quad$ or, $\quad t_i(a + bt_i) = 0.$

$\because \quad t_i \neq 0, \ a + bt_i = 0.$

$\therefore \quad t_i = - \left(\dfrac{a}{b}\right) {}^\circ C.$

2. For a copper-iron thermocouple, one junction of which is maintained at $0\,{}^\circ C$ and the other at $t\,{}^\circ C$ the e.m.f. in microvolts is given by $e = 10.34t - 0.018t^2$. Calculate the temperature of the junction (i) for maximum e.m.f. (ii) for zero e.m.f. [B.U. 1972]

Solution : We have $e = 10.34t - 0.018t^2$

$$\dfrac{de}{dt} = 10.34 - 0.036t.$$

For maximum e.m.f., $\dfrac{de}{dt} = 0.$

i.e., at $t = t_n$, $\dfrac{de}{dt} = 0.$

$\therefore \quad 10.34 - 0.036t_n = 0 \quad$ or, $\quad t_n = \dfrac{10.34}{0.036} = 287.2\,{}^\circ C.$

For zero e.m.f., $e = 0.$

$\therefore \quad 10.34t_i - 0.018t_i^2 = 0.$

$\therefore \quad t_i = \dfrac{10.34}{0.018} = 574.4\,{}^\circ C.$

3. The e.m.f. of a thermocouple of which one junction is at $0\,{}^\circ C$ and the other at $50\,{}^\circ C$ is 25 microvolts. The neutral temperature is $100\,{}^\circ C$. Find the e.m.f. when the junctions are at $0\,{}^\circ C$ and $200\,{}^\circ C$.

Solution : We know that $e = at + bt^2$

and $\quad t_n = -\dfrac{a}{2b}.$

Here $\quad t = 50\,{}^\circ C$, $e = 25$ microvolt and $t_n = 100\,{}^\circ C$.

$\therefore \quad 25 = 50a + 2500b$ \hfill (i)

$\quad\quad 100 = -\dfrac{a}{2b}.$ \hfill (ii)

From Eq. (ii), we get $a = -200b.$

$\therefore \quad 25 = -10000b + 2500b \quad$ or, $\quad -7500b = 25.$

$\therefore \quad b = -\dfrac{1}{300}.$

Substituting the value of b in equation (ii), we have

$$a = \dfrac{2}{3}.$$

$\therefore \quad e = \dfrac{2}{3}t - \dfrac{1}{300}t^2$

$\therefore \quad e_{200} = \dfrac{2}{3} \times 200 - \dfrac{1}{300} \times (200)^2 = \mathbf{0}.$

4. If the e.m.f. equation is given by $E = at + \frac{1}{2}bt^2$ for the e.m.f. set up in a Cu-Pb and in an Fe-Pb circuit, calculate Peltier coefficient and $\sigma_{Cu} - \sigma_{Fe}$. Find also the neutral temperature. Given,

$$a_{Cu} = 2.71, \quad b_{Cu} = 0.008$$
$$a_{Fe} = 16.7, \quad b_{Fe} = -0.029.$$

Solution : From the law of intermediate metals,

$$a_{Cu-Fe} = a_{Cu-Pb} - a_{Fe-Pb} = 2.71 - 16.7 = -13.99$$

$$b_{Cu-Fe} = b_{Cu-Pb} - b_{Fe-Pb} = 0.008 + 0.029 = 0.037.$$

$$\therefore \quad t_n = -\frac{a}{b} = \frac{13.99}{0.037} = \mathbf{378.1\,°C}$$

$$t_i = 2t_n = 756.2\,°C.$$

$$(\sigma_{Cu} - \sigma_{Fe}) = -bT$$

$$\therefore \quad \int_{T_2}^{T_1}(\sigma_{Cu} - \sigma_{Fe})dT = -\frac{b}{2}(T_1^2 - T_2^2) = -\frac{0.037}{2}(373^2 - 273^2)$$

$$= -\frac{0.037}{2} \times 646 \times 100 = -1195\,\mu V.$$

The Peltier coefficients,

$$\pi_1 = T_1\left(\frac{dE}{dt}\right)t_1 = 373(a + b \times 100) = \mathbf{-3838\,\mu V}$$

$$\pi_2 = T_2\left(\frac{dE}{dt}\right)t_2 = 273 \times (a + b \times 0) = -272 \times 13.99 = \mathbf{-3819\,\mu V}.$$

5. Find the neutral and inversion temperature of a thermocouple of which the constants are $a = 10.3$ microvolts/°C and $b = 0.018$ microvolt/°C, the cold junction being at $0\,°C$.   **[B.U. 1968]**

Solution : We know, neutral temperature, $t_n = \dfrac{a}{2b}$ and inversion temperature $t_i = 2t_n$

$$\therefore \quad t_n = \frac{1.03}{2 \times 0.018} = 286.1\,°C, \qquad t_i = 2 \times 286.1 = 572.2\,°C$$

6. The e.m.f. in a thermocouple, one junction of which is kept at $0\,°C$, is given by $E = bt + ct^2$. Find the neutral temperature, and the Peltier and Thomson coefficients.

Solution : $E = bt + ct^2 = b(T - 273) + c(T - 273)^2$

$$\therefore \quad \frac{dE}{dT} = b + 2c(T - 273) \quad \text{and} \quad \frac{d^2E}{dT^2} = 2c$$

At neutral temperature, $\dfrac{dE}{dT} = 0$.

$$\therefore \quad t_n = (T_2 - 273) = -\frac{b}{2c}.$$

Peltier coefficient $\pi = T\dfrac{dE}{dT} = T[b + 2c(T - 273)] = (t + 273)(b + 2ct).$

Thomson coefficient $\sigma = T\dfrac{d^2E}{dT^2} = T \times 2c = 2c(t + 273).$

7. The thermoelectric power of iron is $17.3\,\mu V/°C$ at $0\,°C$ and $12.47\,\mu V/°C$ at $100\,°C$, that of copper is $1.36\,\mu V/°C$ at $0\,°C$ and $2.31\,\mu V/°C$ at $100\,°C$. Calculate the e.m.f. in volts of a copper-iron couple with junctions at $0\,°C$ and $100\,°C$.

Solution : Thermoelectric curve for iron and copper is shown in the figure.

∴ thermo-e.m.f.

$$e = \boxed{} A_1 A_2 B_2 B_1$$

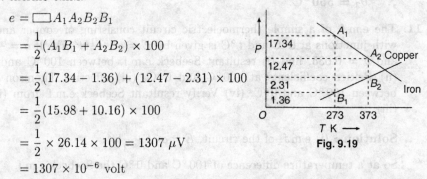

$$= \frac{1}{2}(A_1 B_1 + A_2 B_2) \times 100$$

$$= \frac{1}{2}(17.34 - 1.36) + (12.47 - 2.31) \times 100$$

$$= \frac{1}{2}(15.98 + 10.16) \times 100$$

$$= \frac{1}{2} \times 26.14 \times 100 = 1307 \ \mu V$$

$$= 1307 \times 10^{-6} \text{ volt}$$

Fig. 9.19

8. If, for a certain thermocouple $E = a\theta + b\theta^2$, where $\theta\,°C$ is the temperature of the hot junction, the cold junction being at $0\,°C$, $a = 10$ microvolts/°C and $b = -\frac{1}{40}$ microvolt/°C, find the neutral temperature and the temperature of inversion.

Solution : $\theta_n = -\dfrac{a}{2b} = -\dfrac{10}{-2 \times \frac{1}{40}} = \mathbf{200\,°C}.$

Again, $\theta_1 + \theta_2 = 2\theta_n$

$\theta_1 = 0°$ and $\theta_2 =$ inversion temperature.

According to the condition, $\theta_1 + \theta_2 = 2 \times 200$ or $\theta_2 = \mathbf{400\,°C}.$

9. The e.m.f. equation of a copper-nickel couple in microvolts is $E = 16.34t - 0.021t^2 \ \mu V$ where t is in °C. Calculate (i) the thermoelectric power at $100\,°C$, (ii) the neutral temperature of the couple, (iii) the temperature of inversion and (iv) Peltier coefficient at $100\,°C$. **[C.U. 1990]**

Solution : (i) $E = 16.34t - 0.021t^2$; $\dfrac{dE}{dt} = 16.34 - 0.021 \times 2t.$

So, at a temperature $100\,°C$, thermoelectric power,

$$\left(\frac{dE}{dt}\right)_{t=100\,°C} = 16.34 - 0.021 \times 2 \times 100 = \mathbf{12.14 \ microvolts/°C}.$$

(ii) At neutral temperature, $\theta_n = -\dfrac{a}{2b}$; here, $a = 16.34$ and $b = -0.021$.

∴ $\theta_n = -\dfrac{16.34}{2 \times (-0.021)} = \mathbf{389\,°C}.$

(iii) Inversion temperature, $\theta_i = 2\theta_n = 2 \times 389\,°C = \mathbf{778\,°C}.$

(iv) Peltier coefficient $= T \cdot \dfrac{dE}{dt} = (t + 273)\dfrac{dE}{dT} = (100 + 273) \times 12.14 \ \mu V$

$$= \mathbf{4528.22 \ \mu V}.$$

10. If the cold junction temperature of a thermocouple be $20\,°C$ and the neutral temperature be $285\,°C$, find the temperature of inversion. **[C.U. 1989]**

Solution : Let temperature of the cold junction be θ_1, neutral temperature θ_n and inversion temperature θ_2. Then

$$\theta_n = \frac{\theta_1 + \theta_2}{2}; \quad \text{here, } \theta_1 = 20\,°C; \ \theta_n = 285\,°C; \ \theta_2 = ?$$

$$\therefore \quad 285 = \frac{20 + \theta_2}{2}$$

$$\therefore \quad \theta_2 = 550\,^{\circ}\text{C}.$$

11. The e.m.f. of a simple thermoelectric circuit consisting of copper and iron with junctions at $0\,^{\circ}\text{C}$ and $t\,^{\circ}\text{C}$ is given by $E = at + \frac{1}{2}bt^2$ μV. If $a = -14.00$ and $b = 0.035$, find (i) resultant Seebeck e.m.f. between $100\,^{\circ}\text{C}$ and $0\,^{\circ}\text{C}$, (ii) Peltier coefficients at $100\,^{\circ}\text{C}$ and $0\,^{\circ}\text{C}$, (iii) effective Thomson e.m.f. between $100\,^{\circ}\text{C}$ and $0\,^{\circ}\text{C}$. (iv) Verify resultant Seebeck e.m.f. from (i) and (iii).

Solution : (i) e.m.f. of the circuit, $E = a \cdot t + \frac{1}{2}bt^2$.

So at a temperature difference of $100\,^{\circ}\text{C}$ and $0\,^{\circ}\text{C}$ the Seebeck e.m.f.

$$E_{0\,^{\circ}\text{C}}^{100\,^{\circ}\text{C}} = 100 \times a + \frac{1}{2}(100)^2 b = -14 \times 100 + \frac{1}{2}(100)^2 \times 0.035$$

$$= -1400 + 175 = -\mathbf{1225}\,\boldsymbol{\mu}\mathbf{V}.$$

(ii) Here, $\dfrac{dE}{dT} = \dfrac{dE}{dt} = a + b \cdot t$.

$$\therefore \quad \pi = T \cdot \frac{dE}{dT} = (t + 273)(a + b \cdot t)$$

$$\therefore \quad (\pi)_{100\,^{\circ}\text{C}} = (100 + 273)(-14 + 0.035 \times 100)$$

$$= -373 \times 10.5 = -\mathbf{3916.5}\,\boldsymbol{\mu}\mathbf{V}$$

and $(\pi)_{0\,^{\circ}\text{C}} = 273 \times (-14) = -\mathbf{3822}\,\boldsymbol{\mu}\mathbf{V}$.

(iii) $\dfrac{d^2 E}{dT^2} = \dfrac{d^2 E}{dt^2} = \dfrac{d}{dt}(a + b \cdot t) = b.$

So the effective Thomson e.m.f., $\displaystyle\int_{T_1}^{T_2} -T \cdot \frac{d^2 E}{dt^2} \cdot dT = \int_{T_1}^{T_2} -b \cdot T \cdot dT$

$$= \frac{b}{2}(T_1^2 - T_2^2).$$

At a temperature difference of $100\,^{\circ}\text{C}$, the effective Thomson e.m.f.

$$= \frac{0.035}{2}(273^2 - 373^2) = -\mathbf{1130.5}\,\boldsymbol{\mu}\mathbf{V}.$$

(iv) Total Seebeck e.m.f. $= (\pi)_{100} - (\pi)_0 + \displaystyle\int_0^{100} -T \cdot \frac{T^2 E}{dT^2} \cdot dT$

$$= [-3916.5 - (-3822) + (-1130.5)]\,\mu\text{V}$$

$$= -\mathbf{1225}\,\boldsymbol{\mu}\mathbf{V}.$$

As the result obtained from (i) and (iv) are same, so the Seebeck effect is established.

12. The thermoelectric power of iron with respect to lead at a temperature $t\,^{\circ}\text{C}$ is given by $1734 - 4.87t$ μV/$^{\circ}$C and that of copper with respect to lead by $136 + 0.95t$ μV/$^{\circ}$C. Find the e.m.f. of a Cu-Fe couple with junctions at $20\,^{\circ}\text{C}$ and $200\,^{\circ}\text{C}$.   [C.U. (Hons.) 1965]

Solution : Area of $CDEF$

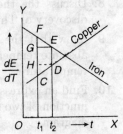

Fig. 9.20

$$= \frac{1}{2}EG \times FG + GH \times EG + \frac{1}{2}CH \times EG$$

$$= \frac{1}{2}EG[FG + 2GH + CH]$$

$$= \frac{1}{2}EG[FC + ED] \quad [\because GH = ED]$$

From Fig. 9.20,

$$FC = (p_1 - q_1), \ ED = (p_2 - q_2) \text{ and } EG = (t_2 - t_1)$$

$$\therefore \text{ e.m.f. } E = \frac{1}{2}EG[FC + ED] = \frac{1}{2}(t_2 - t_1)[(p_1 - q_1) + (p_2 - q_2)]$$

For iron,

at $20\,°C$ temperature, $p_1 = 1734 - 4.87 \times 20 = 1636.6 \ \mu V/°C$

at $200\,°C$ temperature, $p_2 = 1734 - 4.87 \times 200 = 760 \ \mu V/°C$.

For copper,

at $20\,°C$ temperature, $q_1 = 136 + 0.95 \times 20 = 155 \ \mu V/°C$

at $200\,°C$ temperature, $q_2 = 136 + 0.95 \times 200 = 326 \ \mu V/°C$.

So, $E = \dfrac{1}{2}(200 - 20)[(1636.5 - 155) + (760 + 326)]$

$$= \frac{1}{2} \times 180 \times [1481.6 + 436] = 17240 \ \mu V = \mathbf{0.17 \ volt}.$$

Questions

Essay-type

1. Describe briefly Peltier effect and explain how it can be demonstrated. The e.m.f. of a simple thermoelectric circuit, one junction of which is heated while the other is kept at $0\,°C$, is given by $E = bt + ct^2$ where $t\,°C$ is the temperature of the hot junction. Determine the neutral temperature of the couple and Peltier and Thomson coefficients. **[B.U. 1991]**

2. Explain Seebeck effect and Peltier effect. Describe an experimental arrangement to measure the thermo-e.m.f. in a thermocouple and state the type of galvanometer suitable for the arrangement. **[C.U. 1962, '91]**

3. What are meant by Peltier and Thomson effects in thermoelectricity? How would you demonstrate experimentally the Peltier and Thomson effects?

4. What are Seebeck and Peltier effects? Give in short some of the practical uses of thermoelectricity?

5. State and explain the laws of intermediate temperature and intermediate metals in connection with thermoelectricity.

6. The e.m.f. of a thermo electric circuit is given by the relation $E = mT^n$, where the cold junction is kept at $0\,°C$ and T is the temperature of the hot junction in absolute degrees, m and n being constants. Describe an experimental arrangement that will enable you to determine the melting point of some metal by the help of thermocouple and the above relation.

7. Prove that $dE = d\pi + (\sigma_A - \sigma_B)dT$, the symbols having the usual meaning.

8. Discuss the thermodynamics of Peltier effect and show how it led to the discovery of Thomson effect.   [B.U. 1983]

9. Show that the Peltier coefficient at a given junction is the product of the absolute temperature and the rate of change of total e.m.f. in the circuit with temperature.

10. Find an expression for (a) Peltier coefficient and (b) Thomson coefficient at a junction of two metals. Explain how these are represented on a thermoelectric diagram.

11. Derive from thermodynamical considerations, the following relations :

$$\pi = T \cdot \frac{dE}{dT} \text{ and } \sigma_A = -T \cdot \frac{d^2E}{dT^2} \qquad \text{[B.U. 1983, '95; C.U. 1978, '92]}$$

12. The e.m.f. in a thermocouple, one junction of which is kept at $0\,°C$, is given by $e = bt + ct^2$. Find the neutral temperature.   [C.U. 1992]

13. What are the two main consequences of the law of intermediate metals?

14. What do you mean by (i) neutral temperature and (ii) temperature of inversion? Do they depend on cold junction temperature?   [C.U. 1991]

15. In what way Peltier heating is different from Joule heating?

[C.U. 1962, '91, '93, '95]

Short Answer-type

16. Define Thomson coefficient. What do you mean by positive and negative Thomson coefficient?

17. Two wires, one of copper and the other of iron, are twisted together at one end, the other ends being connected to a low resistance galvanometer. Describe and explain the indications of the galvanometer, as the iron-copper junction is gradually heated to redness.

18. In demonstrating Peltier effect, which wire would you prefer—a thick or a thin wire? Give reasons for your answer.

19. Explain (i) Seebeck effect, (ii) Peltier effect and (iii) Thomson effect.

20. Write down an expression for the e.m.f. round a thermocouple taking both Peltier and Thomson effects into account.

21. Why is a copper-iron junction not used to measure the temperatures above $250\,°C$, although a copper-constantan couple is often so employed?

22. Do (i) the neutral temperature, (ii) the temperature of inversion change with the change of cold junction temperature of a thermocouple?   [C.U. 1993]

23. Why is Thomson coefficient sometimes called the specific heat of electricity?

24. What do you mean by thermoelectric power? What is the nature of the graph between thermoelectric power and temperature? What is the graph called?

25. What is the relation between neutral and inversion temperatures?

26. What do you mean by Seebeck effect? Explain this with an experiment.

    What is called a thermocouple? How the direction of thermoelectric current can be found out?

27. If one junction of a copper-iron thermocouple is kept at $0\,°C$ temperature and other junction is heated gradually, how and what will be the change of thermo-e.m.f.?

28. Define neutral temperature and temperature of inversion of a thermocouple and establish the mathematical relation between them.

Numerical Problems

29. For a certain thermocouple, in which the cold junction is kept at $0\,°C$ and the hot junction at $T\,°C$, the variation of e.m.f. with temperature is given by $e = \alpha T + \frac{1}{2}\beta T^2$ where $\alpha = 16.65 \times 10^{-6}$ volt/$°C$ and $\beta = -2.97 \times 10^{-8}$ volt/$°C^2$. Calculate the neutral temperature for the couple. [B.U. 1995]
[**Ans.** $11.21 \times 10^2\,°C$]

30. Find the neutral and inversion temperatures of a thermocouple of which the constants are $a = 10.3$ microvolts/$°C$ and $b = 0.018$ microvolt/$°C$, the cold junction being at $0\,°C$. [B.U. 1968]
[**Ans.** $286.1\,°C$; $572.2\,°C$]

31. One junction of a thermocouple is at $0\,°C$ while the other at $\theta\,°C$. The e.m.f. produced is given by $E = 16.7\theta - 0.019\theta^2$ microvolt. What is its neutral temperature? [**Ans.** $439.5\,°C$]

32. Thermoelectric power of iron is 1734 microvolts per degree at $0\,°C$ and 1247 microvolts per degree at $100\,°C$, that of copper is 136 microvolts at $0\,°C$ and 231 microvolts at $100\,°C$. Calculate the e.m.f. of an iron-copper couple between the temperatures $0\,°C$ and $100\,°C$. [**Ans.** 0.131 volt]

33. A thermocouple is made of iron and constantan. Find the e.m.f. developed per $°C$ difference of temperature between the junctions, given that the thermo-e.m.f.s of iron and constantan against platinum are $+1600$ microvolts and -3400 microvolts per $100\,°C$ difference of temperature. [**Ans.** $50\ \mu V$]

34. The thermoelectric power of iron is $1734 - 4.837t$ and that of copper is $136 + 0.095t$ (where t is the temperature in the Celsius scale). Show that the e.m.f. of an iron-copper couple is $130700\ \mu V$, when the junctions of the thermocouple are at $0\,°C$ and $100\,°C$.

35. For a nickel-aluminium couple the e.m.f. is given by $E = 19.57t - 0.0165t^2$ when the cold junction is at $0\,°C$ and the hot junction at $t\,°C$. Find the thermoelectric power at $50\,°C$ and the e.m.f. when the junctions are at $30\,°C$ and $100\,°C$. [**Ans.** $1220\ \mu V$]

36. The e.m.f. in a simple thermoelectric circuit, one junction of which is heated to $t\,°C$ when the other is kept at $0\,°C$ is given by $E = 15.8t - 0.03t^2$. Calculate the neutral temperature, Peltier and Thomson coefficients of the couple.
[**Ans.** $263.3\,°C$; $\pi = (t + 273)(15 - 0.06t)$; $\sigma = -0.06(t + 273)$]

Chapter 10

Varying Currents

10.1 Introduction

The laws governing the flow of steady currents in conductors are not suitable for finding the value of current when changing. Using Ohm's law we can find the resistance of a conductor in a steady current and thereby the electromotive force required. But if, however, the current varies, the magnetic flux linked with the circuit also changes which means another electromotive force acting in it. When a current is made to pass in a circuit consisting of elements like capacitor, inductor, resistor, the induced e.m.f. generated lasts so long as the current in the circuit is changing. It is, of course, for a very short duration. Phenomena which are not simple periodic functions of time and also which exist for a short duration are known as *transient* or *transient phenomena*.

10.2 Growth of Current in a Circuit Containing Inductance and Resistance

A coil of resistance R, an inductance L and a battery of e.m.f. E are connected in series through the tapping key K as shown in Fig. 10.1. When the circuit is closed, the current in the circuit will be increased up to a maximum value due to self-induction.

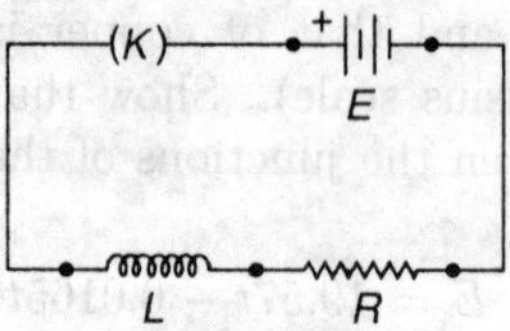

Let i be the current at any instant t. The rate of growth of current will be $\frac{di}{dt}$. The induced e.m.f. in the circuit $L\frac{di}{dt}$ will oppose the e.m.f. of the battery E. Therefore, the effective e.m.f. in the circuit will be $E - L\frac{di}{dt}$. By using Ohm's law we can write,

Fig. 10.1

$$E - L\frac{di}{dt} = Ri \tag{10.1}$$

or, $\dfrac{di}{dt} = \dfrac{E - Ri}{L}$ or, $\dfrac{di}{E - Ri} = \dfrac{1}{L}dt$

or, $\dfrac{Rdi}{E - Ri} = \dfrac{R}{L}dt.$ \hfill (10.2)

Integrating Eq. (10.2), we get

$$\log_e(E - Ri) = -\frac{R}{L}t + k, \tag{10.3}$$

where k is a constant.

Now at $t = 0$, $i = 0$.

Substituting this condition in Eq. (10.3), we have

$$k = \log_e E$$

Therefore, $\log_e\left(E - \dfrac{Ri}{E}\right) = -\dfrac{R}{L}t$

248

or, $\quad \dfrac{E - Ri}{E} = e^{-\frac{Rt}{L}}$

or, $\qquad i = \dfrac{E}{R}\left(1 - e^{-\frac{R}{L}t}\right).$ \hfill (10.4)

From the above equation one can get the expression for the magnitude of current at any instant. It is also clear that the current does not attain steady value as soon as the circuit is closed. But it rises exponentially. The current will be maximum when $e^{-\frac{Rt}{L}} = 0$, i.e., at $t = \infty$. The maximum value of current will be $i_0 = \dfrac{E}{R}$.

$\therefore \quad i = i_0(1 - e^{-Rt/L}).$ \hfill (10.5)

The time at which $\dfrac{Rt}{L} = 1$ is called the *time constant* (λ) of the circuit.

$\therefore \quad \dfrac{R\lambda}{L} = 1, \quad$ i.e., $\quad \lambda = \dfrac{L}{R}.$

Therefore, Eq. (10.5) becomes

$i = i_0\left(1 - e^{-t/\lambda}\right).$ \hfill (10.6)

If $t = \lambda, i = i_0\left(1 - \dfrac{1}{e}\right) = 0.632 i_0 = \dfrac{2}{3} i_0$ (approx.).

So the time constant of an *L-R* circuit may be defined as the time in which the magnitude of the current reaches about $\frac{2}{3}$ of its maximum value.

From Eq. (10.6) it is obvious that greater the value of the time constant λ, the smaller will be the rate of growth of current. Fig. 10.2 shows the nature of the growth of current for different values of λ. The graph will be asymptotic in nature, i.e., the current will be maximum after an infinite time. But practically the current attains its maximum value after several seconds.

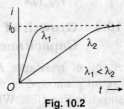

Fig. 10.2

10.3 Decay of Current in a Circuit Containing Inductance and Resistance

Suppose a steady current i is flowing through a circuit having a coil of resistance R, an inductance L and a battery of e.m.f. E, all in series (Fig. 10.3). After the key is cut off the battery, the circuit is made to close again. The current will not instantaneously attain zero value. A self-induced e.m.f. $L\dfrac{di}{dt}$ will appear in the circuit which opposes the decay of current. The differential equation for the e.m.f. will be given by

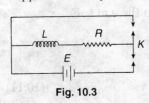

Fig. 10.3

$L\dfrac{di}{dt} + Ri = 0$

or, $\quad \dfrac{di}{i} = -\dfrac{R}{L}dt$ \hfill (10.7)

Integrating Eq. (10.7), we get

$\log_e i = -\dfrac{R}{L}t + k,$ \hfill (10.8)

where k is a constant.

Now at $t = 0$, $i = i_0$

$k = \log_e i_0.$

Hence Eq. (10.8) can be written as

$$\log_e i = -\frac{R}{L}t + \log_e i_0.$$

$$\therefore \quad i = i_0 e^{-\frac{R}{L}t}. \tag{10.9}$$

The time at which $\frac{R}{L}t = 1$ is called the *time constant* (λ) of the circuit. Therefore,

$$\frac{R}{L}\lambda = 1, \quad \text{i.e.,} \quad \lambda = \frac{L}{R}.$$

So the expression for current becomes

$$i = i_0 e^{-t/\lambda}. \tag{10.10}$$

When λ, $i = \frac{1}{e} i_0 = \frac{i_0}{2.718}$.

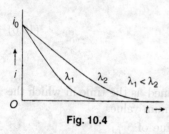

Fig. 10.4

So the time constant of an L-R circuit may be defined as the time in which the magnitude of the current attains $\frac{1}{2.718}$ of its maximum value.

From Eq. (10.10) it is clear that the current falls exponentially. Fig. 10.4 shows the nature of decay of current for different values of λ. Now at $t = \infty$, the current will be zero. But practically the current falls to zero after a few seconds.

10.4 Growth of Charge in a Circuit Containing Resistance and Capacitance (Charging of a Condenser)

A coil of resistance R, a capacitor of capacitance C and a battery of e.m.f. E are all connected in series through the tapping key K as shown in Fig. 10.5. When the circuit is closed the charge on the capacitor instead of attaining its steady value $q = CE$ instantaneously, takes some times, however small it may be.

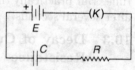

Fig. 10.5

Let Q be the charge on the capacitor at any instant t. The p.d. across the capacitor $V = \frac{Q}{C}$ acts in opposition to the e.m.f. E.

Hence the resultant e.m.f. of the circuit $= E - \frac{Q}{C}$.

If the current flowing through the circuit is i, then

$$E - \frac{Q}{C} = Ri \tag{10.11}$$

or, $\quad E - \frac{Q}{C} = R\frac{dQ}{dt} \quad \left[\because i = \frac{dQ}{dt}\right]$

or, $\quad EC - Q = CR\frac{dQ}{dt}$

or, $\quad \dfrac{dQ}{EC - Q} = \dfrac{1}{CR}dt \tag{10.12}$

Integrating Eq. (10.12), we get

$$\log_e(EC - Q) = -\frac{t}{CR} + k, \tag{10.13}$$

where k is a constant.

Now at time $t = 0$, $Q = 0$.

$\therefore \quad k = \log_e EC$.

Substituting the value of k in Eq. (10.13) we have

$$\frac{EC - Q}{EC} = e^{-t/CR}$$

or, $\quad Q = EC(1 - e^{-t/CR})$. $\hspace{4cm}$ (10.14)

From the above expression we can see that the charge does not attain its steady value as soon as the circuit is closed. The condenser is charged exponentially. It is charged to a maximum value when $e^{-t/CR} = 0$, i.e., $t = \infty$. The maximum value of charge will be $Q_0 = CR$.

$\therefore \quad Q = Q_0(1 - e^{-t/CR})$. $\hspace{4cm}$ (10.15)

Now, the time at which $\dfrac{t}{CR} = 1$, is called the *time constant* (λ) of the circuit. Hence $\lambda = CR$.

Therefore, Eq. (10.15) becomes

$$Q = Q_0(1 - e^{-t/\lambda}).$$ $\hspace{4cm}$ (10.16)

If $t = \lambda$,

$$Q = Q_0\left(1 - \frac{1}{e}\right) \quad \text{or,} \quad Q = 0.632 Q_0 = \frac{2}{3}Q_0 \text{ (approx.)}.$$

So the time constant of a C-R circuit may also be defined as the time in which the condenser attains $\frac{2}{3}$ of the maximum charge (Q_0).

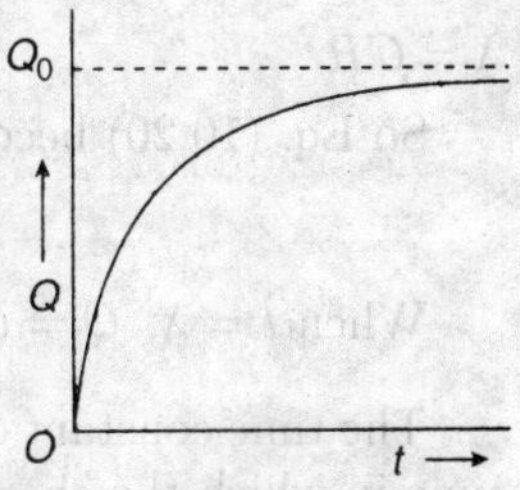

Fig. 10.6 shows the nature of the growth of charge on a condenser. The graph will be asymptotic in nature, i.e., the condenser will be charged to a maximum value at an infinite time. But practically for charging to a maximum value it takes several seconds.

Fig. 10.6

Now the rate of growth of charge at any instant t will be

$$\frac{dQ}{dt} = \frac{d}{dt}\left[Q_0\left(1 - e^{-t/\lambda}\right)\right] = \frac{Q_0}{\lambda}e^{-t/\lambda}$$

$$= \frac{Q_0}{CR}e^{-t/CR} \quad [\because \lambda = CR]$$

$$= \frac{E}{R}e^{-t/CR} \quad [\because Q_0 = CE]$$

$$= i_0 e^{-t/CR} \quad \left[\because i_0 = \frac{E}{R} = \text{max. value of current}\right]$$

$$\therefore \quad i = i_0 e^{-t/CR}.$$ $\hspace{4cm}$ (10.17)

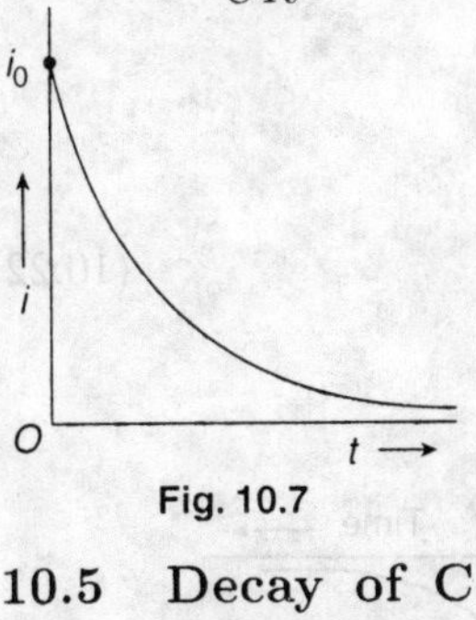

Fig. 10.7

The change of current with time is shown in Fig. 10.7. During the charging, the current decreases exponentially.

10.5 Decay of Charge in a Circuit Containing Resistance and Capacitance (Discharging of a Condenser)

After the condenser is fully charged, the key K is cut off from a and the circuit is again made to close by connecting K with the point b (Fig. 10.8).

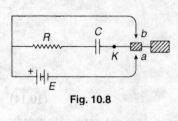

Fig. 10.8

Suppose at any instant t the charge on the condenser is Q and the current through the circuit is $i = \frac{dQ}{dt}$. The differential equation for the e.m.f. will be given by

$$\frac{Q}{C} + Ri = 0 \quad \text{or,} \quad \frac{Q}{C} + R\frac{dQ}{dt} = 0$$

$$\text{or,} \quad \frac{dQ}{Q} = -\frac{dt}{CR}. \tag{10.18}$$

Integrating the above equation, we get

$$\log_e Q = -\frac{t}{CR} + k, \tag{10.19}$$

where $k = $ constant.

Now at time, $t = 0$, $Q = Q_0$.

$\therefore \quad k = \log_e Q_0$.

Hence Eq. (10.19) can be written as

$$\log_e Q = -\frac{t}{CR} + \log_e Q_0$$

$$\text{or,} \quad Q = Q_0 e^{-t/CR}. \tag{10.20}$$

Now the time at which $\frac{t}{CR} = 1$ is called the *time constant* λ of the circuit, i.e., $\lambda = CR$.

So Eq. (10.20) becomes

$$Q = Q_0 e^{-t/\lambda}. \tag{10.21}$$

When $t = \lambda$, $Q = Q_0 \frac{1}{e} = \frac{Q_0}{2.718}$.

The time constant of a C-R circuit during discharging may also be defined as the time in which the charge of the condenser falls to $\frac{1}{2.718}$ th of its maximum charge.

Fig. 10.9 shows the decay of charge on a condenser. At time $t = \infty$, the condenser will completely discharge theoretically. But in practice, the time needs a few seconds only.

Now the rate of decay of charge at any instant t will be

$$\frac{dQ}{dt} = \frac{d}{dt}(Q_0 e^{-t/CR}) = -\frac{Q_0}{CR} e^{-t/CR}$$

$$= -\frac{E}{R} e^{-t/CR} \quad [\because Q_0 = CE]$$

$$= -i_0 e^{-t/CR}. \tag{10.22}$$

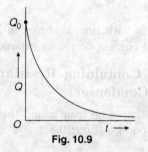

Fig. 10.9

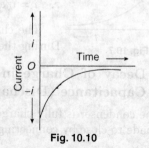

Fig. 10.10

Therefore, the directions of current during charging and discharging of a condenser are opposite in nature. The change of current with time during discharging of a condenser is shown in Fig. 10.10.

10.6   Energy of a Charged Capacitor

Suppose the current flowing through the circuit at any instant be i. So the energy required to produce heat in the resistance R in time $dt = i^2 R dt$.

$\therefore$ total energy required $= \displaystyle\int_0^\infty i^2 R dt$

$$= \int_0^\infty i_0^2 e^{-2t/CR} R dt \quad [\because \quad i = i_0 e^{-t/CR}]$$

$$= Ri_0^2 \int_0^\infty e^{-2t/CR} dt = Ri_0^2 \left[\frac{CR}{2} e^{-2t/CR} \right]_0^\infty$$

$$= \frac{1}{2} R^2 i_0^2 C = \frac{1}{2} E^2 C$$

$$= \text{energy of the capacitor.}$$

Therefore, the energy of a charged capacitor will be equal to the energy required to produce heat.

10.7   Measurement of High Resistance by Leakage

The resistances of the order of 20 MΩ and above can be measured by this method. Suppose a condenser of capacity C is charged by a cell of e.m.f. E. Hence the charge in the capacitor is $Q = EC$. The condenser is allowed to discharge itself through a resistance R for time t and suppose the charge remained on the condenser after discharge is Q_0.

$$\therefore \quad \log_e \frac{Q_0}{Q} = \frac{t}{CR} \quad \text{or,} \quad R = \frac{t}{C \log_e \frac{Q_0}{Q}} = \frac{t}{2.3026 C \log_{10} \left(\frac{Q_0}{Q} \right)}$$

The charges Q and Q_0 may be measured by a calibrated ballistic galvanometer. Suppose θ and θ_0 be the respective throw of the coil.

$$\therefore \quad \frac{Q}{Q_0} = \frac{\theta}{\theta_0}.$$

So we have, $R = \dfrac{t}{2.3026 C \log_{10} \left(\frac{\theta_0}{\theta} \right)}.$ (10.23)

From the above equation R can be evaluated.

A condenser itself has a natural leakage resistance (r') in parallel with the condenser. Therefore, the equivalent resistance of the circuit will be

$$\frac{1}{R} = \frac{1}{r} + \frac{1}{r'}, \quad\quad\quad (10.24)$$

where r is the actual value of the high resistance.

10.8   Charging of a Condenser through Inductance

Suppose a battery of e.m.f. E is connected with a condenser as shown in Fig. 10.11. Immediately after closing the circuit a current will flow through the inductance causing a back e.m.f. $L\frac{di}{dt}$. Therefore, at any instant t, the potential drop across the capacitor will be

$$\frac{Q}{C} = E - L\frac{di}{dt} \quad\quad\quad (10.25)$$

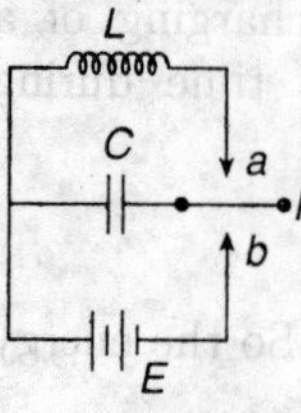

or, $L\dfrac{di}{dt} = E - \dfrac{Q}{C} = \dfrac{EC - Q}{C}$ or, $L\dfrac{d^2Q}{dt^2} = \dfrac{EC - Q}{C}$

or, $\dfrac{d^2Q}{dt^2} = \dfrac{EC - Q}{LC}$. (10.26)

Let us substitute $Q - EC$ by x in the above equation.

Fig. 10.11 $\therefore \quad \dfrac{d^2x}{dt^2} = -\dfrac{x}{LC}$.

Again substituting $\dfrac{1}{LC}$ by ω^2,

$\therefore \quad \dfrac{d^2x}{dt^2} = -\omega^2 x$. (10.27)

Suppose $x = Ae^{mt}$ be the trial solution of Eq. (10.27).

Substituting the value of x and $\dfrac{d^2x}{dt^2}$ in Eq. (10.27) we get

$m^2 + \omega^2 = 0, \quad \therefore \quad m = \pm i\omega$.

Therefore, $x = A_1 e^{i\omega t} + A_2 e^{-i\omega t}$, where A_1 and A_2 are the constants.

$\therefore \quad x = (A_1 + A_2)\cos\omega t + i(A_1 - A_2)\sin\omega t$

$\quad = A_3 \cos\omega t + A_4 \sin\omega t$ (10.28)

where A_3 and A_4 are new constants.

Eq. (10.28) can then be written as

$\quad Q - EC = A_3 \cos\omega t + A_4 \sin\omega t$.

Now at time $t = 0$, $Q = 0$,

$A_3 = -EC$.

Again, at time $t = 0$, $\dfrac{dQ}{dt} = 0$,

$A_4 = 0$.

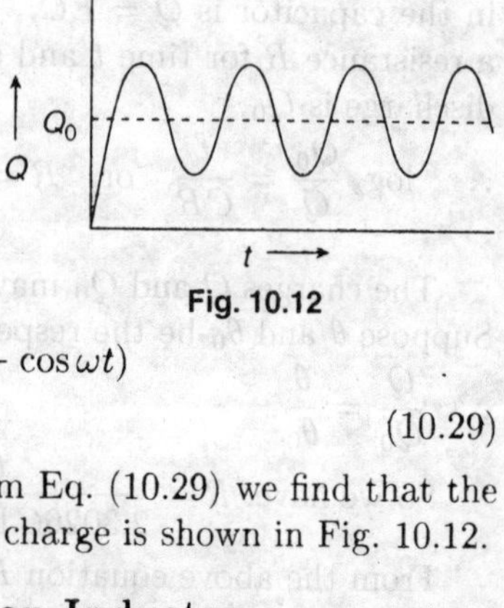

Fig. 10.12

Hence, $Q - EC = -EC\cos\omega t$ or, $Q = EC(1 - \cos\omega t)$

$\quad = Q_0(1 - \cos\omega t)$. (10.29)

Q_0 is the steady charge of the condenser. So from Eq. (10.29) we find that the charge varies in a sinusoidal manner. The nature of charge is shown in Fig. 10.12.

10.9 Discharge of a Condenser through an Inductor

Suppose, the condenser is fully charged after connecting the key at the point b (Fig. 10.11). Now, if the key K is connected at the point a, the condenser will discharge through the inductor of inductance L.

Let the charge of the condenser after time t be Q, and if i be the current flowing through the circuit, then the e.m.f. induced on the inductor

$$= -L\dfrac{di}{dt}$$

and the potential drop across the plate of the condenser $= \dfrac{Q}{C}$.

$\therefore \quad \dfrac{Q}{C} = -L\dfrac{di}{dt}$ or, $\dfrac{Q}{C} + L\dfrac{di}{dt} = 0$

or, $\dfrac{Q}{C} + L\dfrac{d^2Q}{dt^2} = 0 \quad \left[\because i = \dfrac{dQ}{dt} \right]$

or, $\dfrac{d^2Q}{dt^2} + \dfrac{Q}{LC} = 0.$ \hfill (10.30)

Suppose, $\dfrac{1}{LC} = \omega^2.$

$\therefore \quad \dfrac{d^2Q}{dt^2} + \omega^2 Q = 0.$ \hfill (10.31)

The solution of the above equation will be

$Q = A\sin(\omega t + \theta).$ \hfill (10.32)

Now, when $t = 0$ and $\theta = \dfrac{\pi}{2}$, $Q = Q_0$.

$\therefore \quad A = Q_0.$

Hence Eq. (10.32) can be written as

$Q = Q_0 \sin\left(\omega t + \dfrac{\pi}{2}\right)$, where $\omega = \dfrac{1}{\sqrt{(LC)}}$ \hfill (10.33)

From Eq. (10.33) one can easily see that the discharge of the condenser will be oscillatory.

10.10 Charging of a Condenser through a Resistance and an Inductance

Suppose a battery of e.m.f. E is applied to a circuit as shown in Fig. 10.13. Here the e.m.f. of the battery is opposed by the back e.m.f. induced in the inductance and the potential drop across the condenser. If Q be the charge of the condenser and i the current flowing at any instant through the circuit, then we have

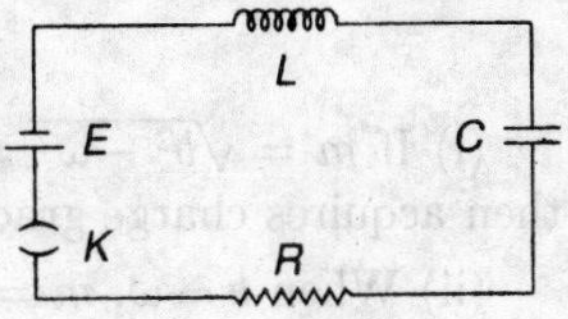

$L\dfrac{di}{dt} + Ri + \dfrac{Q}{C} = E$ or, $L\dfrac{d^2Q}{dt^2} + R\dfrac{dQ}{dt} + \dfrac{Q}{C} = E$

Fig. 10.13

or, $\dfrac{d^2Q}{dt^2} + \dfrac{R}{L}\dfrac{dQ}{dt} + \dfrac{Q}{CL} = \dfrac{E}{L}$

or, $\dfrac{d^2Q}{dt^2} + \dfrac{R}{L}\dfrac{dQ}{dt} + \dfrac{1}{LC}(Q - EC) = 0$

or, $\dfrac{d^2Q}{dt^2} + \dfrac{R}{L}\dfrac{dQ}{dt} + \dfrac{1}{LC}(Q - Q_0) = 0 \quad [\because Q_0 = EC = \text{steady charge}]$

Let us substitute $\dfrac{R}{L} = 2b$, $\dfrac{1}{LC} = \omega^2$ and $Q - Q_0 = x$ in the above equation, when we get

$$\dfrac{d^2x}{dt^2} + 2b\dfrac{dx}{dt} + \omega^2 x = 0.$$ \hfill (10.34)

The solution of the above equation will be

$$x = A_1 e(-b + \sqrt{b^2 - \omega^2})t + A_2 e(-b - \sqrt{b^2 - \omega^2})t,$$ \hfill (10.35)

where A_1 and A_2 are the constants.

$\therefore \quad x = e^{-bt}(A_1 e^{mt} + A_2 e^{-mt})$, where $m = \sqrt{b^2 - \omega^2}.$

The boundary conditions are:

at $t = 0$

$$Q = 0 \quad \text{and} \quad \frac{dQ}{dt} = 0.$$

$$\therefore \quad Q - Q_0 = e^{-bt}(A_1 e^{mt} + A_2 e^{-mt})$$

or, $\quad \dfrac{dQ}{dt} = -be^{-bt}(A_1 e^{mt} + A_2 e^{-mt}) + e^{-bt}(A_1 m e^{mt} - A_2 m e^{-mt}).$ (10.36)

From the condition we have at time $t = 0$, $Q = 0$. Hence we get

$$A_1 + A_2 = -Q_0. \tag{10.37}$$

Again, from the condition at $t = 0$, $\dfrac{dQ}{dt} = 0$,

$$-b(A_1 + A_2) + m(A_1 - A_2) = 0. \tag{10.38}$$

After solving Eqs. (10.37) and (10.38), we get

$$A_1 = -\frac{Q_0}{2}\left(1 + \frac{b}{m}\right) \quad \text{and} \quad A_2 = -\frac{Q_0}{2}\left(1 - \frac{b}{m}\right).$$

Therefore, the final equation becomes

$$Q = Q_0\left[1 - \frac{e^{-bt}}{2}\left\{\left(1 + \frac{b}{m}\right)e^{mt} + \left(1 - \frac{b}{m}\right)e^{-mt}\right\}\right]$$

$$= Q_0\left[1 - \frac{e^{-bt}}{2}\left\{\left(1 + \frac{b}{\sqrt{b^2 - \omega^2}}\right)e^{\sqrt{b^2 - \omega^2}\,t}\right.\right.$$

$$\left.\left. + \left(1 - \frac{b}{\sqrt{b^2 - \omega^2}}\right)e^{-\sqrt{b^2 - \omega^2}\,t}\right\}\right] \tag{10.38a}$$

(i) If $m = \sqrt{b^2 - \omega^2} = +$ve, Eq. (10.38a) cannot be simplified. The condenser then acquires charge gradually as shown in Fig. 10.14 for $b > \omega$.

(ii) When $b \cong \omega$, $m = \sqrt{b^2 - \omega^2}$ is a small quantity.

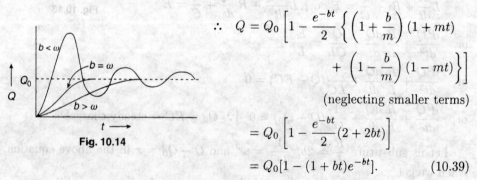

Fig. 10.14

$$\therefore \quad Q = Q_0\left[1 - \frac{e^{-bt}}{2}\left\{\left(1 + \frac{b}{m}\right)(1 + mt)\right.\right.$$

$$\left.\left. + \left(1 - \frac{b}{m}\right)(1 - mt)\right\}\right]$$

(neglecting smaller terms)

$$= Q_0\left[1 - \frac{e^{-bt}}{2}(2 + 2bt)\right]$$

$$= Q_0[1 - (1 + bt)e^{-bt}]. \tag{10.39}$$

The condenser acquires charge gradually as shown in Fig. 10.14 for $b \cong \omega$.

(iii) When $b < \omega$, $m = \sqrt{b^2 - \omega^2} = i\sqrt{\omega^2 - b^2} = im'$ (say)

$$\therefore \quad Q = Q_0\left[1 - \frac{e^{-bt}}{2}\left\{\left(1 + \frac{b}{im'}\right)e^{im't} + \left(1 - \frac{b}{im'}\right)e^{-im't}\right\}\right]$$

$$= Q_0\left[1 - \frac{e^{-bt}}{2}\left\{\left(e^{im't} + e^{-im't}\right) + \frac{b}{im'}\left(e^{im't} - e^{-im't}\right)\right\}\right]$$

$$= Q_0 \left[1 - e^{-bt} \left(\cos m't + \frac{b}{m'} \sin m't \right) \right]$$

$$= Q_0 [1 - e^{-bt} \{ A \cos\theta \cos m't + A \sin\theta \sin m't \}],$$

where $A \cos\theta = 1$ and $A \sin\theta = \frac{b}{m'}$,

i.e., $A = \sqrt{1 + \left(\frac{b}{m'} \right)^2}$ and $\theta = \tan^{-1} \frac{b}{m'}$.

$\therefore \qquad Q = Q_0 [1 - A e^{-bt} \cos(m't - \theta)]$

$$= Q_0 \left[1 - \frac{\omega e^{-bt}}{\sqrt{\omega^2 - b^2}} \cos \left(\sqrt{\omega^2 - b^2} t - \tan^{-1} \frac{b}{\sqrt{\omega^2 - b^2}} \right) \right]. \qquad (10.40)$$

From the above expression we find that the charging is oscillatory. The oscillation gradually decreases as the amplitude of oscillation decreases with time. The charging of the condenser is shown in Fig. 10.14 for $b < \omega$.

The time period of oscillation is given by

$$T = 2\pi \sqrt{\frac{1}{\omega^2 - b^2}} = 2\pi \frac{1}{\sqrt{\frac{1}{LC} - \frac{R^2}{4L^2}}}.$$

Therefore, the frequency of oscillation will be

$$f = \frac{1}{2\pi} \sqrt{\frac{1}{LC} - \frac{R^2}{4L^2}}. \qquad (10.41)$$

Current in the circuit

$$i = \frac{dQ}{dt} = A Q_0 \{ b e^{-bt} \cos(m't - \theta) + m' e^{-bt} \sin(m't - \theta) \}$$

$$= A Q_0 e^{-bt} \{ b \cos(m't - \theta) + m' \sin(m't - \theta) \}.$$

Let us now substitute

$$b = B \cos\phi, \quad m' = B \sin\phi.$$

$\therefore \qquad B = \sqrt{b^2 + m'^2} = \omega^2$ and $\tan\phi = \frac{m'}{b} = \frac{\sqrt{\omega^2 - b^2}}{b}$.

Therefore $i = A Q_0 e^{-bt} B \cos(m't - \theta - \phi)$.

Now, $\tan\theta = \frac{b}{\sqrt{\omega^2 - b^2}} = \cot\phi = \tan\left(\frac{\pi}{2} - \phi \right)$.

$\therefore \qquad \theta + \phi = \left(\frac{\pi}{2} \right)$.

Hence, $i = A Q_0 e^{-bt} B \cos\left(m't - \frac{\pi}{2} \right)$

$$= Q_0 \frac{\omega^2}{\sqrt{\omega^2 - b^2}} e^{-bt} \sin\sqrt{\omega^2 - b^2} t. \qquad (10.42)$$

The expression for current will thus be given by Eq. (10.42).

10.11 Discharging of a Condenser through a Resistance and an Inductance

Suppose a battery of e.m.f. E is connected to a circuit as shown in Fig. 10.15. The condenser is fully charged by connecting K to the point b; then the key is connected

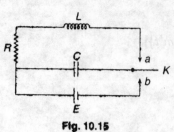

to the point a. So now the condenser begins to discharge through the inductance and the resistance. If Q be the charge of the condenser and i be the current flowing through the circuit at any instant t, then we have

$$L\frac{di}{dt} + Ri + \frac{Q}{C} = 0 \qquad (10.43)$$

or, $\qquad L\frac{d^2Q}{dt^2} + R\frac{dQ}{dt} + \frac{Q}{C} = 0$

or, $\qquad \frac{d^2Q}{dt^2} + 2b\frac{dQ}{dt} + \omega^2 Q = 0, \qquad (10.44)$

where $\quad 2b = \dfrac{R}{L}\quad$ and $\quad \omega^2 = \dfrac{1}{LC}$.

The solution of the above equation will be

$$Q = e^{-bt}(A_1 e^{mt} + A_2 e^{-mt}), \qquad (10.45)$$

where $\quad m = \sqrt{b^2 - \omega^2}$.

A_1 and A_2 are constants and they can be evaluated from the initial condition of the problem.

Now at $\quad t = 0, \; Q = Q_0$.

We get $\quad A_1 + A_2 = Q_0$. $\qquad\qquad\qquad\qquad\qquad (10.46)$

Again at $t = 0$, $\dfrac{dQ}{dt} = 0$

Now, $\quad \dfrac{dQ}{dt} = e^{-bt}m(A_1 e^{mt} - A_2 e^{-mt}) - be^{-bt}(A_1 e^{mt} + A_2 e^{-mt})$

At $\qquad t = 0,$

$$m(A_1 - A_2) - b(A_1 + A_2) = 0 \qquad (10.47)$$

After solving Eqs. (10.46) and (10.47), we get

$$A_1 = \frac{Q_0}{2}\left(1 + \frac{b}{m}\right)$$

$$A_2 = \frac{Q_0}{2}\left(1 - \frac{b}{m}\right).$$

Therefore, the final solution becomes

$$Q = \frac{Q_0 e^{-bt}}{2}\left\{\left(1 + \frac{b}{m}\right)e^{mt} + \left(1 - \frac{b}{m}\right)e^{-mt}\right\}$$

$$= \frac{Q_0 e^{-bt}}{2}\left\{\left(1 + \frac{b}{\sqrt{b^2 - \omega^2}}\right)e^{\sqrt{b^2-\omega^2}\,t}\right.$$

$$\left. + \left(1 - \frac{b}{\sqrt{b^2 - \omega^2}}\right)e^{-\sqrt{b^2-\omega^2}\,t}\right\}. \qquad (10.48)$$

(i) When $m = \sqrt{b^2 - \omega^2} = +$ve, i.e., $b > \omega$, the charge of the condenser decreases exponentially with time and approaches to zero as $t \to \infty$. This discharge is called dead beat discharge. The nature of the discharge is given in Fig. 10.16 for $b > \omega$.

(ii) When $b < \omega$, $m = \sqrt{b^2 - \omega^2} = i\sqrt{\omega^2 - b^2} = im'$ (say).

So from Eq. (10.48),

$$Q = Q_0 \frac{e^{-bt}}{2} \left\{ \left(1 + \frac{b}{im'}\right) e^{im't} + \left(1 - \frac{b}{im'}\right) e^{-im't} \right\}$$

$$= Q_0 \frac{e^{-bt}}{2} \left\{ (e^{im't} + e^{-im't}) + \frac{b}{im'}(e^{-im't} - e^{-im't}) \right\}$$

$$= Q_0 \frac{e^{-bt}}{2} \left\{ 2\cos m't + \frac{2b}{m'}\sin m't \right\}$$

$$= Q_0 e^{-bt} \left\{ \cos m't + \frac{b}{m'}\sin m't \right\}$$

$$= Q_0 e^{-bt} \{ A\cos\theta \cos m't + A\sin\theta \sin m't \},$$

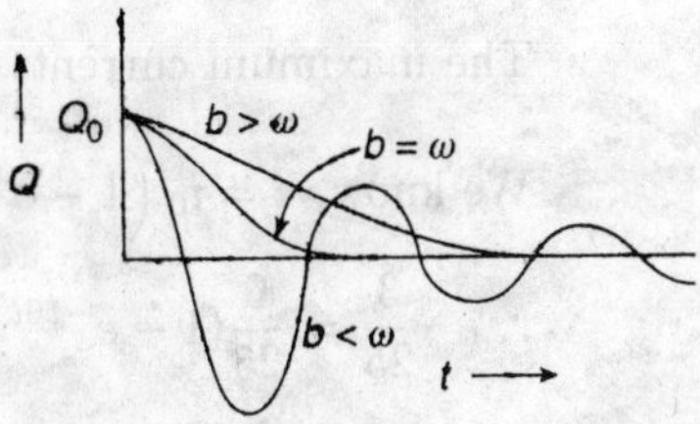

where $A\cos\theta = 1$ and $A\sin\theta = \dfrac{b}{m'}$.

Fig. 10.16

$$A = \sqrt{1 + \left(\frac{b}{m'}\right)^2} = \frac{\omega}{\sqrt{\omega^2 - b^2}} \quad \text{and} \quad \theta = \tan^{-1}\frac{b}{\sqrt{\omega^2 - b^2}}.$$

$$\therefore \quad Q = AQ_0 e^{-bt}\cos(m't - \theta)$$

$$= \frac{\omega Q_0}{\sqrt{\omega^2 - b^2}} e^{-bt}\cos\left(\sqrt{\omega^2 - b^2}\, t - \tan^{-1}\frac{b}{\sqrt{\omega^2 - b^2}}\right). \tag{10.49}$$

From the above expression we find that the discharge is oscillatory in nature. The nature of discharge is shown in Fig. 10.16 for $b < \omega$.

The frequency of oscillation is given by

$$f = \frac{1}{2\pi}\sqrt{\frac{1}{LC} - \frac{R^2}{4L^2}}. \tag{10.50}$$

Current in the circuit

$$i = -AQ_0 e^{-bt} b\cos(m't - \theta) - AQ_0 e^{-bt} m'\sin(m't - \theta)$$

$$= -AQ_0 e^{-bt}\{ b\cos(m't - \theta) + m'\sin(m't - \theta) \}.$$

Let us now substitute

$$b = B\cos\phi, \quad m' = B\sin\phi.$$

$$\therefore \quad B = \sqrt{b^2 + m'^2} = \omega \quad \text{and} \quad \tan\phi = \frac{m'}{b} = \frac{\sqrt{\omega^2 - b^2}}{b}.$$

Therefore $i = AQ_0 e^{-bt} B\cos(m't - \theta - \phi)$.

Now, $\tan\theta = \dfrac{b}{\sqrt{\omega^2 - b^2}} = \cot\phi = \tan\left(\dfrac{\pi}{2} - \phi\right).$

$$\therefore \quad \theta + \phi = \frac{\pi}{2}.$$

So $\quad i = \dfrac{dQ}{dt} = -\dfrac{\omega^2}{\sqrt{\omega^2 - b^2}} Q_0 e^{-bt}\sin\sqrt{\omega^2 - b^2}\, t. \tag{10.51}$

The expression for current is thus obtained by the above equation.

(iii) When $b = \omega$, the damping is such that dead beat discharge becomes most rapid. This stage is called *critical damping*. For a slight increase of the value of ω, the discharge then becomes *oscillatory*.

Examples

1. A telephone operates at a current of 120 mA has an inductance of 10 henries and resistance 100 ohms. If a 24-volt battery having negligible internal resistance is suddenly applied, calculate the operating time.

   Solution : Let the operating time be t when the current $i = 120 \, \text{mA} = \dfrac{3}{25}$ A.

   The maximum current, $i_0 = \dfrac{E}{R} = \dfrac{24}{100} = \dfrac{6}{25}$ A and $L = 10$ henries.

   We know, $i = i_0 \left(1 - e^{-\frac{Rt}{L}}\right)$.

   $\therefore \quad \dfrac{3}{25} = \dfrac{6}{25}(1 - e^{-10t}) \quad \text{or,} \quad \dfrac{1}{2} = 1 - \dfrac{1}{e^{10t}} \quad \text{or,} \quad e^{10t} = 2.$

   or, $\quad 10t = \log_e 2 \quad$ or, $\quad t = \dfrac{\log_e 2}{10} = \dfrac{2.3026 \times 0.3010}{10} = \mathbf{0.0693 \text{ second}}.$

   So the operating time is 0.0693 second.

2. A capacitance of 4 μF is charged through a resistance of 10^6 ohms from a 200-volt supply. How long does it take the capacitor to charge up to 63.2% of its final potential difference?

   Solution : Time required to charge the capacitor up to 63.2% of its final p.d. = its time constant CR.

   $\therefore \quad t = CR = 4 \times 10^{-6} \times 10^6 = \mathbf{4 \text{ seconds}}.$

3. In a C-R circuit if $C = 2.4 \, \mu$F, $R = 0.02$ megohm, in what time will the charge in the capacitor attain half its final value? [$\log_e 2 = 0.6931$]

   Solution : We know, $Q = Q_0(1 - e^{-t/CR})$.

   Here, $\quad C = 2.4 \, \mu\text{F} = 2.4 \times 10^{-6}\text{F},$

   $\qquad\quad R = 0.02 \text{ megohm} = 0.02 \times 10^6 \text{ ohm}$

   and $\quad Q = \dfrac{1}{2}Q_0.$

   $\therefore \quad \dfrac{1}{2}Q_0 = Q_0(1 - e^{-t/CR}) \quad \text{or,} \quad e^{-t/CR} = \dfrac{1}{2} \quad \text{or,} \quad \dfrac{t}{0.048} = \log_e 2.$

   $\therefore \quad t = 0.6931 \times 0.048 = \mathbf{0.0333 \text{ second}}.$

4. In an oscillatory circuit, $L = 0.2$ henry, $C = 0.0012 \, \mu$F. What is the maximum value of the resistance, so that the circuit may oscillate?

   Solution : For the circuit to be oscillatory, we have

   $$\dfrac{R^2}{4L^2} = \dfrac{1}{LC} \quad \text{or,} \quad R^2 = \dfrac{4L}{C}.$$

   So the maximum value of the resistance,

   $$R = \sqrt{\dfrac{4L}{C}}.$$

   Here, $\quad L = 0.2$ henry, $\quad C = 0.0012 \, \mu\text{F} = 0.0012 \times 10^{-6}\text{F}.$

   $\therefore \quad R = \sqrt{\dfrac{4 \times 0.2}{0.0012 \times 10^{-6}}} = \mathbf{2.582 \times 10^4 \text{ ohms}}.$

5. Examine whether the discharge of a condenser is oscillatory if $C = 2 \ \mu F$, $L = 0.15$ henry and $R = 150$ ohms.

   Solution : We know that the discharge is oscillatory, when

   $$\frac{R^2}{4L^2} < \frac{1}{LC}.$$

   Here, $\quad \dfrac{R^2}{4L^2} = \dfrac{(150)^2}{4 \times (0.15)^2} = 25 \times 10^4$

   and $\quad \dfrac{1}{LC} = \dfrac{1}{0.15 \times 2 \times 10^{-6}} = 3.3 \times 10^6.$

   $\therefore \quad \dfrac{R^2}{4L^2} < \dfrac{1}{LC}$, so the **discharge is oscillatory in nature.**

6. If L is 0.01 H and C is 1 μF, find the value of R for which the discharge is critically damped.

   Solution : We have $\dfrac{1}{LC} - \dfrac{R^2}{4L^2} = 0 \quad$ or, $\quad R = \sqrt{\dfrac{4L}{C}}.$

   Here, $\quad L = 0.01$ H, $C = 1 \ \mu F = 10^{-6}$ F.

   $\therefore \quad R = \sqrt{\left(\dfrac{4 \times 0.01}{10^{-6}}\right)} = \sqrt{4 \times 10^4} = 2 \times 10^2 = \textbf{200 ohms}.$

7. (a) A 2-volt battery of negligible internal resistance is applied to a coil of inductance 1 henry and of resistance 1 ohm. Calculate the time required by the current to attain a value half that in the steady state.

   (b) What will be the current after $\frac{1}{5}$ second? [C.U. 1956]

   Solution : (a) We know, $i = i_0 \left(1 - e^{-\frac{R}{L}t}\right).$

   Here, $i = \dfrac{i_0}{2}$, $R = 1$ ohm, $L = 1$ henry.

   $\therefore \quad \dfrac{i_0}{2} = i_0(1 - e^{-1})$

   or, $\quad \dfrac{1}{2} = 1 - e^{-t} \quad$ or, $\quad e^{-t} = \dfrac{1}{2} \quad$ or, $\quad e^t = 2.$

   $\therefore \quad t = \log_e 2 = \textbf{0.693 second}.$

   (b) Here, $i_0 = \dfrac{E}{R} = \dfrac{2}{1} = 2$ amperes.

   $$t = \frac{1}{5} \text{ second} = 0.2 \text{ second}.$$

   $\therefore \quad i = 2(1 + e^{-0.2}).$

8. A 40-μF capacitor in series with a 2000-Ω resistor is connected across a 200-volt dc source. Determine (i) the initial current, (ii) the time constant, (iii) the value of the current when time is equal to the time constant, and (iv) energy stored in the capacitor at time 0.04 second. [C.U. 1965]

   Solution : (i) Initial current, $i_0 = \dfrac{E}{R} = \dfrac{200}{2000} = \textbf{0.1 A}.$

   (ii) Time const., $\lambda = CR = \textbf{0.08 second}.$

(iii) We know current at any instant,

$$i = i_0 e^{-t/CR}.$$

Here, $t = 0.08$ second, $i_0 = 0.1$ A, $CR = 0.08$ second.

$$\therefore \qquad i = 0.1 e^{-1} = \frac{0.1}{2.718} = \textbf{0.0368 A}$$

(iv) We know, $Q = Q_0(1 - e^{-t/CR})$

or, $CV = CE(1 - e^{t/CR})$ or, $V = E(1 - e^{t/CR})$.

Here, $E = 200$ volts, $t = 0.04$ second, $CR = 0.08$ second.

$$\therefore \qquad V = 200\left(1 - e^{-\frac{1}{2}}\right) = \textbf{78.7 volts}.$$

$\therefore$ energy stored $= \dfrac{1}{2}CV^2 = \dfrac{1}{2} \times 40 \times 10^{-6} \times 78.7 \times 78.7$ joule

$$= \textbf{0.1239 joule}.$$

9. A circuit has its resistance 20 ohms and inductance 0.1 henry. If the current through the circuit at any instant be 1 ampere and the same growing at the rate of 20 amperes/second, calculate the e.m.f. applied in the circuit.

Solution : We know, $i = i_0(1 - e^{-Rt/L})$.

$$\therefore \qquad \frac{di}{dt} = i_0 \frac{R}{L} e^{-\frac{R}{L}t} = i_0 \frac{R}{L}\left(\frac{i_0 - i}{i_0}\right) = \frac{R}{L}(i_0 - i).$$

Here, $R = 20$ ohms, $\dfrac{di}{dt} = 20$ amperes/second, $L = 0.1$ henry, $i = 1$ ampere.

$$\therefore \qquad 20 = \frac{20}{0.1}(i_0 - 1).$$

$$\therefore \qquad i_0 = \frac{11}{10} \text{ A}$$

So the applied e.m.f., $E = i_0 \times R = \dfrac{11}{10} \times 20 = \textbf{22 volts}.$

10. The field coil of a dc generator has an inductance of 8 henries and a resistance of 80 ohms. If a dc supply of 100 volts is suddenly applied to the windings, find the time taken for the current to rise to 60% of the final value.

Solution : Time of increase of current, $i = i_0(1 - e^{-Rt/L})$.

Here, $i = \dfrac{60}{100} \times i_0 = \dfrac{3}{5} i_0 = i_0(1 - e^{-80t/8})$

or, $\dfrac{3}{5} = 1 - e^{-10 \cdot t}$ or, $e^{-10t} = \dfrac{2}{5}$ or, $e^{10t} = \dfrac{5}{2} = 2.5$

or, $10t = \log_e 2.5 = 2.3 \times \log_{10} 2.5 = 2.3 \times 0.4$

$$\therefore \qquad t = \textbf{0.092 s}.$$

11. A 2-volt battery of negligible internal resistance is applied to a coil of inductance 1 henry and of resistance 1 ohm. Calculate the time required by the current to attain a value half that in the steady state.

[C.U. 1990, '92; N.B.U. 1983]

Solution : We have, $i = i_0(1 - e^{-Rt/L})$.

Here, $i = \dfrac{i_0}{2}$;   or, $\dfrac{i_0}{2} = i_0(1 - e^{-\frac{1}{1} \cdot t}) = i_0(1 - e^{-t})$

or, $\quad \dfrac{1}{2} = 1 - e^{-t}$ or, $\quad \dfrac{1}{e^t} = \dfrac{1}{2}$ or, $\quad e^t = 2.$

$\therefore \quad t = \log_e 2 = 2.3 \log_{10} 2 = 2.3 \times 0.3010 = \textbf{0.69 s.}$

12. A capacitor of capacitance 0.1 μF and a resistance of 10 megohms in series are charged to a certain potential and then insulated. Find the time the potential will take to fall to half its original value. $\log_e 2 = 0.6931.$

Solution : $Q = Q_0 e^{-t/RC}$ or, $\dfrac{Q}{C} = \dfrac{Q_0}{C} \cdot e^{-t/RC}$ or, $V = V_0 \cdot e^{-t/RC}.$

Here, $V = \dfrac{V_0}{2}$; $R = 10$ megohms $= 10 \times 10^6$ ohms;

$C = 0.1 \ \mu\text{F} = 0.1 \times 10^{-6} \ \text{F}$ or, $CR = 10 \times 10^6 \times 0.1 \times 10^{-6} = 1.$

$\therefore \quad \dfrac{V_0}{2} = V_0 e^{-t}$ or, $\dfrac{1}{2} = \dfrac{1}{e^t}$

or, $\quad e^t = 2.$

So $\quad t = \log_e 2 = \textbf{0.6931 s.}$

13. A capacitor is charged through a resistance of 2 megohms by a battery. It takes $\frac{1}{2}$ s for the charge to reach three quarter of its final value. What is the capacitance of the capacitor?

Solution : $Q = Q_0(1 - e^{-t/CR}).$

Here, $Q = \dfrac{3}{4}Q_0,$ $t = \dfrac{1}{2}$ s, $R = 2$ megohms $= 2 \times 10^6$ ohms.

So, $\quad \dfrac{3}{4}Q_0 = Q_0(1 - e^{-\frac{1}{2 \times C \times 2 \times 10^6}}) = Q_0(1 - e^{-\frac{1}{4 \times 10^6 \times C}})$

or, $\quad e^{-\frac{1}{4 \times 10^6 \times C}} = 1 - \dfrac{3}{4} = \dfrac{1}{4}$ or, $4 = e^{\frac{1}{4 \times 10^6 \times C}}$

i.e., $\quad \dfrac{1}{4 \times 10^6 \times C} = \log_e 4 = 2.3 \log_{10} 4 = 2.3 \times 0.6021 = 1.384.$

$\therefore \quad C = \dfrac{1}{4 \times 1.384} \times 10^{-6} = 0.18 \times 10^{-6} \ \text{F} = \textbf{0.18} \ \boldsymbol{\mu}\textbf{F.}$

14. If a capacitor of 4 microfarads capacitance be allowed to discharge through an inductance of 10 millihenries, calculate the natural frequency of the circuit.

Solution : Natural frequency, $f = \dfrac{1}{2\pi\sqrt{LC}}.$

Here, $C = 4$ microfarads $= 4 \times 10^{-6} \ \text{F}$; $L = 10$ millihenries $= 10 \times 10^{-3} \ \text{H}.$

$\therefore \quad f = \dfrac{1}{2\pi\sqrt{10 \times 10^{-3} \times 4 \times 10^{-6}}} = \dfrac{10^4}{4\pi} = \textbf{796 cycles/s.}$

Questions

Essay-type

1. An e.m.f. E volts, is suddenly applied to a circuit consisting of an inductance and a resistance in series. Investigate the growth of current in the circuit and also its decay when the e.m.f. is withdrawn. What is the time constant of the circuit? [C.U. (Hons.) 1990]

2. Show that the current in a d.c. circuit containing a resistance and an inductance grows exponentially. What do you mean by the time constant of the circuit?   [N.B.U. 1983]

3. Show that in a circuit with a steady e.m.f. and an inductive resistance the current decays exponentially with time when the e.m.f. is suddenly withdrawn.

4. A steady e.m.f. is applied to a circuit consisting of a resistance r and an inductance l. Discuss the growth of current. What do you mean by time constant of the circuit? How does rate of change of current depend on time constant during growth of current?   [C.U. 1982; B.U. 1991]

5. A condenser is being charged from a battery through a resistance in series. Find an expression for the instantaneous charge. What is 'time constant' of the circuit? Sketch the growth curve of the charge, marking the time constant.   [C.U. 1989]

6. Calculate the growth of charge in a capacitor of capacitance C connected in series with a battery of e.m.f. E and a (non-inductive) resistance R. Draw a curve showing the variation of current with time in the above case.

7. A steady d.c. voltage is suddenly applied to a capacitor in series with a resistance. Derive an expression for the instantaneous value of the voltage across the capacitor. What do you mean by the time constant of the circuit?

8. A capacitor having initial charge Q_0 is discharged through a resistance. Find an expression for the charge remaining in the capacitor after t seconds. What is the 'time constant' of the circuit? Sketch the decay curve and mark the time constant.   [C.U. 1991]

Short Answer-type

9. What do you mean by the time constant of (i) an inductive circuit and (ii) a capacitative circuit containing a capacitance and a resistance.

10. A steady current is flowing in a circuit containing an inductance, a resistance and a battery in series. Suddenly the battery is switched off. State the characteristics of decay of current in the circuit. Show, by a graph, the time variation of the current. What will you do to make the current fall (i) very rapidly and (ii) rather slowly?

11. In an inductive circuit, current cannot grow to the steady value all at once. Why? Upon what factor does the rapidity of growth of current depend?

12. A capacitor is being charged by a battery. What factors decide the growth of charge?

13. Generally when an electric motor is switched off, a spark passes between the air gap of the switch contact. Why?

Numerical Problems

14. A capacitance of 2 μF is charged through a resistance of 0.5 megohm from a 200-volt d.c. supply. Calculate (i) the maximum charging current, (ii) time constant of the circuit and (iii) time for the capacitor to charge up to half its final charge.   [Ans. (i) 0.4 mA, (ii) 1 s, (iii) 0.698 s]

15. A circuit contains a resistance of 20 ohms, an inductance of 50 millihenries and a battery. How long after the circuit is closed will the current take to rise to half its maximum value?.   [Ans. 0.00172 s]

16. A coil having a resistance of 15 ohms and an inductance of 10 henries is connected to a 75-volt d.c. supply. Determine the values of the current 0.67 s and 2 s after connection. Given $e = 2.72$ and $e^3 = 20$.   [**Ans.** 3.1 A; 4.75 A]

17. A coil stores 32 J of magnetic field energy and dissipates energy as heat at the rate of 320 watts when a current of 4 A is passed through it. Find the time constant of the circuit when the coil is joined across an ideal battery.

[**Ans.** 0.2 s]

18. A coil having an inductance of 0.45 H and resistance 10 ohms is connected in series with a plug key, a 35-ohm resistor and a battery of e.m.f. 12 volts. At what time after closing the key, will the current strength be half its steady value? What is the value of the steady current?

[**Ans.** 6.93×10^{-3} s; 0.27 A (nearly)]

19. A coil of resistance 15 ohms and self-inductance 10 henries is connected to a 90-volt dc mains. Find the value of current after 2 seconds.   [**B.U. 1989**]

[**Ans.** 5.2 A (nearly)]

20. A condenser of 1 μF capacity is connected in series with a 10 000-ohm resistor across the terminals of a 300-volt battery. Calculate the amount of heat generated in the resistor. $J = 4.18$ joules/cal.   [**Ans.** 1.08×10^{-2} cal]

[**Hints :** Heat generated in the resistor = charging energy of the capacitor $= \frac{1}{2}E^2 \cdot V. \therefore H = \frac{E^2 V}{2J}$]

Chapter 11
Alternating Currents

11.1   Introduction

The flow of electrons in an electrical circuit in which the direction of movement periodically reverses so that the average value over a period becomes zero is called the *alternating current*. This means an alternating current has a positive and an equal negative maximum value during each periodic time. The number of such complete cycles per second is called the *frequency*.

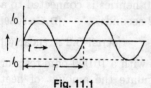

Fig. 11.1

The form of the alternating current (I) which changes sinusoidally with time (t) is shown in Fig. 11.1, where $+I_0$ and $-I_0$ represent maximum positive and negative currents in the time period T. The equation for the instantaneous value of an alternating current can be written as

$I = I_0 \sin \omega t$, where ω = angular velocity (in radian/s) = $2\pi/T$

$$= I_0 \sin \frac{2\pi}{T} t$$

$$= I_0 \sin 2\pi f t \quad (\because \ f = 1/T). \tag{11.1}$$

Similarly, if E_0 be the maximum e.m.f., then at any instant of time t the instantaneous value of the e.m.f. E is given by,

$$E = E_0 \sin \omega t$$

$$= E_0 \sin 2\pi f t. \tag{11.2}$$

11.2   Mean Current and Mean e.m.f.

For a complete cycle of periodic time T, the average value of an alternating current of instantaneous value $I = I_0 \sin \omega t$ is given by

$$I_{av} = \frac{1}{T} \int_0^T I_0 \sin \omega t \, dt = \frac{I_0}{T} \left[-\frac{\cos \omega t}{\omega} \right]_0^T$$

$$= \frac{I_0}{T} \cdot \frac{1}{\omega} \left\{ \left(-\cos \frac{2\pi}{T} \times T \right) - \left(\cos \frac{2\pi}{T} \times 0 \right) \right\}$$

$$= \frac{I_0}{\omega T}(-1 + 1) = 0. \tag{11.3}$$

Thus, the average value over a complete cycle becomes zero. This can alternately be seen in the following way. For the first half of the cycle the average value of current is

$$\frac{1}{T/2} \int_0^{T/2} I_0 \sin \omega t \, dt = \frac{2I_0}{T} \left[-\frac{\cos \omega t}{\omega} \right]_0^{T/2}$$

$$= -\frac{2I_0}{\omega T} \left\{ \left(\cos \frac{2\pi}{T} \times \frac{T}{2} \right) - \left(\cos \frac{2\pi}{T} \times 0 \right) \right\} = -\frac{2I_0}{\omega T}(-1-1)$$

$$= \frac{4I_0}{\frac{2\pi}{T} \cdot T} = \frac{2}{\pi}I_0. \tag{11.4}$$

Similarly, for the next half of the cycle the average value is

$$\frac{1}{T/2} \int_{T/2}^{T} I_0 \sin \omega t \, dt = \frac{2I_0}{T} \left[-\frac{\cos \omega T}{\omega} \right]_{T/2}^{T}$$

$$= -\frac{2I_0}{\omega T} \left\{ \left(\cos \frac{2\pi}{T} \times T \right) - \left(\cos \frac{2\pi}{T} \times \frac{T}{2} \right) \right\} = -\frac{2I_0}{\omega T}(1+1)$$

$$= -\frac{4I_0}{\frac{2\pi}{T} \cdot T} = -\frac{2}{\pi}I_0. \tag{11.5}$$

Eqs. (11.4) and (11.5) indicate that during the two successive halves of the cycle the average currents have equal magnitudes but opposite directions. Consequently, the average value during a complete cycle becomes zero.

By the term mean current or mean e.m.f. in an a.c. circuit is meant the average value of that quantity over a positive half-cycle. Thus we can write,

$$I_{\text{mean}} = \frac{2I_0}{\pi}. \tag{11.6}$$

Similarly, $E_{\text{mean}} = \frac{2E_0}{\pi}. \tag{11.7}$

11.2.1 rms Current and rms e.m.f.

The r.m.s. or root mean square value of an alternating current is defined as the square root of the mean value of the square of that quantity for a complete cycle. Mathematically, the r.m.s. value of current is

$$I_{\text{rms}} = \sqrt{\overline{I^2}},$$

where $\overline{I^2} = \frac{1}{T} \int_0^T I_0^2 \sin^2 \omega t \, dt = \frac{I_0^2}{T} \int_0^T \left(\frac{1 - \cos 2\omega t}{2} \right) dt = \frac{I_0^2}{T} \left[\frac{t}{2} - \frac{\sin 2\omega t}{4\omega} \right]_0^T$

$$= \frac{I_0^2}{T} \left[\frac{T}{2} - \frac{\sin \left(2 \cdot \frac{2\pi t}{T} \right)}{4\pi} \right]_0^T = \frac{I_0^2}{T} \cdot \frac{T}{2} = \frac{I_0^2}{2}.$$

$$\therefore \quad I_{\text{rms}} = \sqrt{\frac{I_0^2}{2}}$$

$$= \frac{I_0}{\sqrt{2}} = 0.707 I_0. \tag{11.8}$$

In a similar way,

$$E_{\text{rms}} = \frac{E_0}{\sqrt{2}} = 0.707 E_0. \tag{11.9}$$

11.2.2 Power and Power Factor

In a d.c. circuit the average power is obtained by the product of load current and the p.d. across the load. In an a.c. circuit also with pure resistive load the average power (W) over a complete cycle is given by

$$W = \frac{1}{T}\int_0^T EI\,dt = \frac{1}{T}\int_0^T E_0\sin\omega t \times I_0\sin\omega t\,dt = \frac{E_0 I_0}{T}\int_0^T \sin^2\omega t\,dt$$

$$= \frac{E_0 I_0}{T}\int_0^T \sin^2\frac{2\pi}{T}t\,dt = \frac{E_0 I_0}{T}\cdot\frac{T}{2}$$

$$= \frac{E_0 I_0}{2} = \frac{E_0}{\sqrt{2}}\cdot\frac{I_0}{\sqrt{2}} = E_{\text{rms}}\cdot I_{\text{rms}}. \tag{11.10}$$

But with inducting load, i.e., when the circuit contains both the resistance (R) and inductance (L) and an alternating e.m.f. $E = E_0\sin\omega t$ is applied to drive a current through them, the current lags behind the e.m.f. by a constant phase angle α, where $\tan\alpha = \frac{L\omega}{R}$. The instantaneous current is then given by $I = I_0\sin(\omega t - \alpha)$ and the average power in such a case is

$$W = \frac{1}{T}\int_0^T EI\,dt = \frac{1}{T}\int_0^T E_0\sin\omega t\cdot I_0\sin(\omega t - \alpha)\,dt$$

$$= \frac{E_0 I_0}{T}\int_0^T \sin\omega t(\sin\omega t\cos\alpha - \cos\omega t\sin\alpha)\,dt$$

$$= \frac{E_0 I_0}{T}\int_0^T (\sin^2\omega t\cos\alpha - \sin\omega t\cos\omega t\sin\alpha)\,dt$$

$$= \frac{E_0 I_0}{T}\cos\alpha\int_0^T \sin^2\omega t\,dt - \frac{E_0 I_0}{T}\sin\alpha\int_0^T \frac{\sin 2\omega t}{2}\,dt$$

$$= \frac{E_0 I_0}{T}\cos\alpha\cdot\frac{T}{2} - \frac{E_0 I_0}{2T}\sin\alpha\times 0 = \frac{E_0 I_0}{2}\cos\alpha = \frac{E_0}{\sqrt{2}}\cdot\frac{I_0}{\sqrt{2}}\cdot\cos\alpha$$

$$= E_{\text{rms}}\cdot I_{\text{rms}}\cdot\cos\alpha. \tag{11.11}$$

The product $E_{\text{rms}} \times I_{\text{rms}}$ is called the apparent power and the factor $\cos\alpha$ which is to be multiplied to get the average power is known as the *power factor of the load.*

11.2.3   Form Factor

The form factor (F) of an alternating current may be defined as,

$$F_{\text{current}} = \frac{\text{r.m.s. value of current}}{\text{mean value of current}}$$

$$= \frac{I_{\text{rms}}}{I_{\text{mean}}} = \frac{I_0/\sqrt{2}}{\frac{2I_0}{\pi}} = \frac{\pi}{2\sqrt{2}} = 1.11. \tag{11.12}$$

Similarly, $F_{\text{emf}} = \dfrac{E_{\text{rms}}}{E_{\text{mean}}} = 1.11.$ \hfill (11.13)

11.3   Circuit Elements in a.c. Circuits

An electric circuit may contain some or all of the following components, viz., inductor (L), capacitor (C) and resistor (R). Using complex numbers, behaviour of an a.c. circuit with (i) L-R, (ii) C-R and (iii) L-C-R in series is discussed below.

11.3.1   An a.c. Circuit with Inductor and Resistor in Series

Let a source of sinusoidal e.m.f. of instantaneous value $E = E_0 e^{j\omega t}$ is applied to a circuit consisting of an inductance L and a resistance R in series (Fig. 11.2), where

E may be considered as the real part of $E_0(\cos\omega t + j\sin\omega t)$. The impressed e.m.f. in driving the instantaneous current I through the circuit will be opposed by the induced back e.m.f. $\left(-L\frac{dI}{dt}\right)$ developed across the inductance L. So from Ohm's law we can write,

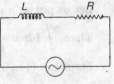

Fig. 11.2

$$\mathbf{I} = \frac{\mathbf{E} - L\frac{d\mathbf{I}}{dt}}{R}$$

or, $\qquad L\dfrac{d\mathbf{I}}{dt} + R\mathbf{I} = \mathbf{E}.$ \hfill (11.14)

Let us put as a solution, $\mathbf{I} = \mathbf{A}e^{j\omega t}$, \hfill (11.15)

where $\mathbf{A}$ may contain both real and imaginary parts.

Then, $\dfrac{d\mathbf{I}}{dt} = j\omega \mathbf{A}e^{j\omega t} = j\varphi\mathbf{I}.$

From Eq. (11.14), $jL\omega\mathbf{I} + R\mathbf{I} = \mathbf{E}$ or, $(jL\omega + R)\mathbf{I} = \mathbf{E}$

or, $\qquad \mathbf{I} = \dfrac{\mathbf{E}}{R + jL\omega} = \dfrac{\mathbf{E}(R - jL\omega)}{(R + jL\omega)(R - jL\omega)}$

$$= \frac{\mathbf{E}(R - jL\omega)}{R^2 + L^2\omega^2}. \tag{11.16}$$

Let $\quad R = a\cos\alpha, \; L\omega = a\sin\alpha$, where a and α are constants.

Then, $a = \sqrt{R^2 + L^2\omega^2}$ and $\tan\alpha = \dfrac{L\omega}{R}.$

$\therefore \qquad \mathbf{I} = \dfrac{\mathbf{E}a(\cos\alpha - j\sin\alpha)}{R^2 + L^2\omega^2} = \dfrac{\mathbf{E}(\cos\alpha - j\sin\alpha)}{\sqrt{R^2 + L^2\omega^2}}$

$$= \frac{\mathbf{E}e^{-j\alpha}}{\sqrt{R^2 + L^2\omega^2}} \tag{11.17}$$

$$= \frac{E_0 e^{j(\omega t - \alpha)}}{\sqrt{R^2 + L^2\omega^2}}. \quad (\because \mathbf{E} = \mathbf{E}_0 e^{j\omega t}) \tag{11.18}$$

Eq. (11.18) shows that the current lags behind the applied e.m.f. by an angle $\alpha = \tan^{-1}\frac{L\omega}{R}.$

If $E = E_0\cos\omega t$, then in the steady condition the current is given by

$$I = \frac{E_0\cos(\omega t - \alpha)}{\sqrt{(R^2 + L^2\omega^2)}}. \tag{11.19}$$

$\sqrt{R^2 + L^2\omega^2}$ is known as the *impedance* of the circuit and $L\omega$ is called the *reactance* of the inductor.

11.3.2 An a.c. Circuit with Capacitor and Resistor in Series

Let a source of sinusoidal e.m.f. of instantaneous value $\mathbf{E} = \mathbf{E}_0 e^{j\omega t}$ is applied to a circuit consisting of a capacitor C and a resistor R in series (Fig. 11.3). If $\mathbf{I}$ be the instantaneous current, then the e.m.f. equation is

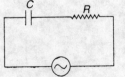

Fig. 11.3

$$\frac{\mathbf{q}}{C} + R\mathbf{I} = \mathbf{E}$$

or, $\quad \dfrac{\int \mathbf{I}dt}{C} + R\mathbf{I} = \mathbf{E}. \quad \left(\because q = \int \mathbf{I}dt\right)$ \hfill (11.20)

Let us put as a solution, $\mathbf{I} = \mathbf{A}e^{j\omega t}$.

Then, $\int \mathbf{I} dt = \dfrac{\mathbf{I}}{j\omega}$.

From Eq. (11.20),

$$\frac{\mathbf{I}}{jC\omega} + R\mathbf{I} = \mathbf{E} \quad \text{or,} \quad \left(\frac{1}{jC\omega} + R\right)\mathbf{I} = \mathbf{E}$$

or,
$$I = \frac{\mathbf{E}}{R + \frac{1}{jC\omega}} = \frac{\mathbf{E}\left(R - \frac{1}{jC\omega}\right)}{R^2 + \frac{1}{C^2\omega^2}}.$$

Let $\quad R = a\cos\alpha, \ \dfrac{1}{C\omega} = a\sin\alpha.$

Then $\quad a = \sqrt{R^2 + \dfrac{1}{C^2\omega^2}}, \ \tan\alpha = \dfrac{1}{C\omega R}.$

$$\therefore \quad \mathbf{I} = \frac{\mathbf{E}(a\cos\alpha + ja\sin\alpha)}{R^2 + \frac{1}{C^2\omega^2}} = \frac{\mathbf{E}ae^{ja}}{R^2 + \frac{1}{C^2\omega^2}}$$

$$= \frac{\mathbf{E}e^{ja}}{\sqrt{\left(R^2 + \frac{1}{C^2\omega^2}\right)}}. \tag{11.21}$$

Eq. (11.21) shows that the current leads the e.m.f. by an angle $\alpha = \tan^{-1}\dfrac{1}{C\omega R}$. Impedance in this case is $\sqrt{R^2 + \dfrac{1}{C^2\omega^2}}$ and $\dfrac{1}{C\omega}$ is the reactance of the capacitor.

11.3.3   An a.c. Circuit with Inductor, Capacitor and Resistor in Series

Let a source of sinusoidal e.m.f. of instantaneous value $\mathbf{E} = \mathbf{E}_0 e^{j\omega t}$ is applied to a circuit consisting of an inductance L, capacitance C and resistance R in series as shown in Fig. 11.4. If $\mathbf{I}$ be the instantaneous current, then the e.m.f. equation is

$$L\frac{d\mathbf{I}}{dt} + R\mathbf{I} + \frac{q}{C} = \mathbf{E}$$

Fig. 11.4   or, $L\dfrac{d\mathbf{I}}{dt} + R\mathbf{I} + \dfrac{\int \mathbf{I} dt}{C} = \mathbf{E}.$ \qquad (11.22)

Let us put as a solution, $\mathbf{I} = \mathbf{A}e^{j\omega t}$.

Then, $\dfrac{d\mathbf{I}}{dt} = j\omega \mathbf{A}e^{j\omega t} = j\omega \mathbf{I}$ and $\int \mathbf{I} dt = \dfrac{\mathbf{I}}{j\omega}$.

From Eq. (11.22),

$$jL\omega\mathbf{I} + R\mathbf{I} + \frac{\mathbf{I}}{jC\omega} = \mathbf{E} \quad \text{or,} \quad \left(jL\omega + R + \frac{1}{jC\omega}\right)\mathbf{I} = \mathbf{E}$$

$$\therefore \quad \mathbf{I} = \frac{\mathbf{E}}{R + j\left(L\omega - \frac{1}{C\omega}\right)} \tag{11.23}$$

or, we can write,

$$\mathbf{I} = \frac{\mathbf{E}\left\{R - j\left(L\omega - \frac{1}{C\omega}\right)\right\}}{R^2 + \left(L\omega - \frac{1}{C\omega}\right)^2}.$$

Let $\quad R = a\cos\alpha, \ L\omega - \dfrac{1}{C\omega} = a\sin\alpha.$

then $a = \sqrt{R^2 + \left(L\omega - \dfrac{1}{C\omega}\right)^2}$ and $\tan\alpha = \dfrac{L\omega - \dfrac{1}{C\omega}}{R}$.

$$\therefore \quad \mathbf{I} = \frac{\mathbf{E}(a\cos\alpha - ja\sin\alpha)}{R^2 + \left(L\omega - \frac{1}{C\omega}\right)^2} = \frac{\mathbf{E}ae^{-j\alpha}}{R^2 + \left(L\omega - \frac{1}{C\omega}\right)^2}$$

$$= \frac{\mathbf{E}e^{-j\alpha}}{\sqrt{R^2 + \left(L\omega - \frac{1}{C\omega}\right)^2}}. \tag{11.24}$$

Eq. (11.24) shows that the current lags behind the applied e.m.f. by an angle $\alpha = \tan^{-1}\frac{L\omega - \frac{1}{C\omega}}{R}$. In the above equation, $\sqrt{R^2 + \left(L\omega - \frac{1}{C\omega}\right)^2} = Z$ (say), is known as the impedance of the circuit and $\left(L\omega - \frac{1}{C\omega}\right)$ is the reactance. The reactance here is of two different types; the inductive reactance $L\omega$ and the capacitative reactance $\frac{1}{C\omega}$ which are of opposite in sign. If we put the inductive reactance $L\omega = X_L$ and the capacitative reactance $\frac{1}{C\omega} = X_C$, then $(X_L - X_C)$ can be represented by X, where X is the total reactance.

Fig. 11.5 shows how the resistance R, the reactance X and the impedance Z are related to the phase angle α vectorially. The triangle thus obtained is known as the *impedance triangle*. In the triangle, the resistance R is drawn along the x-axis while the reactances X_L and X_C are drawn along the +ve and −ve y-axis respectively. The vector $Z(= \sqrt{R^2 + X^2})$ in this case represents the phase of the impressed e.m.f. and so the diagram is often referred to as a vector impedance diagram.

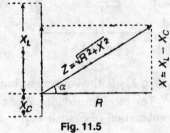

Fig. 11.5

11.4 Resonance

A circuit is called resonant when the frequency of the sinusoidal e.m.f. becomes equal to the natural frequency of the circuit. In practice, a circuit is also said to be resonance when the magnitude of the capacitative reactance is exactly equal to the magnitude of the inductive reactance, i.e., $L\omega = \frac{1}{C\omega}$. Or in other words, in a resonant circuit the reactive component of the impedance vanishes and thereby it behaves as a pure resistance.

For a series resonant circuit the impedance is a minimum while for a parallel resonant circuit it becomes a maximum. A series resonant circuit is sometimes called an *acceptor circuit* and a parallel resonant circuit is called a *rejector circuit*.

11.4.1 Series Resonant Circuit

We have found that in an a.c. circuit with inductor, resistor and capacitor in series, the current $\mathbf{I}$ can be expressed as

$$\mathbf{I} = \frac{\mathbf{E}}{R + j\left(L\omega - \frac{1}{C\omega}\right)}, \tag{11.25}$$

where the impedance $\mathbf{Z}$ is given by

$$\mathbf{Z} = R + j\left(L\omega - \frac{1}{C\omega}\right). \tag{11.26}$$

Now, the reactive component will be inductive for $L\omega > \frac{1}{C\omega}$ and capacitative for $L\omega < \frac{1}{C\omega}$. If the value of the inductor or the capacitor is varied such that $L\omega = \frac{1}{C\omega}$,

Eq. (11.26) reduces to

$$Z = R. \qquad (11.27)$$

The impedance then becomes minimum and the circuit is called *series resonant*.

For a series resonant circuit since

$$L\omega_R = \frac{1}{C\omega_R} \quad \text{or,} \quad \omega_R = \frac{1}{\sqrt{(LC)}},$$

we have $f_R = \dfrac{1}{2\pi\sqrt{(LC)}},$ $(\because \omega_R = 2\pi f_R)$ $\qquad (11.28)$

where f_R is the resonant frequency.

11.4.2 Parallel Resonant Circuit

A parallel resonant circuit is shown in Fig. 11.6, where the capacitor C is connected in parallel to the inductor L. To get an expression for current let us first calculate the total impedance of the circuit. Since L and C are connected in parallel, their equivalent impedance is found from the relation,

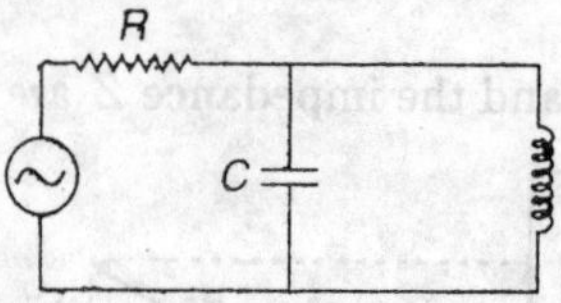

Fig. 11.6

$$\frac{1}{Z_{eq}} = \frac{1}{-j\left(\frac{1}{\omega C}\right)} + \frac{1}{j\omega L} = j\omega C + \frac{1}{j\omega L}$$

$$= \frac{-\omega^2 LC + 1}{j\omega L}$$

$$\text{or,} \quad Z_{eq} = \frac{j\omega L}{1 - \omega^2 LC}, \qquad (11.29)$$

where Z_{eq} is the equivalent impedance of the LC combination.

The total impedance $\mathbf{Z}$ of the circuit can now be obtained by adding the series combination of R with Z_{eq},

i.e., $\mathbf{Z} = R + Z_{eq}$

$$= R + \frac{j\omega L}{1 - \omega^2 LC}. \qquad (11.30)$$

Thus knowing $\mathbf{Z}$, the current $\mathbf{I}$ in the circuit can be written as

$$\mathbf{I} = \frac{\mathbf{E}}{R + \frac{j\omega L}{1 - \omega^2 LC}}. \qquad (11.31)$$

In Eq. (11.30) for $\omega^2 LC = 1$, the term $j\omega L/(1 - \omega^2 LC)$ becomes infinite. The impedance then gives a maximum value and the circuit is called *parallel resonant*. For a parallel resonant circuit since

$$\omega_R^2 LC = 1 \quad \text{or,} \quad \omega_R = \frac{1}{\sqrt{(LC)}},$$

we have, $f_R = \dfrac{1}{2\pi\sqrt{(LC)}},$ $\qquad (11.32)$

where f_R is the resonant frequency.

This is the same relation as obtained in the case of series resonance.

11.5 Q-factor

In a resonant circuit the value of the resistance is significant for determining the current in the circuit. This is important since the resistance is also present in the inductor. The effect is similar in both series and parallel resonant circuits.

However, the former is mathematically easier and so considered here to illustrate some important features.

The magnitude of the current in the series L-C-R circuit is given by

$$I = \frac{E}{\sqrt{\left\{ R^2 + \left(L\omega - \frac{1}{C\omega} \right)^2 \right\}}} \tag{11.33}$$

which can be rearranged as

$$I = \frac{E}{\sqrt{\left\{ R^2 + (L\omega)^2 \left(1 - \frac{1}{LC\omega^2} \right)^2 \right\}}}$$

$$= \frac{E}{R\sqrt{\left\{ 1 + \left(\frac{L\omega}{R} \right)^2 \left(1 - \frac{1}{LC\omega^2} \right)^2 \right\}}}. \tag{11.34}$$

The ratio of inductive reactance ($L\omega$) to resistance (R) is termed as the Q-*factor* of the circuit. At resonance the Q-factor may, therefore, be mathematically expressed as

$$Q_R = \frac{L\omega}{R}. \tag{11.35}$$

11.5.1 Selectivity

If the total resistance in a circuit is low, then the curve obtained by plotting current against frequency has a sharp peak. Such a circuit is called sharply resonant or highly selective. On the other hand, if the internal resistance of the generator is high or the resistance of the circuit has a high value, then the peak becomes not so pronounced and hence the circuit is said to be poorly selective. So for a sharply resonant series circuit the generator impedance must be sufficiently low.

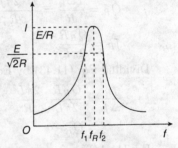

Fig. 11.7

To compare the selectivity of one circuit with another, one must consider the band of frequencies between limits at which the current is minimized by a certain amount, say, $\frac{1}{\sqrt{2}}$ of its maximum value of $\frac{E}{R}$. This happens, as evident from Eq. (11.33), when

$$L\omega - \frac{1}{C\omega} = \pm R. \tag{11.36}$$

As shown in Fig. 11.7, let f_1 and f_2 are two frequencies between which the current $I > \frac{E}{\sqrt{2}R}$. Since the power dissipation at f_1 and f_2 is half of the maximum value, these points on the response curve are calledl as *half-power points*. For f_1 and f_2 let us replace ω in Eq. (11.36) by $(\omega_R \pm \omega')$. Then we have

$$L(\omega_R \pm \omega') - \frac{1}{C(\omega_R \pm \omega')} = \pm R. \tag{11.37}$$

Again, $L\omega_R = \dfrac{1}{C\omega_R}$

i.e., $\qquad C = \dfrac{1}{L\omega_R^2}. \tag{11.38}$

Substituting the value of C in Eq. (10.37), we get

$$L(\omega_R + \omega') - \frac{L\omega_R^2}{(\omega_R + \omega')} = R \quad \text{or,} \quad L\omega_R + L\omega' - \frac{L\omega_R}{1 + \frac{\omega'}{\omega_R}} = R$$

or, $L\omega_R + L\omega' - L\omega_R\left(1 - \dfrac{\omega'}{\omega_R}\right) = R \quad (\because \ \omega_R \gg \omega')$

or, $L\omega_R + L\omega' - L\omega_R + L\omega' = R \quad \text{or,} \ \ 2L\omega' = R.$

$\therefore \qquad \omega' = \dfrac{R}{2L}.$ \hfill (11.39)

Now substituting the value of ω', we have

$$f_1 = \frac{\omega_R - \omega'}{2\pi}$$

$$= f_R - \frac{R}{4\pi L} \tag{11.40}$$

and $f_2 = \dfrac{\omega_R + \omega'}{2\pi}$

$$= f_R + \frac{R}{4\pi L}. \tag{11.41}$$

$\therefore \qquad f_2 - f_1 = \Delta f$

$$= \frac{R}{2\pi L}. \tag{11.42}$$

Further by Eq. (11.35), we have

$$Q_R = \frac{L\omega_R}{R} = \frac{L \cdot 2\pi f_R}{R}$$

$\therefore \qquad f_R = \dfrac{Q_R R}{2\pi L}.$ \hfill (11.43)

Dividing Eq. (11.43) by Eq. (11.42),

$$\frac{f_R}{\Delta f} = \frac{Q_R R}{2\pi L} \cdot \frac{2\pi L}{R}$$

$$= Q_R. \tag{11.44}$$

Eq. (11.44) gives the selectivity of the circuit for a variation of supply frequency. In practice, the supply frequency is altered and the difference in frequency Δf between the half-power points is calculated. When the resonance frequency f_R is divided by this quantity, the Q for the circuit is obtained.

Sometimes the supply frequency is kept constant and the tuning capacitance is varied for getting the Q-value. If C_R is the capacitance at resonance, then the required relation is

$$\frac{C_R}{\Delta C} = Q_R. \tag{11.45}$$

11.6   a.c. Bridge Circuits

The principle of Wheatstone bridge can also be applied for an a.c. source. Analysis of this circuit proceeds similarly as in d.c., except that here complex impedances and currents are used. The detector is a tuned vibration galvanometer or a telephone receiver. At balance, the voltage across the detector is zero and so

$$\frac{\mathbf{Z}_1}{\mathbf{Z}_2} = \frac{\mathbf{Z}_3}{\mathbf{Z}_4}, \tag{11.46}$$

where $\mathbf{Z}_1$, $\mathbf{Z}_2$, $\mathbf{Z}_3$ and $\mathbf{Z}_4$ are the vector impedances of the branches.

The balance condition of Eq. (11.46) involves the equality of two complex numbers. Such independent balance adjustment of both real and imaginary parts are essential in a.c. bridge circuits. This will be evident from the consideration of the generalized Wheatstone network as shown in Fig. 11.8.

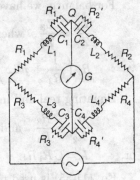

Fig. 11.8

For balance, we can write,

$$\frac{R_1 + jL_1\omega + \frac{R_1'}{1+jC_1R_1'\omega}}{R_2 + jL_2\omega + \frac{R_2'}{1+jC_2R_2'\omega}} = \frac{R_3 + jL_3\omega + \frac{R_3'}{1+jC_3R_3'\omega}}{R_4 + jL_4\omega + \frac{R_4'}{1+JC_4R_4'\omega}}.$$

(a) If $L_1 = L_2 = L_3 = L_4 = 0$ and $R_1' = R_2' = R_3' = R_4' = 0$,

we have $\dfrac{R_1}{R_2} = \dfrac{R_3}{R_4}$. $\hfill$ (11.47)

(b) If $R_1 = R_2 = 0$, $L_3 = L_4 = 0$ and $R_1' = R_2' = R_3' = R_4' = 0$,

we have $\dfrac{jL_1\omega}{jL_2\omega} = \dfrac{R_3}{R_4}$

or, $\dfrac{L_1}{L_2} = \dfrac{R_3}{R_4}$. $\hfill$ (11.48)

(c) If $R_1 = R_2 = 0$, $L_1 = L_2 = L_3 = L_4 = 0$ and $R_1' = R_2' = \infty$, $R_3' = R_4' = 0$,

we have $\dfrac{\frac{1}{jC_1\omega}}{\frac{1}{jC_2\omega}} = \dfrac{R_3}{R_4}$

or, $\dfrac{C_2}{C_1} = \dfrac{R_3}{R_4}$. $\hfill$ (11.49)

(d) If $L_3 = L_4 = 0$ and $R_1' = R_2' = R_3' = 0$,

we have $\dfrac{R_1 + jL_1\omega}{R_2 + jL_2\omega} = \dfrac{R_3}{R_4}$

or, $R_1R_4 + jL_1\omega R_4 = R_3R_2 + jL_2\omega R_3.$ $\hfill$ (11.50)

Equating real and imaginary parts of Eq. (11.50), we have

$$R_1R_4 = R_3R_2$$

or, $\dfrac{R_1}{R_2} = \dfrac{R_3}{R_4}$ $\hfill$ (11.51)

and $L_1\omega R_4 = L_2\omega R_3$

or, $\dfrac{L_1}{L_2} = \dfrac{R_3}{R_4}$. $\hfill$ (11.52)

By Eqs. (11.51) and (11.52),

$$\frac{R_1}{R_2} = \frac{R_3}{R_4} = \frac{L_1}{L_2}.$$ $\hfill$ (11.53)

11.6.1 Inductance Bridge

(i) Maxwell's bridge : The circuit diagram of Maxwell's bridge is shown in Fig. 11.9. It is a very early form of bridge used for measurement of inductance in terms of capacitor and resistances.

For balance, we have

$$\frac{Z_1}{Z_2} = \frac{Z_3}{Z_4}, \quad \text{where} \quad \frac{1}{Z_2} = \frac{1}{R_2} + jC\omega.$$

$$\therefore \qquad R_1\left(\frac{1}{R_2} + jC\omega\right) = \frac{R_3 + jL\omega}{R_4}. \tag{11.54}$$

Equating real and imaginary quantities of Eq. (11.54), we get

$$\frac{R_1}{R_2} = \frac{R_3}{R_4} \quad \text{and} \quad CR_1 = \frac{L}{R_4}$$

or, $\qquad L = CR_1 R_4.$ \hfill (11.55)

Eq. (11.55) is used to calculate the inductance.

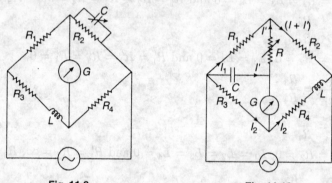

Fig. 11.9   Fig. 11.10

(ii) Anderson's bridge : It is one of the most accurate methods for measuring inductance over a wide range. The circuit diagram of the bridge is shown in Fig. 11.10. For simplicity, let R_4 include the resistance of the inductor L. Then considering Fig. 11.10, we have

$$\mathbf{I}_1 R_1 + (\mathbf{I}_1 + \mathbf{I}')R_2 = \mathbf{I}_2(R_3 + R_4 + jL\omega) \tag{11.56}$$

$$\mathbf{I}_1 R_1 = \mathbf{I}'\left(R + \frac{1}{jC\omega}\right), \tag{11.57}$$

and $\qquad \dfrac{\mathbf{I}'}{jC\omega} = \mathbf{I}_2 R_3.$ \hfill (11.58)

From Eq. (11.57),

$$\mathbf{I}_1 = \mathbf{I}'\left(\frac{R}{R_1} + \frac{1}{jC\omega R_1}\right). \tag{11.59}$$

From Eq. (11.58),

$$\mathbf{I}_2 = \frac{\mathbf{I}'}{jC\omega R_3}. \tag{11.60}$$

Now, Eq. (11.56) can be written as

$$\mathbf{I}_1(R_1 + R_2) + \mathbf{I}'R_2 = \mathbf{I}_2(R_3 + R_4 + jL\omega)$$

or, $\quad \mathbf{I}'\left(\dfrac{R}{R_1} + \dfrac{1}{jC\omega R_1}\right)(R_1 + R_2) + \mathbf{I}'R_2$

$$= \frac{\mathbf{I}'}{jC\omega R_3}(R_3 + R_4 + jL\omega) \quad \text{(putting value of } \mathbf{I}_1 \text{ and } \mathbf{I}_2)$$

or, $\dfrac{(R_1+R_2)R}{R_1} + \dfrac{(R_1+R_2)}{jC\omega R_1} + R_2 = \dfrac{R_3+R_4}{jC\omega R_3} + \dfrac{L}{CR_3}.$ (11.61)

Equating imaginary parts of Eq. (11.61),

$$\dfrac{R_1+R_2}{R_1} = \dfrac{R_3+R_4}{R_3}$$

or, $\dfrac{R_1}{R_2} = \dfrac{R_3}{R_4}$ (11.62)

Equating real parts of Eq. (11.61),

$$\dfrac{(R_1+R_2)R}{R_1} + R_2 = \dfrac{L}{CR_3}.$$

or, $L = CR_3\left[\dfrac{(R_1+R_2)R}{R_1} + R_2\right] = CR_3\left[\left(1+\dfrac{R_2}{R_1}\right)R + R_2\right]$

$$= C\left[\left(R_3 + \dfrac{R_2 R_3}{R_1}\right)R + R_2 R_3\right].$$ (11.63)

From Eq. (11.62), we have $\dfrac{R_2 R_3}{R_1} = R_4$

and hence by Eq. (11.63),

$$L = C[(R_3+R_4)R + R_2 R_3].$$ (11.64)

Using Eq. (11.64) the inductance L can be found out.

11.6.2 Capacitance Bridge

Schering bridge : The circuit diagram of the bridge is shown in Fig. 11.11. It is one of the best methods of determining the capacitance C_1 in terms of the known capacitance C_3. C_4 is a variable capacitor in the circuit.

For balance we have

$$\dfrac{\mathbf{Z}_1}{\mathbf{Z}_2} = \dfrac{\mathbf{Z}_3}{\mathbf{Z}_4} \quad \text{or,} \quad \dfrac{\frac{1}{jC_1\omega}+R_1}{R_2} = \dfrac{1}{jC_3\omega}\left(\dfrac{1}{R_4}+jC_4\omega\right)$$

or, $\dfrac{C_3}{C_1} + jC_3\omega R_1 = \dfrac{R_2}{R_4} + jC_4\omega R_2.$ (11.65)

Equating real and imaginary parts of Eq. (11.65),

$$\dfrac{C_3}{C_1} = \dfrac{R_2}{R_4}$$

and $C_3 R_1 = C_4 R_2$, i.e., $\dfrac{C_3}{C_4} = \dfrac{R_2}{R_1}.$

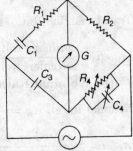

Fig. 11.11

By varying C_4 and R_4 the balance point is found. Then the value of the unknown capacitance C_1 is obtained by

$$C_1 = \dfrac{C_3 R_4}{R_2}.$$ (11.66)

11.7 Instrument Transformers

A transformer is used in an a.c. system for the measurement of voltage, current, power and energy. It is also used for the measurement of frequency, power factor and also finds a wide application in protection circuits of power systems.

Transformers used in connection with measuring instruments for measurement purposes are known as *'Instrument Transformers'*. Thus, when a transformer is used for a measurement of current, it is called *current transformer* (CT). Similarly, if a transformer is used for the measurement of voltage, it is called a *voltage* or a *potential transformer* (PT).

The arrangement for the current measurement by a CT and voltage measurement by a PT are shown in Fig. 11.12(a) and 11.12(b) respectively. In a current transformer the primary winding is so connected that the current to be measured passes through it while the secondary is connected to an ammeter. On the other hand, in a potential transformer, the primary is connected to the voltage

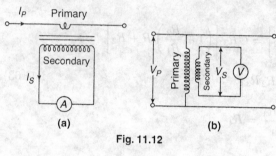

Fig. 11.12

to be measured and the secondary to a voltmeter. In actual practice, the CT steps down the current to the level of an ammeter and the PT steps down the voltage to the level of a voltmeter. The extension of range, however, could be achieved by use of shunts for currents and multipliers for voltage measurements.

11.7.1   Advantages of Instrument Transformers

The instrument transformers have many advantages, some of which are :

(i) If instruments are used in connection with an instrument transformer, their readings do not depend upon their constants (L, C, R).

(ii) Very cheap moderate rating instruments can be used for measuring large current and high voltages.

(iii) Instruments and meters can be standardized so that the overall cost reduces. Several instruments can be operated from a single instrument transformer.

11.7.2   Some Definitions

(a) Transformation Ratio : It is the ratio of the magnitude of the primary phaser to that of the secondary phaser. Thus,

$$\text{Transformation Ratio, } R = \frac{\text{primary phaser}}{\text{secondary phaser}} = \frac{\text{primary current}}{\text{secondary current}} \text{ (for CT)}$$

$$\text{or, } R = \frac{\text{primary voltage}}{\text{secondary voltage}} \text{ (for PT).}$$

(b) Nominal Ratio : It can be defined as

$$\text{Nominal Ratio, } K_n = \frac{\text{rated primary current}}{\text{rated secondary current}} \text{ (for CT)}$$

$$\text{or, } K_n = \frac{\text{rated primary voltage}}{\text{rated secondary voltage}} \text{ (for PT).}$$

(c) Turns Ratio : It can be defined as

$$\text{Turns Ratio, } n = \frac{\text{no. of turns of secondary winding}}{\text{no. of turns of primary winding}} \text{ (for CT)}$$

$$\text{or, } n = \frac{\text{no. of turns of primary winding}}{\text{no. of turns of secondary winding}} \text{ (for PT).}$$

(d) Ratio Correction Factor : It can be defined as

$$\text{Ratio Correction Factor} = \frac{\text{transformation ratio}}{\text{nominal ratio}} = \frac{R}{K_n}.$$

(e) Burden : We can write, total secondary burden

$$= \frac{(\text{secondary induced voltage})^2}{\text{impedance of secondary circuit including impedance of secondary winding}}$$

and secondary burden due to load

$$= \frac{(\text{secondary terminal voltage})^2}{\text{impedance of load on secondary winding}}.$$

(f) Percentage Ratio Error : It can be defined as

$$\text{Percentage Ratio Error} = \frac{\text{nomial ratio} - \text{actual ratio}}{\text{actual ratio}} \times 100 = \frac{K_n - R}{R} \times 100.$$

11.7.3 Current Transformers

It is used with its primary winding connected in series with line carrying the current to be measured. Since the primary is made by a very few turns, so there is no appreciable voltage across it. Its secondary has large number of turns which is exactly determined by the turns ratio. A circuit diagram for the measurement of current and power with a current transformer is shown in Fig. 11.13. The ammeter or the wattmeter current coil is connected directly across the secondary terminals.

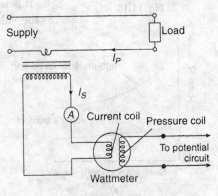

Fig. 11.13

Construction : These are of two different types, viz. (i) wound type and (ii) bar type. In the first type, there is an arrangement of primary winding of more than one full turn wound on a core. In the second type, on the other hand, the primary winding consists of a bar of suitable

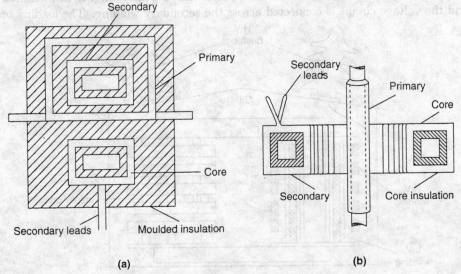

(a)

(b)

Fig. 11.14

size and material forming an integral part of the transformer. Figs. 11.14(a) and 11.14(b) show respectively the wound type and bar type transformers.

11.7.4   Characteristics of Current Transformers

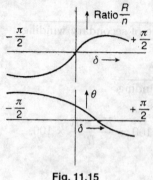

Fig. 11.15

The variation of transformation ratio $\left(\frac{k}{n}\right)$ and phase angle (θ) with δ is shown in Fig. 11.15, where δ represents the angle between secondary induced voltage and secondary current. Variation of ratio R with secondary current is presented in Fig. 11.16(a), while in Fig. 11.16(b) how the phase angle varies with the secondary current has been shown.

These curves are achieved on the assumption that the magnitude of the secondary impedance remains constant.

It is seen from the figure that for negative values of δ, the values of θ are always positive.

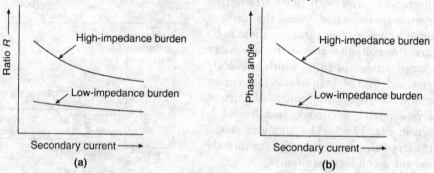

Fig. 11.16

11.7.5   Potential Transformers

Its primary winding is connected across the lines carrying the voltage to be measured and the voltage circuit is connected across the secondary winding. The loading of

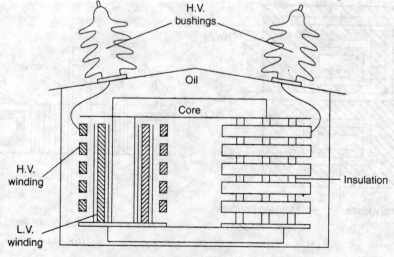

Fig. 11.17

a potential transformer is always small. The design and construction of a potential transformer are similar to those of the power transformer. However, compared to a power transformer a potential transformer has larger core. These are able to carry loads on a thermal basis many times greater than their rated loads. The primary and secondary windings are coaxial to reduce the leakage reactance to a minimum. For oil-filled potential transformers which reduce the transformer size considerably, oil-filled bushings are usually used. Cotton tape and varnished cambric are used as an insulation. A 2-winding single-phase potential transformer is presented in Fig. 11.17.

Capacitive Potential Transformers : If the voltage is above 100 kV (phase), the conventional electromagnetic type of potential transformer becomes too expensive due to insulation requirement. A less expensive capacitive potential transformer can then be used for the purpose. It consists of a capacitance potential divider used in addition to a conventional auxiliary transformer as shown in Fig. 11.18. In this arrangement the capacitance potential divider steps down the voltage to be measured.

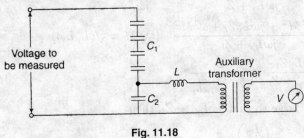

Fig. 11.18

11.7.6   Ideal Transformer

A transformer in electrical power circuit is normally used to either step up or step down a voltage by its two multiturn coils inductively coupled with each other. Any practical transformer has certain losses such as, eddy current loss, hysteresis loss, copper loss, flux leakage, etc. In an ideal transformer all the magnetic flux from the primary winding is intercepted by the secondary winding. We have considered below what is meant by an ideal transformer.

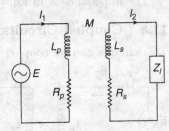

Fig. 11.19

In Fig. 11.19 let the two coils, primary and secondary, be wound on a common magnetic core whose inductances are respectively L_p and L_s. Then,

$$\frac{L_p}{L_s} = \left(\frac{N_p}{N_s}\right)^2, \tag{11.67}$$

where N_p and N_s are the number of turns in the coils.

If all the magnetic flux set up by the first coil links with the other, then the mutual inductance M is given by

$$M = \sqrt{L_p L_s}. \tag{11.68}$$

In the figure, as shown, the primary coil is connected to a generator of e.m.f. **E** while the secondary coil is connected to an impedance Z_t. By applying Kirchhoff's second law to the two meshes, we have

$$(R_p + j\omega L_p)\mathbf{I}_1 - j\omega M \mathbf{I}_2 = \mathbf{E} \tag{11.69}$$

and $(R_s + j\omega L_s + Z_l)\mathbf{I}_2 - j\omega M \mathbf{I}_1 = 0.$ $\hspace{2cm}$ (11.70)

From Eq. (11.70), we get

$$\mathbf{I}_2 = \frac{j\omega M \mathbf{I}_1}{R_s + j\omega L_s + Z_l}. \tag{11.71}$$

Substituting the value of $\mathbf{I}_2$ in Eq. (11.69),

$$(R_p + j\omega L_p)\mathbf{I}_1 + \frac{\omega^2 M^2 \mathbf{I}_1}{R_s + j\omega L_s + Z_l} = \mathbf{E}$$

or, $(R_p + j\omega L_p) + \dfrac{\omega^2 M^2}{R_s + j\omega L_s + Z_l} = \dfrac{\mathbf{E}}{\mathbf{I}_1}.$ $\hspace{1cm}$ (11.72)

If the resistance is negligibly small compared with the inductances of the winding, then the impedance viewed by the generator at the primary terminals is

$$Z = j\omega L_p + \frac{\omega^2 M^2}{j\omega L_s + Z_l} = \frac{-\omega^2 L_p L_s + j\omega L_p Z_l + \omega^2 M^2}{j\omega L_s + Z_l}$$

$$= \frac{-\omega^2 M^2 + j\omega L_p Z_l + \omega^2 M^2}{j\omega L_s + Z_l} \quad (\because M = \sqrt{(L_p L_s)})$$

$$= \frac{j\omega L_p Z_l}{j\omega L_p + Z_l} = \frac{Z_l}{\frac{L_s}{L_p} + \frac{Z_l}{j\omega L_p}}.$$

If L_p is very large so that $j\omega L_p \gg Z_l$, then

$$Z = \frac{Z_l}{L_s/L_p} = \left(\frac{L_p}{L_s}\right) \cdot Z_l$$

$$= \left(\frac{N_p}{N_s}\right)^2 \cdot Z_l \text{ [by Eq. (11.67)]}. \tag{11.73}$$

The impedance Z in Eq. (11.73) gives an expression for an ideal transformer.

11.8 Coupled Circuits

Two circuits can be coupled to each other by using a capacity or an inductance.

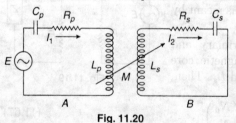
Fig. 11.20

They may also be coupled magnetically by mutual inductance. The coupled circuits are widely used for the reception of radio-signals. We are considering below the theory of magnetic coupling circuits.

Let $\mathbf{I}_1, \mathbf{I}_2$ be the currents and $\mathbf{Z}_1, \mathbf{Z}_2$ be the impedances of the two circuits A and B respectively as shown in Fig. 11.20.

Applying Kirchhoff's law we can write by considering the figure,

$$\mathbf{Z}_1 \mathbf{I}_1 + j\omega M \mathbf{I}_2 = \mathbf{E} \tag{11.74}$$

and $\mathbf{Z}_2 \mathbf{I}_2 + j\omega M \mathbf{I}_1 = 0,$ $\hspace{3cm}$ (11.75)

where $\mathbf{E}$ is the applied sinusoidal e.m.f. In the above equations,

$$\mathbf{Z}_1 = R_p + j\left(L_p \omega - \frac{1}{C_p \omega}\right) \tag{11.76}$$

and
$$\mathbf{Z}_2 = R_s + j\left(L_s\omega - \frac{1}{C_s\omega}\right). \tag{11.77}$$

From Eq. (11.75), we have
$$\mathbf{I}_2 = \frac{-j\omega M\mathbf{I}_1}{\mathbf{Z}_2}. \tag{11.78}$$

Putting the value of $\mathbf{I}_2$ from Eq. (11.78) in Eq. (11.74), we get
$$\mathbf{I}_1\left(\mathbf{Z}_1 + \frac{M^2\omega^2}{\mathbf{Z}_2}\right) = \mathbf{E} \tag{11.79}$$

or,
$$\mathbf{I}_1 = \frac{\mathbf{E}}{\left(\mathbf{Z}_1 + \frac{M^2\omega^2}{\mathbf{Z}_2}\right)} \tag{11.79a}$$

and then from Eq. (11.78), we get
$$\mathbf{I}_2 = -\frac{j\omega M\mathbf{E}}{\mathbf{Z}_2}\bigg/\left(\mathbf{Z}_1 + \frac{M^2\omega^2}{\mathbf{Z}_2}\right)$$

$$= -\frac{j\omega M\mathbf{E}}{\mathbf{Z}_1\mathbf{Z}_2 + M^2\omega^2}. \tag{11.80}$$

Let us put
$$\left.\begin{array}{l}\mathbf{Z}_1 = R_p + jX_1 \\ \text{and} \quad \mathbf{Z}_2 = R_s + jX_2\end{array}\right\}, \tag{11.81}$$

where $\quad X_1 = L_p\omega - \dfrac{1}{C_p\omega} \quad$ and $\quad X_2 = L_s\omega - \dfrac{1}{C_s\omega}$.

From Eq. (10.79), we then have
$$\mathbf{I}_1\left[(R_p + jX_1) + \frac{M^2\omega^2}{(R_s + jX_2)}\right] = \mathbf{E}$$

or,
$$\mathbf{I}_1\left[(R_p + jX_1) + \frac{M^2\omega^2(R_s - jX_2)}{R_s^2 + X_2^2}\right] = \mathbf{E}$$

or,
$$\mathbf{I}_1\left[\left(R_p + \frac{M^2\omega^2 R_s}{R_s^2 + X_2^2}\right) + j\left(X_1 - \frac{M^2\omega^2 X_2}{R_s^2 + X_2^2}\right)\right] = \mathbf{E}. \tag{11.82}$$

Similarly, from Eq. (11.80), we have
$$\mathbf{I}_2 = -\frac{j\omega M\mathbf{E}}{(R_p + jX_1)(R_s + jX_2) + M^2\omega^2}. \tag{11.83}$$

From Eq. (11.82), we find that the primary current $\mathbf{I}_1$ and the e.m.f. $\mathbf{E}$ will be in phase when we put

(i) $X_1 = X_2 = 0 \quad$ and $\quad$ (ii) $X_1 - \dfrac{M^2\omega^2 X_2}{R_s^2 + X_2^2} = 0$.

From condition (i) above, we get
$$L_p\omega - \frac{1}{C_p\omega} = L_s\omega - \frac{1}{C_s\omega} = 0 \quad \text{or,} \quad \omega^2 = \omega_0^2 = \frac{1}{L_pC_p} = \frac{1}{L_sC_s}.$$

Thus we find that for $X_1 = X_2$ the natural frequency of the two circuits must be identical. In this case, therefore, we can write,

$$\mathbf{I}_1 = \frac{\mathbf{E}}{R_p + \frac{M^2\omega_0^2}{R_s}}$$

$$= \frac{R_s\mathbf{E}}{R_pR_s + M^2\omega_0^2} \tag{11.84}$$

and from Eq. (11.80),

$$\mathbf{I}_2 = -\frac{jM\omega_0\mathbf{E}}{R_pR_s + M^2\omega_0^2}. \tag{11.85}$$

From Eq. (11.85), we find for $M = 0$ and $M = \infty, \mathbf{I}_2 = 0$.

The condition for optimum coupling is obtained for a maximum value of I_2. In that case, we have

$$\frac{\delta}{\delta M}\left[\frac{M}{R_pR_s + M^2\omega_0^2}\right] = 0 \quad \text{or,} \quad \frac{1}{R_pR_s + M^2\omega_0^2} - \frac{2M^2\omega_0^2}{(R_pR_s + M^2\omega_0^2)^2} = 0$$

or, $\quad \dfrac{1}{R_pR_s + M^2\omega_0^2}\left[1 - \dfrac{2M^2\omega_0^2}{R_pR_s + M^2\omega_0^2}\right] = 0$

or, $\quad M^2\omega_0^2 = R_pR_s. \tag{11.86}$

Now the coefficient of optimum coupling k can be expressed as

$$k = \frac{M}{\sqrt{L_pL_s}} = \sqrt{\frac{R_pR_s}{L_pL_s\omega_0^2}} = \frac{1}{\sqrt{Q_1Q_2}} \quad \text{[in terms of } Q\text{-factor]}. \tag{11.87}$$

Putting the value of $M^2\omega_0^2$ from Eq. (11.86) in Eq. (11.84), we get

$$\mathbf{I}_1 = \frac{\mathbf{E}}{2R_p} \tag{11.88}$$

and similarly from Eq. (11.85),

$$\mathbf{I}_2 = -\frac{j\mathbf{E}}{2R_pR_s}. \tag{11.89}$$

Thus we find that the phase-difference between primary and secondary currents is $\pi/2$. If we consider $R_p = R_s = R$, then

$$\left.\begin{array}{l} \mathbf{I}_1 = \dfrac{\mathbf{E}}{2R} \\[2mm] \text{and} \quad \mathbf{I}_2 = -\dfrac{j\mathbf{E}}{2R} \end{array}\right\}. \tag{11.90}$$

It is, therefore, found that the current in the primary is the same as that in the secondary and the coupled circuits are thus matched.

From condition (ii) we may be further note that when $\mathbf{I}_1$ is in phase with $\mathbf{E}$,

$$X_1 - \frac{M^2\omega^2 X_2}{R_s^2 + X_2^2} = 0.$$

Let us assume that X_1 and X_2 for the two circuits are same, i.e., $X_1 = X_2 = X$ (say). Then,

$$X^2 = M^2\omega^2 - R_s^2. \tag{11.91}$$

If we put $L_p = L_s = L$ and $C_p = C_s = C$, we get

$$\left(L\omega - \frac{1}{C\omega}\right)^2 = M^2\omega^2 - R_s^2. \tag{11.92}$$

In Eq. (11.92), if $R_s^2 \ll M\omega$, then

$$\left(L\omega - \frac{1}{C\omega}\right)^2 = M^2\omega^2$$

or, $\quad L^2\omega^2 + \dfrac{1}{C^2\omega^2} - \dfrac{2L}{C} = M^2\omega^2.$ \hfill (11.93)

Multiplying both sides of Eq. (11.93) by ω^2/L^2 and rearranging, we get

$$\omega^4 + \frac{1}{C^2 L^2} - \frac{2\omega^2}{LC} - \frac{M^2\omega^4}{L^2} = 0 \quad \text{or,} \quad \omega^4\left(1 - \frac{M^2}{L^2}\right) + \frac{1}{C^2 L^2} - \frac{2\omega^2}{LC} = 0$$

or, $\quad \omega^4(1 - k^2) - 2\omega^2\omega_0^2 + \omega_0^4 = 0, \quad$ where $k = \dfrac{M}{L}.$ \hfill (11.94)

Solving Eq. (11.94), we have

$$\omega^2 = \frac{\omega_0^2(1 \pm k)}{1 - k^2}$$

Thus the two values of ω, where the primary current is in phase with the e.m.f. is

$$\omega = \omega_1 = \frac{\omega_0}{\sqrt{1+k}} \quad \text{and} \quad \omega = \omega_2 = \frac{\omega_0}{\sqrt{1-k}}.$$

The two values of ω are possible, as evident from Eq. (11.91), when

$$M^2\omega^2 > R_s^2.$$

Thus ω_1 and ω_2 are respectively slightly smaller and greater than ω_0, the natural frequency of both the circuits.

The primary current I_1 for condition (ii) to be satisfied as given by Eq. (11.82),

$$I_1\left[R_p + \frac{M^2\omega^2 R_s}{R_s^2 + X^2}\right] = E, \text{ when } X \neq 0$$

or, $\quad I_1[R_p + R_s] = E$ [from Eq. (11.91)]

or, $\quad I_1 = \dfrac{E}{R_p + R_s}.$ \hfill (11.95)

Again, from Eq. (11.83), we have

$$
\begin{aligned}
I &= -\frac{j\omega M E}{R_p R_s - X^2 + jX(R_p + R_s) + M^2\omega^2} \\
&= -\frac{\omega M E}{X(R_p + R_s) - j(R_p R_s + M^2\omega^2 - X^2)} \\
&= -\frac{\omega M E}{X(R_p + R_s) - j(R_p R_s + M^2\omega^2 - M^2\omega^2 + R_s^2)} \\
&= -\frac{\omega M E}{(R_p + R_s)(X - jR_s)} \\
&= -\frac{\omega M E e^{j\alpha}}{(R_p + R_s)\sqrt{(X^2 + R_s^2)}} \quad \left[\text{where } \alpha = \tan^{-1}\frac{R_s}{X}\right].
\end{aligned}
$$

Again, since $X^2 = M^2\omega^2 - R_s^2$,

$$I_2 = -\frac{E e^{j\alpha}}{R_p + R_s}. \hfill (11.96)$$

Discussion : (i) If we put $M^2\omega^2 = X^2 + R_s^2$, two peaks of both primary and secondary currents separated by angular frequencies ω_1 and ω_2 are obtained. For small value of the coefficient of coupling k, the separation $\delta\omega$ can be written as

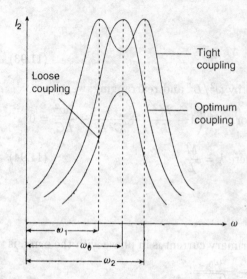

Fig. 11.21

$$\delta\omega = \omega_2 - \omega_1$$

$$= \omega_0 \left(1 + \frac{k}{2}\right) - \omega_0 \left(1 - \frac{k}{2}\right)$$

$$= \omega_0 k. \tag{11.97}$$

It is thus seen that with the increase of the value of k, the separation increases.

In this condition the magnitude of the primary and the secondary currents is

$$\mathbf{I}_1 = \mathbf{I}_2 = \frac{\mathbf{E}}{R_p + R_s}. \tag{11.98}$$

(ii) The two peaks will merge together at ω_0, if $X = 0$.

When $M^2\omega_0^2 = R_p R_s$, the optimum coupling will occur for which

$$\mathbf{I}_1 = \frac{\mathbf{E}}{2R_p} \tag{11.99}$$

and $\quad \mathbf{I}_2 = -\dfrac{j\mathbf{E}}{2\sqrt{R_p R_s}}.$ $\hspace{3cm}$ (11.100)

The coupling is so adjusted that there is almost a uniform response over a narrow band of frequencies expressed as $\frac{\omega_2 - \omega_1}{2\pi}$. Such tuning is called *band-pass tuning*. A plot of ω versus $\mathbf{I}_2$ is presented in Fig. 11.21. The bandwidth in an IF transformer is generally about 8 kHz.

11.9   Electric Shielding

When a conducting sheet is kept in front of an electromagnet excited by using an a.c., the effect of variation of the magnetic field is found to be reduced greatly. This reduction is due to the eddy current generated in the sheet.

In Fig. 11.22, let A be the coil and B the conductor. The coil A is connected with an alternating source of e.m.f. as shown.

Let L represent the self-inductance of B and M represents the mutual inductance between A and B. If I_1 and I_2 are the instantaneous current in A and B respectively, then we can write,

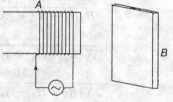

Fig. 11.22

$$L\frac{dI_2}{dt} + M\frac{dI_1}{dt} + RI_2 = 0, \tag{11.101}$$

where R is the resistance of B. If R is neglected, the Eq. (11.101) can be simplified as

$$\frac{d}{dt}(LI_2 + MI_1) = 0$$

or, $\quad LI_2 + MI_1 = \text{constant}.$ $\hfill (11.102)$

It is thus seen that the variation of flux at B is reduced to zero. On the other side of B, any point is practically free from variation of flux. If the separation between A and B is increased, the flux change will be small at all the points near B.

Repulsion : If I_1 be the current in the coil A, then we can write,

$$I_1 = I_0 \sin \omega t. \hfill (11.103)$$

The induced e.m.f. on the conductor, $B = -M \dfrac{dI_1}{dt} = -\omega M I_0 \cos \omega t.$

The instantaneous current in B is given by

$$I_2 = -\frac{\omega M I_0 \cos(\omega t - \alpha)}{\sqrt{L^2\omega^2 + R^2}}, \hfill (11.104)$$

where $\quad \alpha = \tan^{-1} \dfrac{L\omega}{R}.$

If F represents the average force between A and B, then we can write,

$$F \propto \frac{1}{T} \int_0^T I_1 I_2 dt$$

$$= \frac{C}{T} \int_0^T I_1 I_2 dt \quad [\because \; C = \text{constant}] \hfill (11.105)$$

Substituting the values of I_1 and I_2 from Eqs. (11.103) and (11.104) to Eq. (11.105), we get

$$F = \frac{C}{T} \int_0^T \frac{I_0 \sin \omega t \times \{-\omega M I_0 \cos(\omega t - \alpha)dt\}}{\sqrt{L^2\omega^2 + R^2}}$$

$$= -\frac{C I_0^2 \omega M}{T\sqrt{L^2\omega^2 + R^2}} \int_0^T (\sin \omega t \cos \omega t \cos \alpha + \sin^2 \omega t \sin \alpha)dt$$

$$= -\frac{C I_0^2 \omega M}{T\sqrt{L^2\omega^2 + R^2}} \cdot \frac{T}{2} \sin \alpha = -\frac{C I_0^2 \omega M \sin \alpha}{2\sqrt{L^2\omega^2 + R^2}} = -\frac{C I_0^2 \omega M}{2\sqrt{L^2\omega^2 + R^2}} \cdot \frac{L\omega}{\sqrt{L^2\omega^2 + R^2}}$$

$$= -\frac{C I_0^2 \omega^2 M L}{2(L^2\omega^2 + R^2)}. \hfill (11.106)$$

The negative sign in Eq. (11.106) indicates a force of repulsion. When L is very small so that $L^2\omega^2$ is ignored in comparison to R, then

$$F = -\frac{C I_0^2 \omega^2 M L}{2R^2}. \hfill (11.107)$$

It is seen from Eq. (11.107) that for a smaller resistance and a larger frequency, the force of repulsion will be greater.

Examples

1. Express the equation of the alternating e.m.f. for 230 V, 50 cycles/second a.c. supply lines. Find the period of its cyclic variation.

   Solution : We know that if E_0 be the maximum e.m.f., then at any instant t the instantaneous e.m.f. E is given by

   $$E = E_0 \sin \omega t = E_0 \sin 2\pi f t.$$

   Here, $\quad E_0 = \sqrt{2} \times 230 = 325.22$ volts

and $\omega = 2\pi f = 100\pi$ ($\because$ $f = 50$ cycles/second).

$\therefore$ the equation of the alternating e.m.f. is $E = 325.22 \sin 100\pi t$.

The time period, $T = \dfrac{1}{f} = \dfrac{1}{50} = 0.02$ second.

2. The equation of an alternating current is $i = 50 \sin 400\pi t$ ampere. What are the frequency and the peak value of the current? What is the r.m.s. value? Calculate also the form factor of the current.

Solution : We know that the general equation of an alternating current is

$$I = I_0 \sin \omega t = I_0 \sin 2\pi f t.$$

Comparing this with the equation given, viz.,

$$i = 50 \sin 400\pi t,$$

we get $2\pi f = 400\pi$.

   (i) The frequency, $f = \mathbf{200\ cycles/second}$.

   (ii) Peak value of current, $I_0 = \mathbf{50\ amperes}$.

   (iii) The r.m.s. value of current, $I_{\mathrm{rms}} = \dfrac{I_0}{\sqrt{2}} = \dfrac{50}{\sqrt{2}} = \mathbf{35.4\ amperes}$.

   (iv) The form factor of current, $F_{\mathrm{current}} = \dfrac{I_{\mathrm{rms}}}{I_{\mathrm{mean}}}$.

Now, $I_{\mathrm{mean}} = \dfrac{2I_0}{\pi} = \dfrac{100}{\pi}$.

$\therefore$ $F_{\mathrm{current}} = \dfrac{50/\sqrt{2}}{100/\pi} = \dfrac{\pi}{2\sqrt{2}} = \mathbf{1.11}$.

3. A 220-volt (r.m.s.) (pure sine form) 50-cycle a.c. is applied to a current through an ideal rectifier which cuts out completely one-half cycle but offers no impedance to the other half. Calculate the average value of the rectified voltage. Determine the amplitude corresponding to the fundamental frequency.

Solution : We have the r.m.s. value $= \dfrac{E_0}{\sqrt{2}} = 220$ volts.

$\therefore$ $E_0 = 220\sqrt{2} = \mathbf{311.08\ volts}$.

This is the amplitude corresponding to the fundamental frequency.

Again, average rectified voltage $= \dfrac{E_0}{\pi} = \dfrac{311.08}{\pi} = \mathbf{99.07\ volts}$.

4. An alternating current of 50 cycles/second has a maximum value of 100 amperes. Find its value $\frac{1}{600}$ second after the instant the current is zero.

Solution : We have $I = I_0 \sin \omega t = I_0 \sin 2\pi f t$.

Here, $I_0 = 100$ amperes, $f = 50$ cycles/second and $t = \dfrac{1}{600}$ second.

$\therefore$ $I = 100 \sin\left(2\pi \times 50 \times \dfrac{1}{600}\right) = 100 \sin \dfrac{\pi}{6}$

$= 100 \sin 30° = \mathbf{50\ amperes}$ $\left(\because\ \sin 30° = \dfrac{1}{2}\right)$.

5. An alternating e.m.f. is represented by the equation $E = 200 \sin 100\pi t$ volts. What are the frequency and the amplitude of the e.m.f.? If this e.m.f. is applied across a series combination of resistance of 20 ohms and inductance 0.15 henry, calculate the r.m.s. value of the current in the circuit and the phase lag of the current.

Solution : The equation of the e.m.f. at any instant of time t can be written as

$$E = E_0 \sin 2\pi f t.$$

Here, in the given problem, the alternating e.m.f. is represented by the equation,

$$E = 200 \sin 100\pi t.$$

Comparing we get $E_0 = 200$ volts   and $f = \dfrac{100}{2} = 50$ cycles/second.

Again, the r.m.s. value of current,

$$I_{\text{rms}} = \frac{I_0}{\sqrt{2}} = \frac{E_0}{\sqrt{R^2 + L^2\omega^2}} \times \frac{1}{\sqrt{2}}$$

Here, $R = 20$ ohms, $\omega = 2\pi f = 2 \times 3.14 \times 50 = 314$ cycles/second,

$L = 0.15$ henry.

$$\therefore \quad \sqrt{R^2 + L^2\omega^2} = \sqrt{(20)^2 + (0.15 \times 314)^2}$$

$$= \sqrt{(20)^2 + (47.10)^2} = 51.17 \text{ ohms.}$$

Hence we get, $I_{\text{rms}} = \dfrac{200}{\sqrt{2} \times 51.17} = \dfrac{200}{72.35} = \mathbf{2.76 \ amperes.}$

and $\alpha = \tan^{-1}\dfrac{L\omega}{R} = \tan^{-1}\dfrac{47.1}{20} = \tan^{-1} 2.355 = \mathbf{67°.}$

6. An electric lamp of resistance 10 ohms operates on 100 volts d.c. It is required to run the lamp from 220 volts, 50 cycles a.c. supply. Calculate the inductance of the choke coil necessary.

Solution : We have $I_0 = \dfrac{E_0}{\sqrt{R^2 + L^2\omega^2}} = \dfrac{E_0}{\sqrt{R^2 + 4\pi^2 L^2 f^2}}.$

Here, the current required by the lamp,

$$I_0 = \frac{100}{10} = 10 \text{ amperes.}$$

Now, $E_0 = 220$ volts, $R = 10$ ohms, $f = 50$ c.p.s.

$$\therefore \quad 10 = \frac{220}{\sqrt{100 + 4\pi^2 \times (50)^2 \times L^2}} \quad \text{or,} \quad L = \mathbf{6.236 \times 10^{-2} \ henry.}$$

7. An alternating voltage of 100 volts at a frequency of 25 c.p.s. is applied to a circuit containing a resistance of 1.5 ohms and an inductance of 0.01 henry in series. Find the current flowing, the angle of lag and the potential difference across the inductance and resistance.

Solution : Here, $R = 1.5$ ohms, $L = 0.01$ henry, $E_0 = 100$ volts, $f = 25$ c.p.s.

(i) The current,

$$I_0 = \frac{E_0}{\sqrt{R^2 + 4\pi^2 L^2 f^2}} = \frac{100}{\sqrt{(1.5)^2 + 4\pi^2 (0.01)^2 (25)^2}}$$

$$= \frac{100}{2.171} = \textbf{46.06 amperes}.$$

(ii) $\tan \alpha = \dfrac{d\omega}{R} = \dfrac{2\pi f L}{R} = \dfrac{2\pi \times 25 \times 0.01}{1.5} = \dfrac{\pi}{3} = 1.0476.$

$\therefore \quad \alpha = \textbf{46°19}'.$

(iii) Voltage across the resistance $= I_0 \times R = 46.06 \times 1.5 = 69.09$ volts.

(iv) Voltage across the inductance $= I_0 \times L\omega = 46.06 \times 0.01 \times 2\pi \times 25$

$$= \frac{46.06 \times \pi}{2} = \textbf{72.31 volts}.$$

8. An alternating voltage of 100 volts (virtual) is applied to a circuit of resistance 0.5 ohm and self-inductance 0.01 henry, the frequency being 50 cycles per second. What will be the reading of the ammeter included in the circuit.

   Solution : We know that,

   $$\frac{I_0}{\sqrt{2}} = \text{virtual current } I \quad \text{and} \quad \frac{E_0}{\sqrt{2}} = \text{virtual volts } E.$$

   Thus, I (virtual current) $= \dfrac{E \text{ (virtual volt)}}{\sqrt{L^2\omega^2 + R^2}} = \dfrac{E}{\sqrt{L^2(2\pi f)^2 + R^2}}$

   $$= \frac{100}{\sqrt{4\pi^2(50)^2(0.01)^2 + (0.5)^2}} = \textbf{31.4 amperes}.$$

9. An alternating e.m.f. 220 volts at 60 cycles is applied to a coil of 20 ohms resistance and 40 millihenries inductance. Find the current, the angle by which the current lags behind the e.m.f. and the power factor of the circuit.

   Solution : Here, $R = 20$ ohms, $L = 40$ millihenries $= \dfrac{40}{1000} = \dfrac{1}{25}$ henry,

   $f = 60$ cycles/second.

   Now, $\quad I = \dfrac{I_0}{\sqrt{2}} = \dfrac{E_0}{\sqrt{2}} \times \dfrac{I}{Z}$

   where, $\quad Z = \sqrt{R^2 + L^2\omega^2} = \sqrt{R^2 + L^2(2\pi f)^2}$

   $$= \sqrt{(20)^2 + \left(\frac{2\pi \times 60}{25}\right)^2} = \textbf{25.05 ohms}$$

   and $\quad \dfrac{E_0}{\sqrt{2}} = 200$ volts (r.m.s.).

   $\therefore$ the current, $I = \dfrac{220}{25.05} = 8.782$ amperes.

   Again, $\tan \alpha = \dfrac{L\omega}{R} = \dfrac{2\pi \times 60}{25 \times 20} = 0.7541$

   $\therefore \qquad \alpha = \textbf{37°23}'$

   and hence the power factor, $\cos \alpha = \textbf{0.7964}.$

10. Find the magnitude of the current and its phase difference with respect to the applied voltage when an alternating potential of 220 volts and 50 cycles is applied to: (i) a fan having an inductance of 0.2 henry and a resistance of 20 ohms, (ii) a choke-coil having an inductance of 5 henries and negligible resistance.

Solution : (i) The impedance of the fan,

$$Z = \sqrt{R^2 + L^2\omega^2} = \sqrt{R^2 + L^2(2\pi f)^2}$$

Here, $R = 20$ ohms, $L = 0.2$ henry, $f = 50$ cycles/second.

$$\therefore \quad Z = \sqrt{(20)^2 + (0.2)^2 \cdot (2\pi \times 50)^2} = 65.92 \text{ ohms.}$$

Hence current (virtual), $I = \dfrac{220}{65.92} = 3.336$ amperes.

The current lags behind the e.m.f. by an angle α, where

$$\tan\alpha = \frac{L\omega}{R} = \frac{20\pi}{20} = \pi. \quad \therefore \quad \alpha = 72°20'.$$

So lag in time $= \dfrac{72°20'}{360} \times \dfrac{1}{50} = 4 \times 10^{-3}$ second.

(ii) Since the resistance is negligible, we have $R = 0$

and so, $Z = X_L = L\omega = 2\pi \times 50 \times 5 = 500\pi.$

$\therefore$ the current, $I = \dfrac{220}{500\pi} = \mathbf{0.14}$ **ampere.**

Again, $\tan\alpha = \dfrac{L\omega}{R} = \dfrac{500\pi}{0} = \infty.$

$$\therefore \quad \alpha = \frac{\pi}{2} = 90°.$$

So lag in time $= \dfrac{90}{360} \times \dfrac{1}{50} = \dfrac{1}{200}$ **second.**

11. Calculate the current in a circuit consisting of a condenser of capacity 4 μF and a coil in series when the applied voltage is 220 a.c., 50 c.p.s. and the resistance and inductance are 60 ohms and 3 henries respectively. Find also the power factor of the circuit.

Solution : We have $I_0 = \dfrac{E_0}{Z} = \dfrac{E_0}{\sqrt{R^2 + \left(L\omega - \frac{1}{C\omega}\right)^2}}$, where Z is the impedance of the circuit.

Here, $C = 4 \mu F = 4 \times 10^{-6}$ farad, $E_0 = 220$ volts, $f = 50$ c.p.s.,
$R = 60$ ohms, $L = 3$ henries.

Now, $I_0 = \dfrac{220}{\sqrt{(60)^2 + \left(2\pi \times 50 \times 3 - \frac{1}{2\pi \times 50 \times 4 \times 10^{-6}}\right)^2}} = \dfrac{220}{158.8} = \mathbf{1.386}$ **A.**

Power factor,

$$\cos\alpha = \frac{R}{Z} = \frac{60}{158.8} = \mathbf{0.3780}.$$

12. A coil of resistance 20 ohms and inductance 0.15 henry is connected to 110-volt, 60-cycle mains. (i) What are the current and its phase lag? (ii) How much capacity placed in series will reduce the lag to zero?

Solution : (i) Here, $R = 20$ ohms, $L = 0.15$ henry, $f = 60$ cycles/second.

$\therefore$ impedance of the coil $= \sqrt{R^2 + L^2\omega^2}$

$$= \sqrt{(20)^2 + 4\pi^2 \times (60)^2 \times (0.15)^2} = 59.98 \text{ ohms.}$$

So the current, $I = \dfrac{110}{59.98} = \mathbf{1.834}$ **amperes**.

and $\tan\alpha = \dfrac{L\omega}{R} = \dfrac{L \cdot 2\pi f}{R} = \dfrac{0.15 \times 2\pi \times 60}{20} = \dfrac{18\pi}{20} = \mathbf{2.8274}$

$\therefore \quad \alpha = \mathbf{70°31'}.$

(ii) Since the capacity placed in series reduces the lag to zero, the condition is that of resonance.

For resonance, we have

$$L\omega = \dfrac{1}{\omega C} \quad \text{or,} \quad C = \dfrac{1}{\omega^2 L} = \dfrac{1}{4\pi^2 f^2 L}$$

$\therefore \quad C = \dfrac{1}{4\pi^2 \times (60)^2 \times 0.15} = 46 \times 10^{-6}$ farad $= 46\ \mu\text{F}$.

13. A choke coil of resistance 5 ohms and inductance 0.6 henry is connected in series with a capacitance of 10 μF. Calculate the resonant frequency and the voltage magnification of the circuit when tuned to resonance.

   Solution : Here, $R = 5$ ohms, $L = 0.6$ henry, $C = 10\ \mu\text{F} = 10 \times 10^{-6}$ farad.

   We have the resonant frequency,

   $$f = \dfrac{1}{2\pi\sqrt{LC}} = \dfrac{1}{2\pi\sqrt{0.6 \times 10 \times 10^{-6}}} = \dfrac{1}{2\pi}\sqrt{\dfrac{10^6}{6}}$$

   $= 64.98 = \mathbf{65}$ **cycles/second (approx.).**

   Again, the voltage magnification at resonance or Q-factor

   $$= \dfrac{\omega L}{R} = \dfrac{2\pi f L}{R} = \dfrac{2\pi \times 65 \times 0.6}{5} \quad \text{(putting } f = 65 \text{ cycles/second)}$$

   $= \mathbf{49}.$

14. A heating coil of resistance 2 ohms, a condenser of capacity 600 μF and a choke of inductance 0.005 henry are in series. If a p.d. of 100 volts at 50 cycles/second is applied, find (i) the current, (ii) power factor and (iii) power of the circuit.

   Solution : Here, $R = 2$ ohms, $C = 600\ \mu\text{F} = 600 \times 10^{-6}$ farad,

   $$L = 0.005 \text{ henry}, \quad f = 50 \text{ cycles/second}.$$

   Total impedance in the circuit,

   $$Z = \sqrt{R^2 + \left(L\omega - \dfrac{1}{C\omega}\right)^2} = \sqrt{4 + \left(0.005 \times 2 \times \pi \times 50 - \dfrac{10^6}{2\pi \times 50 \times 600}\right)^2}$$

   $= \sqrt{4 + (1.57 - 5.3)^2} = \mathbf{4.22}$ **ohms.**

   (i) Current $= \dfrac{100}{4.22} = \mathbf{23.7}$ **amperes.**

   (ii) Power factor, $\cos\alpha = \dfrac{R}{Z} = \dfrac{2}{4.22} = \mathbf{0.473}$.

   (iii) Power $= 100 \times 23.7 \times 0.473 = \mathbf{1121}$ **watts.**

15. What will be the current and impedance of a reactance of 300 millihenries if a 220 volts/50 cycles AC source is connected with it?

Solution : Impedance, $X_L = \omega \cdot L = 2\pi f \cdot L = 2 \times \dfrac{22}{7} \times 50 \times 300 \times 10^{-3}$ ohms

$$= 94.2 \text{ ohms (approx.)}$$

Apparent current $= \dfrac{220}{94.2} = 2.3$ **amperes (approx.).**

16. An alternating voltage of 100 volts is impressed on a series circuit having an inductance of 1 mH, a capacitance of 0.1 μF and a resistor of 50 ohms. Find (a) the resonance frequency, (b) the p.d. across the inductance and (c) the p.d. across inductor-capacitor combination at resonance. · **[C.U. 1964]**

Solution : (a) We know, resonance frequency, $f = \dfrac{1}{2\pi\sqrt{LC}}$.

$\therefore \quad f = \dfrac{1}{2\pi\sqrt{1 \times 10^{-3} \times 0.1 \times 10^{-6}}} = \dfrac{10^5}{6.28} = \mathbf{1.5 \times 10^4}$ **cycles/second.**

(b) Current in the circuit, $i = \dfrac{100}{50} = 2$ amperes.

So the p.d. due to inductor $= \omega L \cdot i = 2\pi f L \cdot i = 10^5 \times 10^{-3} \times 2$

$$= 2 \times 10^2 = \mathbf{200 \text{ volts.}}$$

(c) At the condition of resonance, $\omega L - \dfrac{1}{\omega C} = 0$

i.e., $\omega L = \dfrac{1}{\omega C}$ `or, $\omega L \cdot i = \dfrac{1}{\omega C} \cdot i$ or, $\omega L \cdot i - \dfrac{1}{\omega C} \cdot i = \mathbf{0}$.

So the p.d. of inductor and capacitor are same but they being opposite, the **combined potential will be zero.**

17. An alternating e.m.f. of r.m.s. value 100 volts and frequency 50 cycles/s is applied to a circuit consisting of an inductance of 5 henries and resistor of 1000 ohms in series. What will be the r.m.s. value of the current flowing in the circuit and its phase lag with respect to e.m.f.? What is the power of the circuit? **[C.U. (Hons.) 1962, (Pass) '88]**

Solution : Impedance of the circuit, $Z = \sqrt{(1000)^2 + (5)^2 \times 4\pi^2 \times (50)^2}$

$$= 1860 \text{ ohms.}$$

$\therefore$ r.m.s. current $= \dfrac{\text{r.m.s. e.m.f.}}{Z} = \dfrac{100}{1860} = \mathbf{0.054 \text{ A}}$.

If ϕ be the phase angle,

$$\tan\phi = \dfrac{L \cdot \omega}{R} = \dfrac{5 \times 2\pi \times 50}{1000} = 1.57 = \tan 57°30'.$$

$\therefore \quad \phi = \mathbf{57°30'}.$

We know, power $=$ r.m.s. voltage $\times$ r.m.s. current $\times \cos\phi$

$$= 100 \times 0.054 \times \cos 57°30' = 100 \times 0.054 \times 0.5373 \text{ watts}$$

$$= \mathbf{2.9 \text{ watts.}}$$

18. Find the capacity of the condenser which is to be introduced in series with a 100 volts, 50 watts lamp to light it from 200 volts (r.m.s.), 50 Hz mains. Find the phase of the current with respect to the applied voltage. **[C.U. 1984]**

Solution : Current of the lamp $= \dfrac{\text{watt}}{\text{volt}} = \dfrac{50}{100} = 0.5$ A;

Resistance of the lamp, $R = \dfrac{\text{volt}}{\text{current}} = \dfrac{100}{0.5} = 200$ ohms.

If a capacitor of C farad is used, then the impedance,

$$Z = \sqrt{R^2 + \frac{1}{\omega^2 C^2}} = \sqrt{R^2 + \frac{1}{4\pi^2 f^2 C^2}}$$

Now, current $= \dfrac{\text{r.m.s. voltage}}{Z}$

$$\therefore \ 0.5 = \frac{200}{\sqrt{R^2 + \dfrac{1}{4\pi^2 f^2 C^2}}} \quad \text{or,} \ \ R^2 + \frac{1}{4\pi^2 f^2 C^2} = (400)^2$$

$$4 \times 10^4 + \frac{1}{4 \times (3.14)^2 \times (50)^2 \times C^2} = 16 \times 10^4$$

or, $\dfrac{1}{4 \times (3.14)^2 \times (50)^2 \times C^2} = 12 \times 10^4$

$$\therefore \ C^2 = \frac{1}{4 \times (3.14)^2 \times (50)^2 \times 12 \times 10^4}$$

$$\therefore \ C = \frac{1}{2 \times 3.14 \times 50 \times 10^2 \times 2\sqrt{3}} \text{ farad} = \frac{10^6}{2 \times 3.14 \times 50 \times 10^2 \times 2\sqrt{3}} \ \mu\text{F}$$

$$= 9.2 \ \mu\text{F}.$$

If ϕ be the phase angle,

$$\tan\phi = \frac{1}{2\pi f C R} = \frac{1}{2 \times 3.14 \times 50 \times 200 \times 9.2 \times 10^{-6}} = 1.73$$

$$\therefore \ \phi = \frac{\pi}{3}.$$

Questions

Essay-type

1. Distinguish between the mean value and the root mean square value of an alternating current, and find the relation between them.

   Deduce an expression for the power consumed in a circuit carrying an alternating current.

2. (a) Define mean, r.m.s. and peak values of an alternating current, and establish their relationships for a sinusoidal current.

   (b) Define form factor and find its value for an alternating current.

3. Define and explain reactance and impedance of an alternating current circuit.

4. Obtain a relation between current and voltage in an alternating current circuit consisting of resistance R and inductance L.

5. An alternating e.m.f. $E = E_0 \sin\omega t$ is applied to the ends of a coil having a resistance R and self-inductance L. Calculate the current in the circuit.

6. Obtain an expression for current when a sinusoidal e.m.f. is applied to a circuit with capacitor and resistor in series.

7. Find a relation between current and voltage in an a.c. circuit with inductor, capacitor and resistor in series.

8. When a circuit is called resonant? Find expressions for series resonant and parallel resonant circuits.

9. Define Q-factor. Obtain its expression at resonance.

10. When a circuit is called highly selective? Calculate an expression for the selectivity of the circuit for a variation of supply frequency.

11. (a) Calculate expressions for the inductance L of (i) Maxwell's bridge and (ii) Anderson's bridge.

    (b) Explain how the capacitance can be determined using a Schering bridge.

12. Find the impedance of an ideal transformer.

13. An alternating current is represented by $i = i_0 \sin pt$. Find the mean and r.m.s. values of the current in terms of the peak value. **[C.U. 1984]**

14. Obtain expressions for the mean value and r.m.s. value of sinusoidal alternating current. Why is the r.m.s. value used to measure the alternating current? **[B.U. 1983]**

15. Distinguish between mean value and root mean square value of an alternating potential. Obtain expressions for the same in the case of a simple harmonically varying potential. **[C.U. 1991]**

16. Define the form factor of an alternating wave. Calculate the value of the same for a pure sinusoidal current.

17. Show how the average, virtual and peak values of an alternating current are related to one another. **[B.U. 1984, '90]**

18. How does a current differ in phase from the applied e.m.f. in a circuit containing an inductance and a resistance? **[B.U. 1983]**

19. An alternating e.m.f. $E = E_0 \sin \omega t$ is applied to the ends of a circuit consisting of a resistor R and a coil of self-inductance L in series. Deduce an expression for the current in the circuit. **[C.U. 1993; N.B.U. 1992; B.U. 1999]**

20. Derive an expression for the instantaneous current of an A.C. circuit consisting of a capacitor and a resistor. **[C.U. 1982, '91, '99]**

21. Deduce an expression for the power consumed in a circuit with resistance and inductance carrying alternating current. **[N.B.U. 1983]**

22. How can the potential differences across a resistor and an inductance connected in series in an A.C. circuit be represented by vector diagram?

23. Show that power absorbed by a coil carrying an alternating current is $E \cdot I \cos \phi$ where E and I are the r.m.s. values of the e.m.f. and the current and ϕ the phase-difference between them.

24. Show that in the case of a purely inductive or capacitative circuit, the power absorbed per cycle is zero. **[N.B.U. 1983]**

25. Deduce an expression for the power consumed in a circuit carrying alternating current. **[C.U. 1999]**

26. An alternating e.m.f. $E = E_0 \sin \omega t$ is applied to the ends of a series circuit consisting of a resistor R, an inductor L and a capacitor C. Find the current through the circuit at any instant. Explain what is meant by the impedance of the circuit and establish the condition for which the resonance occurs.

    [C.U. 1994]

27. What is a transformer? State how an alternating e.m.f. can be (i) stepped up, (ii) stepped down by a transformer. What are the chief causes of energy loss in a transformer?   [B.U. 1984]

28. Derive an expression for the impedance of a self-inductor L, a capacitor C and a resistor R in series when fed by a sinusoidal alternating e.m.f.

[C.U. 1988]

Short Answer-type

29. What is form factor? What is its value for an alternating p.d., and a steady direct p.d.?

30. What is the difference between a.c. and d.c.? How can a coil rotating in a uniform magnetic field produce an alternating current?

31. Distinguish between—(a) mean value and r.m.s. value, (b) resistance and impedance, (c) power and power factor.

32. Explain the terms—(i) the peak value, (ii) the average value, (iii) the r.m.s. value, (iv) power factor.

33. What do you mean by the electrical impedance of a circuit? Does it depend on the frequency? Distinguish between inductive reactance and capacitative reactance. How will the values of the two reactances change if the frequency is (i) increased and (ii) decreased?

34. What is Q-factor? On what factor does it depend?

35. Mention the difference between a series resonant circuit and a parallel resonant circuit. What do you mean by (a) resonance curve and (b) response curve?

[B.U. 1990]

36. When does an L-C-R circuit behave just like a purely resistive circuit? Will the impedance of the circuit then be maximum or minimum? Why is the circuit often called an acceptor circuit?

37. Explain (a) Power factor, (b) Wattless current.   [C.U. 1982]

38. What is impedance triangle? How can you get the impedance and phase from the impedance?

39. What is a choke? For what purpose is it used in an a.c. circuit? 'A choke is more economical than a resistor'—explain the statement.

40. 220 volts a.c. is more dangerous than 200 volts d.c. Explain the statement.

[C.U. 1992, '99]

41. Why is a circuit consisting of a capacitor and inductor in parallel often called a rejector circuit?

Numerical Problems

42. A coil is found to have impedances of 100 Ω and 110 Ω for a.c. frequencies of 50 Hz and 60 Hz respectively. Calculate the inductance of the coil.

[N.B.U. 1992]

[Ans. 0.22 henry]

43. The equation of an a.c. is $i = 50 \sin 400\pi t$. What are the frequency and peak value of the current? What is its r.m.s. value?   [Ans. 200; 50 A; 35.36 A]

44. An alternating e.m.f. is represented by the equation $E = 200 \sin(100\pi)t$ and it is applied across a series combination of a resistor of 20 ohms and an inductance of 0.15 henry. Calculate the r.m.s. value of the current in the circuit and phase lag of the current. [**Ans.** 1.24 A; 66.9° (approx.)]

45. A series circuit consisting of 0.01 henry inductance and 10 ohms resistor is connected across an alternating e.m.f. of 100 V (r.m.s.) at 50 Hz. Find **(i)** the r.m.s. current through the circuit and **(ii)** the voltage across the inductance. [**Ans.** (i) 9.54 A, (ii) 29.97 volts]

46. A 100 volts, 60 watts lamp is to be operated off 220 volts, 50 cycles a.c. mains. What **(i)** pure resistance, **(ii)** pure inductance, placed in series with the lamp will enable it to be correctly used? Which method will be more economical? [**Ans.** (i) 333.3 ohms, (ii) 1 henry (approx.)]

47. An electric lamp marked 100 volts d.c. consumes a current of 1 ampere. It is connected to 200 volts, 50 cycles a.c. mains. Calculate the inductance of the required choke. [**Ans.** 127.4 henry]

48. An alternating pressure of 100 volts (virtual) is applied to a circuit of resistor 0.5 ohm and self-inductance 0.01 henry, the frequency being 50 Hz. What will be the reading of an ammeter included in the circuit? [**Ans.** 31.4 A (approx.)]

49. Find the values of the reactances of a 20-henry choke coil and a 20-μF condenser for a 550-Hz alternating current. [**C.U. 1984**] [**Ans.** 6280 ohms; 159.2 ohms]

50. A resistor of 10 ohms is joined in series with an inductance of 0.5 henry. What capacitor should be put in series with the combination to obtain the maximum current? What is the value of the maximum current? What will be the p.d. across the resistor, the inductance and the capacitor? The circuit is fed with 200-volt, 50-cycle alternating e.m.f.

[**Ans.** 20.24 μF : 20 A; 200 volts; 3142 volts each but oppositely directed]

51. An alternating voltage of 10 volts at 100 cycles is applied to a choke of inductance 5 henries and of resistance 200 ohms. Find the power factor.

[**B.U. 1990**]

[**Ans.** 0.0625]

52. A 20 volts, 5 watts lamp is run from a source of alternating e.m.f. of 200 volts, 50 cycles. Find the capacity of the condenser used in series. [**C.U. 1991**]

[**Ans.** 4 μF]

Chapter 12
Network Theorems

12.1 Introduction

Elements like inductors, resistors and capacitors can never amplify an electrical signal but they have a vital role in electronic circuits containing valves or transistors having amplification properties. Analysis of electronic circuits to get expressions for current, voltage, power, etc. is too complicated unless some methods are properly applied.

An electric network is nothing but an interconnection of electric circuit elements or branches. The current in any part of a network can be easily calculated for a given applied voltage using the two well-known laws of Kirchhoff as stated below :

(i) In any network, the algebraic sum of the currents meeting at a point is zero. Or mathematically,

$$\sum I = 0. \tag{12.1}$$

(ii) In any closed mesh, the algebraic sum of the electromotive forces is equal to the algebraic sum of the products of the resistances R of each part of the mesh and the currents I flowing through them. Mathematically,

$$\sum E = \sum IR$$

or, $\quad \sum E - \sum IR = 0.$ $\hfill (12.2)$

12.2 Some Important Definitions

Before going into the discussion of network theorems, it is desired to introduce some important definitions as given below :

Potential and Current Sources : A hypothetical generator used to maintain its value of potential independence of the output current is known as the *potential source* and is usually indicated by a circle enclosing a wavy line. Similarly, if a hypothetical generator is used to maintain an output current independent of the terminal voltage, then it is known as the *current source* and is indicated by a circle enclosing an arrow.

Active and Passive Networks : If a network contains energy sources as well as other circuit elements, it is called an *active network* while a network containing circuit elements without any energy source is known as the *passive network*.

Distributed and Lumped Networks : If in a network, the inductors, resistors and capacitors are not electrically separated (e.g., transmission line), it is called a *distributed network*. On the other hand, in a *lumped network*, physically separated inductors, resistors and capacitors are represented.

Node and Mesh : A group of elements having two terminals is called a branch. A terminal of any branch is called a *node* (or junction) while a set of branches forming a closed path is known as a *mesh* or loop.

12.3   Mesh Currents

For applying the mesh current method, we have to select closed loops of current
called mesh currents as shown in
Fig. 12.1. In the figure, the current in
Z_A is I_1, the current in Z_B is $(I_1 - I_2)$
and so on. Applying Kirchhoff's voltage
law to each current loop the set of three
equations can be obtained.   Thus we
have

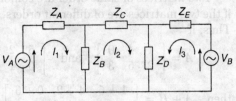

Fig. 12.1

$$I_1 Z_A + (I_1 - I_2)Z_B = V_A \tag{12.3}$$

$$I_2 Z_C + (I_2 + I_3)Z_D + (I_2 - I_1)Z_B = 0 \tag{12.4}$$

$$I_3 Z_E + (I_3 + I_2)Z_D = V_B. \tag{12.5}$$

In Eq. (12.4) above, the sum of the voltage drops is zero since the loop contains
no source. Rearranging we get

$$(Z_A + Z_B)I_1 - Z_B I_2 = V_A \tag{12.6}$$

$$-Z_B I_1 + (Z_B + Z_C + Z_D)I_2 + Z_D I_3 = 0 \tag{12.7}$$

$$Z_D I_2 + (Z_D + Z_E)I_3 = V_B. \tag{12.8}$$

Mesh Equations

The equations for a three-mesh network in general notation can be written as

$$Z_{11}I_1 \pm Z_{12}I_2 \pm Z_{13}I_3 = V_1 \tag{12.9}$$

$$\pm Z_{21}I_1 + Z_{22}I_2 \pm Z_{23}I_3 = V_2 \tag{12.10}$$

$$\pm Z_{31}I_1 \pm Z_{32}I_2 + Z_{33}I_3 = V_3. \tag{12.11}$$

Here Z_{11}, Z_{22} and Z_{33} are the self-impedances of loops one, two and three given
by the sums of the impedances through which I_1, I_2 and I_3 are respectively passing.
Z_{12} is the sum of all impedances common to I_1 and I_2. Similarly, Z_{13} and Z_{23}
are the sums of the impedances common to the mesh currents indicated in the
subscripts. It follows that $Z_{12} = Z_{21}$, $Z_{13} = Z_{31}$ and $Z_{23} = Z_{32}$. If both the
currents pass through the common impedance in the same direction, a positive sign
is used and if not we use a negative sign.

V_1 is the sum of all voltages driving in loop one. Similarly, V_2 and V_3 are the
sums of voltages driving in loops two and three respectively. If the source drives in
the direction of the mesh current, we use a positive sign. On the other hand, if it
drives against the mesh current, a negative sign is used.

12.4   Matrices

A system of rectangular array of numbers, real or complex, enclosed in a pair of
brackets is called a matrix. In the matrix

$$A = \begin{bmatrix} a_{11} & a_{12} & a_{13} & \cdots & a_{1n} \\ a_{21} & a_{22} & a_{23} & \cdots & a_{2n} \\ \cdots & \cdots & \cdots & \cdots & \cdots \\ a_{m1} & a_{m2} & a_{m3} & \cdots & a_{mn} \end{bmatrix} \tag{12.12}$$

each of the mn numbers, i.e., a_{ij} where $i = 1, 2, \ldots, m$ and $j = 1, 2, \ldots, n$, which
constitute an $m \times n$ matrix is called an *element of the matrix*.

Addition and Subtraction of Matrices

Two matrices of same order are conformable for addition or for subtraction. But if the two matrices are of different orders, then those cannot be added or subtracted. Thus, if

$$A = \begin{bmatrix} 1 & 4 & 0 \\ 2 & 5 & 3 \end{bmatrix} \quad \text{and} \quad \begin{bmatrix} 5 & 2 & 6 \\ 0 & 1 & 1 \end{bmatrix},$$

then $\quad A + B = \begin{bmatrix} 1+5 & 4+2 & 0+6 \\ 2+0 & 5+1 & 3+1 \end{bmatrix} = \begin{bmatrix} 6 & 6 & 6 \\ 2 & 6 & 4 \end{bmatrix}$

and $\quad A - B = \begin{bmatrix} 1-5 & 4-2 & 0-6 \\ 2-0 & 5-1 & 3-1 \end{bmatrix} = \begin{bmatrix} -4 & 2 & -6 \\ 2 & 4 & 2 \end{bmatrix}.$

Multiplication of Matrices

The product AB of the $1 \times m$ matrix $A = \begin{bmatrix} a_{11} & a_{12} & a_{13} & \cdots & a_{1m} \end{bmatrix}$ and the

$m \times 1$ matrix $B = \begin{bmatrix} b_{11} \\ b_{21} \\ b_{31} \\ \cdots \\ b_{m1} \end{bmatrix}$ is the 1×1 matrix C. For this each element of the

row is multiplicated by the each corresponding element of the column and then the products are added together. Thus,

$$C = \begin{bmatrix} a_{11} & a_{12} & a_{13} & \cdots & a_{1m} \end{bmatrix} \begin{bmatrix} b_{11} \\ b_{21} \\ b_{31} \\ \cdots \\ b_{m1} \end{bmatrix}$$

$$= [a_{11}b_{11} + a_{12}b_{21} + a_{13}b_{31} + \cdots + a_{1m}b_{m1}]$$

$$= \left[\sum_{k=1}^{m} a_{1k}b_{k1} \right]. \tag{12.13}$$

Let us take a few examples of it.

Example 1 : $\begin{bmatrix} a_{11} & a_{12} \\ a_{21} & a_{22} \\ a_{31} & a_{32} \end{bmatrix} \begin{bmatrix} b_{11} & b_{12} \\ b_{21} & b_{22} \end{bmatrix} = \begin{bmatrix} a_{11}b_{11} + a_{12}b_{21} & a_{11}b_{12} + a_{12}b_{22} \\ a_{21}b_{11} + a_{22}b_{21} & a_{21}b_{12} + a_{22}b_{22} \\ a_{31}b_{11} + a_{32}b_{21} & a_{31}b_{12} + a_{32}b_{22} \end{bmatrix}.$

Example 2 : $\begin{bmatrix} 2 & 3 & 5 \end{bmatrix} \begin{bmatrix} 2 \\ 4 \\ -2 \end{bmatrix} = [2(2) + 3(4) + 5(-21)] = [4 + 12 - 10] = [6].$

Example 3 : $\begin{bmatrix} 2 & 4 & -7 \\ 2 & 1 & 6 \\ 4 & -5 & 7 \end{bmatrix} \begin{bmatrix} I_1 \\ I_2 \\ I_3 \end{bmatrix} = \begin{bmatrix} 2I_1 + 4I_2 - 7I_3 \\ 2I_1 + 1I_2 + 6I_3 \\ 4I_1 - 5I_2 + 7I_3 \end{bmatrix}.$

12.5   Solution by Determinants

Linear equations can be solved by determinants using Cramer's rule. The system of three linear equations in terms of three unknowns x_1, x_2 and x_3 can be written as

$$a_{11}x_1 + a_{12}x_2 + a_{13}x_3 = k_1 \tag{12.14}$$

$$a_{21}x_1 + a_{22}x_2 + a_{23}x_3 = k_2 \qquad (12.15)$$

$$a_{31}x_1 + a_{32}x_2 + a_{33}x_3 = k_3. \qquad (12.16)$$

The three linear equations above may be written in the matrix form as

$$\begin{bmatrix} a_{11} & a_{12} & a_{13} \\ a_{21} & a_{22} & a_{23} \\ a_{31} & a_{32} & a_{33} \end{bmatrix} \begin{bmatrix} x_1 \\ x_2 \\ x_3 \end{bmatrix} = \begin{bmatrix} k_1 \\ k_2 \\ k_3 \end{bmatrix}. \qquad (12.17)$$

Here let $\Delta_a = \begin{bmatrix} a_{11} & a_{12} & a_{13} \\ a_{21} & a_{22} & a_{23} \\ a_{31} & a_{32} & a_{33} \end{bmatrix}$,

then the solution is

$$x_1 = \frac{\begin{vmatrix} k_1 & a_{12} & a_{13} \\ k_2 & a_{22} & a_{23} \\ k_3 & a_{32} & a_{33} \end{vmatrix}}{\Delta_a}, \qquad (12.18)$$

$$x_2 = \frac{\begin{vmatrix} a_{11} & k_1 & a_{13} \\ a_{21} & k_2 & a_{23} \\ a_{31} & k_3 & a_{33} \end{vmatrix}}{\Delta_a} \qquad (12.19)$$

and $\qquad x_3 = \dfrac{\begin{vmatrix} a_{11} & a_{12} & k_1 \\ a_{21} & a_{22} & k_2 \\ a_{31} & a_{32} & k_3 \end{vmatrix}}{\Delta_a}. \qquad (12.20)$

This procedure can be conveniently applied to any system of n linear equations in n unknowns, provided the coefficients determinant is not equal to zero.

12.6 Matrix Methods and Circuit Analysis

We know that the three mesh current equations are :

$$Z_{11}I_1 \pm Z_{12}I_2 \pm Z_{13}I_3 = V_1 \qquad (12.21)$$

$$\pm Z_{21}I_1 + Z_{22}I_2 \pm Z_{23}I_3 = V_2 \qquad (12.22)$$

$$\pm Z_{31}I_1 \pm Z_{32}I_2 + Z_{33}I_3 = V_3. \qquad (12.23)$$

These can be written in the matrix form as

$$\begin{bmatrix} Z_{11} & \pm Z_{12} & \pm Z_{13} \\ \pm Z_{21} & Z_{22} & \pm Z_{23} \\ \pm Z_{31} & \pm Z_{32} & Z_{33} \end{bmatrix} \begin{bmatrix} I_1 \\ I_2 \\ I_3 \end{bmatrix} = \begin{bmatrix} V_1 \\ V_2 \\ V_3 \end{bmatrix} \qquad (12.24)$$

or, $\quad [Z][I] = [V]. \qquad (12.25)$

In Eq. (12.25) above, $[V]$ is the voltage matrix, $[Z]$ the impedance matrix and $[I]$ the current matrix. This equation is known as the *matrix form of Ohm's law*. Obviously, the mesh currents I_1, I_2 and I_3 can be expressed as

$$I_1 = \frac{\begin{vmatrix} V_1 & \pm Z_{12} & \pm Z_{13} \\ V_2 & Z_{22} & \pm Z_{23} \\ V_3 & \pm Z_{32} & Z_{33} \end{vmatrix}}{\Delta_Z}, \qquad (12.26)$$

$$I_2 = \frac{\begin{vmatrix} Z_{11} & V_1 & \pm Z_{13} \\ \pm Z_{21} & V_2 & \pm Z_{23} \\ \pm Z_{31} & V_3 & Z_{33} \end{vmatrix}}{\Delta_Z} \tag{12.27}$$

and $\quad I_3 = \dfrac{\begin{vmatrix} Z_{11} & \pm Z_{12} & V_1 \\ \pm Z_{21} & Z_{22} & V_2 \\ \pm Z_{31} & \pm Z_{32} & V_3 \end{vmatrix}}{\Delta_Z}.$ \hfill (12.28)

If the numerator determinant of each is expanded about the elements of the column containing the voltages, one can get the following set of equations for the mesh currents :

$$I_1 = V_1 \left(\frac{\Delta_{11}}{\Delta_Z}\right) + V_2 \left(\frac{\Delta_{21}}{\Delta_Z}\right) + V_3 \left(\frac{\Delta_{31}}{\Delta_Z}\right) \tag{12.29}$$

$$I_2 = V_1 \left(\frac{\Delta_{12}}{\Delta_Z}\right) + V_2 \left(\frac{\Delta_{22}}{\Delta_Z}\right) + V_3 \left(\frac{\Delta_{32}}{\Delta_Z}\right) \tag{12.30}$$

$$I_3 = V_1 \left(\frac{\Delta_{13}}{\Delta_Z}\right) + V_2 \left(\frac{\Delta_{23}}{\Delta_Z}\right) + V_3 \left(\frac{\Delta_{33}}{\Delta_Z}\right). \tag{12.31}$$

The right-hand side terms of Eq. (12.29), (12.30) and (12.31) are the phasor components due to the various driving voltages.

12.7 Driving Point Impedance

Let us consider a source-free network with two external connections. As shown in Fig. 12.2, let a voltage source V_1 be applied to the external connections so that the resulting mesh current becomes I_1. As there is no other source in the network we have

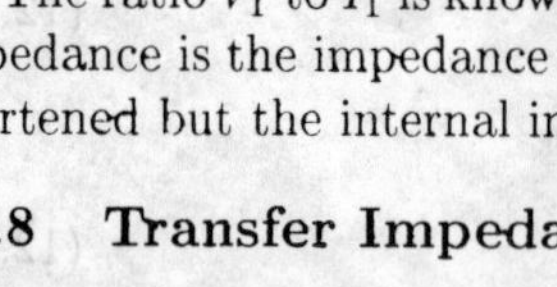

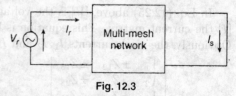

$$I_1 = V_1 \left(\frac{\Delta_{11}}{\Delta_Z}\right) + (0) \left(\frac{\Delta_{21}}{\Delta_Z}\right) + (0) \left(\frac{\Delta_{31}}{\Delta_Z}\right) + \cdots$$

$$= V_1 \left(\frac{\Delta_{11}}{\Delta_Z}\right)$$

Fig. 12.2   or, $\dfrac{V_1}{I_1} = \dfrac{\Delta_Z}{\Delta_{11}}.$ \hfill (12.32)

The ratio V_1 to I_1 is known as the input or driving point impedance. So the input impedance is the impedance to the specified terminals when all internal sources are shortened but the internal impedances are retained.

12.8 Transfer Impedance

The transfer impedance is defined as the ratio of a driving voltage in one mesh to the resulting current at another when other sources are made zero. Let us consider the network of Fig. 12.3 with a voltage V_r driving in mesh r and the resulting current I_s in mesh s.

Then we have

$$I_s = (0) \left(\frac{\Delta_{1s}}{\Delta_Z}\right) + \cdots + V_r \left(\frac{\Delta_{rs}}{\Delta_Z}\right) + \cdots$$

$$+ (0) \left(\frac{\Delta_{ns}}{\Delta_Z}\right) = V_r \left(\frac{\Delta_{rs}}{\Delta_Z}\right)$$

Fig. 12.3

or, $\quad \dfrac{V_r}{I_s} = \dfrac{\Delta_Z}{\Delta_{rs}}.$ \hfill (12.33)

The ratio V_r to I_s is known as the transfer impedance. The double subscripts rs indicate that the source is in mesh r and the resulting current is in mesh s.

12.9 Node Voltages

Node is a common point in a network to two or more circuit elements. If three or more elements are joined at a point, then that node is called a *principal node* or a *junction*. For example, in Fig. 12.4 the points marked 1, 2 and 3 are junctions. A node voltage is defined with respect to a reference node. Thus V_{13} is the voltage between nodes 1 and 3, and V_{23} is that between 2 and 3. However, the notations V_1 for V_{13} and V_2 for V_{23} are used sometimes.

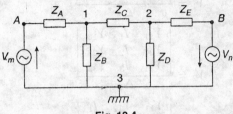

Fig. 12.4

The node voltage method determines the voltages at all principal nodes. Applying Kirchhoff's current law to junctions 1 and 2, the two unknowns V_1 and V_2 are obtained. We have

$$\frac{V_1 - V_m}{Z_A} + \frac{V_1}{Z_B} + \frac{V_1 - V_2}{Z_C} = 0 \tag{12.34}$$

and $\quad \dfrac{V_2 - V_1}{Z_C} + \dfrac{V_2}{Z_D} + \dfrac{V_2 + V_n}{Z_E} = 0$ \hfill (12.35)

Rearranging Eqs. (12.34) and (12.35),

$$\left(\frac{1}{Z_A} + \frac{1}{Z_B} + \frac{1}{Z_C}\right) V_1 - \left(\frac{1}{Z_C}\right) V_2 = \left(\frac{1}{Z_A}\right) V_m \tag{12.36}$$

$$-\left(\frac{1}{Z_C}\right) V_1 + \left(\frac{1}{Z_C} + \frac{1}{Z_D} + \frac{1}{Z_E}\right) V_2 = -\left(\frac{1}{Z_E}\right) V_n \tag{12.37}$$

Putting $1/Z = Y$, equations (12.36) and (12.37) can be expressed in terms of admittances. Thus, we get

$$(Y_A + Y_B + Y_C)V_1 - Y_C V_2 = Y_A V_m \tag{12.38}$$

$$-Y_C V_1 + (Y_C + Y_D + Y_E)V_2 = -Y_E V_n. \tag{12.39}$$

12.10 Nodal Equations

The three nodal equations of a network with four principal nodes can be expressed as

$$Y_{11}V_1 + Y_{12}V_2 + Y_{13}V_3 = I_1 \tag{12.40}$$

$$Y_{21}V_1 + Y_{22}V_2 + Y_{23}V_3 = I_2 \tag{12.41}$$

$$Y_{31}V_1 + Y_{32}V_2 + Y_{33}V_3 = I_3. \tag{12.42}$$

Here, Y_{11}, Y_{22} and Y_{33} are the self-admittances of nodes 1, 2 and 3 given by the sums of the admittances connected to the respective nodes. Y_{12}, Y_{13} and Y_{23} are the mutual admittances of the elements. I_1 is the sum of all the source current at node 1 while I_2 and I_3 are the sums of the driving currents at nodes 2 and 3 respectively.

The three nodal equations can be written in the matrix form as

$$\begin{bmatrix} Y_{11} & Y_{12} & Y_{13} \\ Y_{21} & Y_{22} & Y_{23} \\ Y_{31} & Y_{3}2 & Y_{33} \end{bmatrix} \begin{bmatrix} V_1 \\ V_2 \\ V_3 \end{bmatrix} = \begin{bmatrix} I_1 \\ I_2 \\ I_3 \end{bmatrix}, \tag{12.43}$$

from which we get

$$V_1 = \frac{\begin{vmatrix} I_1 & Y_{12} & Y_{13} \\ I_2 & Y_{22} & Y_{23} \\ I_3 & Y_{32} & Y_{33} \end{vmatrix}}{\Delta_Y}, \tag{12.44}$$

$$V_2 = \frac{\begin{vmatrix} Y_{11} & I_1 & Y_{13} \\ Y_{21} & I_2 & Y_{23} \\ Y_{31} & I_3 & Y_{33} \end{vmatrix}}{\Delta_Y} \tag{12.45}$$

and $$V_3 = \frac{\begin{vmatrix} Y_{11} & Y_{12} & I_1 \\ Y_{21} & Y_{22} & I_2 \\ Y_{31} & Y_{32} & I_3 \end{vmatrix}}{\Delta_Y}. \tag{12.46}$$

If the numerator determinant of each is expanded about the elements of the column containing the currents, one can get the following set of equations for the nodal voltages :

$$V_1 = I_1 \left(\frac{\Delta_{11}}{\Delta_Y}\right) + I_2 \left(\frac{\Delta_{21}}{\Delta_Y}\right) + I_3 \left(\frac{\Delta_{31}}{\Delta_Y}\right) \tag{12.47}$$

$$V_2 = I_1 \left(\frac{\Delta_{12}}{\Delta_Y}\right) + I_2 \left(\frac{\Delta_{22}}{\Delta_Y}\right) + I_3 \left(\frac{\Delta_{32}}{\Delta_Y}\right) \tag{12.48}$$

$$V_3 = I_1 \left(\frac{\Delta_{13}}{\Delta_Y}\right) + I_2 \left(\frac{\Delta_{23}}{\Delta_Y}\right) + I_3 \left(\frac{\Delta_{33}}{\Delta_Y}\right). \tag{12.49}$$

The right-hand side terms of Eqs. (12.47), (12.48) and (12.49) are the phasor components due to the various driving currents.

12.11   Driving Point Admittance

Let us consider a passive network with external circuit as shown in Fig. 12.5. As there is no other current source within the network we have

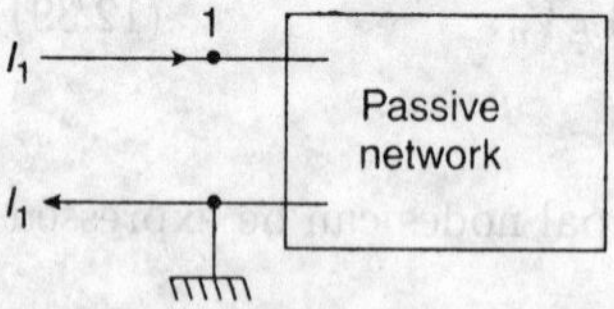

Fig. 12.5

$$V_1 = I_1 \left(\frac{\Delta_{11}}{\Delta_Y}\right)$$

or, $$\frac{I_1}{V_Y} = \frac{\Delta_Y}{\Delta_{11}}. \tag{12.50}$$

Also for an active network

$$V_1 = I_1 \left(\frac{\Delta_{11}}{\Delta_Y}\right) + (0) \left(\frac{\Delta_{21}}{\Delta_Y}\right) + (0) \left(\frac{\Delta_{31}}{\Delta_Y}\right) + \cdots = I_1 \left(\frac{\Delta_{11}}{\Delta_Y}\right)$$

or, $$\frac{I_1}{V_1} = \frac{\Delta_Y}{\Delta_{11}}. \tag{12.51}$$

The ratio I_1 to V_1 of either of the Eqs. (12.50) and (12.51) gives the driving point admittance.

12.12   Transfer Admittance

The transfer admittance is defined as the ratio of a current driving in at one node to the resulting voltage at another when other sources are made zero. In Fig. 12.6, let I_r be the current driving into node r and V_s be the resulting voltage at s. Then we have

$$V_s = (0)\left(\frac{\Delta_{1s}}{\Delta_Y}\right) + \cdots + I_r\left(\frac{\Delta_{rs}}{\Delta_Y}\right) + \cdots$$

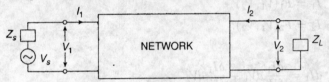

$$+ (0)\left(\frac{\Delta_{ns}}{\Delta_Y}\right)$$

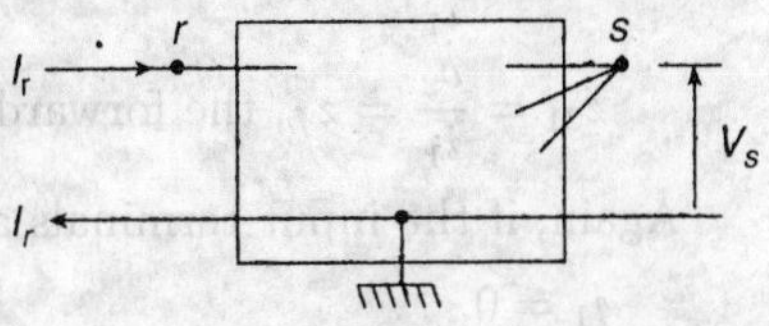

$$= I_r\left(\frac{\Delta_{rs}}{\Delta_Y}\right)$$

Fig. 12.6

or, $\qquad \dfrac{I_r}{V_s} = \dfrac{\Delta_Y}{\Delta_{rs}}.$ $\hfill (12.52)$

The ratio I_r to V_s is known as the *transfer admittance*.

12.13   Parameters of Four-Terminal Network

The circuit performance of a four-terminal network may be expressed conveniently in terms of the input and output currents and the voltages at the four terminals.

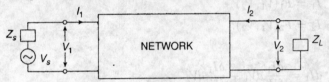

Fig. 12.7

A network connected to a voltage source and a load is shown in Fig. 12.7. The figure indicates the sign convention for the general case.

The functional relationship between the four electrical quantities V_1, V_2, I_1 and I_2 may be expressed in different ways depending on which quantities are considered as dependent variables.

(a) Open-circuit impedance parameters : If the currents I_1, I_2 are considered as the independent variables, we may write,

$$V_1 = f_1(I_1, I_2) \hfill (12.53)$$

$$V_2 = f_2(I_1, I_2) \hfill (12.54)$$

which give $\quad dV_1 = \dfrac{\delta V_1}{\delta I_1} dI_1 + \dfrac{\delta V_1}{\delta I_2} dI_2 \hfill (12.55)$

and $\qquad dV_2 = \dfrac{\delta V_2}{\delta I_1} dI_1 + \dfrac{\delta V_2}{\delta I_2} dI_2. \hfill (12.56)$

Let us denote

$$\frac{\delta V_1}{\delta I_1} = Z_{11}, \quad \frac{\delta V_1}{\delta I_2} = Z_{12}, \quad \frac{\delta V_2}{\delta I_1} = Z_{21}, \quad \frac{\delta V_2}{\delta I_2} = Z_{22}.$$

Therefore, Eqs. (12.55) and (12.56) can be rewritten as

$$v_1 = z_{11}i_1 + z_{12}i_2 \hfill (12.57)$$

$$v_2 = z_{21}i_1 + z_{22}i_2, \hfill (12.58)$$

where the differentials dV_1, dV_2, dI_1 and dI_2 are respectively expressed as v_1, v_2, i_1 and i_2.

If now the output terminals are open-circuited to a.c. so that

$$i_2 = 0,$$

then $\quad z_{11} = \dfrac{v_1}{i_1} = z_i$, the input impedance,

$$z_{21} = \frac{v_2}{i_1} = z_f, \text{ the forward transfer impedance.}$$

Again, if the input terminals are open-circuited to a.c. so that

$$i_1 = 0,$$

then $\quad z_{12} = \dfrac{v_1}{i_2} = z_r$, the reverse transfer impedance,

$$z_{22} = \frac{v_2}{i_2} = z_o, \text{ the output impedance.}$$

Since the above parameters are obtained with either the input or the output open, these are called *open circuit impedance parameters*.

(b) **Short circuit admittance parameters :** If the voltages V_1, V_2 are considered as the independent variables, we may write,

$$I_1 = F_1(V_1, V_2) \tag{12.59}$$
$$I_2 = F_2(V_1, V_2). \tag{12.60}$$

Or, we have

$$dI_1 = \frac{\delta I_1}{\delta V_1} dV_1 + \frac{\delta I_1}{\delta V_2} dV_2 \tag{12.61}$$

and $\qquad dI_2 = \dfrac{\delta I_2}{\delta V_1} dV_1 + \dfrac{\delta I_2}{\delta I_2} dV_2. \tag{12.62}$

Let us denote

$$\frac{\delta I_1}{\delta V_1} = Y_{11}, \quad \frac{\delta I_1}{\delta V_2} = Y_{12}, \quad \frac{\delta I_2}{\delta V_1} = Y_{21}, \quad \frac{\delta I_2}{\delta V_2} = Y_{22}.$$

Therefore, Eqs. (12.61) and (12.62) can be written as

$$i_1 = y_{11}v_1 + y_{12}v_2 \tag{12.63}$$
$$i_2 = y_{21}v_1 + y_{22}v_2. \tag{12.64}$$

If now the output terminals are short-circuited to a.c. so that $v_2 = 0$, then

$$y_{11} = \frac{i_1}{v_1} = y_i, \text{ the input admittance,}$$

$$y_{21} = \frac{i_2}{v_1} = y_f, \text{ the forward transfer admittance.}$$

Again, if the input terminals are short-circuited to a.c. so that $v_1 = 0$, then

$$y_{12} = \frac{i_1}{v_2} = y_r, \text{ the reverse transfer admittance,}$$

$$y_{22} = \frac{i_2}{v_2} = y_o, \text{ the output admittance.}$$

Since the above parameters are obtained with either the input or the output short, they are called *short circuit admittance parameters*.

12.14 Network Theorems

Network problems may be solved by the application of Ohm's and Kirchhoff's laws. In the following subsections some important network theorems are discussed.

12.14.1 Thevenin's Theorem

This theorem as enunciated by Helmholtz and later by Thevenin is applied to resistive networks. The theorem may be stated as follows :

'Any two-terminal network containing linear impedances and energy sources (generators) can be replaced by an equivalent circuit consisting of a voltage source E' and a series impedance Z'. The value of E' is the open circuit voltage at the terminals and Z' is the impedance measured between the terminals when all the energy sources in the network have been replaced by their internal impedances.

In Fig. 12.8(a), an active network of energy source E is connected to a load Z_L while in Fig. 12.8(b), the passive portion of the network is replaced by its equivalent

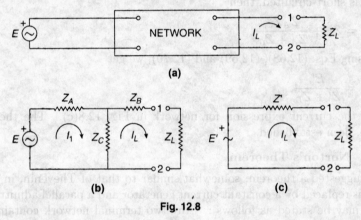

(a)

(b)   **(c)**

Fig. 12.8

T-section. The theorem then states that the circuit of Fig. 12.8(c) with voltage source E' and impedance Z' will be equivalent to that of Fig. 12.8(b) with identical voltages and currents at Z_L.

For the load current I_L the solution of circuit in Fig. 12.8(b) can be made by considering the mesh equations. We have,

$$E = I_1(Z_A + Z_C) - I_L Z_C \tag{12.65}$$

$$0 = I_L(Z_B + Z_C + Z_L) - I_1 Z_C. \tag{12.66}$$

In order to get an expression for I_L, let us substitute the value of I_1 from equation (12.66) to equation (12.65).

From equation (12.66), we have

$$I_1 = \frac{I_L(Z_B + Z_C + Z_L)}{Z_C}. \tag{12.67}$$

From Eq. (12.65),

$$E = \frac{I_L(Z_B + Z_C + Z_L)}{Z_C}(Z_A + Z_C) - I_L Z_C$$

or, $\quad I_L = \dfrac{E}{\frac{(Z_B + Z_C + Z_L)(Z_A + Z_C)}{Z_C} - Z_C}$

$$= \frac{EZ_C}{Z_B(Z_A + Z_C) + Z_A Z_C + Z_L(Z_A + Z_C)}$$

$$= \frac{E\left(\frac{Z_C}{Z_A + Z_C}\right)}{Z_B + \frac{Z_A Z_C}{Z_A + Z_C} + Z_L}. \tag{12.68}$$

[dividing both numerator and denominator by $(Z_A + Z_C)$]

Eq. (12.68) is the expression for load current that would flow in any value of Z_L.

Again, from Fig. 12.8(b), the open circuit voltage at 1, 2 terminals is

$$E' = \frac{E}{Z_A + Z_C} \cdot Z_C$$

$$= E\left(\frac{Z_C}{Z_A + Z_C}\right) \tag{12.69}$$

and if E is short-circuited, then

$$Z' = Z_B + \frac{Z_A Z_C}{Z_A + Z_C}. \tag{12.70}$$

By using Eqs. (12.68), (12.69) and (12.70), we get

$$I_L = \frac{E'}{Z' + Z_L}, \tag{12.71}$$

which is the current expression for network in Fig. 12.8(c). The theorem has, therefore, been established.

12.14.2   Norton's Theorem

Norton suggested a theorem, somewhat similar to that of Thevenin, in which the network is replaced by a constant current generator and a parallel admittance. The theorem may be stated as follows : "Any two terminal network containing linear impedances and energy sources (generators) can be replaced by an equivalent circuit consisting of a current source I' and a parallel admittance Y'. The value of I' is the short circuit current at the terminals and Y' is an admittance measured between the terminals when all the energy sources have been replaced by their internal admittances."

In Fig. 12.9(a), an active network of energy source E is connected to a load Z_L while in Fig. 12.9(b), the network has been converted to the voltage-source

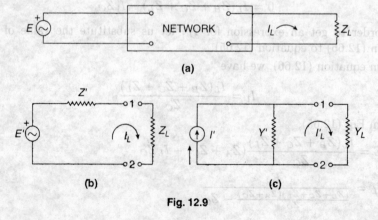

Fig. 12.9

equivalent circuit by Thevenin's theorem. The theorem then states that the circuit of Fig. 12.9(c) with a constant current generator of value I' will be equivalent to that of Fig. 12.9(b).

The load current I_L in Fig. 12.9(c) is given by

$$I_L = \frac{E'}{Z' + Z_L}. \qquad (12.72)$$

Since the reciprocal of impedance is known as admittance, we have

$$Z' = \frac{1}{Y'} \quad \text{and} \quad Z_L = \frac{1}{Y_L} \quad \text{(where } Y' \text{ and } Y_L \text{ are two admittances)} \qquad (12.73)$$

$$\therefore \quad Z' + Z_L = \frac{1}{Y'} + \frac{1}{Y_L} = \frac{Y' + Y_L}{Y'Y_L}$$

or, $$\frac{1}{Z' + Z_L} = \frac{Y'Y_L}{Y' + Y_L}. \qquad (12.74)$$

By Eqs. (12.72) and (12.74),

$$I_L = E' \left(\frac{Y'Y_L}{Y' + Y_L} \right)$$

$$= E'Y' \left(\frac{Y_L}{Y' + Y_L} \right). \qquad (12.75)$$

Next consider the circuit of Fig. 12.9(c) where the constant current generator I' is in parallel with the admittances Y' and Y_L. Using appropriate current division factor, the load current I'_L in the admittance Y_L may be written as

$$I'_L = I' \left(\frac{Y_L}{Y' + Y_L} \right). \qquad (12.76)$$

Again, from Fig. 12.9(b), the short circuit current at 1, 2 terminals is

$$I' = \frac{E'}{Z'} = E'Y'. \qquad (12.77)$$

By Eqs. (12.75) and (12.77), we get

$$I_L = I' \left(\frac{Y_L}{Y' + Y_L} \right). \qquad (12.78)$$

Therefore from Eqs. (12.76) and (12.78), we have

$$I_L = I'_L, \qquad (12.79)$$

which proves the validity of Norton's theorem.

It is found that both Thevenin's and Norton's theorems may be applied to any given network and so their choice is made as required.

12.14.3 Superposition Theorem

The statement of the theorem is as follows : "In a network containing linear impedances and energy sources (generators), the current flowing at any point is the sum of all the currents which would separately flow at that point by each energy source."

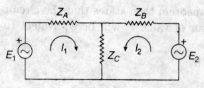

Fig. 12.10

For the verification of the theorem, let us consider the simple network with two generators of e.m.f.s E_1 and E_2, as shown in Fig. 12.10.

Let the currents due to E_1 and E_2 acting together are I_1 and I_2, and suppose the currents due to E_1 acting alone be I_1' and I_2' and also the currents due to E_2 acting alone be I_1'' and I_2''.

When both E_1 and E_2 are applied simultaneously, we have

$$E_1 = I_1(Z_A + Z_C) + I_2 Z_C \qquad (12.80)$$

and $\quad E_2 = I_2(Z_B + Z_C) + I_1 Z_C. \qquad (12.81)$

Now, when E_1 is considered alone,

$$E_1 = I_1'(Z_A + Z_C) + I_2' Z_C \qquad (12.82)$$

and $\quad 0 = I_2'(Z_B + Z_C) + I_1' Z_C, \qquad (12.83)$

and when E_2 is considered to act alone,

$$0 = I_1''(Z_A + Z_C) + I_2'' Z_C \qquad (12.84)$$

and $\quad E_2 = I_2''(Z_B + Z_C) + I_1'' Z_C. \qquad (12.85)$

Adding Eqs. (12.82) and (12.84),

$$E_1 = (I_1' + I_1'')(Z_A + Z_C) + (I_2' + I_2'')Z_C. \qquad (12.86)$$

and adding Eqs. (12.83) and (12.85),

$$E_2 = (I_2' + I_2'')(Z_B + Z_C) + (I_1' + I_1'')Z_C. \qquad (12.87)$$

It is seen that Eqs. (12.86) and (12.87) are respectively identical with Eqs. (12.80) and (12.81), if

$$I_1 = I_1' + I_1''$$

and $\quad I_2 = I_2' + I_2'', \qquad (12.88)$

which must then be true.

The superposition theorem simplifies network calculation in presence of several generators. This is particularly important when generators of different frequencies are present.

12.14.4   Reciprocity Theorem

"In any network of linear impedance, if an e.m.f. applies in one mesh produces a certain current in the second mesh, then the same e.m.f. acting in the second mesh will give an identical current in the first mesh."

For the verification of the theorem let us consider the simple arrangement, shown in Fig. 12.11, where a T-network is inserted between a generator and a load.

Let E be the source of e.m.f. and D the detector. In the said circuit, let the currents be I_1 and I_2 in the two meshes. Further, say,

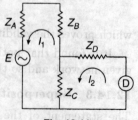

Fig. 12.11

$$Z_1 = Z_A + Z_B + Z_C = \text{self-impedance of mesh 1,}$$

$Z_2 = Z_C + Z_D$ = self-impedance of mesh 2,

and $Z_{12} = Z_C$ = mutual impedance of mesh 1 and mesh 2.

Applying Kirchhoff's law in the mesh 1 and mesh 2, we have

$$E = I_1 Z_1 - I_2 Z_{12} \qquad (12.89)$$

and $0 = I_2 Z_2 - I_1 Z_{12}.$ $\qquad (12.90)$

From Eq. (12.89),

$$I_1 = \frac{E}{Z_1} + \frac{Z_{12}}{Z_1} I_2. \qquad (12.91)$$

Putting the value of I_1 in Eq. (12.90),

$$I_2 Z_2 - \left(\frac{E}{Z_1} + \frac{Z_{12}}{Z_1} I_2 \right) Z_{12} = 0$$

or, $I_2 \left(Z_2 - \dfrac{Z_{12}^2}{Z_1} \right) = \dfrac{E Z_{12}}{Z_1}$ or, $I_2(Z_1 Z_2 - Z_{12}^2) = E Z_{12}.$

$$\therefore \quad I_2 = \frac{E Z_{12}}{Z_1 Z_2 - Z_{12}^2}. \qquad (12.92)$$

Now, interchanging the position of source and detector, we get

$$0 = I_1' Z_1 - I_2' Z_{12} \qquad (12.93)$$

and $E = I_2' Z_2 - I_1' Z_{12}.$ $\qquad (12.94)$

Rearranging Eqs. (12.93) and (12.94), we can write,

$$I_1' Z_1 - I_2' Z_{12} = 0 \qquad (12.95)$$

$$-I_1' Z_{12} + I_2' Z_2 = E. \qquad (12.96)$$

$$\therefore \quad I_1' = \frac{\begin{vmatrix} 0 & -Z_{12} \\ E & Z_2 \end{vmatrix}}{\begin{vmatrix} Z_1 & -Z_{12} \\ -Z_{12} & Z_2 \end{vmatrix}} = \frac{E Z_{12}}{Z_1 Z_2 - Z_{12}^2}. \qquad (12.97)$$

By Eqs. (12.92) and (12.97), we have

$$I_2 = I_1'. \qquad (12.98)$$

Therefore, with the transposition of the source and detector the current remains the same. The source and the detector cannot be interchanged, however, in a special case when they have equal impedances.

12.14.5   Maximum Power Transfer Theorem

This theorem is applicable to all branches of electrical engineering and is particularly important in communication work. The theorem may be stated as follows :

"A two-terminal network will absorb maximum power from a generator if the load impedance is the complex conjugate of the internal impedance of the generator."

For the verification of the theorem, let us consider the circuit diagram of Fig. 12.12.

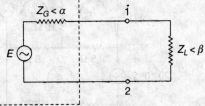

Fig. 12.12

Here, the generator impedance $Z_G \angle \alpha = R_G + jX_G$, where $\tan \alpha = \frac{X_G}{R_G}$ and the load impedance $Z_L \angle \beta = R_L + jX_L$, where $\tan \beta = \frac{X_L}{R_L}$.

Then the current I flowing in the circuit will be

$$I = \frac{E}{(R_L + R_G) + j(X_L + X_G)}. \tag{12.99}$$

$\therefore$ power in the load,

$$P = I^2 R_L$$

$$= \frac{E^2 R_L}{(R_L + R_G)^2 + (X_L + X_G)^2}. \tag{12.100}$$

Maximizing this expression with respect to X_L gives

$$\frac{\delta P}{\delta X_L} = \frac{-2E^2 R_L (X_L + X_G)}{[(R_L + R_G)^2 + (X_L + X_G)^2]^2} = 0. \tag{12.101}$$

So, as far as the variation of X_L is concerned, the maximum power will be achieved for $X_L = -X_G$. Then the power in the load becomes

$$P = \frac{E^2 R_L}{(R_L + R_G)^2}. \tag{12.102}$$

Again, maximising Eq. (12.100) with respect to R_L, we get

$$\frac{\delta P}{\delta R_L} = \frac{E^2 (R_L + R_G)^2 - 2E^2 R_L (R_L + R_G)}{(R_L + R_G)^4} = 0$$

or, $(R_L + R_G)^2 - 2R_L^2 - 2R_L R_G = 0.$ $\tag{12.103}$

Hence, for $R_L = R_G$, the power will be maximum.

The expression for the maximum power P may then be written as

$$P = \frac{E^2 R_L}{(2R_L)^2} = \frac{E^2}{4R_L}. \tag{12.104}$$

We may thus conclude that the power absorbed by the load will be maximum when the resistive components of both the load and generator impedances are equal and also the reactance of the load has an opposite sign to that of the generator, i.e., when the impedance of the load is the complex conjugate of the internal impedance of the generator.

Examples

1. A network is drawn in Fig. 12.13 showing the mesh currents. Write down the equations of mesh current.

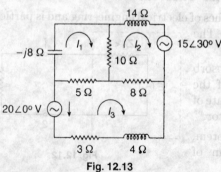

Fig. 12.13

Solution : In loop one, as there is no driving voltage, the sum of the voltage drops equals zero. In loop 2 the $15\angle 30°$ volt source drives against the mesh current and so its sign is negative. Similar is for the loop 3 also. We can now write the equations of mesh current as

$$I_1(-j8) + (I_1 - I_2)10$$
$$+ (I_1 - I_3)5 = 0$$

$$I_2(j4) + (I_2 - I_3)8 + (I_2 - I_1)10 = -(15\angle 30°)$$
$$I_3(3 + j4) + (I_3 - I_1)5 + (I_3 - I_2)8 = -(20\angle 0°).$$

Rearranging

$$(15 - j8)I_1 - 10I_2 - 5I_3 = 0$$
$$-10I_1 + (18 + j4)I_2 - 8I_3 = -(15\angle 30°)$$
$$-5I_1 + 8I_2 + (16 + j4)I_3 = -(20\angle 0°)$$

2. Determine the power output of the voltage source in the circuit of Fig. 12.14 and hence find the power in the resistances of the circuit.

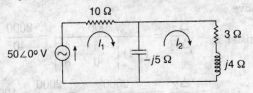

Fig. 12.14

Solution : Here we have

$$\begin{bmatrix} 10 - j5 & j5 \\ j5 & 3 - j1 \end{bmatrix} \begin{bmatrix} I_1 \\ I_2 \end{bmatrix} = \begin{bmatrix} 50\angle 0° \\ 0 \end{bmatrix},$$

from which we get

$$I_1 = \cfrac{\begin{vmatrix} 50\angle 0° & j5 \\ 0 & 3 - j1 \end{vmatrix}}{\begin{vmatrix} 10 - j5 & j5 \\ j5 & 3 - j1 \end{vmatrix}} = \frac{150 - j50}{50 - j25} = 2.83\angle 8.14° \text{ A.}$$

and $I = \cfrac{\begin{vmatrix} 10 - j5 & 50\angle 0° \\ j5 & 0 \end{vmatrix}}{\begin{vmatrix} 10 - j5 & j5 \\ j5 & 3 - j1 \end{vmatrix}} = \frac{-j250}{50 - j25} = 4.47\angle -63.4° \text{ A.}$

∴ the source power,

$$P = VI\cos\theta = 50 \times 2.83 \times \cos(8.14)° = 140 \text{ watts.}$$

Now, the power in the 10 Ω resistor

$$= (I_1)^2 \times 10 = (2.83)^2 \times 10 = \textbf{80 watts}$$

and the power in the 3 Ω resistor

$$= (I_2)^2 \times 3 = (4.47)^2 \times 3 = \textbf{60 watts.}$$

3. Using matrix methods find the input impedance in the network of Fig. 6.15 as seen by the 50-volt source and hence calculate the value of I_1. Find also the mesh currents I_2 and I_3, using the transfer impedances.

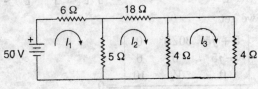

Fig. 12.15

Solution : The input impedance or the driving point to loop one is

$$Z_{input 1} = \frac{\Delta_Z}{\Delta_{11}} = \frac{\begin{vmatrix} 11 & -5 & 0 \\ -5 & 27 & -4 \\ 0 & -4 & 8 \end{vmatrix}}{\begin{vmatrix} 27 & -4 \\ -4 & 8 \end{vmatrix}} = \frac{2000}{200} = 10\ \Omega.$$

So the current, $I_1 = \dfrac{V}{Z_{input 1}} = \dfrac{50}{10} = $ **5 amperes**.

To find mesh currents I_2 and I_3 the transfer impedances are to be calculated first. We have

$$Z_{transfer 12} = \frac{\Delta_Z}{\Delta_{12}} = \frac{2000}{(-1)\begin{vmatrix} -5 & -4 \\ 0 & 8 \end{vmatrix}} = \frac{2000}{40} = 50\ \Omega$$

and $\quad Z_{transfer 13} = \dfrac{\Delta_Z}{\Delta_{13}} = \dfrac{2000}{\begin{vmatrix} -5 & 27 \\ 0 & -4 \end{vmatrix}} = \dfrac{2000}{20} = 100\ \Omega.$

$\therefore$ the mesh currents,

$$I_2 = \frac{V_1}{Z_{transfer 12}} = \frac{50}{50} = \textbf{1 ampere}$$

and $\quad I_3 = \dfrac{V_1}{Z_{transfer 12}} = \dfrac{50}{100} = \textbf{0.5 ampere}.$

4. A network with two voltage sources V_1 and V_2 is drawn in Fig. 12.16. With $V_1 = 30\angle 0°$ volt, find V_2 such that the current in the $2 + j3\ \Omega$ impedance is zero.

If $V_2 = 20\angle 0°$ volt, find also source voltage V_1 which results in zero current in the branch containing V_2.

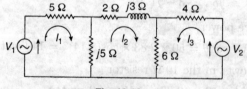

Fig. 12.16

Solution : First part : Considering the network of Fig. 12.16, we can write in matrix form,

$$\begin{bmatrix} 5 + j5 & -j5 & 0 \\ -j5 & 8 + j8 & 6 \\ 0 & 6 & 10 \end{bmatrix} \begin{bmatrix} I_1 \\ I_2 \\ I_3 \end{bmatrix} = \begin{bmatrix} 30\angle 0° \\ 0 \\ V_2 \end{bmatrix}.$$

From this we get

$$I_2 = \frac{\begin{vmatrix} 5 + j5 & 30\angle 0° & 0 \\ -j5 & 0 & 6 \\ 0 & V_2 & 10 \end{vmatrix}}{\Delta_Z} = 0$$

or, $\quad -30\angle 0° \begin{vmatrix} -j5 & 6 \\ 0 & 10 \end{vmatrix} - V_2 \begin{vmatrix} 5+j5 & 0 \\ -j5 & 6 \end{vmatrix} = 0$

or, $\quad -30\angle 0°(50\angle -90°) - V_2(6)(5\sqrt{2}\angle 45°) = 0.$

$\therefore \quad V_2 = \dfrac{-30\angle 0°(50\angle -90°)}{6(5\sqrt{2}\angle 45°)} = \textbf{35.4}\angle\textbf{45°ﾠvolts.}$

Second part : We have

$$I_3 = \dfrac{\begin{vmatrix} 5+j5 & -j5 & V_1 \\ -j5 & 8+j8 & 0 \\ 0 & 6 & 20\angle 0° \end{vmatrix}}{\Delta_z} = 0$$

or, $\quad V_1 \begin{vmatrix} -j5 & 8+j8 \\ 0 & 6 \end{vmatrix} + 20\angle 0° \begin{vmatrix} 5+j5 & -5 \\ -j5 & 8+j8 \end{vmatrix} = 0$

or, $\quad V_1(30\angle -90°) + 20\angle 0°(25+j80) = 0$

$\therefore \quad V_1 = \dfrac{-20\angle 0°(25+j80)}{30\angle -90°} = \textbf{55.8}\angle - \textbf{17.4° volts.}$

5. A network is drawn in Fig. 12.17. What will be its node voltage equations?

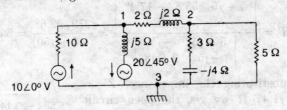

Fig. 12.17

Solution : Applying Kirchhoff's current law to node 1 and node 2, we get

$$\dfrac{V_1 - 10\angle 0°}{10} + \dfrac{V_1 + 20\angle 45°}{j5} + \dfrac{V_1 - V_2}{2+j2} = 0$$

and $\quad \dfrac{V_2 - V_1}{2+j2} + \dfrac{V_2}{3-j4} + \dfrac{V_2}{5} = 0.$

Rearranging we get

$$\left(\dfrac{1}{10} + \dfrac{1}{j5} + \dfrac{1}{2+j2}\right) V_1 - \left(\dfrac{1}{2+j2}\right) V_2 = \dfrac{10\angle 0°}{10} - \dfrac{20\angle 45°}{j5}$$

and $\quad -\left(\dfrac{1}{2+j2}\right) V_1 + \left(\dfrac{1}{2+j2} + \dfrac{1}{3-j4} + \dfrac{1}{5}\right) V_2 = 0.$

6. Determine the Thevenin equivalent circuit for the network shown in Fig. 12.18. Find also the Norton equivalent circuit of the network.

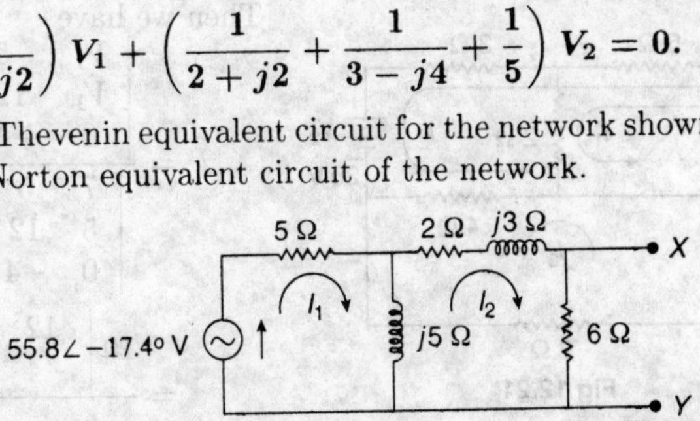

Fig. 12.18

Solution : First part : On the open circuit two mesh currents are there as shown in Fig. 12.18. The mesh current I_2 is given by

$$I_2 = \frac{\begin{vmatrix} 5+j5 & 55.8\angle -17.4° \\ -j5 & 0 \end{vmatrix}}{\begin{vmatrix} 5+j5 & -j5 \\ -j5 & 8+j8 \end{vmatrix}} = \frac{279\angle 72.6°}{83.7\angle 72.6°} = 3.33\angle 0° \text{ A}.$$

∴ the open circuit voltage,

$$V_{xy} = I_2 \times 6 = 3.33\angle 0° \times 6 = 20\angle 0° \text{ volts}.$$

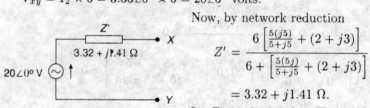

Fig. 12.19

Now, by network reduction

$$Z' = \frac{6\left[\frac{5(j5)}{5+j5} + (2+j3)\right]}{6 + \left[\frac{5(5j)}{5+j5} + (2+j3)\right]}$$

$$= 3.32 + j1.41 \ \Omega.$$

In Fig. 12.19, the Thevenin equivalent circuit is shown.

Second part : Apply a short across terminals XY when the current I_2 becomes

$$I_2 = I' = \frac{\begin{vmatrix} 5+j5 & 55.8\angle -17.4° \\ -j5 & 0 \end{vmatrix}}{\begin{vmatrix} 5+j5 & -j5 \\ -j5 & 2+j8 \end{vmatrix}} = \frac{279\angle 72.6°}{(-5+j50)} = 5.58\angle -23.14° \text{ A}.$$

Now, substituting the impedance, $Z' = 3.32 + j1.41 \ \Omega$ we get the open circuit voltage,

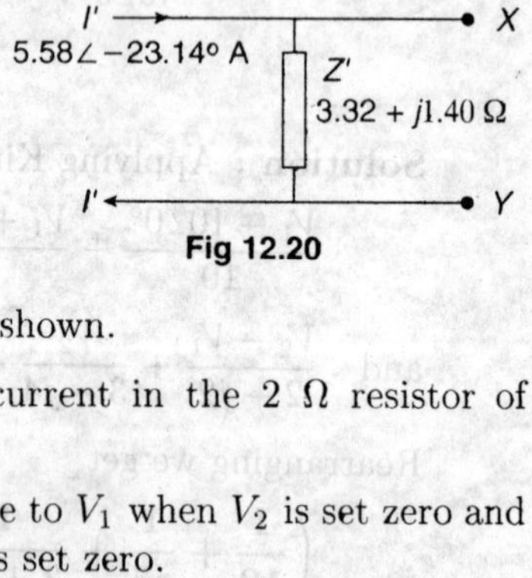

$$V_{oc} = I'Z'$$

$$= 5.58\angle -23.14°(3.32 + j1.41)$$

$$= 20.1\angle -0.14° \text{ volts}.$$

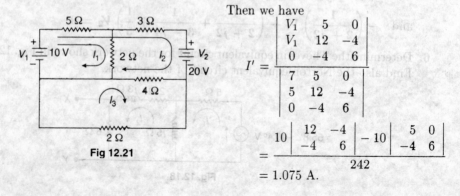

Fig 12.20

In Fig. 12.20, the Norton equivalent circuit is shown.

7. Using superposition principle calculate the current in the 2 Ω resistor of Fig. 12.21.

Solution : Let $I' =$ current in 2 Ω resistor due to V_1 when V_2 is set zero and $I'' =$ current in the same due to V_2 when V_1 is set zero.

Then we have

$$I' = \frac{\begin{vmatrix} V_1 & 5 & 0 \\ V_1 & 12 & -4 \\ 0 & -4 & 6 \end{vmatrix}}{\begin{vmatrix} 7 & 5 & 0 \\ 5 & 12 & -4 \\ 0 & -4 & 6 \end{vmatrix}}$$

$$= \frac{10\begin{vmatrix} 12 & -4 \\ -4 & 6 \end{vmatrix} - 10\begin{vmatrix} 5 & 0 \\ -4 & 6 \end{vmatrix}}{242}$$

$$= 1.075 \text{ A}.$$

Fig 12.21

and $I'' = \dfrac{\begin{vmatrix} 0 & 5 & 0 \\ -V_2 & 12 & -4 \\ 0 & -4 & 6 \end{vmatrix}}{242} = \dfrac{-(-20)\begin{vmatrix} 5 & 0 \\ -4 & 6 \end{vmatrix}}{242} = 2.48$ amperes.

∴ the current I_1 due to the two sources is given by

$$I_1 = I' + I'' \quad \text{(using superposition theorem)}$$

$$= 1.075 + 2.48 = \textbf{3.555 amperes}.$$

8. The network of Fig. 12.22(a) contains a single current source $I = 12\angle 90°$ A. Find the voltage V_2 at node 2. Apply the reciprocity theorem and compare the results.

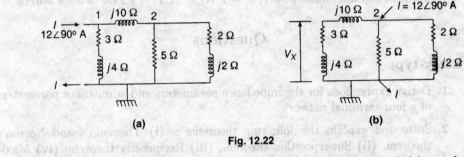

Fig. 12.22

Solution : In matrix form, the two nodal equations of Fig. 12.22(a) may be written as

$$\begin{bmatrix} \left(\frac{1}{3+j4} + \frac{1}{j10}\right) & -\frac{1}{j10} \\ -\frac{1}{j10} & \left(\frac{1}{j10} + \frac{1}{5} + \frac{1}{2+j2}\right) \end{bmatrix} \begin{bmatrix} V_1 \\ V_2 \end{bmatrix} = \begin{bmatrix} 12\angle 90° \\ 0 \end{bmatrix},$$

from which we get

$$V_2 = \dfrac{\begin{vmatrix} 0.12 - j0.26 & 12\angle 90° \\ j0.1 & 0 \end{vmatrix}}{\begin{vmatrix} 0.12 - j0.26 & j0.1 \\ j0.1 & 0.45 - j0.35 \end{vmatrix}}$$

$$= 12\angle 90° \left(\dfrac{-j0.1}{0.161\angle 260.35°}\right) = \textbf{7.45}\angle\textbf{99.65° volts}.$$

Now in Fig. 12.22(b), using the reciprocity theorem, let us apply the current I between node 2 and the reference node in the circuit.

Then we have

$$\left(\dfrac{1}{3+j14} + \dfrac{1}{5} + \dfrac{1}{2+j2}\right) V_2 = 12\angle 90°$$

or, $\quad V_2 = \dfrac{12\angle 90°}{0.563\angle - 34.4°} = 21.3\angle 124.4°$ volts.

∴ the voltage, $V_x = V_2 \left(\dfrac{3+j4}{3+j4+j10}\right) = 21.3\angle 124.4° \left(\dfrac{3+j4}{3+j14}\right)$

$$= 7.45\angle 99.6° \text{ volts}.$$

So the **value of V_2** in Fig. 12.22(a) and V_x in Fig. 12.22(b) **are equal** and hence the reciprocity theorem is proved.

9. The load Z_L in **Fig. 12.23** consists of a pure resistance R_L. Determine the value of R_L for which the source delivers maximum power to the load. Find also the value of the maximum power P.

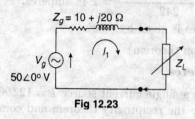

Fig 12.23

Solution : We know that the maximum power transfer occurs when

$$R_L = |Z_g| = |10 + j20| = 22.4 \text{ ohms.}$$

Now, $I = \dfrac{V}{Z_g + R} = \dfrac{50\angle 0°}{10 + j20 + 22.4}$

$$= 1.31\angle - 31.7° \text{ A.}$$

Value of the maximum power, $P = I^2 R_L = (1.31)^2 \times 22.4 = \textbf{38.5 watts}$.

Questions

Essay-type

1. Derive expressions for the impedance parameters and admittance parameters of a four-terminal network.

2. State and explain the following theorems : **(i)** Thevenin's and Norton's theorem, **(ii)** Superposition theorem, **(iii)** Reciprocity theorem, **(iv)** Maximum power transfer theorem.

Short Answer-type

3. State Kirchhoff's laws.

4. Define : **(i)** potential and current sources, **(ii)** active and passive networks, **(iii)** distributed and lumped networks, **(iv)** node and mesh.

5. What are mesh currents?

6. How are the circuits analysed by matrix methods?

7. Define the terms : **(i)** driving point impedance and admittance, **(ii)** the transfer impedance and admittance.

Numerical Problems

8. Determine the currents I_A, I_B and I_C in the circuit shown in Fig. 12.24.

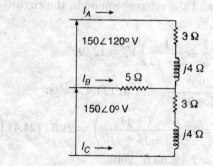

Fig. 12.24

[**Ans.** $I_A = 12.1\angle 46.4°$ A, $I_B = 19.1\angle - 47.1°$ A, $I_C = 22.1\angle 166.4°$ A]

9. (a) A network is shown in Fig. 12.25; select the mesh current and compute Δ_Z. Take a second choice of mesh currents and again compute Δ_Z.

[**Ans.** $61 - j15\ \Omega^2$]

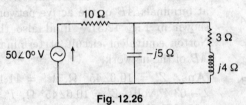

Fig. 12.25

(b) If V_1 and V_2 in the network of Fig. 12.25 are each $50\angle0°$ volts, find the power each supplies to the network. Repeat for a reverse direction on source V_2.

[**Ans.** $P_1 = 191$ watts, $P_2 = 77.1$ watts; $P_1 = \mathbf{327}$ watts, $P_2 = 214$ watts]

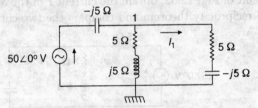

Fig. 12.26

10. Applying nodal method on the circuit of Fig. 12.26, determine the power supplied by the 50-volt source and the power in the two resistors.

[**Ans.** 140 watts, 80 watts, 60 watts]

11. A circuit is shown in Fig. 22.27. Use the nodal method to find I_1.

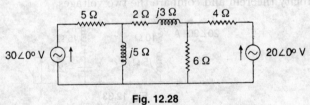

Fig. 12.27   [**Ans.** $5\angle90°$ A]

12. By nodal method find the power in the 6-ohm resistor of Fig. 12.28. Determine also the current in the $2 + j3\ \Omega$ impedance, with the positive direction to the right.

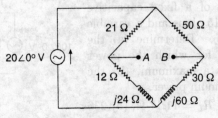

Fig. 12.28

[**Ans.** 39.6 watts, $1.73\angle40°$ A]

13. Find the Thevenin equivalent for the bridge circuit shown in Fig. 12.29.

Fig. 12.29

[**Ans.** In the equivalent circuit, $Z' = 47.4\angle26.8°\ \Omega$ and $V' = 0.328\angle170.5°$ volt]

14. Find the Thevenin equivalent circuit at terminals AB of the active network given in Fig. 12.30. Obtain also the Norton equivalent circuit for the network.

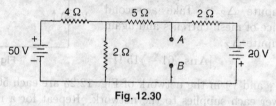

Fig. 12.30

[**Ans.** $Z' = 1.52$ ohms, $V' = 11.18°$ volts; $Z' = 1.52$ ohms, $I' = 7.35$ A]

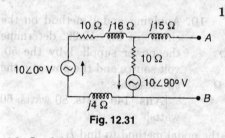

Fig. 12.31

15. Find the Thevenin equivalent circuit at terminals AB of the active network shown in Fig. 12.31. Find also the Norton equivalent circuit at terminals AB of the network.

[**Ans.** $Z' = 10.6∠45°$ Ω, $V' = 11.17$ $∠ -63.4°$ volts; $Z' = 10.6∠45°$ Ω, $I' = 1.05∠251.6°$ A]

16. In the circuit of Fig. 12.32, obtain the current I in the $3 - j4$ ohm impedance, apply the reciprocity theorem and compare the two currents.

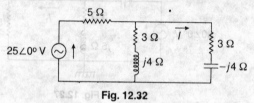

Fig. 12.32

[**Ans.** $2.27∠53.2°$ A]

17. In the circuit of Fig. 12.33, determine the voltage V_Z. Then apply the reciprocity theorem and compare the two voltages.

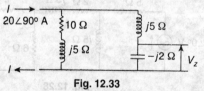

Fig. 12.33

[**Ans.** $35∠ - 12.1°$ volts]

18. In the network of Fig. 12.34, the load consists of a fixed capacitive reactance of 15 ohms and a variable resistance R_L. Determine (a) the value of R_L for which the power transferred is a maximum, (b) the value of maximum power.

[**Ans.** (a) $R_L = 11.17$ Ω, (b) 236 watts]

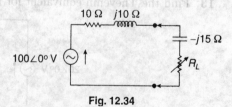

Fig. 12.34

Chapter 13
Galvanometers, Voltmeters and Ammeters

13.1 Introduction

The name of the instrument galvanometer has come after physiologist Luigi Galvani of Italy. A galvanometer is used for detecting the presence of low current or voltage in a circuit or measuring their magnitude. Galvanometers find wide applications in bridge and potentiometer measurements where their function is to indicate the zero value of current. Hence a galvanometer should have a stable zero, a short periodic time and nearly critical damping.

13.2 d'Arsonval Galvanometer

This galvanometer is used commonly in different methods of resistance measurement and in d.c. potentiometer work.

The construction of the d'Arsonval type galvanometer is presented in Fig. 13.1. It has the following important features :

(i) **Moving coil :** It may be either rectangular or circular in shape and consists of a number of turns of fine wire. The coil is suspended in such a fashion that it becomes free to turn about its vertical axis of symmetry. The coil is kept in a radial, horizontal magnetic field in the air-gap between pole pieces and armature (iron core) of a permanent magnet. When the coil is a circular one the armature is spherical in shape while for a rectangular coil it is cylindrical. The iron core is sometimes omitted and the coil is made narrow to reduce the air-gap. In general, the length of the air-gap is about 1.5 mm. The sensitivity of this galvanometer is poor but it has a low moment of inertia and short periodic time.

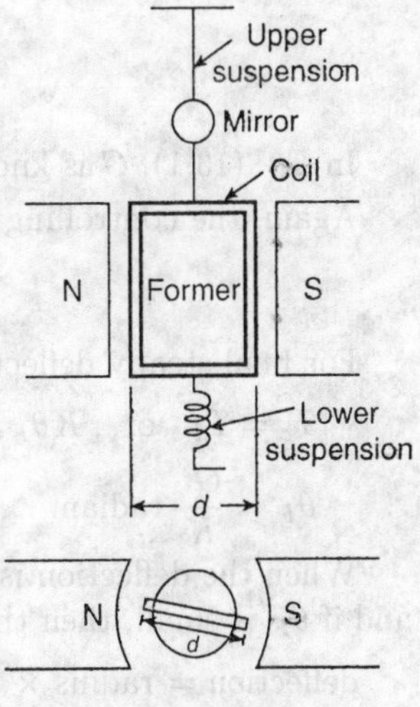

(ii) **Damping :** A damping torque is present there due to production of eddy currents in the metal former on which the coil is mounted. By connecting a low resistance across the galvanometer terminals damping can also be obtained. Since the damping torque

Fig. 13.1

depends upon the resistance used the critical damping can be obtained by adjusting the value of the resistance.

(iii) **Suspension :** The coil is supported by means of flat ribbon suspension which carries current to the coil. In a sensitive galvanometer, the other current connection is a coiled wire known as the lower suspension.

The upper suspension consists of a copper or gold wire of nearly 0.0125 mm or 0.025 mm diameter rolled into the form of a ribbon.

(iv) Indication : The suspension carries a small mirror on which a beam of light is cast. The light is reflected on a scale upon which the deflection is measured. The scale is placed usually about 1 metre away from the instrument.

(v) Zero setting : A torsion head is there for adjusting the position of the coil and also for zero setting.

Torque Equation

Let N = number of turns in the coil,

B = flux density in the air-gap at the coil position in Wb/m^2,

l = length of the vertical side of the coil in m,

d = width of the coil in m,

K = restoring constant of suspension in N-m/rad,

θ_F = final steady deflection in rad.

Then, for a current i the force on each side of the coil

$$= NBil \sin \alpha,$$

where α is the angle between direction of magnetic field and the conductor.

The field is radial and so $\alpha = 90°$.

$\therefore$ force $= Nil$.

Now, the deflecting torque, T_d = force $\times$ distance $= NBild$

$$= NBiA \text{ newton-meter}$$

$$\text{(where } A = ld = \text{area of the coil)}$$

$$= Gi \quad \text{(where } G = NBA\text{).} \tag{13.1}$$

In Eq. (13.1), G is known as the displacement constant of the galvanometer.

Again, the controlling torque exerted by the suspension,

$$T_c = K\theta_F. \tag{13.2}$$

For final steady deflection, we can write

$$T_c = T_d \quad \text{or,} \quad K\theta_F = Gi$$

$$\therefore \quad \theta_F = \frac{Gi}{K} \text{ radian.} \tag{13.3}$$

When the deflection is measured on a mm scale placed at a distance of 1 metre and if θ_F is small, then the deflection is given by

$$\text{deflection} = \text{radius} \times \text{angle turned by the reflected beam} = 1000 \times 2\theta_F$$

$$= 2000 \frac{Gi}{K}. \tag{13.4}$$

13.3 Dynamic Behaviour of a Galvanometer

We know that when a current is made to pass through a galvanometer it does not attain the steady state deflection immediately. There is a period of transition during which the moving system of the galvanometer deflects from its initial position to the final steady position. The dynamic behaviour of the galvanometer during this time is examined by the equation of motion which can help us to study the problems related to speed of response, overshoot and damping.

We have considered below the constants of a galvanometer. These constants are called the *intrinsic constants*.

(i) Inertia constant : A retarding torque is produced due to the inertia of moving system. The inertia torque, T_i, can be written as

$$T_i = J\frac{d^2\theta}{dt^2}, \tag{13.5}$$

where J is the moment of inertia of the moving system about the axis of rotation. J is also known as the inertia constant. θ represents the deflection at any instant of time t.

(ii) Damping constant : Damping occurs by the friction owing to the movement of the coil in the air and also by induced electrical effects. The damping torque T_D can be written as

$$T_D = D\frac{d\theta}{dt}, \tag{13.6}$$

where D is the damping constant.

(iii) Displacement constant : We know that the deflecting torque,

$$T_d = G_i, \tag{13.7}$$

where G is the displacement constant.

(iv) Control constant : A controlling torque is produced owing to the elasticity of the system. This tries to restore the moving system back to its initial position. The controlling torque, T_c, can be written as

$$T_c = K\theta, \tag{13.8}$$

where K is the control constant.

13.4 Torques Acting on a Galvanometer

Four torques are acting at a time on the moving system. Out of these four the deflecting torque T_d tries to accelerate the system while the inertia torque T_i, damping torque T_D and the control torque T_c attempt to retard the system (Fig. 13.2).

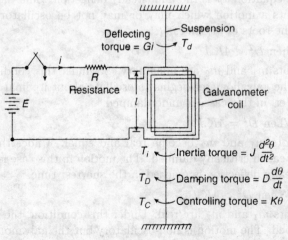

Fig. 13.2

We can write, at any instant of time t,

$$T_i + T_D + T_c = T_d$$

or, $J\dfrac{d^2\theta}{dt^2} + D\dfrac{d\theta}{dt} + K\theta = Gi.$ (13.9)

The solution of this second degree differential equation is the sum of a 'complementary function' representing a transient condition and a 'particular integral' representing a steady state condition.

Complementary Function

The auxiliary equation is

$$Jm^2 + Dm + K = 0.$$ (13.10)

The roots of the above equation are

$$m_1 = \frac{-D + \sqrt{D^2 - 4KJ}}{2J} \quad \text{and} \quad m_2 = \frac{-D - \sqrt{D^2 - 4KJ}}{2J}.$$

Thus we have

$$\theta = Ae^{m_1 t} + Be^{m_2 t},$$ (13.11)

where A and B are constants.

Particular Integral

Under steady state conditions,

$$\frac{d^2\theta}{dt^2} = 0, \quad \frac{d\theta}{dt} = 0 \text{ and } \theta = \theta_F.$$

Substituting the above conditions in Eq. (13.10), the final steady state deflection is

$$\theta_F = \frac{Gi}{K}.$$ (13.12)

Therefore, the complete solution of the differential equation is

$$\theta = Ae^{m_1 t} + Be^{m_2 t} + \theta_r.$$ (13.13)

In the above equation θ_F is the final steady deflection while the term $(Ae^{m_1 t} + Be^{m_2 t})$ represents a motion which may or may not be oscillatory which can be obtained from the-roots of m_1 and m_2.

Case I : When $D^2 < 4KJ$

Both the roots m_1 and m_2 are imaginary. So under this condition the motion is oscillatory. The galvanometer begins to oscillate about its final steady position. The galvanometer, in this case, is underdamped.

Case II : When $D^2 = 4KJ$

Both the roots m_1 and m_2 become real and equal. Under the condition the galvanometer is called critically damped. The motion in this case is non-oscillatory and the final steady deflection is reached in the shortest time.

Case III : When $D^2 > 4KJ$

Both the roots m_1 and m_2 are real. Under this condition, the galvanometer is called overdamped. The motion is non-oscillatory but the galvanometer attains its final steady position in a sluggish manner.

13.5 Underdamped Motion of a Galvanometer

The motion of a galvanometer is underdamped for the condition

$$D^2 < 4KJ.$$

Under this condition m_1 and m_2 are imaginary and may be written as

$$m_1 = \frac{-D + \sqrt{D^2 - 4KJ}}{2J} = \frac{-D + \sqrt{(-1)^2 + 4KJ - D^2}}{2J}$$

$$= -\frac{D}{2J} + j\frac{\sqrt{4KJ - D^2}}{2J} = -\alpha + j\omega$$

and $\quad m_2 = -\dfrac{D}{2J} - j\dfrac{\sqrt{4KJ - D^2}}{2J} = -\alpha - j\omega.$

Substituting the above values of m_1 and m_2 in Eq. (13.13), we get

$$\theta = Ae^{(-\alpha+j\omega)t} + Be^{-(\alpha-j\omega)t} + \theta_F$$

$$= e^{-\alpha t}\{Ae^{j\omega t} + Be^{-j\omega t}\} + \theta_F.$$

Since θ is real and $e^{\pm j\omega t}$ is complex, so A and B must be complex.

Let $\quad A = a + jb \quad$ and $\quad A = c + jd.$

$$\therefore \quad \theta = e^{-\alpha t}[(a + jb)e^{j\omega t} + (c + jd)e^{-j\omega t}] + \theta_F$$

$$= e^{-\alpha t}[(a + jb)(\cos\omega t + j\sin\omega t) + (c + jd)(\cos\omega t - j\sin\omega t)] + \theta_F$$

$$= e^{-\alpha t}[(a + c)\cos\omega t - (b + d)\sin\omega t$$

$$+ j(b + d)\cos\omega t + j(a - c)\sin\omega t] + \theta_F. \qquad (13.14)$$

In Eq. (13.14) the imaginary terms must be equal to zero as θ is a real number. So, for all values of t, $(b + d)\cos\omega t + (a - c)\sin\omega t = 0$.

(i) At $\omega t = 0$,

$$b + d = 0 \quad \text{or}, \quad b = -d.$$

(ii) At $\omega t = \dfrac{\pi}{2}$,

$$a - c = 0 \quad \text{or}, \quad a = c.$$

$$\therefore \quad A = a + jb \quad \text{and} \quad B = a - jb.$$

We can thus conclude that A and B are complex conjugate pair. Eq. (13.14) can, therefore, be written as

$$\theta = 2e^{-at}(a\cos\omega t + d\sin\omega t) + \theta_F. \qquad (13.15)$$

Let $a = \dfrac{F}{2}\sin\phi \quad$ and $\quad d = \dfrac{F}{2}\cos\phi.$

$$\therefore \quad F = 2\sqrt{a^2 + d^2} \quad \text{and} \quad \phi = \tan^{-1}\frac{a}{d}.$$

Hence, we have

$$\theta = Fe^{-at}(\sin\phi\cos\omega t + \cos\phi\sin\omega t) + \theta_F$$

$$= Fe^{-at}\sin(\omega t + \phi) + \theta_F$$

$$= Fe^{-\frac{D}{2J}t}\sin(\omega_d t + \phi) + \theta_F, \qquad (13.16)$$

where ω_d is the angular frequency of damped oscillation and is equal to $\sqrt{4KJ - D^2}/2J.$

Now, at $t = 0$, $\dot{\theta} = 0$.

$\therefore$ from Eq. (13.16), we have

$$0 = F \sin \phi + \theta_F$$

or, $$\sin \phi = -\frac{\theta_F}{F}.$$ (13.17)

Differentiating Eq. (13.16), we get

$$\frac{d\theta}{dt} = -\frac{D}{2J} F e^{-\frac{D}{2J}t}[\sin(\omega_d t + \phi)] + F e^{-\frac{D}{2J}t}[\cos(\omega_d t + \phi)]\omega_d.$$

At $t = 0$, $\dfrac{d\theta}{dt} = 0$

$\therefore$ $$0 = -\frac{D}{2J} F \sin \phi + F \omega_d \cos \phi$$ (13.18)

or, $$\tan \phi = \omega_d \cdot \frac{2J}{D} = \frac{\sqrt{4KJ - D^2}}{2J} \cdot 2\frac{J}{D} = \frac{\sqrt{4KJ - D^2}}{D}.$$

Putting the value of $\sin \phi$ in Eq. (13.18), we have

$$0 = \left(-\frac{D}{2J} F\right) \times \left(-\frac{\theta_F}{F}\right) + F \omega_d \cos \phi$$

or, $$\cos \phi = -\frac{D}{2J\omega_d} \cdot \frac{\theta_F}{F}.$$ (13.19)

From Eqs. (13.17) and (13.19), we have

$$\left(-\frac{\theta_F}{F}\right)^2 + \left(-\frac{D}{2J\omega_d} \cdot \frac{\theta_F}{F}\right)^2 = 1$$

or, $$F = -\theta_F \left[\frac{4J^2\omega_d^2 + D^2}{4J^2\omega_d^2}\right]^{\frac{1}{2}}$$ (13.20)

Now, $\omega_d = \dfrac{\sqrt{4KJ - D^2}}{2J}$.

$\therefore$ $$F = -\theta_F \frac{2\sqrt{KJ}}{\sqrt{4KJ - D^2}}.$$ (13.21)

Putting the above value of F and ϕ in Eq. (13.16), we get

$$\theta = \theta_F \left[1 - \frac{2\sqrt{KJ}}{\sqrt{4KJ - D^2}} e^{-\frac{D}{2J}t} \sin\left(\omega_d t + \tan^{-1}\frac{2J\omega_d}{D}\right)\right]$$

$$= \theta_F \left[1 - \frac{2\sqrt{KJ}}{\sqrt{4KJ - D^2}} e^{-\frac{D}{2J}t} \sin\left(\frac{\sqrt{4KJ - D^2}}{2J}t + \tan^{-1}\frac{\sqrt{4KJ - D^2}}{D}\right)\right]$$

(13.22)

When a current is suddenly made to pass through the coil of an underdamped galvanometer the moving system oscillates about its final steady state position θ_F. This oscillation would be an attenuated sinusoidal motion whose angular frequency is ω_d. The frequency of the damped oscillation is given by,

$$f_d = \frac{\omega_d}{2\pi}$$

$$= \frac{1}{2\pi} \frac{\sqrt{4KJ - D^2}}{2J}.$$ (13.23)

∴ the time-period,

$$T_d = \frac{1}{f_d} = \frac{2\pi}{\omega_d}$$

$$= 2\pi \cdot \frac{2J}{\sqrt{4KJ - D^2}}. \tag{13.24}$$

13.6 Undamped, Critically Damped and Overdamped Motion of a Galvanometer

(i) When damping forces are absent (i.e., $D = 0$) we may get the undamped motion of a galvanometer.

For $D = 0$ instead of ω_d we can write the angular frequency ω_n as

$$\omega_n = \sqrt{\frac{K}{J}} \tag{13.25}$$

and $\quad F = -\theta_F$.

So the frequency of undamped oscillation,

$$f_n = \frac{\omega_n}{2\pi} = \frac{1}{2\pi}\sqrt{\frac{K}{J}} \tag{13.26}$$

and the time-period,

$$T_0 = \frac{1}{f_n} = 2\pi\sqrt{\frac{J}{K}}. \tag{13.27}$$

Also, $\phi_0 = \tan^{-1}\alpha = 90°$. $\tag{13.28}$

Hence, from Eq. (13.16), we get

$$\theta = -\theta_F[\sin(\omega_n t + 90°)] + \theta_F$$

$$= \theta_F(1 - \cos\omega_n t). \tag{13.29}$$

(ii) The critically damped motion of a galvanometer is obtained when

$$D^2 = 4KJ.$$

Under this condition,

$$m_1 = m_2 = -\frac{D}{2J}.$$

The solution in this case,

$$\theta = \theta_F + e^{-\frac{D}{2J}t}[A + Bt], \tag{13.30}$$

where A and B are constants.

Differentiating Eq. (13.30),

$$\frac{d\theta}{dt} = \left[-\frac{D}{2J} \cdot e^{-\frac{D}{2J}t}(A + Bt) + Be^{-\frac{D}{2J}t}\right]$$

$$= e^{-\frac{D}{2J}t}\left[-\frac{D}{2J}(A + Bt) + B\right]. \tag{13.31}$$

At $t = 0$, $\theta = 0$ and $\frac{d\theta}{dt} = 0$.

∴ $\quad 0 = \theta_F + A \quad$ or, $\quad A = -\theta_F \quad$ and $\quad 0 = -\frac{D}{2J}A + B.$

$$\therefore \quad B = -\frac{D}{2J}\theta_F.$$

Hence, the solution is

$$\theta = \theta_F \left[1 - e^{-\frac{D}{2J}t}\left(1 + \frac{D}{2J}t\right)\right]. \tag{13.32}$$

For critically damped motion,

$$D = D_c = 2\sqrt{KJ}.$$

$\therefore$ under critical damping condition,

$$\frac{D}{2J} = \frac{2\sqrt{KJ}}{2J} = \sqrt{\frac{K}{J}} = \omega_n.$$

Thus for a critically damped galvanometer we can write,

$$\theta = \theta_F[1 - e^{-\omega_n t}(1 + \omega_n t)]. \tag{13.33}$$

(iii) The overdamped motion of a galvanometer is non-oscillatory and is obtained when

$$D^2 > 4KJ.$$

Under this condition both the roots m_1 and m_2 are real. The solution in this case is

$$\theta = Ae^{m_1 t} + Be^{m_2 t} + \theta_F. \tag{13.34}$$

13.7   Operational Constants

We have derived the galvanometer equations above in terms of the intrinsic constants J, D and K which are important for a designer. But the user is interested in the so-called operational constants, viz., the critical damping resistance, time-period and the sensitivity.

(i) **Relative Damping :** The damping of a galvanometer can be most conveniently expressed with critical damping case. The ratio of the actual damping constant to the damping constant required for critical damping is known as the *damping ratio*. Mathematically,

damping ratio, $\zeta = \dfrac{D}{D_c}.$

But $\quad D_c = 2\sqrt{KJ};$

$$\therefore \qquad \zeta = \frac{D}{2\sqrt{KJ}}. \tag{13.35}$$

Now, $\quad \dfrac{D}{2J} = \dfrac{D}{2\sqrt{KJ}} \cdot \sqrt{\dfrac{K}{J}}$

$$= \zeta\omega_n. \tag{13.36}$$

$$\tan\phi = \frac{\sqrt{4KJ - D^2}}{D} = \sqrt{\frac{4KJ}{D^2} - 1} = \sqrt{\left(\frac{2\sqrt{KJ}}{D}\right)^2 - 1} = \sqrt{\frac{1}{\zeta^2} - 1}$$

$$= \sqrt{1 - \zeta^2}/\zeta \tag{13.37}$$

$$\sin\phi = \sqrt{1 - \zeta^2} \tag{13.38}$$

$$\cos \phi = \zeta. \tag{13.39}$$

Again, $\dfrac{2\sqrt{KJ}}{\sqrt{4KJ - D^2}} = \sqrt{\dfrac{K}{J}} \cdot \dfrac{2J}{\sqrt{4KJ - D^2}} = \dfrac{\omega_n}{\omega_d}$

But $\dfrac{\omega_n}{\omega_d} = \dfrac{2\sqrt{KJ}}{\sqrt{4KJ - D^2}} = \dfrac{1}{\sqrt{1 - \dfrac{D^2}{4KJ}}} = \dfrac{1}{\sqrt{1 - \dfrac{D^2}{D_c^2}}} \qquad (\because D_c = 2\sqrt{KJ})$

$$= \dfrac{1}{\sqrt{1 - \zeta^2}}$$

or, $\omega_d = \omega_n \sqrt{1 - \zeta^2}.$ \hfill (13.40)

Substituting the above values in Eq. (13.22), we get

$$\theta = \theta_F \left[1 - \dfrac{\omega_n}{\omega_d} e^{-\zeta \omega_n t} \sin(\omega_d t + \phi) \right] \tag{13.41}$$

$$= \theta_F \left[1 - \dfrac{1}{\sqrt{1 - \zeta^2}} e^{-\zeta \omega_n t} \sin\left(\omega_d t + \tan^{-1} \dfrac{\sqrt{1 - \zeta^2}}{\zeta} \right) \right] \tag{13.42}$$

$$= \theta_F \left[1 - \dfrac{1}{\sqrt{1 - \zeta^2}} e^{-\zeta \omega_n t} \sin(\omega_d t + \sin^{-1} \sqrt{1 - \zeta^2}) \right]. \tag{13.43}$$

Now, $\dfrac{T_0}{T_d} = \dfrac{f_d}{f_n} = \dfrac{\omega_d}{\omega_n} = \sqrt{1 - \zeta^2}$

and $\zeta \omega_n = \dfrac{2\pi \zeta}{T_0}.$

$\therefore \qquad \theta = \theta_F \left[1 - \dfrac{1}{\sqrt{1 - \zeta^2}} e^{-\frac{2\pi \zeta t}{T_0}} \sin\left(\dfrac{2\pi}{T_0} \sqrt{1 - \zeta^2} t + \sin^{-1} \sqrt{1 - \zeta^2} \right) \right]$

$$= \theta_F \left[1 - \dfrac{T_d}{T_0} e^{-\frac{2\pi \zeta t}{T_0}} \sin\left(\dfrac{2\pi t}{T_d} + \sin^{-1} \dfrac{T_0}{T_d} \right) \right]. \tag{13.44}$$

Eq. (13.44) describes the motion of the galvanometer in terms of operational constants, viz., relative damping, free period and the sensitivity.

(ii) **Logarithmic Decrement :** The time required for the deflection to reach a maximum value can be found by putting $\frac{d\theta}{dt} = 0$. Differentiating Eq. (13.42), we have

$$\dfrac{d\theta}{dt} = \dfrac{\zeta \omega_n}{\sqrt{1 - \zeta^2}} e^{-\zeta \omega_n t} \sin\left(\omega_d t + \tan^{-1} \dfrac{\sqrt{1 - \zeta^2}}{\zeta} \right)$$

$$- \omega_d e^{-\zeta \omega_n t} \cos\left(\omega_d t + \tan^{-1} \dfrac{\sqrt{1-\zeta^2}}{\zeta} \right) = 0$$

or, $\tan\left(\omega_d t + \tan^{-1} \dfrac{\sqrt{1 - \zeta^2}}{\zeta} \right) = \dfrac{\omega_d}{\zeta \omega_n} = \dfrac{\sqrt{1 - \zeta^2}}{\zeta}.$ \hfill (13.45)

The above equation is true, only if

$\omega_d t = N\pi$ (N is an integer).

The first maximum value of deflection occurs at t_1 for $N = 1$.

$\therefore$ we can write,

$$\omega_d t_1 = \pi \quad \text{or,} \quad t_1 = \frac{\pi}{\omega_d} = \frac{\pi}{\omega_n \sqrt{1 - \zeta^2}}.$$

Putting this values in Eq. (13.43), the first maximum deflection θ_1 becomes

$$\theta = \theta_F \left[1 - \frac{1}{\sqrt{1 - \zeta^2}} e^{-\pi\zeta/\sqrt{1-\zeta^2}} \sin\left(\pi + \sin^{-1}\sqrt{1 - \zeta^2}\right) \right]$$

$$= \theta_F \left[1 + e^{-\pi\zeta/\sqrt{1-\zeta^2}} \right]$$

or, $\theta_1 - \theta_F = \theta_F e^{-\pi\zeta/\sqrt{1-\zeta^2}}.$ \hfill (13.46)

Eq. (13.46) represents the fist overshoot. At $t = t_2$, the first minimum deflection occurs, where $t_2 = 2\pi/\omega_d$. Putting this value in Eq. (13.43),

$$\theta_2 = \theta_F \left[1 - e^{-2\pi\zeta/\sqrt{1-\zeta^2}} \right]$$

or, $\theta_F - \theta_2 = e^{-2\pi\zeta/\sqrt{1-\zeta^2}}.$ \hfill (13.47)

$$\therefore \quad \frac{\theta_F - \theta_2}{\theta_1 - \theta_F} = \frac{e^{-2\pi\zeta/\sqrt{1-\zeta^2}}}{e^{-\pi\zeta/\sqrt{1-\zeta^2}}} = e^{-\pi\zeta/\sqrt{1-\zeta^2}}$$

or, $-\log_e \left(\dfrac{\theta_F - \theta_2}{\theta_1 - \theta_F} \right) = \dfrac{\pi\zeta}{\sqrt{1 - \zeta^2}}.$

Now, the *logarithmic decrement* can be defined as the Naperian logarithm of the ratio of successive swings. Denoting logarithmic decrement by λ we can write,

$$\lambda = \log_e \left(\frac{\theta_1 - \theta_F}{\theta_F - \theta_2} \right) = -\log_e \left(\frac{\theta_F - \theta_2}{\theta_1 - \theta_F} \right)$$

$$= \frac{\pi\zeta}{\sqrt{1 - \zeta^2}} = \pi\zeta \frac{T_d}{T_0} \quad \left(\because \frac{T_0}{T_d} = \sqrt{1 - \zeta^2} \right).$$

Eq. (13.44) can then be written as

$$\theta = \theta_F \left[1 - \frac{T_d}{T_0} e^{-2\lambda t/T_d} \sin\left(\frac{2\pi t}{T_d} + \sin^{-1}\frac{\pi\zeta}{\lambda} \right) \right]$$

$$= \theta_F \left[1 - \frac{\omega_n}{\omega_d} e^{-\omega_d \lambda/\pi} \sin\left(\omega_d t + \sin^{-1}\frac{\pi\zeta}{\lambda} \right) \right]. \hfill (13.48)$$

(iii) Sensitivity

(a) **Current sensitivity** : The current sensitivity of a galvanometer may be defined as the deflection produced by unit current. Thus,

$$\text{current sensitivity,} \ S_i = \frac{\theta_F}{i} = \frac{Gi}{K} \cdot \frac{1}{i} \quad \left(\because \ \theta_F = \frac{Gi}{K} \right)$$

$$= \frac{G}{K} \ \text{rad/A}. \hfill (13.49)$$

In practice the currents involved are small and so for practical work the sensitivity is expressed in terms of scale divisions/μA. Thus,

$$\text{current sensitivity,} \ S_i = \frac{d}{i \times 10^6} \ \text{mm/}\mu\text{A (where } d = \text{deflection in mm).}$$

But, $\dfrac{i}{d} = \dfrac{K}{2000G}$.

$$\therefore \quad S_i = \frac{2000G}{K \times 10^6}$$

$$= \frac{G}{500K} \text{ mm}/\mu\text{A}. \tag{13.50}$$

(b) **Voltage sensitivity :** The voltage sensitivity of the galvanometer may be defined as the scale divisions per unit voltage impressed on the galvanometer. Thus,

voltage sensitivity, S_v = scale divisions per unit voltage

$$= \frac{d}{i \times R_g \times 10^6} \text{ scale div.}/\mu\text{V}.$$

If the galvanometer is placed at a distance of 1 metre and if 1 scale div. is 1 mm, then

$$S_v = \frac{2000G}{KR_g \times 10^6} = \frac{G}{500KR_g} \text{ mm}/\mu\text{V}. \tag{13.51}$$

(c) **Megohm sensitivity :** It is the resistance of the circuit in MΩ so that the deflection will be 1 scale division with 1 volt impressed to the circuit. Due to the negligible coil resistance the megohm sensitivity can, in fact, be defined as the resistance that must be put in series with the galvanometer so that 1 volt gives a deflection of 1 scale division. The megohm sensitivity thus in a true sense represents the current sensitivity. Hence, we can write,

megohm sensitivity, $S_0 = \dfrac{d}{i \times 10^6}$ MΩ/scale div.

If the galvanometer is at a distance of 1 metre and 1 scale div. = 1 mm, then

$$S_0 = \frac{G}{500K} \text{ M}\Omega/\text{mm}. \tag{13.52}$$

13.8   Ballistic Galvanometer

In order to measure the quantity of electricity passing through it one can use a ballistic galvanometer. In magnetic measurements, this quantity of charge is due to an instantaneous e.m.f. which is induced in the search coil connected across the galvanometer. The quantity of charge passing through the galvanometer is proportional to the e.m.f. induced and, therefore, to the change of flux linking with the search coil. Hence, the galvanometer is to be calibrated for studying the charge directly.

Construction

A ballistic galvanometer is of d'Arsonval type. Due to the transitory nature of current passing through, it does not show a steady deflection. Rather it oscillates with decreasing amplitude which is proportional to the charge passing.

The time-period T_0 for undamped oscillations of a galvanometer can be written as

$$T_0 = 2\pi\sqrt{J/K},$$

where J and K are respectively inertia constant and control constant. For a longer time-period, therefore, the moment of inertia of the moving system should be large and the control constant should be small. This is achieved by attaching small weights to the moving system and by using suspensions of smaller stiffness.

A key is connected across the galvanometer terminals. This key short-circuits the galvanometer coil when closed.

Theory

If Q is the charge to be measured, then

$$Q = \int i \, dt$$

or, $\quad i = \dfrac{dQ}{dt}$ \hfill (13.53)

Let the charge Q passes between the time interval $t_0 (= 0)$ to t_1. During this time there is no motion of the coil of the galvanometer. Now the equation of motion can be written as

$$J\frac{d^2\theta}{dt^2} + D\frac{d\theta}{dt} + K\theta = Gi \quad \text{or,} \quad J\frac{d^2\theta}{dt^2} + D\frac{d\theta}{dt} + K\theta = G\frac{dQ}{dt}$$

or, $\quad \dfrac{d^2\theta}{dt^2} + \dfrac{D}{J}\dfrac{d\theta}{dt} + \dfrac{\dot{K}}{J}\theta = \dfrac{G}{J}\dfrac{dQ}{dt}.$

Integrating,

$$\left[\frac{d\theta}{dt}\right]_{t_0=0}^{t_1} + \frac{D}{J}[\theta]_{t_0=0}^{t_1} + \frac{K}{J}\int_0^{t_1}\theta \, dt = \frac{G}{J}Q. \tag{13.54}$$

Since the deflection θ remains zero during t_0 to t_1, therefore, we have

$$\frac{d\theta}{dt} = \frac{G}{J}Q. \tag{13.55}$$

After the passage of charge, i.e., after time t_1, no current flows through the galvanometer and so the deflecting torque becomes zero. The equation of motion after time t_1 is

$$J\frac{d^2\theta}{dt^2} + D\frac{d\theta}{dt} + K\theta = \delta. \tag{13.56}$$

The solution of the above equation can be written in the form as

$$\theta = Fe^{-\frac{D}{2J}t}[\sin(\omega_d t + \phi)] + \phi_F. \tag{13.57}$$

But as the galvanometer does not show any steady state deflection, we can write,

$$\theta = Fe^{-\frac{D}{2J}t}[\sin(\omega_d t + \phi)]. \tag{13.58}$$

Again, since damping is small,

$$\omega_d \approx \omega_n.$$

$\therefore \qquad \theta = F_e^{-\frac{D}{2J}t}[\sin(\omega_n t + \phi)]. \tag{13.59}$

Differentiating Eq. (13.59),

$$\frac{d\theta}{dt} = F\omega_n e^{-\frac{D}{2J}t}[\cos(\omega_n t + \phi)] - Fe^{-\frac{D}{2J}t}\frac{D}{2J}[\sin(\omega_n t + \phi)].$$

At $t = 0$, $\theta = 0$ $\quad$ and $\quad \dfrac{d\theta}{dt} = \dfrac{G}{J}Q.$ \hfill (13.60)

From Eq. (13.59), $F \sin \phi = 0$ or, $\phi = 0$ and from Eq. (13.60),

$$F = \frac{G}{J\omega_n} Q.$$

Hence, Eq. (13.59) can be written as

$$\theta = \frac{G}{J\omega_n} Q e^{-\frac{D}{2J}t} \sin \omega_n t = \frac{G}{J}\sqrt{\frac{J}{K}} Q e^{-\frac{D}{2J}t} \sin \sqrt{\frac{K}{J}} \cdot t$$

$$= AQ e^{-\frac{D}{2J}t} \sin \frac{2\pi}{T_0} t, \tag{13.61}$$

where $\quad A = \dfrac{G}{J}\sqrt{\dfrac{J}{K}}.$

Eq. (13.61) shows that at any instant the deflection θ is proportional to the charge Q. Also the motion of the galvanometer is oscillatory in nature with a decreasing amplitude. A plot of the deflection θ against the time gives a curve as shown in Fig. 13.3. It is seen that the amplitude of the oscillations decreases with time. The maxima of successive oscillations occur at

$$t = \frac{T_0}{4}, \frac{3T_0}{4} \frac{5T_0}{4}, \text{ etc.}$$

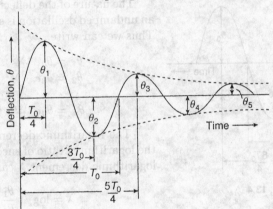

Fig. 13.3

Hence we can write,

$$\theta_1 = AQ e^{-\frac{D}{2J} \cdot \frac{T_0}{4}} \sin \frac{2\pi}{T_0} \cdot \frac{T_0}{4} = AQ e^{-\frac{D}{2J} \cdot \frac{T_0}{4}}.$$

Substituting,

$$T_0 = 2\pi \sqrt{(J/K)},$$

we have

$$\theta_1 = AQ e^{-\frac{D}{2J} \frac{2\pi}{4} \sqrt{\frac{J}{K}}}$$

$$= AQ e^{-\frac{\pi D}{4\sqrt{(JK)}}}. \tag{13.62}$$

Now, we can recall that the logarithmic decrement,

$$\lambda = \pi \zeta \frac{T_d}{T_0}.$$

When damping is small,

$$T_d = T_0.$$

$$\therefore \quad \lambda = \pi\zeta$$

$$= \frac{\pi D}{2\sqrt{(KJ)}}. \tag{13.63}$$

Therefore, Eq. (13.62) can be written as

$$\theta_1 = AQe^{-\lambda/2}. \tag{13.64}$$

Similarly, we can write,

$$\theta_2 = AQe^{-3\lambda/2}, \ \theta_n = AQe^{-(2n-1)\lambda/2}. \tag{13.65}$$

Let us now examine the case when the galvanometer is free from damping, i.e., $D = 0$. The equation of motion of an undamped galvanometer is

$$\theta = AQ \sin \frac{2\pi}{T_0} t \quad \text{[from Eq. (13.61)]}$$

So the amplitude of swings of undamped oscillations is

$$\theta_0 = AQ \sin \frac{2\pi}{T_0} \cdot \frac{T_0}{4}$$

$$= AQ. \tag{13.66}$$

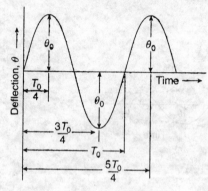

Fig. 13.4

The nature of the deflection-time curve for an undamped oscillation is shown in Fig. 13.4. Thus we can write,

$$\theta_1 = \theta_0 e^{-\lambda/2}$$
$$\theta_2 = \theta_0 e^{-3\lambda/2}$$
$$\dots\dots\dots\dots\dots$$
$$\theta_n = \theta_0 e^{-(2n-1)\lambda/2}.$$

The logarithmic decrement is defined as the logarithm of ratio of successive swings. So logarithmic decrement λ can be written as

$$\lambda = \log_e \left(\frac{\theta_1}{\theta_2} \right).$$

But, $\quad \dfrac{\theta_1}{\theta_2} = \dfrac{e^{-\lambda/2}}{e^{-3\lambda/2}} = e^{\lambda}.$

Similarly, $\dfrac{\theta_2}{\theta_3} = e^{\lambda}$

$$\dots\dots\dots$$

$$\frac{\theta_{n-1}}{\theta_n} = e^{\lambda}.$$

Hence, we get

$$\frac{\theta_1}{\theta_2} \times \frac{\theta_2}{\theta_3} \times \frac{\theta_3}{\theta_4} \times \cdots \times \frac{\theta_{n-1}}{\theta_n} = e^{(n-1)\lambda} \quad \text{or,} \quad \frac{\theta_1}{\theta_n} = e^{(n-1)\lambda}.$$

$$\therefore \text{logarithmic decrement, } \lambda = \frac{1}{n-1} \log_e \left(\frac{\theta_1}{\theta_n} \right). \tag{13.67}$$

Now we have

$$\theta_1 = \theta_0 e^{-\lambda/2} \quad \text{or,} \quad \theta_0 = \theta_1 e^{\lambda/2} = \theta_1 \left(1 + \frac{\lambda}{2} \right) \text{(approx.)}$$

or, $\qquad AQ = \theta_1 \left(1 + \dfrac{\lambda}{2}\right) \quad (\because \theta_0 = AQ).$

$\therefore$ charge, $Q = \dfrac{\theta_1}{A}\left(1 + \dfrac{\lambda}{2}\right)$ $\hfill$ (13.68)

$\qquad = \dfrac{J}{G}\sqrt{\dfrac{K}{J}}\theta_1\left(1 + \dfrac{\lambda}{2}\right) \quad \left(\because A = \dfrac{G}{J}\sqrt{\dfrac{J}{K}}\right).$

Now, $T_0 = 2\pi\sqrt{\dfrac{J}{K}}$

$\therefore \qquad Q = \dfrac{J}{G}\sqrt{\dfrac{K}{J}}\cdot\dfrac{T_0}{2\pi\sqrt{(J/K)}}\cdot\theta_1\left(1 + \dfrac{\lambda}{2}\right)$

$\qquad = \dfrac{K}{G}\cdot\dfrac{T_0}{2\pi}\theta_1\left(1 + \dfrac{\lambda}{2}\right).$ $\hfill$ (13.69)

To eliminate K and G from Eq. (13.69), let a steady current I_g passing through the galvanometer produce a steady deflection θ.

$\therefore \qquad GI_g = K\theta \quad \text{or,} \quad \dfrac{K}{G} = \dfrac{I_g}{\theta}.$

Hence, $Q = \dfrac{I_g}{\theta}\cdot\dfrac{T_0}{2\pi}\left(1 + \dfrac{\lambda}{2}\right)\theta_1$

$\qquad = K_q\theta_1,$ $\hfill$ (13.70)

where $\qquad K_q = \dfrac{I_g}{\theta}\cdot\dfrac{T_0}{2\pi}\left(1 + \dfrac{\lambda}{2}\right).$ $\hfill$ (13.71)

K_q is the constant of the galvanometer. Its unit is coulomb/radian. Sometimes instead of the term constant of galvanometer two other terms, viz., 'ballistic sensitivity' and 'flux linkage sensitivity' are used. Denoting the ballistic sensitivity by S_q and flux linkage sensitivity by S_ϕ we can write,

$S_q = \dfrac{\theta_1}{Q} \text{ rad/C}$ $\hfill$ (13.72)

and $\quad S_\phi = \dfrac{\theta_1}{\Delta\psi} \text{ rad/Wb turn.}$ $\hfill$ (13.73)

Thus we have,

$S_q = \dfrac{1}{K_q}$ $\hfill$ (13.74)

and $\quad S_\phi = \dfrac{1}{K_\phi}.$ $\hfill$ (13.75)

13.9 Fluxmeter

It is a special type of ballistic galvanometer in which the controlling torque is very low while the electromagnetic damping is heavy.

Construction

In Fig. 13.5 we have shown the construction of a fluxmeter. Here a coil of small cross-section is suspended from a spring supported by a single silk thread. The coil can move in the narrow gap of a permanent magnet. There is no arrangement of control springs. With the help of a loose helices of thin annealed silver strips the

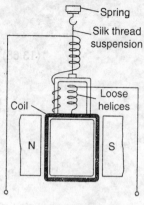

Fig. 13.5

current is led into the coil and hence the controlling torque is reduced to a minimum. The coil in a fluxmeter is formerless and the air friction damping is negligibly small.

Operation

As shown in Fig. 13.6, the fluxmeter is connected with the search coil. The flux linking with the search coil can be changed either by removing the coil from the magnetic field or by reversing the field. An e.m.f. is induced into the search coil owing to the change of flux linking with it. This e.m.f. sends a current through the fluxmeter. The instrument coil is found to deflect during the period the flux linkages change. But due to the high electromagnetic damping in the coil circuit as soon as the change ceases, the coil stops.

Theory

Let at any instant i be the current in the circuit and θ be the deflection of the instrument. We also assume that N be the number of turns of the search coil and ϕ the flux linking with it.

Further, let

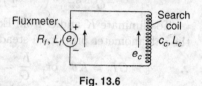

Fig. 13.6

R_f, L_f = resistance and inductance of the fluxmeter respectively

and R_c, L_c = resistance and inductance of the search coil respectively.

The equation of motion is

$$T_i + T_D + T_C = T_d \quad \text{or,} \quad J\frac{d^2\theta}{dt^2} + D\frac{d\theta}{dt} + K\theta = Gi.$$

If the control torque and the air friction damping are small, the above equation reduces to

$$J\frac{d^2\theta}{dt^2} = Gi \quad (\because \ D \text{ and } K \text{ are both zero}). \tag{13.76}$$

The e.m.f. due to any change of flux linked with the search coil,

$$e_c = N\frac{d\phi}{dt}. \tag{13.77}$$

Again, due to the movement of the fluxmeter coil within the field of the magnet a rotational e.m.f. is induced in the coil. This rotational e.m.f., e_f, can be expressed as

$$e_f = G\frac{d\theta}{dt}. \tag{13.78}$$

In addition, there are voltage drops in the resistance and inductance of the circuit; we can, therefore, write,

$$e_c = e_f + (L_f + L_c)\frac{di}{dt} + i(R_f + R_c)$$

or, $$N\frac{d\phi}{dt} = G\frac{d\theta}{dt} + (L_f + L_c)\frac{di}{dt} + i(R_f + R_c)$$

or, $$i = \frac{N\frac{d\phi}{dt} - G\frac{d\theta}{dt} - (L_f + L_c)\frac{di}{dt}}{R_f + R_c}.$$

So, the equation of motion is

$$J\frac{d^2\phi}{dt^2} = \frac{G}{R_f + R_c}\left[N\frac{d\phi}{dt} - G\frac{d\theta}{dt} - (L_f + L_c)\frac{di}{dt}\right]$$

or,
$$N\frac{d\phi}{dt} = \frac{J(R_f + R_c)}{G}\frac{d^2\theta}{dt^2} + G\frac{d\theta}{dt} + (L_f + L_c)\frac{di}{dt}$$

$$= \frac{J(R_f + R_c)}{G}\frac{d\omega}{dt} + G\frac{d\theta}{dt} + (L_f + L_c)\frac{di}{dt};$$

where ω is the angular velocity of the moving coil at any instant t. If T is the time taken by change in flux, we have

$$\int_0^T N\frac{d\phi}{dt}dt = \int_0^T \frac{J(R_f + R_c)}{G}\frac{d\omega}{dt}dt + \int_0^T G\frac{d\theta}{dt}dt + \int_0^T (L_f + L_c)\frac{di}{dt}dt$$

or,
$$\int_{\phi_1}^{\phi_2} Nd\phi = \int_{\omega_1}^{\omega_2}\frac{J(R_f + R_c)}{G}d\omega + \int_{\theta_1}^{\theta_2}Gd\theta + \int_{i_1}^{i_2}(L_f + L_c)di$$

or,
$$N(\phi_2 - \phi_1) = \frac{J(R_f + R_c)}{G}(\omega_2 - \omega_1) + G(\theta_2 - \theta_1) + (L_f + L_c)(i_2 - i_1),\ \ (13.79)$$

where ϕ_1, ϕ_2 are the interlinking fluxes; ω_1, ω_2 are the angular velocities; θ_1, θ_2 are the deflections and i_1, i_2 are the currents. Suffixes 1 and 2 respectively indicate values at the beginning and at the end of the change. But since the angular velocities and currents are zero at the beginning and at the end of the change, we have

$$\omega_1 = \omega_2 = 0 \quad \text{and} \quad i_1 = i_2 = 0.$$

Hence Eq. (13.79) reduces to

$$N(\phi_2 - \phi_1) = G(\theta_2 - \theta_1)$$

or, simply, $\phi = \dfrac{G}{N}\theta.$
$$\hspace{10cm}(13.80)$$

where ϕ is the change in the flux and θ the change in fluxmeter deflection. If G is constant, then we can conclude from the above equation that the change in flux is directly proportional to the change in the deflection and hence the instrument will have a uniform scale.

13.9.1 Use of Shunt with the Fluxmeter

When a large value of flux is to be measured, the fluxmeter deflection may exceed the scale length even when a single turn search coil is used. The range of fluxmeter, for such measurement, may be extended by using a shunt. The circuit diagram for the use of a shunt with a fluxmeter is shown in Fig. 13.7.

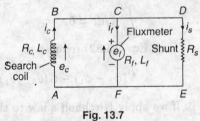

Fig. 13.7

Let $\quad L_c, L_f =$ inductance of the search coil and the fluxmeter respectively,

$R_c, R_f, R_s =$ resistance of search coil, fluxmeter and shunt respectively,

$i_c, i_f, i_s =$ current through search coil, fluxmeter and shunt respectively,

$e_c =$ induced e.m.f. in the search coil due to the change in flux linkages

$$= N\frac{dL}{dt},$$

e_f = generated e.m.f. in the fluxmeter coil due to rotation

$$= G\frac{d\phi}{dt}.$$

If we apply Kirchhoff's law to the mesh $ABCF$, we get

$$e_c = i_c R_c + L_c \frac{di_c}{dt} + i_f R_f + L_f \frac{di_f}{dt} + e_f$$

or, $$N\frac{d\phi}{dt} - L_c\frac{di_c}{dt} - L_f\frac{di_f}{dt} - G\frac{d\theta}{dt} = i_c R_c + i_f R_f.$$

Integrating, as before, we get

$$N(\phi_2 - \phi_1) - L_c(i_{c_2} - i_{c_1}) - L_f(i_{f_2} - i_{f_1}) - G(\theta_2 - \theta_1)$$

$$= R_c \int_0^T i_c dt + R_f \int_0^T i_f dt. \tag{13.81}$$

Since both at the beginning and the end of the flux-change, the currents are equal to zero, we can write,

$$i_{c_2} = i_{c_1} = 0$$

$$i_{f_2} = i_{f_1} = 0.$$

Eq. (13.81) can, therefore, be written as

$$N(\phi_2 - \phi_1) - G(\theta_2 - \theta_1) = R_c \int_0^T i_c dt + R_f \int_0^T i_f dt. \tag{13.82}$$

The equation of motion is

$$J\frac{d^2\theta}{dt^2} = G i_f$$

or, $$i_f = \frac{J}{G}\frac{d^2\theta}{dt^2} = \frac{J}{G}\frac{d\omega}{dt} \quad (\omega = \text{angular velocity at any instant}).$$

Hence, $$\int_0^T i_f dt = \frac{J}{G}\int_0^T \frac{d\omega}{dt}dt = \frac{J}{G}\int_{\omega_1}^{\omega_2} d\omega$$

or, $$\int_0^T i_f dt = \frac{J}{G}(\omega_2 - \omega_1).$$

But $\omega_2 = \omega_1 = 0.$

$\therefore$ $$\int_0^T i_f dt = 0. \tag{13.83}$$

Thus Eq. (13.82) reduces to

$$N(\phi_2 - \phi_1) - G(\theta_2 - \theta_1) = R_c \int_0^T i_c dt. \tag{13.84}$$

If we apply Kirchhoff's law to the mesh $CDEF$, we get

$$e_f + L_f \frac{di_f}{dt} + i_f R_f = i_s R_s$$

or, $$G\frac{d\theta}{dt} + L_f\frac{di_f}{dt} = -i_f R_f + i_s R_s = -i_f R_f + (i_c - i_f)R_s$$

$$= -(R_f + R_s)i_f + i_c R_s.$$

Integrating as before,

$$G(\theta_2 - \theta_1) + L_f(i_{f_2} - i_{f_1}) = -(R_f + R_s)\int_0^T i_f dt + R_s \int_0^T i_c dt.$$

But $i_{f_2} - i_{f_1} = 0$ and $\int_0^T i_f dt = 0$.

$\therefore \qquad G(\theta_2 - \theta_1) = R_s \int_0^T i_c dt$

or, $\qquad \int_0^T i_c dt = \dfrac{G(\theta_2 - \theta_1)}{R_s}.$ \hfill (13.85)

Hence, from Eq. (13.84), we get

$$N(\phi_2 - \phi_1) - G(\theta_2 - \theta_1) = \frac{R_c}{R_s} \cdot G(\theta_2 - \theta_1)$$

or, $\qquad N(\phi_2 - \phi_1) = G\dfrac{R_c + R_s}{R_s}(\theta_2 - \theta_1).$ \hfill (13.86)

If $\qquad \phi_2 - \phi_1 = \phi$ and $\theta_2 - \theta_1 = \theta,$

we get $\qquad \phi = \dfrac{G}{N}\dfrac{R_c + R_s}{R_s}\theta.$ \hfill (13.87)

It is thus found from Eq. (13.87) that the multiplying factor for the shunted fluxmeter is

$$m = \frac{R_c + R_s}{R_s}.$$ \hfill (13.88)

13.9.2 Advantages and Disadvantages of Fluxmeter

Advantages

(i) Its scale is directly calibrated to weber-turns.

(ii) Fluxmeter of industrial form is portable.

(iii) Indication of the meter is independent of the time taken by the flux-change.

Disadvantages

The fluxmeter is—

(i) less accurate and

(ii) less sensitive than the ballistic galvanometer.

13.9.3 Comparison of a Ballistic Galvanometer with a Fluxmeter

Ballistic galvanometer	Fluxmeter
(i) It has a large time-period and a large moment of inertia of the suspended system.	(i) It is also a galvanometer with a very large time-period and a large moment of inertia. Hence, we may call it as a special type of ballistic galvanometer.
(ii) The deflection is independent of the time of passage of the charge.	(ii) In this case also the deflection is independent of the time of passage of the charge.
(iii) In comparison to the time-period the time of passage of charge is very small.	(iii) In a good fluxmeter the time of passage of charge is sufficiently great.

Contd.

Ballistic galvanometer	Fluxmeter
(iv) In a ballistic galvanometer the damping is reduced to zero. The controlling torque is solely due to suspension.	(iv) The controlling torque of the suspension is almost reduced to zero. But in a fluxmeter the electromagnetic damping is increased to a maximum.
(v) The ballistic galvanometer is an absolute device for measuring charge or flux.	(v) It is to be previously calibrated taking known values of flux.
(vi) The time-period in this case is large but not approaching towards infinity.	(vi) The time-period almost approaches to infinity.
(vii) Ballistic galvanometer circuit is a high resistance circuit and the deflection is dependent on the resistance in the circuit.	(vii) The fluxmeter circuit is a low resistance circuit. The deflection here is independent of the circuit resistance if it is less than a limiting value.

13.10   Vibration Galvanometers

These are also of d'Arsonval type with a moving coil suspended between the pieces of a permanent magnet. If an alternating current is made to pass through the moving coil it vibrates with a frequency of the current passing.

This type of galvanometers is used at low audio-frequencies.

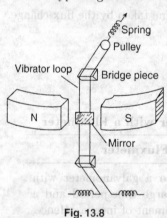

Fig. 13.8

Construction

The construction of Duddell's moving coil vibration galvanometer is shown in Fig. 13.8. It consists of a fine bronze or platinum silver wire which passes over a small pulley at the top and is pulled tight by a spring. The loop of the wire is stretched over two ivory bridge pieces whose separation can be adjusted. Owing to the passage of an a.c. when the moving coil begins to vibrate, the reflected beam from the mirror throws a band of light on the scale. When the galvanometer is properly tuned, the amplitude of vibration becomes very large and so a wide band of light is obtained on the scale.

Theory

Let i be the current passing through the moving coil at any instant t. Then we can write,

$$i = I_m \sin \omega t \qquad (13.89)$$

∴ deflecting torque, $T_d = Gi$

$$= GI_m \sin \omega t. \qquad (13.90)$$

The equation of motion is

$$T_i + T_D + T_C = T_d$$

or, $\quad J\dfrac{d^2\theta}{dt^2} + D\dfrac{d\theta}{dt} + K\theta = GI_m \sin \omega t.$ $\hfill$ (13.91)

The galvanometer is underdamped. So the complementary function is given by

$$\theta = e^{-\frac{D}{2J}t} F[\sin(\omega_d t + \phi)].$$ $\hfill$ (13.92)

Let $\theta = A\sin(\omega t - \alpha)$, where A and α are constants.

$$\therefore \quad \dfrac{d\theta}{dt} = A\omega \cos(\omega t - \alpha) \quad \text{and} \quad \dfrac{d^2\theta}{dt^2} = -A\omega^2 \sin(\omega t - \alpha).$$

Hence, from Eq. (13.91), we have

$$-AJ\omega^2 \sin(\omega t - \alpha) + AD\omega \cos(\omega t - \alpha) + AK \sin(\omega t - \alpha)$$
$$= GI_m \sin \omega t.$$ $\hfill$ (13.93)

Eq. (13.93) holds good for all values of t.

(i) When $\omega = \alpha$,

$$AD\omega = GI_m \sin \alpha.$$

(ii) When $(\omega t - \alpha) = \dfrac{\pi}{2}$,

$$-AJ\omega^2 + AK = GI_m \cos \alpha.$$

Squaring and adding (i) and (ii),

$$A^2 D^2 \omega^2 + A^2(K - J\omega^2)^2 = G^2 I_m^2$$

or, $\quad A = \dfrac{GI_m}{\sqrt{(D\omega)^2 + (K - J\omega^2)^2}}.$

Also taking the ratio of (i) and (ii),

$$\tan \alpha = \dfrac{D\omega}{K - J\omega^2} \quad \text{or,} \quad \alpha = \tan^{-1} \dfrac{D\omega}{K - J\omega^2}.$$

Thus, we have

$$\theta = \dfrac{GI_m}{\sqrt{(D\omega)^2 + (K - J\omega^2)^2}} \sin(\omega t - \alpha).$$ $\hfill$ (13.94)

Hence, the complete solution is

$$\theta = e^{-\frac{D}{2J}t} F[\sin(\omega t + \phi)] + \dfrac{GI_m}{\sqrt{(D\omega)^2 + (K - J\omega^2)^2}} \sin(\omega t - \alpha).$$ $\hfill$ (13.95)

The first term on the r.h.s. is a transient term and effects only for a first few vibrations. So it has little importance. For a particular current the amplitude can be increased by increasing G. This can also be done by decreasing $(D\omega)^2 + (K - J\omega^2)^2$. This requires that

$$K - J\omega^2 = 0 \quad \text{or,} \quad \omega = \sqrt{(K/J)}$$

or, $\quad f = \dfrac{\omega}{2\pi} = \dfrac{1}{2\pi}\sqrt{(K/J)}.$ $\hfill$ (13.96)

A plot of the deflection against frequency is shown in Fig. 13.9. It is seen that for a galvanometer having sharply peaked resonance

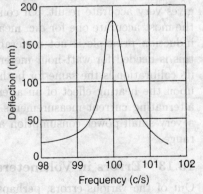

Fig. 13.9

curve a little deviation from the resonance frequency results in a large reduction in deflection.

13.11   Voltmeters and Ammeters

Voltmeters and ammeters are usually classed together as there is no basic difference in principle between these two instruments. A voltmeter carries a current which is proportional to the voltage to be determined. This current of the voltmeter produces the operating torque. On the other hand, in an ammeter this torque is produced by the current to be measured. Therefore, the only difference between them is in the magnitude of the current producing the operating torque.

A voltmeter, in a circuit, is connected across the voltage to be measured. Therefore, it has a high resistance so that the current taken by it becomes very small. An ammeter, on the contrary, has a low resistance and if it is connected in series does not appreciably alter the current. A low range ammeter can, therefore, be suitably used as a voltmeter if a high resistance is connected in series with it.

If R_v represents the resistance of a voltmeter to which a voltages E is applied, then the power loss in the instrument is E^2/R_v. Again, if R_a denotes the resistance of an ammeter in which a current I flows, then the power loss in the instrument is $I^2 R_a$. Therefore, the instrumental power loss will be small for a large value of R_v and small R_a.

13.12   Types of Voltmeters and Ammeters

The commonly used voltmeters and ammeters are of the following types :

   (i) Moving iron

  (ii) Moving coil :

     (a) permanent magnet form

     (b) dynamometer form

 (iii) Induction

 (iv) Thermal

  (v) Electrostatic (voltmeters only).

Out of these, the permanent magnet moving coil type can be used only for the measurement of direct current while the induction type can be used only for alternating current. All the remaining types are suitable for both the currents.

Both moving iron and moving coil types depend for their action on the magnetic effect of current. The moving iron type is the cheapest and if properly designed gives very accurate result. Of course, the permanent magnet moving coil type is the most accurate one for d.c. measurement. Due to high cost and inaccuracy the induction principle is not preferably used for ammeters and voltmeters. Rather this is needed for watt-hour meters. Thermal instrument has the advantage that its calibration is the same for both d.c. and a.c. circuits. Their deflection depends upon the heating effect of an alternating current and hence very suitable for the alternating current measurements. As voltmeters, electrostatic instruments have a very small power consumption and can be constructed to cover a wide voltage range.

13.13   Errors in Voltmeters and Ammeters

Out of the various errors, perhaps the friction and temperature errors are most important.

In order to reduce the effect of friction torque the weight of the moving system should be made as small as possible in comparison to the operating forces. Or in other words, the ratio of torque to weight must be large. Another serious error is owing to the heat generated in the instrument due to a change in the resistance of the working coil. For eliminating the temperature error, the working coil is wound with copper wire. Other errors by heating may come due to expansion of the control spring or some other parts of the instrument. Such errors are usually very small.

13.14 Moving Iron Instruments

These instruments are broadly of two different types, viz., (a) attraction type and (b) repulsion type. In these instruments, the current to be measured is passed through a coil of wire whose number of turns depends on the current to be passed.

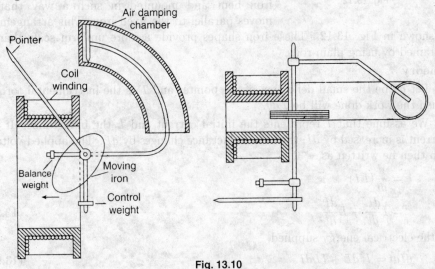

Fig. 13.10

In the attraction type of moving iron instrument, as shown in Fig. 13.10, a small piece of iron is drawn into the core of the coil. In the repulsion form (Fig. 13.11), two rods or pieces of iron are there inside the coil. One of the rods is fixed while the other is movable. These are magnetized similarly when the current passes through the coil and as a result a repulsion of the moving iron from the fixed one occurs. The force of this repulsion is proportional to the square of the current in the coil.

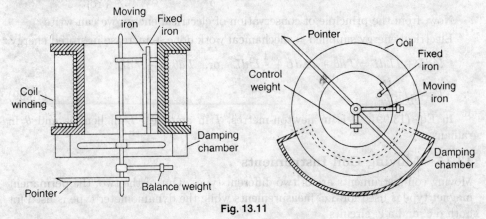

Fig. 13.11

Gravity control is used in the instrument in the earlier days. But nowadays spring control is used almost universally. The method of damping moving iron instruments is by air friction.

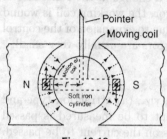

Fig. 13.12

The moving iron in the attraction type is eccentrically pivoted. It consists of thin disc of soft iron which tends to move when the current passes. The shape of the disc is made such that a suitably divided scale is obtained. In the repulsion type, iron shapes may be like of rod or it may consist of a tongue-shaped piece of sheet iron bent into a cylindrical form. The moving iron is made from another piece of sheet iron bent and mounted in such a way that it moves parallel to the fixed iron. This arrangement is shown in Fig. 13.12. These iron shapes provide a more uniform scale than is obtained by using plain rods.

Theory

Let $d\theta$ be the small deflection of the pointer and T is the instrumental torque. Then the work done will be $T d\theta$.

We assume that I represents the initial current and L the inductance. If the current is increased by dI, then the inductance changes by dL. The applied voltage can then be written as

$$e = \frac{d}{dt}(LI)$$

$$= I\frac{dL}{dt} + L\frac{dI}{dt}. \tag{13.97}$$

∴ the electrical energy supplied,

$$eIdt = I^2 dL + ILdI. \tag{13.98}$$

The stored energy changes from $\frac{1}{2}I^2L$ to

$$\frac{1}{2}(I + dI)^2(L + dL).$$

So the change in stored energy $= \frac{1}{2}(I^2 + 2IdI + dI^2)(L + dL) - \frac{1}{2}I^2L$

$$= ILdI + \frac{1}{2}I^2 dL \text{ (neglecting higher orders)}.$$

Now, from the principle of conservation of electrical energy we can write :

Electrical energy supplied = mechanical work done + increase in stored energy.

$$I^2 dL + ILdI = Td\theta + ILdL + \frac{1}{2}I^2 dL \quad \text{or,} \quad Td\theta = \frac{1}{2}I^2 dL.$$

$$\therefore \quad T = \frac{1}{2}I^2 \frac{dL}{d\theta}. \tag{13.99}$$

In Eq. (13.99), T is in newton-metres, I in amperes, L in henries and θ in radians.

13.15 Moving Coil Instruments

Moving coil instruments are of two different types. Out of the two, the permanent magnet type is used for d.c. measurements while the dynamometer type is used for both d.c. and a.c. circuits.

In the permanent magnet type a light rectangular coil is pivoted so that its sides remain in the air-gaps between the two poles of a permanent magnet and a soft iron cylinder. With the flow of current through the coil a deflecting torque is produced due to the reaction between the field of permanent magnet and the magnetic field of the coil (Fig. 13.13). The air-gap between the magnet poles and the iron core is about 0.05 inch. The flux density is uniform and it is in a radial direction.

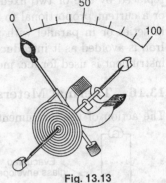

Fig. 13.13

When a current I passes through the moving coil in the direction shown in the figure, forces F, F will act on the two sides of the coil. For N number of turns of the coil the force F can be written as

$$F = NBIl, \tag{13.100}$$

where B is the flux density in the air-gap and l is the active length of the sides of the coil within the air-gap.

Again, if r is the mean distance of the wires forming the sides of the coil from the axis of rotation, then the torque causing the coil to rotate is

$$T = 2rF$$
$$= 2r \times NBIl. \tag{13.101}$$

In a moving coil instrument since the deflecting torque is proportional to current and the controlling torque of the springs is proportional to the deflection θ, we have

$$T_D \propto I \quad \text{and} \quad T_c \propto \theta.$$

In its deflected position, when the moving system is at rest,

$$T_D = T_c.$$

$$\therefore \quad \theta \propto I.$$

Thus the scale is uniformly divided.

The connections of moving coil instrument when used as an ammeter and a voltameter is shown in Fig. 13.14(a) and (b), respectively. Power loss in permanent magnet moving coil instruments is generally lower than the other type of instruments.

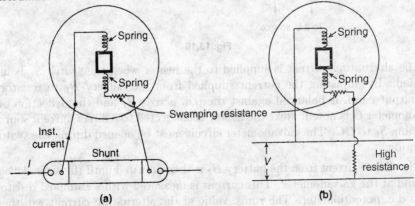

Fig. 13.14

In dynamometer type moving coil instruments, the permanent magnet is replaced by one or two fixed coils. These coils carry the current to be measured or a current proportional to the voltage to be measured and are connected either in series or in parallel with the moving coil. The coils are air-cored, in general. Iron is avoided as it introduces hysteresis, eddy current and other errors when the instrument is used for a.c. measurement.

13.16   Thermal Meters

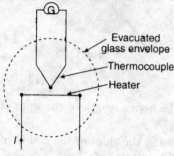

Fig. 13.15

The action of the instrument depends on the heating effect of the current to be measured. A thermal converter is shown in Fig. 13.15. It consists of a heater through which the current to be determined flows and a thermocouple for sensing the rise of temperature at the mid-point of the heater. All these are enclosed in an evacuated glass bulb shown by dashed circle in the figure. This form is called as *vacuo-thermo-junctions*. The thermocouple is in thermal contact with the heater but should be electrically insulated from it.

Instruments of these types have a wide frequency range and are completely free from waveform error.

The vacuo-thermo-junction can be utilized for the precise measurement of alternating currents and voltages with the help of an arrangement shown in Fig. 13.16.

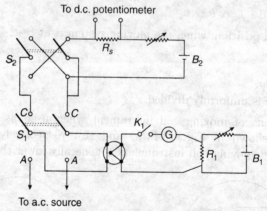

Fig. 13.16

The alternating current is supplied to the heater when the switch S_1 is in AA position. By adjusting the current supplied from the battery B_1 to resistor R_1, the output e.m.f. is balanced against the p.d. across R_1 and the deflection of the galvanometer G is noted. Next the heater is connected to a direct current source by changing S_1 to CC. The galvanometer circuit must be opened during the switching operation.

The direct current from the battery B_2 is then adjusted until the same deflection is found at the galvanometer. This current is measured with a standard resistor R_s and a d.c. potentiometer. The r.m.s. value of the alternating current will then be equal to the direct current.

13.17   Electrostatic Instruments

These instruments are basically voltmeters. Electrostatic voltmeter provides equally correct measurements in a.c. and d.c. circuits. As no iron is present in their working system, they are free from all errors related to magnetic fields in iron. The power loss of this voltmeter is also very small. However, they have the disadvantage that the operation voltages are too small, particularly for low voltages.

Theory

The principle of the electrostatic voltmeter can be established by considering Fig. 13.17. In the figure, plate A is fixed while B is movable and restrained by a spring S connected to the fixed point P. Let for a potential difference of V volts between the plates, a force of attraction F newtons exist between them. If the capacitance between the plate is C farads, then the energy stored is $\frac{1}{2}CV^2$ joules. With the increase of the voltage, a capacitance current will flow, given by

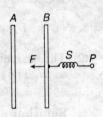

Fig. 13.17

$$i = \frac{dq}{dt} = \frac{d}{dt}(CV) = C\frac{dV}{dt} + V\frac{dC}{dt}.$$

The input energy is

$$V i \, dt = V^2 dC + CV \, dV.$$

The change in stored energy $= \frac{1}{2}(C + dC)(V + dV)^2 - \frac{1}{2}CV^2$

$$= \frac{1}{2}(C + dC)(V^2 + 2V + dV^2) - \frac{1}{2}CV^2$$

$$= \frac{1}{2}V^2 dC + CV \, dV \quad \text{(neglecting higher orders)}.$$

Now, from the principle of conservation of energy :

Input electrical energy = increase in stored energy + mechanical work done

i.e., $V^2 dC + CV \, dV = \dfrac{1}{2}V^2 dC + CV \, dV + F \, dx$

or, $F = \dfrac{1}{2}V^2 \dfrac{dC}{dx}.$ (13.102)

Electrostatic voltmeters are of two different types, viz., quadrant type and the attracted disc type.

Examples

1. A galvanometer shows a deflection of 150 mm on a linear scale 2.5 m distant for a steady current 1 μA. The period of oscillations is 4 seconds and the moment of inertia of the moving system 1×10^{-6} kg-m^2. Calculate the coil circuit resistance required to obtain critical damping. The air damping is neglected.

    Solution : Let the final steady deflection be θ_F radian, r the distance of the scale from the galvanometer and d the deflection on the linear scale. Then,

    $$d = r\theta_F \quad \text{or,} \quad \theta_F = \frac{d}{r} = \frac{150}{2500} = 0.06 \text{ rad.}$$

Again, $\theta_F = \dfrac{Gi}{K}$ or, $G = \dfrac{\theta_F K}{i} = \dfrac{0.06 \times K}{1 \times 10^{-6}} = 60K \times 10^3$.

Period of oscillation, $T_0 = 2\pi\sqrt{\dfrac{J}{K}}$

or, $4 = 2\pi\sqrt{\dfrac{1 \times 10^{-6}}{K}}$ or, $K = 2.47 \times 10^{-6}$ N-m/rad.

Hence, $G = 60 \times 2.47 \times 10^{-6} \times 10^3 = 148.2 \times 10^{-3}$

For critical damping, the coil circuit resistance

$$R = \frac{G^2}{2\sqrt{KJ}} = \frac{(148.2 \times 10^{-3})^2}{2\sqrt{2.47 \times 10^{-6} \times 1 \times 10^{-6}}} = \mathbf{6950\ \Omega}.$$

2. The current sensitivity of a galvanometer is 100 mm/μA with the scale 1 m away. The resistance of the coil is 200 ohms. Determine the voltage sensitivity and the megohm sensitivity.

Solution : Here, the current sensitivity $= 100$ mm/μA,

$$\text{scale distance} = 1 \text{ m}.$$

Now, voltage sensitivity, $S_v = \dfrac{d}{i \times R_g \times 10^{-6}}$ mm/μV

$$= \frac{100}{1 \times 10^{-6} \times 200 \times 10^6} = \mathbf{0.5\ mm/\mu V}.$$

Again, current required for 1 mm deflection is 0.01 μA.

$\therefore$ megohm sensitivity, $S_0 = \dfrac{1}{0.01} = \mathbf{100\ M\Omega/mm}$.

3. A ballistic galvanometer shows a first maximum deflection of 60° for a discharge of 1000 μC. Determine the quantity of electricity, which when discharged through this galvanometer, gives rise to a spot deflection of 10 divisions on a millimeter circular scale 1 metre away.

Solution : We have

charge $Q = K_q\theta_1$ or, $K_q = \dfrac{Q}{\theta_1}$.

Here, $\theta = 60° = \dfrac{\pi}{3}$ rad, $Q = 1000\ \mu$C.

$\therefore$ $K_q = \dfrac{1000}{\pi/3} = \dfrac{3000}{\pi}$ μC/rad.

Again, $\theta = \dfrac{l}{r} = \dfrac{10}{1000} = 0.01$ rad.

$\therefore$ $Q = \dfrac{3000}{\pi} \times 0.01 = 9.56\ \mu$C.

Questions

Essay-type

1. Describe a d'Arsonaval galvanometer. Establish the equation for the torque.

2. Discuss the equation of the dynamic behaviour of galvanometers. Calculate the torque acting on a galvanometer.

3. What is meant by underdamped motion of a galvanometer? Explain mathematically. What is the difference between critically damped and overdamped motion of a galvanometer?

4. Define current and voltage sensitivity of a galvanometer. What do you mean by 'megohm sensitivity'?

5. What is a ballistic galvanometer? What are its uses? Give the construction and theory of the galvanometer.

6. What is a fluxmeter? Give its theory. What are the uses of a shunt with the fluxmeter?

7. Compare a ballistic galvanometer with fluxmeter.

8. Give the construction and theory of the vibration galvanometers. What is a fluxmeter?

9. What is a voltmeter and an ammeter? Mention the different types of voltmeter and ammeters. What are the errors in such instruments?

10. Discuss the construction of (i) moving iron instruments and (ii) moving coil instruments. Give the theory for each of them.

11. Describe briefly about the thermal meters and electrostatic instruments.

Chapter 14
Electrical Equipments

14.1 Introduction

The measurement of a given quantity is essentially the result of comparison between the quantity and a predefined standard. Generally measurement involves using an instrument as a physical means to determine a quantity or variable. Thus one may define an instrument as a device of finding the value or the magnitude of a quantity or variable.

The first instruments were mechanical in nature. However, the principles on which these worked are still not known. The history of development of instruments encompassed three phases as : (i) mechanical instruments, (ii) electrical instruments and (iii) electronic instruments. Out of the three, electrical methods are more rapid than the mechanical methods. But unfortunately an electrical system normally depends in a mechanical meter movement as indicating device. Nowadays most of the scientific and industrial measurements demand very fast responses. The mechanical and electrical instruments cannot cope with these requirements. This has been only possible by using electronic instruments. In this chapter, however, we have discussed only the earlier types of instruments avoiding the electronic systems.

14.2 Generator

Basic Principles

Let us consider a straight conductor O of length l moving with a uniform velocity v in a uniform magnetic field of flux density B in a direction perpendicular to the lines of induction as shown in Fig. 14.1. If the conductor moves through a distance $OP = d$ in time t, then the flux cut by it is given by

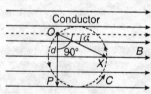

Fig. 14.1

$$N = B \cdot l \cdot d. \tag{14.1}$$

$\therefore$ the induced e.m.f.,

$$e = -\frac{dN}{dt} = -\frac{Bld}{t} = -Blv. \tag{14.2}$$

On the other hand, if the conductor moves a distance $OX = x$ in a direction inclined at an angle α with the lines of force, then the distance traversed perpendicularly to the field is $x \sin \alpha$ and, therefore,

$$N = Blx \sin \alpha.$$

Hence, $e = -\dfrac{dN}{dt} = -Blv \sin \alpha.$ $\tag{14.3}$

If $\alpha = 0$, then $e = 0$ and if $\alpha = 90°$, then e.m.f. is maximum.

Let us next calculate the e.m.f. generated in a rectangular coil. Let $abcd$ be a rectangular loop of a conducting material rotated with uniform angular velocity ω

about an axis XY perpendicular to the field (Fig. 14.2). If the breadth (ab or cd) is $2r$, then the linear velocity of the rotating loop is

$$v = r\omega. \tag{14.4}$$

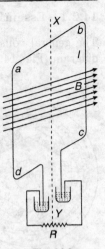

During the rotation of the rectangular loop the planes of rotation of ab and cd remain parallel to the field. As a result they do not cut any lines of force and there is no induced e.m.f. in these portions. But the side ad (or bc) of length l remains perpendicular to the field. Their direction of motion with respect to the field continually changes from 0 to 2π. When the conductors are moving in a direction α with the field, the induced e.m.f. can be written as

$$e = 2Blv \sin \alpha. \tag{14.5}$$

If the loop is replaced by coil of n turns, then the total induced e.m.f. can be expressed as

$$E = 2nBlv \sin \alpha. \tag{14.6}$$

Fig. 14.2

If the time is reckoned in a way that when $t = 0, \alpha = 0$, then at any subsequent instant, $\alpha = \omega t$. Hence,

$$E = 2nBlr\omega \sin \omega t = nB(2rl)\omega \sin \omega t$$
$$= nBA\omega \sin \omega t, \text{ where } A = \text{area of each loop of the coil} \tag{14.7}$$
$$= 2rl.$$

Eq. (14.7) can be rewritten as

$$E = E_0 \sin \omega t, \text{ where } E_0 = nBA\omega. \tag{14.8}$$

In Eq. (14.8) nBA is the total flux through the coil when its normal is parallel to the field.

We have found above that the working of a generator is based upon the induced e.m.f. due to electromagnetic induction in rotating coil. If a rectangular coil of n turns each of area A rotates with an angular velocity ω, then

$$f = \omega/2\pi.$$

If the normal to the coil is initially parallel to the field, then at any subsequent instant t it will be displaced through an angle $\alpha = \omega t$. Therefore, magnetic flux linked with the coil in this position is given by

$$N = n\mu HA \cos \omega t \quad [\because \ B = \mu H]. \tag{14.9}$$

$\therefore$ total induced e.m.f., $E = -dN/dt = n\mu HA w \sin \omega t$

$$= E_0 \sin \omega t, \text{ where } E_0 = n\mu HA\omega.$$

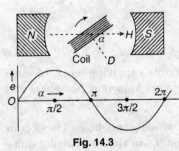

In such a rotating coil the variation of the current is obtained in a simple harmonic manner. Here as the current is reversed in direction alternately during rotation, it is termed as *alternating current* (Fig. 14.3).

In a generator, there is an arrangement to transfer the current from a rotating coil to an external circuit due to which unidirectional or alternating current can be achieved. The gene-

Fig. 14.3

rators can, therefore, be classified as d.c. and a.c. generators.

14.2.1   Essential Parts of a.c. Generator

The general constructions of a generator is discussed below and is shown in the diagram (Fig. 14.4).

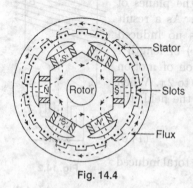

Fig. 14.4

(i) The stator is built of steel laminations having slots for conductors. It is fitted inside a frame of cast iron.

(ii) The rotor poles are fixed to the rim of a steel magnet wheel and this can be rotated. The exciting coils round the poles are connected in series while the two ends are carefully connected to a d.c. source through brushes.

(iii) The armature coils are fitted inside the slots and their both ends are brought out. For a maximum voltage the span of each coil should be a pole pitch.

Single-phase Winding

There is only one coil group for each pair of poles. In concentrated winding there is one slot per pole. For a given number of conductors this type of winding as shown in Fig. 14.5 provides the maximum voltage but the wavefront is not a sinusoidal one. The windings shown are single-layer windings; two-layer windings arranged with two coil-sides per slot are frequently used.

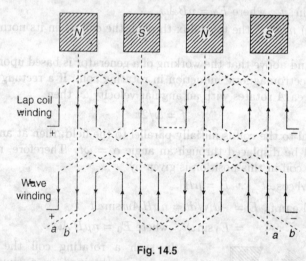

Fig. 14.5

Poly-phase Winding

In this arrangement there are 2 or 3 separate circuits supplying e.m.f. of same frequency but differing in phase by 90° or 120°. These are known as *two-phase* and *three-phase machines* respectively.

In a two-phase winding two separate single-phase windings are housed in slots in different positions relative to the poles so that the e.m.f.s in the two circuits differ in phase by 90°. A skeleton of this is shown in the upper part of Fig. 14.6.

In a three-phase winding three sets of conductors are distributed in slots, the skeleton of which is shown in the lower part of Fig. 14.6.

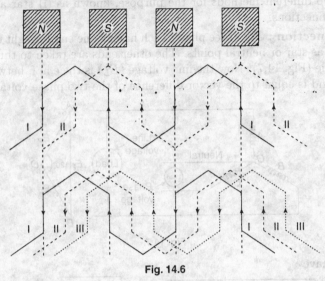

Fig. 14.6

14.2.2 Frequency and e.m.f. Equation

If there be n revolutions per second and $(p/2)$ is the number of pairs of poles, then the frequency of e.m.f. is

$$f = n \cdot (p/2).$$

Again if R is the revolution per minute, then

$$n = R/60.$$

$$\therefore \quad f = \frac{R}{60} \cdot \frac{p}{2} = \frac{Rp}{120}. \tag{14.10}$$

Let us consider the case where Z conductors are connected in series per phase. Time taken by the field per revolution $= (1/n)$ second. Therefore, time taken by the field to move through one pole pitch is given by

$$t = 1/(pn).$$

So the average e.m.f. in each conductor,

$$e = \frac{N}{t} = p \cdot nN \cdot 10^{-8} \text{ volts.}$$

If the waveform is not a sinusoidal one, then the form factor differs from 1.11. Indicating this by K_1, we can express the e.m.f. E as

$$E = K_1 p \cdot nNZ \times 10^{-8} \text{ volts.}$$

Again, if the windings are distributed then the e.m.f.s in different parts of the coil are not in phase. Let the total e.m.f. E for concentrated winding when distributed is reduced to $K_2 E$, where K_2 is called the 'breadth factor'. Then the resultant e.m.f. in all the conductors can be written as

$$E = K_1 K_2 p \cdot NnZ \times 10^{-8} \text{ volts}$$
$$= 2K_1 K_2 fNZ \times 10^{-8} \text{ volts} \quad (\because \ f = np/2). \tag{14.11}$$

14.2.3   Terminals in Three-phase Winding

There are two different methods for the purpose, known as (i) star and (ii) delta (or mesh) connections.

Star connection : The three phases each having one end brought to a common point known as star or neutral points. The other ends are taken to three terminals of the machine (Fig. 14.7). Now the line voltage (E_L) is the e.m.f. between any two phase lines and is equal to the vector difference of the two phase voltages E_p.

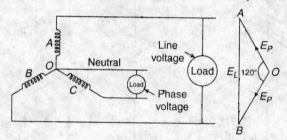

Fig. 14.7

We thus have

$$E_L = \sqrt{E_p^2 + E_p^2 - 2E_p E_p \cos 120°} = E_p \sqrt{2 + 2\cos\frac{\pi}{3}}$$

$$= \sqrt{3}E_p. \tag{14.12}$$

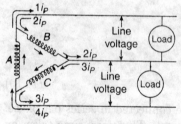

Fig. 14.8

Delta connection : The three phases, in this system, are connected to form a closed circuit (Fig. 14.8). Here the line current is the vector difference of two-phase currents. Mathematically,

$$I_L = \sqrt{3}I_p. \tag{14.13}$$

Power

As a balanced three-phase system consists of three similar circuits, we have

total power $= 3 \times$ power in each phase

$$= 3 \times E_p I_p \cos\phi, \tag{14.14}$$

where ϕ is the phase difference between phase current and phase voltage.

14.3   d.c. Generator

A d.c. generator has the following main components :

(i) A magnet for producing a field.

(ii) An arrangement to produce motion in the conductors.

(iii) An assemblage of conductors placed in the field.

(iv) A contrivance for transferring current to an external circuit.

All the above are accommodated in the field magnet and the armature. The field magnet may have one or more pairs of opposite poles. In Fig. 14.9(a) the field system consists of four poles. The armature, on the other hand, is a cylindrical structure made by sheets of iron or steel. The armature core has a series of longitudinal slots.

The material of the core increases the flux. Solid and laminated cores are shown in Fig. 14.9(b) and (c).

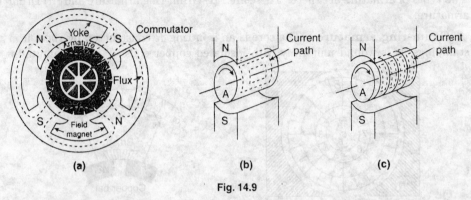

Fig. 14.9

There are three different ways of winding the field coil in relation to the armature coil. These are (i) series-wound machine, (ii) shunt-wound machine and (iii) compound-wound machine. Out of the three in the first mode of winding, the field coil has a few turns of thick wire and the load is in series with the field coil [Fig. 14.10(a)]. In the second mode of winding, the field coil has a large number of turns of wire and the load is connected in parallel with it [Fig. 14.10(b)]. The third type, i.e., the compound-wound machine is nothing but a shunt-wound machine in addition to

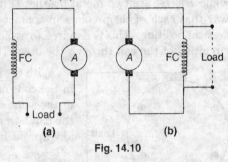

Fig. 14.10

few turns in series. When the series coil is connected in series with the field coil armature parallel combination it is termed as short shunt (Fig. 14.11(a)] while if it is connected in series with the armature it is called a long shunt [Fig. 14.11(b)].

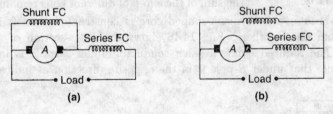

Fig. 14.11

The characteristics of the above three types of d.c. generator having different modes of field coil winding is shown in Fig. 14.12.

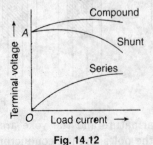

Fig. 14.12

14.3.1   Armature e.m.f. and Commutator Action

Two types of armature are there. These are : (i) Grum-ring armature and (ii) Drum armature.

Grum-ring armature : The core is an iron ring R constructed by sheet iron stampings. It is wound uniformly with insulated copper coils. C is a commutator

Fig. 14.13

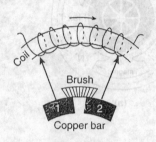

Fig. 14.14

while B_1, B_2 are two metal brushes (Fig. 14.13). Each brush is placed in such a way that each of them comes in contact with the end of the coil when it is in the vertical position. This is required to avoid sparking which may arise owing to short-circuiting of the coil through the brush (Fig. 14.14).

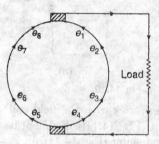

Fig. 14.15

With the rotation of the armature the induced e.m.f. in the coils on each half lying under the same pole are in the same direction (Fig. 14.15). If e_1, e_2, e_3, e_4 are the e.m.f. in different positions, then the total e.m.f. at any instant in each half of the coils is

$$e = e_1 + e_2 + e_3 + e_4 + \cdots$$

and $e = e_5 + e_6 + e_7 + e_8 + \cdots$

Since the position of the coils remains unchanged, the sum of the e.m.f. of different coils remains constant.

Drum armature : A drum-shaped core is constructed by soft iron sheets insulated from one another. Fig. 14.16 shows the cross-section of a four-pole generator. The induced e.m.f. in each conductor under N-pole is in the same direction while that under S-pole is in the opposite direction as indicated by '+' and '−' sign.

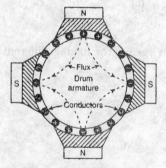

Fig. 14.16

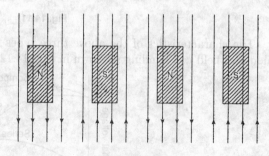

Fig. 14.17

If the periphery of the armature and the yoke are opened, one may get the diagram (Fig. 14.17) where the poles and the conductors are in one plane.

14.3.2 Lap and Wave Windings

Let a conductor (say, a) connected at the back to a conductor (say, b) under the next pole. The conductor is then to be joined at the front with any other conductor either by forward or by backward connections (Fig. 14.18).

Lap winding is a system in which the front and back pitches are unequal. In Fig. 14.19 the scheme of connections with only 16 conductors under 4-poles has been shown. According to the figure, brushes A and B are positive but those at C and D are negative.

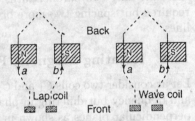

Fig. 14.18

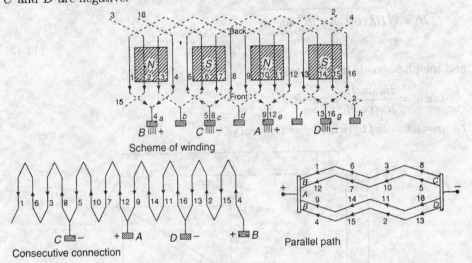

Scheme of winding

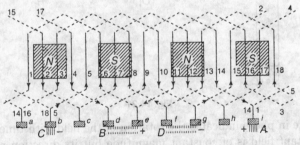

Consecutive connection

Parallel path

Fig. 14.19

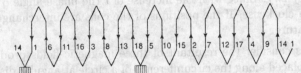

Scheme of winding

Consecutive connection

Parallel path

Fig. 14.20

On the contrary, in a wave winding front and back pitches are often equal. In Fig. 14.20 the schemes of connections with 18 conductors are shown. In this system there are only two parallel paths connecting all conductors. Here two brushes are required but spacing two more brushes are placed in positions as shown by dotted lines.

14.4   Rotating Magnetic Field

Let us consider two coils C_1 and C_2 carrying alternating currents of same amplitude and frequency but differing in phase by $(\pi/2)$. Let the coils be placed in mutually perpendicular planes as shown in Fig. 14.21. The two fields between the coils are represented as $H_0 \cos \omega t$ and $H_0 \sin \omega t$ so that the resultant field is given by

$$H = \sqrt{H_0^2 \cos^2 \omega t + H_0^2 \sin^2 \omega t}$$
$$= H_0 \tag{14.15}$$

and the phase-angle α is expressed as

$$\tan \alpha = \frac{H_0 \sin \omega t}{H_0 \cos \omega t} = \tan \omega t.$$

$$\therefore \quad \alpha = \omega t = 2\pi f t \quad (\text{where } f = \text{frequency}).$$

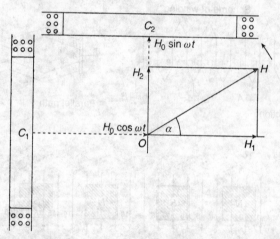

Fig. 14.21

This change in phase indicates the rotation of the field with time. We thus find that the resultant field is of constant magnitude but its direction rotates with an angular velocity $2\pi f$. Since with the increase of t the phase-angle α increases, the rotation is anti-clockwise. If the positions of the coils are interchanged it would be clockwise in nature.

Next, let us consider the resultant of three magnetic fields produced by three identical coils placed along the circumference of a circle at angular distances of 120° from one another (Fig. 14.22). Let each of them be energised by currents differing in phase by $(2\pi/3)$ from the current in two others. The magnitude of the fields thus produced can be written as

$$H_0 \sin \omega t, \ H_0 \sin \left(\omega t - \frac{2\pi}{3}\right), \ H_0 \sin \left(\omega t - \frac{4\pi}{3}\right).$$

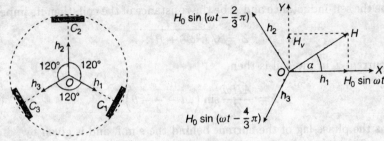

Fig. 14.22

To find the resultant resolve the two other field along and at right angle to $H_0 \sin \omega t$. We thus have, field along $H_0 \sin \omega t$

$$H_h = H_0 \left[\sin \omega t + \sin \left(\omega t - \frac{2\pi}{3} \right) \left(-\cos \frac{\pi}{3} \right) + \sin \left(\omega t - \frac{4\pi}{3} \right) \left(-\cos \frac{\pi}{3} \right) \right]$$

$$= \frac{3}{2} H_0 \sin \omega t.$$

Field $\perp$ to $H_0 \sin \omega t$,

$$H_v = H_0 \left[0 + \sin \left(\omega t - \frac{2\pi}{3} \right) \left(-\sin \frac{\pi}{3} \right) + \sin \left(\omega t - \frac{4\pi}{3} \right) \left(\sin \frac{\pi}{3} \right) \right]$$

$$= \frac{3}{2} H_0 \cos \omega t.$$

Therefore, resultant magnetic field,

$$H = \sqrt{\frac{9}{4} H_0^2 (\sin^2 \omega t + \cos^2 \omega t)} = \frac{3}{2} H_0$$

and the phase-change α is given by

$$\tan \alpha = \frac{\frac{3}{2} H_0 \sin \omega t}{\frac{3}{2} H_0 \cos \omega t} = \tan \omega t.$$

$$\therefore \quad \alpha = \omega t = 2\pi f t. \qquad (14.16)$$

14.4.1 Couple on a Coil in a Rotating Field

When a coil is placed in a rotating magnetic field there will be an induced e.m.f. in the coil which tends to oppose the relative motion of the coil and the field by Lenz's law.

Let A be the effective area of the coil and at any instant t the angular separation between the plane of the coil and the field be ωt (Fig. 14.23). The *flux* passing through the coil is given by

$$N = AH \sin \omega t.$$

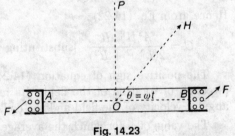

Fig. 14.23

Therefore, induced e.m.f., $e = -\dfrac{dN}{dt} = -\dfrac{d}{dt} (A \cdot H \sin \omega t)$

$$= -AH\omega \cos \omega t$$

$$= AH\omega \sin \left(\omega t - \frac{\pi}{2} \right). \qquad (14.17)$$

If L be the self-inductance and R be the resistance of the coil, then its impedance,

$$Z = \sqrt{L^2\omega^2 + R^2}.\tag{14.18}$$

The current I in the coil is then,

$$I = \frac{AH\omega}{Z}\sin\left(\omega t - \frac{\pi}{2} - \theta\right),\tag{14.19}$$

where θ is the phase-lag of the current behind the e.m.f. and is given by

$$\theta = \tan^{-1}\frac{L\omega}{R}.\tag{14.20}$$

Again, the magnetic moment of the coil $= A \cdot I$. This magnetic moment is directed along the normal OP of the coil. The couple tending to bring the normal in the direction of field H is $AIH\cos\omega t$. Therefore, the direction of the motion of the coil is just opposite to the direction of the motion of the field. The magnitude of the couple is hence obtained as

$$C = -AIH\cos\omega t \quad \text{(considered as negative)}$$

$$= \frac{A^2H^2\omega}{Z}\sin\left(\omega t - \frac{\overline{\pi}}{2} + \theta\right)\cos\omega t$$

or, $$C = -\frac{A^2H^2\omega}{Z}\left[\sin\omega t\cos\left(\frac{\pi}{2}+\theta\right) - \cos\omega t\sin\left(\frac{\pi}{2}+\theta\right)\right]\cos\omega t$$

$$= -\frac{A^2H^2\omega}{Z}\left[\sin\omega t\cos\omega t\cos\left(\frac{\pi}{2}+\theta\right) - \cos^2\omega t\sin\left(\frac{\pi}{2}+\theta\right)\right].\tag{14.21}$$

Considering the average over a complete cycle, we have

$$C = +\frac{A^2H^2\omega}{2Z}\sin\left(\frac{\pi}{2}+\theta\right)$$

$$= \frac{A^2H^2\omega}{2Z}\cos\theta.\tag{14.22}$$

Now since $\tan\theta = \dfrac{L\omega}{R}$, we have

$$\cos\theta = \frac{R}{\sqrt{L^2\omega^2+R^2}}.\tag{14.23}$$

Hence, from Eq. (14.22),

$$C = \frac{A^2H^2\omega R}{2(L^2\omega^2+R^2)} \quad \text{[substituting the value of Z].}\tag{14.24}$$

The positive sign of equation (14.24) shows that the mean couple is in the direction of rotation of the field. Its magnitude is dependent on ω, the relative angular velocity of the field and the coil.

The value of ω for which the average couple becomes maximum is obtained as

$$\frac{dc}{d\omega} = \frac{d}{d\omega}\left[\frac{A^2H^2\omega R}{2(L^2\omega^2+R^2)}\right] = 0$$

or, $$A^2H^2R\frac{L^2\omega^2+R^2-2L^2\omega^2}{2(L^2\omega^2+R^2)^2} = 0$$

or, $$L^2\omega^2 = R^2$$

or, $\quad \omega = R/L.$ (14.25)

Hence, from Eq. (14.24),

$$C = \frac{A^2 H^2}{4L}.$$ (14.26)

Again we have, $\tan \theta = \dfrac{L\omega}{R}.$

Therefore, the value of θ is $\dfrac{\pi}{4}$ for a maximum couple.

The above phenomenon that a closed coil when placed in a rotating magnetic field experiences a couple is applied in the construction of induction motor.

14.5 Induction Motors

This is an a.c. motor which works on the principle of the motion of a coil produced when it is placed in a rotating magnetic field. These motors are manufactured to work on (i) single-phase, (ii) two-phase and (iii) three-phase current supply.

Single-phase Motor

The field produced by a single-phase winding is alternating in nature but it is not a rotating one. It may be looked upon as the resultant of two equal fields rotating with same angular velocity in mutually opposite direction as shown in Fig. 14.24.

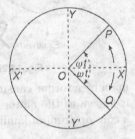

Fig. 14.24

Let the rotating fields be of magnitude H_0 and angular velocity ω. The fields coincide at any instant along OX. After time t, one of the fields advances in the positive direction through an angle ωt and the other in the negative direction by the same angle.

The components along OY are, therefore, written as

$$H_0 \cos\left(\frac{\pi}{2} - \omega t\right), \; H_0 \cos\left(\frac{\pi}{2} + \omega t\right).$$

These two are mutually cancelled.

Again, the components along OX are

$$H_0 \cos \omega t, \; H_0 \cos(-\omega t), \; \text{i.e.,} \; H_0 \cos \omega t, \; H_0 \cos \omega t.$$

Hence, the resultant along OX is $2H_0 \cos \omega t$, which proves that a single alternating field in any direction is the resultant of two equal fields rotating in mutually opposite directions.

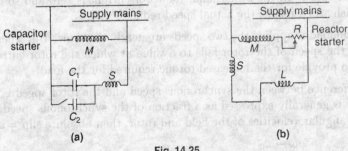

Fig. 14.25

To make the motor self-starting with a single-phase current an initial rotation of the armature is required. In order to achieve this the starting-winding (S) is kept at half-a-pole pitch (90°) distance of the main winding (M) and is parallel with it as shown in Fig. 14.25. The required phase-difference is obtained between the currents in the two windings by several methods. The circuit diagram for the capacitor-starting and the reactor-starting techniques are shown in Figs. 14.25(a) and (b) respectively.

Two-phase Motor

Two pairs of pole-pieces PP_1 and QQ_1 are placed inside and at the ends

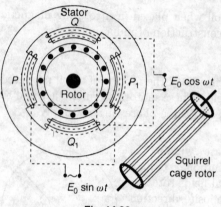

Fig. 14.26

of mutually perpendicular diameters of a soft iron-ring as shown in Fig. 14.26. The currents in each pair of coils are directed in such a manner that in between them there are two alternating magnetic fields. Owing to the action of mutually perpendicular fields a rotating magnetic field is produced inside the ring. The magnetic field is of constant magnitude but during a complete cycle of the a.c. supply a complete revolution is made.

A conducting rectangular loop free to rotate if mounted inside the ring, a current will be induced in it. The coil is then acted upon by a torque causing it to rotate in the same direction as the field. This is what is known as the motor action. In a practical induction motor the rotor consists of a core or drum of laminated soft-iron disc of high permeability.

Poly-phase Motor

Three-phase induction motor is more widely used than any other form of a.c. motor. Here also the working principle is based on the creation of a rotating magnetic field. For the purpose three coils carry current of three phases differing by 120° and are also kept at 120° apart from one another along the circumference of a circle.

Slip in Induction Motor

The couple which acts on the rotor is proportional to the relative velocity of the rotating magnetic field. Therefore, the motor must not run with the same speed as the field. A motor of this type is termed as an asynchronous motor. At the synchronous speed, on the other hand, the rotor-current is zero and so the torque would vanish. As a result, the actual speed reduces.

When no load is applied the two speeds are nearly the same. But when the load is applied, the speed of the rotor falls to a value at which the rotor current is just sufficient to provide for the increased torque required for the load.

The difference between the synchronous speed and the rotor speed is known as the *slip*. It is generally expressed as a fraction of the synchronous speed. If ω and ω_0 are the angular velocities of the field and rotor, then absolute slip $= \omega - \omega_0$.

$\therefore$ fractional slip $= \dfrac{\omega - \omega_0}{\omega}$.

When it is multiplied by 100, the percentage slip is obtained.

14.5.1 Synchronous Motor

If the stator core of an alternator is excited by an a.c. supply, the poles of a rotor would be acted upon by a torque owing to armature (stator). It will be in the same direction for different conductors. But the armature current will be reversed at the end of each half-cycle and the torque also becomes opposite. As a matter of fact, the rotor would not move at all due to inertia.

Let us assume that the rotor has an initial speed causing it to move through one pole-pitch in each half-cycle. The current in each stator conductor, under this condition will be reversed when it finds the next opposite pole facing it. Thus the direction of the torque exerted by the armature conductors remains the same and the rotor begins to move. In this way the machine runs as a motor with a constant speed.

If f represents the frequency, n the revolutions per second and p the number of poles, then for a synchronous motor we can write,

$$f = np.$$

A synchronous motor has a constant speed and it requires start and synchronisation before it is loaded.

14.6 d.c. Motors

An electric motor is a contrivance for converting electrical energy into mechanical energy. Let a conductor of length l carrying a current of i (e.m.u.) be kept at right angle to a magnetic field H. According to Fleming's left-hand rule it is urged on by a force Hil dynes. We assume that a steady current is supplied with the armature and the field coils.

In order to achieve the *equation for the torque*, let N_0 be the flux distributed around each conductor. The field H in which the conductor is placed can then be written as

$$H = \frac{N_0}{Lx},$$

where x is the length occupied along the periphery by each of the conductor. If r be the radius of the armature and Z be the number of conductors, then

$$x = \frac{2\pi r}{Z}.$$

If i_a denotes the total armature current in p parallel paths, then the current in each conductor is (i_a/p). Hence the force on each conductor obtained as Hil is given by

$$\frac{N_0}{Lx} \cdot \frac{i_a}{p} \cdot l = \frac{N_0 Z}{2\pi r} \cdot \frac{i_a}{p}.$$

If N represents the flux per pole, then the total force on all the conductors is

$$F = \sum \frac{N_0 Z}{2\pi r} \cdot \frac{i_a}{p} = \frac{NZ}{2\pi r p} \cdot i_a.$$

So the torque acting on the armature due to this is

$$F \cdot r = \frac{NZ}{2\pi r} \cdot \frac{i_a}{p} \cdot r = \frac{NZi_a}{2\pi p} \quad (r = \text{radius of the armature}).$$

The total torque on the armature for P poles will, therefore, be given by

$$T = \frac{NZi_a}{2\pi p} \cdot P.$$

The above equation shows that

$$T \propto Ni_a.$$

Back e.m.f.

During the rotation of the armature an induced e.m.f. is produced in the coils and the motor functions as a generator. This induced e.m.f. is in a direction opposite to that supplied to them and is called *back e.m.f.* in a motor. Therefore, we have

resultant e.m.f. in armature = supply e.m.f. − back e.m.f.

Let V be the e.m.f. supplied and E the back e.m.f. Then if R_a denotes the armature resistance and i_a the current in it, we can write,

$$R_a i_a = V - E.$$

Speed Equation

Let us assume that f represents the frequency of rotation of the armature. Since the magnitude of the back e.m.f. is controlled by the factors determining the e.m.f. on a generator, we have

$$E \propto Nf$$

or, $\quad f \propto \dfrac{E}{N}$

$$\propto \frac{V_a - R_a i_a}{N} \quad (\because E = V_a = R_a i_a).$$

We thus find that the speed of a motor is directly proportional to the back e.m.f. and inversely as the flux. That means the speed can be increased by weakening the field.

14.6.1   Field Excitation

The field of a d.c. motor can be excited by three different means. In fact, excitation involves the supply of current to the field and the armature coils. This is done by either series, shunt or compound form of windings.

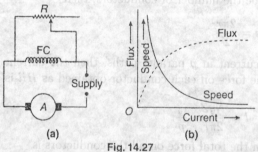

Fig. 14.27

Series Motor : Here as shown in Fig. 14.27(a) the field coil is in series with the armature coil and the same current passes through both. The speed at the start varies inversely to the current and thus the speed-armature current curve shows a rectangular hyperbola [Fig. 14.27(b)].

Shunt Motor : In this type the field coil is in parallel with the armature coil. As a result the current in the field coil is constant while the flux is independent of the load. The motor runs with a constant speed and so it is used for any drive where a constant speed is required as in the driving of lathes. The speed-current curve is presented in Fig. 14.28(a).

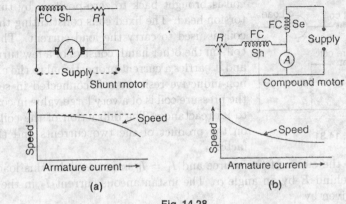

Fig. 14.28

Compound Motor : It has both shunt and series coils between the field and the armature windings [Fig. 14.28(b)]. This type of motor exerts a large starting torque. Adjusting the relative strengths of shunt and series coils the compound motor may be given any characteristics between those of series and shunt motors. As shown in Fig. 14.28(b), in a compound motor a regulating resistance R is placed in series with the shunt coil.

14.6.2 Motor Starters

As soon as a voltage is applied to a motor the armature coil acts like a low resistance circuit and so the current becomes high. When the motor acquires speed the back e.m.f. is developed and then the current falls to a lower value. Thus at the start the current may be so high that it may damage the machine. For its prevention motor starter is required.

In series motor an adjustable resistance R is connected in series with the field coil as shown in Fig. 14.29. H is the arm of the starter switch and M is the arm of the electromagnet.

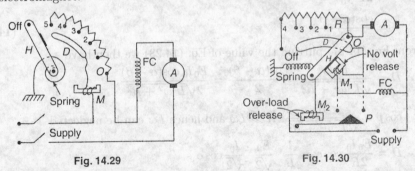

Fig. 14.29   **Fig. 14.30**

In a compound or shunt motor, on the other hand, two electromagnets M_1 and M_2 are used (Fig. 14.30).

14.7 Measurement of Power

The power absorbed in a circuit can be conveniently measured by wattmeter like Kelvin-Watt balance or by the moving coil dynamometer wattmeter.

In the torsion type the pressure coil as shown in Fig. 14.31 is suspended by a fine conducting wire from a torsion head carrying a scale. In actual practice, the moving

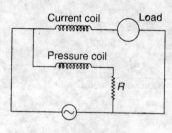

Fig. 14.31

coil is brought back to zero-position by turning the torsion head. The fixed coils constituting the current coils is used to carry the load current. The moving coil, on the other hand, consists of a few turns of wire and it carries a current proportional to the e.m.f. The non-inductive resistance R connected in series with the pressure coil is of a very large value in comparison to its reactance. The diffraction of the coil depends on the product of the two currents and the power factor.

Let E be the e.m.f. of the source and $I_1 = I_0 \sin(\omega t - \alpha)$ be this load current which lags behind E by an angle α. The instantaneous current I_2 in the pressure coil is then given by

$$I_2 = \frac{E_0 \sin(\omega t - \beta)}{\sqrt{L^2 \omega^2 + R^2}},$$

where $E = E_0 \sin \omega t$ and $\beta = \tan^{-1} \frac{L\omega}{R}$. The indication D can then be written as

$$D = \frac{1}{T} \int_0^T I_1 I_2 dt$$

$$= \frac{E_0 I_0}{\sqrt{L^2 \omega^2 + R^2}} \cdot \left[\frac{1}{T} \int_0^T \sin(\omega t - \alpha) \sin(\omega t - \beta) dt \right] \qquad (14.27)$$

Now, the terms within the third bracket can be re-written as

$$\frac{1}{T} \int_0^T \sin(\omega t - \alpha) \sin(\omega t - \beta) dt$$

$$= \frac{1}{2T} \int_0^T \cos(-\alpha + \beta) dt - \frac{1}{2T} \int_0^T \cos(2\omega t - \alpha - \beta) dt$$

$$= \frac{1}{2T} \int_0^T \cos(\alpha - \beta) dt \quad \text{[the second integral being zero]}$$

$$= \frac{\cos(\alpha - \beta)}{2}. \qquad (14.28)$$

From Eq. (14.27) putting the value of Eq. (14.28) we then have

$$D = \frac{E_0 I_0}{\sqrt{L^2 \omega^2 + R^2}} \cdot \frac{\cos(\alpha - \beta)}{2} = \frac{E_0 I_0 \cos(\alpha - \beta)}{2\sqrt{L^2 \omega^2 + R^2}}.$$

Now, $\cos p = \dfrac{R}{\sqrt{L^2 \omega^2 + R^2}}$; $R \gg L\omega$ and hence $L\omega$ can be neglected,

$$\therefore \quad D = \frac{E_0 I_0}{2R} \cos \alpha = \frac{1}{R} \cdot \frac{E_0}{\sqrt{2}} \cdot \frac{I_0}{\sqrt{2}} \cos \alpha$$

$$= \frac{1}{R} \text{ [r.m.s. e.m.f.} \times \text{r.m.s. current} \times \text{power factor].}$$

$$= \frac{1}{R} \times \text{[power in watt].} \qquad (14.29)$$

Thus we find that the indication D is proportional to the true power if $R \gg L\omega$. When $L\omega$ is not negligible the indication is proportional to

$$\frac{E_0 I_0 \cos(\alpha - \beta)}{2\sqrt{L^2 \omega^2 + R^2}} = \frac{E_0 I_0 \cos(\alpha - \beta) \cos \beta}{2R}.$$

$$\therefore \quad \frac{\text{true power}}{\text{apparent power}} = \frac{E_0 I_0 \cos\alpha}{2R} \Big/ \frac{E_0 I_0 \cos(\alpha - \beta)\cos\beta}{2R} = \frac{\cos\alpha}{\cos(\alpha - \beta)\cos\beta}.$$

Thus it appears that,

$$\text{true reading} = \left[\frac{\cos\alpha}{\cos(\alpha - \beta)\cos\beta}\right] \times \text{actual reading.}$$

The bracketted terms are the correction factor. When the power factor of the load is very low a large error will be introduced.

One of the great advantages of a wattmeter is that it can be used in several ranges by using current and potential transformation suitably.

14.7.1 Average Torque

When no current is made to pass, the plane of the pressure coil makes zero angle with the magnetic axis of the current coils. When the current is passed, let the plane of the coil make an angle θ (Fig. 14.32). If A be the area of the moving coil and H the magnetic field due to fixed coils, then the torque τ can be written as

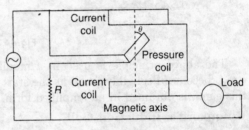

Fig. 14.32

$$\tau = nAHI_2\cos\theta \quad [n = \text{number of turns}]. \tag{14.30}$$

Now, $I_2 = \dfrac{E_0}{R}\sin\omega t$ and $H = aI_1 = aI_0\sin(\omega t - \alpha)$, where $a = $ constant.

$$\therefore \quad \tau = nA\cos\theta[aI_0\sin(\omega t - \alpha)]\left[\frac{E_0\sin\omega t}{R}\right]$$

$$= KE_0 I_0\cos\theta\sin(\omega t - \alpha)\sin\omega t, \text{ where } K \text{ is a new constant.}$$

$$\therefore \text{ average torque} = \frac{1}{T}\int_0^T KE_0 I_0\cos\theta\sin(\omega t - \alpha)\sin\omega t\, dt$$

$$= \frac{KE_0 I_0}{2}\cos\alpha\cos\theta.$$

$$= K\cos\theta \times \text{power.} \tag{14.31}$$

This is the restoring torque due to the spiral spring.

For the torsion type wattmeters since the coil is brought back to its initial position we can write the restoring torque,

$$\tau = K \times \text{ power } \times \cos 0°$$

$$= K \times \text{ power.} \tag{14.32}$$

In a wattmeter reading the errors come due to inductive reactance of the pressure coil and capacity of the pressure coil circuit. In addition, eddy current errors and stray magnetic field errors are also introduced.

14.8 Induction Coil

Let in a circuit, as shown in Fig. 14.33(a), current be supplied by a battery to a primary coil with an arrangement for automatic make-and-break of the circuit. This induces e.m.f. in the secondary. Since the primary circuit includes a resistance and an inductance in series, the current in it grows and decays exponentially as shown in Fig. 14.33(b). The induced secondary current is somewhat oscillatory in nature. The secondary current during growth of the primary currents is in the opposite direction to that of the primary but during the break of the circuit it is in the same direction.

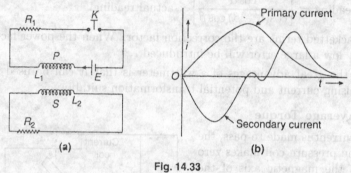

(a)   (b)

Fig. 14.33

The above principle is used in a modified arrangement where the secondary e.m.f. becomes negligibly small at the start of the primary current, while at break this e.m.f. is obtained in an amplified form.

Ruhmkorff's Induction Coil

It is an apparatus where a low e.m.f. is applied at the ends of a primary coil of a few number of turns of a thick wire. This is transformed into an intermittent

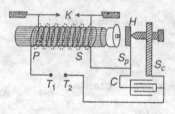

Fig. 14.34

high potential difference obtained at the ends of the secondary winding with a large number of turns of fine wire. Here, as shown in Fig. 14.34, the primary coil P is wound on a bundle of soft iron rods in series with a make-and-break arrangement consisting of a spring (S_p) in contact with a screw (S_c). The spring has a soft iron hammer H which is attracted by the iron core when it is magnetized by the primary current. Owing to the attraction on the hammer piece, the contact between the screw-head and the spring breaks. The primary current is thus broken and the current ceases to flow. The frequency of make-and-break depends on the action of the spring.

The secondary coil S is wound over the primary coil whose ends are connected with the two knobs K separated by a sparking gap. If $\frac{di}{dt}$ is the rate of change of current in the primary, then the induced e.m.f. in the secondary is given by

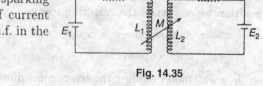

Fig. 14.35

$$e = -M\frac{di}{dt},$$

where M is the mutual inductance.

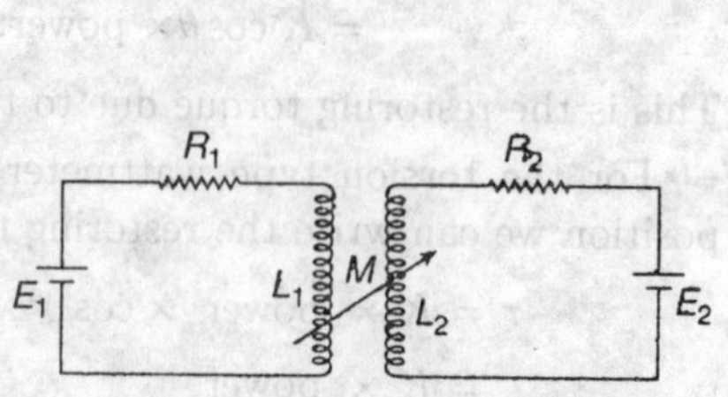

In inducing the secondary e.m.f. the primary current is more effective at 'break' than at 'make'. If the primary circuit is broken, the resistance in the circuit becomes infinity and then the time constant is negligible. So $\frac{di}{dt}$ is very high at break and hence the e.m.f. becomes considerably high. But the sudden collapse of current produces a sparking at the contact point on the screw head. This damages the contact surface. Such arcing is prevented by placing a condenser C across the contact point.

The primary and secondary e.m.f. equations during break may be written as

$$L_1 \frac{di_1}{dt} + M \frac{di_2}{dt} + i_1 R_1 = 0 \qquad (14.33)$$

$$L_2 \frac{di_2}{dt} + M \frac{di_1}{dt} = 0, \qquad (14.34)$$

where L_1, i_1 and R_1 represent the primary inductance, current and resistance while L_2 and i_2 are the secondary inductance and current. The secondary resistance is neglected here for simplification in presence of its inductance.

From Eq. (14.34), we have

$$\frac{di_2}{dt} = -\frac{M}{L_2} \frac{di_1}{dt}. \qquad (14.35)$$

Substituting in Eq. (14.33),

$$\left(L_1 - \frac{M^2}{L_2} \right) \frac{di_1}{dt} + R_1 i_1 = 0. \qquad (14.36)$$

This is an equation of the form,

$$\alpha \frac{dx}{dt} + \beta x = 0,$$

whose solution is

$$x = x_0 e^{-\frac{\beta}{\alpha} - t}.$$

Hence the solution for i_1 is written as

$$i_1 = i_0 e^{-bt}, \qquad (14.37)$$

where $b = \dfrac{R_1}{L_1 - \frac{M^2}{L_2}}$ and $i_0 = $ primary current at break.

Again, we have

$$\int \frac{di_2}{dt} dt = -\frac{M}{L_2} \int \frac{di_1}{dt} dt$$

or, $\qquad L_2 i_2 + M i_1 = K$ (where $K = $ constant). $\qquad (14.38)$

Now, when $i_2 = 0$, $i_1 = i_0$.

$$\therefore \qquad K = M i_0.$$

Hence, we have

$$L_2 i_2 + M i_0 e^{-bt} = M i_0$$

or, $\qquad i_2 = \dfrac{M i_0}{L_2} (1 - e^{-bt}). \qquad (14.39)$

$\therefore$ the maximum value of $i_2 = \dfrac{M i_0}{L_2}$.

When a condenser of capacitance C is connected in series with the primary, the e.m.f. equations for the break of primary circuit are

$$L_1 \frac{di_1}{dt} + M \frac{di_2}{dt} + \frac{q_1}{C} = 0 \qquad (14.40)$$

$$L_2 \frac{di_2}{dt} + M \frac{di_1}{dt} = 0, \qquad (14.41)$$

where we have neglected the primary resistance; q_1 is the charge of the condenser. Considering $i = \frac{dq}{dt}$ or, $\frac{di}{dt} = \frac{d^2q}{dt^2}$, the above equations become

$$L_1 \frac{d^2 q_1}{dt^2} + M \frac{d^2 q_2}{dt^2} + \frac{q_1}{C} = 0 \tag{14.42}$$

$$L_2 \frac{d^2 q_2}{dt^2} + M \frac{d^2 q_1}{dt^2} = 0. \tag{14.43}$$

Multiplying Eq. (14.42) by L_2 and Eq. (14.43) by M, we have

$$L_1 L_2 \frac{d^2 q_1}{dt^2} + M L_2 \frac{d^2 q_2}{dt^2} + L_2 \frac{q_1}{C} = 0 \tag{14.44}$$

$$M L_2 \frac{d^2 q_2}{dt^2} + M^2 \frac{d^2 q_1}{dt^2} = 0. \tag{14.45}$$

Subtracting Eq. (14.45) from Eq. (14.44),

$$(L_1 L_2 - M^2) \frac{d^2 q_1}{dt^2} + L_2 \frac{q_1}{C} = 0. \tag{14.46}$$

Eq. (14.46) is of the form $\frac{d^2 x}{dt^2} + \omega^2 x = 0$, which represents the equation of a simple harmonic motion. The primary current and the charge are there oscillatory in nature. This is due to the addition of a condenser in the circuit.

Now, integrating Eq. (14.41),

$$L_2 i_2 + M i_1 = K,$$

when $i_0 = 0,\ i = i_0$.

$\therefore$ $K = M i_0$.

Hence, we have

$$i_2 = \frac{M}{L_2}(i_0 - i_1). \tag{14.47}$$

Since i_1 oscillates between i_0 and $-i_0$, so the maximum value of i_2 is given by

$$i_2 = 2M \frac{i_0}{L_2}. \tag{14.48}$$

Thus it is seen that when a condenser is used, the maximum value of i_2 is doubled theoretically. However, in practice, this is somewhat less, since in calculation we have ignored the resistances of the winding.

14.8.1   Energy Linked with Mutual Inductance

Considering Fig. 14.31, we can write the e.m.f. equations as

$$L_1 \frac{di_1}{dt} + R_1 i_1 + M \frac{di_2}{dt} = E_1 \tag{14.49}$$

$$L_2 \frac{di_2}{dt} + R_2 i_2 + M \frac{di_1}{dt} = E_2. \tag{14.50}$$

$$\therefore \int_0^t (E_1 i_1 + E_2 i_2)\,dt$$

$$= \frac{L_1 i_1^2}{2} + \frac{L_2 i_2^2}{2} + \int \left((R_1 i_1^2 + R_2 i_2^2)\,dt + \int_0^t M i_1 \frac{di_2}{dt} + M i_2 \frac{di_1}{dt} \right) dt. \tag{14.51}$$

The left-hand side of Eq. (14.51) represents the work done by the cells at time t when current in the two circuits becomes i_1 and i_2. In Eq. (14.51),

$$\int_0^t \left(M i_1 \frac{di_2}{dt} + M i_2 \frac{di_1}{dt} \right) dt = M i_1 i_2.$$

So the potential energy of the magnetic field,

$$W = \frac{1}{2} L_1 i_1^2 + \frac{1}{2} L_2 i_2^2 + M i_1 i_2. \tag{14.52}$$

14.8.2 e.m.f. in the Secondary

The periodic primary current can be expressed into a Fourier series as

$$i_1 = a_0 + \sum_1^\infty a_s \cos s\omega t + \sum_1^\infty b_s \sin s\omega t, \tag{14.53}$$

where $\omega = 2\pi/T$; a_0, a_s, b_s are constants.

Now, the induced e.m.f. in the secondary on open circuit is

$$e = -m \frac{di_1}{dt}$$

$$= +m \sum_1^\infty s\omega a_s \sin s\omega t - m \sum_1^\infty s\omega b_s \cos s\omega t. \tag{14.54}$$

Hence the mean e.m.f. in a couple cycle is

$$\tilde{e} = \frac{1}{t} \int_0^T e\,dt = 0. \tag{14.55}$$

Examples

1. A 100 HP three-phase, delta-connected motor works on a line voltage of 3000 volts. If the power factor is 80% and the efficiency is 84%, find the line current. Hence calculate the phase current.

   Solution : We have

   $$\text{input} = \text{output} \times \frac{100}{84} = \frac{100 \times 746 \times 100}{84} = 88 \times 10^3 \text{ watts.}$$

   Power, $P = \sqrt{3} E_L I_L \cos\phi$

   or, $I_L = \dfrac{P}{\sqrt{3} E_L \cos\phi} = \dfrac{88 \times 10^3}{\sqrt{3} \times 3000 \times 0.8} = \mathbf{21.17 \ A}.$

   Phase current,

   $$I_P = \frac{I_L}{\sqrt{3}} = \frac{21.17}{\sqrt{3}} = 12.22 \text{ A.}$$

2. A star-wound alternator develops a line e.m.f. of 6600 volts. Determine the phase voltage and the total power output when the current in each phase is 300 amperes and the power factor is 0.8.

Solution : Phase voltage, $E_p = \dfrac{6600}{\sqrt{3}} = 3810$ volts.

Power output $= 3 \times E_p I_p \cos\phi = 3 \times 3810 \times 300 \times 0.8$

$$= 2743 \times 10^3 \text{ watts.}$$

Questions

Essay-type

1. Describe briefly the essential parts of d.c. generator.

2. Find the equation for the e.m.f. generated in a d.c. dynamo.

3. Discuss the essential parts of an a.c. generator, obtain the equation for the e.m.f. generated.

   Explain the difference between single-phase, two-phase and poly-phase machines.

4. Draw neat diagrams to show the distributions of e.m.f. from three-phase star-wound and delta-wound alternators. What do you mean by phase voltage and line voltage? Obtain the relations between them.

5. Find the expression for the frequency of the e.m.f. generated by an alternator in terms of number of poles and revolutions per second.

6. What is rotating magnetic field? Explain its production by (i) two coils and (ii) three coils.

   Find an expression for the torque acting on a coil placed in a rotating magnetic field. Hence discuss the outlines of construction of an induction motor.

7. Discuss the principle of an induction motor. What is slip in such a motor?

   Explain how an induction motor can be run with a single phase current.

8. Discuss the construction and theory of a wattmeter.

9. What is an induction coil? Describe the construction of Ruhmkorff's induction coil and give the theory of it.

Chapter 15
Electrolysis

15.1   Introduction

Like solids, liquids may be either insulators or conductors. Aqueous solutions of inorganic salts, acids and bases are some common examples of conducting liquids. These are called *electrolytes*. Let us consider an *electrolytic cell* consisting of a solution of silver nitrate ($AgNO_3$) with two plates of silver called *electrodes* partly inserted in it. We can observe that as the current flows, silver is deposited on the cathode and an equal amount is removed from the anode, the electrolyte remaining unaltered. It has been found from measurement that the mass of silver deposited is proportional to the product of the current for the time by which it flows. The phenomenon is termed as electrolysis.

15.2   Faraday's Laws of Electrolysis

Faraday was the first to make a systematic study of electrolysis. He discovered the simple relations representing the general laws which can be stated as :

(i) *The mass of a substance liberated at an electrode is directly proportional to the total charge passing.*

(ii) *The mass of a substance liberated at an electrode by a unit charge is directly proportional to the chemical equivalent of that substance.* The chemical equivalent of a substance is the atomic weight or for a compound substance group weight, divided by the valence.

The above laws can be expressed analytically in a simple way. If M be the mass of a substance liberated, i the current and t the time of flow, then for the first law,

$$M = Zit, \tag{15.1}$$

where Z is a constant usually expressed in grams per coulomb. It is called the *electrochemical equivalent* of the given substance.

For the second law, let us assume that w represents the atomic or group weight of the substance involved and v its valence. Then,

$$Z = \frac{w}{v}\left(\frac{1}{F}\right). \tag{15.2}$$

F is called the *Faraday's constant*. It is the number of coulombs required to liberate 1.008 grams of hydrogen and its numerical value is 96 490.

15.3   Arrhenius Theory of Electrolytic Dissociation

Arrhenius established an explanation of the principle of electrolysis which was elaborated by the later investigators.

According to this theory, a fraction δ of the molecules of the dissolved substance is separated into two or more parts, each of which bears a charge. These charged

373

carriers are known as *ions*. When an e.m.f. is applied, the positively charged cations move to the cathode and the negatively charged anions to the anode. The continuous arrival of positive charge at one electrode and the negative charge at the other is equivalent to a transfer of charge from one to other. This constitutes the current passing through the electrolyte.

Actually, material liberated may appear on an electrode or it may be involved in some secondary chemical reaction. As for example, the ions in the $AgNO_3$ solution are Ag^+ and NO_3^-. The Ag^+ is deposited in the form of metallic silver on the cathode causing an increase of its mass while NO_3^- is liberated at the anode and it combines with the silver of which the anode is composed. Thus, the silver nitrate formed remains in the solution and the net result is loss of silver by the anode. Simultaneously, the concentration of $AgNO_3$ increases in the vicinity of the anode and decreases in the vicinity of the cathode. With currents of ordinary magnitude the change becomes slow, since even in the dilute solution the amount of ionic charge is relatively great. Eventually, the rate of change of concentration is balanced by diffusion and hence a steady state is reached.

15.4   Evidences of Dissociation in Solution

Van't Hoff showed that gas laws are applicable to a dilute solution. If p represents the osmotic pressure exerted by the solute molecules in the solution and v is the volume of the solution containing one gram-molecule of the solute, then

$$pv = RT, \tag{15.3}$$

where R is the molar gas constant and T the temperature in absolute scale.

Eq. (15.3) can be rewritten as

$$p \cdot \frac{1}{C} = RT, \quad \left(\because v = \frac{1}{C} \right) \tag{15.4}$$

where C is the number of gram-molecules per cc of the solution.

or, $p = CRT$ \tag{15.5}

For a non-electrolyte solute, e.g., sugar, the osmotic pressure is very well given by Eq. (15.5). But for a very diluted NaCl the pressure is nearly two times the value than that obtained by Eq. (15.5). For Na_2SO_4 solution for the same concentration C, the pressure lies between two to three times as much. When all the solute molecules are dissociated, then for each molecule of NaCl two free ions of Na and Cl are obtained. Similarly, for each molecule of Na_2SO_4 we have altogether three ions. As the osmotic pressure is due to the free particles per cc either in the form of ions or molecules, the greatly increased osmotic pressure by dissociation is explained.

15.5   Conduction of Current through an Electrolyte

Let us consider a glass vessel V where a solution of NaCl in water is taken (Fig. 15.1). A and C are two platinum conductors immersed in the solution. Let A and C be connected respectively with the positive and negative terminals of a battery. Due to this connection, the conductor A will behave as an anode and C as a cathode, and an electric field will be established between the two. The positive Na ions and the negative Cl ions will be liberated ultimately as neutral Na and Cl atoms on the cathode C and anode A respectively.

In practice, when an ion of Na is liberated as an atom of Na on C the $+$ve amount of charge carried by it is delivered to C. This charge is neutralised by a charge of $-e$ which flows from the batter to C. In an identical way the $-$ve amount of charge delivered by an ion of chlorine to A passes from A to inside the battery and thus maintains a constant potential. We can, therefore, conclude that by electrolysis of a molecule of NaCl a charge of amount $-e$ moves from A to E and then to C while a charge of $+e$ moves from C to A in the reversed direction.

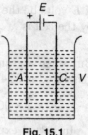

Fig. 15.1

15.6   Ohm's Law in Electrolysis

Let the electrolyte taken be water acidulated with dilute H_2SO_4 and the electrodes

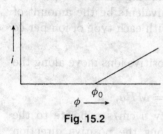

Fig. 15.2

are of platinum. If now a p.d. is applied between the electrodes, then there will be decomposition of water and a current will flow in the circuit. If, however, the p.d. applied is below a certain value ϕ_0, the current will be ceased ultimately. We can, therefore, say in a general way that there will be a decomposition of water continuously if the p.d. between the electrodes exceeds a value ϕ_0. The value of ϕ_0 for acidulated water is about 1.7 volts.

If we plot the current i through the electrolyte against the p.d. ϕ, we may get a graph as shown in Fig. 15.2. The figure shows that the current beyond ϕ_0 is strictly proportional to $(\phi - \phi_0)$. Therefore, Ohm's law applicable in this case may be written as

$$i = \frac{\phi - \phi_0}{R},\qquad(15.6)$$

where R is the resistance of the electrolyte.

The experimental arrangement for the verification of the above discussion can be made with the help of the circuit diagram shown in Fig. 15.3. It will be seen that there is a current flow as indicated by the ammeter A. An explanation for the stoppage of current below ϕ_0 can be explained by the fact that the layers of hydrogen and oxygen collecting on the platinum electrodes constitute a voltaic cell and has an e.m.f. opposed to the applied p.d. The phenomenon is termed as *polarisation*. Hence, for a continuous flow of current the p.d. must exceed the back e.m.f.

The minimum p.d. required to decompose water can be calculated easily. As the chemical combination of hydrogen and water liberates heat energy, it is clear that some energy must be supplied from outside to decompose water.

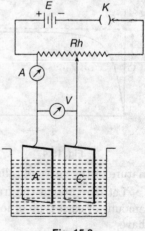

Fig. 15.3

Since electrolysis of a gram-molecule of water liberates two gram-equivalents of hydrogen, the charge that must pass through is given by

$$q = 2 \times 96\,500 \text{ coulombs.}$$

If E volts be the required e.m.f. to perform this decomposition, then the work done by the cell is

$$E \times 2 \times 96\,500 \text{ joules.}$$

But when a gram-molecule of water is formed into hydrogen and oxygen, the heat generated is $68\,400$ calories. Thus, we can write,

$$E \times 2 \times 96\,500 = \frac{68\,400 \times 4.2 \times 10^7}{10^7} \quad \text{or,} \quad E = 1.49 \text{ volts.}$$

In actual experiment, the e.m.f. required is 1.7 volts. The difference between the calculated and the actual value is termed as *overvoltage*.

15.7   Electrical Conductivity

The electrical conductivity can be defined as the charge flowing per second per unit cross-section per unit electric intensity. If M gram-equivalents be the amount of each ion per cc of the solution, then charge associated with each type of ion per cc $= MF$, where F is the faraday.

Let due to the application of an electric field E the positive ions move along the field with a velocity u cm/second.

$\therefore$ the current per unit cross-section along the intensity $= MFu$.

Similarly, let the negative ions move with a velocity v cm/s opposite to the applied field so that the magnitude of the current along the positive direction $= MFv$ (per unit cross-section).

$\therefore$ the current density $= MF(u + v)$.

If σ is the conductivity, then we can write,

$$MF(u + v) = \sigma E$$

or, $\sigma = MF\left(\dfrac{u}{E} + \dfrac{v}{E}\right) = MF(u_0 + v_0).$ (15.7)

In Eq. (15.7) u_0 and v_0 represent the velocities of the two types of ions due to unit intensity. The velocity of drift of the ions due to unit field intensity is called the *ionic mobility*. When the ions are free particles, the mobility is independent of the concentration of the ions or of the solution.

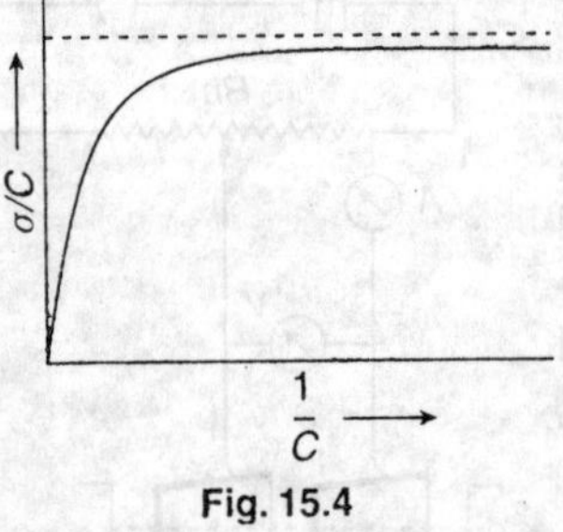

The ratio of electrical conductivity σ to concentration C is called the *equivalent conductivity*. It has been found that the value of σ/C of a solution increases with decrease of concentration. This increase, as was explained by Arrhenius, is due to the increase in the number of dissociated molecules at greater dilution. If we plot σ/C against $1/C$, the nature of the curve obtained may be as shown in Fig. 15.4.

Fig. 15.4

Let α represent the fraction of total molecules undergoing dissociation. So the amount of each type of ions $= \alpha M$ gram-equivalent/cc. Then from Eq. (15.7), we have

$$\sigma = \alpha MF(u_0 + v_0).$$ (15.8)

$\therefore$ the equivalent conductivity, $\lambda_c = \dfrac{\sigma}{C} = \dfrac{\alpha MF(u_0 + v_0)}{M} = \alpha F(u_0 + v_0),$ (15.9)

where we have assumed that M gram-equivalents of solute are present per cc of the solution.

15.8   Migration of the Ions

Let us consider two electrodes A and C, area of each in the liquid is one sq. cm with faces parallel; P be an imaginary partition between them. The electrodes A and C are connected with a source of e.m.f. E (Fig. 15.5).

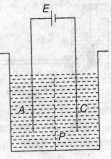

Fig. 15.5

Let M be the concentration per cc in gram-equivalents of each type of ion, t be the time in seconds in which one gram-equivalent of each ion is liberated at the electrodes, u and v be the velocities of migration of the positive and the negative ions respectively. We can now calculate the loss in concentration at the cathode and anode sides of the solution in the following way :

Cathode side

Loss of +ve ions by deposition on $C = 1$ gram-equivalent.

Gain of +ve ions by migration from anode side $= Mut$ gram-equivalent.

$$\therefore \text{ net loss of +ve ions} = 1 - Mut = 1 - \frac{Mu}{M(u+v)} \qquad \left[\text{putting } t = \frac{1}{M(u+v)}\right]$$

$$= 1 - \frac{u}{u+v} = \frac{v}{u+v} \text{ gram-equivalent.}$$

Loss of −ve ions by migration towards $A = Mvt = \dfrac{Mv}{M(u+v)}$

$$= \frac{u}{u+v} \text{ gram-equivalent.}$$

So the net loss in the concentration of the solute $= \dfrac{u}{u+v}$ gram-equivalent.

Anode side

Loss of −ve ions by deposition on $A = 1$ gram-equivalent.

Gain of −ve ions by migration from cathode side $= Mvt$ gram-equivalent.

$$\therefore \text{ net loss of −ve ions} = 1 - Mvt = 1 - \frac{Mv}{M(u+v)} = 1 - \frac{v}{u+v}$$

$$= \frac{v}{u+v} \text{ gram-equivalent.}$$

Loss of +ve ions by migration towards $C = Mut = \dfrac{u}{u+v}$ gram-equivalent.

So the net loss in the concentration of the solute $= \dfrac{u}{u+v}$ gram-equivalent.

At infinite dilution, $\alpha = 1$ and then

$$\lambda_\infty = F(u_0 + v_0), \tag{15.10}$$

when the degree of dissociation is written as

$$\alpha = \frac{\lambda_c}{\lambda_\infty}. \tag{15.11}$$

Knowing λ_∞ for strongly dissociated molecules by extrapolation, the degree of dissociation α can be found out at any concentration.

15.8.1   Determination of Conductivity

The electrical conductivity of an electrolyte can be determined by Kohlrausch's method. The electrolyte is taken in a cell as shown in Fig. 15.6.

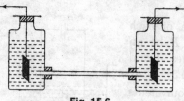

Fig. 15.6

If σ represents the conductivity of the electrolyte, then for a column of liquid of length l and radius R, we have

$$R = \frac{l}{\pi a^2 \cdot \sigma}, \qquad (15.12)$$

where a is the radius of the glass tube. However, due to end errors the length between the two electrodes is indefinite. Therefore, if R_1 and R_2 are the resistances of the electrolyte for lengths l_1 and l_2 respectively, then we can write,

$$R_1 - R_2 = \frac{1}{\pi a^2 \cdot \sigma}(l_1 - l_2). \qquad (15.13)$$

Eq. (15.13) can be utilised to find the conductivity. In the above equation, the resistances R_1 and R_2 are determined by a slide wire metre bridge.

In order to minimise the error due to polarisation an alternating source of e.m.f. is taken. The effect of polarisation in one half-cycle is balanced in the next half. The platinum-coated electrodes used are of large area and thus reduce the polarisation.

The source is a small induction coil or a valve oscillator whose frequency is about 1000 Hz while the detector used is a telephone receiver of suitable impedance.

During the experiment, the temperature of the cell is to be maintained constant as the conductivity of an electrolyte increases with increase of temperature. In this experiment it becomes very difficult to get the position of perfect balance due to the stray capacitance and inductance.

Hence, we can write,

$$\frac{\text{loss in concentration near cathode}}{\text{loss in concentration near anode}} = \frac{\frac{v}{u+v}}{\frac{u}{u+v}} = \frac{v}{u}.$$

If the two electrodes A and C are separated by a distance x and if the p.d. between them is V, then the electric intensity,

$$E = \frac{V}{x}. \qquad (15.14)$$

Thus we can write,

$$\frac{v}{u} = \frac{v/E}{u/E} = \frac{v_0}{u_0} \qquad (15.15)$$

where v_0 and u_0 are known as the ionic mobilities.

The term $\frac{v}{u+v}$ is known as the *transport ratio* or the *migration constant of Hittorf*.

15.8.2 Determination of Migration Constant

The migration constant can be determined by studying the loss in concentration of the electrolyte near the electrodes. The experimental arrangement is shown in Fig. 15.7. B_1 and B_2 are two beakers in which the electrolytes of same concentration are taken. A small siphon connects the beakers electrically. As the diffusion through it tending to equalise concentration is very slow, so the transport

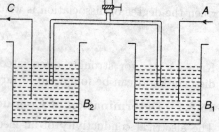

Fig. 15.7

ratio can be calculated by finding the concentrations in B_1 and B_2 before electrolysis and after electrolysis has progressed for a long time.

15.9 Application of Thermodynamics to Reversible Cells

The second law of thermodynamics is applicable to processes which are strictly reversible.

Let us consider a reversible cell of electromotive force E at absolute temperature T and assume that the cell produces current until a charge q has passed round the circuit. In the indicator diagram of Fig. 15.8, PQ represents the passage of the charge q parallel to x-axis. At Q the cell is thermally isolated and let a further infinitesimal change be made to pass. The source of energy is now only the cell itself, and let us assume that the using up of the energy of the cell causes drop of temperature by δT. Thus, the temperature becomes $(T - \delta T)$, and the e.m.f. as

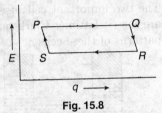

Fig. 15.8

$E - \frac{dE}{dT}\delta T$, where $\frac{dE}{dT}$ is the rate of change of e.m.f. with the temperature. This change is represented by the path QR in the figure. Now, maintaining the temperature $(T - \delta T)$ constant a current is passed in the opposite direction to the first until the charge q is passed through the cell. We then come to the point S. Next a sufficient charge is passed to bring the cell back to its original temperature T. Here the two adiabatic processes represented by QR and SP are identical and every part of the cycle is reversible.

Let us assume that H represents the energy due to chemical reaction in the cell when unit charge is passed by it while h is the heat absorbed from the atmosphere to produce electrical energy when the charge q is passed at the temperature T.

Now, from the second law we have

$$\frac{\text{net work done}}{\text{heat absorbed}} = \frac{T - (T - \delta T)}{T}. \tag{15.16}$$

But the net work done by the cell $= Eq - \left(E - \frac{dE}{dT}\delta T\right)q = q\frac{dE}{dT}\delta T.$

So from the Eq. (15.16),

$$\frac{q\frac{dE}{dT}\delta T}{h} = \frac{\delta T}{T}$$

or, $\quad h = qT \cdot \dfrac{dE}{dT}. \tag{15.17}$

Therefore, the work done in the process PQ is

$$Eq = Hq + h = Hq + qT\frac{dE}{dT}$$

or, $\quad E = H + T\dfrac{dE}{dT}. \tag{15.18}$

Eq. (15.18) is known as Gibbs-Helmholtz equation.

From above, we find that when the temperature coefficient $\frac{dE}{dT} = 0$, $E = H$. Hence, the energy of the current is supplied by the chemical reactions occurring in the cell. This is approximately true for Daniell cell where

$$H = 2.66 \times 4.18 \times 10^7 = 1.112 \times 10^8 \text{ c.g.s. units} \quad \text{and} \quad E = 1.112 \text{ volts.}$$

If the e.m.f. of the cell increases with rise in temperature, $\frac{dE}{dT}$ is +ve and $E > H$. Therefore, to supply the energy necessary for maintaining the current, the heat of the cell is drawn upon and the cell is thereby cooled.

If the e.m.f. of the cell falls with rise in temperature, $\frac{dE}{dT}$ is −ve and $E < H$. In that case the energy liberated by the chemical reaction is greater than that required by the current and so the cell becomes warmer when running.

15.10 Standard Cells

The two important cells used as standards of e.m.f. are of reversible type. These are the (i) Latimer-Clark cell and (ii) Weston or Cadmium cell. There are various patterns of these cells.

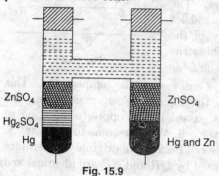

Latimer-Clark Cell : One most useful pattern of the Latimer-Clark cell due to Lord Rayleigh is shown in Fig. 15.9. A platinum wire to serve as terminal is sealed through the bottom of each limb of the H-shaped tube. Mercury is poured in one limb upon which rests a paste of mercurous sulphate and zinc sulphate. In the other limb, upon an amalgam of zinc rests a layer of crystals of zinc sulphate. Above the cross-piece the tubes are filled with zinc sulphate

ZnSO₄ ... ZnSO₄
Hg₂SO₄
Hg ... Hg and Zn

Fig. 15.9

solution. The whole is sealed with corks and paraffin wax.

Following Jager and Kahle, the e.m.f. of the cell can be written as

$$1.4328 - 0.00119(t - 15) - 0.000007(t - 15)^2 \text{ volt,}$$

where t is the temperature in °C.

Weston or Cadmium Cell : In this cell, cadmium amalgam and sulphate replace the zinc amalgam and sulphate of the Latimer-Clark cell. When current is taken from the cell mercury is deposited on the anode by the equation,

$$Cd + Hg_2SO_4 \rightarrow CdSO_4 + 2Hg.$$

The Weston cell replaces the Latimer-Clark cell because it lasts for a longer time and also has a small temperature coefficient. Within 0° to 40 °C the e.m.f. of the cell is given by

$$1.01864 - 0.0000406(t - 20) - 9.5 \times 10^{-7}(t - 20)^2 \text{ volt.}$$

15.11 Concentration Cells

The principle of concentration cells was first pointed out by Helmholtz. In such cells the source of energy is not due to chemical action but to the diffusion occurring between the two solutions of the same substance at different concentrations.

In Fig. 15.10, two solutions of concentrations C_1 and C_2 are separated by a porous partition P. The solutions and the electrodes A and B are made by the same salt of a metal. The two cells may be represented as

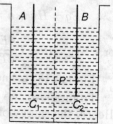

Cu|CuSO₄ (concentrated)|CuSO₄ (dilute)|Cu

Ag|AgNO₃ (concentrated)|AgNO₃ (dilute)|Ag.

Fig. 15.10

If the electrodes are connected by a conductor, then for $C_1 > C_2$, metallic ions deposit on A while those from B go into the solution. Let u and v be the velocities of the positive and negative ions respectively. To examine the mode of change of the concentrations of the two solutions, we may assume that $(u + v)$ gram-equivalent of metal is dissolved at the anode and an equal amount deposited at the cathode. For the silver cell, we have

loss of silver at the cathode by deposition $= (u + v)$,

gain of silver at the cathode by transport $= u$.

∴ net loss of silver $= (u + v) - u = v$.

Also, loss of nitrate by transport $= v$.

So, loss of silver nitrate $= v$ gram-molecules.

Again, gain of silver at the anode by solution $= (u + v)$,

loss of silver at the anode by transport $= u$.

∴ net gain of silver $= (u + v) - u = v$.

Also, gain of nitrate by transport $= v$.

So, gain of silver nitrate $= v$ gram-molecules.

Thus, we find that the result of the process is a transference of $AgNO_3$ by v gram-molecules from the concentrated solution to the dilute solution. If instead of $(u + v)$ gram-atoms of deposition we take unit gram-atom, the transference of $AgNO_3$ becomes equal to $\frac{v}{u+v}$ gram-molecules and $\frac{v}{u+v}$ is the transport ratio of the negative ion. For the other cell, the transference of the salt for unit gram-equivalent of deposit would be $\frac{u}{u+v}$ gram-molecules.

If we substitute $\frac{v}{u+v} = n$, then we have

$$\frac{u}{u + v} = 1 - n.$$

The e.m.f. of the concentration cells can be written as

$$0.0578 \times 2n \log_{10} \frac{C_1}{C_2} \text{ volt.}$$

That means the e.m.f. depends upon the ratio of the concentration. In the silver nitrate cell,

$$n = \frac{61.8}{54 + 61.8} = 0.533.$$

At temperature $18\,°C$ and with ratio of concentrations $10 : 1$,

$$\text{e.m.f.} = 0.0578 \times 2 \times 0.533 = 0.0615 \text{ volt.}$$

As there is no resultant chemical reaction in the concentration cell, putting $H = 0$ in Gibbs-Helmholtz equation, we get

$$E = T \frac{dE}{dT} \quad \text{or,} \quad \frac{dE}{E} = \frac{dT}{T} \quad \text{or,} \quad \frac{E}{T} = \text{constant.}$$

15.12 Secondary Cells or Accumulators

The most satisfactory modern secondary cells, also known as accumulators, are still based on the type produced by Plante in 1859. This can be constructed by using lead electrodes in a solution of sulphuric acid.

Considering e for the charge carried by positive ion, the process of charging may be represented as

Positive plate

$$PbSO_4 + SO_4^{--} + 2H_2O = PbO_2 + 2H_2SO_4 - 2e$$

Negative plate

$$PbSO_4 + 2H^+ = Pb + H_2SO_4 + 2e.$$

For discharge, we can write,

Positive plate

$$PbO_2 + H_2SO_4 + 2H^+ = PbSO_4 + 2H_2O + 2e$$

Negative plate

$$Pb + H_2SO_4 + O^{--} = PbSO_4 + H_2O - 2e.$$

Sometimes modern cells use 'paste' plates with a mixture of lead oxides held in lead grid. These cells, however, have a shorter duration.

There are also alkali cells in which the electrolyte is an aqueous solution of a mixture of alkali hydroxides and the plates are metal structures containing hydroxides of nickel, iron or cadmium.

Questions

Essay-type

1. State and explain the Faraday's laws of electrolysis.

2. Explain the Arrhenius theory of electrolytic dissociation.

3. Discuss how the conduction of current through an electrolyte is made.

4. Write short notes on (i) Latimer-Clark cell and Weston cell, (ii) Concentration cells, (iii) Secondary cells.

5. Explain Ohm's law in electrolyte and verify it experimentally.

Short Answer-type

6. Define conductivity and equivalent conductivity.

7. What is meant by ionic mobility?

8. What do you mean by migration of the ions?

9. How can the conductivity of an electrolyte be determined by using Kohlrausch's method?

10. How is the second law of thermodynamics applied to a reversible cell?

11. What are standard cells?

Chapter 16

Electromagnetism

16.1 Introduction

It was H. C. Oersted who first made some fundamental arrangements for experimentation through which he established that a current of electricity produced a magnetic field in its neighbourhood. The first experimental observation of the interaction between two coils carrying current was performed by André-Marie Ampere. The work was later extended significantly by Oersted, Biot and Savart.

16.2 Ampere's Law

We know that an electric current flowing through a conducting wire is always attributed to a drift of electrons in the direction opposite to that of the impressed electric force. Suppose a point charge q is at rest; then the electric field caused by it along the radius vector will be

$$\mathbf{E} = \frac{1}{4\pi\epsilon_0}\frac{q}{r^3}\mathbf{r}. \tag{16.1}$$

Oersted in 1819 discovered that a current along a conducting wire exerts a torque on a magnet placed near to it. As a result of this the magnet rotates until its axis is at right angles to the wire. In the following year Ampere showed that a torque is also exerted between two circuits. So one can conclude that a magnetic field as well as an electric field are produced by a moving electric charge. The magnitude of the magnetic field is proportional to the speed of the charge. It is to be remembered that a moving charge exerts no force on a magnet moving with it.

The intensity of magnetic field at a point X (Fig. 16.1) at a distance r from the charge will be

$$\mathbf{H} = \frac{\mu_0}{4\pi}\frac{q\mathbf{v} \times \mathbf{r}}{r^3}. \tag{16.2}$$

Magnetic field will be perpendicular to the plane of $\mathbf{v}$ and $\mathbf{r}$. Its magnitude can be written as

$$\mathbf{H} = \frac{\mu_0}{4\pi}\frac{qv \sin\theta}{r^2},$$

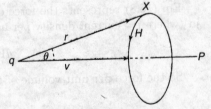

Fig. 16.1

where θ is the angle between v and r.

The magnitude of the magnetic field will remain unaltered on the circumference of a circle through the point X lying in a plane perpendicular to $\mathbf{v}$. Its direction will be everywhere tangent to the circle. On the other hand, if we consider magnetic field at different points on the surface of a sphere with its centre, the magnitude of magnetic field vanishes at the poles $\theta = 0$ and $\theta = \pi$, and is maximum along the equator $\theta = \frac{\pi}{2}$.

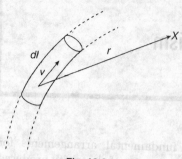

Fig. 16.2

Now consider a small tube of a conducting medium (Fig. 16.2) having cross-section α carrying a current $\mathbf{i}$.

$$\therefore \quad \mathbf{i} = \alpha n e v, \tag{16.3}$$

where n is the number of free charges per unit volume, $\mathbf{v}$ is the mean drift velocity and e is the charge. In case of electrons, the current has the direction opposite to that of $\mathbf{v}$.

The total moving charge in a length dl of the tube is

$$q = \alpha n e \, dl. \tag{16.4}$$

Therefore, the field at X due to a length dl of a current will be

$$d\mathbf{H} = \frac{\mu_0}{4\pi} \frac{(\alpha n e v) \times \mathbf{r}}{r^3} dl = \frac{\mu_0}{4\pi} \frac{\mathbf{i} \times \mathbf{r}}{r^3} dl. \tag{16.5}$$

This is *Ampere's law* for the magnetic field due to a current element $i\,dl$.

From Eq. (16.5), it is possible to deduce the force exerted on a current element by an external magnetic field.

Suppose a magnetic pole m is placed at the point X (Fig. 16.2). Then the force produced by the current element on the pole can be written using Eq. (16.5) as

$$m\,d\mathbf{H} = \frac{\mu_0}{4\pi} \mathbf{i} \times \left(\frac{m\mathbf{r}}{r^3} \right) dl. \tag{16.6}$$

According to Newton's third law of motion, the force exerted on the current element by the magnetic pole is equal and opposite to Eq. (16.6). Now, if $\mathbf{H}$ represents the intensity of magnetic field due to the pole at the current element, then

$$\mathbf{H} = -\frac{\mu_0}{4\pi} \frac{m\mathbf{r}}{r^3}. \tag{16.7}$$

Here the *minus* sign indicates that the radius vector $\mathbf{r}$ is directed towards the pole.

Using Eqs. (16.6) and (16.7) we get the expression of the force $d\mathbf{F}$ on the current element as

$$d\mathbf{F} = \mathbf{i} \times \mathbf{H}\,dl. \tag{16.8}$$

Eq. (16.8) represents the force due to an external field $\mathbf{H}$. Now replacing $\mathbf{i}$ by $\mathbf{j}\alpha$ (where $\mathbf{j}$ = current density per unit area) in Eq. (16.8) we get

$$d\mathbf{F} = \mathbf{j} \times \mathbf{H}\alpha\,dl. \tag{16.9}$$

So the force per unit volume of the current is

$$\mathbf{F} = \mathbf{j} \times \mathbf{H}. \tag{16.10}$$

Again from Eq. (16.8),

$$d\mathbf{F} = \mathbf{i} \times \mathbf{H}\,dl$$

$$= \alpha n e v \times \mathbf{H}\,dl \quad \text{[using Eq. (16.3)]}$$

$$= q\mathbf{v} \times \mathbf{H} \quad \text{[using Eq. (16.4)]}$$

The above expression represents the force on a moving charge due to a magnetic field of intensity $\mathbf{H}$.

If the surrounding space has the permeability μ, then

$$d\mathbf{F} = q\mathbf{v} \times \mathbf{B} \quad (\text{where } B = \mu H) \tag{16.11}$$

If B is in tesla, i in ampere, then dF will be in newton.

16.3   Magnetic Fields of Simple Circuits

(i) **Field due to a circular coil :** The magnetic field at the centre O of a circular coil having radius a can be easily found out using Ampere's law. Using Eq. (16.9) we get the magnitude of the intensity of a magnetic field at the point O (Fig. 16.3) due to current element AB of length dl as

$$dH = \frac{\mu_0}{4\pi} \frac{i}{a^2} dl, \text{ the angle } \theta \text{ between } AB \text{ and } AO \text{ is } \frac{\pi}{2}.$$

Now, $dH = \dfrac{\mu_0}{4\pi} \dfrac{i}{a^2} \cdot a\, d\theta$, where $dl = a\, d\theta$.

$$\therefore \quad H = \frac{\mu_0}{4\pi} \frac{i}{a} \int_0^{2\pi} d\theta = \frac{\mu_0}{4\pi} \cdot \frac{i}{a} \cdot 2\pi = \frac{\mu_0 i}{2a}. \tag{16.12}$$

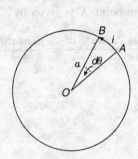

Fig. 16.3

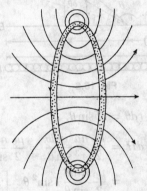

Fig. 16.4

The lines of force in the field of a circular coil are given in Fig. 16.4. If the circular coil consists of n turns, then the magnetic field at the point O will be

$$H = \frac{\mu_0}{2} \frac{ni}{a}. \tag{16.13}$$

Suppose we want to calculate the field at the point X on the axis of the coil (Fig. 16.5) at a distance $x(= OX)$ from the centre O.

Now the field at the point X due to current element AB is

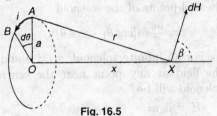

Fig. 16.5

$$dH = \frac{\mu_0}{4\pi} \frac{i a\, d\theta}{r^2}. \tag{16.14}$$

The direction of the field will be at right angles to the plane containing AB and AX.

Two diametrically opposite current elements give rise to fields whose components normal to OX annul each other. Therefore, the resultant field will be along OX

and equals to $dH \cos \beta$. The total field

$$H = \frac{\mu_0}{4\pi} \frac{ia}{r^2} \left[\int_0^{2\pi} d\theta \right] \cos \beta$$

$$= \frac{\mu_0}{4\pi} \frac{ia}{r^2} \left[\int_0^{2\pi} d\theta \right] \frac{a}{r} \quad \left[\because \cos \beta = \cos \angle AOX = \frac{a}{r} \right]$$

$$= \frac{\mu_0}{4\pi} \frac{ia^2}{r^3} \cdot 2\pi = \frac{\mu_0}{4\pi} \frac{2\pi ia^2}{(a^2 + x^2)^{3/2}} \quad \left[\because r^2 = a^2 + x^2 \right]$$

$$= \frac{\mu_0 ia^2}{2(a^2 + x^2)^{3/2}}. \tag{16.15}$$

(ii) Field due to a solenoid : Suppose AB be the axis of a solenoid (Fig. 16.6) having radius a, number of turns per unit length be n and i be the current flowing in each turn.

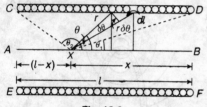

Fig. 16.6

Now consider a small element dl at a distance r from the point X on the axis. This element may be considered as a circular coil of ndl number of turns and field due to this element at the point X is given by

$$dH = \frac{\mu_0}{4\pi} \frac{2\pi nia^2 \cdot dl}{r^3} = \frac{\mu_0 nia^2 dl}{2r^3}.$$

Now, $rd\theta = dl \sin \theta$.

$$\therefore \quad dH = \frac{\mu_0}{2} \frac{na^2 ird\theta}{r^3 \sin\theta} = \frac{\mu_0}{2} \frac{nid\theta}{\sin\theta} \cdot \left(\frac{a}{r}\right)^2$$

$$= \frac{\mu_0}{2} \frac{nid\theta}{\sin\theta} \cdot \sin^2\theta \quad \left[\because \sin\theta = \frac{a}{r} \right]$$

$$= \frac{\mu_0}{2} ni \sin\theta d\theta.$$

For the whole solenoid the total field will be

$$H = \frac{\mu_0}{2} ni \int_{\theta_1}^{\theta_2} \sin\theta d\theta, \text{ where } \theta_1 \text{ and } \theta_2 \text{ be the angles subtended at } X \text{ by}$$

the end points of the solenoid

$$= \frac{\mu_0}{2} ni[\cos\theta_1 - \cos\theta_2]. \tag{16.16}$$

For an infinite solenoid, $\theta_1 = 0$ and $\theta_2 = \pi$, the field at any point near the centre of the solenoid will be

$$H = \mu_0 ni. \tag{16.17}$$

At the end of the solenoid, $\cos\theta_1 = 1$ and $\cos\theta_2 = 0$.

$$\therefore \quad H = \frac{\mu_0}{2} ni. \tag{16.18}$$

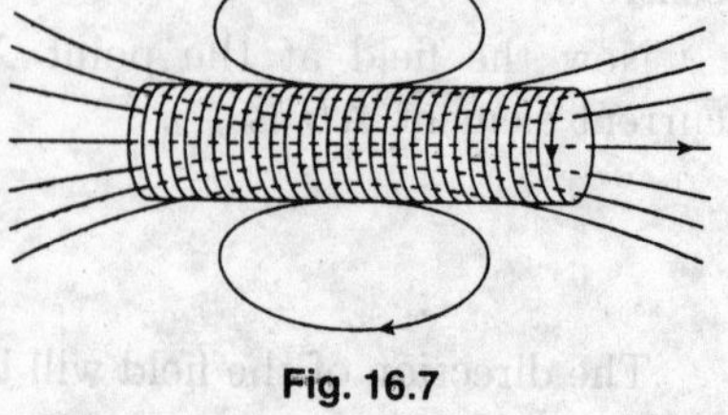

Fig. 16.7

Therefore, half the lines of force passing through the central section of a long solenoid pass out through the sides before reaching the end. The distribution of the lines of force is given in Fig. 16.7.

(iii) Field due to a straight wire : Here we have to calculate the field at a point P due to a straight wire parallel to Y-axis (Fig. 16.8). The field at the point P due to current element idl will be

$$dH = \frac{\mu_0}{4\pi} \frac{idl \sin\theta}{r^2} \qquad (16.19)$$

and is directed out from the plane of the paper.

Now, $CO = l = a\tan\beta$.

$\therefore \quad dl = a\sec^2\beta d\beta = r\sec\beta d\beta$

or, $\quad dl\cos\beta = rd\beta$

or, $\quad dl\sin\theta = rd\beta \quad [\because \sin\theta = \sin(90° + \beta) = \cos\beta]$.

$\therefore \quad dH = \frac{\mu_0}{4\pi} \frac{idl\sin\theta}{r^2} = \frac{\mu_0}{4\pi} \frac{ird\beta}{r^2} = \frac{\mu_0}{4\pi} \frac{id\beta}{r}$

$\qquad = \frac{\mu_0}{4\pi} \frac{i\cos\beta d\beta}{a} \quad \left[\because \cos\beta = \frac{a}{r}\right]$.

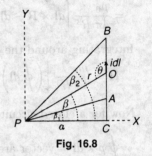

Fig. 16.8

Hence the total field at the point P will be

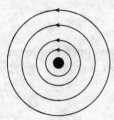

Fig. 16.9

$$H = \frac{\mu_0}{4\pi} \frac{i}{a} \int_{\beta_1}^{\beta_2} \cos\beta d\beta = \frac{\mu_0}{4\pi} \frac{i}{a}[\sin\beta_2 - \sin\beta_1]. \qquad (16.20)$$

If the straight wire is of infinite length, then the field at the point P will be obtained after substituting $\beta_1 = -\frac{\pi}{2}$ and $\beta_2 = \frac{\pi}{2}$. Hence

$$H = \frac{\mu_0}{4\pi} \frac{2i}{a} = \frac{\mu_0 i}{2\pi a}. \qquad (16.21)$$

The lines of force will be circular in planes at right angles to the wire as shown in Fig. 16.9.

(iv) Field due a current-carrying conductor of any shape : Here we shall calculate the field at any point P due to a small circuit of any shape (Fig. 16.10). Suppose the linear dimension of the circuit is small compared with the distance of the point P from the circuit. Let O be the origin of our coordinate system which lies inside the circuit. The axes are so oriented that the Z-axis lies perpendicular to the plane of the circuit and OP lies on the ZX-plane.

Now, the distance of P from O is $\mathbf{R}$.

$\mathbf{R} \equiv R(\hat{i}\sin\theta + \hat{k}\cos\theta)$ and the position vector of the current element AB is $\rho = \hat{i}x + \hat{j}y$.

$\therefore \quad \mathbf{r} = \mathbf{R} - \rho$

or, $\quad r^2 = (\mathbf{R} - \rho)\cdot(\mathbf{R} - \rho) = \mathbf{R}^2 - 2\mathbf{R}\cdot\rho + \rho^2$

here $\rho^2 = x^2 + y^2$

Now, $\mathbf{R}\cdot\rho = R(\hat{i}\sin\theta + \hat{k}\cos\theta)\cdot(\hat{i}x + \hat{j}y)$

$\qquad = Rx\sin\theta$.

$\therefore \quad r^2 = R^2 - 2Rx\sin\theta + \rho^2$.

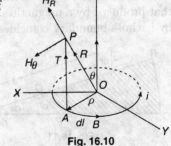

Fig. 16.10

In this problem we have assumed that x and y are small compared with R, and so we neglect higher order terms of x and y.

$\therefore \quad r^3 = (R^3 - 2Rx\sin\theta)^{3/2}$.

From Eq. (16.5) we can write the expression of magnetic field due to the current element AB of length dl at the point P as

$$d\mathbf{H} = \frac{\mu_0}{4\pi} \frac{i \times r}{r^3} dl = \frac{\mu_0}{4\pi} i \frac{dl \times r}{r^3}$$

$$= \frac{\mu_0}{4\pi} i (R^2 - 2Rx \sin\theta)^{-3/2} dl \times r = \frac{\mu_0}{4\pi} i \cdot \frac{1}{R^3} \left(1 + \frac{3x}{R} \sin\theta\right) (dl \times \mathbf{R} - dl \times \rho)$$

$$= \frac{\mu_0}{4\pi} \frac{i}{R^3} \left[dl \times \mathbf{R} - dl \times \rho + \frac{3x}{R} \sin\theta \, dl \times \mathbf{R}\right].$$

Integrating around the circuit we get the total magnetic field at the point P,

$$\mathbf{H} = \frac{\mu_0}{4\pi} \frac{i}{R^3} \left[\left(\oint dl\right) \times \mathbf{R} - \oint (dl \times \rho) + \frac{3}{R} \sin\theta \left(\oint x \, dl\right) \times \mathbf{R}\right]. \qquad (16.22)$$

Now for a closed circuit, $\oint dl = 0$,

$$\oint \rho \times dl = \text{vector area } \mathbf{A} \text{ of circuit along the } Z\text{-axis and}$$

$$\oint x \, dl = \oint x(\hat{i}\, dx + \hat{j}\, dy) = \hat{i} \oint x \, dx + \hat{j} \oint x \, dy$$

$$= \hat{j} A \text{ [the first integral vanishes because of the same upper and lower}$$
limits and the second integral is the area under a curve].

Therefore, the expression for $\mathbf{H}$ becomes

$$= \mathbf{H} = \frac{\mu_0}{4\pi} \frac{i}{R^3} \left[-2A + 3\frac{A \sin\theta}{R} \hat{j} \times \mathbf{R}\right]$$

$$= \frac{\mu_0}{4\pi} \left[\frac{2iA}{R^3} + 3\frac{iA \sin\theta}{R^4} \hat{j} \times \mathbf{R}\right] \qquad (16.23)$$

Resolving H along and perpendicular to R, we get

$$\left. \begin{array}{l} H_R = \frac{\mu_0}{4\pi} \frac{2iA}{R^3} \cos\theta = \frac{\mu_0 iA}{2\pi R^3} \cos\theta \\[2mm] H_\theta = \frac{\mu_0}{4\pi} \frac{iA}{R^3} \sin\theta \end{array} \right\} \qquad (16.24)$$

16.4 Magnetic Shell Equivalent to Current Circuit

Here we shall show that a current circuit will produce the same magnetic field as that produced by a magnetic shell of constant strength equal to the current divided by c whose boundary coincides with the circuit.

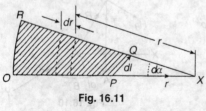

Fig. 16.11

Suppose $OPQR$ is a magnetic shell of strength ϕ (Fig. 16.11) and $d\alpha$ be the angle confined between the sides OP and RQ at the point X. Now we want to calculate the intensity of magnetic field at the point X due to the magnetic shell. The magnetic moment of the elementary shell between the arcs of radii r and $r + dr$ is $\phi r \, d\alpha \, dr$. Therefore, the field at X due to this shell element will be

$$d^2 H = \frac{\phi r \, d\alpha \, dr}{r^3} = \phi d\alpha \frac{dr}{r^2}.$$

After integration we have

$$dH = \phi d\alpha \int_r^\infty \frac{dr}{r^2} = \frac{\phi d\alpha}{r} = \frac{\phi r^2 d\alpha}{r^3}. \tag{16.25}$$

Now $r^2 d\alpha = r \cdot r d\alpha = 2 \times \Delta PQX$.

If **r** is the vector distance PX and $d\mathbf{l}$ is the vector PQ, then $d\mathbf{l} \times \mathbf{r}$ is equal to twice the area of the triangle PQX. Therefore, Eq. (16.25) can be written as

$$dH = \phi \frac{d\mathbf{l} \times \mathbf{r}}{r^3} \tag{16.26}$$

Comparing Eq. (16.26) with Ampere's law one can easily conclude that this equation is identical with that of the field produced by a current element idl provided the strength of the shell ϕ is equal to i/c.

Therefore, one can say that, "*Any conductor carrying a current is equivalent to a simple magnetic shell whose bounding edge coincides with the conductor and whose strength is proportional to the strength of the current.*"

Let $ABCD$ be the circuit of any shape as shown in Fig. 16.12 and we divide this circuit into a number of elementary circuits, viz., $abcd$ by means of network. Suppose that some current i is flowing in each network in the direction as shown in Fig. 16.12. By considering any one branch of the network we see that it is a part of two adjacent circuits and carries equal and opposite currents. So the resultant current will be zero. Only those currents flowing through the peripheral branches are uncompensated. Therefore, the resultant field is identical with that produced in $ABCD$.

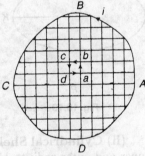

Fig. 16.12

16.5   Circuital Form of Ampere's Law

Here we express Ampere's law in another usual form. Suppose the current circuit is replaced by an equivalent magnetic shell whose periphery coincides with the circuit and whose strength ϕ is equal to i/c. We know that the work done in carrying a unit positive pole from a point on the positive side to an opposite point on the negative side around the edge of a magnetic shell is equal to $4\pi\phi$. Therefore, the work done in case of a current circuit will be equal to

$$W = 4\pi\phi = 4\pi \frac{i}{c}. \tag{16.27}$$

In the above deduction, we have neglected the portion of the path of the pole lying inside the equivalent magnetic shell. The work done in passing through the shell is equal and opposite to that done along the part of the path lying outside the shell. Therefore, the total work done around a closed path is zero. The field in the interior of the equivalent shell differs from the field due to the current circuit. But as the thickness of the equivalent shell is extremely small, the work done on a pole as it passes around the edge of the shell from one point on one side to a point opposite to that other side will not differ appreciably from the work done on the pole as it is completely encircling the circuit.

Suppose the angle between the intensity of magnetic field **H** and an element dl of a closed curve surrounding the current is θ. Then the work done by the field when a unit pole describes a closed path around the current is

$$W = \oint H \cos\theta \, dl = \oint \mathbf{H} \cdot d\mathbf{l} \tag{16.28}$$

The above integral is known as *magnetomotive force.*

Comparing Eqs. (16.27) and (16.28) we get Ampere's law in a circuital form as

$$\oint \mathbf{H} \cdot d\mathbf{l} = \frac{4\pi i}{c}. \tag{16.29}$$

Circuital form of Ampere's law is useful in calculating intensity of magnetic field when symmetry occurs for all points on a closed line of force.

16.6   Intensity from Circuital Theorem

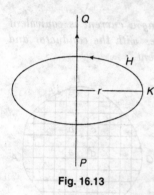

Fig. 16.13

(i) Straight Wire : Consider a wire PQ along which a current of magnitude i is flowing (Fig. 16.13). The intensity of magnetic field at a point K will be normal to the plane containing r and PQ. Therefore, the lines of force are circle around the wire with the centre on PQ. Applying Ampere's circuital theorem,

$$\oint \mathbf{H} \cdot d\mathbf{l} = \frac{4\pi i}{c}$$

or, $2\pi r H = \dfrac{4\pi i}{c}$

$$\therefore \quad H = \frac{2i}{cr}. \tag{16.30}$$

(ii) Cylindrical Shell : Consider a cylinder PQ having inner and outer radii to be a and b along which a current i is flowing (Fig. 16.14).

So the current per unit area $= \dfrac{i}{\pi(b^2 - a^2)}.$

Now we have to calculate the intensity at any point X (not shown in the figure) at a distance r, say, from the axis of the cylinder.

According to Ampere's circuital theorem,

$$\oint \mathbf{H} \cdot d\mathbf{l} = \frac{4\pi i}{c},$$

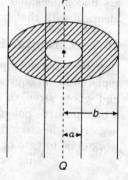

Fig. 16.14

where i is the current enclosed by the circle and passes through that point X where the intensity is to be calculated having centre on the axis of the cylinder.

(a) For a point inside the cylinder $(r < 0)$, $i' = 0$.

$$\therefore \quad H = 0. \tag{16.31}$$

(b) If $a < r < b$, then

$$i' = \pi(r^2 - a^2) \frac{i}{\pi(b^2 - a^2)} = \left(\frac{r^2 - a^2}{b^2 - a^2}\right) i.$$

$$\therefore \quad \oint \mathbf{H} \cdot d\mathbf{l} = 4\pi \left(\frac{r^2 - a^2}{b^2 - a^2}\right) \cdot \frac{i}{c} \quad \text{or,} \quad 2\pi r \cdot H = 4\pi \left(\frac{r^2 - a^2}{b^2 - a^2}\right) \cdot \frac{i}{c}$$

$$\therefore \quad H = \frac{2i}{cr}\left(\frac{r^2 - a^2}{b^2 - a^2}\right). \tag{16.32}$$

(c) If $b < r \leq \infty$,

$$H \cdot 2\pi r = \frac{4\pi i}{c}.$$

$$\therefore \quad H = \frac{2i}{cr}. \tag{16.33}$$

(iii) Toroid : Endless solenoid is known as toroid. Let H be the field inside a toroid of radius r with its centre at O (Fig. 16.15). Suppose n be the number of turns per unit length and i be the current flowing in each turn. So according to Ampere's circuital theorem

$$\oint \mathbf{H} \cdot d\mathbf{l} = \frac{4\pi}{c}(2\pi rni) = \frac{8\pi^2 rni}{c}$$

or, $\quad 2\pi r \cdot H = \dfrac{8\pi^2 r \cdot ni}{c}$

$$\therefore \quad H = 4\pi ni. \tag{16.34}$$

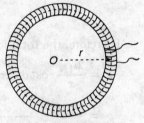

Fig. 16.15

16.7 Force on Two Current-carrying Conductors

Suppose two current elements $i_1 dl_1$ and $i_2 dl_2$ are kept at a distance r from each other as shown in Fig. 16.16.

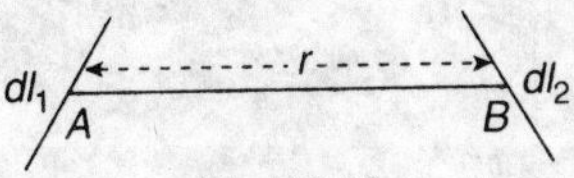

The field due to the current element $i_1 dl_1$ at B will be

$$d\mathbf{H} = \frac{i_1(d\mathbf{l}_1 \times \mathbf{r})}{r^3}.$$

Fig. 16.16

Therefore, force on the current element $i_2 dl_2$ is

$$dF = i_2(d\mathbf{l}_2 \times d\mathbf{H}) = \frac{i_1 i_2 d\mathbf{l}_2 \times (d\mathbf{l}_1 \times \mathbf{r})}{r^3}. \tag{16.35}$$

Similarly, the force on the current element $i_1 dl_1$ due to the current element $i_2 dl_2$ will be same as Eq. (16.35).

(i) Straight Parallel Wires : Suppose P and Q are two straight wires carrying currents i_1 and i_2 respectively. Let r be the distance between the wires [Fig. 16.17(a)].

Now the field produced due to the current flowing along the wire P at a point on the wire Q will be $\frac{2i_1}{r}$.

Therefore, the force per unit length of the wire Q,

$$F = \frac{2i_1 i_2}{r}. \tag{16.36}$$

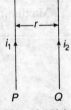

Fig. 16.17(a)

(ii) Two Parallel Co-axial Circular Coils : Consider two parallel co-axial coils of radii a and b respectively [Fig. 16.17(b)].

Field at any point A_2 is $\dfrac{2i_1 \cos\theta}{x}$.

Therefore, the force per unit length of the coil of radius b will be $\frac{2i_1 i_2 \cos\theta}{x}$ and will be directed along $A_1 A_2$. The component of forces normal to the axis will be zero by symmetry. Therefore, the component of forces parallel to the axis will be $\frac{2i_1 i_2 \cos\theta}{x} \cos\theta = \frac{2i_1 i_2}{x} \cos^2\theta$.

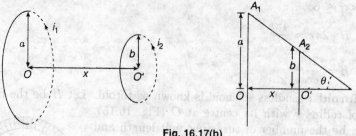

Fig. 16.17(b)

Therefore, the total force on the coil

$$F = \frac{2i_1 i_2}{x} \cos^2\theta \cdot 2\pi b = \frac{4\pi i_1 i_2 b \cos^2\theta}{x}$$

$$= \frac{4\pi i_1 i_2 b}{x} \cdot \frac{x^2 \cdot}{(a-b)^2 + x^2} \qquad \left[\because \cos\theta = \frac{x}{\sqrt{(a-b)^2 + x^2}} \right]$$

$$= 4\pi i_1 i_2 b \cdot \frac{x}{(a-b)^2 + x^2}. \tag{16.37}$$

Now for maximum value of F, $\dfrac{\partial F}{\partial x} = 0$.

$$\therefore \quad \frac{\partial F}{\partial x} = 4\pi i_1 i_2 b \left[\frac{1}{(a-b)^2 + x^2} - \frac{2x^2}{\{(a-b)^2 + x^2\}^2} \right]$$

$$= 4\pi i_1 i_2 b \frac{(a-b)^2 + x^2 - 2x^2}{\{(a-b)^2 + x^2\}^2} = 4\pi i_1 i_2 b \frac{(a-b)^2 - x^2}{\{(a-b)^2 + x^2\}^2}.$$

Now, $\dfrac{\partial F}{\partial x}$ will be zero when $x = a - b$.

Therefore, the force will be maximum if the coils are kept separate at a distance equal to the difference of the radii of the two coils.

Maximum value of the force

$$F_{\max} = 4\pi i_1 i_2 b \cdot \frac{(a-b)}{2(a-b)^2} = \frac{2\pi i_1 i_2 b}{a - b}. \tag{16.38}$$

Examples

1. A current is flowing along a vertical wire. A neutral point is found at a distance of 10 cm from the wire. If the horizontal component of the earth's magnetic field $H = 0.36$ oersted, what will be the magnitude of the current?

   Solution : In Fig. 16.18, N is the neutral point in the (i) the field F due to current flowing along the wire and (ii) the earth's horizontal field H.

   Therefore at N, $F = H$.

   Now, $F = \dfrac{2i}{a} = H$.

   Here, $a = 10$ cm and $H = 0.36$ oersted.

$$\therefore \qquad i = \frac{aH}{2} = \frac{10 \times 0.36}{2} = 1.8 \text{ e.m.u.} = \mathbf{18 \text{ amperes}}.$$

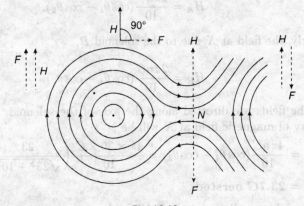

Fig. 16.18

2. A circuit carrying a current I has the form of a square having side l. Find the magnetic intensity at its centre.

   Solution : Suppose $ABCD$ be the square frame carrying a current of I ampere (Fig. 16.19). At the centre O of the square frame the resultant intensity will be equal to the sum of intensities due to each side.

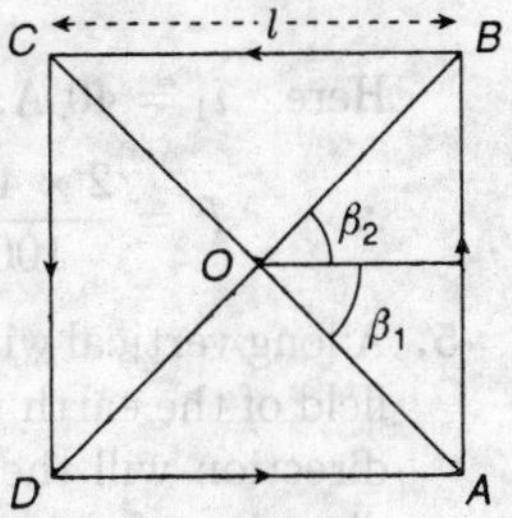

   Now, the intensity of magnetic field at O due to current flowing through the side AB will be

   $$H = \frac{I}{a}(\sin \beta_2 + \sin \beta_1).$$

   Here, $a = \dfrac{l}{2}$ and $\beta_1 = \beta_2 = 45°$.

   Fig. 16.19

   $$\therefore \qquad H = \frac{2I}{l}\left(\frac{1}{\sqrt{2}} + \frac{1}{\sqrt{2}}\right) = \frac{4I}{l\sqrt{2}} = \frac{2\sqrt{2}I}{l} \text{ oersted}.$$

   Therefore, the resultant intensity at $O = \dfrac{4 \times 2\sqrt{2}I}{l} = \dfrac{8\sqrt{2}I}{l}$ **oersted**.

3. Two short solenoids each of radii 10 cm and length 20 cm uniformly round with 30 turns of wire per cm are arranged co-axially with a gap 6 cm between them. Assuming Laplace's formula for the field of a current element, calculate the magnetic field at the centre of the gap due to a current of C ampere flowing through the two solenoids in series.

   Solution : Suppose A and B are two equal solenoids and C be the current flowing through the two solenoids in series (Fig. 16.20).

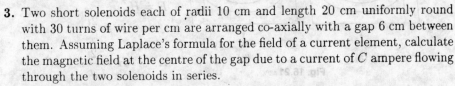

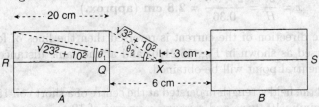

Fig. 16.20

Now the field at the point X due to the solenoid A will be

$$H_A = \frac{2\pi nC}{10}(\cos\theta_1 - \cos\theta_2).$$

Similarly, the field at X due to the solenoid B,

$$H_B = \frac{2\pi nC}{10}(\cos\theta_1 - \cos\theta_2).$$

Both the fields are directed along the axis of the solenoid. Therefore, total intensity of magnetic field at X will be

$$H = \frac{4\pi nC}{10}(\cos\theta_1 - \cos\theta_2) = \frac{4\pi \times 30 \times C}{10}\left(\frac{23}{\sqrt{23^2 + 10^2}} - \frac{3}{\sqrt{3^2 + 10^2}}\right)$$

$$= \mathbf{23.7C \ oersted.}$$

4. Two straight parallel wires each 10 cm long are separated by a distance of 4 cm and are each carrying a current of 40 amperes. What force in dynes will be set up between the wires?

Solution : We know that force per unit length of the wire $F = \dfrac{2i_1 i_2}{100a}$.

Here, $i_1 = 40$ A, $i_2 = 40$ A, $a = 4$ cm.

$\therefore \qquad F = \dfrac{2 \times 40 \times 40}{100 \times 4}$ dynes/cm = 8 dynes/cm.

5. A long vertical wire carries a current of 5 amperes and is placed in the magnetic field of the earth where $H = 0.36$ oersted. Find at what distances and in what direction will the neutral points be located. Will there be any change if the direction of the current be reversed?   [Delhi U. 1961]

Solution : Let the current be flowing vertically upwards through the vertical wire. The magnetic lines of force will be anticlockwise [Fig. 16.21(a)]. Now if the neutral point is situated at a distance x from the wire, then at that point $F = H$.

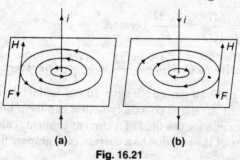

Fig. 16.21

$$\therefore \qquad F = \frac{2i}{x},$$

$$\therefore \qquad H = \frac{2i}{x}.$$

Here, $i = 5$ amperes $= 0.5$ e.m.u., $H = 0.36$ oersted.

$\therefore \qquad x = \dfrac{2i}{H} = \dfrac{2 \times 0.5}{0.36} = \mathbf{2.8 \ cm \ (approx.)}$

If the direction of the current is reversed then the lines of force will also be reversed as shown in Fig. 16.21(b) and at the same distance the position of the neutral point will be obtained.

6. Find the field strength in oersted at the centre of a short coil 15 cm in diameter containing 10 turns and carrying a current of 10 amperes.   [C.U. 1966]

Solution : We know, $F = \dfrac{2\pi n i}{\alpha}$.

Here, $n = 10$, $i = 10$ amperes $= 1$ e.m.u., $\alpha = 7.5$ cm.

$\therefore \quad F = \dfrac{2 \times 3.14 \times 10 \times 1}{7.5} = \mathbf{8.37 \text{ oersteds}}$.

7. Determine the strength of the current in milliamperes which must flow through a narrow solenoid of 1000 turns and of length 1 metre, lying in the magnetic meridian, if the earth's horizontal magnetic field of 0.36 oersted is to be neutralized at the centre.   [Utkal U. 1953]

Solution : We know, magnetic intensity, $F = 4\pi n i$.

At the centre of the coil if the magnetic intensity neutralises the horizontal component of the earth's magnetic field, then $F = 4\pi n i$.

Here, $n = \dfrac{1000}{100} = 10$ turns/cm, $H = 0.36$ oersted.

$\therefore \quad i = \dfrac{H}{4\pi n} = \dfrac{0.36}{4 \times 3.14 \times 10} = 2.86 \text{ e.m.u.} = \mathbf{0.0286 \text{ mA}}$.

8. Suppose two long, straight and parallel wires P and Q are carrying 30 A and 40 A current respectively. What will be the force experienced by one metre of the wire P due to the wire Q if the wires P and Q are kept 10 cm apart?

Solution : We know, $F = \dfrac{2 i_1 i_2}{a} \times l$.

Here, $i_1 = 30$ amperes $= 3$ e.m.u., $i_2 = 40$ amp $= 4$ e.m.u., $a = 10$ cm,

$\quad l = 1$ metre $= 100$ cm.

$\therefore \quad F = \dfrac{2 \times 3 \times 4}{10} \times 100 = \mathbf{240 \text{ dynes}}$.

9. A circular coil of 10 turns has a diameter of 0.12 m and carries a current of 7 A. It is placed in the magnetic meridian where the horizontal component of the earth's magnetic field is 0.4 Oe. In what direction will a compass needle point which is 0.08 m magnetically east of the coil in the line of its axis? $[1 \text{ Oe} = 10^3/4\pi \text{ A m}^{-1}]$

Solution : At a distance x from the centre of the coil, the magnetic intensity on the axis of the coil,

$$F = \frac{1}{4\pi} \cdot \frac{2\pi n i a^2}{(a^2 + x^2)^{3/2}} = \frac{n i a^2}{2(a^2 + x^2)^{3/2}} \text{ A m}^{-1}.$$

Given that, $n = 10$; $i = 7$ A; $a = 0.06$ m; $x = 0.08$ m.

$\therefore \quad F = \dfrac{10 \times 7 \times (0.06)^2}{2[(0.06)^2 + (0.08)^2]^{3/2}} = \dfrac{10 \times 7 \times 36 \times 10^{-4}}{2 \times 10^{-3}} = 126 \text{ A m}^{-1}$.

Again, $H = 0.4$ Oe $= 0.4 \times \dfrac{10^3}{4\pi} \text{ A m}^{-1} = 31.85 \text{ A m}^{-1}$.

If the deflection of the needle is θ,

$$\tan\theta = \frac{F}{H} = \frac{126}{31.85} = 4$$

$\therefore \quad \theta = \mathbf{75°60'}$.

10. Find the field strength in A/m at the centre of a short coil 15 cm in diameter containing 100 turns and carrying a current of 10 amperes.

   Solution : Magnetic intensity at the centre of circular conductor carrying current, $F = \dfrac{ni}{2a}$.

   Given that, $n = 100$; $i = 10$ A; $a = 7.5$ cm $= \dfrac{7.5}{100}$ m.

   $\therefore \qquad F = \dfrac{100 \times 10 \times 100}{2 \times 7.5} = 6\,666.7$ amperes/m.

11. A solenoid 60 cm long is wound with three layers of wire of 800 turns each. If a current of 2 A flows through the solenoid, determine field at a point near the centre in c.g.s. and S.I. systems.

   Solution : According to c.g.s. system, the total number of turns, $N = 3 \times 800$.

   So the number of turns per cm, $n = \dfrac{3 \times 800}{60} = 40$.

   Again, the intensity of the magnetic field at some point within (of the long solenoid),

   $$F = \frac{4\pi n I}{10} = \frac{4 \times 22 \times 40 \times 2}{7 \times 10} = \textbf{100.6 Oe}$$

   According to S.I. system intensity of magnetic field at any point in the long solenoid is

   $$F = ni \text{ ampere/m} = \frac{40 \times 2}{1/100} = \textbf{8} \times \textbf{10}^3 \textbf{ ampere/m}.$$

   $$\left(\text{since } \; n = \frac{40}{1/100} \text{ turn/m} \right)$$

12. A circular coil of radius 2 cm has 500 turns in it and carries a current of 1 A. Its axis makes an angle of 30° with a uniform magnetic field of magnitude 0.4 T that exists in the space. Find the torque acting on the coil.

   Solution : The torque on the coil $\tau = niAB \sin\theta$.

   Given that, $n = 500$; $i = 1$ A; $A = \pi r^2 = \pi(2 \times 10^{-2})$ m^2; $B = 0.4$ T and $\theta = 30°$.

   $\therefore \qquad \tau = 500 \times 1 \times \pi(2 \times 10^{-2})^2 \times 0.4 \times \sin 30°$

   $$= 500 \times 3.14 \times 4 \times 10^{-4} \times 0.4 \times \frac{1}{2} = \textbf{0.13 N-m}.$$

13. A current of 10^{-9} A is established in a circular loop of radius 1 cm. Find the magnetic dipole moment of the current loop.

   Solution : Magnetic dipole moment $\vec{\mu} = ni\vec{A}$.

   Given that, $n = 1$; $i = 10^{-9}$ A and $A = \pi r^2 = 3.14 \times (10^{-2})^2$ m^2

   $\therefore \qquad \vec{\mu} = 10^{-9} \times 3.14 \times 10^{-4} = \textbf{3.14} \times \textbf{10}^{-13} \textbf{ A-m}^{-2}$.

Questions

Essay-type

1. State and explain Ampere's law for the magnetic field. Calculate the magnetic field near an infinitely long straight conductor carrying current.

2. Discuss Ampere's theorem and express it in the circuital form. Using Ampere's circuital law calculate the magnetic field of a cylindrical shell.

3. Obtain an expression of magnetic field inside a finite solenoid. Hence calculate the field inside of toroid.

4. State Laplace's law for the magnetic fields at a point due to a current element. Obtain an expression for the magnetic field at the centre of a circular wire carrying current. **[N.B.U. 1982]**

5. Derive an expression for the magnetic field intensity at a point on the axis of a circular coil of wire carrying electric current. **[B.U. 1990, '96]**

6. Show that the magnetic field inside a long solenoid is ni where n is the number of turns per unit length and i the current in ampere.

7. A straight solenoid of length l and radius r is wound uniformly with n turns of wire carrying a current i. Derive an expression for the intensity of the magnetic field at a point on the axis of the solenoid midway between its ends.

8. State Ampere's theorem of equivalent magnetic shell. Apply Ampere's theorem to determine the intensity of the magnetic field at any point on the axis of a circular coil. **[B.U. 1983, '91]**

9. Deduce an expression for the magnetic potential at any point due to a current in a closed circuit. Hence find the intensity of the magnetic field at any point on the axis of a circular current.

10. What is Ampere's circuital theorem? Explain it. Apply the theorem to find the intensity of the magnetic field due to solenoidal current at a point on its axis.

11. Find the force per unit length of a current-carrying conductor placed in a uniform magnetic field.

12. In the case of a long solenoid, prove that the intensity of the magnetic field at a point well inside is double than that at any end of the solenoid.

13. Find the force due to a small magnet on a circular coil carrying a steady current, the plane of the coil being normal to the axis of the magnet and its centre on the axis.

14. State and explain the law for the intensity of magnetic field at a point due to a current element.

Short Answer-type

15. What is Fleming's left-hand rule? In what connection is this rule applied?

16. What do you mean by the magnetic moment of a circular coil? What is the value?

17. What is called ampere-turn of a solenoid?

18. A small magnetic needle is pivoted on a vertical stand. If a wire carrying a current, is placed along the axis of the needle, how will the needle place itself when the wire is stretched above the needle? What will be the positions of the needle in the following cases : **(i)** the wire is above the needle, **(ii)** the wire is below the needle, **(iii)** the wire is placed in the east-west position?

19. State Laplace or Biot-Savart law.

20. What are Ampere's swimming rule and Maxwell's cork-screw rule? In what connection are these rules applied?

Numerical Problems

21. A wire shaped to a regular hexagon of side 'a' carries a current of 1 ampere. Calculate the strength of the magnetic field at the centre of the hexagon.
[**Ans.** 0.7 oersted]

22. Two similar coils of wire having radius 7 cm and 60 turns have a common axis and are 18 cm apart. Find the strength of the magnetic field (a) at the centre of either coil, (b) at a point on their common axis midway between them.
[**Ans.** 0.2564 oersted, 1.2471 oersted]

23. Calculate the intensity of field at the centre of a square conducting frame carrying a current of 1 ampere, the length of each side of the square being 10 cm. [**Ans.** $\sqrt{2125}$ oersteds]

24. A solenoid of 1000 turns is wound uniformly on a tube in single layer and is carrying a current of 0.1 A. The tube is 50 cm long and 10 cm in diameter. Find out the strength of the magnetic field **(i)** at the centre of the solenoid, **(ii)** at the centres of the end faces.

25. A circular coil of 50 turns and radius 15 cm has a magnetic pole of 300 Wb placed at its centre. When a current flows through the coil, the pole is acted on by a force of 6.25×10^{-2} N. What is the strength of the current in amperes? [**Ans.** 3.14 A]

26. A circular coil consists of 10 turns of fine wire wound in a narrow ring of radius 22 cm. Find the intensity of the magnetic field at the centre of the coil, if a current of 1 A passes through it. [**Ans.** 0.29×10^{-4} T]

27. A long vertical wire carries a current of 15 A and is placed in the earth's magnetic field ($H = 0.36 \times 10^{-4}$ T). How far from the wire will the neutral point be situated? What will be the change if the current in the wire is reversed? [**Ans.** 8.33 cm; in opposite direction at the same distance]

28. Two straight wires, each 10 cm long, are parallel to one another and are separated by a distance of 2 cm. They carry currents of 30 A and 40 A respectively. Calculate the force experienced by either of the wires.
[**Ans.** 1.2×10^{-3} N]

29. A magnetic field of intensity 12.6×10^{-4} T has to be obtained at the centre of a solenoid 20 cm long and 5 cm in diameter. Find the number of ampere-turns required. [**Ans.** 207 (nearly)]

30. A current flowing through a solenoid of 200 turns closely wound along an axial length of 50 cm produces a field of 30×10^{-4} T at a point well inside the solenoid. What is the strength of the current? [**Ans.** 5.9 A]

31. A solenoid of length 20 cm and radius 2 cm is closely wound with 200 turns. If the current in the windings be 5 A, calculate the magnetic field at the centre of one end of the solenoid. [**Ans.** 0.063 T]

32. A long straight wire carries a current of 50 A. An electron moving at 10^7 m/s is 5 cm from the wire at a given instant. Find the force acting on the electron if its velocity is directed towards the wire at that instant. $e = 1.6 \times 10^{-19}$ C. [**Ans.** 3.2×10^{-16} N]

33. Two long straight wires lie parallel to each other, separated by a distance of 10 cm in a medium of permittivity 1.5. If one carries a current of 12 A and the other a current of 5 A in the opposite direction, find the force each wire exerts on the other.   **[Ans. 1.8×10^{-4} N/m]**

34. The number of turns per cm of a solenoid of length 40 cm and radius 10 cm is 50. If a current of 500 mA flows through the solenoid, calculate the magnetic field at the centre of the solenoid.   **[C.U. 1982]**

                                                   [Ans. 28.13×10^{-4} T]

35. An electric current of 1.5 A flows round a circular coil of radius 1.5 cm. Calculate the strength of the magnetic field on the axis of the coil at a point 20 cm distant from the plane of the coil.   **[C.U. 1967]**

                                                   [Ans. 0.01356 oersted]

36. A solenoid of 400 turns wound uniformly round a glass tube 20 cm long has its diameter 2 cm and conveys a current of 1 amp through it. Find the strength of the magnetic field at the (i) centre and (ii) ends of the solenoid.

                                                   [Ans. 28.12 oersteds]

Chapter 17
Electromagnetic Induction

17.1   Introduction

In 1831 English physicist Michael Faraday noticed that a magnet might induce a current in a neighbouring fixed circuit. By careful experiment he found that a galvanometer in the circuit exhibits a momentary deflection when the magnet is approaching or receding. Further observation also revealed that the same effect is produced by moving a second circuit in which a current is passing toward or away from the first or by keeping the second circuit fixed and changing the current in it. The phenomenon of current induction was noted by Henry in America even earlier but the discovery is generally attributed to Faraday as he was the first to publish his observations.

17.2   Electromotive Force

When a steady current flows through a conductor, a potential drop will exist between the two terminals of the conductor. This potential difference is maintained by a source such as battery, dynamo, etc. All such sources convert some kinds of energy into electrical energy. Suppose a constant potential difference V volts is maintained between two terminals of a conductor by a battery. As a result of this an electric field E is established in the conductor, the line integral of which over a path between two points (A, B) is equal to the electromotive force V of the battery,

$$V = \int_A^B \mathbf{E} \cdot d\mathbf{l}. \tag{17.1}$$

Now, during the flow of current, the battery must do work to keep V constant. If q be the charge that flows through the conductor, then the work done by the battery is

$$W = Vq = \int_A^B q\mathbf{E} \cdot d\mathbf{l}.$$

Therefore, the e.m.f. of the battery is

$$V = \frac{1}{q} \int_A^B q\mathbf{E} \cdot d\mathbf{l}. \tag{17.2}$$

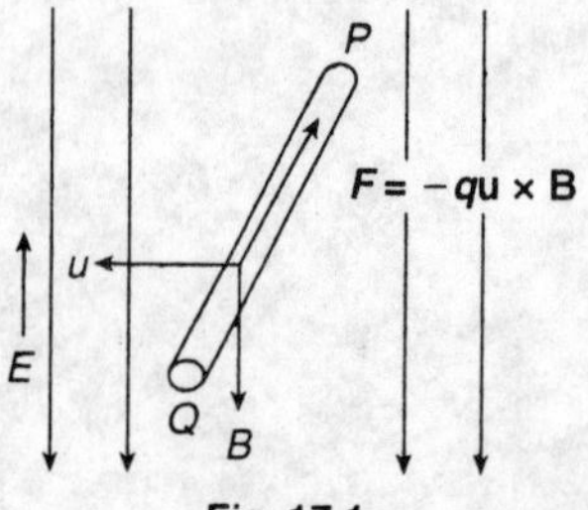

Fig. 17.1

Consider a metal bar PQ which is moving with a constant velocity u (Fig. 17.1) A magnetic field $\mathbf{B}$ is applied normal to the direction of $\mathbf{u}$. Each electron of the metal bar will experience a magnetic force $(\mathbf{u} \times \mathbf{B})$. The free electrons will move towards the end of the bar and produce an electric field $\mathbf{E}$ given by

$$\mathbf{E} = -\mathbf{u} \times \mathbf{B}. \tag{17.3}$$

400

∴ the potential difference between the ends of the bar is

$$V_{ba} = \int_b^a \mathbf{E} \cdot d\mathbf{l}$$

$$= u\mathbf{BL}, \tag{17.4}$$

where L = length of the metal bar.

This potential difference, however, produces no flow of current.

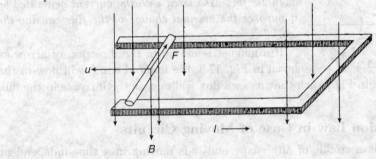

Fig. 17.2

But if the bar is a part of a circuit as shown in Fig. 17.2, current will flow. The line integral of the force on a charge q round the circuit is

$$\oint q\mathbf{E} \cdot d\mathbf{l} = qu\mathbf{BL}.$$

The e.m.f. induced in the closed circuit due to the motion of the conductor will be

$$V = \frac{1}{q} \oint (q\mathbf{E} \cdot d\mathbf{l}) = u\mathbf{BL}. \tag{17.5}$$

The above e.m.f. is called *motional e.m.f.*, since it depends on the velocity of the conductor and not on its position.

Now, $u\mathbf{BL}$ is nothing but the magnetic flux per unit time through the area swept out by the bar. Hence, $u\mathbf{BL}$ will be the rate of change of flux through the circuit.

$$\text{e.m.f. } |\epsilon| = u\mathbf{BL} = \frac{d\phi}{dt}. \tag{17.6}$$

17.3 Faraday's Law of Electromagnetic Induction

Michael Faraday observed that :

(a) If a magnet is moved about in a neighbourhood of a closed circuit (no source of e.m.f. is present) of wire, then a current will be induced in the wire so long as the movement lasts, but will disappear as soon as the movement is ceased.

(b) The same effect is produced in the reverse case, i.e., the circuit is moving and the magnet is kept static.

(c) A transient current is induced in a loop of wire when the current in another adjacent circuit is turned on and off. So a transient current is induced in a circuit when the flux linked through the circuit is changing. This phenomenon is called magnetic induction. Summing Faraday's observation the following 'flux rule' is obtained :

"When the magnetic flux through the circuit is changing, an electromotive force is induced in the circuit, the magnitude of which is proportional to the rate of change of flux."

If ϵ be the e.m.f. and ϕ, the flux, then

$$|\epsilon| \propto \frac{d\phi}{dt}. \tag{17.7}$$

The direction of induced e.m.f. is obtained by the method what is known as the *Lenz's law*. This law states that :

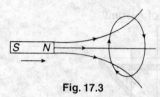

"The direction of the induced e.m.f. is such that the magnetic flux associated with the current generated by it, opposes the original change of the flux causing the e.m.f."

Fig. 17.3

If a magnet is moved in the direction of arrow as shown in Fig. 17.3, the induced e.m.f. will flow in the direction [shown in Fig.] such that its own flux will oppose the increase in the flux of the magnet.

17.4   Induction Law in Case of Moving Circuits

Suppose ABC is a circuit of any shape and it is moving in a time-independent magnetic field **B** with a velocity **v** as shown in Fig. 17.4. Now consider an elementary section of length $d\mathbf{l}(PQ)$. After time t it will move to the position $P'Q'$ at a distance vdt from PQ. If the velocity of free electrons relative to the circuit be **u**, then their velocity relative to the field will be **u + v**.

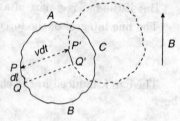

Fig. 17.4

Therefore, each electron will experience a force $[e(\mathbf{v} + \mathbf{u}) \times \mathbf{B}]$. The component of this force along $d\mathbf{l}$ is $[e(\mathbf{v} + \mathbf{u}) \times \mathbf{B}]\hat{\imath}$, where $\hat{\imath}$ is a unit vector in the direction PQ. Now $\hat{\imath}$ is parallel to **u**. Therefore,

$$\mathbf{u} \times \mathbf{B} \cdot \hat{\imath} = 0. \tag{17.8}$$

Hence, $\quad [e(\mathbf{v} + \mathbf{u}) \times \mathbf{B}] \cdot \hat{\imath} = e\mathbf{v} \times \mathbf{B} \cdot \hat{\imath} + e\mathbf{u} \times \mathbf{B} \cdot \hat{\imath}$

$$= e\mathbf{v} \times \mathbf{B} \cdot \hat{\imath}. \tag{17.9}$$

From the above equation it is clear that an electric field $\mathbf{v} \times \mathbf{B} = \mathbf{E}$ will be induced in the circuit, the component of which along the wire being $\mathbf{v} \times \mathbf{B} \cdot \hat{\imath}$.

The e.m.f. induced in the circuit will be the line integral of the field **E** round the circuit. Therefore, the induced e.m.f.,

$$\epsilon = \oint (\mathbf{v} \times \mathbf{B}) \cdot \hat{\imath} dl. \tag{17.10}$$

As the circuit is moving, after time dt the elementary section dl will sweep out an area $PP'Q'Q = \mathbf{v}dt \times \hat{\imath} dl$. Therefore, the flux passing through the element is

$$(\mathbf{v}dt \times \hat{\imath} dl) \cdot \mathbf{B}.$$

The flux over the entire band,

$$d\phi = \oint \mathbf{B} \cdot (\mathbf{v}dt \times \hat{\imath} dl), \quad \text{i.e.,} \quad \frac{d\phi}{dt} = \oint \mathbf{B} \cdot (\mathbf{v} \times \hat{\imath} dl)$$

$$= -\oint (\mathbf{v} \times \mathbf{B}) \cdot \hat{\imath} dl. \tag{17.11}$$

Combining (17.10) and (17.11), we get

$$\epsilon = -\frac{d\phi}{dt}. \tag{17.12}$$

17.5 Integral and Differential Form of Faraday's Law

The induced e.m.f. is equal to the line integral of the induced electric field $\mathbf{E}$ around the coil, i.e.,

$$\epsilon = \oint \mathbf{E} \cdot \hat{\imath} dl$$

and the flux through the coil

$$\phi = \int_s \mathbf{B} \cdot \hat{\imath} ds, \quad \text{where} \quad ds = \text{area } PP'Q'Q.$$

Therefore, Eq. (17.12) can be written as

$$\oint \mathbf{E} \cdot \hat{\imath} dl = -\int_s \frac{d\mathbf{B}}{dt} \cdot \hat{\imath} ds. \tag{17.13}$$

Eq. (17.13) is known as integral form of Faraday's law. Using Stokes' theorem,

$$\oint \mathbf{E} \cdot \hat{\imath} dl = \int_s \text{curl } \mathbf{E} \cdot \hat{\imath} ds' = -\int \frac{\delta \mathbf{B}}{\delta t} \cdot \hat{\imath} ds.$$

$$\therefore \quad \int \left(\text{curl } \mathbf{E} + \frac{\delta \mathbf{B}}{\delta t} \right) \cdot \hat{\imath} ds = 0. \tag{17.14}$$

Here we replace the total time derivative by partial derivative because we consider only the change in the field $\mathbf{B}$ with time at the fixed position of the elementary area.

Now Eq. (17.14) is true for any arbitrary surface. Therefore, we can write,

$$\text{curl } \mathbf{E} = \nabla \times \mathbf{E} = -\frac{\partial \mathbf{B}}{\delta t}. \tag{17.15}$$

The above equation is known as differential form of Faraday's law.

If we take divergence of Eq. (17.15), we find that

$$\nabla \cdot \nabla \times \mathbf{E} = -\frac{\delta}{\delta t}(\nabla \cdot \mathbf{B}) = 0.$$

Therefore, $\nabla \cdot \mathbf{B}$ must be independent of time at every point. The above condition will be fulfilled if we assume

$$\nabla \cdot \mathbf{B} = 0, \tag{17.16}$$

i.e., $\mathbf{B}$ is always solenoidal.

From Faraday's law as expressed in Eq. (17.15) two important conclusions can be made :

(a) If magnetic field changes with time, the electric field no longer remains conservative.

(b) All magnetic poles occur in pairs positive and negative.

Hence, from Faraday's law of electromagnetic induction we can see how the electric and magnetic fields are interrelated.

17.6 Self-inductance and Mutual Inductance

When a current flows in a circuit, a magnetic flux ϕ is linked through the circuit due to its own field. This flux is proportional to the current I flowing through the circuit, i.e.,

$$\phi = LI, \tag{17.17}$$

where L is a constant.

Now, suppose the magnetic field changes with time.

$$\therefore \quad \frac{d\phi}{dt} = \frac{d\phi}{dI} \cdot \frac{dI}{dt} = L\frac{dI}{dt}$$

or, $\quad L = \dfrac{d\phi}{dI}.$ (17.18)

The quantity L is called self-inductance and it depends on the geometry of the circuit.

From Eqs. (17.12) and (17.18), we can write

$$\epsilon = -\frac{d\phi}{dt}$$

or, $\quad \epsilon = -L\dfrac{dI}{dt}.$ (17.19)

Therefore, we can define the self-inductance as the e.m.f. induced in the circuit when the rate of change of current is unity.

The unit of self-inductance is *henry*. It is defined as the self-inductance of a coil when an e.m.f. of one volt is produced provided the change of current being 1 ampere per second.

$\therefore \quad$ 1 henry $= 10^9$ e.m.u. of self-inductance.

Now, suppose a coil carries a current I_1 and a second coil in which a current I_2 is flowing being brought near to the first coil. Then there will be a linkage of flux through the first coil due to the current flowing in the second,

$$\phi_1 = L_{12}I_2,$$ (17.20)

where L_{12} is a constant.

Similarly, there will be a linkage of flux through the second coil due to current in the first,

$$\phi_2 = L_{21}I_1,$$ (17.21)

where L_{21} is a constant.

The potential energy of the system will be

$$U_p = -\phi_2 I_2 = -\phi_1 I_1 \quad \text{or,} \quad -L_{21}I_1 I_2 = -L_{12}I_2 I_1$$

or, $\quad L_{21} = L_{12} = M$ (say).

The constant M is called the mutual inductance between the two circuits. It may be defined as the flux linked with the second coil due to unit current flowing through the first coil.

The potential energy of the system,

$$U_p = -\phi_1 I_1 = -I_1 \int B_1 \hat{\imath}_1 ds = -I_1 \int \nabla \times A_{12} \cdot \hat{\imath}_1 ds,$$

where A is the vector potential and $B = \nabla \times A$

$$= -I_1 \int A_{12} \cdot \hat{\imath}_1 dl_1 \quad \text{(using Stokes' theorem)}$$

$$= -I_1 \int \left[\frac{\mu}{4\pi} \int \frac{I_2 \hat{\imath}_2 dl_2}{|r|} \right] \cdot \hat{\imath}_1 dl_1$$

$$= -\frac{\mu}{4\pi} I_1 I_2 \int \int \frac{\hat{\imath}_1 dl_1 \cdot \hat{\imath}_2 dl_2}{|r|}.$$ (17.22)

Again, $U_p = -MI_1I_2$. (17.23)

Comparing Eqs. (17.22) and (17.23) we can write

$$M = \frac{\mu}{4\pi} \int \int \frac{\hat{i}_1 dl_1 \hat{i}_2 dl_2}{|r|}.$$ (17.24)

Eq. (17.24) is known as *Neumann's formula*.

17.7 Energy in Magnetic Fields

(i) Magnetic energy in an inductor : Suppose a resistance of value R, an inductor having self-inductance of value L and a battery E of e.m.f. ϵ are connected in series as shown in Fig. 17.5. Let I be the current flowing in the circuit at any instant t.

$$\therefore \quad \epsilon - L\frac{dI}{dt} = RI.$$ (17.25)

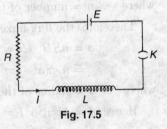

If dQ be the charge moved through the circuit, then the work done by the e.m.f. ϵ will be

$$dW = \epsilon dQ = \epsilon I dt \quad [\because dQ = I dt]$$

or, $$\frac{dW}{dt} = \epsilon I = \left(RI + L\frac{dI}{dt}\right)I \quad \text{[from Eq. (17.25)]}$$

$$= RI^2 + LI\frac{dI}{dt}.$$

Fig. 17.5

Therefore, total work done will be

$$W = \int \frac{dW}{dt} \cdot dt = R\int I^2 dt + L\int I dI$$

$$= R\int I^2 dt + \frac{1}{2}LI^2.$$ (17.26)

The first term of the above expression represents the energy dissipated in the form of joule heat and the second term is the energy stored in the inductance.

(ii) Magnetic energy stored in a series of inductances : Here we make the assumption that the initial current in all circuits at $t = 0$ is zero and attain their equilibrium value at time $t = T$.

The induced e.m.f. in the kth circuit will be

$$\epsilon_k = \frac{d\phi_k}{dt}.$$

Let the current in each circuit and the flux through it be some fraction α of the equilibrium values.

$$\therefore \qquad I_k(t) = \alpha I_k \quad \text{and} \quad \phi_k(t) = \alpha \phi_k.$$

Therefore, total work done by the kth circuit will be

$$W_k = \int_0^T \epsilon_k I_k(t) dt = \int_0^T \phi_k \frac{d\alpha}{dt} \cdot \alpha I_k dt = I_k \phi_k \int_0^1 \alpha d\alpha = \frac{1}{2}I_k \phi_k.$$

Therefore, for all circuits,

$$W = \frac{1}{2}\sum_k I_k \phi_k.$$

Now $\phi_k = L_k I_k + \sum_{j \neq k} M_{kj} I_j$.

$\therefore \qquad W = \frac{1}{2} \sum_k L_k I_k^2 + \frac{1}{2} \sum_k \sum_{\substack{j \\ k \neq j}} M_{kj} I_j I_k.$ $\qquad (17.27)$

Therefore, for a pair of inductances,

$$W = \frac{1}{2} L_1 I_1^2 + \frac{1}{2} L_2 I_2^2 + M_{12} I_1 I_2. \qquad (17.28)$$

17.8   Calculation of Self-inductance

(i) Self-inductance of an infinite solenoid : Suppose the solenoid is infinitely long. Then the field inside the solenoid except at ends is approximately

$\qquad B = 4\pi n I,$

where n = number of turns per unit length   and I = current in e.m.u.

Therefore, the flux linked with n turns per cm of the solenoid will be

$\qquad \phi = nSB \quad (S = \text{area of each turn})$

$\qquad = n \cdot \pi a^2 \cdot 4\pi n I,$

where a = radius of the solenoid.

Hence, $\phi = 4\pi^2 n^2 a^2 I = LI$

$\therefore \qquad L = 4\pi^2 n^2 a^2$ e.m.u.

If μ be the permeability of the core, then

$\qquad L = \mu 4\pi^2 n^2 a^2 I$ e.m.u.

$\qquad = \mu 4\pi^2 n^2 a^2 I \times 10^{-9}$ henry. $\qquad (17.29)$

(ii) Self-inductance of co-axial cylinder : Suppose we have two infinite hollow cylinders of radii a and b; one being the return circuit of the other as shown in Fig. 17.6.

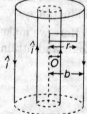

From Ampere's circuital law, we know that the field is confined in the space between two cylinders and is given by $B = \frac{2I}{r}$ at a distance r from the axis.

Therefore, the flux passing through the elementary area of radial width dr and axial length unity will be

Fig. 17.6 $\qquad\qquad\qquad\qquad d\phi = B \cdot ds = 2I \frac{dr}{r}.$

Therefore, the total flux $\phi = 2I \int_a^b \frac{dr}{r} = 2I \log_e \frac{b}{a}.$

Thus, the self-inductance of the system per unit length will be

$\qquad L = 2 \log_e \frac{b}{a}$ e.m.u.

$\qquad = 2 \log_e \frac{b}{a} \times 10^{-9}$ henry. $\qquad (17.30)$

(iii) Self-inductance of two inductances

(a) Connected in series : In series connection of two inductances and the fluxes produced by the two inductances are in the same direction.

Suppose the current flowing through the coil be I.

From Fig. 17.7 the sum of induced e.m.f. in the above combination will be

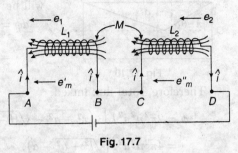

$$\epsilon = e_1 + e'_m e_2 + e''_m$$

$$= -L_1 \frac{dI}{dt} - M \frac{dI}{dt} - L_2 \frac{dI}{dt} - M \frac{dI}{dt}$$

$$= -(L_1 + L_2 + 2M) \frac{dI}{dt}$$

$$= -L \frac{dI}{dt}.$$

Fig. 17.7

Therefore, self-inductance of the above circuit,

$$L = L_1 + L_2 + 2M. \tag{17.31}$$

(b) Connected in parallel : In this case the sum of induced e.m.f. as shown in Fig. 17.8 will be

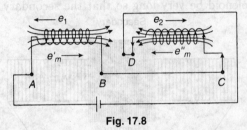

Fig. 17.8

$$\epsilon = e_1 + e'_m + e_2 + e''_m$$

$$= -L_1 \frac{dI}{dt} + M \frac{dI}{dt} - L_2 \frac{dI}{dt} + M \frac{dI}{dt}$$

$$= -(L_1 + L_2 - 2M) \frac{dI}{dt}$$

$$= -L \frac{dI}{dt}.$$

$\therefore$ self-inductance in case of parallel connection,

$$L = L_1 + L_2 - 2M. \tag{17.32}$$

(iv) Self-inductance of two parallel wires : Suppose two parallel wires each of radius a are kept separated from each other by a distance d, and I be the current flowing through the wires in the directions as shown in Fig. 17.9.

The field at the point P at a distance r from the lower wire will be

$$B = \frac{2I}{r} + \frac{2I}{d - r}.$$

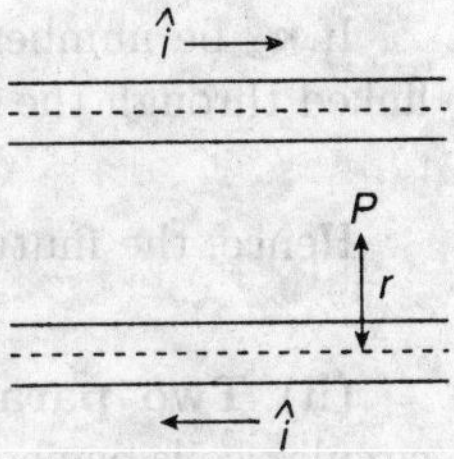

Fig. 17.9

Therefore, flux linked per unit length of the circuit,

$$\phi = 2I \int_a^{d-a} \left(\frac{1}{r} + \frac{1}{d - r} \right) dr = 4I \log_e \frac{d - a}{a}.$$

Therefore, self-inductance per unit length is

$$L = 4 \log_e \frac{d - a}{a} \text{ e.m.u.} \tag{17.33}$$

(v) Self-inductance of a finite solenoid : Consider a solenoid of length l and radius a having n number of turns per unit length. Now at any point P (Fig. 17.10) inside the solenoid the field due to flow of current I will be

$$B = 2\pi nI \{\cos(\pi - \theta_1) + \cos \theta_2\},$$

where θ_1 and θ_2 are the angles made by the two ends of the solenoid at P

$$= 2\pi nI \left\{ \frac{x}{\sqrt{x^2 + a^2}} + \frac{l - x}{\sqrt{(l - x)^2 + a^2}} \right\} \quad (\text{where } OP = x).$$

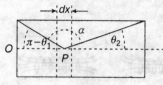

Fig. 17.10

Therefore, the flux linked through ndx turns will be

$$d\phi = \pi a^2 Bn dx$$

$$= 2\pi^2 n^2 a^2 I \left\{ \frac{x dx}{\sqrt{x^2 + a^2}} + \frac{(l-x) dx}{\sqrt{(l-x)^2 + a^2}} \right\}.$$

Therefore, total flux linked,

$$\phi = 2\pi^2 n^2 a^2 I \left[\sqrt{x^2 + a^2} - \sqrt{(l-x)^2 + a^2} \right]_0^1$$

$$= 4\pi^2 n^2 a^2 I \{ \sqrt{l^2 + a^2} - a \}.$$

$\therefore$ self-inductance, $L = 4\pi^2 n^2 a^2 \{ \sqrt{l^2 + a^2} - a \}.$ (17.34)

17.9   Calculation of Mutual Inductance

(i) Two solenoids : Let us consider two solenoids, one of which is wound outside the other (Fig. 17.11). Let the inner solenoid be very long so that the secondary may be wound over the primary about the central region of the primary.

If I be the current flowing through the primary, then the field far from the ends will be

$$B = 4\pi n_1 I.$$

If A be the cross-section of the primary, the flux through each turn of the secondary is

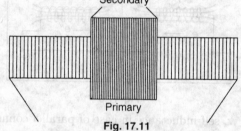

Fig. 17.11

$$B \cdot A = 4\pi n_1 I A$$

If n_2 be number of turns per unit length of the secondary, then the total flux linked through the secondary will be

$$\phi = 4\pi n_1 n_2 A I.$$

Hence, the mutual inductance of the two solenoids is

$$M = 4\pi n_1 n_2 A \text{ e.m.u.} \tag{17.35}$$

(ii) Two parallel co-axial circular coils : Suppose two parallel co-axial circular coils as shown in Fig. 17.12 are kept x distance apart, one of which has a radius r_2, small compared with the radius r_1 of the other. Let I be the current flowing in the coil of radius r_1. Then the field at the point P is

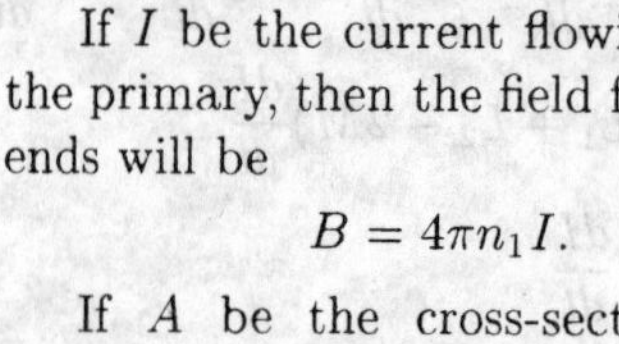

$$B = \frac{2\pi r_1^2 I}{(r_1^2 + x^2)^{3/2}}.$$

Fig. 17.12

This field is supposed to be constant over the circuit of radius r_2. Therefore, the flux linked with this coil,

$$\phi = B \cdot \pi r_2^2 = \frac{2\pi^2 r_1^2 r_2^2}{(r_1^2 + x^2)^{3/2}} I.$$

Therefore, the mutual inductance of the system is

$$M = \frac{2\pi^2 r_1^2 r_2^2}{(r_1^2 + x^2)^{3/2}} \text{ e.m.u.} \tag{17.36}$$

Examples

1. A coil of resistance 100 Ω is placed in a magnetic field of flux 10^5 e.m.u. The coil has 100 turns and a galvanometer of resistance 400 Ω is connected in series with it. Find the average e.m.f. and current if the coil is moved in $\frac{1}{10}$ second from the given field to a field 0.2×10^5 e.m.u.

Solution : Change of flux, $d\phi = (10^5 - 0.2 \times 10^5)$ maxwell

$$= 0.8 \times 10^5 \text{ maxwell}.$$

Total number of turns = 100

and $dt = \frac{1}{10}$ second.

$\therefore$ induced e.m.f., $\epsilon = 100 \times \frac{d\phi}{dt} = 100 \times 0.8 \times 10^5 \times 10$ e.m.u.

$$= 0.8 \times 10^8 \text{ e.m.u.} = \mathbf{0.8 \text{ volt}} \quad (\because 1 \text{ volt} = 10^8 \text{ e.m.u.})$$

Current flowing through the circuit,

$$I = \frac{\epsilon}{R} = \frac{0.8}{400 + 100} \text{ ampere} = \mathbf{1.6 \times 10^{-3} \text{ ampere}}.$$

2. A metal bar rotates in a field of flux 10^8 e.m.u. at the rate of 100 revolutions/second. Find the induced e.m.f.

Solution : Induced e.m.f., $\epsilon = \frac{d\phi}{dt}$.

Here, $d\phi = 10^8$, $dt = \frac{1}{100}$ second.

$\therefore \qquad \epsilon = 10^8 \times 10^{-2}$ e.m.u. $= 0.01$ volt.

3. An air-cored solenoid of diameter 1 cm and 1 metre long has 1000 number of turns. Find the coefficient of self-induction.

Solution : We know, $L = 4\pi^2 n^2 a^2 l$

$$= \frac{4\pi^2 N^2 a^2}{l}, \text{ where } N = \text{total number of turns}.$$

$$\therefore \quad L = \frac{4 \times (3.14)^2 \times (1000)^2 \times (0.5)^2}{100} \text{ e.m.u.}$$

$$= 9.86 \times 10^4 \text{ e.m.u.} = \mathbf{9.86 \times 10^{-4} \text{ henry}}.$$

4. An air-cored solenoid of length 100 cm and radius 5 cm has 1000 turns. Calculate the energy stored in joules when a current of 1 ampere flows through it.

Solution : Energy stored $= \frac{1}{2}Li^2$

Here, $L = \frac{4\pi^2 N^2 a^2}{l}$ e.m.u.$= \frac{4 \times 9.86 \times (1000)^2 \times (5)^2}{100}$ e.m.u.

$$= 9.86 \times 10^6 \text{ e.m.u.} = 9.86 \times 10^{-2} \text{ henry}.$$

$\therefore$ energy stored $= \frac{1}{2} \times 9.86 \times 10^{-2} \times 1^2 = \mathbf{4.93 \times 10^{-3} \text{ joule}}.$

5. A car ignition coil consists of two insulated coils, one of 16000 turns and the other of 400 turns, wound over each other. The length of each coil is 10 cm and the turns have the radius of 3 cm. A current of 3 amperes is passed through the primary coil and broken in about 10^4 seconds. Calculate the voltage induced in the secondary circuit.

Solution : We know that

$$\epsilon = -\frac{d\phi}{dt} = -M\frac{dI}{dt}.$$

Mutual inductance, $M = N_1 N_2 l \pi r^2$.

$$\therefore \qquad \epsilon = -4\pi N_1 N_2 l \pi r^2 \frac{dI}{dt}.$$

Here, $N_1 = 16000$, $N_2 = 400$, $l = 10$ cm, $r = 3$ cm.

$$\frac{dI}{dt} = \frac{3}{10^4} = 3 \times 10^{-4} \text{ ampere/second}$$

$$\therefore \qquad \epsilon = 4 \times 16000 \times 400 \times 10 \times (3.14)^2 \times 9 \times 3 \times 10^{-4} \text{ e.m.u.}$$

$$= \frac{4 \times 9.86 \times 16 \times 4 \times 3 \times 9 \times 10^2}{10^8} \text{ volts}$$

$$= 0.068152 \text{ volt.}$$

6. A magnetic field of 100 oersteds is applied at right angles to a coil of 50 turns and having area 50 sq. cm. If the coil be removed from the field in $\frac{1}{20}$ second, what will be the induced e.m.f. of the coil?

Solution : We know, induced e.m.f., $e = \dfrac{dN}{dt}$.

Again, $N = HAn$

Here, $H = 100$ oersteds, $A = 50$ sq. cm, $n = 50$ turns.

$$\therefore \qquad N = 100 \times 50 \times 50 = 25 \times 10^4 \text{ maxwellian turns.}$$

Therefore, $e = \dfrac{25 \times 10^4}{\frac{1}{20}}$ e.m.u. $= 5 \times 10^6$ e.m.u. $= \dfrac{5 \times 10^6}{10^8}$ volt $= \mathbf{0.05 \text{ volt.}}$

7. What is the e.m.f. induced between the rails by a train travelling at a speed of 120 km/hour? Suppose the distance between the rail = 1.5 metres and the vertical component of the earth's magnetic field, $H = 0.36$ oersted.

Solution : The number of lines of force passing through the two lines per second,

$$\frac{dN}{dt} = Hlv.$$

Here, $H = 0.36$ oersted , $l = 1.5$ metres $= 150$ cm,

$$v = 120 \text{ km/hour} = \frac{10000}{3} \text{ cm/second.}$$

$$\therefore \qquad \frac{dN}{dt} = 0.36 \times 150 \times \frac{10000}{3} = \frac{36 \times 150 \times 100}{3} = 180000$$

$\therefore$ induced e.m.f., $e = 180000$ e.m.u. $= 180000 \times 10^{-8}$ volt

$$= \mathbf{0.0018 \text{ volt.}}$$

8. Find the self-inductance of a solenoid 40 cm long and radius 4 cm having 200 turns. Assume $\mu = 1$.   **[C.U. 1969]**

Solution : We know, $L = \dfrac{4\pi^2 n^2 a^2 \mu}{l} \times 10^{-9}$ henry

Here, $\mu = 1$, $l = 40$ cm, $n = 200$, $a = 4$ cm.

$$\therefore \qquad L = \frac{4 \times 3.14 \times 3.14 \times 200 \times 200 \times 4 \times 4 \times 1}{40} \times 10^{-9} \text{ henry}$$

$$= \mathbf{0.00063 \text{ henry}}.$$

9. A solenoid 50 cm long and of radius 3 cm has 20 turns of wire per cm. A second coil of 1000 turns is wound upon the middle part of the solenoid. Calculate—(i) the mutual inductance of the coils and (ii) the self-inductance of the solenoid. **[M.U. 1956]**

Solution : (i) We know, $M = \dfrac{\mu 4\pi n_1 n_2 A}{l} \times 10^{-9}$ henry

Here, $\mu = 1$, $n_2 = 1000$, $\dfrac{n_1}{l} = 20$, $A = \pi a^2 = 3.14 \times 9$ sq. cm.

$$\therefore \qquad M = (4 \times 3.14 \times 20 \times 1000 \times 3.14 \times 9) \times 10^{-9} \text{ henry}$$

$$= 7.098 \times 10^{-3} \text{ henry}$$

(ii) We know, $L = \dfrac{4\pi^2 n_1^2 a^2 \mu}{l} \times 10^{-9}$ henry

$$= (4 \times 9.86 \times (20)^2 \times 50 \times 9 \times 10^{-9}) \text{ henry}$$

$$= \mathbf{7.098 \times 10^{-3} \text{ henry}}.$$

10. A circular copper disc of radius 10 cm rotates 1200 revolutions per minute with its plane perpendicular to a magnetic field. If the induced e.m.f. between the centre and the edge of the disc be 6.28 mV, find the intensity of the field. **[B.U. 1983]**

Solution : Area of the disc $= \pi r^2 = \pi \times (10 \times 10^{-2})^2 \text{ m}^2 = \pi \times 10^{-2} \text{ m}^2$.

Area per unit rotation $= \pi \times 10^{-2} \text{ m}^2$.

So the area covered by the disc per minute $= \pi \times 10^{-2} \times 1200 \text{ m}^2$

Thus the area covered per second $= \dfrac{\pi \times (10^{-2}) \times 1200}{60} = 0.2\pi \text{ m}^2$.

If B be the intensity then the flux associated with the disc $= 0.2\pi \times B$

$\therefore$ induced e.m.f. $= 0.2\pi \times B = 6.28 \times 10^{-3}$ [6.28 mV $= 6.28 \times 10^{-3}$ V]

$$\therefore \quad B = \mathbf{10^{-2} \text{ T}}.$$

11. An aeroplane, having a wing span of 30 m, flies due north at a speed of 90 m/s. Calculate the p.d. between the tips of the wings over a given locality if the earth's magnetic field is 24 Wb/m² and the dip is 60°.

Solution : In this case, $E = B_V \cdot l \cdot v$ volts.

Again, if the angle of dip be 60°, then,

$$B_V = \mu_0 H \cdot \sin 60° = (4\pi \times 10^{-7}) \times 24 \times 0.866 \text{ Wb/m}^2$$

$$= 1.306 \times 10^{-5} \text{ tesla}$$

Given, $l = 30$ m and $v = 90$ m/s.

$$\therefore \quad E = 1.306 \times 10^{-5} \times 30 \times 90 \text{ volts} = \mathbf{0.035 \text{ volt}}.$$

2. A coil of 100 turns having an average area of 100 cm² for each turn is held in a uniform field of 5×10^{-3} T, the direction of the field being at right angles to the coil. The field is removed in $\frac{1}{100}$th of a second. Calculate the average e.m.u. induced in the coil.

Solution : Here, the intensity of the magnetic field $= 5 \times 10^{-3}$ T.

The number of lines of force passing through per unit area $= 5 \times 10^{-3}$.

So the lines of force associated with each turn of the coil

$$= 5 \times 10^{-3} \times 100 \times (10^{-2})^2 = 5 \times 10^{-5}.$$

Hence, the number of lines of force associated with the whole coil

$$\phi = 5 \times 10^{-5} \times 100$$

$$\therefore \quad e = \frac{d\phi}{dt} = \frac{5 \times 10^{-5} \times 100}{\frac{1}{100}} = \mathbf{5 \times 10^7 \ e.m.u.}$$

13. A coil of wire of certain radius has 600 turns and a self-inductance of 108 mH. What will be the self-inductance of a second similar coil with 500 turns?

[B.U. 1998]

Solution : As in a circular coil of wire the self-inductance (L) is proportional to the square of the number of turns (n^2) of the wire, we have

$$L \propto n^2.$$

$$\therefore \quad \frac{L_1}{L_2} = \frac{n_1^2}{n_2^2}; \quad \text{given that } L_1 = 108 \text{ mH}, \ n_1 = 600; \ n_2 = 500; \ L_2 = ?$$

Thus $L_2 = \dfrac{n_2^2}{n_1^2} \cdot L_1 = \left(\dfrac{500}{600}\right)^2 \times 108 = \mathbf{75 \ mH}.$

14. A solenoid produces flux of 30 000 maxwells in an iron core when a current of 2 A flows through it. If it has 400 turns, calculate its coefficient of self-induction in c.g.s. systems. Find also the value in SI system.

Solution : According to c.g.s. system, the magnetic flux associated per turn due to 1 A current $= \frac{30\,000}{2} = 15\,000$ maxwells.

Due to this current, the total flux in the solenoid

$$= 15\,000 \times 400 = 6 \times 10^6 \text{ maxwells.}$$

$\therefore$ the induced e.m.f. due to a change of 1 A/s current

$$= 6 \times 10^6 \times 10^{-8} \text{ volt} = \mathbf{0.06 \ volt}$$

According to SI method, the magnetic flux associated in each turn due to 1 A of current

$$= \frac{30\,000}{2} = 15\,000 \text{ maxwell} = 15000 \times 10^{-8} \text{ Wb} \ (1 \text{ maxwell} = 10^{-8} \text{ Wb})$$

$$= 15 \times 10^{-5} \text{ Wb}.$$

Due to this current the flux in the whole solenoid

$$= 15 \times 10^{-5} \times 400 = 6 \times 10^{-2} \text{ Wb}.$$

So, the induced e.m.f. due to the change of 1 A/s current $= 6 \times 10^{-2}$ volts i.e., the self-inductance of the solenoid $L = \mathbf{0.06 \ H}$.

Questions

Essay-type

1. State the laws of electromagnetic induction. Calculate the mutual inductance of two similar co-axial coils.

2. A solenoid of finite length l and radius r is wound with n turns of wire. If i be the current flowing through each turn of the coil, calculate the self-inductance of the solenoid.

3. Deduce, in henries, the value of the self-inductance in air-medium of a circular coil of radius 'a' metre and 'n' number of turns.   **[B.U. 1994]**

4. Prove theoretically that induced e.m.f. is equal to the rate of change of flux.

5. Calculate the self-inductance of a solenoid with an iron core.

6. Deduce, from the first principle, the expression for the inductance of a long solenoid and the energy stored in it by passing a direct current I ampere units through it.

7. Explain what is meant by coefficient of self-induction and coefficient of mutual induction. Calculate the value of coefficient of self-induction in a very long solenoid.

8. What do you mean by mutual induction? Define the coefficient of mutual inductance. Obtain an expression for the coefficient of mutual inductance of two co-axial solenoids.

Short Answer-type

9. Define self-induction in different ways. Why is it known as electric inertia?
          [B.U. 1983]

10. Distinguish between self-induction and mutual induction. What are their practical units? Why is self-induction analogous to inertia?

11. What is Fleming's left-hand rule? Mention the area where the rule is applied.

12. A metallic loop is placed in a non-uniform magnetic field. Will an e.m.f. be induced in the loop?

13. What are the laws of electromagnetic induction? What decides (i) the duration, (ii) the direction and (iii) the magnitude of an induced e.m.f. in a circuit?

14. If the magnetic field outside a copper box is suddenly changed, what happens to the magnetic field inside the box?

15. Two circular loops are placed co-axially but separated by a distance. A battery is suddenly connected to one of the loops establishing a current in it. Will there be any current induced in the other loop? If yes, when does the current start and when does it stop? Do the loops attract each other or repel?

16. Two resistors A and B of equal ohmic resistance are connected in parallel. A battery with a key is connected with the system. A is of negligible self-inductance while B has a high self-inductance. Describe and explain how the currents through A and B change with time (i) when the key is closed and (ii) when the key is opened.

17. Define (i) coefficient of self-induction and (ii) coefficient of mutual induction. Show that the coefficient of self-induction of a circular coil of given radius is proportional to the square of the number of turns it possesses.

Numerical Problems

18. A solenoid produces flux of 30 000 maxwells in an iron core when a current of 2 amperes flows through it. If it has 400 turns, calculate its coefficient of self-induction. **[Ans. 0.06 henry]**

19. A coil of 100 turns of area 20 sq. cm is wound on an iron core for which $\mu = 1000$ and is held at right angles to a field of 50 oersteds. It is removed in $\frac{1}{10}$ second. The resistance of the coil is 4 ohms and it is in series with a galvanometer of resistance 6 ohms. Find the average current induced in the circuit. **[Ans. 1 amp]**

20. Find the inductance of a coil of 100 turns wound on a paper tube 25 cm long and radius 4 cm. **[Ans. 2.527×10^{-4} henry]**

21. A conducting circular loop is placed in a uniform magnetic field of induction $B = 0.02$ T, with its plane perpendicular to the field. Somehow, the radius of the loop starts shrinking at a constant rate of 1 mm/s. Find the induced e.m.f. in the loop at an instant when the radius is 2 cm. **[Ans. 2.5 μV]**

22. A straight piece of wire is free to slide on two smooth parallel rails laid 1 metre apart. The wire, the rails and a magnetic field of strength 0.1 T are at right angles to one another. If a potential difference of 100 volts is maintained between the rails, what velocity will the wire finally attain? **[C.U.(Hons.) 1961]**

[Ans. 1 km/s]

23. A field of 2×10^{-2} T acts at right angles to a coil of area 100 cm^2 with 50 turns. The coil is removed from the field in $\frac{1}{10}$th of a second. Find the average e.m.f. produced in it in practical units. **[Ans. 0.1 volt]**

24. A square loop of side l, having turns n is rotated with a uniform angular velocity ω about one of its diagonals which is kept fixed in a horizontal position. A uniform magnetic field B exists in the vertical direction. Find the e.m.f. induced in the coil. **[Ans. $nBl^2\omega \sin\omega t$]**

25. A solenoid 1 metre long and 10 cm in diameter has 5000 turns. Calculate (i) the self-inductance in henry, (ii) the energy stored in joule when a current of 2 A flows through it. Assume the solenoid to be air-cored.

[Ans. (i) 0.0247 henry, (ii) 0.0494 joules]

26. A solenoid is 40 cm long and has 10 turns per cm. Each turn of the solenoid has an area of 50 cm^2. What is the value of the coefficient of self-induction of the solenoid? **[Ans. 2.51×10^{-6} H]**

Chapter 18

Electromagnetic Waves

18.1 Introduction

Physicist J. C. Maxwell put forward his electromagnetic theory in 1865, where he established successfully the general equation for the electromagnetic wave describing the nature of the field of electric and magnetic forces. Light was assumed by Maxwell to be nothing but electromagnetic waves and therefore, the velocity with which these waves traverse in free space is the same as the velocity of light in free space. Maxwell's electromagnetic concept of light has later supported various experimental data and hence the electromagnetic theory is found to be of immense importance both in radio-physics and optics.

18.2 Maxwell's Equations

The basic laws of electricity and magnetism are

(i) Gauss's theorem as applied to electrostatic field

$$\text{div } \mathbf{D} = \rho, \tag{18.1}$$

where $D = \epsilon E$, ϵ being the permittivity of the medium and E be the electric intensity.

(ii) Gauss's theorem as applied to magnetic field,

$$\text{div } \mathbf{B} = 0, \tag{18.2}$$

where B being the magnetic induction.

(iii) Faraday's law of induction

$$\text{curl } \mathbf{E} = -\frac{\partial \mathbf{B}}{\partial t}. \tag{18.3}$$

(iv) Ampere's circuital theorem

$$\text{curl } \mathbf{H} = \mathbf{j}, \tag{18.4}$$

where j being the current density.

Eqs. (18.1), (18.2) and (18.3) are valid for both static and dynamic fields. But Ampere's circuital theorem is obtained from steady state observations and so its validity for time varying fields have to be examined.

Now taking the divergence of both sides of Eq. (18.4), we get

$$\vec{\nabla}(\vec{\nabla} \times \mathbf{H}) = \vec{\nabla} \cdot \mathbf{j} = 0. \tag{18.5}$$

The above equation is also true for steady field. Suppose the current changes with time. In this case the result is incompatible with the principle of conservation of energy, i.e., the equation of continuity.

$$\nabla \cdot \mathbf{j} + \frac{\partial \rho}{\partial t} = 0. \tag{18.6}$$

415

Maxwell said that the difficulty in case of time varying fields arose due to incomplete definition of the total current density.

Now from Eq. (18.6)

$$\vec{\nabla} \cdot \mathbf{j} = -\frac{\partial \rho}{\partial t} = -\frac{\partial}{\partial t}(\cdot \vec{\nabla} \mathbf{D}), \text{ using Eq. (18.1)}$$

$$= \vec{\nabla}\left(-\frac{\partial \mathbf{D}}{\partial t}\right)$$

or, $\nabla\left(\mathbf{j} + \dfrac{\partial \mathbf{D}}{\partial t}\right) = 0.$ \hfill (18.7)

Therefore, $\mathbf{j}$ in Ampere's circuital theorem must be replaced by $\mathbf{j} + \frac{\partial \mathbf{D}}{\partial t}$. Taking the above modification of circuital form of Ampere's law we can obtain

$$\vec{\nabla} \times \mathbf{H} = \mathbf{j} + \frac{\partial \mathbf{D}}{\partial t}. \tag{18.8}$$

The vector $\mathbf{j}$ is called *conduction* or *charge transported current density* and the second term which arises from the variation of electric displacement with time is called *displacement current density*.

Therefore, the equations which the field vectors $\mathbf{E}$, $\mathbf{B}$, $\mathbf{D}$ and $\mathbf{H}$ satisfy are

(i) $\nabla \cdot \mathbf{D} = \rho$

(ii) $\nabla \cdot \mathbf{B} = 0$

(iii) $\nabla \times \mathbf{E} + \dfrac{\partial \mathbf{B}}{\partial t} = 0$

(iv) $\nabla \times \mathbf{H} = \mathbf{j} + \dfrac{\partial \mathbf{D}}{\partial t}$

$\left. \phantom{\begin{matrix} a \\ b \\ c \\ d \end{matrix}} \right\}$ \hfill (18.9)

The above equations are known as Maxwell's equations for electromagnetic field.

18.3   Electrostatic and Magnetostatic Field Energies

(i) Electrostatic field energy : Suppose a small charge $\delta\rho$ is added to the field. Here we assume that no work is done on mechanical constraints. Now due to addition of small charge, the work done will be

$$\delta W = \int \phi \delta \rho \, dv, \text{ where } \phi \text{ is the potential at any point of the field.}$$

$$= \int \phi \delta(\vec{\nabla} \cdot \mathbf{D}) dv \quad [\because \ \nabla \cdot D = \rho]$$

$$= \int \phi \vec{\nabla} \cdot \delta \mathbf{D} dv$$

$$= \int \vec{\nabla}(\phi \delta \mathbf{D}) dv - \int \delta \mathbf{D} \cdot \vec{\nabla} \phi dv$$

$$[\text{using vector identity, } \vec{\nabla}(\mathbf{A}\phi) = \phi \vec{\nabla} \cdot \mathbf{A} + \mathbf{A} \cdot \vec{\nabla} \phi]$$

$$= \int (\phi \cdot \delta \mathbf{D}) ds - \int \delta \mathbf{D} \vec{\nabla} \phi dv. \tag{18.10}$$

Now the field decreases as the inverse second power, the potential as the inverse first power and the differential area of integration increases as the square of the distance, so the surface term can be made arbitrarily small by letting the boundary surface go to the infinity. The first term of the Eq. (18.10) can be neglected and we get

$$\delta W = -\int \delta \mathbf{D} \cdot \vec{\nabla} \phi dv$$

$$= \int \mathbf{E} \delta \mathbf{D} dv. \tag{18.11}$$

The integration of Eq. (18.11) cannot be performed unless E is a given function of D. As E and D are related by a dielectric constant K, the energy becomes

$$U_E = \int_0^D \delta W = \int_0^D \int \mathbf{E} \cdot \delta \mathbf{D} dv$$

$$= \int \int \frac{K\epsilon_0 \delta(E^2)}{2} dv = \frac{1}{2} \int K\epsilon_0 E^2 dv$$

$$= \frac{1}{2} \int^{'} \mathbf{E} \cdot \mathbf{D} dv. \tag{18.12}$$

(ii) Magnetostatic field energy : Suppose a battery with an electromotive field E' is feeding energy both into a magnetic field and into heat losses.

$$\mathbf{j} = \sigma(\mathbf{E} + \mathbf{E}') \tag{18.13}$$

Taking scalar product of $\mathbf{E}'$ with $\mathbf{j}$, we get

$$\mathbf{E}' \cdot \mathbf{j} = \frac{j^2}{\sigma} - \mathbf{E} \cdot \mathbf{j}. \tag{18.14}$$

The left-hand side of Eq. (18.14) represents the time rate of work done by the battery. The first term of the right-hand side gives the heat loss due to joule effect and the second term represents the rate at which energy is fed into the magnetic field. In case of slowly varying fields the displacement current may be neglected and the fourth Maxwell's equation becomes $\vec{\nabla} \times \mathbf{H} = \mathbf{j}$.

Substituting in Eq. (18.14), we get

$$\mathbf{E}' \cdot (\vec{\nabla} \times \mathbf{H}) = \frac{(\vec{\nabla} \times \mathbf{H})^2}{\sigma} - \mathbf{E} \cdot (\vec{\nabla} \times \mathbf{H}). \tag{18.15}$$

Now integrating over all space we get the total power expended by the battery

$$\int \mathbf{E}' \cdot (\vec{\nabla} \times \mathbf{H}) dv = \int \frac{(\vec{\nabla} \times \mathbf{H})^2}{\sigma} dv - \int \mathbf{E} \cdot (\vec{\nabla} \times \mathbf{H}) dv. \tag{18.16}$$

Using the identity $\vec{\nabla} \cdot (\mathbf{E} \times \mathbf{H}) = \mathbf{H}(\vec{\nabla} \times \mathbf{E}) - \mathbf{E}(\vec{\nabla} \times \mathbf{H})$

$$\int E \cdot (\nabla \times H) dv = \int \mathbf{H}(\vec{\nabla} \times \mathbf{E}) dv - \int \vec{\nabla}(\mathbf{E} \times \mathbf{H}) dv$$

$$= -\int \mathbf{H} \cdot \frac{\partial \mathbf{B}}{\partial t} dv - \int \vec{\nabla}(\mathbf{E} \times \mathbf{H}) dv \quad \left[\because \nabla \times E = -\frac{\partial B}{\partial t} \right]$$

$$= -\int \mathbf{H} \frac{\partial \mathbf{B}}{\partial t} dv - \int (\mathbf{E} \times \mathbf{H}) ds, \tag{18.17}$$

using divergence theorem.

We know that $\mathbf{E} \times \mathbf{H}$ falls off as the fifth inverse power, so the surface integral can be neglected. Therefore, Eq. (18.17) becomes

$$\int \mathbf{E}'(\vec{\nabla} \times \mathbf{H})dv = \int \frac{(\vec{\nabla} \times \mathbf{H})^2}{\sigma}dv + \int \mathbf{H}\frac{\partial B}{\partial t}dv. \qquad (18.18)$$

The first term on the right-hand side represents the joule heat loss and the second term is the rate at which energy is fed into the field. So the variation of magnetic field energy δu_m is given by

$$\delta u_m = \int H \cdot \delta B dv. \qquad (18.19)$$

For a medium which magnetize linearly the above integration may be carried out as in Eq. (18.11) and we get

$$U_m = \frac{1}{2} \int H \cdot B dv. \qquad (18.20)$$

18.4   Field Energy and Field Momentum : Poynting Theorem

Here we shall find out the expression for the electromagnetic energy in time dependent situations.

We know that the force on a moving charge will be

$$\mathbf{F} = q(\mathbf{E} + \mathbf{V} \times \mathbf{B}), \qquad (18.21)$$

where $\mathbf{V}$ is the velocity of the moving charge.

Therefore, the rate of work done on this charge is

$$\mathbf{F} \cdot \mathbf{V} = q(\mathbf{E} + \mathbf{V} \times \mathbf{B}) \cdot \mathbf{V}$$
$$= q\mathbf{E} \cdot \mathbf{V}. \qquad (18.22)$$

Note that the magnetic field is perpendicular to the velocity of charge and hence performs no work.

Assuming the existence of continuous distribution of charge, the total rate of work done for a given volume will be

$$\int \rho(\mathbf{E} \cdot \mathbf{V})dv = \int (\mathbf{E} \cdot \mathbf{j})dv, \qquad (18.23)$$

where ρ is the volume distribution of charge.

Now $\displaystyle\int (\mathbf{E} \cdot \mathbf{j})dv = \int \left[\mathbf{E}\left(\vec{\nabla} \times \mathbf{H} - \frac{\partial \mathbf{D}}{\partial t}\right)\right] dv$ [using Maxwell's fourth equation]

$$= \int \mathbf{E}(\vec{\nabla} \times \mathbf{H})dv - \int \mathbf{E}\frac{\partial \mathbf{D}}{\partial t}dv$$

$$= \int \vec{\nabla}(\mathbf{H} \times \mathbf{E})dv + \int \mathbf{H}(\vec{\nabla} \times \mathbf{E})dv - \int \mathbf{E}\frac{\partial \mathbf{D}}{\partial t}dv,$$

[using the identity $\vec{\nabla}(\mathbf{E} \times \mathbf{H}) = \mathbf{H}(\vec{\nabla} \times \mathbf{E}) - \mathbf{E}(\vec{\nabla} \times \mathbf{H})$]

$$= \int \vec{\nabla}(\mathbf{H} \times \mathbf{E})dv - \int \mathbf{H}\frac{\partial \mathbf{B}}{\partial t}dv - \int \mathbf{E}\frac{\partial \mathbf{D}}{\partial t}dv,$$

[using Maxwell's third equation]

$$= \int \vec{\nabla}(\mathbf{H} \times \mathbf{E})dv - \int \left[E\frac{\partial \mathbf{D}}{\partial t} + H\frac{\partial \mathbf{B}}{\partial t} \right] dv \qquad (18.24)$$

Using the divergence theorem to transform the first integral of Eq. (18.24)

$$\int (\mathbf{E} \cdot \mathbf{j})dv = \int_s (\mathbf{H} \times \mathbf{E})ds - \int_v \left(\mathbf{E}\frac{\partial \mathbf{D}}{\partial t} + \mathbf{H}\frac{\partial \mathbf{B}}{dt} \right) dv,$$

where v is the volume of the boundary surface s.

$$\therefore \quad -\int_v \left(\mathbf{E}\frac{\partial \mathbf{D}}{\partial t} + \mathbf{H}\frac{\partial \mathbf{B}}{\partial t} \right) dv = \int (\mathbf{E} \cdot \mathbf{j})dv + \int (\mathbf{E} \times \mathbf{H})ds. \qquad (18.25)$$

For a liner media,

$$\int_v \left(\mathbf{E}\frac{\partial \mathbf{D}}{\partial t} + \mathbf{H}\frac{\partial \mathbf{B}}{\partial t} \right) dv = \frac{\partial}{\partial t} \int \frac{1}{2}(\mathbf{E} \cdot \mathbf{D} + \mathbf{B} \cdot \mathbf{H})dv$$

$$\therefore \quad -\frac{\partial}{\partial t} \int \frac{1}{2}(\mathbf{E} \cdot \mathbf{D} + \mathbf{B} \cdot \mathbf{H})dv = \int (\mathbf{E} \cdot \mathbf{j})dv + \int (\mathbf{E} \times \mathbf{H})ds. \qquad (18.26)$$

Now the electromagnetic field consists of electric and magnetic fields. So the total electromagnetic energy will be the sum of energies as given in Eqs. (18.12), (18.20).

$$\therefore \quad \epsilon_M = \frac{1}{2}[\mathbf{E} \cdot \mathbf{D} + \mathbf{B} \cdot \mathbf{H}] \text{ will be the electromagnetic energy density.}$$

The left-hand side of Eq. (18.26) can be recognised as the rate at which the energy stored in the electromagnetic field decreases. The first term of the right-hand side gives the rate at which the electromotive forces are doing work. The second term demands careful consideration. The vector $\mathbf{E} \times \mathbf{H}$ has the dimensions of $\frac{\text{energy}}{\text{area} \times \text{time}}$ and hence the second term may be interpreted as representing the flow of energy through the boundary per unit time. The vector $\mathbf{N} = \mathbf{E} \times \mathbf{H}$ gives the rate at which the energy flows across unit area of the boundary and is known as *Poynting vector*.

Eq. (18.26), therefore, can be written in differential form as

$$\frac{d\epsilon_M}{dt} + \text{ div } \mathbf{N} = -\mathbf{E} \cdot \mathbf{j}. \qquad (18.27)$$

If the conductivity of the medium $\sigma = 0$, then

$$\mathbf{j} = \sigma \mathbf{E} = 0.$$

Therefore, Eq. (18.27) becomes

$$\frac{d\epsilon_M}{dt} + \text{ div } N = 0. \qquad (18.28)$$

Eq. (18.28) has the form analog to the equation of continuity. The volume density of the conserved quantity is ϵ_M and the current density is N. This analogy leads us the identification of Poynting vector $\mathbf{N}$ with the flux of electromagnetic energy. Therefore, Eq. (18.26) represents the law of conservation of energy and gives us the theorem known as 'Poynting theorem' which states that the decrease of electromagnetic energy per unit time in a certain volume is equal to the work done by the field forces per unit time plus the flux flowing outwards per unit time.

The force on a system will be

$$F = \int_v (\rho \mathbf{E} + \mathbf{j} \times \mathbf{B}) dv.$$

If p represents the momentum of all particles, then

$$\frac{d\mathbf{p}}{dt} = \int_v (\rho \mathbf{E} + \mathbf{j} \times \mathbf{B}) dv$$

$$= \int_v \left[(\vec{\nabla} \cdot \mathbf{D}) \mathbf{E} + \left(\vec{\nabla} \times \mathbf{H} - \frac{\partial \mathbf{D}}{\partial t} \right) \times \mathbf{B} \right] dv$$

[using Maxwell's first and fourth equation]

$$= \int_v \left[(\vec{\nabla} \cdot \mathbf{D}) \mathbf{E} + \mathbf{B} \times \frac{\partial \mathbf{D}}{\partial t} - \mathbf{B} \times (\vec{\nabla} \times \mathbf{H}) \right] dv$$

$$= \int_v \left[(\vec{\nabla} \cdot \mathbf{D}) \mathbf{E} + \left(\mathbf{D} \times \frac{\partial \mathbf{B}}{\partial t} \right) - \frac{\partial}{\partial t} (\mathbf{D} \times \mathbf{B}) - \mathbf{B} \times (\vec{\nabla} \times \mathbf{H}) \right] dv$$

$$\left[\text{using the identity, } \frac{\partial}{\partial t} (A \times B) = A \times \frac{\partial B}{\partial t} + B \times \frac{\partial A}{\partial t} \right]$$

or, $$\frac{d\mathbf{p}}{dt} + \frac{d}{dt} \int_v (\mathbf{D} \times \mathbf{B}) dv$$

$$= \int \left[(\vec{\nabla} \cdot \mathbf{D}) \mathbf{E} + (\vec{\nabla} \cdot \mathbf{B}) \mathbf{H} - \mathbf{D} \times (\vec{\nabla} \cdot \mathbf{E}) - \mathbf{B} \times (\vec{\nabla} \times \mathbf{H}) \right] dv. \qquad (18.29)$$

We know that $\vec{\nabla} \cdot \mathbf{B} = 0$, so addition of $(\vec{\nabla} \cdot \mathbf{B}) \mathbf{H}$ in the above will not change the result.

The second term on the left-hand side of the above expression represents the momentum. It is not associated with the mass of the particles and consists only of fields, it is termed as electromagnetic momentum p_e. The vector $\mathbf{g} = [\mathbf{D} \times \mathbf{B}]$ is called the *momentum density*.

Again, the momentum density vector

$$\mathbf{g} = [\mathbf{D} \times \mathbf{B}] = [\epsilon \mathbf{E} \times \mu \mathbf{H}] = \epsilon \mu [\mathbf{E} \times \mathbf{H}] = \epsilon \mu \mathbf{N}.$$

Therefore, momentum vector $\mathbf{g}$ is related with the Poynting vector $\mathbf{N}$.

18.5   The Wave Equation

Here we shall show that the field generated by the moving charges may leave the source and travel through space in the form of waves.

Taking curl of the Maxwell's third equation one can obtain

$$\vec{\nabla} (\vec{\nabla} \times \mathbf{E}) = -\vec{\nabla} \times \frac{\partial \mathbf{B}}{\partial t} = -\frac{\partial}{\partial t} (\vec{\nabla} \times \mathbf{B}) = -\mu \frac{\partial}{\partial t} (\vec{\nabla} \times \mathbf{H})$$

$$= -\mu \frac{\partial}{\partial t} \left(\mathbf{j} + \frac{\partial \mathbf{D}}{\partial t} \right), \text{ from Maxwell's fourth equation}$$

$$= -\mu \frac{\partial}{\partial t} \left(\mathbf{j} + \epsilon \frac{\partial \mathbf{E}}{\partial t} \right).$$

Using the vector identity, $\vec{\nabla} \times (\vec{\nabla} \times \mathbf{E}) = \vec{\nabla} (\vec{\nabla} \cdot \mathbf{E}) - \vec{\nabla}^2 \mathbf{E}$.

$$\therefore \quad \vec{\nabla} (\vec{\nabla} \cdot \mathbf{E}) - \vec{\nabla}^2 \mathbf{E} = -\mu \frac{\partial}{\partial t} \left(\mathbf{j} + \epsilon \frac{\partial \mathbf{E}}{t} \right).$$

Now in the charge free region, $\vec{\nabla} \cdot E = \frac{1}{\epsilon} \cdot \vec{\nabla} D = e^\rho = 0 \quad [\because \rho = 0]$

$$\therefore \quad \vec{\nabla}^2 E = \mu \frac{\partial}{\partial t}\left(\sigma E + \epsilon \frac{\partial E}{\partial t}\right) = \mu\sigma \frac{\partial E}{\partial t} + \mu\epsilon \frac{\partial^2 E}{\partial t^2}$$

or, $\quad \vec{\nabla}^2 E - \mu\epsilon \frac{\partial^2 E}{\partial t^2} - \mu\sigma \frac{\partial E}{\partial t} = 0.$ \hfill (18.30)

Eq. (18.30) is known as general wave equation. In case of conducting medium, the third term of Eq. (18.30) is dominant, hence the equation becomes

$$\vec{\nabla}^2 E - \mu\sigma \frac{\partial E}{\partial t} = 0. \tag{18.31}$$

For non-conducting medium the equation will be

$$\vec{\nabla}^2 E - \mu\epsilon \frac{\partial^2 E}{\partial t^2} = 0. \tag{18.32}$$

Taking the curl of Maxwell's fourth equation exactly similar equations for H can be obtained.

$$\vec{\nabla}^2 H - \mu\epsilon \frac{\partial^2 H}{\partial t^2} - \mu\sigma \frac{\partial H}{\partial t} = 0 \tag{18.33}$$

and $\quad \vec{\nabla}^2 H - \mu\epsilon \frac{\partial^2 H}{\partial t^2} = 0.$ \hfill (18.34)

The solutions of differential Eqs. (18.32) and (18.34) represents waves travelling with velocity

$$v = \sqrt{\frac{1}{\mu\epsilon}}.$$

From Eqs. (18.32) and (18.34) it can be concluded that any time variations in electric or magnetic field are propagated with the same velocity $v = \sqrt{\frac{1}{\mu\epsilon}}$. The type of wave which is obtained from the solution of Eqs. (18.32) and (18.34) are plane waves.

We know that a plane wave is a wave in which the wave amplitude remains constant over all points of a plane perpendicular to the directions of propagation. This plane will constitute a wavefront which propagates with a velocity v in a direction normal to itself. Suppose, we choose the direction of propagation to be coincided with the X-axis. Therefore, the general wave equation takes the form

$$\frac{\partial^2 \Psi}{\partial x^2} - \frac{1}{v^2}\frac{\partial^2 \Psi}{\partial t^2} = 0. \tag{18.35}$$

The general solution of the above equation will be

$$\Psi(x, t) = A e^{i(kx - \omega t)} + B^{-i(kx + \omega t)}, \tag{18.36}$$

where A and B are constants and $k = \frac{\omega}{v}$. Here we may assume that the plane wave field equations

$$E(x, t) = E_0 e^{i(kx - \omega t)} \tag{18.37}$$

$$H(x, t) = H_0 e^{i(kx - \omega t)}. \tag{18.38}$$

In the above equation we have assumed that **E** and **H** are in phase. The proof of this statement is given below.

Let us suppose that the phase difference between $\mathbf{E}$ and $\mathbf{H}$ be α, i.e.,

$$\left.\begin{array}{l} \mathbf{E} = \mathbf{E}_0 e^{i(kx - \omega t)} \\[2mm] \mathbf{H} = \mathbf{H}_0 e^{i(kx - \omega t + \alpha)} \end{array}\right\} . \tag{18.39}$$

Now both the fields must satisfy Maxwell's equation $\vec{\nabla} \times \mathbf{E} = -\frac{\partial \mathbf{B}}{\partial t}$.
$\mathbf{E}$ travells in the X-direction, so the $\frac{\partial}{\partial y}$, $\frac{\partial}{\partial z}$ of E will be zero.

$$\therefore \quad \frac{\partial E_z}{\partial x} = \frac{\partial B_y}{\partial t} \quad \text{and} \quad \frac{\partial E_y}{\partial x} = -\frac{\partial B_z}{\partial t}$$

$$\text{or,} \quad \frac{\partial E_z}{\partial x} = \mu \frac{\partial H_y}{\partial t} \quad \text{and} \quad \frac{\partial E_x}{\partial x} = -\mu \frac{\partial H_z}{\partial t} .$$

From the last equation we get

$$ikE_{0y}e^{i(kx - \omega t)} = -\mu\omega H_{0z}e^{i(kx - \omega t + \alpha)} .$$

Equating the real parts of the above equation, we have

$$kE_{0y}\cos(kx - \omega t) = \mu\omega H_{0z}\cos(kx - \omega t + \alpha) .$$

The above equation must be true for all values of x and t. This will be true only when $\alpha = 0$. Hence $\mathbf{E}$ and $\mathbf{H}$ always remain in phase. The ratio of the amplitudes of the field vectors $Z_0 = \frac{E_0}{H_0}$ has the dimension of impedance and known as intrinsic impedance of the medium.

Transverse Nature of Electromagnetic Waves

If the wave propagates in any arbitrary direction, we have

$$\mathbf{E}(\mathbf{r}, t) = \mathbf{E}_0 e^{-i(\mathbf{k} \cdot \mathbf{r} - \omega t)}, \tag{18.40}$$

$$\mathbf{H}(\mathbf{r}, t) = \mathbf{H}_0 e^{i(\mathbf{k} \cdot \mathbf{r} - \omega t)}, \tag{18.41}$$

where $\mathbf{k}$ being the propagation vector.

Substituting Eq. (18.40) in Maxwell's first relation $\vec{\nabla} \cdot D = \rho$, and remembering that in charge-free region $\rho = 0$, we get

$$\vec{\nabla} \cdot \{\mathbf{E}_0 e^{i(\mathbf{k}\mathbf{r} - \omega t)}\} = 0, \tag{18.42}$$

which leads to $\mathbf{k} \cdot \mathbf{E} = 0$.

Similarly, substituting Eq. (18.41) in Maxwell's second equation we get $\mathbf{k} \cdot \mathbf{H} = 0$. From the above result we find that $\mathbf{E}$ and $\mathbf{H}$ are normal to the propagation vector $\mathbf{k}$. Therefore, electromagnetic plane waves are transverse wave.

Now Maxwell's third relation is

$$\vec{\nabla} \times \mathbf{E} = -\frac{\partial \mathbf{B}}{\partial t} \quad \text{or,} \quad \vec{\nabla} \times \mathbf{E} = -\mu \frac{\partial \mathbf{H}}{\partial t}$$

$$\text{or,} \quad \vec{\nabla} \times \mathbf{E}_0 e^{i(\mathbf{k}\mathbf{r} - \omega t)} = -\mu \frac{\partial}{\partial t}\left\{\mathbf{H}_0 e^{i(\mathbf{k}\mathbf{r} - \omega t)}\right\}$$

$$\text{or,} \quad \vec{\nabla} \cdot e^{i(\mathbf{k}\mathbf{r} - \omega t)} \times \mathbf{E}_0 = i\mu\omega \mathbf{H}_0 e^{i(\mathbf{k}\mathbf{r} - \omega t)}$$

$$\text{or,} \quad i\mathbf{k} \times \mathbf{E} = i\mu\omega \mathbf{H}$$

$$\text{or,} \quad \mathbf{k} \times \mathbf{E} = \mu\omega \mathbf{H}. \tag{18.43}$$

From the Eq. (18.43) we may conclude that $\mathbf{H}$ is perpendicular to both $\mathbf{k}$ and $\mathbf{E}$. Hence $\mathbf{E}$ and $\mathbf{H}$ are perpendicular to each other. The vectors $\mathbf{k}$, $\mathbf{H}$ and $\mathbf{E}$ will constitute a right-handed orthogonal set as shown in Fig. 18.1.

The velocity of electromagnetic wave in free space is given by

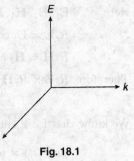

$$v_0 = \sqrt{\frac{1}{\mu_0 \epsilon_0}},$$

here $\epsilon_0 = 8.8547 \times 10^{-12}$ and $\mu_0 = 4\pi \times 10^{-7}$.

$\therefore \quad v_0 = 2.99 \times 10^{10}$ cm/second.

This velocity is same as the velocity of light in vacuum. So light is simply a form of electromagnetic radiation.

Fig. 18.1

The direct verification of the existence of electromagnetic waves was done by Hertz.

Hertz Experiment

In his experiment, H. R. Hertz took two sheets of metal (40 cm × 40 cm) and placed them in a vertically coplanar position with the centres at 60 cm apart. Two highly polished brass-spheres are attached to each sheets. The brass spheres are kept 2 cm apart. An induction coil is connected between these two spheres. The square metal sheets will form an open type capacitor as shown in Fig. 18.2.

Hertz used a circle of thick wire to detect the radiation. Two sparking knobs separated by a small gap are connected with the two ends of the wire. The coil is

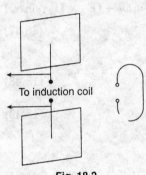

To induction coil

placed in the vertical plane so that it will cut the lines of force and an e.m.f. will be induced in the coil. Due to high potential difference of the knob, sparking will take place.

If the natural period of the coil coincides with the period of oscillation of the electromagnetic waves, a maximum sparking will take place due to resonance. The detector will not response if the coil is set in the horizontal plane.

Fig. 18.2

The frequencies of electromagnetic waves produced by Hertz were lower than that of light waves. But the properties deduced by Maxwell were actually verified by this experiment. He showed that electromagnetic waves are reflected, refracted and they produce interference.

18.6   Energy Flux in a Plane Wave

We know that Poynting vector **N** gives the rate of flow of energy per unit area. Here we shall calculate the Poynting vector for a plane electromagnetic wave where field vectors are expressed in terms of complex amplitudes.

Since the field vectors **E** and **H** vary harmonically with time, the average energy flow will be equal to average of Poynting vector $\langle N \rangle$ over a complete period.

$\therefore \quad \langle N \rangle = \langle R_e \mathbf{E} \times R_\epsilon \mathbf{H} \rangle,$ \hfill (18.44)

where R_e stands for the real part.

As the field vectors are complex we can express **E** and **H** in the following form :

$$\left. \begin{array}{l} \mathbf{E} = (\mathbf{E}_1 + i\mathbf{E}_2)e^{-i\omega t} \\ \mathbf{H} = (\mathbf{H}_1 + i\mathbf{H}_2)e^{-i\omega t} \end{array} \right\}. \hfill (18.45)$$

Here $\mathbf{E}_1, \mathbf{E}_2, \mathbf{H}_1, \mathbf{H}_2$ are all real.

$\therefore$ $R_e\mathbf{E} = \mathbf{E}_1 \cos \omega t + \mathbf{E}_2 \sin \omega t$

            $R_e\mathbf{H} = \mathbf{H}_1 \cos \omega t + \mathbf{H}_2 \sin \omega t.$

Therefore, $R_e\mathbf{E} \times R_e\mathbf{H} = (\mathbf{E}_1 \times \mathbf{H}_1) \cos^2 \omega t + (\mathbf{E}_2 \times \mathbf{H}_2) \sin^2 \omega t$

$$+ \{(\mathbf{E}_1 \times \mathbf{H}_2) + (\mathbf{E}_2 \times \mathbf{H}_1)\} \sin \omega t \cos \omega t.$$

We know that for a complete period,

$$\langle \sin^2 \omega t \rangle = \langle \cos^2 \omega t \rangle = \frac{1}{2} \quad \text{and} \quad \langle \sin \omega t \cos \omega t \rangle = 0.$$

$\therefore$ $\langle R_e\mathbf{E} \times R_e\mathbf{H} \rangle = \frac{1}{2}[(\mathbf{E}_1 \times \mathbf{H}_1) + (\mathbf{E}_2 \times \mathbf{H}_2)].$ (18.46)

Let us now calculate the value of $R_e(\mathbf{E} \times \mathbf{H}^*)$.

$$\mathbf{E} = (\mathbf{E}_1 + i\mathbf{E}_2)e^{-i\omega t} = (\mathbf{E}_1 + i\mathbf{E}_2)(\cos \omega t - i \sin \omega t)$$

$$\mathbf{H}^* = (\mathbf{H}_1 - i\mathbf{H}_2)e^{i\omega t} = (\mathbf{H}_1 - i\mathbf{H}_2)(\cos \omega t + i \sin \omega t).$$

$\therefore$ $R_e(\mathbf{E} \times \mathbf{H}^*) = (\mathbf{E}_1 \times \mathbf{H}_1) \cos^2 \omega t + (\mathbf{E}_1 \times \mathbf{H}_2) \cos \omega t \sin \omega t$

$$+ (\mathbf{E}_2 \times \mathbf{H}_1) \cos^2 \omega t - (\mathbf{E}_2 \times \mathbf{H}_1) \cos \omega t \sin \omega t$$

$$- (\mathbf{E}_1 \times \mathbf{H}_2) \cos \omega t \sin \omega t - (\mathbf{E}_1 \times \mathbf{H}_1) \sin^2 \omega t$$

$$+ (\mathbf{E}_2 \times \mathbf{H}_1) \cos \omega t \sin \omega t + (\mathbf{E}_2 \times \mathbf{H}_2) \sin^2 \omega t$$

$$= (\mathbf{E}_1 \times \mathbf{H}_1) + (\mathbf{E}_2 \times \mathbf{H}_2).$$ (18.47)

Comparing Eqs. (18.46) and (18.47), we get

$$\langle R_e\mathbf{E} \times R_e\mathbf{H} \rangle = \frac{1}{2}(\mathbf{E} \times \mathbf{H}^*).$$ (18.48)

$\therefore$ $\langle N \rangle = \frac{1}{2}R_e(\mathbf{E} \times \mathbf{H}^*).$ (18.49)

Now from Eq. (22.43), we have

$\mathbf{k} \times \mathbf{E} = \omega\mu\mathbf{H}.$

$\therefore$ $\mathbf{H} = \dfrac{\mathbf{k} \times \mathbf{E}}{\omega\mu}$ or, $\mathbf{H}^* = \dfrac{\mathbf{k} \times \mathbf{E}^*}{\omega\mu}$

or, $\mathbf{E} \times \mathbf{H}^* = \dfrac{1}{\omega\mu}[\mathbf{E} \times (\mathbf{k} \times \mathbf{E}^*)] = \dfrac{1}{\omega\mu}[(\mathbf{E} \cdot \mathbf{E}^*)\mathbf{k} - (\mathbf{E} \cdot \mathbf{k})\mathbf{E}^*]$

$$= \dfrac{1}{\omega\mu}|E_0|^2\mathbf{k}.$$

$\therefore$ $\langle N \rangle = \dfrac{1}{2}R_e(\mathbf{E} \times \mathbf{H}^*) = \dfrac{1}{2\omega\mu}|E_0|^2\mathbf{k}$

$$= \dfrac{|E_0|^2}{2} \cdot \left(\dfrac{\epsilon}{\mu}\right)^{\frac{1}{2}} \hat{e}_k,$$ (18.50)

where $\mathbf{k} = k\hat{e}_k$; $\hat{e}_k$ is the unit vector in the direction of propagation and $\frac{\omega}{v} = \frac{\omega}{\sqrt{\epsilon\mu}} = k$.

If the wave propagates along X-direction, the field vectors $\mathbf{E}$ and $\mathbf{H}$ will act along Y- and Z-directions, respectively. Consider a rectangular box with a, b and c being the length of its sides as shown in Fig. 18.3.

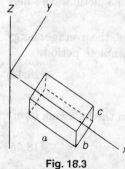

Fig. 18.3

The electromagnetic energy density is $\frac{1}{2}(\mathbf{E} \cdot \mathbf{D} + \mathbf{B} \cdot \mathbf{H})$. Hence the total energy will be given by

$$\mathbf{U} = \frac{1}{2} \int (\mathbf{E} \cdot \mathbf{D} + \mathbf{B} \cdot \mathbf{H}) dv.$$

Here $\mathbf{E} = \hat{e}_y E_0 e^{i(kx - \omega t)} = \hat{e}_y E_0 \cos(kx - \omega t)$

$\mathbf{H} = \hat{e}_z H_0 e^{i(kx - \omega t)} = \hat{e}_z H_0 \cos(kx - \omega t).$

$\therefore \quad (\mathbf{E} \cdot \mathbf{D} + \mathbf{B} \cdot \mathbf{H}) = [\epsilon_0 (\mathbf{E} \cdot \mathbf{E}) + \mu_0 (\mathbf{H} \cdot \mathbf{H})]$

$$= \epsilon_0 E_0^2 \cos^2(kx - \omega t) + \mu_0 H_0^2 \cos^2(kx - \omega t).$$

Therefore, $\mathbf{U} = \dfrac{1}{2} \displaystyle\int_0^a \int_0^b \int_0^c [\epsilon_0 E_0^2 \cos^2(kx - \omega t) + \mu_0 H_0^2 \cos^2(kx - \omega t)] dx\,dy\,dz$

$$= \frac{bc}{2} \int_0^a [\epsilon_0 E_0^2 \cos^2(kx - \omega t) + \mu_0 H_0^2 \cos^2(kx - \omega t)] dx$$

$\therefore \quad \langle U \rangle = \dfrac{1}{T} \cdot \dfrac{bc}{2} \displaystyle\int_0^T \int_0^a [\epsilon_0 E_0^2 \cos^2(kx - \omega t) + \mu_0 H_0^2 \cos^2(kx - \omega t)] dx\,dt$

$$= \frac{bc}{2} \int_0^a \frac{1}{2} [\epsilon_0 E_0^2 + \mu_0 H_0^2] dx$$

$$= \frac{abc}{4} [\epsilon_0 E_0^2 + \mu_0 H_0^2]. \tag{18.51}$$

Therefore, time average of the energy density

$$\langle U_d \rangle = \frac{1}{4}(E \cdot D^* + B \cdot H^*) = \frac{1}{4}(\epsilon E^2 + \mu H^2)$$

$$= \frac{1}{4} \left[\epsilon |E_0|^2 + \mu \frac{\mathbf{k} \times \mathbf{E}}{\omega \mu} \cdot \frac{\mathbf{k} \times \mathbf{E}^*}{\omega \mu} \right]$$

$$= \frac{1}{4} \left[\epsilon |E_0|^2 + \frac{\mu k}{\omega \mu} \cdot \frac{k}{\omega \mu} |E_0|^2 \right]$$

$$= \frac{1}{4} \left[\epsilon |E_0|^2 + \frac{\mu \cdot \omega^2 \mu t}{\omega^2 \mu^2} |E_0|^2 \right] \quad [\because \omega(\mu t)^{1/2} = k]$$

$$= \frac{\epsilon}{2} |E_0|^2. \tag{18.52}$$

Hence, $\langle N \rangle = \dfrac{1}{2} \left(\dfrac{\epsilon}{\mu} \right)^{\frac{1}{2}} \hat{e}_k |E_0|^2 = \langle U_d \rangle \dfrac{1}{\sqrt{\mu t}} \hat{e}_k$

$$= v \langle U_d \rangle \hat{e}_k. \tag{18.53}$$

Therefore, time averaged energy will flow in the direction of propagation of the wave with the same velocity as the wave and we can say

$\therefore \quad \langle \text{ energy } \rangle = \text{ phase velocity } \times \langle \text{ energy density } \rangle.$

18.7 Plane Waves in a Conducting Medium

We know from Eqs. (18.30) and (18.33) that both electric and magnetic fields satisfy identical equations,

$$\vec{\nabla}^2 \mathbf{E} - \mu \epsilon \frac{\partial^2 \mathbf{E}}{\partial t^2} - \mu \sigma \frac{\partial \mathbf{E}}{\partial t} = 0 \tag{18.54}$$

and $\vec{\nabla}^2 \mathbf{H} - \mu \epsilon \dfrac{\partial^2 \mathbf{H}}{\partial t^2} - \mu \sigma \dfrac{\partial \mathbf{H}}{\partial t} = 0.$ $\tag{18.55}$

Let us now assume that the field vectors varies harmonically with time, i.e.,

$$\mathbf{E}(\mathbf{r}, t) = \mathbf{E}_0 e^{i(\mathbf{k} \cdot \mathbf{r} - \omega t)} \tag{18.56}$$

$$\mathbf{H}(\mathbf{r}, t) = \mathbf{H}_0 e^{i(\mathbf{k} \cdot \mathbf{r} - \omega t)}. \tag{18.57}$$

Using Eqs. (18.54) and (18.56), we have

$$-k^2 \mathbf{E}(\mathbf{r}, t) + \mu \epsilon \omega^2 \mathbf{E}(\mathbf{r}, t) + i \mu \sigma \omega \mathbf{E}(\mathbf{r}, t) = 0$$

or, $\quad [-k^2 + \mu \epsilon \omega^2 + i \mu \sigma \omega] \mathbf{E}(\mathbf{r}, t) = 0 \tag{18.57a}$

or, $\quad k^2 - \mu \epsilon \omega^2 - i \mu \sigma \omega = 0$

or, $\quad k^2 = \mu \epsilon \omega^2 \left(1 + \dfrac{i\sigma}{\epsilon \omega} \right). \tag{18.58}$

The first term of the Eq. (18.58) corresponds to the displacement current and the second to the conduction current. The dispersion relation of electromagnetic waves in vacuum can be obtained by putting $\sigma = 0$ in Eq. (18.58) and one gets the well-known established dispersion relation,

$$k^2 = \mu \epsilon \omega^2 = \frac{\omega^2}{v^2}$$

i.e., $\quad k = \dfrac{\omega}{v}. \tag{18.59}$

From Eq. (18.58) we see that the propagation vector is a complex quantity. So we have solved Eq. (18.58) for the real and imaginary parts of k.

Assuming $k = a + i\beta$, we get

$$\alpha = \omega \sqrt{\frac{\mu \epsilon}{2}} \left[1 + \left\{ 1 + \left(\frac{\sigma}{\omega t} \right)^2 \right\}^{\frac{1}{2}} \right]^{\frac{1}{2}} \tag{18.60}$$

and $\quad \beta = \omega \sqrt{\frac{\mu \epsilon}{2}} \left[-1 + \left\{ 1 + \left(\frac{\sigma}{\omega t} \right)^2 \right\}^{\frac{1}{2}} \right]^{\frac{1}{2}}. \tag{18.61}$

Using Eqs. (18.60) and (18.61) the field vectors can be written as

$$E = E_0 e^{-\beta \mathbf{r}} e^{i(\alpha \mathbf{r} - \omega t)}$$

$$H = H_0 e^{-\beta \mathbf{r}} e^{i(\alpha \mathbf{r} - \omega t)}. \tag{18.62}$$

Two features of Eq. (18.62) are immediately evident. The conductivity gives rise to exponential damping of the wave and the electric and magnetic fields are no longer in phase. When a plane wave is propagated in a conducting medium, the oscillating electric field in the wave sets up currents and so some energy must be dissipated as heat in the medium. This results into attenuation of the wave. The quantity B is called *absorption coefficient* and it gives the measure of attenuation.

18.8   Skin Depth

The third term of Eq. (18.57a) arises from the term involving $\frac{\partial E}{\partial t}$ in Eq. (18.54), i.e., from conduction current and the second term from the displacement current. In most of the conducting media the conduction current dominates the displacement current. Thus, for a good conducting medium, one can neglect the middle term of Eq. (18.54).

i.e., $\quad\quad \vec{\nabla}^2 E = \mu \sigma \dfrac{\partial \mathbf{E}}{\partial t}. \tag{18.63}$

The solution of the above equation will be

$$\mathbf{E} = \dot{\mathbf{E}}_0 e^{-\beta r} e^{i(kr - \omega t)}. \tag{18.64}$$

For a good conductor $\dfrac{\sigma}{\omega t} \gg 1$, provided the frequency is not too high.

From Eqs. (18.60) and (18.61),

$$\alpha = \beta = \sqrt{\frac{\omega \sigma \mu}{2}} = \frac{1}{\delta} \text{ (say)}. \quad \therefore \ \delta = \sqrt{\frac{2}{\omega \sigma \mu}}.$$

Hence, $\quad E = E_0 \exp\left(-\dfrac{r}{\partial}\right) \exp i \left(\dfrac{r}{\delta} - \omega t\right).$ \hfill (18.65)

The value of β is very large, and within a very short distance from the surface the amplitude of the electric intensity acquires negligible value. From the Eq. (18.65) we find that at $r = \delta$ the amplitude decreases to $\frac{1}{e}$th its value at the surface. The quality δ is the measure of penetration of electromagnetic wave into a good conductor and is called *skin depth*. Skin depth (δ) is defined to be the distance from the surface at which the attenuation of the wave is $\frac{1}{e}$th of its value at the surface of the conductor.

18.9 Reflection and Refraction of Plane Waves at a Plane Interface

Suppose plane waves are incident on a boundary between two media. Some of its incident energy crosses the boundary and some is reflected. Electromagnetic theory offers a simple explanation for this phenomena.

Let us consider a plane wave travelling in the direction of k_1 in the medium '1' characterized by constants μ_1, ϵ_1 and incident on the plane boundary between media '1' and '2' (Fig. 18.4). The medium '2' is characterized by the constants μ_2 and ϵ_2.

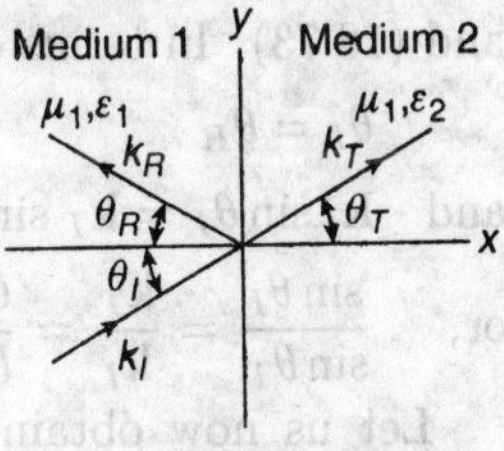

The field vectors for the incident, reflected and transmitted wave can be expressed as

Fig. 18.4

$$\left. \begin{array}{l} \mathbf{E}_I = \mathbf{E}_{0I} \exp\{i(\mathbf{k}_1 \cdot \mathbf{r} - \omega_I t)\} \\[4pt] \mathbf{E}_R = \mathbf{E}_{0R} \exp\{i(\mathbf{k}_R \cdot \mathbf{r} - \omega_R t)\} \\[4pt] \mathbf{E}_T = \mathbf{E}_{0T} \exp\{i(\mathbf{k}_T \cdot \mathbf{r} - \omega_T t)\} \end{array} \right\}. \tag{18.66}$$

and $\quad \left. \begin{array}{l} \mathbf{H}_1 = \dfrac{\mathbf{k}_1 \times \mathbf{E}_1}{\omega_I \times \mu_I} \\[10pt] H_R = \dfrac{\mathbf{k}_R \times \mathbf{E}_R}{\omega_R \mu_1} \\[10pt] H_T = \dfrac{\mathbf{k}_T \times \mathbf{E}_T}{\omega_T \mu_2} \end{array} \right\}. \tag{18.67}$

The subscripts I, R and T are for incident, reflected and transmitted waves respectively.

The tangential components of both the field vectors E and H must be continuous across the boundary. So the boundary condition cannot be satisfied by a single progressive wave. The continuity of tangential fields across the boundary at all points and all times is possible, only if the exponentials are the same at the boundary for all three fields. Thus we are justified in assuming throughout Eqs. (18.66) and

(18.67) that the frequency remains unchanged in the transmitted and reflected waves. Thus,

$$\omega_I = \omega_R = \omega_T \tag{18.68}$$

and we have the further conditions that

$$\mathbf{k}_I \mathbf{r} = \mathbf{k}_R \mathbf{r} = \mathbf{k}_T \mathbf{r} \tag{18.69}$$

over the boundary surface. It is evident from Eq. (18.69) that all the propagation vectors are coplanar. We put the origin of the co-ordinate vector $\mathbf{r}$ in the boundary plane for convenience specified by the unit vector $\mathbf{n}$ so that $\mathbf{n} \cdot \mathbf{r} = 0$ is the equation of the plane, then

$$\mathbf{n} \times (\mathbf{n} \times \mathbf{r}) = (\mathbf{n} \cdot \mathbf{r})\mathbf{n} - \mathbf{r} = -\mathbf{r} \tag{18.70}$$

on the boundary.

Substituting the relation (18.70) in Eq. (18.69) yields

$$\mathbf{k}_I \cdot \mathbf{n} \times (\mathbf{n} \times \mathbf{r}) = \mathbf{k}_R \cdot \mathbf{n} \times (\mathbf{n} \times \mathbf{r}) = \mathbf{k}_T \cdot \mathbf{n} \times (\mathbf{n} \times \mathbf{r})$$

or, $\mathbf{k}_I \times \mathbf{n} \cdot (\mathbf{n} \times \mathbf{r}) = \mathbf{k}_R \times \mathbf{n} \cdot (\mathbf{n} \times \mathbf{r}) = \mathbf{k}_T \times \mathbf{n} \cdot (\mathbf{n} \times \mathbf{r}).$ (18.71)

Now Eq. (18.71) can be written as

$$(\mathbf{k}_I - \mathbf{k}_R) \times \mathbf{n} \cdot (\mathbf{n} \times \mathbf{r}) = 0 \tag{18.72}$$

$$(\mathbf{k}_I - \mathbf{k}_T) \times \mathbf{n} \cdot (\mathbf{n} \times \mathbf{r}) = 0. \tag{18.73}$$

Now the propagation vectors $\mathbf{k}_I$ and $\mathbf{k}_R$ in the same medium are equal in magnitude and $|\mathbf{k}_I|/|\mathbf{k}_T| = \frac{U_2}{U_1}$, the ratio of phase velocities in the two media. Therefore, the laws of reflection and refraction can be obtained from Eqs. (18.72) and (18.73). In terms of angles we can write

$$\theta_I = \theta_R \tag{18.74}$$

and $\mathbf{k}_I \sin \theta_I = \mathbf{k}_T \sin \theta_T$

or, $\dfrac{\sin \theta_I}{\sin \theta_T} = \dfrac{\mathbf{k}_T}{\mathbf{k}_I} = \dfrac{U_1}{U_2}$, which is *Snell's law*. (18.75)

Let us now obtain the relations between the various amplitudes of the field vectors which satisfy the boundary conditions.

$$\mathbf{n} \times (\mathbf{E}_I + \mathbf{E}_R) = \mathbf{n} \times \mathbf{E}_T \tag{18.76}$$

and $\dfrac{\mathbf{n} \times (\mathbf{H}_I + \mathbf{H}_R)}{\mu_1} = \dfrac{\mathbf{n} \times \mathbf{H}_T}{\mu_2}.$ (18.77)

The magnetic amplitudes of Eq. (18.77) can be written in terms of the electric fields. For simplicity we assume that $\mu_1 = \mu_2$.

$$\therefore \quad \mathbf{n} \times (\mathbf{k}_I \times \mathbf{E}_I + \mathbf{k}_R \times \mathbf{E}_R) = \mathbf{n} \times (\mathbf{k}_R \times \mathbf{E}_T). \tag{18.78}$$

The orientation of $\mathbf{E}$ is arbitrary. But one may consider it as the sum of two components at right angles.

(a) E at right angles to the plane of incidence :

The field vectors are shown in Fig. 18.5. When $\mathbf{E}$ is perpendicular to the plane of incidence, all the electric field vectors are tangential to the surface. The conditions (18.76) and (18.78) yield

$$E_{0I} + E_{0R} = E_{0T} \tag{18.79}$$

and $k_I E_{0I} \cos \theta_I - k_I E_{0R} \cos \theta_R = k_T E_{0T} \cos \theta_T$

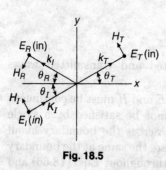

Fig. 18.5

or, $\quad (E_{0I} - E_{0R}) \cos \theta_I = \dfrac{k_T}{k_I} E_{0T} \cos \theta_T.$ $\hfill$ (18.80)

After solving Eqs. (18.79) and (18.80), we get

$$\frac{E_{0R}}{E_{0I}} = \frac{\cos \theta_I - \frac{k_T}{k_I} \cos \theta_T}{\cos \theta_I + \frac{k_T}{k_I} \cos \theta_T}$$

$$= \frac{\cos \theta_I - \frac{n_2}{n_1} \cos \theta_T}{\cos \theta_I + \frac{n_2}{n_1} \cos \theta_T} \hfill \text{(18.80a)}$$

$$= \frac{\cos \theta_I - \frac{\sin \theta_L}{\sin \theta_T} \cos \theta_T}{\cos \theta_I + \frac{\sin \theta_L}{\sin \theta_T} \cos \theta_T} \quad [\because n_1 \sin \theta_I = n_2 \sin \theta_I]$$

$$= \frac{\sin(\theta_T - \theta_I)}{\sin(\theta_T + \theta_I)} \hfill \text{(18.81)}$$

and $\quad \dfrac{E_{0T}}{E_{01}} = \dfrac{2 \cos \theta_I}{\cos \theta_I + \frac{k_T}{k_I} \cos \theta_T}$

$$= \frac{2 \cos \theta_I \sin \theta_T}{\sin(\theta_I + \theta_T)}. \hfill \text{(18.82)}$$

If $n_2 > n_1$, the ratio $\frac{E_{0R}}{E_{0I}}$ is negative which indicates that a phase change of π occurs in reflection of waves. The ratio $\frac{E_{0T}}{E_{0I}}$ is always positive.

The reflection coefficient R is defined as the ratio of energy flux reflected from the interface to the flux incident on it.

i.e., $\quad R = \dfrac{\mathbf{n}\langle N_R \rangle}{\mathbf{n}\langle N_I \rangle} = \dfrac{|\mathbf{E}_R \times \mathbf{H}_R^*|}{\mathbf{E}_I \times \mathbf{H}_I^*} \cdot \dfrac{E_{0R}^2}{E_{0I}^2},$

where $\mathbf{N}_R$ and $\mathbf{N}_I$ are the Poynting vectors.

Using Eq. (18.81), we get

$$R = \frac{\sin^2(\theta_T - \theta_T)}{\sin^2(\theta_T + \theta_I)}. \hfill \text{(18.83)}$$

Similarly, the transmission coefficient,

$$T = \frac{\mathbf{n} \cdot \langle \mathbf{N}_T \rangle}{\mathbf{n} \cdot \langle \mathbf{N}_I \rangle} = \frac{|\mathbf{E}_T \times \mathbf{H}_T^*|}{|\mathbf{E}_I \times \mathbf{H}_I^*|} = \frac{E_{0T}^2}{H_{0I}^2} \frac{n_2 \cos \theta_T}{n_1 \cos \theta_1}$$

$$= \frac{4 \cos^2 \theta_I \sin \theta_T}{\sin^2(\theta_I + \theta_T)} \cdot \frac{\sin \theta_I}{\sin \theta_T} \cdot \frac{\cos \theta_T}{\cos \theta_I} = \frac{\sin 2\theta_I \sin 2\theta_T}{\sin^2(\theta_I + \theta_T)}. \hfill \text{(18.84)}$$

Therefore, $R + T = 1$.

In case of normal incident, we have

$$R = \left(\frac{n_1 - n_2}{n_1 + n_2} \right) \quad \text{and} \quad T = \frac{n_2}{n_1} \cdot \left(\frac{2n_1}{n_1 + n_2} \right)^2. \hfill \text{(18.85)}$$

(b) E in the plane of incidence.

The field vectors are shown in Fig. 18.6.

The boundary conditions (18.76) and (18.78) yield

$$E_{0I} \cos \theta_I - E_{0R} \cos \theta_R = E_{0T} \cos \theta_T$$

i.e., $\quad (E_{0I} - E_{0R}) \cos \theta_1 = E_{0T} \cos \theta_T$ $\hfill$ (18.86) and $k_I E_{0I} + k_1 E_{0R} = K_T E_{0T}$

or, $E_{0I} + E_{0R} = \dfrac{k_T}{k_I} E_{0T}.$ \hfill (18.87)

After solving Eqs. (18.86) and (18.87) we obtain

$$\frac{E_{0R}}{E_{01}} = \frac{\cos\theta_I - \frac{n_1}{n_2}\cos\theta_T}{\cos\theta_I + \left(\frac{n_1}{n_2}\right)\cos\theta_T} \hfill (18.87a)$$

$$= \frac{\cos\theta_I - \frac{\sin\theta_T}{\sin\theta_I}\cos\theta_T}{\cos\theta_I + \frac{\sin\theta_T}{\sin\theta_I}\cos\theta_T}$$

Fig. 18.6

$$= \frac{\sin\theta_I\cos\theta_I - \sin\theta_T\cos\theta_T}{\cos\theta_I\sin\theta_I + \sin\theta_T\cos\theta_T}$$

$$= \frac{\tan\theta_I - \tan\theta_T}{\tan\theta_I + \tan\theta_T}$$

$$= \frac{\tan(\theta_I - \theta_T)}{\tan(\theta_I + \theta_T)} \hfill (18.88)$$

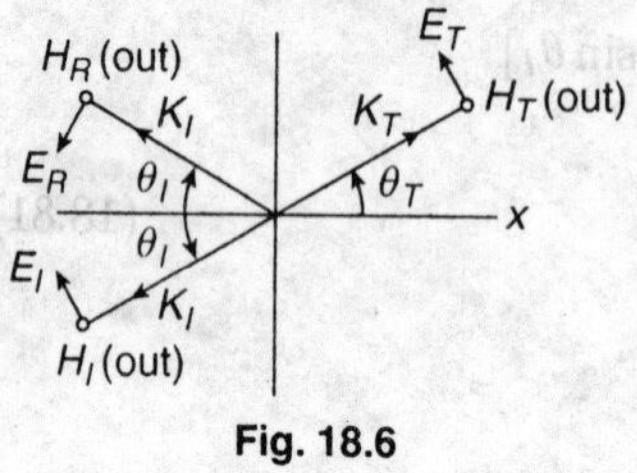

and $\dfrac{E_{0T}}{E_{0I}} = \dfrac{2\sin\theta_T\cos\theta_1}{\sin(\theta_I + \theta_T)\cos(\theta_I - \theta_T)}.$ \hfill (18.89)

Relations (18.81), (18.82), (18.87) and (18.88) are known as Fresnel's relations. Let us now consider the case when $n_1 = n_2$ (i.e., $\theta_1 = \theta_2$).

From Eq. (18.81) we find that if the angle of incidence lies between 0 and $\frac{\pi}{2}$, $\frac{E_{0R}}{E_{01}} \neq 0$. But when **E** is polarized in the plane of incidence Eq. (18.88) shows that $\frac{E_{0R}}{E_{0I}} = 0$ and so the reflection coefficient is equal to zero. In other words, we can write that if the wave is incident at an angle $\theta_I = \frac{\pi}{2} - \theta_T$, it passes through the interface without reflection. This angle is called *Brewster's angle*.

$\therefore$ $\theta_B = \dfrac{\pi}{2} - \theta_T.$

Using Snell's law of refraction one can write,

$$\frac{\sin\theta_B}{\sin\theta_T} = \frac{n_2}{n_1} \quad \text{or,} \quad \frac{\sin\theta_B}{\sin\left(\frac{\pi}{2} - \theta_B\right)} = \frac{n_2}{n_1}$$

i.e., $\tan\theta_B = \dfrac{n_2}{n_1}$

$\therefore$ $\theta_B = \tan^{-1}\left(\dfrac{n_2}{n_1}\right).$ \hfill (18.90)

If an unpolarized light wave is incident on the interface at an Brewster's angle, the component of E polarized normal to the plane of incidence will be reflected and so the reflected wave is plane polarized normal to the plane of incidence and for this the angle θ_B is also known as *polarizing angle*.

18.10   Total Internal Reflection

Suppose the wave is incident from a medium of higher refractive index on the surface of a medium of lower refractive index ($n_2 < n_1$).

$\therefore$ $\dfrac{\sin\theta_T}{\sin\theta_I} = \dfrac{n_1}{n_2}.$ \hfill (18.91)

Consider the case when $\theta_T = \frac{\pi}{2}$. The angle of incidence in this case is represented by θ_C and known as critical angle.

$$\therefore \quad \sin \theta_C = \frac{n_2}{n_1}. \tag{18.92}$$

So when the wave is incident at an angle which is equal to the critical angle of that medium, there will be only reflected wave.

Let us now represent the angle of transmission θ_T in terms of θ_I and θ_C.

We have $\sin \theta_T = \dfrac{n_1}{n_2} \sin \theta_I = \dfrac{\sin \theta_I}{\theta_C}$ [using Eq. (18.92)]

$$\therefore \quad \cos \theta_T = \sqrt{1 - \sin^2 \theta_T}$$

$$= \sqrt{1 - \frac{\sin^2 \theta_I}{\sin^2 \theta_C}}. \tag{18.93}$$

When $\theta_I > \theta_C$, $\cos \theta_T$ becomes an imaginary number. So we can write

$$\cos \theta_T = \sqrt{1 - \frac{\sin^2 \theta_I}{\sin^2 \theta_C}} = iQ.$$

$$\therefore \quad Q = \sqrt{\frac{\sin^2 \theta_I}{\sin^2 \theta_C} - 1}$$

From Eq. (18.80a),

$$\frac{E_{0R}}{E_{0I}} = \frac{\cos \theta_I - \frac{n_2}{n_1} \cos \theta_T}{\cos \theta_I + \frac{n_2}{n_1} \cos \theta_T} = \frac{\cos \theta_I - \frac{n_2}{n_1} iQ}{\cos \theta_I + \frac{n_2}{n_1} iQ}.$$

$$\therefore \quad \left| \frac{E_{0R}}{E_{0I}} \right|^2 = 1, \quad \text{i.e.,} \quad |E_{0R}| = |E_{0I}|.$$

Similarly, from Eq. (18.87a), we obtain

$$\left| \frac{E_{0R}}{E_{0I}} \right|^2 = 1$$

i.e., $|E_{0R}| = E_{0I}$. \hfill (18.94)

So the wave is totally reflected. This phenomenon is called *total internal reflection*.

Let us now calculate the average rate of flow of energy across the boundary.

The rate of flow of energy

$$= \langle \mathbf{N} \rangle \cdot \hat{n} = \frac{1}{2} Re(\mathbf{E}_T \times \mathbf{H}_T^*) \cdot \hat{n}$$

$$= \frac{1}{2} Re \left(\mathbf{E}_T \times \frac{\mathbf{K}_T \times \mathbf{E}_T^*}{\mu \omega} \right) \cdot \hat{n}$$

$$= \frac{1}{2\mu\omega} Re[(\mathbf{E}_T \cdot \mathbf{E}_T^*)\mathbf{K}_T - (\mathbf{E}_T \cdot \mathbf{K}_T)\mathbf{E}_T^*] \cdot \hat{n}$$

$$= \frac{1}{2\mu\omega} Re(\mathbf{E}_T \cdot \mathbf{E}_T^*)\mathbf{K}_T \cdot \hat{n} \quad [\because \ \mathbf{E}_T \perp \mathbf{K}_T]$$

$$= \frac{1}{2\mu\omega} Re|E_{0T}|^2 \mathbf{K}_T \cos \theta_T$$

$$= \frac{1}{2\mu\omega} Re \, iQ K_T |E_{0T}|^2. \tag{18.95}$$

The above expression is purely imaginary.

$\therefore \quad \langle N \rangle \cdot \hat{n} = 0.$

So we can conclude that if the wave is incident on the surface at an angle greater than the critical angle, the total energy is reflected and there will be no refracted wave.

18.11 Metallic Reflection

We have, for incident, reflected and transmitted waves :

$$\mathbf{E}_I = E_{0I} \exp\{i(K_I \cdot r - \omega t)\} \tag{18.96}$$

$$\mathbf{E}_R = E_{0R} \exp\{i(K_I \cdot r - \omega t)\}$$

$$\mathbf{E}_T = E_{0T} \exp\{i(K_T \cdot r - \omega t)\}$$

$$\left.\begin{aligned}
\mathbf{H}_I &= \frac{\mathbf{K}_I \times \mathbf{E}_I}{\omega \mu_1} \\[2mm]
\mathbf{H}_R &= \frac{\mathbf{K}_I \times \mathbf{E}_R}{\omega \mu_1} \\[2mm]
\mathbf{H}_T &= \frac{\mathbf{K}_T \times \mathbf{E}_T}{\omega \mu_2}
\end{aligned}\right\} \tag{18.97}$$

From Eq. (18.58) the propagation vector $\mathbf{K}_T$ of the conducting medium (medium 2) can be written as

$$\mathbf{K}_T^2 = \epsilon_2 \mu_2 \omega^2 \left[1 + \frac{i\sigma}{\epsilon_2 \omega}\right]. \tag{18.98}$$

The boundary conditions will satisfy the following equations.

$$E_{0I} - E_{0R} = E_{0T} \tag{18.99}$$

and $\qquad \mathbf{K}_I(E_{0I} + E_{0R}) = \mathbf{K}_T E_{0T}. \tag{18.100}$

From Eqs. (18.99) and (18.100), we get

$$\left.\begin{aligned}
E_{0R} &= \frac{\mathbf{K}_T - \mathbf{K}_I}{\mathbf{K}_T + \mathbf{K}_I} E_{0I} \\[2mm]
E_{0T} &= \frac{2\mathbf{K}_I}{\mathbf{K}_T + \mathbf{K}_I} E_{01}
\end{aligned}\right\} \tag{18.101}$$

Substituting the values of K_I and K_T in the above equations, we have

$$E_{0R} = \frac{\sqrt{\epsilon_e \mu_e \omega^2}\left(1 + \frac{i\sigma}{\epsilon_2 \omega}\right)^{\frac{1}{2}} - \omega(\epsilon_1 \mu_1)^{\frac{1}{2}}}{\sqrt{\epsilon_2 \mu_2 \omega^2}\left(1 + \frac{i\sigma}{\epsilon_2 \omega}\right)^{\frac{1}{2}} + \omega(\epsilon_1 \mu_1)^{\frac{1}{2}}} E_{0I} \tag{18.102}$$

and $\qquad E_{0T} = \dfrac{2\omega(\epsilon_1 \mu_1)^{\frac{1}{2}}}{\sqrt{\epsilon_2 \mu_2 \omega^2}\left(1 + \frac{i\sigma}{\epsilon_2 \omega}\right)^{\frac{1}{2}} + \omega(\epsilon_1 \mu_1)^{\frac{1}{2}}} E_{0I}. \tag{18.103}$

(i) In the case of a perfect conductor $\sigma = \infty$.

$\therefore \quad E_{0R} = E_{0I} \quad$ and $\quad E_{0T} = 0.$

Therefore, the wave is completely reflected.

(ii) In the case of a good conductor, $\dfrac{\sigma}{\epsilon_e \omega} \gg 1.$

Here $\quad K_T = \alpha + i\beta = (1+i)\sqrt{\dfrac{\omega\sigma\mu_2}{2}}$

$$= \frac{1+i}{\delta}, \qquad\qquad (18.104)$$

where δ is the skin depth.

Substituting the value of $\mathbf{K}_T$ in Eq. (18.102), we get

$$E_{0R} = \frac{\frac{1+i}{\delta} - \omega(\epsilon_1\mu_1)^{\frac{1}{2}}}{\frac{1+i}{\delta} + \omega(\epsilon_1\mu_1)^{\frac{1}{2}}} E_{0I}$$

$$= \frac{\left\{\frac{1}{\delta} - \omega(\epsilon_1\mu_1)^{\frac{1}{2}}\right\} + \frac{i}{\delta}}{\left\{\frac{1}{\delta} + \omega(\epsilon_1\mu_1)^{\frac{1}{2}}\right\} + \frac{i}{\delta}} E_{0I}. \qquad\qquad (18.105)$$

The reflection coefficient R is given by

$$R = \frac{|E_{0R}|^2}{|E_{0I}|^2} = \frac{\{1 - \omega(\epsilon_1\mu_1)^{\frac{1}{2}}\delta\}^2 + 1}{\{1 + \omega(\epsilon_1\mu_1)^{\frac{1}{2}}\delta\}^2 + 1}$$

$$\simeq 1 - 2\omega(\epsilon_1\mu_1)^{\frac{1}{2}}\delta.$$

$\left[\because \dfrac{\sigma}{\epsilon_2\omega} \gg 1,\ \omega(\epsilon_1\mu_1)^{\frac{1}{2}}\delta \ll 1,\ \text{so we neglect the higher order terms}\right]$

$$\therefore \qquad R = 1 - 2\sqrt{\frac{2\omega\epsilon_1\mu_1}{\sigma\mu_2}}. \qquad\qquad (18.106)$$

Assuming $\mu_1 = \mu_2$, we get

$$R = 1 - 2\sqrt{\frac{2\omega\epsilon_1}{\sigma}}.$$

The transmission coefficient, $T = 1 - R$

$$= 2\sqrt{\frac{2\omega\epsilon_1}{\sigma}}. \qquad\qquad (18.107)$$

Examples

1. The intensity of sunlight reaching the earth's surface is 2 calories per sq. cm per minute. Calculate the strength of the magnetic and electric fields of the sunlight.

Solution : Rate of flow of energy through unit area

$$= \frac{1}{2}[E \cdot D + B \cdot H] = \frac{1}{2}[\epsilon E^2 + \mu H^2]$$

$$= \frac{1}{2}\left[\epsilon E^2 + \frac{\epsilon}{\mu} \cdot \mu E^2\right] \qquad \left[\because \frac{H}{E} = \sqrt{\frac{\epsilon}{\mu}}\right]$$

$$= \epsilon E^2 \text{ (in SI unit)}$$

$$= \mu H^2 \text{ (in SI unit)}.$$

Now rate of flow of energy per unit time

$$= 2 \text{ cal/cm}^2/\text{min} = \frac{2 \times 4.2 \times 10^7}{60} \text{ ergs/cm}^2/\text{s}.$$

$$\therefore \quad \frac{2 \times 4.2 \times 10^7}{60} = \frac{c}{4\pi} \times E^2.$$

$$\therefore \quad E = \sqrt{\frac{4 \times 3.14}{3 \times 10^{10}} \times \frac{2 \times 4.2 \times 10^7}{60}} = 2.42 \times 10^{-2} \text{ e.s.u.}$$

Similarly, $H = 2.42 \times 10^{-2}$ e.m.u/cm.

2. The amount of solar energy received by the earth is about 2 cal/min/cm². What are the maximum values of the amplitudes of the electric and magnetic fields of radiation.

Solution : We have $E = \dfrac{E_0}{\sqrt{2}}$, where $E_0 = $ maximum value

$$\therefore \qquad E_0 = \sqrt{2}E = \sqrt{2} \times 2.42 \times 10^{-2} \text{ e.s.u./cm}$$

$$= 3.42 \times 10^{-2} \text{ e.s.u./cm.}$$

Similarly, $H_0 = 3.42 \times 10^{-2}$ e.m.u./cm.

3. If an alternating field $E = E_0 \cos \omega t$ is applied to a conductor, then prove that at any frequency below the optical frequency the displacement current is negligibly small compared to conduction current.

Solution : Given $E = E_0 \cos \omega t$ and according to Ohm's law, $\vec{J} = \sigma \vec{E}$.

So the conduction current, $|\vec{J}| = \sigma E_0 \cos \omega t$. \hfill (i)

But the displacement current, $\vec{J}_d = \dfrac{\delta \vec{D}}{\partial t} = \dfrac{\partial}{\partial t}(\epsilon \vec{E})$ $\quad [\because \vec{D} = \epsilon \vec{E}]$

$$\therefore \quad [\vec{J}_d] = \epsilon_r \cdot \epsilon_0 \frac{\partial}{\partial t}[E_0 \cos \omega t] = -\omega \epsilon_r \epsilon_0 E_0 \sin \omega t$$

$$= \omega \epsilon_r \epsilon_0 E_0 \cos\left(\omega t + \frac{\pi}{2}\right). \hfill \text{(ii)}$$

Dividing (ii) by (i), we get

$$\frac{|\vec{J}_d|}{|\vec{J}|} = \frac{\omega \epsilon_r \epsilon_0 E_0 \cos\left(\omega t + \frac{\pi}{2}\right)}{\sigma E_0 \cos \omega t} = \frac{\omega \epsilon_r \cdot \epsilon_0}{\sigma}.$$

In the case of a good conductor, $\epsilon_r = 1$ and $\sigma = 10^7$ ohms/metre; $\epsilon_0 = 9 \times 10^{-12}$

$$\therefore \quad \frac{|\vec{J}_d|}{|\vec{J}|} = \frac{2\pi f \times 9 \times 10^{-12}}{10^7} = f \times 10^{-17}.$$

Optical frequency, $f_{OP} = 10^{15}$ Hz.

$$\therefore \quad \frac{|\vec{J}_d|}{|\vec{J}|} = 10^{15} \times 10^{-17} = \frac{1}{100}.$$

So it is proved that **displacement current is significantly small compared to conduction current.**

4. Starting from the equation of continuity prove that the charge density of a conductor can follow the following equation $\frac{\sigma}{\epsilon} \cdot \rho + \frac{\delta \rho}{\partial t} = 0$.

Solution : From the equation of continuity, we get

$$\vec{\nabla} \cdot \vec{J} + \frac{\delta \rho}{\partial t} = 0 \quad \text{or,} \quad \text{div } \vec{J} + \frac{\delta \rho}{\partial t} = 0.$$

According to Ohm's law, $\vec{J} = \sigma\vec{E}$.

So, $\operatorname{div}(\sigma\vec{E}) + \dfrac{\delta\rho}{\partial t} = 0$ or, $\sigma(\operatorname{div} \vec{E}) + \dfrac{\delta\rho}{dt} = 0$

or, $\dfrac{\sigma}{\epsilon}(\operatorname{div} \epsilon\vec{E}) + \dfrac{\delta\rho}{t} = 0$

or, $\dfrac{\sigma}{\epsilon}(\operatorname{div} \vec{D}) + \dfrac{\delta\rho}{dt} = 0$ $(\because \vec{D} = \epsilon\vec{E})$

or, $\dfrac{\sigma}{\epsilon} \cdot \rho + \dfrac{\delta\rho}{dt} = 0$ $(\because \operatorname{div} \vec{D} = \rho)$. **(Proved)**.

5. If a capacitor is charged with steady current, show that the displacement current $I_d = C \cdot \dfrac{dV}{dt}$ and it is equal to the conduction current.

Solution : Displacement current $I_d = J_d \cdot \alpha$ (α = cross-sectional area)

i.e., $I_d = \alpha \cdot \dfrac{\delta D}{\partial t}$ $\left[\because J_d = \dfrac{\delta D}{\partial t} \right)$

$\qquad = \alpha \dfrac{\partial}{\partial t}(\epsilon E) = \epsilon \cdot \alpha \dfrac{\partial E}{\partial t}$

$\qquad = \dfrac{\epsilon \cdot \alpha}{d} \cdot \dfrac{\delta V}{\partial t}$ $\left[\because E = \dfrac{V}{d}; \ d = \text{distance between two plates} \right]$

But the capacitance of the capacitor, $C = \dfrac{\epsilon \cdot \alpha}{d}$.

$\therefore \quad I_d = C\dfrac{\delta V}{\partial t} = \dfrac{\partial}{\partial t}(C \cdot V) = \dfrac{\partial q}{\partial t} = I_c$ $[\because q = C \cdot V]$

i.e., **the displacement current (I_d) is the same as the conduction current**.

Questions

Essay-type

1. The Ampere's law in general is not in accordance with the conservation law of charge. Prove that how Maxwell with the help of the concept of displacement current solved this apparent discrepancy.

2. What do you mean by equation of continuity? Establish the equation and explain it.

3. In electric and magnetic field vector establish the equation of electromagnetic wave. Also establish the expression for velocity of the wave.

4. Write down the four Maxwell's equation related to electromagnetic wave and explain how these equations establish the laws of electrostatics, magnetostatics and electromagnetostatics.

5. Give a description of Hertz's experiment related to production and detection of electromagnetic waves.

6. Write down the Maxwell's field equations. Clearly explain their physical significance.

7. What is meant by displacement current density? Establish the four field equations of Maxwell.

8. Calculate the electrostatic and magnetostatic field energies.

9. Derive an expression for the Poynting's vector and explain its significance. Discuss what do you mean by Poynting's theorem.

10. Show that the electromagnetic waves travel through a medium with a velocity $v = \frac{1}{\sqrt{\mu\epsilon}}$.

11. Prove that the electromagnetic waves are transverse in nature and the electric and the magnetic intensity vectors are at right angles to one another and they are in the plane of the wave.

12. Describe with a suitable diagram the Hertz experiment of electromagnetic wave.

13. Calculate the total energy in a plane wave. What is meant by skin depth?

14. Obtain the laws of reflection and refraction of electromagnetic waves. Find expressions for them.

15. Find expressions for total internal reflection and metallic reflection of electromagnetic waves.

Short Answer-type

16. What is displacement current?

17. State Maxwell's equations related to electromagnetic waves. Give the symbols used and write down the units.   **[K.U. 2001]**

18. In a non conducting medium with no charge what will be the forms of the Maxwell's equations?   **[K.U. 2001]**

19. The displacement current flows through the gap between two plates of a capacitor when the charge of the capacitor

    (i) is increased   (ii) is reduced   (iii) has no change   (iv) becomes zero.

    Which one is correct?

20. Mention the difference between conduction current and displacement current.

21. If a capacitor is charged with steady current

    (i) $J_d = 0$ but $J \neq 0$ (ii) $J_d \neq 0$ but $J = 0$ (iii) $J_d > J$ (iv) $J_d = J$.

    Which one is correct?

22. An electric field $\vec{E}$ and magnetic field $\vec{B}$ is present. The fields are not mutually perpendicular.

       (i) It is not possible.

      (ii) No electromagnetic wave flows through that zone.

     (iii) Electromagnetic wave can flow through that zone.

     (iv) Electromagnetic wave must flow through that zone.

    Which one is correct?

23. Div $\vec{B} = 0$. Give an interpretation of this equation.

24. If c be the velocity of light in vacuum, then

    (i) $c = \dfrac{1}{\sqrt{\epsilon_0 \mu_0}}$ (ii) $c = \dfrac{1}{\epsilon_0 \mu_0}$ (iii) $c = \sqrt{\epsilon_0 \mu_0}$ (iv) $c = \sqrt{\dfrac{\epsilon_0}{\mu_0}}$.

    Which one is correct?

Numerical Problems

25. One kilowatt lamp is radiating energy uniformly. Determine the average intensity of electric field at a distance of 5 metres from it.

    [**Ans.** 0.345 volt/cm]

26. What is the maximum magnetic intensity in a plane radiowave in which the maximum intensity is 100 microvolts/metre?   [**Ans.** 2.7×10^{-4} amp/m]

27. Starting from Maxwell's equation $\vec{\nabla} \times \vec{E} = -\frac{\partial \vec{B}}{\partial t}$ and $\vec{\nabla} \times \vec{H} = \vec{J} + \frac{\partial \vec{D}}{\partial t}$, prove that div $\vec{B} = 0$ and div $\vec{D} = \rho$.

28. An alternating e.m.f., $E = E_0 \cos \omega t$ of frequency 10^{20} Hz is applied to a conductor. Prove that the displacement current in the conductor is much greater than the conduction current. The σ of the conductor is 10^3 ohm/m.

29. A parallel plate capacitor has its area of the plate $= A$, the distance between the plates $= d$. The capacitor is charged with current i. A plate of area $\frac{A}{2}$ is kept in parallel to the plates of the capacitor and within them. What will be the displacement current coming out from that imaginary surface? [**Ans.** $\frac{i}{2}$]

Chapter 19
Radiation, Scattering and Dispersion

19.1 Introduction

It is an experience to all that if a stone is thrown into a pond a disturbance is observed on the water surface, known as water waves. Further, if a horn is sounded, the sound waves are generated and as a result we listen the horn. In a similar way, we have electromagnetic waves which like the other waves have got the following two characters : (i) energy is propagated to distant points and (ii) the disturbance travels through the medium without any transference of the medium itself. The relation between the radiation fields and their sources can be obtained if the fields are expressed in terms of electromagnetic potentials. In this chapter the phenomena of radiation, scattering and dispersion of the electromagnetic waves have been critically discussed.

19.2 Retarded Potentials

We know that in a changing magnetic field, curl $\mathbf{E}$ is not zero. So electric field cannot be derived from a scalar potential. Again, div $\mathbf{B}$ vanishes under all conditions and, therefore, the magnetic field can be derived from a vector potential $\mathbf{A}$, where

$$\mathbf{B} = \vec{\nabla} \times \mathbf{A}. \tag{19.1}$$

If Eq. (19.1) is assumed to be valid, then the electric field $\mathbf{E}$ can be written as

$$\mathbf{E} = -\vec{\nabla}\phi - \frac{\partial A}{\partial t}. \tag{19.2}$$

Let us now define div $\mathbf{A}$ by Lorentz condition,

$$\vec{\nabla}\mathbf{A} + \mu\epsilon\frac{\partial \phi}{\partial t} + \mu\sigma\phi = 0. \tag{19.3}$$

To obtain the equations satisfied by the potentials, we introduce the Eqs. (19.1), (19.2) and (19.3) into Maxwell's 1st and 4th equations. We have the following symmetrical set of equations :

$$\vec{\nabla}^2 \mathbf{A} - \mu\epsilon\frac{\partial^2 \mathbf{A}}{\partial t^2} - \mu\sigma\frac{\partial \mathbf{A}}{\partial t} = -\mu j \tag{19.4}$$

$$\vec{\nabla}^2 \phi - \mu\epsilon\frac{\partial^2 \phi}{\partial t^2} - \mu\sigma\frac{\partial \phi}{\partial t} = -\frac{\rho}{\epsilon}. \tag{19.5}$$

The Eqs. (19.4) and (19.5) are known as homogeneous wave equations. Their solutions are expressible in terms of integrals over the charge and current distribution.

In static case Eq. (19.5) reduces to Poisson's equation,

$$\vec{\nabla}^2 \phi = -\frac{\rho}{\epsilon_0}. \tag{19.6}$$

The solution of the above equation is of the form,

$$\phi(x_\alpha) = \frac{1}{4\pi\epsilon_0} \int \frac{\rho(x'_\alpha)}{r(x_\alpha, x'_\alpha)} dv'. \tag{19.7}$$

In Fig. 19.1, dv' is a small volume element. The potentials are to be computed at the point P. This is done by integrating ρ throughout the volume by assuming ρ as a function of x'_α.

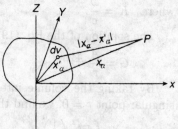

Fig. 19.1

Let us now modify the solution (19.7) in case of time dependent term in Eq. (19.5).

The general equation satisfied by both $\mathbf{A}$ and ϕ will be

$$\Box\psi(x_\alpha, t) = -g(x_\alpha, t), \tag{19.8}$$

where the operator $\Box$ known as the D' Alembertion operator and defined by

$$\Box = \vec{\nabla}^2 - \mu\epsilon\frac{\partial^2}{\partial t^2}. \tag{19.9}$$

Let us assume that the function $g(x_\alpha, t)$ can be analysed by Fourier integral of the form

$$g(x_\alpha, t) = \int_{-\infty}^{\infty} g_\omega(x_\alpha)e^{-i\omega t}d\omega. \tag{19.10}$$

$$\therefore \quad g_\omega(x_\alpha) = \frac{1}{2\pi}\int_{-\infty}^{\infty} g(x_\alpha, t)e^{i\omega t}dt. \tag{19.11}$$

In the similar way the general potential $\psi(x_\alpha, t)$ can be written in term of Fourier components,

$$\psi(x_\alpha, t) = \int_{-\infty}^{\infty} \psi\omega(x_\alpha, t)e^{-i\omega t}d\omega \tag{19.12}$$

$$\therefore \quad \psi_\omega(x_\alpha) = \frac{1}{2\pi}\int_{-\infty}^{\infty} \phi(x_\alpha, t)e^{i\omega t}dt. \tag{19.13}$$

After substituting Eqs. (19.10) and (19.12) in Eq. (19.8) we find that $\psi_\omega(x_\alpha)$ will satisfy the following differential equation,

$$\vec{\nabla}^2 \psi_\omega + \frac{\omega^2}{c^2}\psi_\omega = -g_\omega. \tag{19.14}$$

We may try to compute the solution of the above equation by the superposition of unit point solutions corresponding to a source at the point x'_α given by $g_\omega(x_\alpha) = \delta(x_\alpha - x'_\alpha)$, where $\delta(x_\alpha - x'_\alpha)$ is the Dirac δ function. Therefore, each unit source potential will satisfy the following equation :

$$\vec{\nabla}^2 G(x_\alpha, x'_\alpha) + \frac{\omega^2}{c^2}G(x_\alpha, x'_\alpha) = -\delta(x_\alpha - x'_\alpha), \tag{19.15}$$

where G is a function of both x_α and x'_α. The solution corresponding to the frequency ω of the source is given by the superposition of

$$\psi_\omega(x_\alpha) = \int g_\omega(x'_\alpha)G(x_\alpha, x'_\alpha)dv'. \tag{19.16}$$

The solution of Eq. (19.16) will be spherically symmetric in $r(= x_\alpha \sim x_\alpha')$ and so at all points except $r = 0$, the solution will be similar to the solution of the following equation :

$$\frac{1}{r}\frac{d^2(rG)}{dr^2} + K^2G = 0, \tag{19.17}$$

where $K = \dfrac{\omega}{c}$.

The solution of the Eq. (19.17) will be of the form,

$$G = \frac{A}{r}e^{\pm ikr}. \tag{19.18}$$

By taking the volume integral of Eq. (19.15) over the neighbourhood of the singular point $r = 0$, we find that G behaves as $\frac{A}{r}$. Again, we know that

$$\int \vec{\nabla}^2\left(\frac{1}{r}\right)dv' = -4\pi, \tag{19.19}$$

which leads to the result,

$$-4\pi A = -1 \quad \text{i.e.,} \quad A = \frac{1}{4\pi}.$$

Therefore, $G = \dfrac{1}{4\pi r}e^{\pm ikr}.$ \tag{19.20}

Substituting the solution of G in Eq. (19.16), we have

$$\psi_\omega(x_\alpha) = \frac{1}{4\pi}\int \frac{g_\omega(x_\alpha')}{r(x_\alpha, x_\alpha')}e^{\pm ikr(x_\alpha, x_\alpha')}dv'. \tag{19.21}$$

Using Eqs. (19.21) and (19.12) we can write,

$$\psi(x_\alpha, t) = \frac{1}{4\pi}\int\int \frac{g_\omega(x_\alpha')e^{-i(\omega t \pm kr)}}{r(x_\alpha, x_\alpha')}d\omega dv'. \tag{19.22}$$

We may now introduce a new time,

$$t'(x_\alpha, x_\alpha') = t \pm \frac{r}{c} = t \pm \frac{Kr}{\omega},$$

which corresponds to the shifting of the origin of time by an amount equal to the time taken by the charges to be propagated from the point x_α' to the point P.

$$\therefore \quad \psi(x_\alpha, t) = \frac{1}{4\pi}\int \frac{g(x_\alpha', t')}{r(x_\alpha, x_\alpha')}dv'. \tag{19.23}$$

Mathematically, both plus and minus signs of the relation $t' = t \pm \frac{r}{c}$ will be valid. But physically the solution with minus sign will have some significance. Here we consider the effect at x_α with sources at x_α' and hence the minus sign will correspond to the cause preceding the effect. The solution (19.23) with minus sign is known as *retarded potential solution*.

Now we denote by the symbol [ ] that the variables within the bracket are to be evaluated at the retarded time t'. The solution of Eqs. (19.4) and (19.5) can be written as

$$A(x_\alpha, t) = \frac{\mu_0}{4\pi}\int \frac{[j(x_\alpha')]}{r(x_\alpha, x_\alpha')}dv' \tag{19.24}$$

and $\phi(x_\alpha, t) = \dfrac{1}{4\pi\epsilon_0}\displaystyle\int \frac{[\rho(x_\alpha')]}{r(x_\alpha, x_\alpha')}dv'.$ \tag{19.25}

These potentials (19.24) and (19.25) are called *retarded potentials*.

19.3 The Hertz Potential

We know that charges and currents cannot be specified independently. So for the calculation of radiation fields it is advantageous to express charges and currents by a single function which is chosen in such a way that the equation of continuity must be satisfied. In the similar radiation field can be represented by a single potential so that Lorentz condition is satisfied.

The current and charge densities are derived from a single vector $P(x'_\alpha, t)$, known as *polarization vector* by the relation,

$$\vec{\rho} = -\vec{\nabla} \cdot \mathbf{P} \tag{19.26}$$

$$\mathbf{j} = \frac{\partial \mathbf{P}}{\partial t}. \tag{19.27}$$

A vector which combines the vector potential A and scalar potential ϕ and also satisfies the Lorentz condition is called *Hertz vector* (sometimes it is called *Hertz potential*).

$$\mathbf{A} = \frac{1}{c^2} \frac{\partial \mathbf{Z}}{\partial t} \quad \text{and} \quad \phi = -\vec{\nabla} \mathbf{Z}. \tag{19.28}$$

Hertz vector $\mathbf{Z}$ obeys the inhomogeneous wave equation with $\mathbf{P}$ as the source.

$$\vec{\nabla}^2 \mathbf{Z} - \frac{1}{c^2} \frac{\partial^2 \mathbf{Z}}{\partial t^2} = -\frac{\mathbf{P}}{\epsilon_0}. \tag{19.29}$$

The retarded potential solution of the above equation will be given by

$$\mathbf{Z}(x_\alpha) = \frac{1}{4\pi\epsilon_0} \int \frac{[\mathbf{P}(x'_\alpha)]}{r(x_\alpha x'_\alpha)} dv'. \tag{19.30}$$

The Fourier components are

$$\mathbf{Z}_\omega = \frac{1}{4\pi\epsilon_0} \int \frac{\mathbf{P}_\omega(x'_\alpha) e^{ikr}}{r(x_\alpha x'_\alpha)} dv'. \tag{19.31}$$

Let us now assume

$$\mathbf{C} = \vec{\nabla} \times \mathbf{Z}, \tag{19.32}$$

then the magnetic field is given by

$$\mathbf{B} = \frac{1}{c^2} \frac{\partial \mathbf{C}}{\partial t} \tag{19.33}$$

and the electric field by

$$\mathbf{E} = \vec{\nabla} \times \mathbf{C}. \tag{19.34}$$

Eq. (19.34) will be true only outside the source where $\vec{\nabla} \cdot \mathbf{E} = 0$.

19.4 Computation of Radiation Fields

Here we assume that the fields are observed at distances large compared with the extent of the source distribution and the extent of source is negligible compared with the radiation of the outgoing wave. In other words, we can say that the distance to the observer is large compared to the dimensions of the source.

Under the above assumption, the function $\frac{e^{ikr}}{r}$ is slowly varying function relative to the variation of P. So it is expressed in power series in terms of the distance $\xi = |\vec{\xi}|$ of the source point from the origin of the charge distribution.

$$\therefore \quad \frac{e^{ikr}}{r} = ik \sum_{0}^{\infty} (2n+1) P_n(\cos\Theta) j_n(k\xi) h_n(kR),$$ (19.35)

where R is the distance of the observation point from the origin.

Equation (19.35) is valid for $R > \xi$.

Here $P_n(\cos\Theta)$ is the Legendre Polynomial of order n, Θ is the angle between ξ and R, $j_n(k\xi)$ and $h_n(kR)$ are the spherical Bessel and Hankel functions. $P_n(\cos\Theta)$ can be expressed in terms of the angular co-ordinates of the source (θ', ϕ') and of the field point (θ, ϕ).

$$P_n(\cos\Theta) = \sum_{m=-n}^{n} (-1)^m P_n^m(\cos\theta) P_n^{-m}(\cos\theta') e^{im(\phi-\phi')}.$$ (19.36)

The Hertz potential becomes

$$\mathbf{Z} = \frac{ike^{-ikr}}{4\pi\epsilon_0} \sum_n \sum_m (2n+1)(-1)^m P_n^m(\cos\theta) h_n(kR) e^{im\phi'}$$

$$\times \int P(\xi) j_n(k\xi) P_n^{-m}(\cos\theta') e^{-im\phi} dv'.$$ (19.37)

Now for $k\xi \ll 1$,

$$j_n(k\xi) \simeq \frac{2^n n!}{(2n+1)!} (k\xi)^n$$ (19.38)

and for $kR \gg 1$,

$$h_n(kR) \cdot (-i)^{n+1} \frac{e^{ikR}}{kR}.$$ (19.39)

Therefore, for the wavelength, large compared with the dimension of the source, the radiation fields corresponding to the nth term in the expansion may be calculated from

$$Z_\omega^{(n)} = (-i)^n \frac{e^{ikR}}{4\pi\epsilon_0 R} \cdot \frac{2^n n!}{(2n)!} \int (k\xi)^n \mathbf{P}_\omega P_n(\cos\Theta) dv'.$$ (19.40)

For $n = 0$, $\int \mathbf{p}_\omega dv' = \mathbf{p}_1$, gives the electric dipole moment of the charge distribution. Hence the corresponding Hertz potential will be as follows :

$$\mathbf{Z}_\omega(x_\alpha) = \frac{e^{ikR}}{4\pi\epsilon_0 R} \int \mathbf{p}_\omega(x'_\alpha) dv'$$

$$= \frac{e^{ikR}}{4\pi\epsilon_0 R} \mathbf{p}_1$$ (19.41)

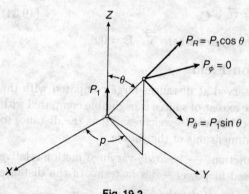

Fig. 19.2

and the direction of $\mathbf{p}_1$ is taken to be parallel to the polar axis (Fig. 19.2). From Fig. 19.1 we can write the components of the polarization vector as

$$Z_R = \frac{p_1 \cos\theta e^{ikR}}{4\pi\epsilon_0 R}$$ (19.42)

$$Z_\theta = -\frac{p_1 \sin\theta e^{ikR}}{4\pi\epsilon_0 R}$$ (19.43)

$$Z_\phi = 0.$$ (19.44)

Now $\mathbf{C} = \vec{\nabla} \times \mathbf{Z}.$

If curl of Z is expressed in polar co-ordinates we find that the only component of C is C_ϕ.

$$C_\phi = \frac{p_1 \sin\theta}{4\pi\epsilon_0 R}\left(\frac{1}{R} - ik\right)e^{ikR}. \tag{19.45}$$

Therefore, the magnetic field will be

$$H_\phi = -\frac{i\omega}{4\pi}p_1 \sin\theta \left(\frac{1}{R^2} - \frac{ik}{R}\right)e^{ikR} \tag{19.46}$$

and the components of the electric field in a similar way can be written as

$$E_R = \frac{1}{R\sin\theta}\frac{\partial}{\partial\theta}(\sin\theta C_\phi) = \frac{p_1 \cos\theta}{2\pi\epsilon_0 R^2}\left(\frac{1}{R} - ik\right)e^{ikR}$$

$$E_\theta = -\frac{1}{R}\frac{\partial}{\partial R}(RC_\phi) = \frac{p_1 \sin\theta}{4\pi\epsilon_0 R}\left(\frac{1}{R^2} - \frac{ik}{R} - K^2\right)\epsilon^{ikR}. \tag{19.47}$$

The first and the second term of Eq. (19.46) will represent respectively the induction field and the radiation field. Eq. (19.47) has three terms which represent static dipole field, transition field and radiation field respectively.

Hence the radiation fields alone will be

$$H_\phi = -\frac{\omega k p_1 \sin\theta e^{ikR}}{4\pi R} \tag{19.48}$$

$$E_\theta = -\frac{k^2 p_1 \sin\theta e^{ikR}}{4\pi\epsilon_0 R}. \tag{19.49}$$

The fields are mutually perpendicular. For the radiation zone, $E_r = 0$. So the field distribution will be spherical with the magnetic field as the circles of latitude and the electric field as the circles of longitude. The field will be maximum at the equator and minimum at the poles. Electric field lines produced by an oscillating dipole are shown in the Fig. 19.3. This field is periodic radially, with radial spacing equal to the wavelength λ.

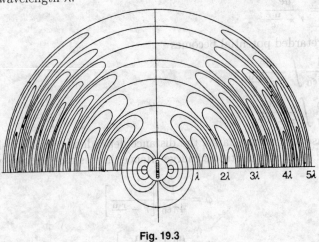

Fig. 19.3

19.5 Lienard-Wiechert Potentials

Here we use the retarded potentials to compute the radiation from a single charged particle, say, an electron. The calculation of the potentials will depend upon the position and the velocity of the charge at the retarded time $t' = t - \frac{r}{c}$ in Fig. 19.4.

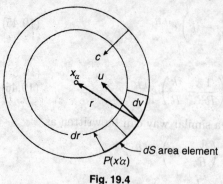

Now we do not know how this charge is distributed geometrically within the electron. If we assume that the charge has zero physical extent, many difficulties arise. In our calculation we shall assume that the electron has a finite radius and we shall consider only those properties which are independent of the magnitude of the radius.

Fig. 19.4

Now suppose that the velocity of the electron is comparable to c. Here we assume that (i) the total charge of the electron is e and (ii) within an unspecified but small volume, all parts of the electronic charge moves with a velocity **u**. Let $r(x_\alpha, x'_\alpha)$ be the retarded radius vector (Fig. 19.4). Now if the electron is at rest, the amount of charge that the sphere will cross during the time dt will be $[\rho]dSdr$ where $[\rho]$ is the retarded charge density. In other words, we can say that a quantity of charge which is less than $[\rho]dSdr$ by an amount $[\rho]dS\frac{u \cdot r}{r}dt$ will be crossed by the sphere.

Therefore, the observed amount of charge,

$$de = [\rho]dSdr - [\rho]\frac{u \cdot r}{r}dSdt$$

$$= [\rho]dv' - [\rho]\frac{\mathbf{u} \cdot \mathbf{r}}{cr}dv' \quad [\because \ dt = \frac{dr}{c} \text{ and } dSdr = dv']$$

$$= [\rho]dv'\left\{1 - \frac{\mathbf{u} \cdot \mathbf{R}}{cr}\right\}$$

$$= \frac{[\rho]dv'}{r}\left\{r - \frac{\mathbf{u} \cdot \mathbf{r}}{c}\right\}.$$

$$\therefore \quad \frac{[\rho]dv'}{r} = \frac{de}{r - \frac{\mathbf{u} \cdot \mathbf{r}}{c}}.$$

Hence, the retarded potential becomes

$$\phi = \frac{1}{4\pi\epsilon_0}\int \frac{de}{r - \frac{\mathbf{r} \cdot \mathbf{u}}{c}} \tag{19.50}$$

$$A = \frac{\mu_0}{4\pi}\int \frac{ude}{r - \frac{\mathbf{r} \cdot \mathbf{u}}{c}}. \tag{19.51}$$

In the case of a point charge, the distance dependent terms are slowly varying and $\int de = e$, the total electron's charge. Hence, in this case the potentials may be written as

$$\phi = \frac{1}{4\pi\epsilon_0}\left[\frac{e}{r - \frac{\mathbf{r} \cdot \mathbf{u}}{c}}\right] \tag{19.52}$$

$$A = \frac{\mu_0}{4\pi}\left[\frac{e\mathbf{u}}{r - \frac{\mathbf{r} \cdot \mathbf{u}}{c}}\right]. \tag{19.53}$$

Eqs. (19.52) and (19.53) are known as the *Lienard-Wiechert potentials of a single electron*. These expressions are dependent on the velocity of the electron but independent of the extent of the charge.

19.6 Fields of a Charge in Uniform Motion

The fields of a moving charge can be found from the relations,

$$\mathbf{E} = -\vec{\nabla}\phi - \frac{\partial \mathbf{A}}{\partial t}, \tag{19.54}$$

$$\mathbf{B} = \vec{\nabla} \times \mathbf{A}. \tag{19.55}$$

From Lienard-Wiechert potentials we can only evaluate the fields in terms of the retarded positions and velocities of the charge, because the relation between the present position and retarded position is not in general known to us. In case of uniform motion the potentials and fields can be computed in terms of the present position of the charge at time t.

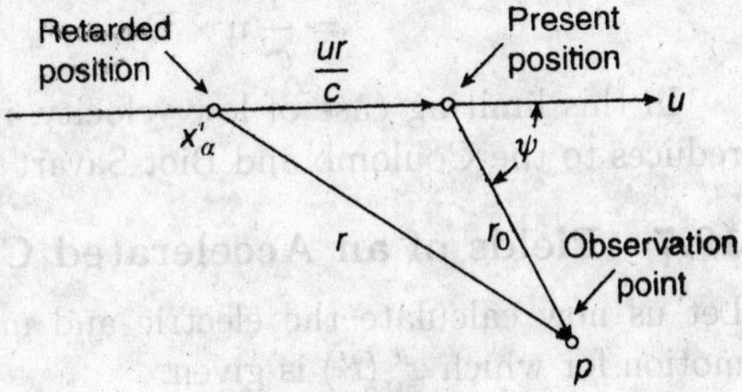

Fig. 19.5

Suppose an electron is moving with a uniform velocity in the x-direction (Fig. 19.5). Let us now calculate the Lienard-Wiechert denominator, $d = r - \frac{\mathbf{r} \cdot \mathbf{u}}{c}$ in terms of the present position of the electron. By the geometry of the figure we can write

$$\mathbf{r_0} \times \mathbf{u} = \mathbf{r} \times \mathbf{u}$$

and $$d^2 = r_0^2 - \left(\frac{\mathbf{r_0} \times \mathbf{u}}{c}\right)^2. \tag{19.56}$$

$$\therefore \quad d = \sqrt{x_0^2 + y_0^2 + z_0^2 - \frac{u^2}{c^2}(y_0^2 + z_0^2)}$$

$$= \sqrt{x_0^2 + \left(1 - \frac{u^2}{c^2}\right)(y_0^2 + z_0^2)} \tag{19.57}$$

$$= r_0 \sqrt{1 - \frac{u^2}{c^2}\sin^2\psi}. \tag{19.58}$$

Eqs. (19.57) and (19.58) represent the Lienard-Wiechert denominator in terms of the present position co-ordinate and the angle ψ between u and r_0.

Now the time derivative may be written in terms of the spatial derivative, i.e.,

$$\frac{\partial}{\partial t} = -u\frac{\partial}{\partial x}. \tag{19.59}$$

Using Eqs. (19.54), (15.58) and (15.59), we get the components of the electric field as

$$E_x = \frac{ex_0}{4\pi\epsilon_0 d^3}\left(1 - \frac{u^2}{c^2}\right) \tag{19.60}$$

$$E_y = \frac{ey_0}{4\pi\epsilon_0 d^3}\left(1 - \frac{u^2}{c^2}\right) \tag{19.61}$$

$$E_z = \frac{ez_0}{4\pi\epsilon_0 d^3}\left(1 - \frac{u^2}{c^2}\right). \tag{19.62}$$

Vectorially the electric field can be written as

$$E = \frac{e r_0 \left(1 - \frac{u^2}{c^2}\right)}{4\pi\epsilon_0 d^3}.$$ (19.63)

Similarly, the magnetic field can be written as

$$\mathbf{B} = \vec{\nabla} \times \mathbf{A} = \frac{\mu_0 e}{4\pi} \frac{u \times r_0}{d^3} \left(1 - \frac{u^2}{c^2}\right)$$

$$= \frac{1}{c^2} \mathbf{u} \times \mathbf{E}.$$ (19.64)

In this limiting case of low velocity, i.e., $u \to 0$, field Eqs. (19.63) and (19.64) reduces to the Coulomb and Biot-Savart fields respectively.

19.7 Fields of an Accelerated Charge

Let us now calculate the electric and magnetic fields of a charge e in arbitrary motion for which $x'_\alpha(t')$ is given.

The Lienard-Wiechert potentials are given by

$$\phi(x_\alpha, t) = \frac{e}{4\pi\epsilon_0 d}$$ (19.65)

and $\quad A(x_\alpha, t) = \frac{e}{4\pi\epsilon_0 c^2} \cdot \frac{\mathbf{u}}{d},$ (19.66)

where $d = r - \frac{\mathbf{u} \cdot \mathbf{r}}{c}$ is a function of both retarded source point and the field point co-ordinates. The relation between field and source point variables are

$$r(x_\alpha, x'_\alpha) = \left[\sum (x_\alpha - x'_\alpha)^2\right]^{1/2}$$

$$= c(t - t').$$ (19.67)

Now only the time variation with respect to t' is given, we must transform partial derivatives $\frac{\partial}{\partial t}\big|_{x_\alpha}$ and $\vec{\nabla}\big|_t$ into $\frac{\partial}{\partial t'}\big|_{x_\alpha}$ in order to calculate the fields.

Now $\quad \dfrac{\partial r}{\partial t'}\bigg|_{x_\alpha} = -\dfrac{\mathbf{r} \cdot \mathbf{u}}{r}.$ (19.68)

Therefore, from Eq. (19.67) one can write,

$$\frac{\partial r}{\partial t} = c\left(1 - \frac{\partial t'}{\partial t}\right) = \frac{\partial r}{\partial t'} \cdot \frac{\partial t'}{\partial t} = -\frac{\mathbf{r} \cdot \mathbf{u}}{r} \cdot \frac{\partial t'}{\partial t}$$

or, $\quad 1 - \dfrac{\partial t'}{\partial t} = -\dfrac{\mathbf{r} \cdot \mathbf{u}}{cr} \dfrac{\partial t'}{\partial t}$

or, $\quad \dfrac{\partial t'}{\partial t} = \dfrac{1}{1 - \frac{\mathbf{r} \cdot \mathbf{u}}{cr}} = \dfrac{r}{d}.$ (19.69)

$\therefore \quad \dfrac{\partial}{\partial t} = \dfrac{r}{d} \dfrac{\partial}{\partial t'},$ (19.70)

which will be the desired transformation.

Similarly, for the operator. $\vec{\nabla}$ we can write,

$$\nabla r = -c\nabla t' = \nabla_1 r + \frac{\partial r}{\partial t'}\nabla t'$$

$$= \frac{\mathbf{r}}{r} - \frac{\mathbf{r} \cdot \mathbf{u}}{r}\nabla t',$$ (19.71)

where ∇_1 represents the differentiation with respect to x_α at constant retarded time t'.

Now $\quad -c\nabla t' = \dfrac{\mathbf{r}}{t} - \dfrac{\mathbf{r}\cdot\mathbf{u}}{r}\nabla t'$ or, $\quad -c\nabla t'\left(1 - \dfrac{\mathbf{r}\cdot\mathbf{u}}{cr}\right) = \dfrac{\mathbf{r}}{r}$

or, $\quad \nabla t' = -\dfrac{\mathbf{r}}{cd}.$ $\hspace{6cm}$ (19.72)

Therefore, the operator ∇ can be written as

$$\nabla = \nabla_1 - \frac{\mathbf{r}}{cd}\frac{\partial}{\partial t'}, \hspace{5cm} (19.73)$$

which will be the required transformation of the operator $\vec{\nabla}$.

Now the fields can be computed from the relation,

$$\mathbf{E} = -\vec{\nabla}\phi - \frac{\partial \mathbf{A}}{\partial t} \hspace{5cm} (19.74)$$

and $\quad B = \vec{\nabla} \times A.$ $\hspace{6cm}$ (19.75)

Using Eqs. (19.65), (19.66), (19.70), (19.73) and (19.74), we have

$$\frac{4\pi\epsilon_0}{e}\mathbf{E} = \frac{1}{d^2}\vec{\nabla}d - \frac{\partial}{\partial t}\frac{\mathbf{u}}{dc^2} = \frac{1}{d^2}\vec{\nabla}_1 - \frac{r}{cd^3}\frac{\partial d}{\partial t'} - \frac{r}{d^2c^2}\mathbf{u} + \frac{ru}{c^2S^2}\frac{\partial s}{\partial t'}.$$

Now, $\nabla_1 S = \dfrac{\mathbf{r}}{r} - \dfrac{\mathbf{u}}{c}.$

$\therefore \quad \dfrac{4\pi\epsilon_0}{e}\mathbf{E} = \dfrac{1}{d^3}\left(\mathbf{r} - \dfrac{r\mathbf{u}}{c}\right)\left(1 - \dfrac{u^2}{c^2}\right) + \dfrac{1}{c^2S^3}\left\{\mathbf{r}\times\left[\left(\mathbf{r} - \dfrac{r\mathbf{u}}{c}\right)\times\mathbf{u}\right]\right\}.$ $\quad$ (19.76)

Similarly, we get

$$\frac{4\pi\epsilon_0 c^2}{e}\mathbf{B} = \frac{\mathbf{u}\cdot\mathbf{r}}{d^3}\left(1 - \frac{u^2}{c^2}\right) + \frac{1}{cS^3}\frac{\mathbf{r}}{r}\times\left\{\mathbf{r}\times\left[\left(\mathbf{r} - \frac{r\mathbf{u}}{c}\right)\times\mathbf{u}\right]\right\}. \quad (19.77)$$

Comparing Eqs. (19.76) and (19.77), we get

$$\mathbf{B} = \frac{\mathbf{r}\times\mathbf{E}}{rc}. \hspace{5cm} (19.78)$$

Hence, the magnetic field is always perpendicular to **E** and to the retarded radius vector **r**.

19.8   Scattering of Radiation

Suppose an electromagnetic wave is incident on charged particles. The energy will be absorbed by the particles and then re-emitted into space. This process is known as *scattering of the incident radiation by the charged particles*.

Let a plane monochromatic linearly polarized wave is incident on a charged particle having a charge q. The wave will be

$$E = E_0 \exp[i(k_0 r - \omega_0 t)] \hspace{4cm} (19.79)$$

and the charged particle will experience a force due to the electric field,

$$\mathbf{F} = q\mathbf{E}. \hspace{5cm} (19.80)$$

Here we assume that the velocity acquired by the charged particle $v \ll c$, so that the treatment will be a non-relativistic one and we neglect the second term of the Lorentz force,

$$\mathbf{F} = q\mathbf{E} + q\mathbf{V} \times \mathbf{B}. \hspace{4cm} (19.81)$$

Now equation of motion of the particle

$$F = m\ddot{r} = qE = qE_0 \exp[i(k_0 r - \omega_0 t)]. \tag{19.82}$$

We know that the radiation fields in terms of dipole moment will be

$$\mathbf{p}(t) = q\mathbf{r}(t) \tag{19.83}$$

$$\ddot{\mathbf{p}}(t) = q\ddot{\mathbf{r}}(t)$$

$$= q \cdot \frac{q}{m} E. \tag{19.84}$$

Again, the time average of the power radiated per unit solid angle will be

$$\left\langle \frac{d\omega}{d\Omega} \right\rangle = \frac{q^2 (\ddot{\mathbf{r}})^2}{16\pi^2 \epsilon_0 c^3} \sin^2 \theta = \frac{\langle \ddot{p} \rangle^2}{16\pi^2 \epsilon_0 c^3}$$

$$= \frac{q^4 E_0^2 \sin^2 \theta}{16\pi^2 m^2 \epsilon_0 c^3}, \text{ using Eq. (19.84).} \tag{19.85}$$

Differential scattering cross-section is defined as

$$\frac{d\sigma}{d\Omega} = \frac{\text{energy scattered per unit solid angle per unit time}}{\text{energy incident per unit area per unit time}}$$

$$\therefore \quad \frac{d\sigma}{d\Omega} = \frac{\left\langle \frac{d\omega}{d\Omega} \right\rangle}{\langle \text{incident flux} \rangle} = \frac{q^4 E_0^2 \sin^2 \theta / (16\pi^2 m^2 \epsilon_0 c^3)}{\sqrt{\frac{t_0}{\mu_0}} E_0^2}$$

$$= \left(\frac{q^2}{4\pi\epsilon_0 mc^2} \right)^2 = \sin^2 \theta, \tag{19.86}$$

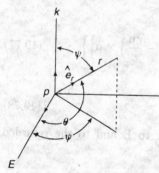

Fig. 19.6

where θ is the angle between $\mathbf{p}$ and the direction of outgoing radiation (Fig. 19.6).

Now if the incident radiation is unpolarized, then we take average overall possible azimuthal orientations of $\mathbf{E}$.

From Fig. 19.6 we see that

$$\cos \theta = \cos \psi \sin \phi.$$

$$\therefore \quad \sin^2 \theta = 1 - \cos^2 \psi \sin^2 \psi.$$

$$\therefore \quad \langle \sin^2 \theta \rangle = 1 - \langle \cos^2 \psi \rangle \sin^2 \phi$$

$$= 1 - \frac{1}{2} \sin^2 \phi = \frac{1}{2} (1 + \cos^2 \phi).$$

$$\therefore \quad \left\langle \frac{d\sigma}{d\Omega} \right\rangle_{\text{unpolarized}} = \left(\frac{q^2}{4\pi\epsilon_0 mc^2} \right) \langle \sin^2 \theta \rangle$$

$$= \left(\frac{q^2}{4\pi\epsilon_0 mc^2} \right)^2 \frac{1 + \cos^2 \phi}{2}. \tag{19.87}$$

The angle ϕ is called the angle of scattering because it is the angle between the directions of the incident radiation and the scattered radiation.

The total cross-section,

$$\langle \sigma \rangle_{\text{unpolarized}} = \int \frac{d\sigma}{d\Omega} \cdot d\Omega = \left(\frac{q^2}{4\pi\epsilon_0 mc^2} \right)^2 \int \frac{1 + \cos^2 \phi}{2} \sin \phi d\phi d\psi$$

$$= \frac{8\pi}{3} \left(\frac{q^2}{4\pi\epsilon_0 mc^2} \right)^2. \tag{19.88}$$

Scattering of unpolarized EMW by charged particle is known as *Thomson scattering*.

In the case of an electron, $q = e$.

$$\langle \sigma \rangle = \frac{8\pi}{3} \left(\frac{e^2}{4\pi\epsilon_0 mc^2} \right)^2$$

$$= \frac{8\pi}{3} r_0^2, \qquad \qquad \qquad (19.89)$$

where $r_0 = \dfrac{e^2}{4\pi\epsilon_0 mc^2}$ is the classical electron radius.

For scattering by free electron Thomson scattering cross-section will be

$$\sigma = 0.66 \times 10^{-28} m^2.$$

19.9   Radiation Damping

The effect of electromagnetic radiation on the motion of the charged particle is known as *radiation damping*.

The Newton's equation of motion for a particle having mass m and charge e under an external force F_e is given by

$$m\dot{\mathbf{V}} = \mathbf{F}_e \qquad \qquad \qquad (19.90)$$

In the radiation field the particle will be accelerated. We know that an accelerated particle emits radiation. So we must take into account the effect of this radiation on the particle. We have modified Eq. (19.90) by adding a reaction force F_r with F_e.

$$\therefore \quad m\dot{\mathbf{V}} = \mathbf{F}_e + \mathbf{F}_r. \qquad \qquad \qquad (19.91)$$

We know that the energy radiated in unit time by a moving charge e is

$$W = \frac{e^2 (\dot{V})^2}{6\pi\epsilon_0 c^3}. \qquad \qquad \qquad (19.92)$$

According to conservation of energy the work done by $\mathbf{F}_r$ will be equal to negative of energy radiated.

$$\therefore \quad \int_{t_1}^{t_2} \mathbf{F}_r \mathbf{V}_{dt} = -\frac{e^2}{6\pi\epsilon_0 c^3} \int_{t_1}^{t_2} \dot{V} \cdot \dot{V} dt$$

$$= -\frac{e^2}{6\pi\epsilon_0 c^3} \left[V \cdot \dot{V} \right]_{t_1}^{t_2} + \frac{e^2}{6\pi\epsilon_0 c^3} \int_{t_1}^{t_2} V \cdot \ddot{V} dt.$$

In case of periodic motion we may neglect the integrated term.

$$\therefore \quad \int_{t_1}^{t_2} \mathbf{F}_r \cdot \mathbf{V} dt = \frac{e^2}{6\pi\epsilon_0 c^3} \int_{t_1}^{t_2} V \cdot \ddot{V} dt$$

or, $$\int_{t_1}^{t_2} \left(\mathbf{F}_r - \frac{e^2}{6\pi\epsilon_0 c^2} \ddot{V} \right) \mathbf{V} dt = 0.$$

$$\therefore \quad \mathbf{F}_r = \frac{e^2}{6\pi\epsilon_0 c^3} \ddot{\mathbf{V}}$$

$$= m\tau \ddot{\mathbf{V}}, \qquad \qquad \qquad (19.93)$$

where $\tau = \dfrac{e^2}{6\pi\epsilon_0 mc^3}$.

Eq. (19.91) becomes

$$m\dot{\mathbf{V}} = \mathbf{F}_e + m\tau\ddot{\mathbf{V}}$$

or, $$m(\dot{\mathbf{V}} - \tau\ddot{\mathbf{V}}) = \mathbf{F}_e.$$ (19.94)

The above equation is known as *Abraham-Lorentz equation*.

19.10   Dispersion in Dilute Gases

In case of dilute gases the mutual interaction between the particles can be neglected. When the electromagnetic waves are propagated through the gas, the electrons of the molecules will be displaced from their position of equilibrium and the molecules are polarized. Let us assume that a linear restoring force is acted on the electrons and the damping is proportional to the velocity.

The equation of motion of the nth electron can be written as

$$m[\ddot{\mathbf{r}}_n + l_n\dot{\mathbf{r}}_n + \gamma_n\mathbf{r}_n] = e\mathbf{E},$$ (19.95)

where l_n and γ_n are constants which measure the damping and restoring force respectively.

From Eq. (19.95) we have

$$\ddot{\mathbf{r}}_n + l_n\dot{\mathbf{r}}_n + \gamma_n\dot{\mathbf{r}}_n = \frac{e}{m}\mathbf{E_0}\exp(-i\omega t).$$

The solution of the above equation is

$$\mathbf{r}_n(t) = \frac{\left(\frac{e}{m}\right)\mathbf{E_0}}{(\omega_n^2 - \omega^2) - il_n\omega}\exp(-i\omega t).$$ (19.96)

The corresponding dipole moment,

$$\mathbf{p}_n = e\mathbf{r}_n(t) = \frac{\frac{e^2}{m}\mathbf{E_0}}{(\omega_n^2 - \omega^2) - il_n\omega}.$$ (19.97)

If N is the total number of electrons per unit volume of the gas and f be the fraction of the total electrons which have the characteristic resonance frequency ω_n, then the total dipole moment will be

$$\mathbf{p} = \sum_n Nf p_n$$

$$= E\sum_n \frac{\left(\frac{e^2}{m}\right)Nf}{(\omega_n^2 - \omega^2) - il_n\omega}.$$ (19.98)

Now $\mathbf{p} = \epsilon_0\chi E$, where χ = the electric susceptibility.

$$\therefore \quad \chi = \frac{\mathbf{p}}{\epsilon_0 E} = \sum_n \frac{\left(\frac{e^2}{m\epsilon_0}\right)Nf}{(\omega_n^2 - \omega^2) - il_n\omega}.$$ (19.99)

Again, the dielectric constant ϵ can be expressed as

$$\epsilon = 1 + \chi = 1 + \sum_n \frac{\left(\frac{e^2}{m\epsilon_0}\right)Nf}{(\omega_n^2 - \omega^2) - il_n\omega}.$$

Hence, the refractive index n can be found from the relation,

$$n^2 = \epsilon = 1 + \sum_n \frac{\left(\frac{e^2}{m\epsilon_0}\right)Nf}{(\omega_n^2 - \omega^2) - il_n\omega}.$$ (19.100)

The above equation is known as *dispersion relation*.

When $\omega < \omega_n$, all terms in Eq. (19.100) are positive and $\epsilon > 1$. But for $\omega > \omega_n$, $\epsilon < 1$. In the neighbourhood of ω_n the case is somewhat peculiar. The real part then vanishes and the term will be imaginary and large. The variation of ϵ is shown in Fig. 19.7.

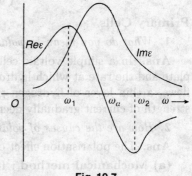

If $\frac{dn}{d\omega} > 1$, the dispersion is said to be normal and if $\frac{dn}{d\omega} < 1$, the dispersion is said to be anomalous. From Fig. 19.7 it is clear that anomalous dispersion occurs between the two frequencies ω_1 and ω_2, i.e., in the region $\frac{dn}{d\omega} < 1$.

Fig. 19.7

Questions

Essay-type

1. What do you mean by retarded potential? Find expressions for it.

2. Clearly explain what do you mean by Hertz potential.

3. Establish the equations for the Lienard-Wiechert potentials of a single electron. Find the fields of a charge in uniform motion.

4. Calculate the electric and magnetic fields of an accelerated charge.

5. Explain what do you mean by scattering of radiation and radiation damping.

6. What is meant by **(i)** normal and **(ii)** anomalous dispersion? Establish the dispersion equation.

Review Short Questions on *Current Electricity*
(with Answers)

Primary Cells

1. *What do you mean by polarisation effect of a voltaic cell?*

Ans. In a simple voltaic cell, the rate of evolution of hydrogen from copper plate and the rate at which hydrogen coming out are not same. So when a current flows, a thin layer of hydrogen gradually deposited on the copper plate and the strength of current gradually decreases. This effect is known as polarisation effect.

2. *How are the causes of polarisation minimised?*

Ans. The polarisation effect can be minimised or prevented by three methods :

(a) Mechanical method : In this method, the hydrogen bubbles are brushed off from the copper plate frequently.

(b) Chemical method : In this method, hydrogen is converted into water by using oxidising agent.

(c) Electrochemical method : In this method two solutions are used. When hydrogen meets the second solution, ions of the same metal as that of the positive plate are liberated.

3. *Show how the effects of local action and polarisation are avoided in a Daniell cell.*

Ans. In a Daniell cell, local action is prevented by using an amalgamated zinc rod which serves as the negative plate. Copper vessel is used for positive plate and concentrated solution of copper sulphate is used as the depolariser and this solution is always kept saturated by allowing it to come in contact with copper sulphate crystals. The hydrogen ions react with copper sulphate solution producing copper ions and sulphuric acid. So the effect of polarisation is removed.

4. *What is a standard cell and why is it so called?*

Ans. The cell for which the e.m.f is practically constant, known as standard cell.

In voltaic cells, the e.m.f is gradually decreased. Hence they cannot be used where constant flow of current is required. In a standard cell, the e.m.f. and the current remain constant. So they are called standard cell.

5. *On what factors does the e.m.f. of a cell depend?*

Ans. The e.m.f. of a cell depends on the temperature and on the materials used for positive and negative plates of the cell.

6. *What is contact potential difference?*

Ans. When two different metals are placed in contact with each other, there exists a potential difference at the point of contact of the metals, known as contact potential difference.

7. *Mention the requisites of a good voltaic cell.*

Ans. The requisites of a good voltaic cell are as under :

(i) It should be free from local action and polarisation,

(ii) e.m.f. should be high.

(iii) Current must be steady during the supply.

(iv) No chemical action should take place when the cell is not giving a current.

Electromagnetism

8. *From what experiment Oersted concluded that a wire carrying an electric current produces a magnetic field?*

Ans. H. C. Oersted placed a magnetic needle very near to the current-carrying wire. He found that the needle is deflected. The deflection of magnetic needle indicates the presence of a magnetic field round the current-carrying conductor.

9. *State Ampere's rule to find the direction of the magnetic field round the current-carrying wire.*

Ans. Suppose a man is swimming along the wire in the direction of the current with his face directed towards the needle, then the north pole will be deflected towards his left hand.

10. *On what factors does the deflection of the needle depend?*

Ans. The deflection of the needle depends on the strength of the current and the number of turns of wire.

11. *What will be the nature of lines of force due to (i) linear and (ii) circular current?*

Ans. **(i)** For a straight wire, the lines of force will be circular with their centres situated on the axis of the wire.

(ii) For a circular wire, the magnetic lines of force are straight lines and parallel to one another and they are perpendicular to the plane of the coil.

12. *State Laplace's law for the intensity of magnetic field due to a current element.*

Ans. The Laplace's law states that "the intensity of the magnetic field F at any point due to a current element is directly proportional to **(i)** length dl of the element, **(ii)** the strength i of the current, **(iii)** the sine of the angle α between the direction of the element and the line joining the point (where the intensity is required) to the mid-point of the element and inversely proportional to **(iv)** the square of the distance r of the given point from the element.

Mathematically, it is expressed as

$$F \propto \frac{idl \sin \alpha}{r^2}.$$

13. *What do you mean by 'electromagnetic unit of current'?*

Ans. The strength of the current which flows through a wire having length 1 cm, bent into an arc of a circle of 1 cm radius produces a force of 1 dyne on a unit north pole placed at the centre of the circle is known as electromagnetic unit of current.

14. *If a current of strength 'i' flows through an infinitely long straight conductor, what will be the intensity of the field at a distance 'a' from the conductor?*

Ans. For an infinitely long straight conductor, the intensity of field at a point is expressed as

$$F = \frac{2i}{a}.$$

15. *Write the expression of the field due to circular current at a point on the axis.*

Ans. The field at a point on the axis of a circular current is given by

$$F = \frac{2\pi na^2 i}{(a^2 + x^2)^{3/2}},$$

where n = number of turns of the coil, a = radius of the coil,

        i = strength of the current,

        x = distance of the point from the centre of the coil.

16. *What is a solenoid?*

Ans. A solenoid is a cylindrical coil of wire acting as a magnet when carrying electric current.

17. *Write the expression of intensity of field, in c.g.s. system at any point on the axis of a long solenoid in terms of the number of turns of the coil and the strength of the current.*

Ans. Intensity of field at any point on the axis of the solenoid is

$$F = 4\pi ni,$$

where i = strength of the current,

        n = number of turns per unit length of the coil.

18. *How is the c.g.s. electromagnetic unit of current related to the practical unit of current?*

Ans. Practical unit of current is Ampere.

1 e.m.u. = 10 amperes.

19. *State Ampere's Theorem.*

Ans. Ampere's theorem states that a closed current-carrying conductor is equivalent to a simple magnetic shell, the bounding edge of which coincides with the conductor, and the moment of the shell is proportional to the strength of the current.

20. *What do you understand by the equivalence of a magnetic shell and a coil carrying a current?*

Ans. In the case of a coil of radius a, the force exerted on unit N-pole placed on the axis of the coil at a distance x from its centre due to the current i will be $\frac{2\pi a^2 i}{x^3}$.

If the coil is replaced by a shell of strength ϕ having area equal to that of the coil, the force on a unit N-pole at the same point on the axis will be $\frac{2\pi a^2 \phi}{x^3}$.

Hence the magnetic shell is equivalent to the coil if $i = \phi$.

Thus the magnetic field at any point due to a current in a closed loop is identical with that of a magnetic shell of equal area when the strength of the shell is equal to the strength of the current.

21. *What will be the work done in carrying a magnetic pole round a closed circuit?*

Ans. The work done in carrying a unit pole round a circuit is $4\pi i$, where i is the strength of the current.

22. *Write the names of classification of galvanometers.*

Ans. The galvanometers are generally classified into two categories :

(1) Suspended Needle Galvanometer and **(2)** Suspended Coil Galvanometer.

23. *What are the precautions necessary to use a tangent galvanometer?*

Ans. Precautions :

(i) The deflection should be near $45°$.

(ii) The needle must be situated at the centre of the circular scale.

(iii) The suspended fibre must be torsion-free.

(iv) The pointer should be placed at right angle to the axis of the needle.

(v) The coil of the galvanometer should lie in the magnetic meridian.

24. *Explain how the sensitiveness of the tangent galvanometer can be increased.*

Ans. The sensitiveness of the tangent galvanometer can be increased if the ratio $\frac{r}{n}$ (where r is the radius of the coil and n be the number of turns) is as small as possible. This can be done by increasing the number of turns of the coil and by decreasing the radius of the coil.

25. *What are the forces acting on the needle of a tangent galvanometer when deflected by the action of a current passing through the coil?*

Ans. When a current is passed through the coil of the galvanometer, the deflection of the needle occurs under the action of two couples —one due to restoring forces produced by the earth's horizonal component H and the other due to the deflecting forces due to the current.

26. *Give a short description of Helmholtz double-coil galvanometer.*

Ans. Helmholtz double-coil galvanometer consists of two identical co-axial coils placed at a distance equal to the radius of the coil. The coils are joined in series and the direction of the current is such that the field at the half-way between the coils is double that due to one coil alone.

27. *Explain how the sensitiveness of a moving coil D'Arsonval galvanometer can be made maximum.*

Ans. The sensitiveness of the D'Arsonval galvanometer can be made maximum by increasing the factor nAH as large as possible and at the same time by decreasing restoring couple per unit twist, C, as small as possible. But the large number of turns, n, will increase the resistance of the coil, and the area A also cannot be made very large for in that case the apparatus becomes large. Again, the suspension fibre should be such that it is capable of carrying current. So the only remaining factor H, the field strength of the magnet, can be made strong enough to increase the sensitiveness of the galvanometer.

28. *Make a comparison between the suspended needle galvanometer and the suspended coil galvanometer.*

Ans.

Suspended needle galvanometer	*Suspended coil galvanometer*
(i) Both transient current and steady current can be measured.	(i) Here also both transient and steady current can be measured
(ii) The strength of magnetic field may vary.	(ii) The strength of the magnetic field is fixed.
(iii) The coil must lie in the magnetic meridian.	(iii) The coil need not be placed in the magnetic meridian.
(iv) Here the deflecting force is due to current.	(iv) Here the deflecting force is due to magnet.
(v) Restoring force is due to the earth's horizontal component.	(v) Restoring force is due to torsion fibre.
(vi) Sensitivity is small.	(vi) Sensitivity is large.

29. *What is the difference between a deadbeat galvanometer and a ballistic galvanometer?*

Ans. In a deadbeat galvanometer, the coil returns to its original position from its deflected position very quickly after the withdrawal of current. The oscillation of the coil stops due to generation of eddy currents in the conducting frame of the coil which oscillates in the fixed magnetic field.

The ballistic galvanometer is used to measure a sudden transient charge passing through it. The damping of the coil is avoided by using non-conducting frame of the coil.

30. *Why does an ammeter have a low resistance?*

Ans. An ammeter has low resistance, so that the magnitude of the current in the circuit remains almost unaltered and the loss due to heating of the resistance is practically nil.

31. *What modification is necessary to make the ammeter a direct reading voltmeter?*

Ans. The shunt of the ammeter is to be removed and then a suitable high resistance is to be joined in series so as to convert an ammeter into a direct reading voltmeter.

d.c. Circuits

32. *State Kirchhoff's laws for the distribution of currents in a network of conductors.*

Ans. Kirchhoff's Laws : (a) First Law—The algebraic sum of currents meeting at a point in an electric circuit is zero. **(b) Second Law**—In any closed mesh, the algebraic sum of the products of current and resistance of each part of the mesh is equal to the total electromotive force in that mesh.

33. *What is meant by the e.m.f. of a cell?*

Ans. The e.m.f. of a cell is the potential drop between the two terminals of the cell in the open condition. Again, the electromotive force drives the electric charge through the circuit.

34. *Distinguish e.m.f. from potential difference.*

Ans. Differences between e.m.f. and potential difference are given below :

(i) The potential difference between the terminals is a result of the action of e.m.f.

(ii) The potential difference and the e.m.f. of a cell act in opposite direction. So they are equal in an open circuit.

(iii) The direction of potential difference depends on the direction of current but the e.m.f. has always the same direction in the circuit.

(iv) In a closed circuit when the e.m.f. and the potential difference are in the same direction, the e.m.f. of the cell > p.d. between its terminals. When the e.m.f. and the p.d. are in opposite direction, e.m.f. < p.d. between the terminals.

(v) Both e.m.f. and p.d. are expressed in the same unit.

35. *State Ohm's law.*

Ans. Ohm's law states that under identical condition of temperature the current flowing through a conductor is directly proportional to the potential difference between its two ends provided all physical conditions remain unchanged.

If V_A and V_B are the potential at the two ends of the conductor respectively and i be the current flowing through the conductor, then

$$\frac{V_A - V_B}{i} = \text{constant (say, } R).$$

This constant is called the resistance of the conductor.

36. *What do you mean by c.g.s. unit of current, resistance, e.m.f. and charge?*

Ans. c.g.s. Unit of Current : It is the current which produce one dyne force on a unit north magnetic pole when it is placed at the centre of a circular arc of wire having radius one centimetre and the length of the wire is one centimetre.

c.g.s. unit of Resistance : If a potential difference of one c.g.s. unit causes a current of one c.g.s. unit to flow through the conductor, then the resistance of that conductor is said to be one c.g.s. unit of resistance.

c.g.s. unit of e.m.f. : The e.m.f. which delivers one unit current through a unit resistance is said to be one c.g.s. unit of e.m.f.

c.g.s. unit of Charge : One c.g.s. unit of charge is that quantity of electricity conveyed in one second by one unit of current.

37. What are the relation between c.g.s. unit and practical unit of current, resistance, charge and e.m.f.?

Ans. The practical unit of current is ampere.

10 amperes = 1 c.g.s. unit of current.

The practical unit of resistance is ohm.

1 ohm = 10^9 c.g.s. unit of resistance.

The practical unit of charge is coulomb.

10 coulombs = 1 c.g.s. unit of quantity of charge.

The practical unit of e.m.f. is volt.

1 volt = 10^8 c.g.s. unit of e.m.f.

38. *Write the mathematical formula which express the relation of the resistance of a conductor with its length and cross-sectional area.*

Ans. The resistance of a conductor is given by $R = \rho \frac{L}{A}$,

where R = resistance of the conductor,

L = its length,

A = area of the conductor,

ρ = a constant, known as specific resistance of the material of the conductor.

39. *Define specific resistance and conductivity.*

Ans. Specific resistance may be defined as the resistance of a conductor having unit length and unit cross-sectional area.

The reciprocal of the specific resistance is called conductivity.

40. *Explain why nichrome wire is used to make a high resistance.*

Ans. The specific resistance of nichrome is very high of the order of 110 micro-ohms per cm cube. So nichrome is used for making high resistances.

41. *How do you account the difference in behaviour of the temperature coefficient of resistance of a metal from that of an electrolyte?*

Ans. In metal, the thermal motion of the molecules increases with temperature and interferes with the motion of the electrons strongly. So the resistance increases with temperature, whereas in electrolytes, as the temperature increases the viscosity of water decreases very rapidly. From this one can conclude that the temperature coefficient of electrolyte is negative.

42. What is supra-conductivity?

Ans. At low temperatures mercury, lead and some alloys offer no resistance to the flow of current at their respective critical temperatures. This property is known as supra-conductivity.

43. *For what purpose the shunt is used?*

Ans. To protect a galvanometer from being damaged by the flow of high current, a shunt is used. Shunt is nothing but a resistance which is connected in parallel with the galvanometer resistance so that a small fraction of the total current flows through the coil of the galvanometer.

44. *What will be the current flowing through the galvanometer having resistance G when it is shunted by a resistance S?*

Ans. The current through the galvanometer will be

$$i_g = \frac{S}{G+S}i,$$

where i is the main current.

45. '*The resistance of the shunt should be $\frac{1}{9}$th of the resistance of the galvanometer in order that $\frac{1}{10}$th of the total current may pass through the galvanometer.*'—*Justify the above statement.*

Ans. Suppose a current i_g flows through the galvanometer of resistance G which is shunted by a resistance S. So we have

$$i_g = \frac{S}{G+S}i.$$

But according to the question, $\dfrac{S}{G+S} = \dfrac{1}{10}$

or, $\dfrac{G+S}{S} = 10$ or, $\dfrac{G}{S} = 9.$

$\therefore$ $S = \dfrac{1}{9}G.$

Hence the resistance of the shunt should be $\frac{1}{9}$th of the resistance of the galvanometer in order that $\frac{1}{10}$th of the total current may pass through the galvanometer.

46. *Explain why constant total current shunt is used instead of simple shunt.*

Ans. When a shunt is inserted in a circuit, the equivalent resistance will be decreased. So the main current is changed. This difficulty is overcome by using constant current shunt.

47. *Explain why the wire of a metre-bridge is made of same material and uniform cross-section.*

Ans. It is necessary that the resistance of the wire must be proportional to the length of the wire. The resistance of a wire having length L and cross-sectional area A is given by $R = \rho\frac{L}{A}$, where ρ is the specific resistance of the material of the wire. So it is evident that ρ and A must be constant for a wire to make R

proportional to *L*. So the wire of a metre-bridge is made of same material and of uniform cross-seciion.

48. *When does the bridge become most sensitive?*

Ans. If the resistances in the four arms of the bridge are equal, the bridge becomes most sensitive.

49. *Why a metre-bridge cannot be used to measure high resistances?*

Ans. If two high resistances are introduced in the two gaps, the current practically flows through the wire of the bridge. So the bridge becomes most insensitive. For this reason metre-bridge is not suitable to measure high resistances.

50. *Which apparatus between a galvanometer and a battery is inserted between the junction of the two arms having greater resistance and the junction of the two arms having smaller resistance?*

Ans. Between a galvanometer and a battery, the one which has the greater resistance is placed between the junction of the two arms having greater resistances and the other is placed between the junction of the two arms having smaller resistances.

51. *Is it necessary to use a shunt if an ordinary unpivot type galvanometer is used in the metre-bridge?*

Ans. No shunt is necessary if the galvanometer be ordinary unpivot type.

52. *What are the sources of errors to measure a resistance with the help of a metre-bridge?*

Ans. Sources of errors :

(a) If the soldering of the wire at its ends to the copper plate is imperfect, the joint and copper plates introduce small resistance to their respective arms.

(b) Thermo-currents and Joule heating are produced if a current is passed for a long time through the wire.

(c) The Wheatstone bridge is unsuitable for the purpose of comparing very low resistances.

53. *Will you get correct value of the resistance with a long or with a short wire of the metre-bridge?*

Ans. In measuring the resistance a long wire is used so that end error due to imperfect soldering will not affect the result.

54. *What is the limitation in comparing two nearly equal resistances by a metre-bridge?*

Ans. The difference between the two resistances must be smaller than the total resistance of the bridge wire.

55. Do you prefer a wire of a pure metal or of an alloy for use in a metre-bridge?

Ans. The temperature coefficient of an alloy is less than that of a pure metal. So a wire of an alloy is preferred to a wire of a pure metal.

56. *What is a Post Office (P.O.) Box?*

Ans. It is a compact form of the Wheatstone bridge. It consists of three sets of coils of manganin wire which form three arms of the Wheatstone bridge.

57. *Is it possible to measure a very high resistance by P.O. Box?*

Ans. The measurement of resistance by a P.O. box is based on Wheatstone bridge principle which is found to be insensitive if the resistances of the two arms are large. The P.O. box is, therefore, unsuitable for the purpose of measuring high resistances.

58. *If the resistance coils of a P.O. Box is calibrated at* 0 °C, *will they give the same value at* 32 °C?

Ans. The resistance of a metal increases with temperature. So the resistance coils will not give the same value at 32 °C.

59. *What material would you select to construct a standard* one-ohm *coil?*

Ans. The coil should be made of either manganin or constantan because of its high specific resistance and low temperature coefficient.

60. *When does the half-deflection method fail to measure the resistance of the galvanometer?*

Ans. If the resistance of the galvanometer is very high in comparison with the shunt resistance, half-deflection method gives satisfactory results. So this method fails for a very low resistance galvanometer.

61. *What is the range of temperature that can be measured by platinum resistance thermometer?*

Ans. The range of temperature which can be measured by a platinum resistance thermometer is between −200 °C and 1200 °C.

62. *Why is platinum selected to construct a thermometer?*

Ans. The resistance of platinum is fixed for a fixed temperature. So it is used to construct a thermometer.

63. *What is platinum scale of temperature?*

Ans. The scale where the relation, $t_\rho = \frac{R_t - R_0}{R_{1000} - R_0} \times 100$, is used known as platinum scale of temperature,

where t_ρ = temperature obtained from platinum scale,

     R_t = resistance of platinum at temperature t °C,

     R_{100} = resistance of platinum at 100 °C,

     R_θ = resistance of platinum at 0 °C.

64. *Write the relation between platinum temperature t_ρ and the temperature t on the gas thermometer.*

Ans. The relation between t and t_ρ is given by

$$t = t_\rho + \delta \left(\frac{t}{100} - 1 \right) \frac{t}{100},$$

where δ is a constant which can be determined from the knowledge of platinum resistance of three known temperatures.

65. *What is the fundamental interval of a platinum resistance thermometer? What will be its value?*

Ans. $(R_{100} - R_0)$ is the fundamental interval of a platinum resistance thermometer. Its value is approximately one ohm.

66. *Write the advantages and disadvantages of a platinum thermometer.*

Ans. Advantages :

(i) The range of temperature is wide from −200 °C to 1200 °C.

(ii) Between 0 °C and 630 °C the readings are reliable up to 0.02 °C.

Disadvantages :

(i) It takes an appreciable time to attain the temperature of the bath due to its low conductivity.

(ii) Changing temperature cannot be measured by it.

(iii) Capacity is very large.

67. *What is a potentiometer and where it is used?*

Ans. A potentiometer consists of ten wires of uniform cross-section, each one metre in length stretched parallel to each other on a wooden board. They are joined in series.

The potentiometer is used to measure current, internal resistance of a cell and potential difference.

68. *What do you mean by the terms low, ordinary and high resistances?*

Ans. Resistances below one ohm are known as low resistances.

Resistances between 1 ohm and 1000 ohms are regarded as ordinary resistances and the resistances above 1000 ohms are termed as high resistances.

69. *Mention the methods which are generally used to measure low, ordinary and high resistances.*

Ans. Low resistances are generally measured by using a potentiometer.

The measurement of ordinary resistances are generally based on the principle of Wheatstone Bridge. High resistance is measured by the method of substitution.

Thermoelectricity

70. *What are thermocouple and thermoelectric current?*

Ans. A couple formed by any two dissimilar metals, soldered together at both ends are called thermocouple.

When one junction of the couple is kept in a hot bath and another junction in a cold bath, an electric current will flow. This current is known as thermoelectric current.

71. *Suppose a thermocouple is made of bismuth and antimony. In what direction the thermoelectric current will flow?*

Ans. We know that a current will flow across the cold junction from one metal occurring later in the thermoelectric series than the other. Thus, in a thermo-couple described in the question, current flows from antimony to bismuth.

72. *Write the thermoelectric series.*

Ans. Thermoelectric series **(i)** Bismuth, **(ii)** Copper, **(iii)** Lead, **(iv)** Silver, **(v)** Iron, **(vi)** Antimony.

73. *How is thermoelectric e.m.f. originated in a thermocouple?*

Ans. The number of free electrons differs from metal to metal. So when the junctions of the thermocouple are kept at different temperatures, the rate of diffusion of electrons at the junctions is not equal. At equilibrium one metal becomes positively charged and the other negatively charged. Hence there will be a resultant e.m.f. across the junctions. When the temperatures of both the junctions are equal, the thermoelectric e.m.f. becomes zero.

74. *State the fundamental laws of thermoelectricity.*

Ans. (a) Laws of Intermediate Metal : The thermoelectric e.m.f. across a junction for metals A and D at any given temperature is the sum of the electromotive force across the junctions A-B, B-C and C-D at that temperature.

(b) Laws of Intermediate Temperature : The thermoelectric e.m.f. for a couple with junctions at temperatures T_1 and T_2 is the algebraic sum of the e.m.f. of two couples of the same metals, one with junctions at T_1 and T_2, and the other with junctions at T_2 and T_3.

75. *Define the terms : (a) Neutral Temperature, (b) Temperature of Inversion, (c) Thermoelectric Diagram and (d) Thermoelectric Power.*

Ans. (a) Neutral Temperature : Neutral temperature may be defined as the temperature of the hot junction at which the e.m.f. is maximum.

(b) Temperature of Inversion : The temperature of inversion is the temperature of the hot junction at which the e.m.f. vanishes. If the temperature is further increased the reversal of the e.m.f. and the current occur.

(c) Thermoelectric Diagram : The e.m.f. of a thermocouple varies with temperature. This variation is represented by a graph where the ordinates represent the e.m.f. and the temperature of the hot junction is plotted along the abscissa, the temperature of the cold junction is kept at $0\,°\text{C}$. The diagram will be a parabola. This diagram is called thermoelectric diagram.

(d) Thermoelectric Power : The rate of change of e.m.f. with temperature is called thermoelectric power. It may also be defined as the slope of the tangent of the thermoelectric graph at the given temperature.

76. *What will be the nature of the graph which takes into account the variation of thermoelectric power with temperature?*

Ans. The variation of thermoelectric power with temperature is a straight line.

77. *What is Peltier effect?*

Ans. If the junctions of the thermocouple are kept at the same temperature and a current is made to flow round the circuit, one junction will be heated and the other will be cooled. This effect is reversed with the reversal of the direction of current. This effect is known as Peltier effect.

78. *Compare Peltier effect and Joule effect.*

Ans.

Peltier effect	*Joule effect*
(i) In Peltier effect, the heat developed or absorbed, when a current i passes for t second through a junction whose Peltier coefficient is π, will be equal to $\pi i t$.	(i) In Joule effect, the heat developed, when a current i passes through a resistance R for t second, is equal to $i^2 R t$.
(ii) The junction will be heated or cooled depending on the direction of current.	(ii) The heat developed is independent of the direction of current.
(iii) The amount of heat produced is proportional to the strength of the current.	(iii) The amount of heat produced is proportional to the square of the current.
(iv) Peltier effect is a reversible process.	(iv) Joule effect is an irreversible process.

79. *By what reasoning was Lord William Kelvin led to assume that Peltier effect is not the only thermoelectric effect?*

Ans. Lord Kelvin calculated the total e.m.f. generated in the thermocouple by applying the laws of heat engine because the Peltier effect is a reversible process. He found that the e.m.f. is directly proportional to the temperature difference of hot junction and cold junction. But from the experimental results, it is found that the graph connecting the e.m.f. and temperature difference will be a parabola. These facts led Lord Kelvin to assume that Peltier effect is not the only thermoelectric effect.

80. *What is Thomson effect?*

Ans. If different parts of a conductor are at different temperatures, heat will be absorbed or produced due to passage of a current along that conductor. This effect is called Thomson effect.

81. *Distinguish between Thomson's Positive Effect and Thomson's Negative Effect.*

Ans. If a conductor of copper (or substances like silver, zinc, antimony, cadmium, etc.) is unequally heated and a current passes from the colder part to hotter part, heat will be absorbed. When the direction of current is reversed, the effect will also reverse. This effect is known as Thomson's Positive Effect.

But if a conductor of iron (or bismuth, cobalt, nickel, platinum, etc.) is unequally heated and a current is allowed to pass through it from colder to hotter part, heat will be produced. The reversal of this effect occurs with the reversal of the direction of current. This effect is called Thomson's Negative Effect.

82. *Give the definitions of Peltier coefficient and Thomson coefficient.*

Ans. Peltier coefficient—Peltier coefficient is the amount of heat liberated or absorbed at the junction of a thermocouple when one unit of charge flows through it.

Thomson coefficient—Thomson coefficient is the amount of heat absorbed or generated between the two points of a conductor having different temperatures when one unit of charge flows per second.

83. *Write the mathematical expression of e.m.f. in a thermocouple.*

Ans. Total e.m.f. $= (\pi_2 - \pi_1) - \int_{T_1}^{T_2} (\sigma_A - \sigma_B)dt,$

where π_1 and π_2 are respectively the Peltier coefficients at temperatures T_1 and T_2. σ_A and σ_B are the Thomson coefficients for metals A and B of the thermocouple.

84. *What will be the mathematical expression for Peltier and Thomson coefficients?*

Ans. Peltier coefficient : $\pi = T\dfrac{de}{dT}.$

Thomson coefficient : $\sigma_A - \sigma_B = T\dfrac{d^2e}{dT^2}.$

85. *Assume the e.m.f. of a thermocouple is given by $e = at + bt^2$ in centrigrade scale. Calculate the Peltier and Thomson coefficients.*

Ans. We know that Peltier coefficient is given by

$$\pi = T\frac{de}{dT}.$$

Here $T = t + 273$.

Therefore, $\pi = (t + 273) \dfrac{d}{dT}(at + bt^2) = (t + 273)(a + 2bt)$.

Again, the Thomson coefficient is given by

$$\sigma_A - \sigma_B = T\frac{d^2 e}{dT^2} = (t + 273) \cdot 2b.$$

86. *Among all the thermoelectric effects, which is mostly used in the measurement of temperature?*

Ans. Of all the thermoelectric effects, Seebeck effect is generally used to measure the temperature.

87. *For what purposes the Duddel Thermo-galvanometer is used?*

Ans. The Duddel Thermo-galvanometer is used to detect and measure very small currents. It is equally applicable to both d.c. and a.c.

88. *What is a thermopile?*

Ans. A number of thermocouples of antimony and bismuth joined in series to produce a large e.m.f. for a small difference of temperature between their junctions is known as thermopile. A very small amount of radiant heat of the order of 0.001 °C can be measured by a thermopile.

89. *Give the relation between work and heat.*

Ans. When work is transformed into heat or *vice versa*, the quantity of heat is mechanically equivalent to the amount of work done. This is expressed as

$$W = JH,$$

where J is known as Joule's constant.

90. *What do you mean by the mechanical equivalent of heat?*

Ans. If two points in a circuit are in potential difference of 1 volt, then the amount of work done to pass one coulomb of electricity through it is called the mechanical equivalent of heat.

91. *Find the amount of heat produced by a current of i ampere flowing through a resistance of R ohm per second.*

Ans. Suppose the potential drop across the resistance is E. Now if Q amount of charge is passed in t seconds, the work done $= EQ$

$$= iR \cdot it = i^2 Rt.$$

$\therefore$ heat developed, $H = \dfrac{i^2 Rt}{J}$.

Therefore, the amount of heat produced per second is $i^2 R$ watt.

92. *State Joule's laws of heating effect of current.*

Ans. Joule's laws of heating effect of current are given below :

(i) The amount of heat developed in a conductor for a given time is directly proportional to the square of the current, i.e., $H \propto i^2$, when R and t are constants.

(ii) The amount of heat developed in a conductor for a given time and current is directly proportional to the resistance of the conductor, i.e., $H \propto R$ when i and t are constants.

(iii) The amount of heat developed in a given conductor for a given current is directly proportional to the time of flow of current, i.e., $H \propto t$ when i and R are constants.

93. *Define watt,* kilowatt *and* kilowatt-hour.

Ans. watt : Watt is the SI unit of power which is equivalent to one joule per second and corresponds to the rate of energy in an electric circuit where the potential difference is one volt and the current one ampere.

i.e., watt = ampere × volt.

kilowatt : It is the practical unit of power and equal to 1000 watts.

kilowatt-hour : When power of 1000 watts is consumed for one hour, then the total energy consumed is known as kilowatt-hour.

94. *What do you mean by '200 volts-100 watts' electric bulb?*

Ans. If a potential difference of 200 volts exists between two terminal points of the electric bulb, the power consumed per second will be 100 watts.

95. *Write some important applications of heating effect of current.*

Ans. The instruments based on heating effect of current are electric lamps, heaters, electric fuse, electric welding, arc lamp, etc.

96. *What is electromagnetic induction?*

Ans. The phenomenon of the production of induced current is called electromagnetic induction.

97. *State the Faraday's laws of electromagnetic induction.*

Ans. Faraday's laws of electromagnetic induction are the following :

(1) First law : Whenever the number of magnetic lines of force through a circuit varies, an instantaneous e.m.f. is induced in that circuit.

(2) Second law : The rate of variation of the magnetic lines of force is proportional to the induced e.m.f. at any instant, i.e,

$$e = -\frac{dN}{dt}.$$

98. *What is Lenz's law?*

Ans. The direction of induced current is such that it opposes the relative motion to which it is due. This is known as Lenz's law.

99. *Write down Fleming's right-hand rule which gives the direction of induced current.*

Ans. Fleming's right-hand rule states that if the thumb, and the first two fingers of the right hand are kept at a right angle such that the first finger gives the direction of magnetic field, the thumb that of motion, then the second finger gives the direction of the induced current.

100. *Explain what is meant by (a) Coefficient of self-inductance, (b) Coefficient of mutual induction.*

Ans. (a) Coefficient of self-inductance : It may be defined as the e.m.f. induced in the coil when the rate of change of current is unity.

e.m.f. induced in a coil, $e = -L\dfrac{di}{dt}$.

Therefore, when $\dfrac{di}{dt} = 1,\ \ e = -L.$

(b) Coefficient of mutual induction : The coefficient of mutual induction is numerically equal to induced e.m.f. in one circuit when the rate of change of current in the other circuit is unity.

If a current i flows through a circuit, then the magnetic flux passes through the other circuit, $N = Mi$, where M is the coefficient of mutual induction.

$\therefore$ induced e.m.f., $e = -M\dfrac{di}{dt}$.

Therefore, when $\dfrac{di}{dt} = 1$, $e = -M$.

101. *What is the practical unit of self-induction?*

Ans. The practical unit is henry.

If the rate of change of current is 1 ampere per second and the induced e.m.f. is 1 volt, then the coefficient of self-induction of the coil is 1 henry.

102. *Show that the co-efficient of self-inductance is twice the work done in establishing magnetic flux by unit current flowing through the circuit.*

Ans. The work done in time dt,

$$dW = eidt = -Li\frac{di}{dt} \cdot dt,$$

where e is the induced e.m.f. when the current i flows through the circuit.

Therefore, total work done,

$$W = -\int_0^{i_m} Li\frac{di}{dt} \cdot dt = -L\int_0^{i_m} idi$$

$$= -\frac{1}{2}Li_m^2.$$

If i_m = maximum current = 1,

then $L = -2W$.

Therefore, the coefficient of self-inductance is twice the work done when the current in the circuit is one unit.

103. *On what factors does the self-induction depend?*

Ans. The self-induction depends on

(i) shape of the coil   (ii) area of the coil

(iii) manner of winding   (iv) number of turns of the coil.

104. *Discuss in a few words how a coil of insulated wire can be made non-inductive.*

Ans. The wire is first doubled upon itself and then wound over a bobbin. In such a coil the induced e.m.f. in one half is cancelled by the e.m.f. induced in the other half due to the flow of current in the opposite direction in two halves of the coil. So the coil wound in this way is non-inductive.

105. *What will be the self-inductance of a circular coil?*

Ans. Suppose the circular coil of n turns has radius r and the permeability of the medium be μ. If H be the intensity of the magnetic field at the centre of the coil, then

total flux, $N = \pi r^2 n\mu H$.

If the current at any instant be i, then

$$H = \frac{2\pi ni}{r}.$$

Therefore, total flux, $N = 2\pi^2 n^2 r i \mu$.

$$\therefore \quad \frac{dN}{dt} = 2\pi^2 \mu n^2 r \frac{di}{dt}.$$

$\therefore$ induced e.m.f., $e = L\dfrac{di}{dt}$.

$$\therefore \quad \frac{dN}{dt} = L\frac{di}{dt} = 2\pi^2 \mu n^2 r \frac{di}{dt}.$$

Hence, $L = 2\pi^2 n^2 r \mu$ e.m.u.

106. *Find the self-inductance of a solenoid.*

Ans. Suppose the length of the solenoid having a number of turns n and area A be l. The current i flows through the solenoid.

Therefore, intensity of magnetic field, $H = \dfrac{4\pi n i}{l}$.

$\therefore$ total magnetic flux, $N = \dfrac{4\pi n i}{l} A \cdot n = \dfrac{4\pi n^2 A i}{l}$.

$$\therefore \quad \frac{dN}{dt} = \frac{4\pi n^2}{l} A \frac{di}{dt}.$$

But $\quad \dfrac{dN}{dt} = L\dfrac{di}{dt}$.

$$\therefore \quad L = \frac{4\pi n^2 A}{l} \text{ e.m.u.}$$

107. *What will be the mutual inductance between two similar, parallel and co-axial coil having radius r and number of turns n, separated by a distance x.*

Ans. The mutual inductance M of the above mentioned coil is

$$M = \frac{2\pi^2 \mu n^2 a^4}{(a^2 + x^2)^{3/2}} \text{ e.m.u.,}$$

where μ is the permeability of the medium.

108. *What is an eddy current?*

Ans. When a conducting material is placed near a varying magnetic field, an e.m.f. and thereby a current will be induced in it. This induced current is called eddy current. The magnitude of eddy current depends on the resistance of the conducting material and the rate of change of magnetic flux.

109. *How is the effect of eddy current utilised?*

Ans. The generation of eddy current is used to damp the oscillation of a needle or a coil in a galvanometer. Eddy currents are also utilised to melt metals and to prepare alloys.

110. *What will be the value of self-inductance for parallel cable wires?*

Ans. The self-inductance L of a parallel cable wire is

$$L = 4\log_e \frac{d - r}{r} \text{ per unit length,}$$

where d = distance between the wires,

$\qquad r$ = radius of each wire.

111. *Write the expression for (a) current reduction factor,(b)ballisiic reduction factor and (c) the quantity of charge flowing through the coil of the moving magnet ballistic galvanometer.*

Ans. (a) Current reduction factor of the galvanometer,

$$K' = \frac{H}{G},$$

where H = the earth's horizontal intensity,

G = intensity of the suspended magnet when unit current flows through the coil

(b) Ballistic reduction factor of the galvanometer,

$$K = \frac{H}{G}\frac{T}{\pi},$$

where T is the time-period of the magnet.

(c) Charge flowing through the coil,

$$Q = K \sin\frac{\theta}{2},$$

where θ is the value of throw when a charge q flows through the coil.

112. *What will be the time-period of the magnet of the galvanometer?*

Ans. Time-period of the magnet

$$T = 2\pi\sqrt{\frac{I}{MH}},$$

where M = magnetic moment of the magnet,

I = moment of inertia of the magnet,

H = horizontal intensity of the earth's magnetic field.

113. *Write the mathematical expression of the current reduction factor, of the moving coil ballistic galvanometer.*

Ans. Current reduction factor,

$$K = \frac{C}{nAH},$$

where n = number of turns of the coil,

A = area of the coil,

H = intensity of radial magnetic field,

C = couple per unit twist.

114. *Define logarithmic decrement of the ballistic galvanometer.*

Ans. Suppose $\theta_1, \theta_2, \theta_3, \theta_4, \ldots$ be the successive throws to left and right, then

$$\frac{\theta_1}{\theta_2} = \frac{\theta_2}{\theta_3} = \frac{\theta_3}{\theta_4} = \cdots = d \text{ (constant)}.$$

d is called the decrement and $\log_e d$ is known as logarithmic decrement.

115. *'In a circuit with a steady e.m.f. and an inductive resistance, the current decays exponentially with time when the e.m.f. is suddenly withdrawn', justify the statement.*

Ans. When the e.m.f. is suddenly withdrawn, the instantaneous current in the circuit containing inductance L and resistance R is expressed as

$$L\frac{di}{dt} + Ri = 0.$$

After integration we get $\log i = -\dfrac{R}{L}t + \text{constant.}$

Suppose, $i = i_m$, when $t = 0$.

$\therefore$ constant $= \log i_m$.

So the current at any instant,

$$\log i = -\frac{R}{L}t + \log i_m.$$

$\therefore \quad i = i_m e^{-(R/L)t}.$

From the above equation we find that the current at any instant decays exponentially with time.

116. *Write the value of time constant in a circuit having steady e.m.f. and (a) inductive resistance, (b) capacitance and resistance.*

Ans. (a) Time constant in a circuit having inductive resistance,

$$\lambda = \frac{L}{R},$$

where $L =$ self inductance of the coil.

(b) Time constant in a circuit having resistance and capacitance,

$$\lambda = \frac{1}{CR},$$

where $C =$ capacity of the condenser.

117. *Find the energy required to build up a current i in a circuit of self-inductance L.*

Ans. The rate of storage of energy in the medium surrounding the coil of self-inductance L

$$= Li\frac{di}{dt}.$$

Therefore, total energy required to build up a current i in a circuit of self-inductance L

$$= \int_0^i Li\frac{di}{dt} \cdot dt = \int_0^i Li\,di = \frac{1}{2}Li^2.$$

118. *Show that the energy of the charged condenser of capacity C is $\frac{1}{2}CE^2$, where E is the e.m.f. applied across the capacitance.*

Ans. We know that energy of the supplied battery is partly spent to charge the condenser and partly to heat the resistance.

Work done in heating the resistance

$$= \int_0^\infty i^2 R\,dt.$$

But $i = i_m e^{-(t/CR)}$

$\therefore$ work done $= Ri_m^2 \int_0^\infty e^{-2(t/CR)} dt = \frac{1}{2} CR^2 i_m^2$

$$= \frac{1}{2} CE^2 \text{ which is equal to the energy of the charged condenser.}$$

Alternating Current

119. *What is alternating current?*

Ans. If a coil is rotated in a uniform magnetic field, the induced e.m.f. is sinusoidal and given by the formula $E = E_m \sin \omega t$. So the e.m.f. and also the current flows through the coil alternatively in the opposite directions. Such a current is called alternating current.

120. *Find the average and root mean square value of an alternating current.*

Ans. (a) **Calculation of average alternating current :** Suppose the instantaneous current is given by $i = i_m \sin \theta$ where i_m is the maximum current flowing through the coil and θ is the angle of rotation of the coil from its initial position.

So the average current for a half-cycle is

$$i_{av} = \frac{1}{\pi} \int_0^\pi i_m \sin \theta d\theta = \frac{1}{\pi} [-\cos \theta]_0^\pi i_m = \frac{2}{\pi} i_m.$$

$\therefore$ average current $= \frac{2}{\pi} \times$ maximum current.

(b) **Calculation of root mean square value of alternating current :** Suppose the current at any instant is given by $i = i_m \sin \theta$. So the mean of square of current

$$i_{mean} = \frac{1}{\pi} \int_0^\pi i_m^2 \sin^2 \theta d\theta = \frac{i_m^2}{2\pi} \int_0^\pi (1 - \cos 2\theta) d\theta = \frac{i_m^2}{2}.$$

Therefore, root mean square value of current

$$i_{r.m.s.} = \frac{i_m}{\sqrt{2}} = \frac{1}{\sqrt{2}} \times \text{maximum value of current.}$$

121. *What is the relation among the average, root mean square and maximum values of the alternating current?*

Ans. Average current $= \frac{2}{\pi} \times$ maximum current.

Root mean square current $= \frac{1}{\sqrt{2}} \times$ maximum value of current.

$\therefore$ maximum current $= \frac{\pi}{2} \times$ average current $= \sqrt{2} \times$ root mean square current.

122. *In the calculation of average current, why is the average taken over a half-cycle?*

Ans. The average value of the current over a full-cycle is zero because during one half-cycle the current is positive while during other half-cycle it is negative. So the average is taken over a half-cycle.

123. *Write the expression for mean power in a.c. circuit when (i) the circuit is non-inductive and (ii) the circuit is inductive.*

Ans. (i) Non-inductive circuit :

$$\text{Mean power} = \frac{1}{2}E_m i_m,$$

where E_m = maximum e.m.f., i_m = maximum current.

(ii) Inductive circuit :

$$\text{Mean power} = \frac{1}{2}E_m i_m \cos\alpha$$

where E_m = maximum e.m.f., i_m = maximum current,

α = phase lag of current behind the e.m.f.

124. *An alternating e.m.f., $E_m \sin\omega t$ is applied to a circuit containing resistance and self-inductance. Write down the differential equation for the current and the expression for the current and impedance when the steady state is reached.*

Ans. The differential equation for current when an e.m.f. $E_m \sin\omega t$ is applied to a circuit containing resistance R and self-inductance L is given by

$$L\frac{di}{dt} + Ri = E_m \sin\omega t.$$

The expression for current at the steady state will be

$$i = \frac{E_m}{\sqrt{R^2 + L^2\omega^2}}\sin(\omega t - \theta),$$

where θ is the phase difference between the e.m.f. and the current and given by

$$\tan\theta = \frac{L\omega}{R}.$$

The expression for impedance Z is given by

$$Z = \sqrt{R^2 + L^2\omega^2}.$$

125. *An alternating e.m.f., $E_m \sin\omega t$ is applied to a circuit containing resistance R, inductance L and capacitance C. What will be the differential equation for charge?*

Ans. The differential equation for charge will be

$$L\frac{d^2q}{dt^2} + R\frac{dq}{dt} + \frac{q}{C} = E_m \sin\omega t.$$

126. *What will be the impedance in the above case and the condition for which resonance occurs?*

Ans. The impedance of the circuit will be

$$Z = \sqrt{R^2 + \left(\omega L - \frac{1}{\omega C}\right)^2}.$$

The condition for resonance is

$$\omega L = \frac{1}{\omega C}.$$

127. *Why is an electromagnet used in preference to a permanent magnet?*

Ans. An electromagnet is used in preference to a permanent magnet due to following reasons :

(a) By adjusting the strength of the current and the number of turns of the coil, the magnetic strength can be varied. In a permanent magnet, the strength is fixed.

(b) The electromagnet may be demagnetised completely and again it can be used as a magnet when necessary, which is not possible for a permanent magnet.

(c) The polarity of the electromagnet may be changed by changing the direction of the current, whereas it is fixed for a permanent magnet.

128. *Explain the terms : (a) Vector diagram, (b) Wattless current and (c) Skin effect*

Ans. (a) Vector diagram : An alternating current and an alternating e.m.f. are vector quantities. So they can be represented diagrammatically by vectors. The diagram thus obtained is called vector diagram.

(b) Wattless current : In an *L-R* circuit, if the inductance is so great that resistance can be neglected, then the current is entirely wattless. This current is called wattless current.

(c) Skin effect : When an alternating e.m.f. of high frequency is applied at the ends of a uniform wire, the current instead of spreading uniformly over the cross-section, is confined to the surface-layer of the wire. This effect is called skin effect.

129. *Explain how the speed of an electric fan is regulated by the regulator knob.*

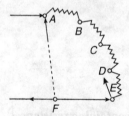

Ans. The circuit diagram shows how the speed of an electric fan is regulated by making use of a regulator knob. When the adjustable contact maker is at *A*, current enters at *A* and leaves through the low resistance contact maker causing the current high. A minimum current is achieved for the metal contact at *E*. No current will be there for the metal contact at *F* which is a point outside the circuit.

130. *Explain why an electric heater used in a d.c. line can also be used in an a.c. line.*

Ans. From Joule's law we know that the heating is proportional to the square of the current. So, if the amount of current remains the same, the heat generated will also remain constant whatever may be the direction of current. Therefore, a d.c. heater may also be used in an a.c. line.

131. *What is induced current?*

Ans. The current produced in a closed coil due to the relative motion between it and a magnetic field is known as the induced current.

132. *The e.m.f. and internal resistance of a cell are E and r respectively. If a resistance R is connected with the cell, calculate the condition for maximum power from the external resistance.*

Ans. We have, the rate of supply of power

$$= \left(\frac{E}{R+r} \right)^2 \times R = \frac{E^2 R}{(R+r)^2} = \frac{E^2 R}{(R-r)^2 + 4Rr}.$$

The rate of supply of power will be maximum when $[(R-r)^2 + 4Rr]$ is minimum, i.e., when $(R - r)^2 = 0$ or, $R = r$. This is the necessary condition.

133. *The e.m.f. and internal resistance of a cell are E and r respectively. A resistance of R ohm is connected with the cell. Establish Ohm's law employing the principle of conservation of energy.*

Ans. If i be the current flowing through the circuit, then the rate of production of heat $= (i^2R + i^2r)$.

It is evident from the principle of conservation of energy that the cell utilised has supplied energy at the same rate as above. The rate of supply of energy by the cell $= E_i$.

$$\therefore \qquad E_i = i^2R + i^2r \quad \text{or,} \quad i = \frac{E}{R + r}.$$

This is Ohm's law.

134. *A current is passed through a steel wire, heating it red. The half of the wire is immersed in cold water. Why does the unimmersed half of the wire heat up still more?*

Ans. The temperature of that portion of the wire immersed in water decreases causing a decrease of its resistance. As a result the flow of current through the wire increases. As the resistance of the portion not immersed is large, the amount of heat developed in that portion is also greater.

135. *Same current flows through the line wires and the filament of the electric bulb but only the latter gets white hot. Explain why.*

Ans. The resistance of the filament is large while that of the line wire is low. Now from Joule's law we know that the amount of heat developed is proportional to the resistance when the current and the time of flow are constant. Hence the filament will be more heated.

136. *Is electromagnetic induction necessarily accompanied by the flow of induced currents? Illustrate your answer with an example.*

Ans. If there be a change in the number of lines of force linked up with the circuit, then an e.m.f. will be produced. If the circuit is closed the induced current will flow but if the circuit remains open, induced e.m.f. will be developed without any flow of current.

137. *If a copper plate is kept in front of a magnet, which is moved to and fro in front of the plate so that its distance varies in a regular way, the plate gets warm. How do you explain this effect?*

Ans. There will be an eddy current on the surface of the copper plate due to the change in the magnetic lines of force associated with the plate. Hence heat will be developed on the plate and it will be warm.

138. *For a d.c. line how will you identify the positive and the negative terminals?*

Ans. In a beaker dil. H_2SO_4 is taken and the two terminals separated by a distance are immersed in it. Huge amount of gas will be evolved by one terminal. This is hydrogen gas and the terminal is marked negative. From the other terminal oxygen gas is evolved by a little amount. That terminal is obviously positive.

139. *An electric bulb is first connected in a d.c. circuit and then in an a.c. circuit. For both the cases, the voltage measured across the bulb by a voltmeter is the same. It is seen that the bulb glows more brightly in the second case. Justify.*

Ans. The voltage across the two terminals of the bulb in the d.c. circuit is constant. But in an a.c. circuit we record the r.m.s. value of the voltage. The maximum voltage is $\sqrt{2}$ times the r.m.s. voltage. For that reason the bulb in an a.c. circuit glows more.

140. *It is asked to two students whether one has to use a high resistance or a low resistance to get a large heating effect. One of them uses the equation $P = i^2 R$ and says 'high' while the other uses the equation $P = V^2 R$ and says 'low'. Comment.*

Ans. If wires are connected in parallel and a constant p.d. is applied between the ends, the value of the p.d. (V) is same for all the wires but current (i) is different for different wires. Under this condition it cannot be concluded that $P \propto R$. Since V is constant, so $P = \frac{V^2}{R}$ equation is to be applied in this case. That means the rate of production of heat is inversely proportional to the resistance of the wire when the wires are connected in parallel.

Further, if the resistances are connected in series, the same amount of current flows through each of them but the p.d. across each wire is different. So in this case $P = i^2 R$ is to be applied.

141. *In an off-circuit, the voltmeter reading across a battery is 2.2 volt while it is 1.9 volt in an on-circuit. If the current in the circuit be 1 ampere, find the internal resistance of the battery.*

Ans. We have the internal resistance, $r = \dfrac{E - V}{i}$.

Here, $E = 2.2$ volt, $V = 1.9$ volt, $i = 1$ ampere.

$$\therefore \quad r = \frac{2.2 - 1.9}{1} = 0.3 \ \Omega.$$

142. *Why does the resistance of carbon decrease with the rise of temperature?*

Ans. If R_t and R_0 are the resistances at $t°C$ and $0°C$ respectively, then we have

$$R_t = R_0(I + \alpha t),$$

where α is a constant, whose value depends on the particular material of the conductor.

For carbon since the temperature coefficient of resistance α is negative, so its resistance decreases with the rise of temperature. This is also true for electrolytes.

143. *Explain why in electric heater wires of alloys are used instead of wires of pure metal.*

Ans. This is because the resistivity of alloys is greater than that of a pure metal. So for producing heat at the same rate with the same current passing through the heater-wire, it requires the length of alloy-wire smaller than that of a pure metal wire.

144. *A galvanometer of 100 Ω resistance when shunted suitably becomes 1 Ω. Find the resistance of the shunt.*

Ans. We have, the resistance of the shunted galvanometer

$$G_s = \frac{SG}{S + G} \quad \text{or} \quad S = \frac{GG_s}{G - S_s},$$

where G is the resistance of the galvanometer without shunt and S is the shunt resistance.

Here $G = 100\ \Omega$ and $G_s = 1\Omega$

$\therefore \qquad S = \dfrac{100 \times 1}{100 - 1} = \dfrac{100}{99} = 1.01\ \Omega.$

145. How can an ammeter be converted into a voltmeter and vice versa?

Ans. In order to convert an ammeter into a voltmeter a high resistance R is connected in series with the ammeter. Since

$$i = \dfrac{V}{G_a + R} \qquad [G_a = \text{ammeter resistance}]$$

So the required $R = \dfrac{V - iG_a}{i}.$

Similarly in order to convert a voltmeter into an ammeter, a low resistance S is to be connected in parallel with the voltmeter. If G_v is the voltmeter resistance, then

$$i_v = i\left(\dfrac{S}{S + G_v}\right),$$

where i represents the maximum current in the desired range of the ammeter. For the maximum potential difference of the range of the voltmeter, its full scale deflection current can be written as

$$i_v = \dfrac{V}{G_v}.$$

146. Why is it potentiometer and not a voltmeter used for the accurate measurement of the e.m.f. of a cell?

Ans. If a voltmeter is connected between the two electrodes of a cell its reading provides the value of the e.m.f. of the cell, since the internal residence of the cell is negligibly small in comparison to the high resistance of the voltmeter. However, if the internal resistance is not neglected then the voltmeter reading becomes slightly smaller than the e.m.f. of the cell.

On the other hand, for the measurement of the e.m.f. of a cell by potentiometer a suitable length of the wire is accurately determined across which the potential difference becomes equal and opposite to the e.m.f. of the cell. Thus in this method the e.m.f. can be measured accurately.

147. If a current of 2 amperes flows through a circular coil of 1000 turns and of mean radius 100 cm, calculate the strength of the magnetic field at the centre.

Ans. Strength at the centre,

$$F = \dfrac{2\pi n i}{a}.$$

Here, $n = 1000$, $i = 2$ amperes $= \dfrac{2}{10}$ e.m.u., $a = 100$ cm.

$\therefore \qquad F = \dfrac{2 \times 3.14 \times 1000 \times 2}{100 \times 10} = 12.56$ Oe.

148. If 2 amperes current is made to pass through a long straight conductor 20 cm long at an angle of 30° with the direction of a magnetic field of strength 400 Oe, calculate the effective force on the conductor.

Ans. The effective force F can be written as

$$F = H i l \sin\theta = 400 \times 0.2 \times 20 \times \sin 30° = 800 \text{ dynes.}$$

149. *For using a tangent galvanometer, why is it required to set the plane of the coil in the magnetic meridian?*

Ans. The tangent galvanometer works on tangent law. For this the strength of the magnetic field (F) at the centre of the coil of the galvanometer is required to be at right angle to the horizontal component of the earth's magnetic field (H).

If the plane of the coil of the galvanometer be set along north and south, i.e., in the magnetic meridian, then only $F \perp H$ and the tangent law applies on the needle.

150. *On what factor does the reduction factor of a tangent galvanometer depend?*

Ans. If a be the radius, n be the number of turns of the coil and H be the horizontal intensity of the earth's magnetic field, then the reduction factor K can be written as

$$K = \frac{aH}{2\pi n}.$$

151. *How is the sensitivity of a galvanometer related with its reduction factor?*

Ans. The less is the reduction factor, the greater is the sensitivity.

152. *A single coil tangent galvanometer and a Helmholtz double coil galvanometer of same size and same number of turns of coil are given to you. Show that the sensitivity of the double coil galvanometer is more.*

Ans. If K_s represents the reduction factor of a single coil galvanometer and K_d represents the same for a double coil galvanometer, then

$$K_s = \frac{aH}{2\pi n},$$

$$K_d = \frac{5\sqrt{5}}{16}\left(\frac{aH}{2\pi n}\right) = \frac{5\sqrt{5}}{16}K_s.$$

$$\therefore \quad \frac{K_d}{K_s} = \frac{5\sqrt{5}}{16} < 1, \quad \text{i.e.,} \quad K_d < K_s.$$

So the sensitivity of the double coil galvanometer is more.

153. *At what temperature is the thermoelectric power zero?*

Ans. At the temperature of inversion E is maximum and hence the thermoelectric power $\frac{dE}{dt}$ is zero.

154. *What is the relation between henry and e.m.u. of inductance?*

Ans. 1 henry = 10^9 e.m.u. of inductance.

155. *Why is a resistance coil doubled on itself before winding?*

Ans. A resistance coil is doubled on itself before winding to make it a non-inductive one.

156. *For an L-R circuit, $L = 20$ H and $R = 2.5$ Ω. Calculate the time constant of the circuit.*

Ans. Time constant λ of an λ-R circuit can be written as

$$\lambda = \frac{L}{R}.$$

Here, $L = 20$ H, $R = 2.5\Omega$.

$$\therefore \qquad \lambda = \frac{20}{2.5} = \textbf{8 seconds.}$$

157. *The capacitance of a C-R circuit is 2μF and resistance 12 MΩ. Calculate the time constant of the circuit.*

Ans. Time constant λ of a C-R circuit can be written as

$\lambda = CR$.

Here, $C = 2\mu$ F $= 2 \times 10^{-6}$ F, $R = 12$ M$\Omega = 12 \times 10^6$ Ω

$\therefore$ $\lambda = 2 \times 10^{-6} \times 12 \times 10^6 = $ **24 seconds**.

158. *As soon as the battery is disconnected with the magnetising coil of an electromagnet, the pointer of an ammeter returns to zero reading immediately and does not move slowly—explain the reason.*

Ans. In a cut-off circuit due to the air-gap, the resistance R becomes very high and so the time constant $\frac{L}{R}$ becomes negligibly small. As a result, the current decays to zero value immediately as the circuit is broken. So the pointer of an ammeter immediately returns to zero reading.

159. *Express the equation of alternating e.m.f. for '230V-50 cycles/s' a.c. supply line.*

Ans. At any instant of time t the equation of an alternating e.m.f. is written as

$E = E_0 \sin \omega t$.

Here $E_0 = \sqrt{2} \times 230$ volts, $\omega = 2\pi f = 100\pi$

$\therefore$ $E = \sqrt{2}.230 \sin 100\pi t$.

160. *An alternating e.m.f. is expressed as*

$$E = 100 \sin 100\pi t \text{ volts.}$$

Find its amplitude and frequency.

Ans. The general equation of an alternating e.mf. can be expressed as

$$E = E_0 \sin \omega t.$$

Comparing the above equation with the equation $E = 100 \sin 100\pi t$, we get

$E_0 = $ **100 volts**

$2\pi f = 100 T$ or, $f = $ **50 cycles/s**.

161. *The equation of an alternating current is written as*

$$I = 200 \sin 400\pi t.$$

Find the peak value, r.m.s. value and frequency of the current.

Ans. The general equation of an alternating current can be expressed as

$$I = I_0 \sin 2\pi f t.$$

Comparing the above equation with the equation,

$$I = 200 \sin 400\pi t,$$

we get peak current, $I_0 = $ **200 amperes**,

r.m.s. current, $I_{rms} = \dfrac{I_0}{\sqrt{2}} = \dfrac{200}{\sqrt{2}} = $ **141.4 amperes**.

Again, $2\pi f = 400\pi = f = $ **200 cycles/s**.

162. *A voltmeter in an a.c. circuit shows 220 volts and ammeter 2 amperes. Calculate the effective resistance of the circuit.*

Ans. Effective resistance $= \dfrac{\text{virtual e.m.f.}}{\text{virtual current}} = \dfrac{220 \text{ volts}}{2 \text{ amperes}} = \mathbf{110\ \Omega}.$

163. *In a 230V-50 c.p.s. supply line (a) what is the period of alternating current and (b) at what intervals of time does the current reverse?*

Ans. (a) Here, frequency $(f) = 50$ c.p.s.

$\therefore$ period $(T) = \dfrac{1}{f} = \dfrac{1}{50} = \mathbf{0.02}$ **second.**

(b) Current reverses its direction at the intervals of $\dfrac{T}{2}$ each.

We have $T = 0.02$ second.

$\therefore \quad \dfrac{T}{2} = \dfrac{0.02}{2} = \mathbf{0.01}$ **second.**

164. *In a 230V-50 c.p.s. supply line, at what intervals of time (a) the magnitude of current is zero and (b) the current attains its pick value in the same direction?*

Ans. (a) The magnitude of current is zero at the intervals of $\dfrac{T}{2}$ each $= \mathbf{0.01}$ **second.**

(b) In the same direction the current attains peak value at intervals of T each $= \mathbf{0.02}$ **second.**

165. *On what factors does the impedance of an a.c. (a) L-R circuit and (b) C-R circuit depend?*

Ans. (a) For an L-R circuit, the impedance Z is written as

$$Z = \sqrt{R^2 + L^2\omega^2} = \sqrt{R^2 + 4\pi^2 L^2 f^2}.$$

So the impedance in this case depends on the inductance L, resistance R and the frequency f of the circuit.

(b) For a C-R circuit, the impedance Z can be expressed as

$$Z = \sqrt{R^2 + \frac{1}{C^2\omega^2}} = \sqrt{R^2 + \frac{1}{4\pi^2 f^2 C^2}}.$$

So the impedance in this case depends on the capacitance C, resistance R and the frequency f of the circuit.

166. *An alternating current of frequency 50 Hz is made to pass through a choke coil of negligible resistance and of 1 henry inductance. Calculate the inductive reactance and the power factor of the circuit.*

Ans. The inductive reactance,

$$X_L = L\omega = 2\pi f L = 2 \times 3.14 \times 50 \times 1 = \mathbf{314\ \Omega}.$$

Again, the power factor, $\cos\alpha = \dfrac{R}{Z}.$

Here, $R = 0$

$\therefore \qquad \cos\alpha = \dfrac{0}{Z} = \mathbf{0}$

167. *How is the frequency of a series resonant circuit is obtained?*

Ans. The impedance of an L-C-R circuit can be expressed as

$$Z = \sqrt{R^2 + \left(L\omega - \frac{1}{C\omega}\right)^2}.$$

When the inductive reactance $L\omega$ becomes equal to the capacitive reactance $\frac{1}{C\omega}$, the circuit becomes a resonance. At resonance,

$$L\omega_R = \frac{1}{C\omega_R} \quad \text{or,} \quad \omega_R^2 = \frac{1}{LC}.$$

$$\therefore \quad f_R = \frac{1}{2\pi\sqrt{(LC)}} \quad [\because \omega_R = 2\pi f_R]$$

The above equation gives the frequency of a series resonant circuit.

168. *What do you mean by an acceptor and a rejector circuit?*

Ans. A series resonant circuit is called an acceptor circuit while a parallel resonant circuit is called a rejector circuit.

169. *What are the devices by which (i) a small direct p.d., (ii) small alternating p.d. can be converted into a large one?*

Ans. (i) This can be done using Ruhmkorff's induction coil. If a small direct p.d. is obtained across its primary coil, a large p.d. is obtained across its secondary.

(ii) This can be done by using a step-up transformer. If a small alternating p.d. is applied across its primary coil a large p.d. is obtained across its secondary.

170. *Using* 220V-50 c.p.s. *supply line, how a p.d. of* 22 volts *and* 22 KV *can be obtained?*

Ans. A suitable step-down transformer for the low p.d. and a step-up transformer for the high p.d. are to be connected to 220s volts of the given a.c. supply line. If n_p and n_s are respectively the number of turns of the primary and the secondary coil of the transformer and if the virtual voltage applied across the primary coil be V_p and voltage across the secondary be V_s, then we have

$$\frac{n_s}{n_p} = \frac{V_s}{V_p}.$$

For the required low voltage of 22 volts,

$$\frac{n_s}{n_p} = \frac{22}{220} = \frac{1}{10}.$$

For the required high voltage of 22 KV,

$$\frac{n_s}{n_p} = \frac{22 \times 10^3}{220} = \frac{100}{1}.$$

Physical Optics

Chapter 20

Velocity of Light

20.1 Introduction

The velocity of light provides one of the most important universal constants. It is the highest velocity and is also the velocity with which X-rays, γ-rays, electromagnetic waves and similar types of radiations propagate. From very early days, it became an established fact that sound propagates with a finite velocity. But as the methods adopted for determination of velocity of sound were unsuccessful in the case of light, the obvious conclusion was that light has a velocity which is infinitely large.

20.2 Romer's Method for Finding the Velocity of Light

To determine the velocity of light Romer a Danish Astromomer by his observations of the eclipses of one of the satellites of Jupiter, noted that the interval between two successive eclipses, as observed from the Earth is not constant but changes according to the relative positions of the Earth and the Jupiter.

Romer calculated this discrepancy from a consideration that light took an appreciable time to travel from the Jupiter to the Earth and he succeeded in determining the velocity of light.

The principle of the method can be explained from Fig. 20.1. Let S be the position of the Sun and E_1, E_2 and J_1, J_2 be the positions of the Earth and the Jupiter in their respective orbits at different instants of time.

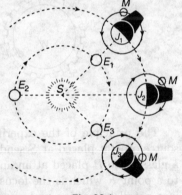

We assume that the first eclipse of the satellite M takes place when the Earth and the Jupiter are at E_1 and J_1, being on the same side of the Sun. As light takes time to travel through a certain distance, the first eclipse will be seen on the Earth $E_1 J_1/c$ seconds later than the actual time of occurrence, where c is the velocity of light. After each eclipse, the Earth will move farther away from

Fig. 20.1

the Jupiter due to their different rates of revolution in their orbits. As a result the distance between them will increase until it becomes maximum when the Earth and the Jupiter will be **in opposition**.

Let n eclipses occur during the interval when the Earth and the Jupiter are in **conjunction** (i.e., at $E_1 J_1$) and when they are in **opposition** (i.e., at $E_2 J_2$). Then the interval between the first and the last of these eclipses is $n \cdot t$, where t is the actual period of the eclipse.

Therefore, the observed interval

$$T_1 = n \cdot t + \frac{E_2 J_2 - E_1 J_1}{c} = n \cdot t + \frac{d}{c}, \qquad (20.1)$$

where $E_2 J_2 - E_1 J_1 = d$, the diameter of the Earth's orbit.

Further, when the Earth and the Jupiter come to the position of conjunction $E_3 J_3$, then the observed interval T_2 will be less than the true interval by $\frac{d}{c}$, as the distance between the Earth and the Jupiter is less than that when they were in opposition. Hence, we have

$$T_2 = n \cdot t - \frac{d}{c}. \tag{20.2}$$

Thus, from Eqs. (20.1) and (20.2), we get

$$c = \frac{2d}{T_1 - T_2} \tag{20.3}$$

Romer calculated T_1 and T_2 and found, $T_1 - T_2 == 33.3$ minutes; taking d equal to 191×10^6 miles from astronomical data, the velocity of light was calculated as $190\,000$ miles per second. Subsequent experiments showed that velocity of light in vacuum is $186\,000$ miles per second.

20.3 Fizeau's Terrestrial Method to Determine the Velocity of Light

The method implemented by Fizeau to determine the velocity of light depends on the eclipsing of a source of light by the teeth of a rapidly rotating wheel.

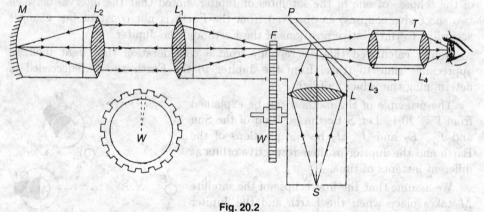

Fig. 20.2

The principle of the experiment can be explained using Fig. 20.2. A bright source of light placed at S sends out rays which after traversing the lens L fall on a glass plate P placed at an angle of $45°$. Then after reflection the rays converge to a point F which is the focus of the lens L_1. The rays of light emerge from L_1 in a parallel direction and after traversing a distance of about 4 miles fall on the lens L_2 and are brought to a focus on the surface of a concave mirror M having its centre of curvature in a position coincident with the centre of the lens L_2. So the rays are reflected back from the mirror along their own paths and after traversing the lens L_1 form an image at F as viewed by the eyepiece T.

A toothed wheel W rotated rapidly round an axle is so arranged that its teeth pass one after another through the point F. When the wheel rotates slowly, the light passing through F will be alternately stopped by a tooth and allowed to come out between two consecutive teeth. The image seen by the eyepiece will thus alternately appear and disappear. If the speed is increased, then due to persistence of vision a permanent image may be seen. If the speed of the wheel be so adjusted that the light which has escaped between two consecutive teeth and after reflection at the mirror M, returned to F is stopped by the tooth, the image will not be visible.

Let θ be the angle of rotation of the wheel. If the wheel makes n revolutions per second and if m be the number of teeth in the wheel, then the time required for the wheel to turn, so that a tooth may occupy a position previously occupied by a space, is determined. As in the time so determined, the light has travelled from F to M and back again to F, the velocity of light can be obtained by dividing the distance traversed by the time taken.

Let T be the time taken by light to travel from F to M and back again to F and let MF be equal to D. The velocity of light is then given by

$$c = \frac{2D}{T}. \tag{20.4}$$

Now, if n be the number of revolutions of the wheel per second, then its angular velocity is $2\pi n$. So, the time taken by the wheel to rotate through θ is same as $\frac{\theta}{2\pi n}$ which is equal to T.

Therefore, the first eclipse will occur when

$$T = \frac{2D}{c} = \frac{\theta}{2\pi n}. \tag{20.5}$$

If the speed is so adjusted that the next space comes at F in time T, then the bright image will be seen and for this the wheel rotates through an angle 2θ. If, again, the speed is increased and adjusted so that the second eclipse occurs in time T, then for the second eclipse,

$$\frac{2D}{c} = \frac{3\theta}{2\pi n_3} \tag{20.6}$$

Thus in this case, the wheel rotates through 3θ and makes n_3 revolutions per second. In a similar way, for the pth eclipse,

$$\frac{2D}{c} = \frac{(2p-1)\theta}{2\pi n_{2p-1}}.$$

$$\therefore \quad c = \frac{4\pi n_{2p-1}D}{(2p-1)\theta}. \tag{20.7}$$

Let m be the number of teeth on the wheel and the angular width of a space and a tooth are equal, then

$$2m\theta = 2\pi, \quad \text{or,} \quad \theta = \frac{\pi}{m}.$$

Putting value of θ in Eq. (20.7), we get

$$c = \frac{4mn_{2p-1}D}{2p-1}. \tag{20.8}$$

Using Eq. (20.8), the velocity of light c can be determined. The value of c thus obtained was 3.13×10^{10} cm per second.

20.4 Foucault's Method to Find c

By this method the velocity of light is determined inside a laboratory. Light from an illuminated slit S falls on a transparent glass plate. After passing through it light falls on an achromatic lens L and the emergent light after being reflected from the plane mirror R converges to a point M_1 on the concave mirror whose centre of curvature lies on the axis of rotation of R (Fig. 20.3). The plane mirror R can be rotated round an axis perpendicular to the plane of the paper. If the mirror R is stationary, the light reflected normally at the concave mirror M_1 will retrace its path and after passing through the lens form an image coincident with S. The returned light will appear to diverge from a virtual image S' behind the plane mirror R and form an image at I after reflection from the glass plate. Let during the time taken by the light to travel from R to M_1 and back again, the mirror is moved through a certain angle α. Then the reflected light makes an angle 2α with its original path and appears to proceed from the virtual image s' behind the mirror (not shown) and forms the real image at S' or at I', where dotted rays meet after reflection from the glass plate.

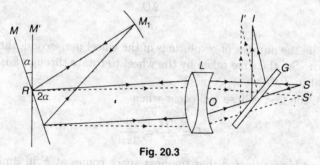

Fig. 20.3

The velocity of light c is then given by $\frac{2RM}{T}$, where T is the time taken by the light to travel from R to M_1 and back again, i.e., through $2RM_1$.

During the time T, the mirror R has turned through an angle MRM' which is equal to α. If we know the angular velocity of the rotating mirror R, then the time taken by the mirror to turn through an angle α is obtained and is equal to T.

Let the mirror makes n revolutions per second. Then the angular velocity $= 2\pi n$ radians per second.

Therefore, the time required to turn through the angle α

$$= \frac{\alpha}{2\pi n} = T. \tag{20.9}$$

To find the angle α, the images s and s' (not shown) may be taken as the virtual images of the point M_1 for the two positions of the mirror and are situated on the circumference of a circle having its centre on the axis of rotation of the mirror and passing through M_1. The arc ss' subtends an angle 2α at the centre of the circle. Hence, $ss' = 2\alpha \times D$, where $RM_1 = D$.

$$\therefore \quad \alpha = \frac{ss'}{D} \tag{20.10}$$

Next, instead of considering M_1 as the object for the two positions of the mirror, we consider s and s' as the object, and S and S' as their corresponding images.

We then have, $\frac{ss'}{SS'} = \frac{D+a}{b}$ (where $a =$ distance between the lens and the mirror and $b =$ the distance between the lens and the line joining the images S and S').

Hence, $ss' = \frac{(D+a)}{b}x$ (where $x = SS'$).

So from Eq. (20.10),

$$\alpha = \frac{(D+a)x}{2Db}. \tag{20.11}$$

Thus from Eqs. (20.9) and (20.11), we get

$$T = \frac{\alpha}{2\pi n} = \frac{(D+a)x}{2Db + 2\pi n}. \tag{20.12}$$

∴ the velocity of light, $c = \dfrac{2D}{T} = \dfrac{8\pi D^2 bn}{(D+a)x}. \tag{20.13}$

Using Eq. (20.13) the velocity of light can be determined. The value obtained by this method was 2 98 000 kilometres per second.

20.4.1 Defects in the Method

(i) The displacement x of the image was rather small. To make x large, D should be increased, but this will cause the angle subtended at R to be small, so that intensity will decrease. (ii) It was difficult to measure x due to existence of a background illumination.

20.4.2 Velocity of Light in Liquids

Foucault determined velocity of light in liquids by placing a tube filled with a liquid. The velocity of light in water or any liquid medium optically denser than air, was seen to be less than that in air. This result was agreed with the *Wave Theory of Light*.

20.5 Michelson's Method to Find c

Michelson modified Foucault's method by placing the lens between the fixed concave mirror and the revolving plane mirror to obtain a greater displacement of the image by increasing the distance between the two mirrors. The experimental arrangement of the method is shown in Fig. 20.4.

As shown, light from an illuminated slit S passes through a glass plate G, falls on the mirror M, which is capable of rotation about a vertical axis. Light being reflected from M passes through an achromatic lens L and gets reflected from a concave mirror OR whose centre of curvature is coincident with the centre of the lens. Thus the incident ray is reflected normally at the mirror OR, retraces its path and after passing through the lens and being reflected from M and G forms an image at S_1.

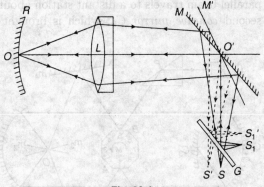

Fig. 20.4

When the mirror M is rotated at a high speed, the image is displaced to S_1'. If during the time taken by the light to travel from O' to O and back again, the mirror is moved through a certain angle α, the reflected light makes an angle 2α with its original path and appears to proceed from S' to form the image at S_1'.

We assume, $SO' = e$, $O'L = d$ and $OL = D$.

If c be the velocity of light and T be the time taken by the light to travel from M to R and back, then we can write,

$$T = \frac{2(D+d)}{c}. \tag{20.14}$$

During the time T, the mirror M has turned through an angle α and so $\alpha = \omega T = 2\pi n T$, where ω is the angular velocity and n the number of revolutions of the mirror M per second.

As the reflected ray turns through double the angle α through which the mirror is turned in time T, we have

$$SS' = S_1 S_1' = 2\alpha e = 4\pi n T \cdot e.$$

Now, if the displacement $SS' = S_1 S_1' = x$, then

$$x = 4\pi n T \cdot e \quad \text{or,} \quad T = \frac{x}{4\pi n e}.$$

Putting the value of T in Eq. (20.14), we get

$$c = \frac{8\pi n e(D + d)}{x}. \tag{20.15}$$

In the actual experiment the values were as follows : $D = 1865$ ft, $d = 135$ ft, $x = 11.2$ cm and $n = 258$ revolutions per second.

The value of c determined by this method was 3×10^{10} cm per second which is close to the standard value 2.99735×10^{10} cm/second.

20.6   Michelson's Octagonal Mirror Method to Find c

Octagonal rotating mirror method of Michelson is an accurate method of finding the velocity of light.

The experimental arrangement is shown in Fig. 20.5. Light from an illuminated slit S falls on the face A of the octagonal mirror M and is reflected from it. The reflected ray of light being further reflected from mirror m_1 falls on plane mirror m_2 to be again reflected by it. This reflected light falls on first *concave mirror* C_1 at its focal distance from O and thereby it is reflected as a parallel beam. This parallel beam travels to a distant station about 22 miles away and falls on a similar second *concave mirror* C_2, which is brought to a focus on the surface of third concave mirror C_3. It is then reflected back to the concave mirror C_2, wherefrom it returns as a parallel beam back to the concave mirror C_1. The light beam is then reflected by the plane mirror m_3 kept at right angles to and above m_2 and goes on to the plane mirror m_4 which reflects it on to the upper face B of the rotating mirror. Thus a final image is formed after being refracted through a right-angled prism P which is at the field of view of the micrometer eyepiece E.

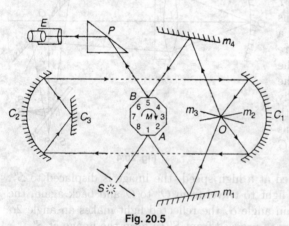

Fig. 20.5

Arranging the apparatus properly, the eyepiece is adjusted, so that the image of the slit falls on the cross-wire of the eyepiece. The *octagonal mirror AB* is then turned round and its speed of rotation is adjusted. The image again falls on the cross-wire when one face of the mirror is exactly occupied by the next, while the light travels from A to the distant mirror and back again to mirror B.

We assume, n = number of rotations of the rotating mirror per second,

m = number of sides of the rotating mirror,

and d = distance between two stations.

Then, $2d$ = total distance traversed by light.

The time taken by one face to be exactly occupied by the next face is given by

$$t = \frac{1}{mn} \text{ second.}$$

So the velocity of light, $c = \dfrac{2d}{1/mn} = 2mnd.$

As in the experiment, we have $m = 8$,

$\therefore$ $c = 16nd.$ (20.16)

In this method, the speed of rotation was found by a *stroboscopic arrangement* using an electrically maintained tuning fork having a known low frequency.

From the knowledge of n and d, the velocity of light is determined using Eq. (20.16).

Again, let θ be the angle of rotation of the mirror in time t required for one face to be exactly occupied by the next face, and ω be the angular velocity of rotation. As $\theta = 45°$, we get

$$t = \frac{\theta}{\omega} = \frac{\theta}{2\pi n} = \frac{45°}{2\pi n} = \frac{\pi}{8\pi n} = \frac{1}{8n}.$$

So the velocity of light, $c = \dfrac{2d}{1/8n} = 2 \times 8 \times nd = 16nd$, where $m = 8$ = number of faces.

Thus we may write, in general, $c = 2mnd.$ (20.17)

The mean velocity obtained by Michelson was 2.99797×10^8 m/s.

20.6.1   Advantages and Limitations of Michelson's Method

The determination of velocity of light by this method has a number of *advantages* and *limitations*.

The *advantages* are : (i) the distance between the two stations was sufficiently large; (ii) it *does not* require the measurement of any displacement of the image as in Foucault's method; (iii) the image remains at the point of intersection of the cross-wires only for a *certain* speed of rotation and appears or disappears abruptly; (iv) the **brightness** of the image is sufficient to ensure accurate measurements.

The *limitations* of the method are : (i) it is difficult to keep the speed of rotation *constant* for a long time. It can be maintained for a *few seconds only* in practice in which observations is to be completed; (ii) at very high speeds of rotation, there is a *risk of breakage* of the sides of the rotating mirror. However, Michelson reduced the risk by increasing the number of sides of the mirror.

20.7   Pease and Pearson's Modification of Michelson's Method

Though Michelson's method is an accurate method for the determination of the velocity of light, it *cannot* be used to find the velocity directly in vacuum. Pease and Pearson modified the method to find the velocity of light directly in vacuum.

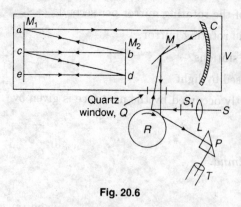

Fig. 20.6

The experimental arrangement of Pease and Pearson's method is shown in Fig. 20.6. In the figure S is an *arc lamp* wherefrom light is focused on the *slit* S_1 with the lens L. It strikes the upper half of one of the faces of a multifaceted *rotating cylinder* R whose all the 32 faces are plane polished. After being reflected from R, light enters into *vacuum tube* V of 1.6 km long through *quartz window* Q, to fall on the plane mirror M. The light reflected by M then strikes the concave mirror C whose focal length is about 15 m and travels to the opposite end of the tube V to fall on the plane mirror M_1. It suffers a reflection at a on M_1 to return to the slightly inclined similar mirror M_2 wherefrom it back to M_1 and again to M_2 by successive reflections. The light finally strikes M_1 *normally* at e to retrace its path to go back to the concave mirror C. On reflection from M, it strikes the lower half of the *same face* of the rotating cylinder R, to observe through the telescope T after being totally reflected from the prism P.

20.8　Kerr Cell Method to Find c

This method is based on the use of a Kerr cell as an *electro-optic shutter*. A *Kerr cell* uses the property known as the *Kerr electro-optic effect*. A Kerr cell consists of a small glass vessel with two parallel metal electrodes sealed into it and immersed in an appropriate insulating liquid like pure nitrobenzene (Fig. 20.7). When a high voltage is applied across the electrodes, the cell acts as a *uniaxial crystal* with *optic axis parallel to the field*.

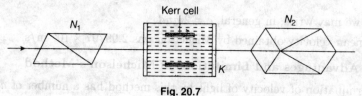

Fig. 20.7

We assume that a Kerr cell K is placed between two crossed Nicol prisms N_1 and N_2, where N_1 acts as a *polariser* and N_2 as an *analyser*. In absence of the field, no light will be transmitted by the analyser. But when the field is 'on', the liquid inside the cell becomes doubly refracting and some light passes through N_2. If the Kerr cell is oriented at an angle 45° to the incident plane polarised light, it breaks into *two equal* components with vibrations parallel and perpendicular to the field. They move with different velocities through the cell and produce *elliptically polarised* light on emergence. The horizontal component of vibration is allowed transmission through the analyser, N_2. When high frequency a.c. voltage is applied to the cell, it acts as an *electro-optic shutter* allowing light to pass when the field is maximum and to stop when the field is zero.

The experimental arrangement to find **velocity of light by Kerr cell method** is show in Fig. 20.8. S is the light source wherefrom light is focused by a lens L_1 on to the Kerr cell K_1, sandwiched between the crossed Nicol prisms N_1, N_2. Light on emergence from N_2, is rendered parallel by the lens L_2 to fall upon the plane mirror M. The reflected parallel beam from M is focused on to an *identical* Kerr cell K_2. Using the lens L_3, light on emergence is allowed to fall on the Nicol prism N_3, being crossed with N_2. The light is then received by the eye E through the lens L_4.

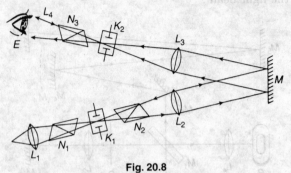

Fig. 20.8

Since N_1 and N_2 are crossed, *no light* comes out of N_2 and so no light is visible to the eye. If a h.f. a.c. voltage is simultaneously applied to K_1 and K_2, the inside liquid becomes doubly refracting at the moment the voltage is maximum and some light will be transmitted by N_2.

If n be the frequency of the a.c. voltage used, it will fall from maximum to zero in time $1/4n$. Let d be the effective distance the light travels between the cells K_1 and K_2. Then we have the velocity of light,

$$c = \frac{d}{1/4n} = 4nd. \tag{20.18}$$

However, there is a *limitation* of the method. It is practically difficult to exactly match the characteristics of the two identical Kerr cells.

20.9 Anderson's Method to Find Velocity of Light

The experimental arrangement of Anderson's method using Kerr cell as an *electro-optic shutter* is shown in Fig. 20.9.

In the figure, S is a mercury lamp wherefrom light, rendered parallel by the lens L_1, is passed through the Kerr cell K. It is sandwiched between two crossed Nicol prisms N_1 and N_2. Light emerging from N_2 is focused on the diaphragm D_1 by the lens L_2. From D_1 light strikes a *semi-silvered* glass plate M_1. It divides the light into *two* parts : (a) a part is reflected to fall on the plane mirror M_2 after passing through the diaphragm D_2 and the lens L_3; (b) the other part is transmitted and on reflection from the plane mirror M_3 falls *normally* on the concave mirror M_4. Both the beams retrace their paths and on passing through the semi-silvered glass plate M_1 are focused on to the *photocell P* by the lens L_4. The position of M_2 is adjusted for getting phase difference π that occurs between the two beams. Thus the photocell would show a *minimum response* to the h.f. variations in light intensity. The concave mirror M_4 is then replaced by another concave mirror M_4' which will reflect light on to the plane mirror M_5 and next to mirror M_6 where it falls *normally* to retrace its path. The position of M_2 is adjusted further for *minimum response* of photocell. D_2 is used to *match* the light intensities of the beams that travel in different paths. If the matching is better, more accurate would be the position of minimum intensity.

We assume that the distance from M_1 to M_4 be x, and y be the distance from M_1 to M_2.

Hence, $2x - 2y = m\lambda/2,$ (20.19)

where m is an integer and λ is the wavelength corresponding to high frequency used for modulating the light beam.

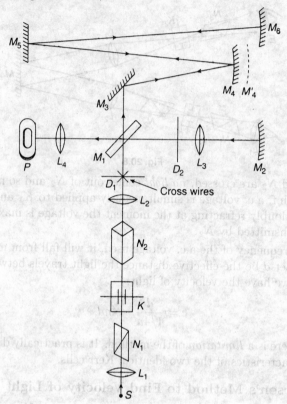

Fig. 20.9

Let s be the distance of M_4 from M_6 and δs be the change in path when M_4 is substituted by M_4' and δy be the shift of the plane mirror M_2, then

$$(2s + 2\delta s + 2x) - (2y - 2\delta y) = (2n + m)\frac{\lambda}{2}$$

or, $2(s + \delta s) + 2\delta y = n\lambda.$ (20.20)

In actual experiment Anderson used $n = 11$; δs was obtained by a micro-calliper and hence λ can be computed. If N be the known frequency of the oscillator, then we have

velocity of light, $c = n\lambda.$ (20.21)

Anderson took about 3000 observations and then introducing correction for vacuum he obtained the value of the velocity of light as

$$c = 299776 \pm 6 \text{ km/s}.$$

Advantages and Source of Error

The advantages of the method are : (i) to avoid the use of two Kerr cells and (ii) the use of a photocell instead of the eye.

The main source of error is the difficulty to arrange for both the beams in using the same position of the photocell.

20.10   Velocity of Light in Vacuum

In various terrestrial experiments, we measure the velocity of light in air. However, in vacuum, the velocity of light is different. The refractive index μ of a medium can be written as

$$\mu = \frac{\text{velocity of light in vacuum}}{\text{velocity of light in the medium}}.$$

Thus by multiplying the velocity of light measured in air by the refractive index of air, one may get the velocity of light in vacuum.

The most accurate value of the velocity of light, in vacuum, is given by

$$c = (2.9986 \pm 0.003) \times 10^8 \text{ m/s}.$$

The velocity of light is generally taken as 3×10^8 m/s.

20.11   Importance of Velocity of Light

The importance of velocity of light is discussed below :

(i) The ratio between the magnitude of various electrical quantities, measured in electromagnetic or electrostatic units involves velocity of light.

As for example,

$$\frac{1 \text{ e.m.u. of capacity}}{1 \text{ e.s.u. of capacity}} = c.$$

Similarly, $\dfrac{1 \text{ e.m.u. of charge}}{1 \text{ e.s.u. of charge}} = c$ and $\dfrac{1 \text{ e.m.u. of potential}}{1 \text{ e.s.u. of potential}} = \dfrac{1}{c}$, so on.

(ii) Experiments reveal that electromagnetic radiation travels with a velocity equal to that of light. So, if ν and λ be the frequency and wavelength of the radiation respectively, then $\nu\lambda = c$. This relation provides the frequency or the wavelength of the radiation.

(iii) The absolute refractive index of a medium is the ratio of velocity of light in vacuum and the velocity of light in the medium.

(iv) According to the Quantum Theory, the momentum of a wave of frequency ν is $p = \frac{h\nu}{c}$ (where p = momentum and h = Planck's constant).

(v) According to the theory of relativity, mass and energy are equivalent to each other. The conversion formula, $E = mc^2$, involves the velocity of light (where E = energy produced; m = mass converted and c = the velocity of light).

(vi) According to the theory of relativity, the mass of a body depends on its velocity. If the velocity of the body be equal to that of light, the mass becomes infinite which is evident from the relation,

$$m = \frac{m_0}{\sqrt{1 - v^2/c^2}}$$

(where m_0 = rest mass of the body; m = mass of body when it is moving with a velocity v).

Examples

1. Calculate the time taken by a beam to travel through a glass pane of thickness 1 mm and refractive index 1.5. Velocity of light through air is 3×10^8 m/s.

Solution : We have from the definition of refractive index,

$$1.5 = \frac{\text{velocity of light in air, } c}{\text{velocity of light in the medium, } v}$$

or, $v(\text{glass}) = 3 \times 10^8/1.5$

Also, thickness of glass, $d = 1 \text{ mm} = 10^{-3} \text{ m.}$

So the time taken by the beam to travel through the medium,

$$t = \frac{d}{v} = \frac{10^{-3}}{3 \times 10^8/1.5} = \frac{1.5 \times 10^{-3}}{3 \times 10^8} = \mathbf{5 \times 10^{-12}} \text{ s.}$$

2. In a Kerr cell method for finding the velocity of light, the response of the photocell was minimum when the path difference was 171.8 m and frequency of modulation 9.6 MHz. If the value of integral was 11, calculate the velocity of light.

Solution : Given that the path difference = 171.8 m and $n = 11$.

$$\therefore \quad 2 \times 171.8 = 11 \times \lambda \quad \text{or,} \quad \lambda = \frac{2 \times 171.8}{11}.$$

Again, the frequency of modulation, $N = 9.6 \text{ MHz} = 9.6 \times 10^6 \text{ Hz}$. Therefore, by using the relation, $c = N\lambda$, we get

velocity of light, $c = 9.6 \times 10^6 \times 2 \times 171.8/11 = \mathbf{2.9986 \times 10^8} \text{ m/s.}$

3. In Michelson's experiment, the octagonal mirror was making 250 r.p.s. and the distance between the concave mirror C_2 and the octagonal mirror was 75 km. Find the velocity of light.

Solution : Given that, $n = 250 \text{ rev/s}$; $d = 75 \text{ km}$. Therefore, the velocity of light,

$$c = 16nd = 16 \times 250 \times 75 \text{ km/s} = 300000 \text{ km/s} = \mathbf{3 \times 10^8} \text{ m/s.}$$

4. In Fizeau's method of determining the speed of propagation of light by means of a toothed wheel, the wheel has 150 teeth and an equal number of spaces of equal width. If the distance of the mirror be 12 km, at what speed (in revolution per minute) of the wheel the first eclipse occurs?   **[C.U. 1947]**

Solution : We have, $c = \dfrac{4mn_{2p-1}D}{2p - 1}$.

Given that $m = 150$, $p = 1$, $D = 12 \times 1000 \times 100$ cm, $c = 3 \times 10^{10}$ cm/second.

So the speed, $n = \dfrac{3 \times 10^{10} \times 60}{4 \times 150 \times 12 \times 10^5} = \mathbf{2500}$ **revolutions per min.**

5. Given that the distance of the mirror is 8000 yards, that the revolving disc has 720 teeth and that the first eclipse occurs when the angular velocity of the disc is $13^3/4$ revolutions per second, calculate the speed of propagation of light.

Solution : We have, $c = \dfrac{4mn_{2p-1}D}{2p - 1}$.

Here, $m = 720$, $p = 1$, $D = 8000 \times 3$ feet, $n = 13^3/4$ revolutions/second.

$$\therefore \quad c = \frac{4 \times 720 \times 55 \times 8000 \times 3}{4} = \mathbf{9.504 \times 10^8} \text{ feet/second}$$

$$= \mathbf{180 \times 10^2} \text{ miles/second.}$$

Questions

Essay-type

1. Describe some modern method for measuring the velocity of light and discuss its merits and demerits.

2. Describe Fizeau's method for finding the velocity of light, giving a neat diagram. What are its disadvantages, and how have some of these been subsequently minimised?

   What value did Fizeau obtain and what is the present accepted value in c.g.s. units?

3. Describe Foucault's rotating mirror method of measuring the velocity of light and the effect upon the displacement of the image of putting a column of water between the rotating and the fixed mirrors.

4. Describe an apparatus which can be arranged in a laboratory for determining the velocity of light. Mention some of its defects and state how they were subsequently minimised.

   Explain how the measurement of velocity of light in water shows that the emission theory of light cannot be accepted as true.

5. Describe and explain Michelson's rotating mirror method of finding the velocity of light, and compare its merits and demerits with those of other methods.

6. Describe Pease and Pearson's modification of Michelson's method for an accurate measurement of the velocity of light.

7. What is a Kerr cell? Describe the Kerr cell method for the determination of the velocity of light in vacuum.

8. Describe Anderson's method for determining the velocity of light. What is the value obtained by him and the present-day accepted value?

9. Describe Michelson's method of determining the velocity of light. State the advantages of this method over other methods.

10. Describe in a general way Kerr cell method of determination of the velocity of light.

Short Answer-type

11. Is the velocity of light in vacuum a fundamental constant? Why?

12. What is the present-day accepted value for the velocity of light in vacuum?

13. What is Kerr effect? What is a Kerr cell?

14. Why is the velocity of light of great significance in Physics?

15. How is refractive index of a medium related to the velocity of light in vacuum?

16. Why is a Kerr cell called an electro-optic shutter? Explain.

17. Could the velocity of a material particle be increased indefinitely? Explain.

18. Is the speed of light in vacuum different for lights of different colours? Does the speed of light in some media depend on the direction of propagation? If so, name such a medium.

19. Write down the advantages and limitations of Michelson's rotating mirror method for the determination of the velocity of light.

Numerical Problems

20. Light travels to a target and back in 0.5 s in carbon disulphide. Calculate the distance of the target if the refractive index of carbon disulphide is 1.46.

[**Ans.** 51.37×10^6 m]

21. In Michelson's method, the octagonal mirror makes 625 revolutions per second. If the distance between the plane mirror and the rotating mirror is 30 km, calculate the velocity of light. [**Ans.** 3×10^8 m/s]

22. In the rotating mirror method used to measure the velocity of light which travelled from Mt. Wilson to Mt. San Antonio, no shift of the observed source of light was obtained with an 8-face mirror rotated at a speed of 530 r.p.s. If the measured distance of the light travelled (in one direction) was 354.3×10^2 m, calculate the velocity of light. [**Ans.** $\simeq 3 \times 10^8$ m s^{-1}]

23. A certain monochromatic radiation has a wavelength of 5000 Å in water. What is the wavelength in (i) vacuum and (ii) carbon disulphide? Given, μ for water = 1.33 and μ for CS$_2$ = 1.628. [**Ans.** 6667 Å; 4102 Å]

Chapter 21
Wave Theory of Light

21.1   Introduction

The wave theory of light was first proposed by the Dutch physicist Huygens. According to him, light propagates in the form of *wave* generated by the mechanical vibrations of a homogeneous medium called *ether*. However this medium was a *hypothetical medium* and was endowed with properties of both *elasticity and inertia* so that a wave motion can propagate through it. The mechanical disturbance propagates from the point of its 'origin in all directions through the medium. Huygens considered that light waves were longitudinal in character which was later proved to be wrong. Subsequently, Fresnel and Young explained light waves to be *transverse* in nature.

The wave theory of light was highly successful to explain many of the optical phenomena.

21.2   Huygens' Principle of Light Propagation

Huygens assumed a light source as a homogeneous hypothetical medium, ether which sends out light waves in all directions. It is these waves that carry energy with them and transmitted in all directions.

Let us assume that S is a point source of light which sends out energy in all directions in the form of waves. After a short time Δt, all the particles of the medium will be on the surface AB and be in *some state of vibration*. This means that the particle will be in the *same phase*. AB is drawn with S as centre and radius $c\Delta t$, where c is the velocity of propagation of the waves. The surface AB is called the *primary wavefront*. A **wavefront** *is defined as the locus of all such points that are in the same state of vibration, i.e., in the same phase.*

In a *homogeneous medium*, for a *point source* of light, the *wavefront* is a *sphere* [Fig. 21.1(a)]. If the source is situated at a large distance, then a small portion of the spherical wavefront may be looked upon as a plane. This is illustrated in Fig. 21.1(b). So the rays of light diverging from or converging to a point give rise to a *spherical wavefront*. A parallel beam of light on the other hand, gives rise to a *plane wavefront*. The *direction along which the disturbance propagates in a homogeneous medium is known as the* ray. Therefore, a *ray* is always *normal to the* *wavefront.*

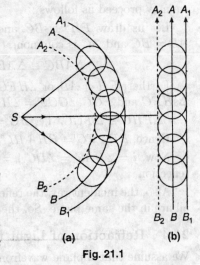

(a)   (b)

Fig. 21.1

According to **Huygens' principle**, *"Each point on the primary wavefront is looked upon as the centre of a new disturbance which sends out secondary wavelets. Therefore, a series of secondary wavelets are sent out in all directions that propagate through space with the same velocity in an isotropic homogeneous medium."* After an interval of time, the envelope of the secondary wavelets produces the *secondary wavefront.*

To locate the position of the new wavefront after an interval Δt, a number of points are taken on AB and with each such point as centre and radius $c\Delta t$, spheres are drawn. These spheres represent the secondary wavelets. The surface A_1B_1 touching all such spheres in the *forward direction* is then the *new wavefront.* This explains how light wave propagates following Huygens' principle. The principle assumes that *wavelets are effective only at the points where they are touched by their enveloping surface.*

21.3 Reflection of Light from Wave Theory

Let PQ be the reflecting surface and AB be the plane wavefront incident on it (Fig. 21.2). If the wavefront strikes the reflector at A making an angle i with it, the angle i is the *angle of incidence*, being equal to the angle between the normal and the

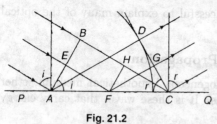

Fig. 21.2

incident ray at A. Then A becomes the source of secondary wavelets that tend to spread out in surrounding space. By the time the disturbance from B reaches to the reflector at C, the secondary waves from A will have a radius BC. We draw a sphere with A as centre and a radius equal to BC. A plane through C, touching the sphere at D, will then be the reflected wavefront CD.

The disturbance from any point E on the incident wavefront, after reflection by the reflector at F, must reach the reflected wavefront in the time the disturbance from A reaches D. Let FG be drawn perpendicular to CD, then $(EF + FG)$ must be equal to AD or BC. In order to show that CD is the *true reflected wavefront*, we may proceed as follows :

Let us draw $FH \perp BC$ and we take right-angled $\Delta sABC$ and ADC. As $AD = BC$ and AC is common,

$$\Delta ABC \equiv \Delta ADC \quad \text{or,} \quad \angle BAC = \angle DCA = r. \tag{21.1}$$

Further, $FH \parallel AB$ or $\angle HFC = \angle BAC = \angle DCA = \angle GCF$. In right-angled $\Delta sHFC$ and FGC, $\angle GCF = \angle HFC$, FC is common.

$\therefore \quad \Delta FHC \equiv \Delta FGC$ i.e. $FG = HC$.

Hence, $EF + FG = BH + HC = BC$. Hence, CD is the *true reflected wavefront.*

Now, $i = \angle BAC = \angle DCA = r$ or, $i = r$. Thus, angle of incidence = angle of reflection.

Also, the incident ray, the reflected ray and the normal at the point of incidence, all are in the same plane. So, the *laws of reflection* are *proved by the wave theory.*

21.4 Refraction of Light from Wave Theory

We assume that a plane wavefront AB be incident on the plane refracting surface PQ that separates two media a and b (Fig. 21.3) where the velocities of the waves are c_1 and c_2 ($c_1 > c_2$).

If the point A of the wavefront touches the refracting surface, the point B is away from it and by the time the disturbance from B reaches C at the surface of separation, secondary waves from A have acquired a radius AD in the medium b. Hence, we can write,

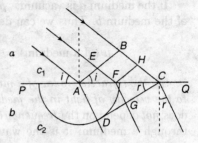

Fig. 21.3

$$\frac{AD}{c_2} = \frac{BC}{c_1}.$$

We draw a sphere with A as centre and AD as radius. The *tangent plane CD* through C touching the sphere will give the *refracted wavefront* (Fig. 21.3). If CD be the *true* refracted wavefront, then the disturbance from any point E on the incident wavefront should, after refraction at F on the surface of separation, reach G on CD during the time disturbance from A reaches D. Then we have

$$\frac{EF}{c_1} + \frac{FG}{c_2} = \frac{AD}{c_2} \quad \left(\text{or,} \quad \frac{BC}{c_1} \right).$$

To show this we draw $FH \perp BC$. But, we have $BC = BH + HC$.

Hence, $\dfrac{BC}{c_1} = \dfrac{BH}{c_1} + \dfrac{HC}{c_1} = \dfrac{EF}{c_1} + \dfrac{HC}{c_1} \quad (\because BH = EF)$.

Now, Δs ABC and FHC are similar. Further, Δs ADC and FGC are similar. So we have

$$\frac{FC}{AC} = \frac{HC}{BC} \tag{21.2}$$

and

$$\frac{FC}{AC} = \frac{FG}{AD}. \tag{21.3}$$

Hence from Eqs. (21.2) and (21.3),

$$HC/BC = FG/AD \quad \text{or,} \quad AD/BC = FG/HC.$$

Now using Eq. (21.2) we have

$$c_2/c_1 = FG/HC \quad \text{or,} \quad HC/c_1 = FG/c_2.$$

Thus it is shown that CD *is the true refracted wavefront*.

Again, $\angle BAC = i =$ angle of incidence; $\angle ACD = r =$ angle of refraction.

Therefore, $\dfrac{\sin i}{\sin r} = \dfrac{\sin \angle BAC}{\sin \angle ACD} = \dfrac{BC}{AC} \cdot \dfrac{AC}{AD} = \dfrac{BC}{AD} = \dfrac{c_1}{c_2} = \text{constant},$ (21.4)

using Eq. (21.2).

This is the famous Snell's law. The constant is the *refractive index*, $_a\mu_b$, of the medium b with respect to the medium a.

Again, the incident ray, the refracted ray and the normal at the point of incidence—all lie in the same plane. So the *laws of refraction* are established from the wave theory of light.

Now from Eq. (21.4), we may write the expression for $_a\mu_b$ as

$$_a\mu_b = \frac{\text{velocity of light in medium } a}{\text{velocity of light in medium } b}$$

If the medium a is vacuum, $_a\mu_b$ is written as μ_b or simply μ, the *refractive index* of the medium b. Thus we can define μ as

$$\mu \text{ (of a medium)} = \frac{\text{velocity of light in vacuum (or air)}}{\text{velocity of light in the medium}}.$$

So, *the refractive index of a medium is the ratio of the velocity of light in vacuum to the velocity of light in the medium.* Further, the refractive index μ of a medium does *not* depend on the *frequency* of the wave. This is because when light propagates through a medium, it is the wavelength that changes but the frequency remains unaltered.

21.5   Refraction of Spherical Wave at a Spherical Surface

The relation for refraction of spherical wave at a spherical surface according to the wave theory can be derived in the following way :

21.5.1   Concave Spherical Surface

As shown in Fig. 21.4, let CAB represent a portion of a concave spherical refracting surface. It separates a medium of refracting index μ and air. P is its centre of curvature and R is the radius of curvature. O is a luminous point object on the principal axis OA and BFC is the portion of the spherical wave touching the surface at C and B. If c_1, c_2 be the velocities of the wave in air and in the medium of index μ respectively, then $\mu = c_1/c_2$. According to Huygens' construction, every point on the wavefront BFC represents source of secondary waves. Points B and C send disturbances into the medium but the other points send them partly in air and then in the medium.

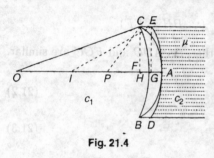

Fig. 21.4

Let t be the time taken by the disturbance from F to reach A in air. Then at that time, we assume that the disturbance from C reaches E in the medium. Hence, we can write,

$$\frac{AF}{c_1} = \frac{CE}{c_2} \quad \text{or,} \quad CE = AF \times \frac{c_2}{c_1} = \frac{AF}{\mu}. \tag{21.5}$$

In the same time t, the disturbance from B also reaches D in the medium. In this way, the disturbance from all points on the incident wavefront after time t will be on the wavefront DAE, the *refracted wavefront* originating from I. So, I is the *virtual image* of O.

Let us draw $CH \perp OA$ and $EG \perp OA$. Here, $CH = EF = y$ (say).

Now, we have $AO = u$, $AI = v$ and $AP = R$. From the geometry of a circle, we get

$$CH^2 = AH \times 2R \quad \text{or,} \quad AH = \frac{CH^2}{2R} = \frac{y^2}{2R}. \tag{21.6}$$

In a similar way,

$$FH = \frac{y^2}{2u}, \quad AG = \frac{y^2}{2v}. \tag{21.7}$$

From the figure, $CE = HG$ and from Eq. (21.5), $AF = \mu \times CE = \mu \times HG$,

$\therefore \quad AH - HF = \mu(AH - AG) \quad \text{or,} \quad \mu AG - HF = (\mu - 1)AH$

or, $\mu \dfrac{y^2}{2v} - \dfrac{y^2}{2u} = (\mu - 1)\dfrac{y^2}{2R}$ [using Eqs. (21.6) and (21.7)]

or, $\dfrac{\mu}{v} - \dfrac{1}{u} = \dfrac{\mu - 1}{R}.$ (21.8)

Now, by sign convention, u, v, R are all negative. Therefore we get the same relation as derived in Eq. (21.8) after substituting the signs for u, v and R.

21.5.2 Convex Spherical Surface

As shown in Fig. 21.5, let BAC be the portion of a convex refracting spherical surface of refractive index μ. Its centre of curvature is at P, separating the medium air and medium of index μ. Let c_1 and c_2 be the velocities of the wave in air and in the medium of refractive index μ respectively so that $\mu = c_1/c_2$ $(c_1 > c_2)$. EAF is a wavefront diverging from the luminous point source O. According to Huygens' construction, each point on the wavefront EAF is a source of secondary wave. Points E and F send disturbances in air but other points send them partly in air and partly in the medium. We assume that t be the time taken by the disturbance from

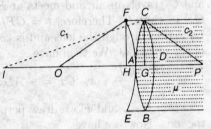

Fig. 21.5

F to reach C in air. Then, in the same time, the disturbance from A will reach at D into the medium. We can, therefore, write,

$$\frac{CF}{c_1} = \frac{AD}{c_2} \quad \text{or,} \quad CF = \frac{c_1}{c_2}AD = \mu AD. \tag{21.9}$$

Disturbances from all other points on incident wavefront EF will reach the wavefront CDB originating from I. So I is the *virtual image* of O formed by refraction. We now draw $FH \perp OA$ and $CG \perp OA$ (extended). We have, $HG = CF = \mu AD$, [using Eq. (21.9)]

or, $AH + AG = \mu(AG + GD)$ or, $(\mu - 1)AG = AH - \mu GD.$ (21.10)

Now we have $CG = FH = y$ (say). Also, $AO = u$, $AI = v$ and $AP = R$.

From the geometry of a circle, we can write,

$$AH = \frac{y^2}{2u}, \quad GD = \frac{y^2}{2v} \quad \text{and} \quad AG = \frac{y^2}{2R}.$$

Putting these values in Eq. (21.10),

$$(\mu - 1)\frac{y^2}{2R} = \frac{y^2}{2u} - \mu\frac{y^2}{2v} \quad \text{or,} \quad \frac{\mu - 1}{R} = \frac{1}{u} - \frac{1}{v}. \tag{21.11}$$

By sign convention, both u and v are negative but R is positive. Substituting the signs for u, v and R in Eq. (21.11), we get

$$\frac{\mu - 1}{R} = \frac{1}{v} - \frac{1}{u}. \tag{21.12}$$

21.6 Lens-maker's Formula by Wave Theory

The formula for thin convex lens is derived below by using the wave theory of light :

We assume that A and D are the poles of two spherical surfaces of radii of curvature R_1 and R_2 respectively of the thin convex lens L of refractive index μ

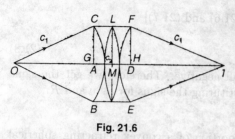

Fig. 21.6

(Fig. 21.6). O is a luminous point object placed on the principal axis, giving out spherical waves. Let c_1 and c_2 be the velocities of the waves in air and in the medium of refractive index μ respectively (where $c_1 > c_2$). Further let BAC be a portion of a spherical wavefront touching the pole A at any instant.

According to Huygens' principle, the pole A becomes the origin of secondary waves that move over the thickness AD in the lens medium in time t. Hence, we have $t = AD/c_2$. The disturbance from B and C travels in air and meets at E and F respectively following paths BE and CF in time t. Therefore, $t = CF/c_1$ and FDE is the spherical wavefront *after refraction* through the lens and is *convergent* with centre I. So I is the *real image* of the object O. We then have

$$\frac{AD}{c_2} = \frac{CF}{c_1} \quad \text{or,} \quad CF = \frac{c_1}{c_2} AD = \mu AD. \tag{21.13}$$

From C, L and F we draw perpendiculars CG, LM and FH respectively on the axis. Now, we have

$$GH = CF = \mu \cdot AD, \quad \text{[using Eq. (21.13)]}$$

or, $GA + AD + DH = \mu \cdot AD$

or, $GA + DH = (\mu - 1)AD = (\mu - 1)(AM + MD).$ \hfill (21.14)

Further, $AO = u$, $ID = v$ and $CG = LM = FH = y$, (say). From geometry of the circle, we get

$$GA = \frac{y^2}{2u}, \quad AM = \frac{y^2}{2R_1}, \quad MD = \frac{y^2}{2R_2} \quad \text{and} \quad DH = \frac{y^2}{2v}.$$

Substituting these values in Eq. (21.14),

$$\frac{y^2}{2u} + \frac{y^2}{2v} = (\mu - 1)\left(\frac{y^2}{2R_1} + \frac{y^2}{2R_2}\right) \quad \text{or,} \quad \frac{1}{u} + \frac{1}{v} = (\mu - 1)\left(\frac{1}{R_1} + \frac{1}{R_2}\right).$$

By sign convention we find that in this case v and R_1 are positive, while u and R_2 are negative. Hence, we get

$$\frac{1}{v} - \frac{1}{u} = (\mu - 1)\left(\frac{1}{R_1} - \frac{1}{R_2}\right). \tag{21.15}$$

When the object is at infinity, the image is formed at focus, i.e., for $u = \infty$, $v = f$. Hence from Eq. (21.15), we get

$$\frac{1}{f} = (\mu - 1)\left(\frac{1}{R_1} - \frac{1}{R_2}\right). \tag{21.16}$$

This is the required Lens-maker's Formula.

Examples

1. A light wave of frequency 6×10^{10} Hz is passed through a liquid. The wavelength measured in liquid is 3×10^{-3} m. Find (i) wavelength in vacuum, (ii) refractive index of the liquid and (iii) speed of light in liquid. Given : velocity of light in vacuum $= 3 \times 10^8$ m/s.

Solution.: (i) Let λ_1, λ_2 be the wavelengths in vacuum and liquid respectively, and n be the frequency of light. We have,

$$c_1 = n\lambda_1, \quad c_2 = n\lambda_2,$$

where c_1 = velocity of light in vacuum and c_2 = velocity of light in liquid.

Hence, $c_2 = 6 \times 10^{10} \times 3 \times 10^{-3} = \mathbf{18 \times 10^7 \ m}$

Further, $\dfrac{\lambda_1}{\lambda_2} = \dfrac{c_1}{c_2}$ or, $\lambda_1 = \dfrac{c_1}{c_2}\lambda_2 = \dfrac{3 \times 10^8}{18 \times 10^7} \times 3 \times 10^{-3} = \mathbf{5 \times 10^{-3} \ m}$

Refractive index, $\mu = \dfrac{c_1}{c_2} = \dfrac{3 \times 10^8}{18 \times 10^7} = \mathbf{1.66}$.

2. The velocity of light in air is 3×10^8 m/s. Find the velocity and wavelength of sodium light ($\lambda = 5893$ Å) in glass of refractive index 1.658.

Solution : Let c_1 be the velocity of light in air and c_2 be that in glass of refractive index μ. We then have

$$\mu = \frac{c_1}{c_2} \quad \text{or,} \quad c_2 = \frac{c_1}{\mu} = \frac{3 \times 10^8}{1.658} = \mathbf{1.809 \times 10^8 \ m/s}.$$

If λ_1 be 5893 Å for sodium light in air and λ_2 be that in glass, then we have

$$c_1 = n\lambda_1, \quad c_2 = n\lambda_2, \quad n = \text{frequency}$$

or, $\dfrac{\lambda_1}{\lambda_2} = \dfrac{c_1}{c_2} = \mu$.

So the wavelength of sodium light in glass, $\lambda_2 = \dfrac{\lambda_1}{\mu} = \dfrac{5893}{1.658} = \mathbf{3554 \ Å}$.

3. It is found that the optical paths of a monochromatic light are identical when it goes through 3.50 cm in water or 3.00 cm in glass. Calculate the refractive index of glass when that of water is 1.33.

Solution : When light propagates through a distance d in a medium of refractive index μ, its optical path $= \mu d$, we then have

$$\mu_{\text{glass}} \times 3.00 \ \text{cm} = \mu_{\text{water}} \times 3.50 \ \text{cm} = 1.33 \times 3.50 \ \text{cm}$$

or, $\mu_{\text{glass}} = \dfrac{1.33 \times 3.50}{3.00} = 1.55$.

4. White light is a mixture of wavelengths between 400 nm and 800 nm. If such light goes through water having a refractive index 1.33, what would be the limits of wavelength in that medium?

Solution : When light of wavelength λ_0 in vacuum propagates into a medium of refractive index μ, the wavelength in the medium becomes $\lambda = \lambda_0/\mu$.

Hence, corresponding to $\lambda_0 = 400$ nm, $\lambda = 400/1.33 = 300$ nm

and corresponding to $\lambda_0 = 800$ nm, $\lambda = 800/1.33 = 600$ nm.

Therefore, the required **limits of wavelength in water are 300 nm and 600 nm**.

5. The refractive index of fused quartz is 1.472 for light of $\lambda = 400$ nm and is 1.452 for light of $\lambda = 760$ nm. Find the speeds of light of these wavelengths in fused quartz.

Solution : Let v_1 be the speed corresponding to $\lambda_1 = 400$ nm and v_2 be that corresponding to $\lambda_2 = 760$ nm in fused quartz.

Now, from the definition of μ, we get

$$1.472 = \frac{\text{velocity of light in vacuum}}{\text{velocity of light in quartz}} = \frac{3 \times 10^8 \text{ m}}{v_1}$$

and $\quad 1.452 = \dfrac{3 \times 10^8 \text{ m}}{v_2}.$

Solving for v_1 and v_2, we get

$$v_1 = 2.04 \times 10^8 \text{ m/s}; \; v_2 = 2.07 \times 10^8 \text{ m/s}.$$

6. A glass plate 3 mm thick with a refractive index 1.5 is placed between a point source and a screen 3 cm away. The source emits light of wavelength 6000 Å in vacuum. What is the length of the optical path between the source and the screen? How many waves are there between the source and the screen?

[C.U. 1991, '99]

Solution : The air path between the source and the screen $= 3 - 0.3 = 2.7$ cm. Now, the equivalent air path for thickness of glass plate $=$ thickness $\times$ refractive index $= 0.3 \times 1.5 = 0.45$ cm.

Hence, total optical path $= 2.7 + 0.45 = \mathbf{3.15\ cm}$.

Further, the number of waves $= \dfrac{\text{optical path}}{\text{wavelength}} = \dfrac{3.15}{6000 \times 10^{-8}} = \mathbf{52500}.$

Questions

Essay-type

1. State Huygens' principle and show how it can be used to explain the laws of reflection of light? [C.U. 1983]

2. Clearly explain Huygens' principle and deduce the laws of refraction from it.
[C.U. 1976; B.U. 1976; N.B.U. 1982]

3. Deduce on the basis of the incidence of spherical waves, the object-image relation of a lens.

4. State the fundamental postulates of undulatory theory of light. Account for the formation of image by refraction through lenses on wave theory and hence prove the relation
$$\frac{1}{v} - \frac{1}{u} = (\mu - 1)\left(\frac{1}{r_1} - \frac{1}{r_2}\right).$$

5. Briefly outline the wave theory of light. What is a wavefront?

6. Apply Huygens' principle to explain the reflection of a plane wave at a plane surface.

7. Explain clearly Huygens' principle for the wave propagation of light.

8. Explain the laws of refraction of light on the basis of the wave theory. What is meant by refractive index and how is it related to the velocities of light in different media?

9. Derive the refraction formula for a thin concave lens on the basis of wave theory.

10. Account for the formation of images by refraction through lenses on wave theory and prove the relation,

$$\frac{1}{v} - \frac{1}{u} = (\mu - 1)\left(\frac{1}{R_1} - \frac{1}{R_2}\right),$$

where the symbols have their usual significance.

11. Derive a relation for refraction of a spherical wave at a spherical surface according to the wave theory of light.

12. Derive the lens-maker's formula for a thin convex lens on the wave theory of light.

Short Answer-type

13. What is a wavefront? What is the nature of the wavefront when the wave travels a great distance from the source?   [C.U. 2000; N.B.U. 2002]

14. Why is light called electromagnetic waves? Explain whether the nature of light is transverse or longitudinal?   [N.B.U. 2002]

15. Discuss briefly the refraction of light and Huygens' principle.   [B.U. 2000]

16. What is the shape of wavefront at a finite distance if the waves start from a point source?

Numerical Problems

17. The optical path of a monochromatic light is the same if it goes through 2 cm of glass or 2.25 cm of water. If the refractive index of glass is 1.50, what is the index of water?   [**Ans.** 1.33]

18. A beam of wavelength 0.16 m strikes the surface of a refracting medium of $\mu = 1.33$. What will be the wavelength in the refracting medium?
[**Ans.** 0.12 m]

19. A ray of light strikes at an angle of incidence 55°. If the reflected and refracted rays are perpendicular to each other, find the refractive index of the medium.
[**Ans.** 1.428]

20. If the refractive index of glass is 1.50 and velocity of light in air is 3×10^8 m/s, find the velocity of light in glass.   [**Ans.** 2×10^8 m/s]

21. The speed of yellow light in a certain liquid is 2.4×10^8 m/s. Find the refractive index of the liquid.   [**Ans.** 1.25]

22. Wavelength of sodium light in air is 589 nm. Find (a) the frequency in air, (b) its wavelength in water ($\mu = 1.33$), (c) its frequency in water and (d) its speed in water. [**Ans.** 5.09×10^{14} Hz; 443 nm; 509×10^{14} Hz; 2.25×10^8 m/s]

Chapter 22
Interference of Light

22.1   Introduction

If two waves from two different sources of light traverse in the same part of a medium, the disturbance at any point of the medium is the resultant of the component disturbances acting independently of the other. When the waves reach the point in the same phase, the effects will be added and the resultant amplitude will be the sum of the amplitudes of the component vibrations at any instant. On the other hand, if the waves are in the opposite phase, the effects will be diminished and the amplitude of the resultant vibration will be the difference between the amplitudes of the component vibrations. This principle is known as the *principle of interference*. If the amplitudes of the component vibrations are equal in magnitude but opposite in directions, the amplitude of the resultant disturbance will be zero and the waves will destroy each other. This is known as *destructive interference*. If the phases are same, the addition of amplitudes causes what is called reinforcement or augmentation. Thus interference is based on the principle of superposition which states that the optical effect *at a point at any instant* where two waves meet or cross is the algebraic sum of the optical effects which would have been produced by each of the individual waves.

22.2   Graphical Study of Interference

Let A and B be two sources of light very close to each other, from which monochromatic waves are proceeding towards a screen S to be superposed on it (Fig. 22.1). The displacement of a particle and hence the intensity of light at the point of superposition, will have maximum or minimum according as the waves reach the particle in the same or in the opposite phases respectively. The waves will be in same phase when the trough or crest of one wave becomes superposed respectively on the trough or crest of the other. The phases will be opposite if the trough of one wave is superposed on the crest of the other.

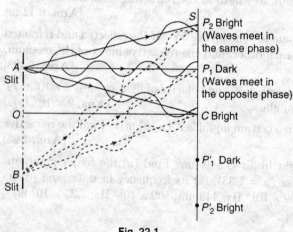

Fig. 22.1

The condition for the two waves to meet in the same or in the opposite phase depends on two factors : (i) the phase difference of the waves at the instant they leave the sources and (ii) the path difference of the point of superposition of the waves on the screen from the two sources. If now, the source A emits troughs or crests just when B is emitting troughs or crests, then the phase difference of the two waves at the instant of their start from the sources will be zero. If the waves are in opposite phases at the start, then it will be π. These conditions are fulfilled only if the two sources are coherent, i.e., if they are derived from a single source and are identical in all respect.

If the path difference of a point on the screen from two sources be *even multiples of half of the wavelength*, i.e., $2n\lambda/2$, where λ is the wavelength of the light illuminating the two sources, then the waves reach in the same phase and the resultant intensity will be maximum. If this path difference be *odd multiples of half of the wavelength*, i.e., $(2n+1)\frac{\lambda}{2}$, then the waves will reach there in opposite phases and the resultant intensity will be minimum. As drawn in Fig. 22.1, the central point C on the screen is equidistant from the sources A and B. Obviously the path difference of the waves is zero. The waves from A and B reach the point C in the same phase and a bright band is formed at C, this bright band is known as the central bright band. If the path difference of waves from A and B is $\frac{\lambda}{2}$, then the waves will reach at P_1 in the opposite phases and a dark band is produced. If the path difference of two waves from A and B is $\frac{2\lambda}{2}$, then waves will reach at P_2 in the same phase and a bright band will be obtained at P_2. The band referred to as **first order** bright band. In this way alternate dark and bright bands are produced on either side of the central band as the path difference changes from *odd to even multiples of half of the wavelength*. Thus the intensity of light will be alternately minimum and maximum. This gives an interpretation of the interference of light graphically.

22.3   Mathematical Expression for Interference

Let two waves of equal wavelength and amplitude, differing in phase are superposed. The displacements of the individual waves at any instant t are given by

$$y_1 = a \sin \frac{2\pi}{\lambda}(Vt - x_1) \tag{22.1}$$

and $$y_2 = a \sin \frac{2\pi}{\lambda}(Vt - x_2). \tag{22.2}$$

These two waves reach a point simultaneously with a difference of phase equal to $\frac{2\pi}{\lambda} \cdot e$ [where e = the path difference = $(x_2 - x_1)$.]

The resultant displacement at the instant t is then given by

$$y = y_1 + y_2 = a \sin \frac{2\pi}{\lambda}(Vt - x_1) + a \sin \frac{2\pi}{\lambda}(Vt - x_2)$$

$$= 2a \cos \frac{\pi}{\lambda}(x_2 - x_1) \sin \frac{2\pi}{\lambda}\left[\frac{2Vt - (x_1 + x_2)}{2}\right]$$

$$= 2a \cos \frac{\pi}{\lambda} \cdot e \sin \frac{2\pi}{\lambda}\left[Vt - \frac{(x_1 + x_2)}{2}\right]. \tag{22.3}$$

Eq. (22.3) shows that the amplitude of the resultant wave is $2a \cos \frac{\pi}{\lambda} \cdot e$. The amplitude will change with e between 0 [when $e = \frac{\lambda}{2}, 3\frac{\lambda}{2}, \cdots, (2n+1)\frac{\lambda}{2}$] and $2a$ [when $e = 0, \lambda, 2\lambda, \ldots, n\lambda$].

The *intensity* of light which is proportional to the *square of the amplitude*, will vary between 0 and $(2a)^2$ or $4a^2$ (i.e., 4 times the intensity due to a single wave).

It thus follows that (i) a minimum intensity (i.e., a dark band) is obtained when the path difference between the two waves is equal to *odd multiple of half a wavelength,* and (ii) a maximum intensity, i.e., for bright band, the path difference between the two waves should be equal to an *even multiple of half a wavelength.*

22.3.1 Distribution of Energy

Fig. 22.2 reveals the distribution of energy. It is seen that when the intensity is maximum the amplitude has a value equal to $2a$. So the intensity of bright points varies as $4a^2$ while that at the dark points is zero. According to the conservation law of

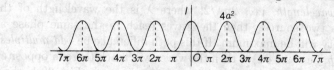

Phase difference

Fig. 22.2

energy we find the energy is not destroyed but is transferred from points of minimum intensity to points of maximum intensity. The intensity in the absence of interference is uniform and is equal to $2a^2$ at every point but it changes from 0 to $4a^2$ due to interference.

22.4 Conditions for Production of Interference

(i) There must be two sources of light which will emit continuous waves of same wavelength and periodic time. If the periods of the two waves differ, the intensity at a point will change continuously and the resulting effect at a point will not be constant.

(ii) The waves from two sources at the start should have either the same phase or some constant difference in phase. The phase difference changes not only in different sources but also in different portions of a given source. Two independent sources cannot produce interference. For production of interference, we have to use two *coherent sources,* i.e., two sources which have been derived from the same source. A source and its virtual image, or two virtual images of same source may produce such coherent sources.

(iii) The two sources should be narrow. A wide source of light is nothing but a large number of fine sources existing side by side. Each set of two sources will produce its own interference bands. The overlapping of a number of such bands will cause general illumination.

(iv) The amplitude of two waves should be preferably same. This will produce complete darkness at a point of minimum intensity. Some general illumination will always occur.

(v) The two sources should be very close to each other. Otherwise the maxima and minima will be produced very close to each other, and they may overlap.

22.5 Production of Coherent Sources

For producing continuous interference of light waves, we need two sources to emit waves of the same wavelength, having phase difference either equal to zero or some constant value. The phase relation of light waves varies with time not only for two independent sources but also for different portions of a given source. This causes general illumination and renders interference impossible. So for production of interference there must be two coherent sources, derived from the same source.

Any variation of phase at the time of emission affects the two sources equally and so the light waves starting from the two sources will be in the same phase or in constant phase difference.

Two coherent sources can be obtained by applying the following methods :

(a) A narrow illuminated slit and its virtual image are formed by reflection. This is used in **Lloyd's single mirror experiment**.

(b) Two virtual images of same source (narrow illuminated slit) are formed by reflection. This is used in **Fresnel's double mirror experiment**.

(c) Two virtual images of same source (narrow illuminated slit) are formed by refraction. This is used in **Fresnel's bi-prism experiment**.

(d) Splitting the amplitude of a wavefront into two parts (by reflection or refraction or by both), they are re-united later to produce interference. This is used in **Newton's rings** and **Michelson's interferometer experiments**.

22.6   Young's Experiment

In 1800 AD, English physicist Thomas Young first showed that two beams of light rays could be superposed in a manner so as to give rise to alternate zones of bright-

ness and darkness. He called the phenomenon as interference between two light waves. In his apparatus as shown in Fig. 22.3. Young allowed sunlight to pass through a pin-hole L and then at a short distance away this was passed through two pin-holes A and B subsequently. He replaced A and B by slits and L being illuminated by a monochromatic source.

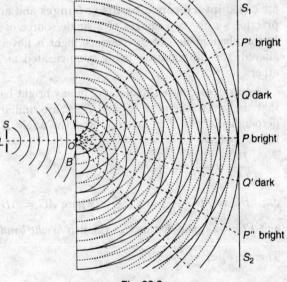

Fig. 22.3

Now, according to Huygens principle the slits A and B behave as new sources to produce circular waves. These waves are of transverse type. The crests of the waves are shown by solid circular lines and the troughs by broken lines. The solid straight lines on the right hand side of AB are the loci of the points of intersection where crests reinforce crests and troughs reinforce troughs. The points where these lines meet the screen $S_1 S_2$ are the position of maximum intensity and so produce constructive interference. The broken straight lines are the loci of the points of intersection where crests and troughs from A and B superpose. The points where the broken lines meet $S_1 S_2$ correspond to minimum intensity and produce destructive interference.

22.6.1   Theory of Young's Experiment

As shown in Fig. 22.4, let A and B be two narrow slits at a distance d wherefrom light waves of same wavelength and amplitude radiate. We assume that they start from A and B in the same phase. If a screen S be kept at a distance D away in front of the sources, a number of alternate *bright* and *dark bands* will be seen if monochromatic light is used.

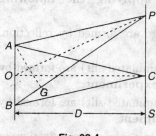

Fig. 22.4

We join A and B and let O be its mid-point. Through O we draw a line OC perpendicular to AB and the screen S. As AC and BC are equal, light waves starting from A and B in the same phase will reach the point C also in the same phase and reinforce one another. Thus the point C will be a bright point. We now determine the nature of illumination at any point, say P, situated at a distance CP. Let us join PA, PB and PO. With P as centre and PA as radius describes the circular arc AG. If AB is very small in comparison to PA, AG will be straight and perpendicular to both PB and PO. Then $BP - AP =$ the **distance** or **path retardation** of the wave from B with respect to that from A. Now, for the point P to be *bright*, we must have $BG = 2n\frac{\lambda}{2}$ and for the point p to be *dark*, we must have $BG = (2n+1)\frac{\lambda}{2}$.

Therefore, due to the *interference of light* originating from two neighbouring sources of light we have alternate bright and dark bands on either side of C. These are called **interference bands** or **fringes** and are equidistant from each other. In practice we use two images of a single source of light as the originators of waves. In the phenomenon of interference, light is never destroyed but its distribution is altered, the illumination being compensated at one place at the expense of the other.

Next, to calculate the distance of any bright band from the central band we note that the two triangles BAG and POC are similar, as AG and AB are respectively perpendiculars to PO and OC and the angle BAG is equal to the angle POC. Hence we have

$$\frac{PC}{OC} = \frac{BG}{AB} = \frac{BG}{AG}.$$

$$\therefore \quad BG = AG \cdot \frac{PC}{OC} = d \cdot \frac{x_n}{D} \quad \text{(where } AG = AB = d)$$

and $PC = x_n$, the distance of the nth *bright band* from the centre C, also $OC = D$.

Therefore, $x_n = \frac{D}{d} \cdot BG$.

For the nth **bright band**, $BG = 2n\frac{\lambda}{2}$.

So, $\quad x_n = \frac{D}{d} 2n \frac{\lambda}{2} = \frac{D}{d} n\lambda$

or, $\quad \lambda = \frac{x_n}{nD}$. $\hspace{6cm}$ (22.4)

Eq (22.4) gives a method of determining the *wavelength of a monochromatic light*.

The distance between the centres of the nth and $(n+1)$th bright band, i.e., the **width of a bright band** is then obtained from

$$\alpha = x_{n+1} - x_n = \frac{D}{d}[(n+1)\lambda - n\lambda] = \frac{D}{d}\lambda \quad \text{or,} \quad \lambda = \frac{d}{D} \cdot \alpha \qquad (22.5)$$

We find from Eq. (22.5) that the expression for the width of a band is independent of the order of the band. Thus with a monochromatic light the bands are **equi-spaced**. The relation can also be used to find λ, the wavelength.

22.7 Lloyd's Single Mirror

Lloyd in 1834 performed an experiment on the basis of division of wavefront. His experimental arrangement is shown in Fig. 22.5. MN is a plane mirror and S_1 is a narrow slit illuminated by monochromatic light placed in front of the mirror. S_1 produces a virtual image S_2 and thus they form *coherent sources* satisfying the conditions of interference. Direct rays S_1P, S_1Q from the slit S_1 and the reflected rays MP, NQ, which are assembled to be coming from the image S_2 get superposed. In this way the region of interference is confined within the space bounded by S_2M and S_2N produced on the Screen.

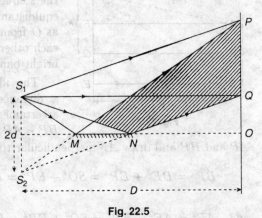

Fig. 22.5

Let us draw a perpendicular from the mid-point of the line S_1S_2 on the screen where the intersection point is O. Thus in Lloyd's experiment less than half of the interference pattern is available. To make the central band visible, a thin mica sheet is kept in the path of the direct ray from S_1 causing an upward displacement of the whole fringe system and then the central band becomes visible. The central band becomes a *dark band* instead of a bright one as because the reflected beam from S_2 having suffered reflection at a denser medium, undergoes a phase change of π while the direct beam from S_1 does not undergo such phase change. Consequently, when the interfering beams arrive at the central band position, they have exactly opposite phase or a phase difference of π and thus producing destructive interference.

Let $2d =$ distance between the two coherent sources S_1 and S_2, $\lambda =$ wavelength of the light used, $D =$ distance between the line of sources and the screen. Then we can write, the fringe width, $y = \frac{D.\lambda}{2d}$ or, $\lambda = \frac{2d.y}{D}$. From a knowledge of D, y and $2d$, the wavelength of light can be determined.

22.8 Determination of Wavelength of Light by a Bi-prism

A bi-prism (CED) is an obtuse-angled prism made up of two right-angled prisms placed base to base (Fig. 22.6). The acute angles at C and D are of the order of one minute. A narrow illuminated slit at O is placed in the same height as the prism, so that the length of the slit becomes parallel to the edge of the prism.

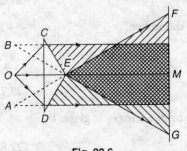

Fig. 22.6

After refraction from the upper and lower halves of the prism, light will appear to come from the virtual images B and A to produce interference. The interference fringes so formed become very narrow and parallel to the edge of the bi-prism. They are focused in the focal plane of the eyepiece kept at M and seen in a magnified form.

22.8.1 Theory of Fringe Formation

In Fig. 22.7, A and B are two virtual images of narrow source S, formed by the

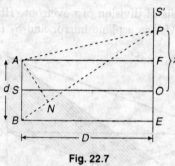

Fig. 22.7

bi-prism. Let d be the separation between A and B. A screen $\acute{S}'$ is placed at a distance D from the source S. The point O on the screen being equidistant from A and B, the two waves meeting at O from the two virtual sources will augment each other. The point O will be the centre of a bright band.

The illumination at any other point P at a distance x from O on the screen can be ascertained by calculating the path difference $BP - AP$ between the two waves. Let us join AP and BP and draw AN perpendicular to BP. We then have

$$BP^2 = BE^2 + EP^2 = SO^2 + EP^2 = D^2 + \left(x + \frac{d}{2}\right)^2$$

and $AP^2 = AF^2 + FP^2 = SO^2 + FP^2 = D^2 + \left(x - \frac{d}{2}\right)^2.$

Thus we get

$$BP^2 - AP^2 = \left\{D^2 + \left(x + \frac{d}{2}\right)^2\right\} - \left\{D^2 + \left(x - \frac{d}{2}\right)^2\right\}$$

$$= \left(x + \frac{d}{2}\right)^2 - \left(x - \frac{d}{2}\right)^2 = 2dx$$

or, $(BP - AP)(BP + AP) = 2dx.$

Hence the path difference, $BP - AP = \frac{2dx}{BP + AP}$. As A and B are very close and P lies very near to O, we can write $BP = AP = SO = D$.

Therefore, the path difference, $BP - AP = \frac{2dx}{2D} = \frac{d}{D} \cdot x.$

For the point P to be on a bright fringe, the path difference,

$$BN = BP - AP = \frac{d}{D} \cdot x = 2n\frac{\lambda}{2}$$

or, $x = \frac{D}{d}n\lambda.$ (22.6)

For the point P to be on a dark fringe, the path difference,

$$BN = \frac{d}{D} \cdot x = (2n + 1)\frac{\lambda}{2}$$

or, $x = \frac{D}{d}(2n + 1)\frac{\lambda}{2}.$ (22.7)

Now, the distance a between two consecutive bright fringes is given by

$$a = x_{n+1} - x_n = \frac{D}{d}(n + 1)\lambda - \frac{D}{d}n\lambda = \frac{D}{d}\lambda.$$ (22.8)

In a similar way, the distance between two consecutive dark fringes

$$= x_{n+1} - x_n = \frac{D}{d}(2n+3)\frac{\lambda}{2} - \frac{D}{d}(2n+1)\frac{\lambda}{2} = \frac{D}{d}\lambda = a. \tag{22.9}$$

We thus find that the distance between consecutive bright or dark fringes is the same. In an actual experiment, the cross-wire of the eyepiece is made to coincide with the central bright band and then moved by a micrometer screw to another chosen bright band and its position is noted.

Now, we have the distance of the nth band from the central band, $x_n = \frac{D}{d}n\lambda$.

Hence, $\quad a = \frac{x_n}{n} = \frac{D}{d}\lambda.$ \hfill (22.10)

In actual experiment, let $n = 8$; then x_8 is obtained from micrometer readings and dividing x_n by 8, a is obtained. The distance D is measured from the slit to the focal plane of the eyepiece by the scale of the optical bench on which the slit, the bi-prism and the eyepiece are fitted on uprights. In order to measure d,

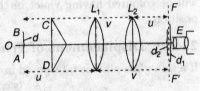

Fig. 22.8

the distance between the two virtual images, a convex lens is kept between the eyepiece and the bi-prism (Fig. 22.8). The distance between the slit and the eyepiece is made greater than four times the focal length of the lens so that for two positions (L_1, L_2) of the lens, two sets of images will be observed by the eyepiece. The distance d_1 and d_2 between the images of A and B for the two positions of the lens are determined with the micrometer screw of the eyepiece and then the actual distance d, between A and B is obtained from the expression $d = \sqrt{d_1 d_2}$ (Fig. 22.7).

The expression $d = \sqrt{d_1 d_2}$ can be deduced in the following way :

For the position L_1 of the lens,.

$$\frac{d}{d_1} = \frac{u}{v}, \tag{22.10a}$$

where u and v are object and image distances respectively from the lens. Again, for position L_2 of the lens, u and v become interchanged, i.e., object and image distance then become v and u respectively. In that case.

$$\frac{d}{d_2} = \frac{v}{u}. \tag{22.11}$$

From Eqs. (22.10) and (22.11), we get

$$\frac{d}{d_1} \times \frac{d}{d_2} = \frac{u}{v} \times \frac{v}{u} \quad \text{or,} \quad d^2 = d_1 d_2;$$

$$\therefore \quad d = \sqrt{d_1 d_2}. \tag{22.12}$$

Next, from the expression, $a = \frac{D}{d}\lambda$ or, $\lambda = \frac{d.a}{D}$ the wavelength λ of the monochromatic light can be found out.

In the measurement of the wavelength of monochromatic light by this method the following adjustments are required :

(i) The slit, the bi-prism and the eyepiece should be adjusted to the same height. (ii) The line joining the slit to the refracting edge of the bi-prism should be parallel to the scale along the bed of the optical bench. (iii) The slit should be narrow and parallel to the edge of the bi-prism. (iv) The cross-wires of the eyepiece should be focused and kept in the vertical position. (v) The plane face of the bi-prism should be at right angles to the length of the bed. (vi) Correction for index error should be made in the measurement of D

22.9 White Light Fringes

We know that the distance x_n of the nth bright band from the central one is $x_n = \frac{D}{d} n \lambda$.

For the central band $n = 0$, and hence x_n is zero for all wavelengths. For another bright band of particular order number, x_n is greater for the light of longer wavelength and less for the light of shorter wavelength. Now, as λ_r for red light is greater than λ_v for violet light, all other bright bands other than the central one will be coloured having violet in the innermost position and red in the outermost position.

22.10   Displacement of Fringes by Interposition of Glass Plate

If a thin glass plate is interposed in the path of light from any one of the two sources

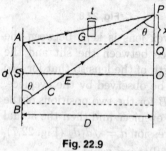

Fig. 22.9

(say, A) the central bright band will be displaced to other point due to the alteration of the path difference. In Fig. 22.9, let a thin glass plate of refractive index μ and thickness t be placed in the path AP of light proceeding from A. As the velocity of light in glass differs from that in air, the path difference changes and so the central fringe moves to certain other position.

The path difference δ between the rays BP and AP is given by

$$\delta = BP - AP = BC + CP - \{(AP - t) + \mu t\}$$

$$= BC - (\mu - 1)t \quad (\because AP \simeq CP).$$

The point P will be at the centre of the nth bright band when this path difference is $2n \cdot \frac{\lambda}{2}$, i.e., $n\lambda$. Thus, we have $BC - (\mu - 1)t = n\lambda$; but $\frac{BC}{d} = \frac{x}{D}$ (approx.), where x is the distance of P at which the nth bright fringe is formed in the absence of the glass plate.

or, $BC = \dfrac{xd}{D}$. $\therefore$ $\dfrac{xd}{D} - (\mu - 1)t = n\lambda$

or, $x = \dfrac{D}{d}\{n\lambda + (\mu - 1)t\}$.   (22.13)

The distance x_0, where the central bright fringe will be formed on placing the glass pate in the path AP, is obtained by substituting $n = 0$. Thus, we get

$$x_0 = \frac{D}{d}(\mu - 1)t.$$ (22.14)

In this case, x_0 is positive, as $\mu > 1$. It means that the central bright fringe will be shifted upwards on placing the glass plate in the path AP.

If $n = 1$, $x_1 = \dfrac{D}{d}\{\lambda + (\mu - 1)t\}$.

So the fringe width, $a = x_1 - x_0 = \dfrac{D}{d}\{\lambda + (\mu - 1)t\} - \dfrac{D}{d}(\mu - 1)t$

$$= \frac{D}{d}\lambda = \text{constant.}$$ (22.15)

Therefore, the interposition of the glass plate produces no changes of the width of the fringes.

From Eq. (22.15),

$$\frac{D}{d} = \frac{a}{\lambda}. \tag{22.16}$$

From Eqs. (22.14) and (22.16),

$$x_0 = \frac{a}{\lambda}(\mu - 1)t. \tag{22.17}$$

From a knowledge of x_0, a, μ and t, λ can be found out. Knowing x_0, a, λ and μ, the thickness t can also be calculated.

If monochromatic light is used the fringes appear all alike and so the shift x_0 of the central bright fringe cannot be measured. This difficulty is overcome by using white light, when all fringes except the central one appear coloured. So it becomes possible to localise the position to which the central fringe is displaced. The shift is measured accurately using monochromatic source of light.

22.11   Colours of Thin Films

If ordinary white light falls on a transparent surface like a soap bubble or a film of oil spread on the surface of water, brilliant colours are observed in general. The colours vary with the *thickness* of the film and disappear altogether when the thickness exceeds a certain limit. These colours are formed by the interference of light waves from the upper and the lower surfaces of the film.

22.12   Retardation

We assume that the ray AB falls on a parallel-sided film of refractive index μ and thickness t. The ray will be split up into a reflected ray BC and a refracted ray BD (Fig. 22.10). The refracted ray is partly reflected at D along DE to suffer refraction at E and emerge from the film along EF. As the bounding surfaces of the plate of the film are parallel, the ray BC and EF will be parallel and are relatively retarded and they will reinforce or weaken each other accordingly as they are in the same or opposite phases. In order to calculate the retardation, produce ED to L making $DL = DB$ and join LB. The line LB will then be perpendicular to the parallel faces of the film and if the thickness of the film be t we have, $LB = 2t$. We then draw EP and BM perpendiculars to BC and ED respectively (Fig. 22.10). Then BM and EP will be the successive positions of the wavefront *reflected* from the front and the rear surfaces.

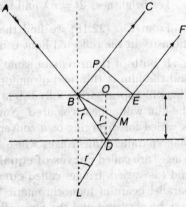

Fig. 22.10

The *path retardation* δ between the two rays BC and EF is then given by

$$\delta = \mu(BD + DM + ME) - BP = \mu(LM + ME) - BP \quad (\because DB = DL)$$

$$= \mu LM \quad (\because \mu ME = BP)$$

$$= \mu LB \cos r = \mu \cdot 2t \cos r \quad (\because \angle BLD = r),$$

where r is the angle of refraction.

As the reflections at B and D occur under opposite conditions, a further difference of path equal to $\lambda/2$ is introduced between the two rays. Then whole path retardation

$$= 2\mu t \cos r \pm \frac{\lambda}{2}, \qquad (22.18)$$

where λ is the wavelength in air.

Now, the condition for the rays BC and EF to **interfere** is written as,

$$2\mu t \cos r \pm \frac{\lambda}{2} = (2n \pm 1)\frac{\lambda}{2} \text{ (for \textbf{dark bands}) or, } 2\mu t \cos r = n\lambda. \qquad (22.19)$$

In a similar way the condition for the rays BC and EF to **reinforce** each other is

$$2\mu t \cos r \pm \frac{\lambda}{2} = \frac{2n\lambda}{2} \text{ or, } 2\mu t \cos r = (2n \pm 1)\frac{\lambda}{2} \text{ (for \textbf{bright bands}),} \qquad (22.20)$$

where n is any positive integer including zero.

For transmitted light, the conditions for brightness and darkness will be opposite to the conditions for reflected light as there is no sudden change of phase if the film is optically denser than the media above and below it.

So, for the **bright bands,** $2\mu t \cos r = n\lambda$ $\qquad (22.21)$

and for the **dark bands,** $2\mu t \cos r = (2n \pm 1)\frac{\lambda}{2}.$ $\qquad (22.22)$

If $\mu = 1$, and the film is viewed normally, i.e., $r = 0$, the conditions will be as follows :

Case of Reflected Light.

For brightness $2t = (2n \pm 1)\frac{\lambda}{2}$ and for darkness $2t = n\lambda$.

Case of Transmitted Light

For brightness $2t = n\lambda$ and for darkness $2t = (2n \pm 1)\frac{\lambda}{2}$.

From Eq. (22.18) we find that the interference effect, i.e., the fluctuation in intensity in the reflected light is due to either of the *two variables* r and t.

If both of them remain same, i.e., if the beam incident on the film is *parallel* and the film is thin and of uniform *thickness*, no fringes can be observed and the film will appear either fully bright or dark. But with a parallel beam of white light, the film will appear coloured. Now, if one of the variables, say t, is constant and r is varied for diverging or a converging beam of monochromatic light incident on a plane parallel film, fringes will be observed due to varying path difference. These fringes are called **curves of equal inclination**. On the other hand, if r is constant and t is varied, fringes called **curves of equal thickness** will be observed with a parallel beam of monochromatic light. With white light bright bands all colours may be observed and the film will show variety of colours.

22.13 Newton's Rings

Newton developed a method to study the colours of thin films in a very simple way. A plano-convex lens of large radius is kept on a glass plate AB so that the convex side touches the plane surface. The thickness of the film of air between the lens and the plate increases gradually from the central point E at which the lens touches the plate. Near the point of contact the thickness of the air film will be very small compared to the wavelength of light and so at the point of contact, the central ring is dark if observed by reflected light. This occurs as neutralisation is effected by the path difference $\lambda/2$ introduced by reflection under opposite conditions. As the lens is a portion of a sphere, concentric circles are drawn, each of which is the locus of a point whose distance from the glass plate is constant. In Fig. 22.11, E is the point of contact and R, the radius of curvature of the convex surface of the lens.

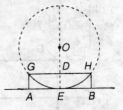

Fig. 22.11

If viewed normally by reflected light, the points G and H equidistant from E, will lie on a bright or dark circle according as twice the distance GA or HB is equal to an *odd* or *even* number of half wavelength of the incident light. We assume that EO be the radius of the circle of which the curved section of the lens is a part. Let $GA = DE = HB = t$, and the diameter of the ring observed be equal to d.

From geometry of the figure, we have

$$(2R - t)t = \left(\frac{d}{2}\right)^2 \quad \text{or,} \quad t = \frac{d^2}{8R},$$

neglecting t^2 as it is very small compared to $2Rt$.

For G and H to be situated on a **bright ring** we can write,

$$2t = \frac{d^2}{4R} = (2n + 1)\frac{\lambda}{2}.$$

Again, for a **dark ring**, $2t = \frac{d^2}{4R} = n\lambda$, where n has the values 0, 1, 2, 3, etc. for the 1st, 2nd, 3rd, 4th, etc., ring respectively.

Now, let d_n be the diameter of the nth bright ring and d_{n+m} is the diameter of the $(n + m)$th bright ring.

Then we have $\dfrac{d_n^2}{4R} = (2n + 1)\dfrac{\lambda}{2}$ and $\dfrac{d_{n+m}^2}{4R} = (2n + 2m + 1)\dfrac{\lambda}{2}$.

Hence, $\dfrac{d_{n+m}^2 - d_n^2}{4R} = 2m \cdot \dfrac{\lambda}{2} = m\lambda$

or, $\qquad \lambda = \dfrac{d_{n+m}^2 - d_n^2}{4Rm}.$ $\hfill (22.23)$

Using Eq. (22.23) the wavelength of light λ can be determined.

If the radii of the nth and $(n + m)$th dark ring are measured, then we can write,

$$\lambda = \frac{d_{n+m}^2 - d_n^2}{4Rm} = \frac{r_{n+m}^2 - r_n^2}{Rm}, \hfill (22.24)$$

where r_n and r_{n+m} are the radii of the nth and $(n + m)$th dark rings respectively.

The reason to measure the diameters of two rings rather than their radii is that the central spot is not well-defined in general and its position cannot be read accurately.

22.13.1 Experimental Arrangement

The lens L is kept on the glass plate P and the combination is placed inside a wooden box with darkened sides. A glass plate G is placed above the combination at an angle of $45°$ to the vertical. The arrangement is shown in Fig. 22.12.

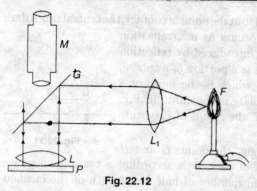

A parallel beam of yellow light from a flame F falls on the glass plate G by the condensing lens L_1 and is thrown downwards on to the air film. The rings are observed by the travelling microscope M set above the plate G and the diameters are measured. For this experiment an extended source of light is required for the perception of the general colour of the film.

Fig. 22.12

22.13.2   Measurement of Refractive Index of a Liquid

A few drops of the experimental liquid are put on the glass plate and the lens is placed on the liquid so that liquid film is formed between the lens and the plate. Using monochromatic light the diameters of nth and $(n + m)$th dark rings are measured by a microscope. If the diameters are d_n and d_{n+m} respectively, then

$$d_n^2 = \frac{4n\lambda R}{\mu} \quad \text{and} \quad d_{n+m}^2 = \frac{4(n+m)\lambda R}{\mu}.$$

$$\therefore \quad d_{n+m}^2 - d_n^2 = \frac{4m \cdot \lambda \cdot R}{\mu} \quad \text{or,} \quad \mu = \frac{4m \cdot \lambda \cdot R}{d_{n+m}^2 - d_n^2}. \tag{22.25}$$

With the help of a spherometer, R is measured. Using Eq. (22.25) μ can then be determined. Alternately, if R is unknown, the diameters of nth and $(n + m)$th dark rings are first measured with air-film for which we can write,

$$D_{n+m}^2 - D_n^2 = 4m\lambda R. \tag{22.26}$$

It is repeated also for liquid film,

$$d_{n+m}^2 - d_n^2 = \frac{4m\lambda R}{\mu}, \tag{22.27}$$

Hence, we get

$$\mu = \frac{D_{n+m}^2 - D_n^2}{d_{n+m}^2 - d_n^2}. \tag{22.28}$$

22.14   Formation of Newton's Rings by Two Curved Surfaces

Let two curved surfaces of radii of curvature R_1 and R_2 respectively have enclosed a thin film of air between them. The curved surfaces are in contact with each other at O (Fig. 22.13). If we see from above, we find the first surface concave of radius of curvature R_1 and the second surface convex of radius of curvature R_2. If a monochromatic ray of light falls at A, it will be split up into two parts as shown. They being coherent will produce interference pattern of alternate dark and bright rings.

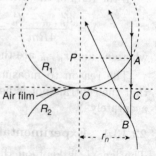

Fig. 22.13

The thickness of the film at A may be written as $AB = AC + CB$.

Again, $(AP)^2 = OP(2R_1 - OP) = 2R_1 \times OP$

[OP being small $(OP)^2$ may be ignored]

Therefore, $(AP)^2 = 2R_1 \times AC$ or, $r_n^2 = 2R_1 \times AC$

or, $\qquad AC = \dfrac{r_n^2}{2R_1}$ (where $r_n = AP$ = the radius of the nth dark ring).

In a similar way,

$$CB = \frac{r_n^2}{2R_2}; \quad \text{Therefore,} \quad AB = \frac{r_n^2}{2}\left(\frac{1}{R_1} + \frac{1}{R_2}\right). \tag{22.29}$$

If t be the thickness of the film AB, then

$$t = \frac{r_n^2}{2}\left(\frac{1}{R_1} + \frac{1}{R_2}\right). \tag{22.30}$$

Now, for nth dark ring, $2t = n\lambda$,

so, $\qquad r_n^2\left(\dfrac{1}{R_1} + \dfrac{1}{R_2}\right) = n\lambda. \quad (n = 1, 2, 3, \ldots, \text{etc}) \tag{22.31}$

Further, for nth bright ring, $2t = (2n+1)\lambda/2$,

so $\qquad r_n^2\left(\dfrac{1}{R_1} + \dfrac{1}{R_2}\right) = (2n+1)\lambda/2 \quad (n = 0, 1, 2, 3, \ldots, \text{etc.}) \tag{22.32}$

For different values of n, we may get the radii of different dark and bright rings. When viewed from top, both the curved surfaces appear concave (shown in Fig. 22.14). Then the thickness, $AB = AC - BC$.

But, $\quad AC = \dfrac{r_n^2}{2R_1}$ and $\quad BC = \dfrac{r_n^2}{2R_2}.$

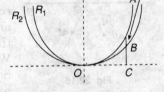

Fig. 22.14

Therefore, the thickness,

$$t = AB = AC - BC = \frac{r_n^2}{2}\left(\frac{1}{R_1} - \frac{1}{R_2}\right). \tag{22.32a}$$

For nth dark ring, $2t = n\lambda$;

hence $\quad r_n^2\left(\dfrac{1}{R_1} - \dfrac{1}{R_2}\right) = n\lambda \quad (n = 1, 2, 3, \ldots, \text{etc.}) \tag{22.33}$

For nth bright ring, $2t = (2n+1)\lambda/2$;

So, $\quad r_n^2\left(\dfrac{1}{R_1} - \dfrac{1}{R_2}\right) = (2n+1)\lambda/2 \quad (n = 0, 2, \ldots, \text{etc.}) \tag{22.34}$

22.15 Change of Phase by Reflection

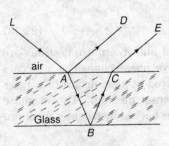

Fig. 22.15

In their paths light waves undergo phase change by reflection. When the waves are reflected at a *denser* medium at an air-glass interface, the reflected waves have a phase change of π compared to the incident waves.

Let a light wave of wavelength λ travel a distance t in a medium of refractive index μ. Then the phase change that occurs due to this path is given by

$$\delta = \frac{2\pi t}{\lambda}. \tag{22.35}$$

When reflection at a denser medium produces a phase change of π, then

$$\delta = \pi = \frac{2\pi t}{\lambda} \quad \text{or,} \quad t = \lambda/2. \qquad (22.36)$$

Thus in order to take into account of reflection at a denser medium, we must add or subtract $\lambda/2$ to the optical path. Fig. 22.15 shows an incident ray of light LA partly refracted at A from air to glass and then reflected at B, the glass-air interface. The optical path from A to $C = \mu(AB + BC)$, where μ is the refractive index of glass. There is no phase change at B due to reflection as this occurs at an interface with the *less* dense medium air. On the other hand, a phase change equivalent to a path $\lambda/2$ occurs, when LA is reflected at A along AD, as this is a reflection at a denser medium, glass.

Stokes' Proof

Let A and B are two media separated by a plane surface, the medium B being denser than the medium A. A light wave of amplitude a is incident at O in the

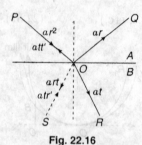

Fig. 22.16

direction PO on the surface of separation (Fig. 22.16). A part of the light is reflected along OQ and the remaining part is refracted along OR into the medium B. If the coefficient of reflection in the medium A be r and the coefficient of refraction in the medium B be t, then the amplitude of the reflected wave along $OQ = a.r$, while the amplitude of the refracted wave along $OR = a.t$. When there is no loss of energy, then the reflected and the refracted beams OQ and OR are made to retrace their paths. Then we get back the original beam PO of amplitude a. When a wave of amplitude ar is made to retrace its path along QO, the wave on incident at O, will give rise to a reflected wave along OP, with amplitude $= a.r.r. = ar^2$ and a refracted wave along OS with amplitude $= a.r.t$. In a similar way on retracing its path, the wave OR of amplitude at will be split up into two parts, one reflected and the other refracted at O. The reflected wave of amplitude $a.t.r'$ will go along SO (r' being the coefficient of reflection) and the refracted wave of amplitude att' will move along OP (t' being the coefficient of transmission).

As originally we had an incident wave PO of amplitude a and no wave along OS, we can write,

$$att' + a.r^2 = a$$

or, $\quad tt' = 1 - r^2.$ $\qquad (22.37)$

Also $\quad art + atr' = 0$

$$r' = -r. \qquad (22.38)$$

Eq. (22.38) shows that the coefficients of external and internal reflections are equal but of opposite signs. It means that a relative phase change of π occurs between two sets of reflected waves, one being reflected at the surface of a rarer medium, while the other suffering reflection at the denser medium. Thus a phase change of π occurs due to reflection at a surface which is backed by a denser medium.

22.16   Michelson's Interferometer

The schematic arrangement of the interferometer is shown in Fig. 22.17. It has two highly polished mirrors M_1 and M_2 silvered on their front surfaces and placed

perpendicular to each other.
The mirror M_2 is fixed and the
mirror M_1 is moved backwards
along the normal to its surface
by using a micrometer screw.

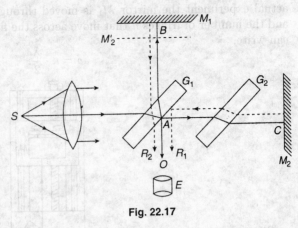

A parallel-sided glass plate
G_1 silvered on its back is
placed at an angle of 45° to
the light coming out·from a
lens.   At˙ the focus of an
extended source of light S
(e.g., a bright sodium flame)
is placed.   A part of the
incident light passes straight

Fig. 22.17

through the plate G_1 and
through another plate G_2 of equal thickness and is reflected back from the plane
mirror M_2 and on reaching the plate G_1 is partly reflected along R_1. Instead of
passing through G_1, part of the incident light is reflected at its back surface and
travels to the mirror M_1 meeting the same normally and is reflected back and partly
transmitted through G_1 along the direction R_2. In this way, the incident ray has
been split up into rays which after traversing different paths are finally brought
back to traverse the same path. In Fig. 22.17, the reflected rays from M_2 and M_1
are shown slightly displaced. In fact, the rays R_1 and R_2 coincide and pass on to
the eyepiece E along the direction between R_1 and R_2.

The object of using another glass plate G_2 of same thickness as G_1 kept parallel
to it, is that the two rays traverse exactly the same thickness of glass; otherwise the
light reflected from the mirror M_2 would only traverse the glass plate once, while
the light reflected from the mirror M_1 would do so three times.

If there is a path difference between the two beams, then the beams will be in a
condition to interfere. On the other hand, if $AB = AC$, i.e., if the path difference
is zero, the beams will not interfere. Also, if AB is not equal to AC, the mirror M_1
and M_2 enclose an air-film of thickness $(AB - AC)$ and a system of *circular fringes*
is observed in the eyepiece E. If the mirrors M_1 and M_2 are not at right angles
such that M_1 and M_2 intersect each other, fringes will be *straight* and parallel to
the line in intersection.

Uses of the Interferometer

 (i) Measurement of the wavelength of monochromatic light.

 (ii) Measurement of thickness of a very thin film.

 (iii) Testing the smoothness of a glass surface.

 (iv) Standardisation of meter in terms of wavelength.

22.16.1 Determination of Wavelength of a Monochromatic Light Using
Michelson's Interferometer

Fig. 22.18 reveals the sectional sketch of a compact interferometer of Michelson
type. To determine the wavelength of a monochromatic light, the interferometer is
adjusted, so that AB and AC are *nearly* equal and that the mirrors M_1 and M_2
are perpendicular to each other. Circular fringes are observed in the eyepiece with
a monochromatic light and the cross-wires are adjusted on a particular fringe. In

actual experiment the mirror M_1 is moved through a distance δ parallel to itself and the number of fringes n that move across the field of view is counted. Then we can write,

$$\delta = n \cdot \frac{\lambda}{2}. \tag{22.39}$$

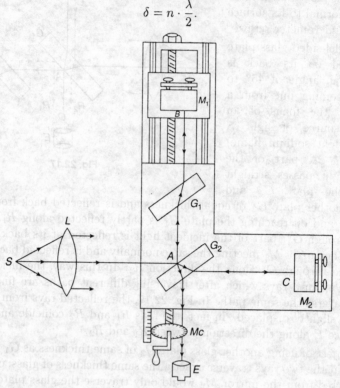

Fig. 22.18

The movement of the mirror through a distance $\lambda/2$ will cause the displacement of each fringe into the position occupied before by the adjacent fringe. Hence, from Eq. (22.39) the wavelength λ is calculated.

Examples

1. The inclined faces of a bi-prism ($\mu = 1.5$) make angles of $1°$ with the base of the prism. The slit is 10 cm from the bi-prism and is illuminated by light of $\lambda = 5900$ Å. Find the fringe-width observed at a distance of 1 m from the bi-prism.

Solution : Here $\mu = 1.5$, $\lambda = 5900$ Å $= 590 \times 10^{-10}$ m,

base angle, $\alpha = 1° = \pi/180$ radian,

source-bi-prism distance, $x = 10$ cm $= 0.1$ m,

screen-bi-prism distance, $y = 1.0$ m.

We can write, fringe width $\beta = \dfrac{\lambda(x + y)}{2(\mu - 1)\alpha}$.

Putting the values,

$$\beta = \frac{5900 \times 10^{-10}(0.1 + 1.0)}{2(1.5 - 1)\pi/180} = \frac{5900 \times 1.1 \times 10^{-10} \times 180}{2 \times 0.5 \times \pi} = 0.0000372 \text{ m}.$$

2. Calculate the fringe-width of interference pattern produced in Young's double slit experiment with two slits 10^{-3} m apart on a screen 1 m away. Wavelength of light is 5893 Å.

Solution : Here, $D = 1$ m, $d = 10^{-3}$ m, $\lambda = 5893$ Å $= 5893 \times 10^{-10}$ m.

Therefore, the fringe width,

$$\beta = \frac{D}{d}\lambda = \frac{1}{10^{-3}} \times 5893 \times 10^{-10} \text{ m} = \mathbf{5893 \times 10^{-7} \text{ m}}.$$

3. When a thin sheet of transparent material of thickness 7.2×10^{-6} m is introduced in the path of one of the interfering beams, the central fringe shifts to a position occupied by the sixth bright fringe. If $\lambda = 6 \times 10^{-7}$ m, find the refractive index of the sheet material.

Solution : Here, thickness $t = 7.2 \times 10^{-6}$ m, $\lambda = 6 \times 10^{-7}$ m;

Given, shift in central fringe $= 6\beta$. Now, from the relation, $x_0 = \beta(\mu - 1)t/\lambda$, we have

$$6\beta = \frac{\beta}{\lambda}(\mu - 1)t = \frac{\beta}{6 \times 10^{-7}}(\mu - 1) \times 7.2 \times 10^{-6}$$

or, $\quad \mu - 1 = \dfrac{6 \times 6 \times 10^{-7}}{7.2 \times 10^{-6}} = 0.5, \quad \therefore \quad \mu = 1.5$.

4. Interference fringes are produced by bi-prism in the focal plane of a reading microscope which is 1 m away from the slit. A lens interposed between bi-prism and microscope gives two images of the slit in two positions : 4.05 mm in one position, 2.90 mm in the other. If the wavelength of light used is $\lambda = 5893$ Å, find the distance between consecutive bands.

Solution : Here, $\lambda = 5893$ Å $= 5893 \times 10^{-10}$ m; $D = 1$ m; $d_1 = 4.05$ mm $= 4.05 \times 10^{-3}$ m; $d_2 = 2.9$ mm $= 2.9 \times 10^{-3}$ m.

So, $\quad d = \sqrt{d_1 d_2} = \sqrt{4.05 \times 2.9} \times 10^{-3} = 3.427 \times 10^{-3}$ m.

Now the distance between consecutive bands $=$ fringe-width $= \beta$.

So, $\quad \beta = \dfrac{D}{d}\lambda = \dfrac{1.0 \times 5893 \times 10^{-10}}{3.427 \times 10^{-3}} = \mathbf{0.172 \times 10^{-3} \text{ m}}$

5. In a bi-prism experiment, fringes were first observed with sodium light of wavelength 5890 Å and fringe-width was measured to be 0.347 mm. Na-light was then replaced by white light and central fringe located. On introducing a thin glass sheet in half of the beam, the central fringe was shifted by 2.143 mm. Calculate the thickness of the sheet if μ of glass is 1.542.

Solution : Here, $\lambda = 5890 \times 10^{-10}$ m; $\mu = 1.542$; $\beta = 0.342$ mm; $x_0 = 2.143$ mm. Let n be the number of fringes in x_0, $n = 2.143/0.342$.

We have $\quad (\mu - 1)t = n\lambda, \quad$ or, $\quad t = \dfrac{n\lambda}{\mu - 1}$.

So the thickness, $t = \dfrac{2.143 \times 5890 \times 10^{-10}}{0.342 \times 0.542} = \mathbf{6.81 \times 10^{-6} \text{ m}}$.

6. What should be the thickness of a non-reflecting layer to be deposited on glass surface corresponding to wavelength 6000 Å? Refractive index of the layer is 1.35.

Solution : We have, the condition for minimum thickness of a non-reflecting coating dictates :

$$t = \lambda/4\mu.$$

where t = thickness, λ = wavelength of light and μ = refractive index of coating.

Here, $\mu = 1.35$, $\lambda = 6000$ Å $= 6000 \times 10^{-10}$ m $= 6 \times 10^{-7}$ m and $t =?$

Therefore, $t = \dfrac{6 \times 10^{-7}}{4 \times 1.35} = \mathbf{1.11 \times 10^{-7}}$ **m.**

7. Newton's rings are observed in reflected light of $\lambda = 5.9 \times 10^{-7}$ m. The diameter of the 10th dark ring is 0.5 cm. Find the radius of curvature of the lens and the thickness of the air film.

Solution : Here, $\lambda = 5.9 \times 10^{-7}$ m, $D_{10} = 0.5$ cm $= 0.5 \times 10^{-2}$ m.

We have $D_n^2 = 4n\lambda R$ 'or, $R = \dfrac{D_n^2}{4n\lambda}$.

So, $R = \dfrac{(0.5 \times 10^{-2})^2}{4 \times 10 \times 5.9 \times 10^{-7}} = \mathbf{1.059}$ **m.**

Now, we have

$$2t = \frac{r^2}{R} \quad \text{or,} \quad t = \frac{r^2}{2R} = \frac{(D/2)^2}{2R} = \frac{D^2}{8R}.$$

$$\therefore \qquad t = \frac{D_n^2}{8R} = \frac{(0.5 \times 10^{-2})^2}{8 \times 1.059} = \mathbf{2.95 \times 10^{-6}} \text{ m.}$$

8. Show that the diameter D_n of the nth Newton's ring, when two surfaces of radii R_1 and R_2 are placed in contact, is given by

$$\frac{1}{R_1} \pm \frac{1}{R_2} = \frac{4n\lambda}{D_n^2}.$$

Solution : Newton's rings are produced by the interference between waves reflected from upper and lower surfaces of air-film of varying thickness enclosed between two surfaces. This is shown in Fig. 22.19.

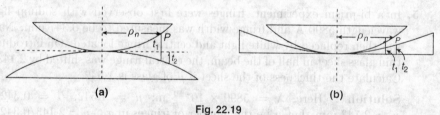

Fig. 22.19

If the radii of curvature of the surfaces are large and incidence of light be almost normal, then the *effective* path difference between interfering waves is given by

$$\Delta = 2t + \lambda/2 \quad \text{(where } t \text{ is the film-thickness).}$$

Therefore, for a dark ring we have

$$2t + \frac{\lambda}{2} = (2n + 1)\frac{\lambda}{2} \quad \text{or,} \quad 2t = n\lambda. \tag{22.38}$$

If ρ_n be the radius of a ring corresponding to a point P, where thickness is t and R_1, R_2 be the radii of curvature of the two surfaces, then

$$t = t_1 + t_2 = \frac{\rho_n^2}{2R_1} \pm \frac{\rho_n^2}{2R_2} \quad \text{or,} \quad 2t = \rho_n^2 \left(\frac{1}{R_1} \pm \frac{1}{R_2} \right).$$

Putting the value of $2t$ in Eq. (22.38),

$$\rho_n^2 \left(\frac{1}{R_1} \pm \frac{1}{R_2} \right) = n\lambda \quad \text{or,} \quad \frac{D_n^2}{4} \left(\frac{1}{R_1} \pm \frac{1}{R_2} \right) = n\lambda \quad \text{(where diameter } D_n = 2\rho_n\text{)}.$$

Hence, $\dfrac{1}{R_1} \pm \dfrac{1}{R_2} = \dfrac{4n\lambda}{D_n^2}$ **(Proved).**

9. Newton's rings are formed with reflected light of $\lambda = 5.895 \times 10^{-7}$ m with a liquid between the plane and the curved surface. The diameter of the 5th dark ring is 0.3 cm and the radius of curvature of the curved surface is 1 m. Calculate the refractive index of the liquid.

   Solution : Here, $\lambda = 5.895 \times 10^{-7}$ m, $D_5 = 0.3$ cm $= 0.3 \times 10^{-2}$ m and $R = 1$ m. For the nth dark ring, we can write,

   $$\frac{\mu D_n^2}{4R} = n\lambda \quad \text{or,} \quad \mu = \frac{4Rn\lambda}{D_n^2}.$$

   Therefore, $\mu = \dfrac{4 \times 1 \times 5 \times 5.895 \times 10^{-7}}{(0.3 \times 10^{-2})^2} = \mathbf{1.31}$

10. In Newton's ring arrangement, a source emitting two wavelengths $\lambda_1 = 6 \times 10^{-7}$ m and $\lambda_2 = 5.9 \times 10^{-7}$ m. It is found that nth dark ring due to one wavelength coincides with $(n+1)$th dark ring due to the other. Find the diameter of nth dark ring if the radius of curvature of the lens is 0.9 m.

    Solution : We can write, $(D_n^2)_{\lambda_1} = (D_{n+1}^2)_{\lambda_2}$.

    i.e., $\quad 4nR\lambda_1 = 4(n+1)R\lambda_2 \quad \text{or,} \quad n\lambda_1 = (n+1)\lambda_2$.

    Putting the values,

    $$n \times 6 \times 10^{-7} = (n+1) \times 5.9 \times 10^{-7}.$$

    Solving we get $n = 49$.

    Hence, $D_n = D_{49} = \sqrt{4 \times 49 \times 0.9 \times 6 \times 10^{-7}} = 1.0288 \times 10^{-2}$ m.

11. Newton's rings are formed with reflected light of wavelength 5890×10^{-10} m using a plano-convex lens and plane glass plate, with liquid between them. The diameter of the 10th ring is 4.2 mm and the radius of curvature of the curved surface of the lens is 100 cm. Find the refractive index of the liquid if the ring is (i) dark and (ii) bright.

    Solution : Here, $n = 10$, $R = 100$ cm $= 1$ m and $\lambda = 5890 \times 10^{-10}$ m, $D_{10} = 4.2$ mm $= 4.2 \times 10^{-3}$ m.

    (i) When ring is *dark,*

    $$\mu = \frac{4Rn\lambda}{D_n^2} = \frac{4 \times 1 \times 10 \times 5890 \times 10^{-10}}{(4.2 \times 10^{-3})^2} = \mathbf{1.336}.$$

    (ii) When the ring is *bright,*

    $$\mu = \frac{4R(2n-1)\lambda}{2D_n^2} = \frac{4 \times 1 \times 19 \times 5890 \times 10^{-10}}{2 \times (4.2 \times 10^{-3})^2} = \mathbf{1.269}.$$

12. In a Young's slit experiment, the separation of four bright fringes is 2.5 mm, when the wavelength used is 6.25×10^{-5} cm. The distance from the slits to the screen is 80 cm. Calculate the separation of the two slits.

    Solution : Given fringe width $y = \dfrac{2.5}{4} = 0.625$ mm $= 0.0625$ cm.

    Now, we can write,

    $$y = \frac{D}{2d} \cdot \lambda \quad \text{or,} \quad 2d = \frac{D}{y} \cdot \lambda = \frac{80 \times 6.25 \times 10^{-5}}{0.0625} = 0.8 \text{ mm} = \mathbf{0.08 \text{ cm.}}$$

13. A Fresnel bi-prism with acute angle of $1°30'$ and of a material whose $\mu = 1.5$ is used to form interference fringes with light of wavelength 6536 Å. The distance between the sources and the prism is 20 cm and that between the prism and the screen is 80 cm. Find the width of the fringes.

    Solution : The distance between the source and the prism, $a = 20$ cm;

    $$\alpha = 1°30' = \frac{\pi}{180} \times \frac{3}{2} = \frac{\pi}{120} \text{ radians.}$$

    We can write, $2d = 2a(\mu - 1) \cdot \alpha = 2 \times 20 \times (1.5 - 1) \times \dfrac{\pi}{120} = \dfrac{\pi}{6}$.

    $$D = 20 + 80 = 100 \text{ cm.}$$

    Now we have, $y = \dfrac{D}{2d} \cdot \lambda = \dfrac{100 \times 6 \times 6536 \times 10^{-8}}{\pi}$ cm $= \mathbf{0.0124 \text{ cm.}}$

14. A bi-prism is kept at a distance of 5 cm from a narrow slit illuminated by sodium light. Distance between two virtual sources formed by the bi-prism is 0.05 cm. If the distance of the screen from the bi-prism be 75 cm, calculate the fringe width. Wavelength of light $\lambda = 5890$ Å.

    Solution : We can write, $y = \frac{D}{2d} \cdot \lambda$, where D = distance between the slit and the screen $= 75 + 5 = 80$ cm; $2d$ = distance between the virtual sources $= 0.05$ cm and λ = wavelength of the light used $= 5890$ Å $= 5890 \times 10^{-8}$ cm.

    Putting the given values in the expression of y,

    we get $y = \dfrac{80 \times 5890 \times 10^{-8}}{0.05} = \mathbf{0.0942 \text{ cm.}}$

15. In an experimental arrangement with Fresnel's bi-prism, sodium light is used and bands 0.0196 cm in width are observed at a distance of 100 cm from the slit. A convex lens is then placed between the observer and the prism so as to give an image of the sources at a distance of 100 cm from the slit. The distance apart of the images is found to be 0.7 cm, lens being 30 cm from the slit. Calculate the wavelength of sodium light.

    Solution : As the slit is 30 cm from the lens, the object distance $u = 30$ cm and the image distance, $v = 100 - 30 = 70$ cm. So, the magnification of the image $= \dfrac{v}{u} = \dfrac{70}{30} = \dfrac{7}{3}$.

    Now, distance apart of the images being 0.7 cm, the size of the object, i.e., the distance between the two coherent sources, $2d = 0.7 \times \frac{3}{7} = 0.3$ cm. Also $D = 100$ cm and the fringe width, $y = 0.0196$ cm.

    We have $\lambda = \dfrac{2d}{D} \cdot y$.

    So, $\lambda = \dfrac{0.3 \times 0.0196}{100} = 5880 \times 10^{-8}$ cm $= \mathbf{5880 \text{ Å.}}$

16. In a Newton's ring apparatus, the radius of curvature of the lower surface of the convex lens is 10 meters. The Kth and $(K + 6)$th dark rings are found to have radii 3 mm and 7 mm respectively. Find the wavelength of the light used.

Solution : Let r_k be the radius of Kth dark ring, then $r_k^2 = K \cdot \lambda \cdot R (R =$ radius of curvature) and for $(K + 6)$th dark ring, $r_{k+6}^2 = (K + 6) \cdot \lambda \cdot R$.

Subtracting we get $r_{k+6}^2 - r_k^2 = \lambda.R(K + 6 - K) = 6.\lambda.R$.

or, $\lambda = \dfrac{r_{k+6}^2 - k_k^2}{6.R} = \dfrac{(0.7)^2 - (0.3)^2}{6 \times 10 \times 100} = \mathbf{0.66 \times 10^{-4} \ cm}$.

17. Newton's rings are seen with reflected light using a plane glass plate and a plano–convex lens, the radius of curvature of the curved surface being 90 cm with a small quantity of liquid between them. If the wavelength of light used is 5893 Å and if the diameters of the nth and $(n + 10)$th bright rings are 2.18 mm and 4.51 mm, find the refractive index of the liquid.   **[N.B.U. 1983]**

Solution : We have $\mu = \dfrac{4m.\lambda.R}{d_{m+n}^2 - d_n^2}$.

Given, $m = (n+10-n) = 10$; $\lambda = 5893$ Å $= 5893 \times 10^{-8}$ cm; $d_{m+n} = 4.51$ mm $= 0.451$ cm; $d_n = 2.18$ mm $= 0.218$ cm and $R = 90$ cm.

Substituting we get

$$\mu = \frac{4 \times 10 \times 5893 \times 10^{-8} \times 90}{(0.451)^2 - (0.218)^2} = \frac{4 \times 9 \times 10^{-6} \times 5893}{0.669 \times 0.233} = \frac{36 \times 5893}{669 \times 233} = \mathbf{1.36}.$$

18. In a Newton's ring experiment, the diameters of fifth and fifteenth dark rings are 0.336 cm and 0.590 cm respectively. If the radius of curvature of the curved surface of the plano–convex lens used be 100 cm, find the wavelength of the light used.   **[C.U. 2004]**

Solution : We have, $\lambda = \dfrac{D_{n+m}^2 - D_n^2}{4.m.R} = \dfrac{(0.590)^2 - (0.336)^2}{4 \times (15 - 5) \times 100}$

$$= \frac{0.926 \times 0.254}{4 \times 10 \times 100} = \mathbf{5880 \times 10^{-8} \ cm}.$$

19. A Michelson's interferometer is set for the white light straight fringes. When a mica sheet of thickness 0.005 cm is put in front of the fixed mirror, then to bring back the coloured fringes to their original position, the movable mirror is moved by 0.0025 cm. Calculate the refractive index of mica.

Solution : If μ be the refractive index of mica sheet of thickness t, then the increase in optical path is $(\mu - 1)t$. Let l be the distance moved by the movable mirror to bring back the coloured fringes in position, then

$(\mu - 1)t = l$ or, $\mu - 1 = l/t$

or, $\mu = 1 + \dfrac{l}{t} = 1 + \dfrac{0.0025}{0.005} = 1 + 0.5 = \mathbf{1.5}$.

20. The wavelength of two components of D-lines of sodium are 5890 Å and 5896 Å. By how much distance one of the mirrors of Michelson's interferometer be moved so as to obtain consecutive positions of maximum distinctness.

Solution : Given $\lambda_1 = 5890$ Å $= 5890 \times 10^{-10}$ m; $\lambda_2 = 5896$ Å $= 5896 \times 10^{-10}$ m. If l be the distance over which one of the mirrors is to be moved to pass from the position of one maximum intensity to the next, then we can write

$$\lambda_1 - \lambda_2 = \frac{\lambda_1 \lambda_2}{2l}, \quad l = \frac{\lambda_2 \lambda_2}{2(\lambda_1 - \lambda_2)}$$

or, $\quad l = \dfrac{5890 \times 10^{-10} \times 5896 \times 10^{-10}}{2(5896 - 5890) \times 10^{-10}} = \dfrac{5890 \times 5896 \times 10^{-10}}{2 \times 6}$

$\quad = \mathbf{0.2894 \times 10^{-3}}$ **m**.

21. In Michelson's interferometer 100 fringes cross the field of view when the movable mirror is displaced through 0.02948 mm. Calculate the wavelength of monochromatic light used.

Solution : We have $n = 100$, $l = 0.02948$ mm

$$= 0.02948 \times 10^{-3} \text{ m and } \lambda = ?$$

We have, $n\lambda/2 = l$, $\lambda = 2l/n$,

or, $\qquad \lambda = \dfrac{2 \times 0.02948 \times 10^{-3}}{100} = 5896 \times 10^{-10} \text{ m} = \mathbf{5896 \text{ Å}}$

Questions

Essay-type

1. Deduce an expression for the intensity of light at a point due to superposition of waves coming from two light sources. Hence find the condition of destructive and constructive interference. [C.U. 2005]

2. What do you mean by the interference of light? Explain the phenomenon by illustration. Describe briefly the phenomenon in relation to the law of conservation of energy.

3. Explain the effect of introducing a thin plate of glass in the path of one of the interfering beams. Show how this method is used for finding the refractive index of glass and the wavelength of light.

4. Derive the expressions for the position and width of the interference fringes produced by two monochromatic point sources, mentioning the conditions of interference.

5. Explain with a diagram how and where a Fresnel's bi-prism forms an interference pattern of light. Obtain an expression for the separation of fringes in the above patterns. [C.U. 1999]

6. How can the wavelength of monochromatic light be measured with the help of a Fresnel's bi-prism? Give the theory of the method and the arrangement of the apparatus. [C.U. 1985; N.B.U. 1982]

7. What are Newton's rings? Explain how such rings are formed. Deduce an expression for the diameter of the nth dark ring. [C.U. 1988]

8. Explain the formation of colours in thin transparent films. Given the theory of Newton's rings, show how from study the wavelength of monochromatic light is determined. [C.U. 1982]

9. Two planes AB and CD inclined to each other at an angle α enclose a wedge-shaped film. A beam of light is incident on the plane AB and is partially reflected and refracted. The refracted light is again partially reflected at the plane CD and is then refracted from the plane AB. This beam interfered with the beam reflected at AB at the point P.

    (i) Find the conditions for the intensity at P to be maximum and minimum.

    (ii) Why is the fringe obtained from the experiment called localised fringe?

    (iii) Why is an extended source required for a permanent fringe system?

                                                   [C.U. 2000]

10. Describe how the wavelength of a monochromatic beam of light can be measured by Newton's ring experiment. Deduce the working formula.

                         [C.U. 1982, 2004; N.B.U. 1983; B.U. 1999]

11. Explain the formation of Newton's ring and deduce an expression for the diameter of the rings. How can Newton's rings be used to determine the refractive index of a liquid?

12. Explain the phenomenon of interference of light. Describe and explain Young's experiment demonstrating interference of light.

13. Explain analytically the interference of light on the basis of wave theory. Explain briefly the phenomenon of interference in relation to the law of conservation of energy.

14. What are coherent sources? How are they produced? Explain.

15. Find an expression for fringe-width in case of Young's double-slit expression. What is the shape of the fringes?

16. State and explain, in brief, the conditions for the interference of light for (i) observance, (ii) good contrast and (iii) stationary interference pattern.

17. Give the theory and experimental arrangement of Lloyd's mirror to measure the wavelength of monochromatic light.

18. Discuss the formation of fringes by Lloyd's single mirror and explain why the central fringe is black. Find an expression for the fringe-width.

19. Give Stokes' treatment to explain the change of phase when reflection takes place at a denser medium.

20. Explain the effect of introducing a thin plate of glass in the path of one of the interfering beams. Show how this method is used for finding the refractive index and the wavelength of light.

21. Calculate the displacement of fringes when a thin transparent sheet is introduced in the path of one of the interfering beams in bi-prism. Show how this method is used for finding the thickness of a mica plate.

22. Describe Fresnel's bi-prism. Explain the formation of interference fringes by it with a monochromatic source. Describe in detail how the wavelength of monochromatic source of light can be determined with its help.

23. In a Fresnel's bi-prism arrangement, show that $d = 2x(\mu - 1)\alpha$, where x is the distance of the source from the bi-prism base and α the refracting angle of the prism.

24. Derive an expression for the wavelength of monochromatic light source used in Newton's rings experiment in terms of diameters of rings and radius of curvature of the lens used.

25. Describe the formation of Newton's rings by reflected light. Describe an arrangement to produce such rings.

26. Derive the expression for the radius of nth dark as well as bright rings to show that while diameters of dark rings are proportional to the square root of simple numbers, those of bright rings are proportional to the square root of odd simple numbers.

27. Explain the method of Newton's rings for determining the refractive index of rare liquids. Derive the necessary formula.

28. Describe the principle of construction and working of Michelson's interferometer.

29. Explain how circular fringes are produced in Michelson's interferometer. Show that the radii of circular fringes are proportional to the square root of natural numbers.

30. Describe Michelson's interferometer. How will you use it to calibrate a metre in terms of a standard wavelength?

Short Answer-type

31. What are constructive and destructive interference? Does destructive interference violate the principle of conservation of energy?

$$\text{[C.U. 2004; N.B.U. 2001]}$$

32. What is the relation between path-difference and phase-difference?

$$\text{[C.U. 2005]}$$

33. Why two different sources of light cannot produce sustained interference?

$$\text{[B.U. 2005]}$$

34. Are interference fringes produced by monochromatic light coming from two different sources? If not, why? [C.U. 1982, '83]

35. Enumerate the necessary conditions for producing sustained interference fringes. What are called coherent sources? [N.B.U. 2001; Vid. U. 2002]

36. What do you mean by coherent sources of light? [C.U. 2004]

37. What do you understand by (i) fringes of equal inclination and (ii) fringes of equal thickness? [B.U. 2004]

38. Is the central fringe of Newton's ring bright or dark? [B.U. 2004]

39. The central fringe of Newton's rings is dark. In the case of white light, the fringes are coloured. Why? [B.U. 1983; Tripura U. 1993]

40. Why is an extended source necessary to observe the colour of thin films?

$$\text{[B.U. 1983]}$$

41. Is the principle of conservation of energy violated in the phenomenon of interference? Explain.

42. Enumerate the methods of production of coherent sources, with one example for each.

43. State, in brief, the condition for observing a good and sustained interference pattern.

44. How will you locate the fringe of zero order in bi-prism experiment? Explain what happens when the eyepiece is moved away from the source.

45. Explain what happens in bi-prism experiment when (i) white light is used to illuminate the slit and (ii) the edge of the prism is not parallel to the slit.

46. Explain why the central fringe in Lloyd's mirror is black.

47. Can two real sources of light act as coherent sources? Explain.

48. Compare the Lloyd's mirror fringes with those of the bi-prism.

49. Can we obtain interference pattern if two coherent sources are separated by a distance less than a wavelength of light? Explain.

50. In case of Young's double-slit experiment, if one slit is covered with green transparent paper and the other with blue transparent one, what will be the effect on interference pattern?

51. Does the interference phenomenon give any information about the longitudinal or transverse nature of light?

52. Show that the fringe-width decreases with the order in Newton's rings.

53. Why is a broad source of light necessary for observing colours in thin films, when a narrow source is required for bi-prism experiment?

54. Why do we see colours when white light falls on a thin film of transparent medium?

55. How does the interference pattern by reflection in thin films differ from that of refraction? Why?

56. How will you test the flatness of a surface by interference of light?

57. What will happen in Newton's ring experiment if the glass plate is replaced by a plane mirror?

58. Lenses coated with non-reflecting thin film appear purple in colour when seen in reflected light. Why?

59. Give important applications of the Michelson's interferometer.

60. What are the shape of interference fringes obtained with Michelson's interferometer?

Numerical Problems

61. In a Young's double-slit experiment the slits are separated by 0.2 cm and the screen is placed 1 m away. The slits are illuminated by yellow light ($\lambda = 5896\text{Å}$). Calculate the fringe-width. **[C.U. 2005]**
    [Ans. 2948×10^{-5} cm]

62. In Lloyd's single-mirror interference experiment, the slit source is at a distance of 2 mm from the plane of the mirror. The screen is kept at a distance of 1.5 metres from the source. Calculate the fringe-width. Wavelength of light used = 5890 Å. **[Ans. 0.022 cm]**

63. In Fresnel's bi-prism experiment, on inserting a thin glass plate of thickness 6×10^{-4} cm in the path of one of interfering beams, it is found that the central fringes shift to the position previously occupied by the 5th bright fringe. If the wavelength of light used be 6000 Å, find the refractive index of glass.
    [C.U. 2001]
    [Ans. 1.5]

64. In an experiment with a bi-prism, it is found that the central fringe shifts, when a thin plate of glass is inserted in the path of one of the interfering beams, to the position previously occupied by the *tenth* bright fringe. Calculate the thickness of the plate if its refractive index is 1.5 and the wavelength of the light used is 6000 Å.   [C.U. 2001]

[Ans. 0.012 mm]

65. Fringes are produced by a Fresnel's bi-prism in the focal plane of a telescope which is 100 cm from the slit. A lens inserted between the prism and the telescope gives two images of the slit in two positions. In one case, the two images of the slit are 4.05 mm and in the other case, 2.9 mm apart. If sodium light ($\lambda = 5893 \times 10^{-8}$ cm) is used, find the fringe-width.

[C.U. 1985; B.U. 1994]

[Ans. 0.172 mm]

66. A bi-prism made of glass (r.i. = 1.5) with refracting angle 2° is used to produce interference fringes with light of wavelength 6000 A.U. Calculate the fringe-width when the slit and the focal plane of eyepiece are at distances 20 cm and 80 cm respectively from the bi-prism.   [N.B.U. 1982]

[Ans. 0.0086 cm]

67. Newton's rings are formed with reflected light of wavelength 5895×10^{-8} cm with a liquid between the plane surface of a glass plate and curved surface of a convex lens. The diameter of 5th dark ring is 0.3 cm and the radius of curvature of curved surface of the lens 100 cm. Calculate the refractive index of the liquid.   [B.U. 1999; N.B.U. 2001]

[Ans. 1.31]

68. In Newton's ring experiment, if the diameters of the 3rd and 23rd rings are 0.181 cm and 0.501 cm respectively and if the radius of curvature of the curved surface of the plano-convex lens be 50 cm, calculate the wavelength of the light.   [C.U. 1986, 2002]

[Ans. 5456 Å]

69. Newton's rings are formed by light reflected normally from a plano-convex lens and a plane glass plate with a liquid between them. The diameters of nth and $(n + 10)$th bright rings are measured as 2.18 mm and 4.51 mm. Calculate the refractive index of liquid. Given, radius of curvature of lens = 90 cm and the wavelength of light used = 5893 Å.   [N.B.U. 1983]

[Ans. 1.36]

70. In a bi-prism experiment, the eyepiece is placed at a distance of 1.2 m from the source. The distance between the virtual sources was found to be 7.5×10^{-4} m. Find the wavelength of light if the eyepiece is to be moved transversely through a distance of 1.888×10^{-2} m for 20 fringes.   [Ans. 5900 Å]

71. The inclined faces of a bi-prism of refractive index 1.50 make an angle of 2° with the base. A slit illuminated by a monochromatic light is placed at a distance of 10 cm from the bi-prism. If the distance between the two dark fringes observed at a distance of 1 m from the bi-prism is 0.18 mm, find the wavelength of light used.   [Ans. 5727 Å]

72. Calculate the separation between the coherent sources formed by a bi-prism whose inclined faces make angle of 2° with the base, the slit source being 10 cm away from the bi-prism and refractive index of the material of bi-prism being 1.5.   [Ans. 0.00349 m]

73. In bi-prism experiment, fringes were first observed with sodium light of wavelength 5890 Å and the fringe-width was measured to be 0.347 mm. Sodium light was then replaced by white light and central fringe was located. On introducing a thin glass sheet in half of the beam, the central fringe was shifted by 2.143 mm. Calculate the thickness of the glass sheet, if the refractive index of glass is 1.542. **[Ans. 6.71×10^{-6} m]**

74. Fringes are produced by a monochromatic light of $\lambda = 5.45 \times 10^{-7}$ m. A thin plate of glass of index 1.50 is then placed normally in the path of one of the interfering beams and the central bright band of the fringe system is found to move into the position previously occupied by the third bright band from the centre. Calculate the thickness of the plate. **[Ans. 3.27×10^{-6} m]**

75. If a slit illuminated by sodium light (5893 Å) is placed 0.15 cm from the plane of the Lloyd's mirror, what will be the distance between the consecutive bands formed 1 m away from the slit. **[Ans. 0.002 cm]**

76. When a thin piece of glass 3.4×10^{-4} cm thick is placed in the path of interfering beams in a bi-prism experiment, it is found that the central bright fringe shifts through a distance equal to the width of 4 fringes. Find the refractive index of the glass piece. **[Ans. 1.6424]**

77. Two coherent sources whose intensity ratio is 81 : 1 produce interference fringes. Deduce the ratio of maximum to minimum intensity of the fringe system. **[Ans. 25 : 16]**

78. Consider a non-reflecting film of refractive index 1.38. Assume that its thickness is 9×10^{-6} cm. Calculate the wavelength in the visible region for which the film will be non-reflecting. **[Ans. 4968 Å]**

79. In a double-slit arrangement, fringes are produced using light of $\lambda = 4800$ Å. One slit is covered by thin glass plate of $\mu = 1.4$ and the other by another glass plate of the same thickness but of index 1.7. The result is a shift in the central bright fringe to the position of the original 5th bright fringe from the centre. Find the thickness of the plates. **[Ans. 8.0×10^{-6} m]**

80. When a wedge-shaped air-film is viewed by a monochromatic source of light incident normally, the interference fringes 4 mm apart are observed. If the air space is filled with water of $\mu = 1.33$, how far apart will the fringes be observed? **[Ans. 3×10^{-3} m]**

81. A wedge-shaped air-film, having an angle of 40 seconds is illuminated by a monochromatic light and fringes are observed vertically through a microscope. The distance measured between the consecutive bright fringes is 0.12×10^{-2} m. Calculate the wavelength of light used. **[Ans. 4656 Å]**

82. A parallel beam of light of $\lambda = 5890$ Å is incident on a thin glass plate of $\mu = 1.5$, such that the angle of refraction inside the plate is 60°. Calculate the *smallest* thickness of glass plate which will appear dark by reflection. **[Ans. 3.927×10^{-7} m]**

83. A plano-convex lens of radius 3 m is placed on an optically flat glass plate and is illuminated by monochromatic light. The diameter of the 8th ring in the transmitted system is 0.72 cm. Calculate the wavelength of light used. **[Ans. 5760 Å]**

84. In an experiment with Jamin's interferometer for determining the refractive index of air, a shift of 150 fringes was observed when all the air was removed

from the tube placed in one of the optical paths. If the wavelength of light used is 4000 Å in air and the length of the tube is 0.2 m, calculate the refractive index of air.

[**Ans. 1.0003**]

85. In a Michelson's interferometer, a thin plate is introduced in the path of one of the beams and it is found that 50 bands had crossed the line of observation. If the wavelength of light used is 5896 Å and $\mu = 1.4$, determine the thickness of the plate.

[**Ans. 4968 Å**]

86. In an experiment with Michelson's interferometer, the distance travelled by the mirror for two successive positions of maximum distinctness was 0.2945 mm. If the mean wavelength for the two components of sodium D-line is 5893 Å, calculate the difference between the two wavelengths.

[**Ans. 5.896 Å**]

Chapter 23
Diffraction of Light

23.1   Introduction

We know that light rays travel in straight lines and when these rays are allowed to pass by the edge of an obstacle a distinct shadow is formed whose boundary line is marked by a straight line drawn from the source to the screen and grazing the edge of the obstacle. When a careful investigation is made, it shows that the shadow is not distinct and perfectly dark, but the light gradually fades away. At a short distance below the line drawn through the source and the edge of the obstacle a complete darkness sets in. In order to explain this phenomenon, we have to consider the fact that according to the *Wave Theory of Light,* the propagation of light is approximately rectilinear and light waves of extremely small wavelengths exhibit a slight bending in passing by the edge of an obstacle. This bending of light waves round the edge of an obstacle causing a rapid diminution in the intensity of light within its geometrical shadow is called the *diffraction of light.*

23.2   Distinction between the Interference and Diffraction Phenomena

Interference	Diffraction
(a) Interference fringes are the result of interaction of light waves arriving from different wavefronts but derived from the same source.	(a) Diffraction fringes are the result of interaction of light waves arriving from different parts of the same wavefront.
(b) All the bright bands have uniform intensity.	(b) All the bright bands have not the same intensity.
(c) Regions of minimum light intensity are perfectly dark.	(c) Regions of minimum light intensity are not perfectly dark.
(d) Interference fringes may or may not have same width.	(d) Diffraction fringes have never same width.

23.3   Types of Diffraction

There are two main types of diffraction phenomena.   These are (i) Fresnel's diffraction and (ii) Fraunhofer's diffraction phenomena.

Fresnel type of diffraction : (i) In this type, the source of light or the screen or both are at finite distances from the obstacle. No lenses are used to make the light rays parallel or convergent.

(ii) The incident wavefront is either spherical or cylindrical and are never plane.

(iii) Fresnel's diffraction is produced when light waves suffer bending or diffraction at a straight edge, a narrow slit, a thin wire, a small circular obstacle or a hole. A zone plate is an example of this type of diffraction.

(iv) As the incident wavefront is not plane the phase of the secondary wavelets have not same value at all the points of the aperture or the obstacle producing diffraction.

Fraunhofer type of diffraction : (i) In this type, the source of light and the screen are virtually at infinite distances from the aperture or the obstacle producing diffraction. This may be realised by placing a convex lens at a distance equal to its focal length from the source, so that a parallel beam may fall on the aperture. Then a second convex lens is used to focus the emergent parallel beam after diffraction on the screen. This interposition of two lenses removes the source and the screen to infinite distance.

(ii) In this case, the incident wavefront is plane and so the phase of vibration is same at every point of the aperture.

(iii) With this type of diffraction we get plane diffraction grating and concave reflection grating.

23.4 Fresnel's Half-period Zones

According to Huygens' principle, each point on a wavefront transmits its secondary wavelets. Fresnel assumed that these wavelets interfere among themselves to produce the resultant intensity at any point. To act this resultant intensity due to the whole wavefront, Fresnel divided the wavefront into a number of zones called *Fresnel's half-period zones.*

As shown in Fig. 23.1, let a plane wavefront $ABCD$ of wavelength λ move from left to right. Let P be the external point at which the resultant intensity is to be found out. From P we draw a perpendicular PO to the wavefront where the point O is called the pole of the wavefront relative to P. We assume $PO = p$ and with P as centre and radii $p + \lambda/2, p + 2\lambda/2, p + 3\lambda/2, \ldots$, etc., let us draw a series of spheres the sections of which by the wavefront are concentric circles. The area of the innermost circle is known as the *first half-period zone;* the annular area between the first and the second circles is called the *second half-period zone* and so on. In this way, nth half-period zone is the annular area between the $(n-1)$th and the nth circles.

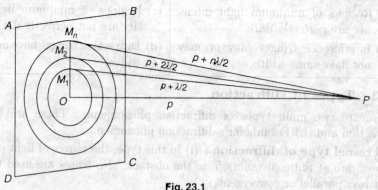

Fig. 23.1

Now, from Fig. 23.1, the area of the nth half-period zone,

$$S = \pi(OM_n^2 - OM_{n-1}^2)$$
$$= \pi[\{(p + n\lambda/2)^2 - p^2\} - \{(p + \overline{n-1}\lambda/2)^2 - p^2\}]$$
$$= \pi[(pn\lambda + n^2\lambda^2/4) - \{p(n-1)\lambda + (n-1)^2\lambda^2/4\}]$$

$$= \pi \left[v\lambda + \frac{\lambda^2}{4} \{ n^2 - (n-1)^2 \} \right]$$

$$= \pi \left[p\lambda + \frac{\lambda^2}{4} (2n-1) \right]$$

$$\simeq \pi p\lambda. \tag{23.1}$$

(λ^2 is ignored compared to $p\lambda$, as $p \gg \lambda$.)

So we can say that, *the area of the nth zone is independent of the order n of the zone. This implies that the area of each zone is nearly equal;* however, it increases slightly with the order n.

Again, if d_n be the average distance of the nth zone from P, then we have

$$d_n = \frac{1}{2} [(p + n\lambda/2) + \{ p + (n-1)\lambda/2 \}]$$

$$= p + (2n-1)\lambda/4. \tag{23.2}$$

Amplitude due to a zone at the point P

The factors on which the amplitude of the disturbance due to a zone at P depends are : (i) the area of the zone, (ii) the average distance of the zone and (iii) the obliquity factor. The amplitude due to a zone is

(a) inversely proportional to the average distance of the zone from P,

(b) directly proportional to the area of the zone as more the area, more would be the number of point sources in it,

and (c) directly proportional to the obliquity factor $(1+\cos\theta_n)$, where θ_n represents the angle made by the direction of P from the nth zone with OP.

Therefore, the amplitude A_n due to the nth zone is expressed as

$$A_n \propto \pi \frac{[p\lambda + (2n-1)\lambda^2/4]}{p + (2n-1)\lambda/4} (1 + \cos\theta_n)$$

$$\propto \pi\lambda(1 + \cos\theta_n). \tag{23.3}$$

As n increases, θ_n increases but $\cos\theta_n$ decreases. Thus the amplitude of the disturbance at P due to a zone will decrease gradually as the order n of the zone increases.

To find the resultant amplitude due to the entire wavefront, let $A_1, A_2, \ldots, A_n$ be the amplitudes at P due to the first, second, $\ldots, n$th zone respectively. Again, the average distance of P from any two consecutive zones differs by $\lambda/2$ (half-period) and the waves from two successive zones reach P in *opposite phase*.

Thus the resultant amplitude at P due to the wavefront $ABCD$ is written as

$$A = A_1 - A_2 + A_3 - A_4 + \cdots + (-1)^{n-1} A_n. \tag{23.4}$$

Now, as A_2 is slightly smaller than A_1 but slightly greater than A_3, we can write,

$$A_2 = \frac{1}{2}(A_1 + A_3); \quad A_4 = \frac{1}{2}(A_3 + A_5), \cdots, \text{etc.} \tag{23.5}$$

to a close approximation.

Hence the equation (23.4) may be written as

$$A = \frac{A_1}{2} + \left(\frac{A_1}{2} - A_2 + \frac{A_3}{2} \right) + \left(\frac{A_3}{2} - A_4 + \frac{A_5}{2} \right) + \cdots \tag{23.6}$$

the last term being $\frac{A_n}{2}$ if n is *odd*, or $\frac{A_{n-1}}{2} - A_n$ if n is *even*.

Using Eq. (23.5) we get

$$A = \frac{A_1}{2} + \frac{A_n}{2}, \text{ when } n \text{ is odd} \tag{23.7}$$

and $A = \dfrac{A_1}{2} + \dfrac{A_{n-1}}{2} - A_n, \text{ when } n \text{ is } even.$ (23.8)

(As the value of each bracketed term is essentially zero.)

But n is extremely large and due to the obliquity factor $A_{n-1} = A_n = 0$.

So, $A = \dfrac{1}{2}A_1.$ (23.9)

Hence, the amplitude due to the whole wavefront at a point is half that due to the first half-period zone alone. The contributions due to other half-period zones are cancelled by mutual interference.

It may be mentioned that as the intensity is proportional to the square of the amplitude, the intensity at P for the entire wavefront is *one-fourth* the intensity due to the *first half-period zone.*

23.4.1   Rectilinear Propagation of Light by Wave Theory

When an opaque obstacle of dimensions very large in comparison to the wavelength

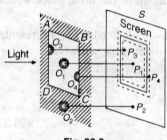

Fig. 23.2

of light λ is kept between a source and a screen, a distinct shadow may be obtained on the screen. This shows that light travels from the source to the screen in a straight line. This phenomenon is called *rectilinear propagation of light*. We assume that a plane wavefront of wavelength λ be incident normally on a rectangular aperture $ABCD$ as shown in Fig. 23.2. A screen S is kept parallel to the aperture at some distance. We shall get an uniform illumination inside the full-line rectangle in S while a complete darkness is obtained outside it.

Let us take a point P_1 inside the full-line rectangle, the corresponding pole being O_1 which is at a large distance compared to λ from the edge of the aperture. Thus a large number of half-period zones can be drawn around O_1 before the edge of the aperture intersects them. Consequently, all the effective zones are exposed and the resultant amplitude at P_1 is half that due to the first zone. All the points close to P_1 are also illuminated equally.

We now choose another point P_2 outside the rectangle but inside the geometrical shadow with pole Q_2. All the effective half-period zones are cut off and so the resultant amplitude at P_2 becomes zero and so there is complete darkness. If we take points like P_3 and P_4 that are within the dotted rectangles, then for P_3, the pole is O_3 just inside the aperture. The effective area of the zones that intersect the edge diminishes rapidly. For P_4 with pole at O_4 just outside the aperture, the effective area of the zones increases rapidly. In both the cases, the theory of half-period zones is inapplicable and so intensity at P_3 and P_4 cannot be decided. Thus there is almost uniform illumination at all points inside the inner dotted-rectangle and complete darkness at all points outside the outer dotted-rectangle. Thus the wave theory of light explains the rectilinear propagation of light approximately.

23.5 Zone Plate

Zone plate is an optical device designed to put a stop to the light from alternate half-period zones. It is constructed by drawing a series of concentric circles on a white paper-sheet. The radii of the circles are proportional to the square root of natural numbers, i.e., $\sqrt{1} : \sqrt{2} : \sqrt{3}$: etc. The different zones formed are alternately *painted black* and a highly reduced photograph of this drawing is taken on a plate of glass. The negative so obtained is the **zone plate**. When odd zones are transparent and even zones are opaque, it is called a *positive zone plate*. While even zones are transparent and odd zones are opaque, it is called a *negative zone plate*. In Fig. 23.3, the positive zone plate and negative zone plate are shown in (a) and (b) respectively.

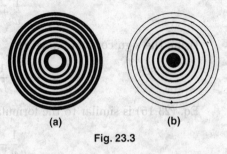

(a)   (b)

Fig. 23.3

A zone plate behaves like a convergent lens and produces image of a light source placed at a suitable distance.

Theory

In Fig. 23.4, O is a point source of monochromatic light producing spherical waves of wavelength λ whose effect at a point I on the screen is to determine. Let us consider an imaginary plane through P of a transparent medium, perpendicular to the plane of the paper and the line OI. The plane is divided into zones which are bounded by circles with centre at P and radii $PM_1 = r_1, PM_2 = r_2, \ldots, PM_n = r_n$. We can write,

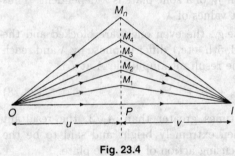

Fig. 23.4

$$OM_1 + IM_1 = OP + IP + \lambda/2 \qquad (23.10)$$

$$OM_2 + IM_2 = OP + IP + 2(\lambda/2) \qquad (23.11)$$

$$\ldots\ldots\ldots\ldots = \ldots\ldots\ldots\ldots\ldots$$

$$OM_n + IM_n = OP + IP + n(\lambda/2) \qquad (23.12)$$

The annular rings so formed are half-period zones for I, as the path-difference between corresponding points of two consecutive zones is $\lambda/2$. We assume,

$$OP = u \quad \text{and} \quad IP = v.$$

Then, $OM_n = (u^2 + r_n^2)^{1/2} = u(1 + r_n^2/u^2)^{1/2}$

$$= u + r_n^2/2u \quad (\text{as } u \gg r_n).$$

Similarly, $IM_n = v + r_n^2/2v.$

Now, from Eq. (23.12) we get

$$u + \frac{r_n^2}{2u} + v + \frac{r_n^2}{2v} = u + v + \frac{n\lambda}{2}$$

or, $\quad r_n^2 \left(\dfrac{1}{u} + \dfrac{1}{v} \right) = n\lambda.$ $\qquad (23.13)$

Eq. (23.13) shows that $r_n \propto \sqrt{n}$, as u, v, λ are constants. This justifies why the radii of the concentric circles in preparing the zone plate were proportional to $\sqrt{1} : \sqrt{2} : \sqrt{3} : \cdots$.

We can write from Eq. (23.13),

$$\frac{1}{u} + \frac{1}{v} = \frac{n\lambda}{r_n^2}. \tag{23.14}$$

Using the sign convention we get

$$\frac{1}{v} - \frac{1}{u} = \frac{n\lambda}{r_n^2} = \frac{1}{f_n} \quad \text{(where } f_n = r_n^2/n\lambda\text{)}. \tag{23.15}$$

Eq. (23.15) is similar to the formula of convex lens,

$$\frac{1}{v} - \frac{1}{u} = \frac{1}{f}. \tag{23.16}$$

Hence, the zone plate may behave like a convergent lens whose focal length is given by

$$f_n = r_n^2/n\lambda. \tag{23.17}$$

Eq. (23.17) reveals that the focal length f_n of a zone plate is λ-dependent. Thus a zone plate has different foci for different values of λ.

In a zone plate, the alternate zones (e.g., the even ones) are blocked and the waves from the transparent zones (1st, 3rd, 5th, etc.) differ in phase by λ and reach the points I in the same phase. Hence, the resultant amplitude A at I is

$$A = A_1 + A_3 + A_5 + \ldots \tag{23.18}$$

The resultant amplitude is now many times greater than $A_1/2$, the resultant amplitude due to all the zones. I is then extremely bright and said to be the image of O. This clearly interprets the focusing action of the zone plate.

23.5.1 Comparison between Zone Plate and Convex Lens

Similarity

A zone plate behaves like a convex lens. As the focal length of both depends on the wavelength λ, both of them suffer from chromatic aberration. Also the relation between the conjugate distances is similar to zone plate and convex lens.

Dissimilarity

There is no one-to-one correspondence between the two and in many ways they differ from each other. In contrast to convex lens, the zone plate has multiple focal lengths. For a point-source zone plate forms a series of point-images of diminishing intensity. For a convex lens, all the rays reaching an image-point have the same optical path, but not so for a zone plate where the paths between the rays for two consecutive transparent zones differ by λ. Also, the focal length for red is less than that for violet (i.e., $f_r < f_v$) for a zone plate, while for a convex lens $f_r > f_v$. Hence, when order of colours in chromatic effect is considered, we find that one is just the reverse of the other.

23.5.2 Phase Reversal Zone Plate

Instead of blocking the light from alternate zones, if an additional optical path $\lambda/2$ is introduced between the light waves from consecutive zones, the amplitudes from each successive zone will be reinforced. Such a zone plate, designed by Wood, is called a *phase reversal zone plate*. In order to prepare it, the following procedures are adopted sequentially :

(i) A glass plate is chemically cleaned and coated with a thin layer of gelatine solution and dried.

(ii) The coated plate is then sensitized by immersing it in a dilute solution of $K_2Cr_2O_7$ for a few seconds and dried in dark.

(iii) Next the plate is placed in contact with an usual zone plate and exposed to sunlight. The light passes through the transparent zones to act upon the gelatine for making it insoluble in water. However, the gelatine in contact with opaque zones remains water-soluble.

(iv) Thereafter, the glass plate is immersed in water to dissolve the gelatine of unexposed parts so, that the optical paths from consecutive zones on the plate get an additional optical path of $\lambda/2$.

The phase reversal zone plate provides four times more intense image in comparison to an ordinary zone plate.

23.6 Diffraction at a Straight Edge

We consider a narrow slit S placed perpendicular to the plane of the paper as shown in Fig. 23.5. A be the sharp straight edge of an opaque obstacle AB, and XY a screen, both are placed parallel to the slit. The slit is illuminated with a monochromatic light of wavelength λ. SA is joined and extended to meet the screen at M.

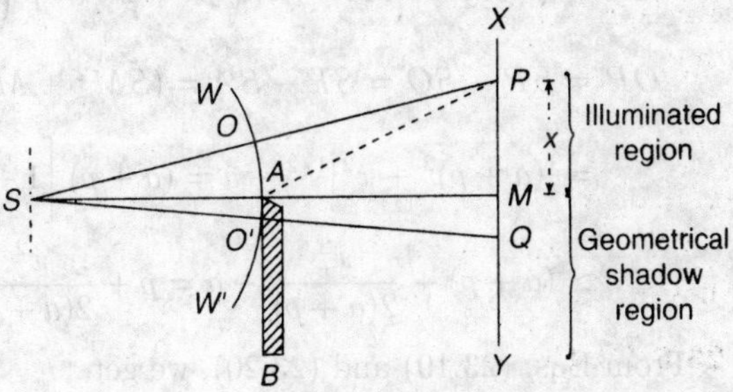

When there is no diffraction at the edge A, uniform illumination is obtained on the screen above M and geometrical shadow below it. Under this condition, a few bright and dark bands of unequal width are observed but those are

Fig. 23.5

poor contrast and varying intensities that run parallel to the length of the slit in the region above and near M. Below M, the intensity falls rapidly and becomes zero at a small but finite distance from M. Thus the **diffraction pattern** due to a straight edge is obtained.

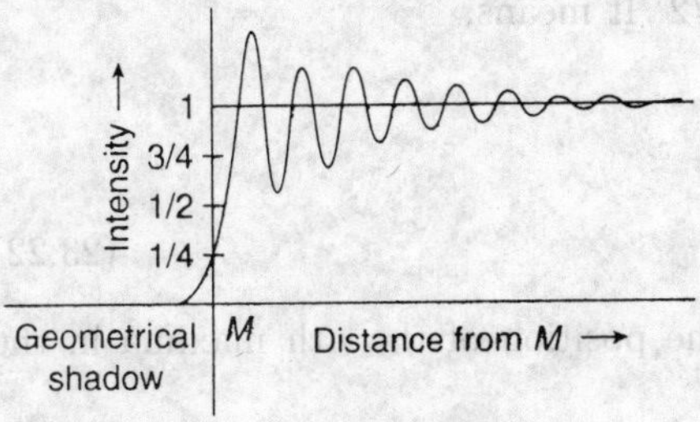

Fig. 23.6

In Fig. 23.6, the intensity distribution of the diffraction pattern is illustrated. The figure shows that the intensity decreases rapidly in the geometrical shadow but a number of bright and dark bands are noted outside till uniform illumination sets in.

Explanation

In Fig. 23.5, let WW' be the section of the cylindrical wavefront originating from S. P is a point at a distance x above M on the screen. PS is joined to intersect

WW' at O, which is the pole of the wavefront with respect to P. To get the intensity at P, the wavefront is divided (with O as pole) into half-period elements. The effect at P depends on the number of half-period elements contained in OA and OW of the wavefront. The effect at M is due to the upper half of wavefront only, so that the displacement at M is half the displacement that would have occurred if the entire wavefront were effective. So the intensity at M is one-fourth of that at a point far away from M, where the whole wavefront is effective.

When we consider the geometrical shadow, we find that the pole O moves through A towards W' and half-period elements 1,2,3,... are intercepted and the intensity gradually diminishes. On the other hand, if we move away from M towards X, half-period elements 1,2,3,... are exposed. The illumination at P is due to the complete half of wave surface OW and the resultant of number of half-period elements contained in OA.

The amplitude at P will exhibit maximum or minimum depending on whether OA contains an odd or even number of half-period elements. The intensity at a maximum goes on decreasing while at a minimum it goes on increasing, till at a large distance from M uniform illumination is produced.

Theory

In Fig. 23.5, the number of half-period elements in AO depends on the path difference $AP - OP$. Substituting $SA = a, AM = p$ and $MP = x$, we get

$$AP = \sqrt{AM^2 + MP^2} = (\sqrt{p^2 + x^2}) = p\left(1 + \frac{x^2}{p^2}\right)^{1/2} \simeq p\left(1 + \frac{x^2}{2p^2}\right) \quad (23.19)$$

$$OP = SP - SO = SP - SA = (SM^2 + MP^2)^{1/2} - SA$$

$$= [(a+p)^2 + x^2]^{1/2} - a = (a+p)\left[1 + \frac{x^2}{(a+p)^2}\right]^{1/2} - a$$

$$\simeq (a+p) + \frac{x^2}{2(a+p)} - a = p + \frac{x^2}{2(a+p)}. \quad (23.20)$$

From Eqs. (23.19) and (23.20), we get

$$AP - OP = \frac{x^2}{2p} - \frac{x^2}{2(a+p)} = \frac{ax^2}{2p(a+p)}. \quad (23.21)$$

P is a **maximum** if $AP - OP = (2n+1)\lambda/2$. It means,

$$\frac{ax^2}{2p(a+p)} = (2n+1)\frac{\lambda}{2}$$

or, $\quad x = \sqrt{\dfrac{p(a+p)(2n+1)\lambda}{a}} = k\sqrt{2n+1}, \quad (23.22)$

where k is a constant. Eq. (23.22) gives the position of the nth maxima in the diffraction pattern.

In a similar way, P is a **minimum** if $AP - OP = n\lambda$. It means,

$$\frac{ax^2}{2p(a+p)} = n\lambda$$

or, $\quad x = \sqrt{\dfrac{p(a+p)2n\lambda}{a}} = k\sqrt{2n}. \quad (23.23)$

This gives the position of nth minima in the pattern.

Thus the distances of successive maxima from M are achieved by putting $n = 0, 1, 2$, etc., in Eq. (23.22). Thus we have

$$x_1 = k; \quad x_2 = k\sqrt{3}; \quad x_3 = k\sqrt{5}; \quad x_4 = k\sqrt{7}; \text{ etc.}$$

Hence separation between successive maxima are

$$x_2 - x_1 = k(\sqrt{3} - 1) = 0.73k$$
$$x_3 - x_2 = k(\sqrt{5} - \sqrt{3}) = 0.50k$$
$$x_4 - x_3 = k(\sqrt{7} - \sqrt{5}) = 0.43k$$
$$\text{etc.,}$$

which are in decreasing order. So the bands are not equally spaced. The separation between successive minima also decreases gradually.

Determination of Wavelength

A straight edge (e.g., a sharp razor blade) is set with its edge parallel to the slit on the optical bench. The slit is illuminated with light of wavelength λ. Diffraction bands of unequal width and diminishing intensity are noted in the field of view of the micrometer eyepiece. The positions of the first maximum and a distant one is noted. Let the 5th one is another clearly visible maximum. We can then write,

$$x_1 = \sqrt{\frac{p(a+p)\lambda}{a}} \quad \text{and} \quad x_5 = \sqrt{\frac{p(a+p) \times 11\lambda}{a}}.$$

$$\therefore \quad x_5 - x_1 = \sqrt{\frac{p(a+p)\lambda}{a}}(\sqrt{11} - 1). \tag{23.24}$$

The distance p from the edge to the eyepiece and the distance a between the slit and the edge are measured. Then from a knowledge of $(x_5 - x_1)$, the unknown wavelength λ can be determined.

23.7 Fresnel's Diffraction at a Circular Aperture

In Fig. 23.7, let AB be the narrow circular aperture placed in the path of light. S is a monochromatic point source. The diffraction pattern may be obtained on a screen XY held parallel to the slit. O is the centre of the slit and the line joining S and O is extended to get P on the screen. Let P_1Q_1 be the section of a spherical wavefront to touch the aperture at any instant. The aperture forms the geometrical shadow above M and below N. The amplitude at P is the resultant of a large number of wavelets emanating from the wavefront AOB. Let with respect to P, the pole of the wavefront is O and we assume that

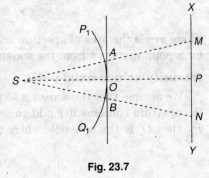

Fig. 23.7

wavefront is divided into half-period zones round O. The intensity at the axial point P is to be determined.

If P exposes only the first zone, then the amplitude at P will be A_1. When the whole wavefront is exposed, the resultant amplitude at P is only $A_1/2$. Therefore, the intensity at P is **four times** the intensity due to the whole wavefront. P is then extremely **bright** and thus giving a position of maximum intensity. When the screen is moved towards the aperture so that the first and the second zones are exposed, then the amplitude at P is $A_1 - A_2$, which is nearly zero, giving the position of minimum. When three zones are allowed, the resultant amplitude at P is $A_1 - A_2 + A_3$, this is again large making the intensity very high. Therefore, P gives a maximum or minimum according as the aperture allows an odd or an even number of half-period zones. Thus the point P will be alternately bright or dark.

Distance of maximum or minimum intensity

Let, as shown in Fig. 23.8, a be the distance of the aperture AB from the source S and b the distance of the screen XY from AB. If r be the radius of the aperture, the path difference Δ for waves reaching P along SAP and SOP is expressed as

$$\Delta = (SA + AP) - (SO + OP) = (a^2 + r^2)^{1/2} + (b^2 + r^2)^{1/2} - (a + b)$$

$$= a(1 + r^2/a^2)^{1/2} + b(1 + r^2/b^2)^{1/2} - (a + b)$$

$$= a(1 + r^2/2a^2) + b(1 + r^2/2b^2) - (a + b) = \frac{r^2}{2}\left(\frac{1}{a} + \frac{1}{b}\right)$$

or, $\quad \dfrac{1}{a} + \dfrac{1}{b} = \dfrac{2\Delta}{r^2}.$ \hfill (23.25)

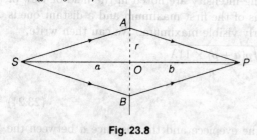

Fig. 23.8

If for the position of the screen, n half-period zones are contained in the aperture, then the path difference $\Delta = n\lambda/2$ or, $2\Delta = n\lambda$.

Hence from Eq. (23.25),

$$\frac{1}{a} + \frac{1}{b} = \frac{n\lambda}{r^2}. \qquad (23.26)$$

P would be **maximum**, when n is *odd* and **minimum** when n is *even*.

If the incident light is parallel, $a = \infty$ or, $1/a = 0$.

$\therefore$ from Eq. (23.26), we get

$$\frac{1}{b} = \frac{n\lambda}{r^2} \quad \text{or,} \quad n = \frac{r^2}{b\lambda} = \frac{\pi r^2}{\pi b\lambda}, \qquad (23.27)$$

where πr^2 is the area of aperture and $\pi b\lambda$ is that of a half-period zone, constructed for a point distant b from the wavefront.

Intensity at non-axial point

We assume that the screen is so placed that the intensity at P is maximum and the aperture contains five odd zones. If we move away from the axis to the point P', then O' is the new pole where the line SP' meets the wavefront. Let, in this

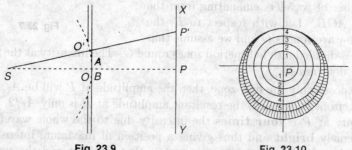

Fig. 23.9   **Fig. 23.10**

position, the first four zones be fully exposed with about half of the 5th and 6th zones as shown in Fig. 23.10. The resultant amplitude at P' is then given by

$$A_1 - A_2 + A_3 - A_4 + \frac{1}{2}A_5 - \frac{1}{2}A_6 = \frac{1}{2}A_1 + \left[\frac{1}{2}(A_1 + A_3) - A_2\right]$$

$$+ \left[\frac{1}{2}(A_3 + A_5) - A_4\right] - \frac{1}{2}A_6$$

$$= \frac{1}{2}A_1 - \frac{1}{2}A_6.$$

This corresponds to the **minimum**.

If we proceed further to another point so that the first three zones are fully exposed with nearly half of the 4th, 5th, 6th and 7th zones, then similar computation for amplitude at that point will show that this is a position of maximum. In this way along PX, there is a series of points with alternate maximum and minimum.

When the aperture is large, the rings will be visible only near the geometrical shadow with intensity rapidly diminishing within the shadow. At a point inside, the intensity becomes zero. When the aperture is small so as to contain only a fraction of the first half-period zone with respect to P, then the point P will be bright. The bright point will be surrounded by alternate bright and dark rings. However, it depends on whether the aperture contains an even or odd number of fractional zones.

23.8 Fresnel's Diffraction at a Rectangular Aperture

Let us consider a rectangular aperature of width AB, placed between a narrow slit S (illuminated with light of wavelength λ) and a screen XY, both being perpendicular to the plane of paper (Fig. 23.11). As shown, WW' is the section of a cylindrical wavefront from S and incident on AB. From the rectilinear propagation of light we know that the region $A'B'$ would be uniformly illuminated but above A' and below B', it should be completely dark. However, the illumination on the screen depends on the width AB. Three distinct situations may arise : (i) wide aperture; (ii) narrow aperture and (iii) very narrow aperture.

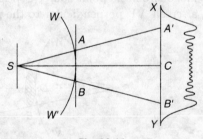

Fig. 23.11

(i) **Wide aperture :** In this situation, there is uniform illumination at the centre C and unequally spaced bands in the region $A'B'$. The contrast of the bands near A' and B' are poor. Above A' and below B', the intensity rapidly falls to zero.

If the aperture AB is wide, it behaves as two independent straight edges A and B. Hence we may get as in straight edge, unequally spaced bands with poor contrast near A' and B' within the region $A'B'$. These bands merge into uniform illumination near C. The intensity exhibits a rapid fall to zero in the region of geometrical shadow (i.e., above A' and below B').

(ii) **Narrow aperture :** In this situation, the centre C of the region $A'B'$ may appear bright or dark. Near A' and B' in the illuminated region, we may get unequally spaced bands with poor contrast. Above A' and below B', equally spaced bands are noticed.

C becomes bright or dark according as AB contains an odd or even number of half-period strips of each half of wavefront. If AB contains three half-period strips of each half wavefront, then the amplitude at C is

$$A = 2(A_1 - A_2 + A_3)$$

and this indicates a maximum.

If there are two half-period strips, then the amplitude at C would be

$$A = 2(A_1 - A_2), \tag{23.28}$$

and this indicates a minimum.

Thus, with more and more opening up of the aperture, the centre of the illuminated region becomes alternately bright and dark.

(iii) Very narrow aperture : In this case, the aperture contains a fraction of the first half-period strip in each half of wavefront. Then C is bright and no bands are seen in region $A'B'$. In geometrical shadow, equi-spaced bands are observed.

C is always bright as disturbances at C due to both halves of wavefront are in phase. As we go towards A' or B' from C, the disturbance at any point is also due to a fraction of first half-period strip from each half-wavefront and are in phase. Thus in region $A'B'$, the intensity is always a maximum and no bands can be seen. In the geometrical shadow beyond A' and B', the number of half-period strips in AB may be more than one. Thus the intensity at a point is maximum or minimum according as this number is odd or even. So we get equi-spaced dark and bright bands.

23.9   Diffraction at an Opaque Circular Disc

Let us consider a small circular opaque disc AB, placed in the path of light of a monochromatic point source S [Fig. 23.12(a)]. The diffraction pattern is found on a screen XY perpendicular to the plane of the paper.

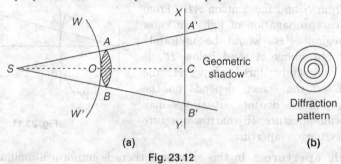

(a)   **(b)**

Fig. 23.12

The pattern has a 'bright' spot at the centre C of the geometrical shadow $A'B'$, which is surrounded by a number of bright rings within the shadow. Outside $A'B'$, brighter and broader rings are formed.

We assume that WW' be the trace of a spherical wavefront incident on the disc with O as its pole with respect to C. To get the intensity at C, the wavefront is divided into half-period zones. Some of the central zones are obstructed by AB and the intensity at C is owing to the exposed zones only. Let A_1, A_2, A_3,..., etc., be the amplitude due to the first, second, third, ... zones. If the disc is too small so that it obstructs only the first zone, then the resultant amplitude at C is

$$A = A_2 - A_3 + A_4 - A_5 + \cdots \simeq \frac{1}{2}A_2. \tag{23.29}$$

Thus, half the amplitude of second zone = intensity, $I \propto \frac{1}{4}A_2^2$. This is same as that in absence of the disc when $I \propto \frac{1}{4}A_1^2$. Therefore, C is almost as bright as it be when the disc is absent. When the disc-area increases so as to cover the first two zones, the amplitude at C is

$$A = A_3 - A_4 + A_5 - A_6 + \cdots \simeq \frac{1}{2}A_3. \qquad (23.30)$$

So, intensity, $I \propto \frac{1}{4}A_3^2$.

Thus at C, I is proportional to $A_2^2/4, A_3^2/4$, etc., as the disc covers 1, 2, etc. zones. Therefore, C is always bright but the intensity decreases gradually as disc-size increases or the screen moved towards the disc. The concentric alternate bright and dark rings inside the geometrical shadow are produced by interference between the exposed parts of wavefront above A and below B. The rings outside the shadow are unequally spaced 'diffraction' rings which are similar to a straight edge. The diffraction pattern is shown in Fig. 23.12(b).

23.10   Fraunhofer Diffraction at a Single Slit

Let us consider a parallel beam of monochromatic light incident normally on a slit AB placed perpendicular to the plane of the paper. If the beam emerging from the slit is received on a screen S kept perpendicular to the plane of a paper, we may get a bright image ab of the slit. The size and shape of the image is to be made

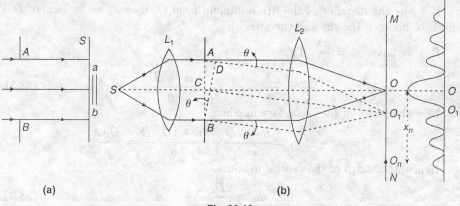

(a)   (b)

Fig. 23.13

identical to that of the slit. Rays from S are made parallel by a convex lens L_1 so that a plane wavefront is incident on a narrow slit AB of width a. When the light passing through the slit is received on a screen MN, we get a sharp and bright image of the slit AB at O on the screen. The narrower the slit AB, the sharper should be the image. But this does not happen as the rays of light do not strictly follow the law of rectilinear motion. In fact, while passing through the slit AB, the rays will be diffracted in different directions. The image is found to be flanked on both sides by alternate dark and bright bands. This diffraction pattern consists of a bright central band opposite to the slit flanked on either side by dark and bright fringes.

We consider a point O on the screen [Fig. 23.13(b)] which lies on the normal to the slit through its mid-point C. The wavefront reaching the slit AB has all points on it between A and B in phase. These points act as secondary centres. The point O corresponds to the image of the slit formed by undiffracted beam in a direction

$\theta = 0$ (where θ is measured from the normal to AB). In this direction, the waves from the secondary sources like A, B, C, etc., have no path-difference and hence all the waves arrive in phase at O, making the point very bright. This point is known as the central maximum and has the maximum intensity. We next consider a beam diffracted at an angle θ and travelling parallel to CO_1. The lens L_2 will collect the beam at O_1. Now, all the wavelets diffracted from the slit and reaching the point O_1 do not travel the same path and so they are not in phase at O_1. In order to get the path-difference, we draw BD perpendicular to CO_1. The path difference between the waves emitted from the two extreme ends A and B of the slit, $AD = AB \sin \theta = a \sin \theta$.

To get the resultant amplitude at O_1, we divide the wavefront AB into two halves. The top point A of the upper half CA and the top point C of the lower half BC will send out waves to O_1 to have a path-difference of $\lambda/2$, where it is assumed that $a \sin \theta = \lambda$. So, the resultant amplitude at O_1 is zero. All other pairs of corresponding points in the two halves of AB have a path-difference of $\lambda/2$. Thus the brightness at O_1 is zero. If θ be the angle of diffraction, giving the first minima on both sides of the central maximum O, then $a \sin \theta = \lambda$ or, $\sin \theta = \lambda/a$. Similarly, if θ_n be the angle of diffraction giving the nth minima on both sides of the central maximum, then $a \sin \theta_n = n\lambda$ where $n = 1, 2, 3, \ldots$, etc., or, $\theta_n = \frac{n\lambda}{a}$ (taking $\sin \theta_n = \theta_n$)

Width of the secondary maxima

If x_n be the distance of the nth minimum from O, then $\theta_n = \frac{x_n}{D}$ (where $D =$ distance between the slit and the screen).

But we have, $\theta_n = \dfrac{n\lambda}{a}$. Thus,

$$\frac{x_n}{D} = \frac{n\lambda}{a} \quad \text{or,} \quad x_n = \frac{n \cdot \lambda \cdot D}{a}. \tag{23.31}$$

Now the width of the secondary maxima,

$$\beta = x_n - x_{n-1} = \frac{n \cdot \lambda \cdot D}{a} - \frac{(n-1)\lambda \cdot D}{a} = \frac{D \cdot \lambda}{a}. \tag{23.32}$$

Hence, the width of the central maxima,

$$\beta_0 = \frac{2D \cdot \lambda}{a}. \tag{23.33}$$

If the lens L_2 is placed very near the slit AB or if the screen is far away from the lens L_2, then $\beta = \frac{\lambda \cdot f}{a}$, where f is the focal length of the lens L_2 and $\beta_0 = \frac{2f\lambda}{a}$ ($\because f = D$).

We now assume the path-difference $AD = a \sin \theta = 3\lambda/2$, and imagine the wavefront AB divided into three equal parts wherein the waves from the extreme ends of the upper two parts have a path-difference λ. These two parts of the wavefront produce darkness while the third part produces a fringe of light less bright than the central maximum, due to the whole wavefront between A and B. Hence for the first maximum on both sides of the central maximum, we get $a \sin \theta = 3\lambda/2$. Most of the light incident of AB is diffracted into the central bright fringe.

If θ'_n be the angle of diffraction for nth subsidiary maximum, then we can write,

$$a \sin \theta'_n = (2n + 1)\lambda/2 \text{ where } n = 1, 2, 3, \ldots, \text{ etc.}$$

$$\text{or,} \quad \sin \theta'_n = \frac{(2n+1)\lambda}{2a} \quad \text{or,} \quad \theta'_n = (2n+1)\frac{\lambda}{2a}. \tag{23.34}$$

If x_n be the distance of nth maxima from the central maximum, then we have

$$x_n = \frac{(2n+1)\lambda f}{2a}.\tag{23.35}$$

Thus we may say that

$$a\sin\theta = \lambda,\ 2\lambda,\ 3\lambda,\dots,2n\cdot\lambda/2\dots \text{ minima}$$

$$a\sin\theta = 0,\ \frac{3\lambda}{2},\ \frac{5\lambda}{2},\dots,(2n+1)\lambda/2\dots \text{ maxima.}$$

The position of the secondary maxima lies between the minima on either side of the central maxima and so their intensity falls rapidly when one moves outwards. When the intensity of central maximum is taken as I_0, the intensity for the next maximum corresponding to $a\sin\theta = 3\lambda/2$ is nearly $I_0/9$ and that of the

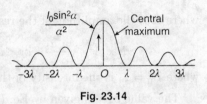

Fig. 23.14

third maximum is $I_0/25$. The positions of maxima and minima as well as their proportionate intensity have been presented graphically in Fig. 23.14. The crests in the figure signify maxima and the troughs minima. The amplitudes of the crests provide their corresponding intensities.

When the slit width a is too small and is equal to 2λ (say), then $\sin\theta = \frac{\lambda}{a} = \frac{1}{2}$ or, $\theta = 30°$. The light waves then spread round through $30°$ on either side of the slit.

If the slit width a is large, then $\sin\theta$ and hence θ is very small. The central band is now very thin and the other maxima and minima approach close to the central band. As a result the diffraction fringe almost disappears and we get a perfect image of the slit at O.

If white light is used to illuminate the slit AB, the subsidiary maxima will be coloured but then the central maxima will be white.

It is interesting to note that while the central band in Fraunhofer pattern is always bright, that in the Fresnel pattern may be dark or bright depending on the number of half-period zones covering the slit.

23.10.1 Intensity Distribution in the Diffraction Pattern due to Single Slit

As shown in Fig. 23.15, the path-difference AD between the secondary waves emitted from the extreme points A and B of the slit is $a\sin\theta$. This is equivalent to a phase-difference

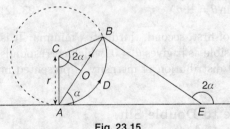

Fig. 23.15

$$2\alpha = \frac{2\pi}{\lambda}\cdot a\sin\theta.\tag{23.36}$$

Let the incident plane wavefront on the slit AB be divided into a large number of small strips of same width. The resultant amplitude due to all the individual small strips is obtained by vector polygon method. Here the chord AB will give the resultant amplitude due to all the wavelets. So, from the figure, chord

$$AB = 2AO = 2r\cdot\sin\alpha,\tag{23.37}$$

where C is the centre and r is the radius of the circular arc.

The length of the arc ADB is directly proportional to the width a of the slit. Thus the length of the arc $ADB = k \cdot a = A$ (say).

Further, $2\alpha = \dfrac{\text{arc}ADB}{\text{radius}} = \dfrac{A}{r}$ or, $2r = \dfrac{A}{\alpha}$.

So, chord $AB = \dfrac{A}{\alpha} \cdot \sin\alpha$ [from Eq. (23.37)]

or, $\qquad\qquad R = A \cdot \dfrac{\sin\alpha}{\alpha}$, $\qquad\qquad\qquad\qquad\qquad$ (23.38)

where R is the amplitude of the resultant vibration. So, the resultant intensity is

$$I \propto A^2 \cdot \frac{\sin^2\alpha}{\alpha^2} \quad \text{or,} \quad I = R_0^2 \cdot \frac{\sin^2\alpha}{\alpha^2} = I_0 \frac{\sin^2\alpha}{\alpha^2}, \qquad (23.39)$$

where $R_0^2 = I_0$ is the intensity of the principal maximum.

The value of α is given by Eq. (23.36) as

$$\alpha = \frac{\pi}{\lambda} \cdot a \sin\theta. \qquad\qquad\qquad\qquad (23.40)$$

Hence the magnitude of intensity at any point on the screen is a function of α and thus a series of maximum and minimum will be obtained.

Principal maximum

The resultant amplitude is obtained from Eq. (23.38) as

$$R = \frac{A}{\alpha} \cdot \sin\alpha = \frac{A}{\alpha}\left[\alpha - \frac{\alpha^3}{\angle 3} + \frac{\alpha^5}{\angle 5} - \cdots\right] = A\left[1 - \frac{\alpha^2}{\angle 3} + \frac{\alpha^4}{\angle 5} - \cdots\right]. \qquad (23.41)$$

R will be maximum if the negative terms disappear. This is possible when $\alpha = \frac{\pi}{\lambda}\alpha\sin\theta = 0$ or, $\theta = 0$. So, the maximum value of R is A and the maximum intensity I_0 is proportional to A^2. This happens when $\theta = 0$ or on the point O on the screen.

Position of minima

From Eq. (23.39), we find that the intensity is minimum, i.e., zero when $\sin\alpha = 0$ or, $\alpha = \pm\pi, \pm 2\pi, \pm 3\pi, \cdots, \pm n\pi$.

But we have $\alpha = \dfrac{\pi \cdot a \sin\theta}{\lambda}$.

Therefore, $\dfrac{\pi \cdot a \sin\theta}{\lambda} = \pm n\pi$ or, $a \sin\theta = \pm n\lambda$, $\qquad\qquad$ (23.42)

where $n = 1, 2, 3$, etc., gives the direction of first, second, third, etc., minima. It is interesting to note that $n = 0$ is not admissible as it gives $\theta = 0$, which corresponds to the principle maximum. The graphical distribution of intensity is presented in Fig. 23.14.

23.11   Fraunhofer Diffraction due to Double Slit

In Fig. 23.16, AB and CD are two slits, each of width a and separated by a distance b. A plane wavefront of wavelength λ is incident on the slits so that the waves emerging from the slits are focused on a screen MN by a convex lens L. The points on the wavefront incident on the slits have same phase and they behave as secondary sources of coherent nature. The undiffracted waves (i.e., $\theta = 0$) coming out of the slits are focused on the point O by the lens L. As the point O is equidistant from the slits, there will be no path-difference between the waves emerging from the slits. So, the waves will interfere constructively to make the point O bright.

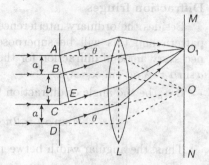

Fig. 23.16

We next consider a point O_1 away from O. The resultant amplitude at O_1 is the algebraic sum of the amplitudes due to the individual waves. Although the amplitudes by the individual waves are of same magnitude but their phases are not same as the point O_1 is not equidistant from the slits AB and CD. If the waves emerging from the corresponding points A and C of the slits and arrive at O_1 with a path-difference of $\lambda/2$, the point O_1 will be a minimum. The points A and C act like two separate coherent sources to produce ordinary interference.

Interference fringes

From Fig. 23.16, the path-difference between A and $C = CE = (a + b)\sin\theta$, (where θ is the angle of diffraction).

Thus, for O_1 to be the first interference minimum,

$$(a + b)\sin\theta = \frac{\lambda}{2}. \tag{23.43}$$

If θ_n be the angle of diffraction for nth interference minimum, then

$$(a + b)\sin\theta_n = (2n + 1)\lambda/2, \tag{23.44}$$

where $n = 0, 1, 2, \ldots$, etc.

Putting $n = 0, 1, 2$, etc., we get different interference minima on both sides of O. Between each two minima, there will be a maximum, the condition for which is $(a + b)\sin(\theta'_n = 2n \cdot \lambda/2$ where θ'_n is the angle of diffraction for nth interference maximum.

Considering the interference minima, for $n = 0$,

$$(a + b)\sin\theta_1 = \lambda/2 \quad \text{or,} \quad \sin\theta_1 = \frac{\lambda}{2(a + b)}. \tag{23.45}$$

For $n = 1, (a + b)\sin\theta_2 = 3\lambda/2 \quad \text{or,} \quad \sin\theta_2 = \frac{3\lambda}{2(a + b)}. \tag{23.46}$

Therefore, the angular width between two consecutive interference minima

$$= \sin\theta_2 - \sin\theta_1 = \frac{3\lambda}{2(a + b)} - \frac{\lambda}{2(a + b)} = \frac{\lambda}{a + b}. \tag{23.47}$$

In a similar way, considering the interference maxima, for $n = 1$, we get

$$(a + b)\sin\theta'_1 = \lambda. \tag{23.48}$$

For $n = 2, (a + b)\sin\theta'_2 = 2\lambda. \tag{23.49}$

Therefore, the angular width between two consecutive interference maxima

$$= \sin\theta'_2 - \sin\theta'_1 = \frac{2\lambda}{a + b} - \frac{\lambda}{a + b} = \frac{\lambda}{a + b} \tag{23.47a}$$

We thus find that the interference fringes are equispaced.

Diffraction fringes

Besides the ordinary interference fringes, each slit will form its own diffraction pattern and this will be superposed on the interference pattern. If α be the necessary angle of diffraction for the first minimum for a single slit, then we have, $a \sin \alpha = \lambda$ or, $\sin \alpha = \lambda/a$.

If α_n be the angle of diffraction for nth minimum,

$$a \sin \alpha_n = 2n \cdot \lambda/2 \quad \text{or,} \quad \sin \alpha_n = \frac{n\lambda}{a}.$$

Thus, the angular width between two consecutive diffraction minima

$$= \sin \alpha_2 - \sin \alpha_1 = \frac{2\lambda}{a} - \frac{\lambda}{a} = \frac{\lambda}{a}. \tag{23.50}$$

Comparing Eqs. (23.47) and (23.50) we find that the angular width of diffraction minima is much greater than angular width of interference minima. It means that between first two diffraction minima there will be many interference minima. In a singular way, there will be many interference maxima and minima between the central diffraction band. This is shown in Fig. 23.17.

23.11.1   Intensity Distribution in the Diffraction Pattern due to Double Slit

Let us consider the secondary waves diffracted in a direction inclined at an angle θ with the initial direction. Then the resultant amplitude due to all the wavelets diffracted from each slit is $A \cdot \frac{\sin \alpha}{\alpha}$ and the resultant phase in this direction is

$$\alpha = \frac{\pi \cdot a \sin \theta}{\lambda}. \tag{23.51}$$

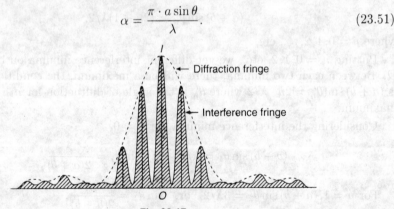

Fig. 23.17

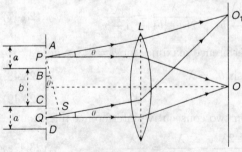

Fig. 23.18

Now the phase-difference between the wavelets coming from the two extreme ends of a slit along a direction θ is 2α and so the resultant having a phase-difference α is supposed to act at the middle points P and Q of the slit AB and CD respectively (Fig. 23.18). Hence the two slits are equivalent to two coherent sources placed at their middle points P and Q, each sending a wave of amplitude $\left(\frac{A \sin \alpha}{\alpha}\right)$ in a direction θ to the normal. Thus the resultant amplitude at the point O_1 on the screen is due to the interference of these two waves originating in the same phase α but having a certain phase-difference δ on reaching the point O_1. In order to find the path-difference, we drop a perpendicular PS from P on QS (Fig. 23.18). The path-difference, $QS = PQ \sin \theta = (a+b) \sin \theta$. So, the phase-difference between the rays is

$$\delta = \frac{2\pi}{\lambda}(a+b) \sin \theta = 2\beta \quad \text{(say)}. \tag{23.52}$$

Now, the resultant amplitude R at O_1 is obtained by the vector addition method of amplitudes. This is illustrated in Fig. 23.19, where $PQ = QD = A \cdot \frac{\sin \alpha}{\alpha}$ are the component amplitudes and $\angle DQF = \delta$, the phase-difference between the component waves. Therefore, we have

$$R^2 = PQ^2 + QD^2 + 2PQ \cdot QD \cdot \cos \delta$$

$$= \left(\frac{A \sin \alpha}{\alpha}\right)^2 + \left(\frac{A \sin \alpha}{\alpha}\right)^2 + 2 \cdot \left(\frac{A \sin \alpha}{\alpha}\right)\left(\frac{A \sin \alpha}{\alpha}\right) \cdot \cos \delta$$

$$= \left(\frac{A \sin \alpha}{\alpha}\right)^2 [2 + 2 \cos \delta]$$

$$= 4\frac{A^2 \sin^2 \alpha}{\alpha^2} \cdot \cos^2 \frac{\delta}{2} = 4 \cdot \frac{A^2 \sin^2 \alpha}{\alpha^2} \cdot \cos^2 \beta.$$

Thus the resultant intensity I at O_1 is proportional to the square of the resultant amplitude R and is expressed as

$$I \propto 4 \cdot \frac{A^2 \cdot \sin \alpha}{\alpha^2} \cdot \cos^2 \frac{\delta}{2} = 4 \cdot R_0^2 \cdot \frac{\sin^2 \alpha}{\alpha^2} \cdot \cos^2 \beta. \tag{23.53}$$

The intensity in the resultant pattern thus depends on :

(i) $R_0^2 \cdot \frac{\sin^2 \alpha}{\alpha^2}$ which gives diffraction pattern of a single slit and (ii) $\cos^2 \beta$ which gives interference pattern due to light waves from the two slits. Thus the resultant intensity distribution in the Fraunhofer diffraction pattern produced by two parallel slits, each of width 'a' and separated by a distance 'b' is a product of the single slit diffraction pattern and the interference pattern due to two point sources separated by a distance b.

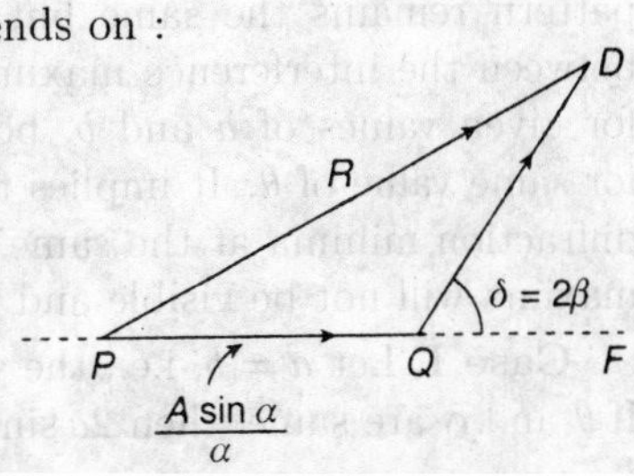

Fig. 23.19

Dependence of intensity on diffraction factor $\left(R_0^2 \dfrac{\sin^2 \alpha}{\alpha^2}\right)$

The diffraction factor gives a principal maxima in the direction $\alpha = 0$ which corresponds to the point O in Fig. 23.14. The maximum exhibits either side alternate minima and secondary maxima of reducing intensity. The minima are obtained in the direction given by

$$\sin \alpha = 0 \quad \text{or,} \quad \alpha = \frac{\pi \cdot a \sin \theta}{\lambda} = \pm m\pi \quad \text{or,} \quad a \sin \theta = \pm m\lambda,$$

(where $m = 1, 2, 3$, etc., excluding zero).

The positions of secondary maxima due to this term are given by

$$\alpha = \pm \frac{3\pi}{2}, \ \pm \frac{5\pi}{2}, \ \pm \frac{7\pi}{2}, \cdots, \text{etc.}$$

Dependence of intensity of interference factor ($\cos^2 \beta$)

Considering the interference factor, we note that for minima $\cos^2 \beta = 0$. This gives

$$\beta = \frac{\pi}{\lambda}(a+b)\sin\theta = \pm(2n+1)\pi/2 \quad \text{or,} \quad \sin\theta = \frac{(2n+1)\lambda}{2(a+b)}$$

(where $n = 0, 1, 2, 3,$ etc.)

$$\text{or,} \quad \theta = \frac{\lambda}{2(a+b)}, \frac{3\lambda}{2(a+b)}, \frac{5\lambda}{2(a+b)}, \cdots \tag{23.54}$$

In a similar way maxima occur for those values of θ for which $\cos^2 \beta = 1$. This gives

$$\beta = \frac{\pi}{\lambda}(a+b)\sin\theta = \pm n\pi \quad \text{or,} \quad (a+b)\sin\theta = \pm n\lambda$$

$$\text{or,} \quad \theta = \frac{\lambda}{a+b}, \frac{2\lambda}{a+b}, \frac{3\lambda}{a+b}, \cdots, \text{etc.} \tag{23.55}$$

23.11.2 Missing Order in the Diffraction Pattern due to Double Slit

In the diffraction pattern due to double slit, the slit width is taken to be equal to a and the spacing between the two slits equal to b. If θ be the angle of diffraction for nth maximum due to interference, then we have

$$(a+b)\sin\theta = n\lambda. \tag{23.56}$$

Further, if α be the angle of diffraction for pth minimum due to diffraction, then

$$a\sin\alpha = p \cdot \lambda. \tag{23.57}$$

From Eqs. (23.56) and (23.57), it is seen that if a is kept constant, the diffraction pattern remains the same but keeping a constant and changing b, the spacing between the interference maxima changes. Eqs. (23.56) and (23.57) indicate that for given values of a and b, both the equations may be simultaneously satisfied for same value of θ. It implies that certain interference maxima correspond to the diffraction minima at the same position on the screen. When this happens, those maxima will not be visible and they are called the missing orders.

Case I. Let $a = b$, i.e., the slit width is equal to the spacing between the slits. If θ and α are same, then $2a\sin\theta = n\lambda$ and $a\sin\theta = p\lambda$.

$$\therefore \quad \frac{n}{p} = 2 \quad \text{or,} \quad n = 2p. \tag{23.58}$$

If we put $p = 1, 2, 3,$ etc., then $n = 2, 4, 6,$ etc.

Therefore, second, fourth, sixth, etc., orders of interference maxima will be missing in the diffraction pattern. There will be produced three interference maxima in the central diffraction maximum.

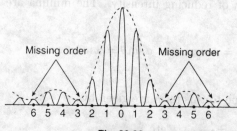

Missing order   Missing order

6 5 4 3 2 1 0 1 2 3 4 5 6

Fig. 23.20

Case II. Let $2a = b$, i.e., the spacing between the slits is double of the width of the slits. If θ and α are same, then $3a\sin\theta = n\lambda$ and $a\sin\theta = p\lambda$.

$$\therefore \quad \frac{n}{p} = 3 \quad \text{or,} \quad n = 3p. \tag{23.59}$$

If we put $p = 1, 2, 3, \cdots$, etc., then $n = 3, 6, 9, \cdots$, etc.

Therefore, third, sixth, ninth, etc. orders of interference maxima will be missing from the diffraction pattern. On both sides of the central maximum, the number of interference maxima is 2 and so there will be five interference maxima in the central diffraction maximum (Fig. 23.20).

Case III. Let $a + b = a$, then $b = 0$, i.e., the slits have joined to form a single slit of width $2a$. Since $b = 0$, we can say that all the interference maxima will be missing and the diffraction pattern will be similar to a single slit of width $2a$.

23.12 Diffraction Grating

A diffraction grating is an arrangement where a large number of parallel equidistant slits of same width are kept side by side. Gratings are formed by drawing lines on a well-polished thin uniform sheet of glass with a sharp diamond point. The number of lines drawn vary from 7000 to 8000 per centimetre or more. Grating are of two types, viz., (i) transmission grating and (ii) reflection grating.

23.13 Diffracting by a Plane Transmission Grating

Let in Fig. 23.21, $ABCD$ represent the section of a plane transmission grating, perpendicular to the plane of the paper. The width of the clear space be a and that of the ruling be b. The distance $(a + b)$ is called the *grating element*. Points like A and C or B and D separated by a distance $(a + b)$ are known as *corresponding points*.

Let a plane wavefront be incident normally on the surface of the grating. The transmitted light consists of a large number of secondary wavelets issuing from clear spaces. From each points of the incident wavefront, a large number of rays are given out in different directions. In Fig. 23.21, AE, BF, CG and DH are rays diffracted at an angle θ with the normal to the grating surface.

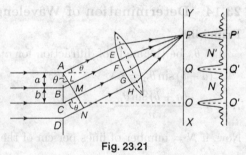

Fig. 23.21

They fall on a convex lens and are brought to focus at the point P on a screen. P would be bright or dark according as the rays produce constructive or destructive interference.

We now draw a line $ALMN$ perpendicular to the parallel diffracted beam of rays. There is no phase-difference between the rays arriving the plane $ABCD$ and no further phase-difference is introduced after passing through the plane $ALMN$. Thus the only phase change occurred between different rays, is due to the difference in paths traversed by the rays from the plane $ABCD$ to the plane $ALMN$. Next we consider the rays AE and CG from two corresponding points A and C. The path-difference $CM = (a + b) \sin \theta$. Also, the path-difference between the rays from two other corresponding points B and $D = (DN - BL) = (a + b + a) \sin \theta - a \sin \theta = (a + b) \sin \theta$.

So, the path-difference between the rays from any two corresponding points $= (a + b) \sin \theta$ and hence rays at P would interfere constructively and a maximum will be produced at P, when $(a + b) \sin \theta = n\lambda$. On the other hand, they interfere destructively and produce a minimum, if $(a + b) \sin \theta = (2n + 1)\lambda/2$ (where n is any integer).

If $n = 0$, we get $\theta = 0$. This gives central bright maximum at O due to undiffracted beam. As we go along the screen either above or below O, one may get dark point N when $(a + b) \sin \theta = \lambda/2$ (putting $n = 0$ in the condition of minima) and bright point Q again when $(a + b) \sin \theta = \lambda$ (putting $n = 1$ in the condition of maxima) and dark point (N) again when $(a + b) \sin \theta = 3\lambda/2$ (putting $n = 1$ in the condition of minima). Thus alternate bright and dark points are followed. The bright points are known as *diffraction spectra*.

The bright point nearest to O is known as the *first order spectrum* $(n = 1)$ and the next one $(n = 2)$, the *second order spectrum* and so on. The central maximum $(n = 0)$ is also called *zero order spectrum*.

For the nth order spectrum, we have

$$(a + b) \sin \theta_n = n\lambda \quad \text{(where } \theta_n = \text{diffraction angle)}$$

or, $\quad \sin \theta_n = \dfrac{n\lambda}{a + b} = n \cdot N \cdot \lambda,$ \hfill (23.60)

where $N = \frac{1}{a+b}$ = number of lines per unit length of the grating.

When white light is used, each wavelength of the incident white light will form its own maxima with the result that each maximum will consist of a band of seven colours. As angle of diffraction $\theta \propto \lambda$, the red will have a greater angle of diffraction than violet. It means that the inner edge of each maximum will be coloured violet and the outer edge will be red-coloured.

23.14   Determination of Wavelength by a Diffraction Grating

Principle

Let θ_n be the angle of diffraction for nth order spectrum. Then we can write,

$$(a + b) \sin \theta_n = n\lambda.$$

$\therefore \quad \lambda = \dfrac{(a + b) \sin \theta_n}{n}.$ \hfill (23.61)

Now, if N = number of lines per cm of the grating, then $N = \dfrac{1}{a + b}$.

$\therefore \quad \lambda = \dfrac{\sin \theta_n}{N \cdot n}.$ \hfill (23.62)

Thus, knowing N, n and θ_n, the wavelength λ can be determined.

Procedure

The plane transmission grating G is mounted on the prism-table P of an ordinary spectrometer. The grating is so mounted that its plane is perpendicular to the prism-table. Parallel rays coming out from the collimator C are incident on its surface normally as shown in Fig. 23.22. The ruled surface of the grating must face the telescope T. The collimator and the telescope are so adjusted for parallel rays and the instrument is levelled properly. The number of lines per centimetre of the grating should be determined experimentally with the help of a radiation of known wavelength. Sodium light is generally used for the purpose.

The sodium light is placed in front of the slit S of the collimator. Keeping the telescope in line with the collimator, the image of the slit is made coincident with the cross-wire of the telescope, the position of the telescope is read from the vernier and the circular scales. If the telescope is turned slowly either on left or on right, then at some position again the image of the slit will be visible. This will give the first order spectrum for $n = 1$. The position of the telescope is again read coinciding the cross-wire with the image. The difference of these two readings will give the angle θ_1 for diffraction for the first order. Getting this angle on both sides of the central maximum, the mean value is to be noted. Then putting $n = 1$, $\lambda = 5896 \times 10^{-8}$ cm, the wavelength of sodium light, and the value of θ_1, we get N. The experiment can be repeated by turning the telescope further and getting the angles of diffraction for second, third and higher orders of spectra. The unknown source of

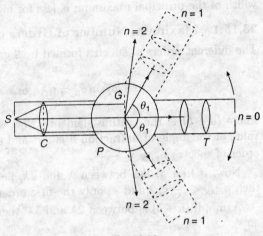

Fig. 23.22

radiation is then placed in the position of sodium light and the same process is repeated to find λ using Eq. (23.62).

23.15 Width of Principal Maxima in Grating Spectra

The angular separation between the first minima on either side of the principal maximum of any order is known as the angular width of the principal maximum of that order. We consider the nth order principal maximum for which the angle of diffraction is θ_n. Then, we have

$$(a + b)\sin\theta_n = n\lambda. \qquad (23.63)$$

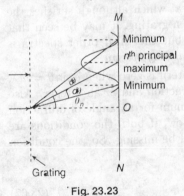

Fig. 23.23

Let $(\theta_n \pm d\theta)$ indicate the directions of the first secondary minima on the two sides of the nth principal maximum as shown in Fig. 23.23. Then,

$$(a + b)\sin(\theta_n \pm d\theta) = n\lambda \pm \lambda/S, \qquad (23.64)$$

where S is the total number of lines in the grating.

Dividing Eq. (23.64) by Eq. (23.63) we get

$$\frac{(a + b)\sin(\theta_n \pm d\theta)}{(a + b)\sin\theta_n} = \frac{n\lambda + \lambda/S}{n\lambda}$$

or, $$\frac{\sin\theta_n \cos d\theta \pm \cos\theta_n \sin d\theta}{\sin\theta_n} = 1 \pm \frac{1}{nS}.$$

For small values of $d\theta$ we have $\cos d\theta = 1$ and $\sin d\theta = d\theta$.

$$\therefore \quad 1 \pm \cot\theta_n \cdot d\theta = 1 + \frac{1}{nS} \quad \text{or,} \quad \cot\theta_n \cdot d\theta = \frac{1}{nS}$$

or, $$d\theta = \frac{1}{nS\cot\theta_n}. \qquad (23.65)$$

In Eq. (23.65), $d\theta$ refers to half the angular width of the nth principal maximum. Eq. (23.65) shows that $d\theta$ is inversely proportional to S, the total number of lines in the grating. Thus the angular width of the principal maximum of any given order is narrower for a grating of higher number of lines. Further, $d\theta$ is inversely proportional to $n \cot \theta_n$; the value of $n \cot \theta_n$ is more for higher orders and so the width of the principal maximum is less for higher orders.

23.15.1   Maximum Number of Orders of Spectra Available in a Grating

The different orders of spectra formed by a grating can be expressed as

$$(a+b)\sin\theta_n = n\lambda \quad \text{or,} \quad n = \frac{(a+b)\sin\theta}{\lambda}, \tag{23.66}$$

where $(a+b)$ is the grating element. Now we know that the maximum possible value of the angle of diffraction θ is $90°$ and so $\sin\theta = 1$. The maximum possible order of spectra $n_{max} = \frac{(a+b)}{\lambda}$.

Now, if $(a+b)$ lies between λ and 2λ, i.e., the grating element $(a+b) < 2\lambda$, then $n_{max} < \frac{2\lambda}{\lambda} < 2$ and so only the first order spectrum is visible.

Again, if $(a+b)$ is between 2λ and 3λ, then first two orders will be seen and so on.

Let the diffraction gratings have 5000 lines/cm. Then the value of $(a+b)$ is $\frac{1}{5000}$. As sodium light is of wavelength 5896×10^{-8} cm, the maximum value of n is given by

$$n_{max} = \frac{(a+b)\times 1}{\lambda} = \frac{1}{5000} \times \frac{10^8}{5896} = 3.4 \text{ (approx.)}.$$

So, in this case, the grating will produce three complete orders of spectra along with a part of a fourth order.

23.16   Absent Spectra in a Grating

It is found sometimes that a given order of spectra, which although satisfies the condition of maxima, is absent and is invisible. In a grating, it may be seen that first, second and fourth order spectra are visible but the third order spectra is missing. Such spectra are called *absent spectra* or *missing spectra*.

We know that the intensity of the single slit pattern is zero when $a\sin\theta = m\lambda$, where a is the width of the slit, θ the angle of diffraction and m an integer. Also in a diffraction grating the condition for nth maximum for an angle of diffraction θ is $(a+b)\sin\theta = n\lambda$ (where n is an integer). Now, if both the conditions are simultaneously satisfied, then nth order spectra will be missing. So, the condition for nth order spectra being absent is

$$\frac{a+b}{a} = \frac{n}{m}. \tag{23.67}$$

If the slit and the opaque portion of the grating are of equal width, i.e., if $a = b$, then

$$\frac{n}{m} = \frac{2}{1} = \frac{2}{1}, \frac{4}{2}, \frac{6}{3}, \frac{8}{4}, \ldots, \text{etc.}$$

This reveals that second, fourth, sixth, i.e., even orders of spectra will be absent.

Further, for $b = 2a$, i.e., if the opaque portion has a width twice the width of a slit, then,

$$\frac{n}{m} = \frac{3}{1} = \frac{3}{1}, \frac{6}{2}, \frac{9}{3}, \text{etc.}$$

Then third, sixth, ninth, etc. spectral orders will be absent.

23.17 Dispersive Power of Grating

A grating has dispersive power similar to a prism. For nth order of spectra in a grating, we have

$$\sin \theta_n = \frac{n\lambda}{a+b}, \tag{23.68}$$

i.e., $\theta_n \propto \lambda$.

If the wavelength varies slightly from λ to $\lambda + d\lambda$, the angle of diffraction will also vary slightly from θ_n to $(\theta_n + d\theta)$. Now, $\frac{d\theta}{d\lambda}$ is a measurement of the change in angular position per unit wavelength change. This ratio is called the *dispersive power* of the grating.

Differentiating Eq. (23.68) we have,

$$\cos \theta_n \cdot d\theta = \frac{n}{(a+b)} \cdot d\lambda = n \cdot N \cdot d\lambda$$

or, $$\frac{d\theta}{d\lambda} = \frac{n \cdot N}{\cos \theta_n}, \tag{23.69}$$

where $N = \frac{1}{a+b} = $ number of lines per centimetre of the grating.

We thus find that the dispersion increases with order n of the spectra. The width of the second order spectra is thus twice the width of the first order spectra. For $n = 0$, $\frac{d\theta}{d\lambda} = 0$, i.e., there is no dispersion and so there is no spectrum in the zero order. Formation of spectrum commences with the first order and increases with N, the number of lines per centimetre of the grating. A grating with higher value of N or smaller value of the grating element $(a+b)$ will produce wider spectrum for any given order. For higher order, θ_n increases and so $\cos \theta_n$ decreases increasing dispersive power. For a given order n, the dispersion increases when $\cos \theta_n$ is small, i.e., when θ_n is large. This corresponds to the red wavelengths of the spectrum for normal incidence on the grating.

23.18 Comparison between Grating Spectrum and Prism Spectrum

(i) In a prism spectrum, the red light suffers the least deviation and the violet the most; while in a grating spectrum, it is exactly the reverse, i.e., the violet suffers the least deviation and the red the most.

(ii) A prism produces only one spectrum but grating produces a number of spectra on both sides of the central maximum.

(iii) Prism spectrum depends on the material of the prism. Grating spectrum is independent of the material of the grating.

(iv) In a prism spectrum, θ is not proportional to λ and so the spectrum is irrational. In a grating spectrum, $\theta \propto \lambda$ and so the spectrum is *rational*.

(v) The resolving power of a prism is less than that of a grating. The resolving power of a prism depends on the material of the prism and the wavelength of the light used but the resolving power of a grating depends on the number of order (n) and the total number of lines on the grating.

(vi) The intensity of prism spectrum is higher than the intensity of grating spectrum.

23.19 Resolving Power

If two objects or their images lie extremely close to each other, it is not possible for the eye always to see them separated, rather they may appear as one object or one image. It has noted that the eye can see two objects as distinctly separate, only if they subtend an angle greater than 1 minute at eye. If the angle subtended is less than 1 minute, their separate existence cannot be identified. The process of separation of two very close objects is called *resolution* and the ability of an optical instrument to produce separate images of such objects is called its *resolving power*.

The resolving power is defined as the ratio of the wavelength of a line in the spectrum to the least difference in the wavelength of the next line which can just be seen as separated. It is equal to $\lambda/d\lambda$ where $d\lambda$ is the difference in the wavelengths of the two spectral lines just separated.

The resolving power of a telescope or microscope is defined as the smallest angle subtended at the objective of the instrument by two point objects which can just be distinguished as separate entities. It is equal to λ/d, where λ is the wavelength of light used and d the diameter of the aperture of the objective of the instrument. If rays of light from a point object pass through a lens, the image formed is not a sharp point image but a series of alternate bright and dark rings are produced with a bright centre. The aperture of the lens then acts like a circular hole to the incident light and produces Fraunhofer diffraction pattern. If the object points are very close to each other, the diffraction patterns of the two will overlap and the object points cannot be identified as seperate entities.

Rayleigh's Criterion

For determining the ability of a lens to exhibit the separate existence of two such close object points, Rayleigh suggested that, two equally bright point sources can be regarded as separate if the central maximum of one pattern coincides exactly with the first minimum of the other. This is called *Rayleigh's criterion of resolution*.

23.20 Resolving Power of a Diffraction Grating

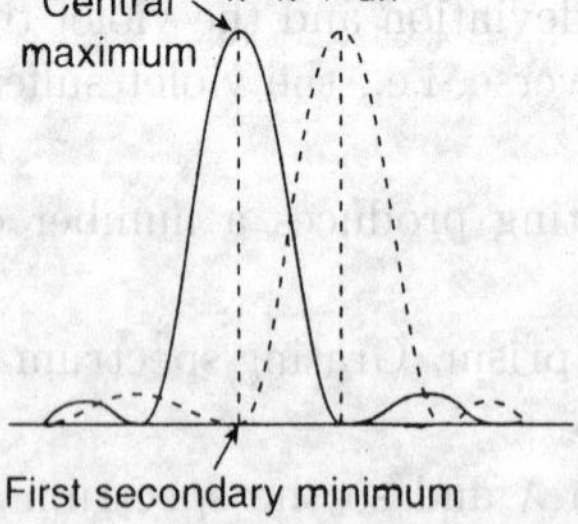

Central maximum λ $\lambda + d\lambda$

First secondary minimum

Fig. 23.24

A grating produces two distinguishable images of the same slit formed by lights of wavelengths λ and $\lambda + d\lambda$. The smaller the wavelength difference $d\lambda$, the larger is the resolving power of the grating. According to Rayleigh criterion, a grating will just resolve the wavelengths λ and $\lambda + d\lambda$ if the first minimum of one, say $\lambda + d\lambda$, is superposed on the central maximum of the other (Fig. 23.24). In this case, we may define the resolving power of the grating $= \frac{\lambda}{d\lambda}$.

In Fig. 23.25, GG' is the effective part of a plane transmission grating on which light is normally incident. Let the total number of lines in the effective part of the grating $= N$ and grating element $= a + b$.

We consider the nth order spectra and let θ be the angle of diffraction giving the nth order maximum for wavelength λ. If GA and $G'A'$ are the two parallel diffracted rays from the two extreme points G and G' of the grating, then their path-difference,

$$GM = N(a+b)\sin\theta \quad [\because GG' = N(a+b)].$$

Now, for nth maximum, the path-difference between two corresponding points (having a distance $a + b$) is given by

$(a + b) \sin \theta = n\lambda.$

$\therefore \quad GM = N \cdot n \cdot \lambda.$ (23.70)

We assume that the angle θ is slowly increased to $(\theta + d\theta)$ so that the diffracted rays GB and $G'B'$, producing destructive interference, cause first subsidiary minimum for λ. Then the path-difference between these rays $= GM'$ and it will be greater than GM by λ as in that case the rays coming from the top point G and from the mid-point and the lowermost point G' will have a path-difference of $\lambda/2$ to produce destructive interference.

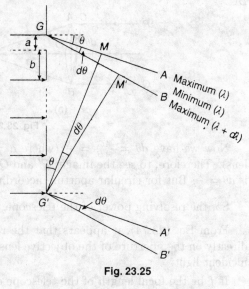

Fig. 23.25

So, $\quad GM' = GM + \lambda = N \cdot n \cdot \lambda + \lambda$

$\qquad\qquad = \lambda(N \cdot n + 1) \qquad (23.71)$

Further, if the diffracted rays GB and $G'B'$ produce nth maximum for $(\lambda + d\lambda)$, then according to the condition of maxima, we have

$$GM' = GG' \sin \angle GG'M = N(a + b) \sin(\theta + d\theta)$$

$$= Nn \cdot (\lambda + d\lambda) \qquad\qquad (23.72)$$

Now, if the wavelengths λ and $\lambda + d\lambda$ are to be resolved, then according to Rayleigh criterion, Eqs. (23.71) and (23.72) should be equal. We then have

$$\lambda(N \cdot n + 1) = N \cdot n(\lambda + d\lambda) \quad \text{or,} \quad \lambda = N \cdot n \cdot d\lambda$$

or, $\quad \dfrac{\lambda}{d\lambda} = N \cdot n.$ (23.73)

Thus, the resolving power $= N \cdot n =$ total number of lines in the grating $\times$ order number of the spectrum. Eq. (23.73) shows that the resolving power of a grating is proportional to (i) the total number of lines (N) in the grating and (ii) the order number (n) of the spectrum.

23.21   Resolving Power of a Telescope

The resolving power of a telescope is defined as the reciprocal of the angular separation that two distant point objects must have, so that their images just resolved according to Rayleigh's criterion.

We consider two distant point objects P and Q situated in front of a telescope objective AB [Fig. 23.26(a)] and they subtend an angle $d\theta$ at the objective. The image of each point object is a Fraunhofer diffraction pattern consisting of a central bright point surrounded by alternate dark and bright rings. We assume that P' and Q' be the central bright points of the two images respectively. According to Rayleigh criterion, these two images are to be resolved if the position of the central maximum of the image P' coincides with the first minimum of the image Q' and vice versa [Fig. 23.26(b)]. As the object points P and Q are far away, the wavefronts will be plane. Let AB and BC be the wavefronts due to the points P and Q respectively. As $AP' = BP'$, the point P' due to the wavefront AB will be a bright point. For just resolution, P' should be the first minimum due to the wavefront BC. For the purpose, the necessary condition is $AC = \lambda$. All the secondary waves destructively interfere with each other and so P' will be the first minimum due to the wavefront BC.

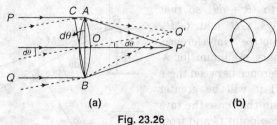

(a)   **(b)**

Fig. 23.26

Now we have $d\theta = \frac{AC}{AB} = \frac{\lambda}{a}$ (where $a = AB =$ the aperture of the objective lens). Therefore, to see the images P' and Q' just resolved, the necessary condition is $d\theta = \frac{\lambda}{a}$. But for circular aperture according to Airy, $d\theta = \frac{1.22\lambda}{a}$.

So, the resolving power of the telescope $= \dfrac{1}{d\theta} = \dfrac{a}{1.22\lambda}.$ (23.74)

From Eq. (23.74), it appears that the resolving power of a telescope depends directly on the aperture of the objective lens and inversely as the wavelength of the incident light.

If f be the focal length of the telescope objective, then we can write,

$$d\theta = \frac{r}{f} = \frac{1.22\lambda}{a}.$$

$$\therefore \quad r = \frac{1.22\lambda f}{a},$$ (23.75)

where r is the radius of the central bright image.

Eq. (23.75) shows that with smaller values of λ and f and larger values of a, the radius r of the central bright image is small. This indicates that the diffraction patterns will apear sharper and so the resolving power will be higher.

23.22   Resolving Power of a Spectrometer

We have seen that the resolving power is defined by the ratio $\lambda/d\lambda$, where $d\lambda$ is the smallest difference in wavelength that can just be resolved at the wavelength λ. It

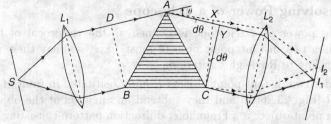

Fig. 23.27

gives the ability of the instrument to form separate spectral images of two neighbouring wavelengths λ and $\lambda + d\lambda$ in the wavelength region λ. According to Rayleigh criterion of resolution, two close wavelengths will appear resolved if the angular separation between their spectral lines is greater than the limit of resolution of the telescope of the spectrometer. To find the resolving power of a prism, let light rays consisting of two close wavelengths λ and $\lambda + d\lambda$ fall on the collimator lens L_1 of the spectrometer from the slit S. The rays are made parallel by the lens L_1 and are incident on AB of the prism placed in the position of minimum deviation. On emergence from the prism the rays are dispersed and the rays AX and AY corresponding to the wavelengths $\lambda + d\lambda$ and λ are found. The set of emerging parallel rays are then collected by the lens L_2 to form their maxima at I_1 and I_2 respectively. The two sets of rays of wavelengths λ and $(\lambda + d\lambda)$ get deviated through angles $(\theta + d\theta)$ and θ respectively. When BD, CX and CY are drawn perpendiculars on DA, AX and AY respectively, then we have BD as the incident wavefront and CX and CY as the emergent wavefronts for the wavelengths $\lambda + d\lambda$ and λ respectively. We can then write,

$$DA + AY = \mu BC \tag{23.76}$$

for the wavelength λ. Similarly, for $\lambda + d\lambda$, we have

$$DA + AX = (\mu - d\mu)BC, \tag{23.77}$$

where $(\mu - d\mu)$ is the refractive index of the material of the prism corresponding to the wavelength $\lambda + d\lambda$.

From Eqs. (23.76) and (23.77), $AY - AX = d\mu \cdot BC$.

But $AY - AX \simeq XY = CY \cdot d\theta = a \cdot d\theta$ $[a = CY = $ the aperture of $L_2]$

or, $\quad d\mu \cdot BC = a \cdot d\theta$.

So, the change in the angle of deviation of two wavelengths λ and $(\lambda + d\lambda)$ is obtained as

$$d\theta = d\mu \cdot \frac{BC}{a} = d\mu \cdot \frac{t}{a}, \tag{23.78}$$

where $t = BC = $ thickness of the base of the prism.

Now, we know that for resolution, the angle $d\theta$ in Eq. (23.78) must be at least equal to λ/a. So,

$$d\theta = d\mu \cdot \frac{t}{a} = \lambda/a \quad \text{or,} \quad \lambda = d\mu \cdot t.$$

$$\therefore \quad \frac{\lambda}{d\lambda} = t \cdot \left(\frac{d\mu}{d\lambda}\right). \tag{23.79}$$

Eq. (23.79) gives the expression for the resolving power of the prism at the position of minimum deviation. It shows that the resolving power depends on the thickness (t) of the base of the prism but is independent of the refracting angle of the prism.

Examples

1. The diameter of the first ring of a zone plate is 1 mm. If plane waves $(\lambda = 5000 \text{ Å})$ fall on the plate, where should the screen be placed so that light is focused to the brightest spot?

Solution : The focal length of the zone plate,

$$f_n = \frac{r_n^2}{n\lambda} \quad \text{(where } r_n = \text{radius of the } n\text{th zone).}$$

Let $r_1 = $ radius of the first $(n = 1)$ zone, then $f_1 = r_1^2/\lambda$.

Given, $r_1 = 0.50$ mm $= 0.05$ cm, $\lambda = 5000$ Å $= 5000 \times 10^{-8}$ cm.

Therefore, $f_1 = \dfrac{0.05 \times 0.05}{5000 \times 10^{-8}} = \mathbf{50}$ **cm**.

So, the screen is to be placed at a distance of **50 cm** from the zone plate.

2. The central circle of a zone plate has a radius of 0.07 cm. Light of wavelength 5000 Å coming from (i) an object at infinity, (ii) an object 147 cm away from the plate falls on it. Find the position of the principal image in each case.

Solution : We have the focal length of the zone plate,

$$f = \frac{r_n^2}{n\lambda} = \frac{0.07^2 \text{ cm}^2}{1 \times 5000 \times 10^{-8} \text{ cm}} = 98 \text{ cm}.$$

Let u and v be the distances of object and principal image from the zone plate. Then,

$$\frac{1}{u} + \frac{1}{v} = \frac{1}{f}.$$

(i) Given, $u = \infty$, $f = 98$ cm, $v = ?$

We then have

$$\frac{1}{\infty} + \frac{1}{v} = \frac{1}{98} \quad \text{or,} \quad v = \mathbf{98 \text{ cm}}.$$

(ii) Given, $u = 147$ cm, $f = 98$ cm, $v = ?$

Hence, $\dfrac{1}{147} + \dfrac{1}{v} = \dfrac{1}{98} \;\Rightarrow\; v = \mathbf{294 \text{ cm}}.$

3. An object is placed at 20 cm from a zone plate and the brightest image is situated at 20 cm from the zone plate with light of $\lambda = 4000$ Å. Calculate the number of Fresnel's zones in a radius of 1 cm of the plate.

Solution : We have from the zone-plate formula,

$$\frac{1}{u} + \frac{1}{v} = \frac{n\lambda}{r_n^2} = \frac{1}{f}.$$

Given, $u = v = 20$ cm. So, $1/f = 1/20 + 1/20 \;\Rightarrow\; f = 10$ cm.

Now, let the radius of nth zone be $r_n = 1$ cm. Then using the relation,

$$\frac{n\lambda}{r_n^2} = \frac{1}{f}, \; n = \frac{r_n^2}{f\lambda} = \frac{1^2}{10 \times 4000 \times 10^{-8}} = \mathbf{2500}.$$

4. A zone plate is made such that the radii of the circles defining the zones are the same as the radii of Newton's rings formed between a plane surface and a surface whose radius of curvature is 150 cm. Find the primary focal length of the zone plate.

Solution : The radii r_n of Newton's dark rings are obtained from

$$r_n^2 = n\lambda R \; (n = 1, 2, 3, \ldots)$$

(where R = radius of curvature of the curved surface).

Now, the primary focal length of the zone plate is expressed as

$$f = \frac{r_n^2}{n\lambda} \; (n = 1, 2, \ldots) \;\Rightarrow\; r_n^2 = n\lambda f.$$

Hence, $n\lambda f = n\lambda R$ or, $f = R = \mathbf{150 \text{ cm}}.$

5. When a circular aperture of diameter 2 mm is illuminated by a plane wave of light, the most intense point on the axis is at a distance of 200 cm from the aperture. Calculate the wavelength of light.

Solution : Let AB be the aperture and P the most intense axial point (Fig. 23.28). Now, for P to be most intense, only one half-period zone is to be allowed by AB.

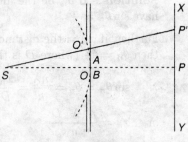

For this, we can write, $PA = p + \lambda/2$, where $p = PO$.

If r be the radius of the aperture, then

$$r^2 = OA^2 = (p + \lambda/2)^2 - p^2 \simeq p\lambda.$$

Fig. 23.28

$$\therefore \quad \lambda = \frac{r^2}{p} = \frac{0.1 \times 0.1}{200} = 5 \times 10^{-5} \text{ cm} = 5000 \text{ Å}.$$

6. Fringes are seen within the shadow of a thin wire held vertically in front of a narrow slit illuminated by monochromatic light. Find the diameter of the wire if the fringe-width at a distance of 4 m from the wire is 1.8 mm and the wavelength of light used is 5400 Å.

Solution : The fringe-width β in the diffraction pattern of fringes due to a narrow wire is

$$\beta = \frac{D}{d}\lambda \text{ or, } d = \frac{D}{\beta}\lambda.$$

Given, D = screen to wire distance = 4 m = 400 cm here; d = dia. of the wire. Here, $\beta = 1.8$ mm = 0.18 cm, $\lambda = 5400 \times 10^{-8}$ cm.

$$\therefore \quad d = \frac{400 \times 5400 \times 10^{-8}}{0.18} = \textbf{0.12 cm.}$$

7. Light of $\lambda = 6000$ Å falls normally on a diaphragm with a round hole of 6 mm dia. A screen is placed behind the diaphragm 3 m away. How many Fresnel's zones can be accommodated in the diaphragm hole? Will the centre of the pattern on the screen be dark or bright? Explain.

Solution : Let n be the required number of Fresnel's zones. Then,

$$PA = p + n\frac{\lambda}{2}.$$

If r be the radius of the hole, we can write,

$$r^2 = \left(p + n\frac{\lambda}{2}\right)^2 - p^2 \simeq pn\lambda,$$

(ignoring $n^2\lambda^2/4$, which is very small).

$$\therefore \quad n = \frac{r^2}{p\lambda}.$$

Given, $r = 3$ mm = 0.3 cm; $p = 3$ m = 300 cm and $\lambda = 6000 \times 10^{-8}$ cm.

$$\therefore \quad n = \frac{0.3 \times 0.3}{300 \times 6000 \times 10^{-8}} = 5.$$

As the hole has odd number of Fresnel's zones, the centre of the pattern will be **bright**.

8. Find the distance between the central maximum and the first minimum on a screen, 100 cm away from a single slit, 0.1 mm wide and illuminated by a light of wavelength 5890 Å.   [N.B.U. 2001]

Solution : If θ_n be the angle of diffraction for the nth minimum, then we have $\sin \theta_n = \frac{n\lambda}{a}$.

Further, if x_n = the distance of the nth minima from the central maximum, then $\theta_n = \frac{x_n}{D}$ (where D is the distance between the slit and the screen).

$$\therefore \quad \sin \theta_n = \theta_n = \frac{n\lambda}{a} = \frac{x_n}{D} \quad (\theta_n \text{ is very small})$$

or, $\quad x_n = \dfrac{n \cdot \lambda \cdot D}{a}.$

For $n = 1$, i.e., for 1st minima, $x_1 = \frac{1 \cdot \lambda \cdot D}{a}$; here, $\lambda = 5890$ Å $= 5890 \times 10^{-8}$ cm, $D = 100$ cm and $a = 0.1$ mm $= 10^{-2}$ cm.

$$\therefore \quad x_1 = \frac{5890 \times 10^{-8} \times 100}{10^{-2}} = \textbf{0.589 cm}.$$

9. A single slit forms diffraction pattern of Fraunhofer class with white light. The second maximum in the pattern for red light of wavelength 7000 Å coincides with the third maximum of an unknown wavelength. Calculate the unknown wavelength.   [C.U. 2001]

Solution : The distance of the nth maximum from the principal maximum in the case of the diffraction pattern due to a single slit, is given by

$$x_n = \frac{(2n + 1)f \cdot \lambda}{2a}.$$

For the second maximum of 7000 Å wavelength, $x_2 = \dfrac{5 \cdot f \times 7000}{2a}.$

For the third maximum of the unknown wavelength, $x'_3 = \dfrac{7 \cdot f \times \lambda}{2a}.$

According to condition, $x_2 = x'_3.$

$$\therefore \quad \frac{5 \cdot f \times 7000}{2a} = \frac{7 \cdot f \times \lambda}{2a} \quad \text{or,} \quad \lambda = \frac{5}{7} \times 7000 = \textbf{5000 Å}.$$

10. Monochromatic light of wavelength 6.56×10^{-5} cm falls normally on a diffraction grating 2 cm wide. The first order spectrum is produced at an angle of $18°44'$ from the normal. What is the total number of lines on the grating? $\sin 18°44' = 0.3129$.

Solution : We have $\sin \theta_n = \lambda \cdot N \cdot n$. Here, $n = 1$, $\theta_n = 18°44'$, $\lambda = 6.56 \times 10^{-5}$ cm.

Therefore, $\sin 18°44' = 6.56 \times 10^{-5} \times 1 \times N$

or, $\quad\quad 0.3129 = 6.56 \times 10^{-5} \times N$

$$\therefore \quad\quad N = \frac{0.3129}{6.56 \times 10^{-5}} = \textbf{4769.8 lines/cm}.$$

Since the grating is 2 cm wide, the total number of lines on it = $4769.8 \times 2 =$ **9539**.

11. The width of each slit of a double slit is 0.15 mm and they are separated by a distance of 0.45 mm. If the double slit produces Fraunhofer diffraction, find the missing orders.

Solution : Missing orders are obtained when interference maxima $(a + b)\sin\theta = n\lambda$ coincide with diffraction minima, $a\sin\theta = p \cdot \lambda$. Here, $a = 0.15$ mm and $b = 0.45$ mm.

$$\therefore \quad \frac{n}{p} = \frac{a+b}{a}; \text{ here, } \frac{n}{p} = \frac{0.15+0.45}{0.15} = \frac{0.6}{0.15} = 4 \quad \text{or, } n = 4p.$$

If $p = 1, 2, 3, \ldots$, etc., $n = 4, 8, 12, \ldots$, etc., this shows that 4th 8th, 12th, etc., order of interference maxima will be missing in the diffraction spectra.

12. A plane transmission grating gives an angle of diffraction of a line to be 30° in the first order, for a wavelength 6×10^{-5} cm. Find the number of lines per cm of the given grating.   [C.U. 2003]

Solution : For a grating, we have, $N = \dfrac{\sin\theta_n}{\lambda \cdot n}$.

In this case, $\lambda = 60 \times 10^{-5}$ cm; $n = 1$; $\theta_n = 30°$.

$$\therefore \quad N = \frac{\sin 30°}{6 \times 10^{-5} \times 1} = \frac{1}{2 \times 6 \times 10^{-5} \times 1} = \textbf{8333 lines per cm}.$$

13. A diffraction grating has 6×10^5 lines per metre and is illuminated normally by white light (4000-7000 Å). Calculate the angular spread of the diffracted spectra. What is the longest wavelength that can be seen in the highest order spectra?

Solution : The grating has lines $N = 6 \times 10^5$ lines/m.

For the 1st order, $n = 1$,

$$\therefore \quad \sin\theta_v = 6 \times 10^5 \times 4000 \times 10^{-10} = 0.24 \quad \text{or, } \theta_v = 13°53'.$$

Similarly, $\sin\theta_r = 6 \times 10^5 \times 7000 \times 10^{-10} = 0.42$.

$$\therefore \quad \theta_r = 24°50'.$$

Hence, the angular spread for 1st order $= 24°50' - 13°53' = 10°57'$.

For the second order, $n = 2$, $\sin\theta = 2 \cdot N \cdot \lambda$.

$$\therefore \quad \sin\theta_v = 2 \times 6 \times 10^5 \times 4000 \times 10^{-10} = 0.48.$$

$$\therefore \quad \theta_v = 28°41'.$$

Similarly, $\sin\theta_r = 2 \times 6 \times 10^5 \times 7000 \times 10^{-10} = 0.84$ or, $\theta_r = 57°8'$.

Hence, the angular spread in the second order $= 57°8' - 28°41' = 28°27'$.

For the third order, $n = 3$ and $\sin\theta = 3 \cdot N \cdot \lambda$.

$$\therefore \quad \sin\theta_v = 3 \times 6 \times 10^5 \times 4000 \times 10^{-10} = 0.72 \quad \text{or, } \theta_v = 46°3'.$$

$$\sin\theta_r = 3 \times 6 \times 10^5 \times 7000 \times 10^{-10} > 1;$$

so this is impossible. Thus all of the third order cannot be seen.

The longest wavelength which can be seen corresponds to $\sin\theta = 1$

or, $\quad \theta = 90°$. So, $1 = 3 \times 6 \times 10^5 \times \lambda$.

or, $\quad \lambda = \dfrac{2}{3 \times 6 \times 10^5}$ metres $= 5556$ Å.

14. A parallel beam of light of wavelength 5.893×10^{-5} cm is incident normally on a diffraction grating. The angle between the two first order spectra on either side of the normal is $27°42'$. Find the number of ruling per centimetre on the grating.

Solution : The first order spectrum occurs at an angle,

$$\theta = \frac{1}{2} \times 27°42' = 13°51'.$$

We have $\sin \theta = N \cdot n \cdot \lambda$.

$$\therefore \quad \sin 13°51' = N \times 1 \times 5.893 \times 10^{-5}$$

or, $N = \dfrac{\sin 13°51'}{5.893 \times 10^{-5}} = \dfrac{0.2393}{5.893 \times 10^{-5}} = \mathbf{4060 \ rulings/cm \ (approx.).}$

15. A plane diffraction grating at normal incidence gives a green line $\lambda = 5.40 \times 10^{-5}$ cm in a certain spectral order superposed on a violet line $\lambda = 4.05 \times 10^{-5}$ cm of 'the next higher order. If the angle of diffraction is $30°$, obtain the number of lines per cm of the grating. **[C.U. 1990, '99]**

Solution : We know, $\sin \theta_n = N \cdot n \cdot \lambda$.

We assume that the green line be in the nth order; the violet line will then be in the $(n + 1)$th order.

For the green line, $\sin 30° = N \cdot n \times 5.40 \times 10^{-5}$.   (i)

For the violet line, $\sin 30° = N \cdot (n + 1) \times 4.05 \times 10^{-5}$.   (ii)

$\therefore \quad N \cdot n \times 5.40 \times 10^{-5} = N \cdot (n + 1) \times 4.05 \times 10^{-5}$ or, $n = 3$.

Putting this value in Eq. (i), we have

$$\sin 30° = N \times 3 \times 5.40 \times 10^{-5}.$$

$$\therefore \quad N = \frac{\sin 30°}{3 \times 5.40 \times 10^{-5}} = \frac{1}{2 \times 3 \times 5.40 \times 10^{-5}} = \mathbf{3087 \ per \ cm.}$$

16. What is the smallest resolvable wavelength difference, in the second order spectrum, produced by a diffraction grating having 15000 lines to the centimetre when the incident light has a mean wavelength of 6000 Å?

Solution : Let the smallest resolvable wavelength difference be $d\lambda$. For the resolving power of a grating, we can write,

$$\frac{\lambda}{d\lambda} = N \cdot n \quad \text{or,} \quad d\lambda = \frac{\lambda}{N \cdot n}.$$

Given, $\lambda = 6000 \times 10^{-8}$ cm; $N = 15000$ and $n = 2$.

$$\therefore \quad d\lambda = \frac{6000 \times 10^{-8}}{15000 \times 2} = 0.2 \times 10^{-8} = \mathbf{0.2 \ \text{Å}.}$$

17. The diameter of the pupil of human eye is 2 mm and the refractive index of the liquid inside the eye is 1.44. Assuming the effective wavelength of white light to be 5.6×10^{-5} cm, calculate the resolving power of human eye.

Solution : According to Airy,

$$\frac{1}{d\theta} = \frac{d}{1.22\lambda} \quad \text{(where } d = \text{diameter of the lens aperture)}$$

or, $d\theta = \dfrac{1.22\lambda}{d}$.

The refractive index of the liquid inside the eye being 1.44, the wavelength of white light inside the eye is $\lambda = \frac{5.6 \times 10^{-5}}{1.44}$ cm.

$$\therefore \quad d\theta = \frac{1.22 \times 5.6 \times 10^{-5}}{1.44} \times \frac{1}{0.2} \text{ radian } [d = 2 \text{ mm} = 0.2 \text{ cm}]$$

$$= \frac{1.22 \times 5.6 \times 10^{-5}}{1.44} \times \frac{180}{0.2 \times 3.14} \text{ degree}$$

$$= \frac{1.22 \times 5.6 \times 10^{-5} \times 180 \times 60}{1.44 \times 0.2 \times 3.14} \text{ minute} \doteq \textbf{0.8 minute (approx.)}.$$

18. Two lines in the second order spectrum formed by a plane transmission grating are just resolved. If the lines are due to wavelengths 5890 Å and 5896 Å, find the number of lines in the grating.

Solution : The resolving power of a grating is given by $\frac{\lambda}{d\lambda} = N \cdot n$.

Given, $\lambda = 5890$ Å; $d\lambda = 5896 - 5890 = 6$ Å; $n = 2$.

So, $\quad \frac{5890}{6} = N \times 2 \quad$ or, $\quad N = \frac{5890}{6 \times 2} = \textbf{491 (nearly)}.$

19. Two monochromatic light waves of length λ and $\lambda + d\lambda (d\lambda \ll \lambda)$ are incident normally on a plane grating having grating element $(a + b)$. Show that the dispersive power of the grating in the nth order is given by

$$\left[\left(\frac{a+b}{n} \right)^2 - \lambda^2 \right]^{-\frac{1}{2}}.$$

Solution : For the nth order spectrum of a grating,

$$(a + b) \sin \theta = n\lambda. \tag{i}$$

Differentiating, $(a + b) \cos \theta \cdot d\theta = \lambda \cdot d\lambda.$

Hence, dispersive power, $\dfrac{d\theta}{d\lambda} = \dfrac{n}{(a + b) \cos \theta}.$ $\qquad$ (ii)

From Eq. (i), we have

$$\cos \theta = \sqrt{1 - \sin^2 \theta} = \sqrt{1 - \left(\frac{n\lambda}{a + b} \right)^2}$$

Substituting this value in Eq. (ii), we get

$$\frac{d\theta}{d\lambda} = \frac{n}{(a + b)\sqrt{1 - \left(\frac{n\lambda}{a+b} \right)^2}} = \frac{n}{\sqrt{(a + b)^2 - n^2\lambda^2}} = \frac{1}{\left[\left(\frac{a+b}{n} \right)^2 - \lambda^2 \right]^{\frac{1}{2}}}.$$

So, the dispersive power of the grating $= \left[\left(\dfrac{a+b}{n} \right)^2 - \lambda^2 \right]^{-\frac{1}{2}}.$

Questions

Essay-type

1. Discuss, in detail, the diffraction pattern obtained when a sharp, straight edge is held in the path of a monochromatic beam of light.

2. What is a zone plate? Compare its functions with those of a lens.

3. Explain the formation of diffraction pattern when a monochromatic beam of light passes through a narrow rectangular aperture.   [B.U. 1983]

4. Deduce an expression for the intensity pattern due to diffraction in a single slit experiment. Also, show your result graphically.   [N.B.U. 2001]

5. Describe with necessary theory the diffraction pattern produced by a narrow slit illuminated by a parallel beam of monochromatic light incident normally on the slit.   [C.U. 1999]

6. What is diffraction of light? A parallel beam of monochromatic light is incident on a double slit. Discuss the nature of the diffraction pattern observed. How will the pattern be changed if one of slits is covered?

                                                                    [C.U. 1980]

7. A narrow circular aperture is held in front of a fine hole and a screen is placed at a certain distance on the other side. Explain the effect observed on the screen when a source of monochromatic light is placed close to the pinhole. What will be the changes in illumination when the circular aperture is gradually increased in size?

8. Discuss the positions of maxima and minima. What do you mean by missing order?   [Vid. U. 2002]

9. Show that the resultant intensity distribution in the Fraunhofer diffraction pattern produced by two parallel slits each of width 'b' and separated by a distance 'd' is a product of the single slit (width 'b') diffraction pattern and the interference pattern produced by two point sources separated by a distance 'd'.

10. Explain the action of a diffraction grating and describe how to use it to measure the wavelength of light.   [C.U. 2000; N.B.U. 1983, 2000]

11. Describe a plane transmission grating and explain how a spectrum is produced by it.   [C.U. 1987, '94]

12. Explain with theory the formation of spectrum by a plane transmission grating. What is the difference between grating spectrum and prism spectrum?   [C.U. 1984]

13. Develop the theory of diffraction grating and derive the conditions for absent spectra. What is the condition which must be satisfied if the 3rd order spectrum is to be absent?

14. Distinguish between the dispersive power and the resolving power of a diffraction grating and derive expression for them. Discuss their dependence on the order of the spectrum as well as the lines on the grating.

                                                                [C.U. (Hons.) 1967]

15. Explain what is meant by the resolving power of diffraction grating. Show that the resolving power is given by the product of the total number of rulings and the order number of the spectrum.   [B.U. 1999; C.U. 1991, 2002]

Short Answer-type

16. How is zone plate constructed? Compare a zone plate with a convex lens.
                                                        [C.U. 2000; N.B.U. 2001]

17. Define 'half-period zone'. How can a plane wavefront be devided into a number of half-period zones with respect to an external point?

18. What is diffraction of light? Explain clearly the difference between interference and diffraction. [C.U. 2002, '03]

19. What is the difference between Fresnel and Fraunhofer classes of diffraction? [C.U. (Hons.) 1949, '65]

20. What is grating element? What is its relation with the number of rulings on the grating?

21. "A zone plate may be regarded as a convex lens with multiple foci." Justify the statement.

22. A narrow slit is illuminated by a beam of parallel white light. How will the central band appear? Will the subsidiary maximum be coloured? Why are secondary maxima less intense than the central maximum? [C.U. 2001]

23. Draw a diagram showing the diffraction pattern produced by a double slit on which a parallel beam of monochromatic light incident normally.

24. Parallel monochromatic light is incident normally on a slit. How will the diffraction pattern be modified if (i) the slit width is very small and (ii) the slit width is large?

25. What would be the effects, if the distance between the rulings in a grating was (a) very large, (b) very small compared with the wavelength?

26. How does a grating spectrum differ from a prism spectrum? [C.U. 2001, '03]

27. On what factors does the dispersive power of a grating depend?

28. How is a zone plate constructed? What is a phase reversal zone plate?

29. What is a zone plate? Write down the expression for its focal length?

30. What are the factors on which the amplitude of light waves from a half-period zone at observation point depend?

31. In what essential respects the case of propagation of sound waves differ from that of light waves?

32. Why is diffraction effect in light difficult to observe?

33. Why do we get bright spot at the centre of the image of an opaque object when its size is extremely small?

34. What is the cause of light streaks one sees while looking at a strong source of light with half-shut eyes?

35. What is the relation between the wavelength of wave and size of the obstacle for diffraction to take place?

Numerical Problems

36. How many lines per cm are there in a grating which produces a deviation of $30°$ in the second order spectrum of light of wavelength 6×10^{-5} cm?

[C.U. 1984]
[**Ans.** 4166 Å]

37. A circular aperture of 0.6 mm diameter is illuminated by parallel monochromatic light. The diffracted light is received on a distant screen which is gradually moved towards the aperture. The centre of the circular path of light first becomes dark when the screen is 50 cm from the slit. Calculate the wavelength of light used. [**Ans.** 6400 Å]

38. ·A parallel beam of light consisting of two wavelengths 4000 Å and 7500 Å falls on a grating for which distance between successive grating elements is 0.001 cm. Calculate the difference in angular deviations of these two spectral lines in the second order.   [**Ans.** 2° (approx.)]

39. A parallel beam of light is incident normally on a plane grating having 4250 lines per cm and the second order spectra is formed at an angle of 30°. Calculate the wavelength of the monochromatic light.   [**N.B.U. 1983**]
                                                          [**Ans.** 5882 Å]

40. A plane grating has 15000 lines per inch. Find the angular separation between the lines having wavelengths 5048 Å and 5016 Å in the second order spectrum.
                                                          [**C.U. 1989**]
                                                          [**Ans.** 16′]

41. Monochromatic beam of light of wavelength 6.28×10^{-5} cm falls normally on a plane grating consisting of identical parallel wires equidistant from one another. The first order spectrum is observed at 15′ from the zero position. Calculate the grating element.   [**Ans.** 0.0143 cm (approx.)]

42. Light, which is a mixture of two wavelengths 5000 Å and 5200 Å is incident normally on a plane transmission grating, having 10000 lines per cm. A lens of focal length 100 cm is used for observing the spectrum on a screen. Calculate the spectration of the two lines in the first order spectrum.   [**Ans.** 2 cm]

43. A plane diffraction grating is illuminated by a source which emits two spectral lines of wavelength 420×10^{-7} cm and 600×10^{-7} cm. Show that the 3rd order line of one of these wavelengths is diffracted through a greater angle than the 4th order of the other wavelength.

44. Monochromatic light of wavelength 5.9×10^{-7} metre falls normally on a diffraction grating and produces a first order maximum at an angle of 19°30′. When the same grating is used with different monochromatic source, the first order maximum is observed at an angle of 15°6′. Calculate (a) the wavelength of the second source and (b) the highest order which is observable with the second source.   [**C.U. 1992**]
                                       [**Ans.** (a) 4.6×10^{-5} cm, (b) 3]

45. Monochromatic light of wavelength 5200 Å falls normally on a diffraction grating having 4.5×10^3 lines per cm. What is the angular separation between the third and the fourth order images?   [**N.B.U. 1991**]
                                                          [**Ans.** 25°48′]

46. A diffraction grating used at normal incidence gives a line $\lambda_1 = 6000$ Å in a certain order superimposed on another line $\lambda_2 = 4500$ Å of the next higher order. If the angle of diffraction be 30°, how many lines are there in a cm of the grating?   [**C.U. 1999**]
                                                          [**Ans.** 2778]

47. Calculate the least width that a grating must have in order to resolve two sodium D-lines in the second order, the grating having 800 lines per cm. The wavelengths of the D-lines of sodium are 5896 Å and 5890 Å respectively.
                                                          [**Ans.** 0.614 cm]

48. A grating has 1000 lines ruled on it. In the region of wavelength $\lambda = 6000 \times 10^{-8}$ cm, what will be the difference between two wavelengths which would just appear to be separated in the first order spectrum?   [**C.U. 1986**]
                                                          [**Ans.** 6×10^{-8}]

49. How many orders will be visible, if the wavelength of the incident light is 5000 Å and the number of lines on the grating be 7620 to an inch?

[**Ans.** Up to 6th order]

50. In an experiment using a spectrometer in normal adjustment fitted with a plane transmission grating and using monochromatic light of wavelength 5.89×10^{-10} cm, diffraction maxima were obtained with telescope setting at $153°44'$, $124°5'$, $76°55'$ and $47°16'$, the central maxima being at $100°30'$. Show that these observations are consistent with normal incidence. Calculate the number of rulings per cm of the grating.

[**Ans.** 6800]

51. Find the first three focal lengths of a zone plate for which the radius of the first zone is 0.3 mm, for light of $\lambda = 5000$ Å. [**Ans.** 18 cm, 6 cm, 3.6 cm]

52. What is the radius of the first zone in a zone plate if the focal length is 20 cm for light of $\lambda = 5000$ Å? [**Ans.** 0.0316 cm]

53. A zone plate is illuminated with sodium light ($\lambda = 5896$ Å) placed at a distance of 1.5 m. If the image of the point source is obtained at a distance of 3 m on the other side, what will be the power of the equivalent lens which may replace the zone plate without disturbing the set-up? Also, calculate the radius of the first zone of the plate. [**Ans.** +1D; 0.0768 cm]

54. Find the radii of the first three transparent zones of a zone plate whose first focal length is 1 m for $\lambda = 5893$ Å. [**Ans.** 0.0767 cm, 0.133 cm, 0.172 cm]

55. In a diffraction experiment due to a straight edge, the distance between the slit-source ($\lambda = 6000$ Å) and the straight edge is 6 m, and that between the straight edge and eyepiece is 4 m. Find the positions of the first three maxima and their separation.

[**Ans.** 0.200 cm, 0.346 cm, 0.447 cm; 0.146 cm, 0.101 cm]

56. A zone plate gives a series of image of a point source on its axis. If the strongest and the second strongest images are at distances 30 cm and 6 cm respectively from the zone plate, both on the same side remote from the source, calculate the distance of the source from the zone plate, the principal focal length and the radius of the first zone ($\lambda = 5 \times 10^{-5}$ cm).

[**Ans.** 30 cm; 15 cm; 0.0274 cm]

57. A very narrow vertical slit illuminated with light of $\lambda = 5.9 \times 10^{-5}$ cm casts a shadow of a vertical copper wire of 0.1 cm dia, and 20 cm away from the slit, on a screen 3 m away from the wire. Calculate the total number of bands inside the shadow. [**Ans.** 9]

58. A fine aperture is placed at a distance of 12 cm from a sharp razor blade edge held vertically at a distance of 25 cm from the screen. If the aperture be illuminated by light of $\lambda = 5890$ Å, calculate the height of the 6th bright band above the line joining the edge to aperture. [**Ans.** 0.243 cm]

59. A parallel beam of $\lambda = 6000$ Å is normally incident on a circular opening in an opaque screen. What should be the radius of the opening such that the intensity at a point 50 cm from the screen is 4 times the intensity on it when the screen is absent? Find the distance through which the screen should be moved towards the point to reduce the intensity at the point to zero.

[**Ans.** 0.055 cm; 25 cm]

60. A circular aperture of 1.2 mm dia. is illuminated with plane waves of monochromatic light. The diffracted light is received on a distant screen, which is gradually moved towards the aperture. The centre of the circular path of light first becomes dark when the screen is 30 cm from the aperture. Find the wavelength of light used? **[Ans.** 6000 Å**]**

61. Light of $\lambda = 6000$ Å passes through a narrow circular aperture of radius 0.09 cm. At what distance along the axis will the first maximum intensity be observed? **[Ans.** 135 cm**]**

62. Parallel monochromatic light of 6000 Å falls normally on a circular aperture of diameter 0.12 cm and is viewed from the opposite side along a line through the centre of the hole and normal to its plane. Calculate the three largest distances from the hole at which the intensity is (i) maximum, (ii) zero.
[Ans. (i) 60 cm, 20 cm, 12 cm; (ii) 30 cm, 15 cm, 10 cm**]**

63. A parallel beam of microwaves ($\lambda = 0.8$ cm) is incident on a circular aperture of adjustable radius. If a detector is placed on the axis of aperture 80 cm behind it and the radius of the aperture is gradually increased, at what value of the radius would the response of the detector be maximum? **[Ans.** 8 cm**]**

64. A screen is placed at a distance of 60 cm from a circular aperture of 0.6 cm radius. Find the radius of the first half-period zone for light of $\lambda = 6000$ Å. How many zones are contained in the circular aperture? **[Ans.** 0.06 cm; 100**]**

Chapter 24
Polarization of Light

24.1 Introduction

The interference and diffraction properties of light proved that light propagates in the form of a wave. But, the nature of this wave motion is not obtained from this property. This was established only after getting the knowledge of the phenomenon of **polarization.** In **longitudinal waves,** the particles in the medium vibrate about their mean positions, along the direction of the propagation of the wave while in **transverse waves** the particles of the medium vibrate at right angles to the direction of the propagation of the wave. Sound wave is an example of longitudinal wave while light wave is the example of transverse wave.

24.2 Unpolarized and Polarized Light

Unpolarized light is the light which vibrates in all possible directions at **right angles** to the direction of its propagation. The average effect of these vibrations indicates that in unpolarized light, the vibrations are *symmetrically distributed* in a plane perpendicular to the direction of propagation of light. Such light having same property in all directions is known as **unpolarized light** (Fig. 24.1). However, if somehow, the symmetrical distribution of the vibrations is made lost, the light is then partially polarized. More precisely, if vibrations in all directions **except one** are removed, the light is said to be **linearly** or **plane polarized.** Thus, if vibrations take place only in one direction perpendicular to the direction of propagation of light, then it is said to be **linearly** or **plane polarized.**

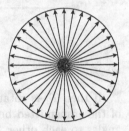

Fig. 24.1

There are two other types of polarized light, known as **circularly polarized** light and **elliptically polarized** light. In circularly polarized light, the vibrations are along a circle and in elliptically polarized light, the vibrations are along an ellipse, both lying in a plane perpendicular to the direction of propagation.

24.3 Representation of Unpolarized and Polarized Light

We know that an unpolarized light consists of vibrations in all directions with equal probability, in a plane normal to the direction of propagation. It is usually

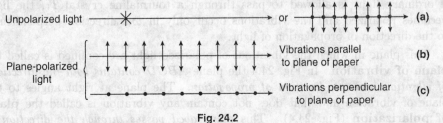

Unpolarized light ——————⁎—————————→ or ↑↑↑↑↑↑↑↑↑→ (a)

Plane-polarized light

↑↑↑↑↑↑↑↑↑ Vibrations parallel to plane of paper (b)
↓↓↓↓↓↓↓↓↓

•••••••••• Vibrations perpendicular to plane of paper (c)

Fig. 24.2

represented by a *star* or *dots* and *arrows,* as shown in Fig. 24.2(a). In polarized light, when the *vibrations* are parallel to the paper, it is indicated by a straight *arrow* as shown in Fig. 24.2(b).

On the other hand, if the *vibrations* lie in a direction perpendicular to the plane of the paper, it is represented by a *dot* as shown in Fig. 24.2(c).

24.4   Polarization of Light Wave

Let us take a tourmaline crystal T_1, cut parallel to the crystallographic axis and passed a beam of unpolarized light normally through it (Fig. 24.3). On rotating the crystal about the ray as the axis, the character of the light transmitted by it remains unaltered. Let now another similar crystal T_2 of tourmaline be kept parallel to the first. It is then observed that light is *almost completely transmitted* by the second crystal so that the intensity becomes *maximum* in this position of the crystal-pair.

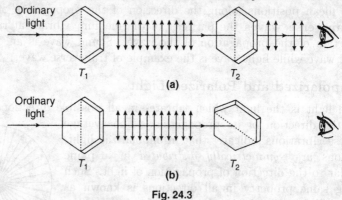

Fig. 24.3

If then T_2 is rotated about an axis parallel to the incident light, the intensity of the transmitted beam *decreases,* and becomes *zero,* when the axes are at right angles to each other. This reveals that no light is transmitted through the second crystal T_2. If the second crystal is rotated further, light is transmitted again and the intensity becomes maximum when both T_1 and T_2 are parallel.

This experiment demonstrates that when light is passed through the first crystal, it has acquired such a property as to prevent its passage through the second crystal when it is at a definite orientation. In practice, when light passes through the first crystal, it absorbs vibrations in all directions except those parallel to the crystallographic axis. Thus the unabsorbed vibrations are only transmitted. The transmitted light has vibrations in *one* direction only and so the transmitted light is *polarized*. The experiment further proves that *light is transverse* in nature.

24.5   Plane of Polarization

If ordinary light is allowed to pass through a tourmaline crystal T_1, the light becomes polarized and the vibrations occur only in *one* direction perpendicular to the direction of propagation of light.

This plane in which the vibrations of polarized light are confined is called the **plane of vibration**. In Fig. 24.4 the plane *ABCD contains both the directions of vibration and the direction of propagation.* The plane at right angles to the plane of vibration and that does not contain any vibration is called the **plane of polarization** (Fig. 24.4). This plane *abcd passes through the direction of propagation and is perpendicular to the plane of vibration.*

Various methods are there for producing plane polarized light. These are :

(i) By simple reflection,

(ii) By double refraction,

(iii) By dichroism or selective absorption.

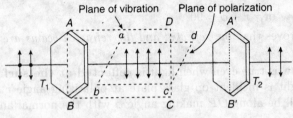

Fig. 24.4

A device used to divide the unpolarized light into two components and eliminates one of the two is known as a **polarizer.**

24.6   Brewster's Law

Malus noted that when unpolarized light is allowed to fall on the surface of a transparent material, both the reflected and the refracted beams are then partially plane polarized.

For a particular angle of incidence, called the **polarizing angle,** *the reflected beam is completely plane polarized.*

Brewster observed that there exists a simple relation between the polarizing angle ϕ and the refractive index μ of the reflector relative to the surrounding medium. This relation can be expressed as

$$\mu = \tan \phi. \qquad (24.1)$$

This is known as **Brewster's law.**

The polarizing angle of glass relative to air is nearly 57°. If we take $\mu_{glass} = 1.5$, then Brewster's law gives $\phi = \tan^{-1}(1.5) \simeq 57°$.

As a corollary to Brewster's law, one may say that if light is incident at the polarizing angle, the refracted beam is at right angles to the reflected beam. This can be proved in the following way :

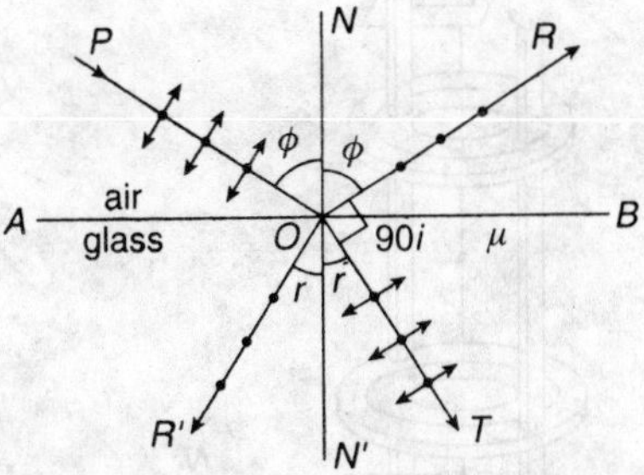

Let PO be the beam of unpolarized light incident on the surface AB of a transparent material at polarizing angle ϕ. OR and OT are the corresponding reflected and refracted beams and r be the angle of refraction (Fig. 24.5).

Fig. 24.5

Now, from Brewster's law, we can write,

$$\mu = \tan \phi = \frac{\sin \phi}{\cos \phi}. \qquad (24.2)$$

Again, by Snell's law, we get

$$\mu = \frac{\sin \phi}{\sin r}. \qquad (24.3)$$

Combining Eqs. (24.2) and (24.3), we get

$$\frac{\sin \phi}{\cos \phi} = \frac{\sin \phi}{\sin r}.$$

$$\therefore \quad \cos \phi = \sin r \quad \text{or,} \quad \sin(90° - \phi) = \sin r$$

$$\text{or,} \quad 90° - \phi = r \quad \text{or,} \quad r + \phi = 90°. \tag{24.4}$$

Eq. (24.4) proves that *the reflected and the refracted beams are at right angles to each other.*

Brewster's law is true even when light is **reflected at the surface of a rarer medium.** If light is incident on glass plate at polarizing angle r along TO, the refracted ray will be along OP making angle ϕ with the normal and the reflected ray along OR'.

Then the index of medium relative to air, μ, is written as

$$\frac{\sin r}{\sin \phi} = \frac{1}{\mu}.$$

Now we have

$$\tan r = \frac{\sin r}{\cos r} = \frac{\sin r}{\sin \phi} = \frac{1}{\mu}. \tag{24.5}$$

In the plane of incidence, ray OR' will be plane polarized.

24.7   Production and Detection of Polarized Light by Reflection

A very simple instrument that can be used to *produce* and *detect* plane polarized light by reflection is the **Biot's polariscope.** As shown in Fig. 24.6(a), it consists of two polished glass plates P_1, P_2 blackened on their back and mounted at the two ends of a cylindrical tube. The plates P_1 and P_2 can be rotated about the axis of the tube and also about a diameter of the cross-section of the tube. The amount of rotations can be recorded on circular scales.

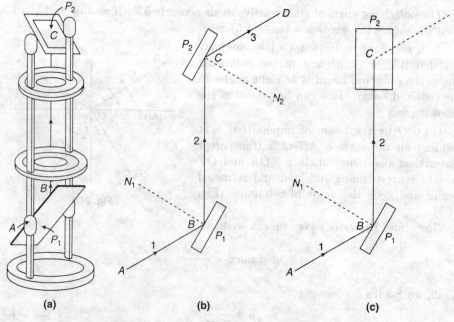

| (a) | (b) | (c) |

Fig. 24.6

If the planes of P_1 and P_2 are parallel to each other, the light is reflected from P_1 and P_2 [Fig. 24.6(b)]. When the incident ray 1 is incident at *polarizing angle* (57°), the reflected ray 2 is *completely plane polarized* with vibrations normal to the plane of incident of P_1. But P_2 being parallel to P_1, their planes of incidence are also parallel and the ray 2 incident on P_2 has its vibrations perpendicular to the plane of incidence of P_2. As only vibrations perpendicular to the plane of incidence are reflected, the intensity of the ray 3 reflected from P_2 will be *maximum*. However, if the plate P_2 is rotated about the ray 2 to have an orientation normal to P_1, the vibrations in ray 2 become parallel to the plane of incidence of P_2 and *no light* is reflected from P_2 in this orientation [Fig. 24.6(c)]. Thus by rotating P_2, the intensity of ray 3 is varied with *zero as minimum*. This implies that the ray 2 is *completely plane polarized*.

If light is incident on P_1 at an angle *other than* the polarizing angle, the ray 2 will only be *partially* polarized. In this situation, the intensity of ray 3, on rotating P_2, will vary between a *maximum* and a *non-zero minimum*. Therefore, in order to produce plane polarized light, the inclination of P_1 relative to the incident ray 1 is to be so adjusted that on rotating P_2, the intensity of ray 3 varies and is zero when $P_2 \perp P_1$.

Plate P_1 which makes the ray 2 polarized is known as the **polarizer** while the plate P_2 which demonstrates that the ray 2 is polarized is known as the **analyzer.**

24.8 Double Refraction

We know that if the refracting medium is isotropic, the physical properties are same in all directions. On the other hand, in *anisotropic substance*, particularly in crystals except those with cubic symmetry, the physical properties are different in different directions. Quartz calcite, tourmaline are examples of anisotropic materials. It has been noted that if a beam of un-polarized light AB is passed through a calcite crystal, the refracted light breaks up into *two refracted rays* (Fig. 24.7). One of these two rays obeys the laws of refraction whose vibrations are perpendicular to the principal section. This ray is known

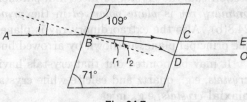

Fig. 24.7

as the **ordinary ray** (*O*-ray). The other ray does not follow the laws of refraction and has vibrations in the principal section. This ray is termed as **extraordinary ray** (*E*-ray). The optical phenomenon of splitting of light into two refracted rays is known as *double refraction,* and the crystal that shows this property is called *doubly refracting crystal.*

24.9 Calcite Crystal—Its Optic Axis and Principal Section

Calcite is a *colourless, transparent* crystal. It is chemically hýdrated *calcium carbonate,* $CaCO_3$, and is also called *iceland spar.*

In crystallography, it belongs to rhombohedral class of hexagonal system whose *six* faces are parallelograms, each with angles 101°55′ and 78°5′ [Fig. 24.8(a)]. At the *two* opposite corners A and B, the three obtuse angles (of 101°55′) meet which are called the **blunt corners.** At the six other corners, there is one obtuse and two acute angles.

Optic axis

A line passing through any one of the blunt corners (i.e., either A or B) and equally inclined to the three faces that meet at the corner gives the direction of the **optic axis** of the crystal. Thus, optic axis of a crystal is a direction and not any particular line and so an optic axis can be drawn through every point in the crystal.

The **characteristics** of the optic axis are the following :

(i) The crystal is symmetrical about the optic axis.

(ii) Optic axis is a direction and not any particular line.

(iii) The velocities of ordinary and extraordinary rays along the optic axis are same.

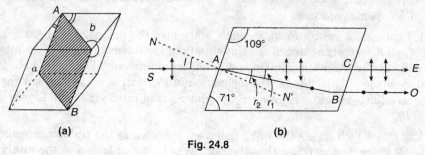

(a)   (b)

Fig. 24.8

Principal plane

A plane containing the optic axis and perpendicular to the two opposite faces is termed as a **principal plane** or **principal section** of the crystal. As there are six faces in the crystal, for every point inside the crystal, there are three principal sections, one for each pair of opposite faces. $AaBb$ is the principal plane for the top and the bottom face of calcite [Fig. 24.8(a)]. As shown in the figure, a principal section cuts the crystal surfaces in a parallelogram with angles 71° and 109°. The *ordinary ray* is *plane polarized* in the *principal plane* as shown by dots in Fig. 24.8(b). Also the extraordinary ray is plane polarized in a plane perpendicular to the principal plane, as shown by arrowed lines in Fig. 24.8(b).

It may be pointed out that crystals having one optic axis are called **uniaxial** *crystals*, e.g., quartz and calcite while crystals having two optic axis are known as **biaxial** *crystals*, e.g., mica.

Principal refractive indices of a crystal

In a crystal, the velocity of O-ray is constant, being same in all directions, while the velocity of E-ray is not a constant and changes with directions. However, both of them move with the same velocity along the optic axis.

Uniaxial crystals have *two principal refractive indices* μ_O and μ_E. μ_O corresponds to O-ray and μ_E corresponds to E-ray. They may be defined as :

$$\mu_O = \frac{\text{velocity of light in vacuo}}{\text{velocity of ordinary ray}}$$

$$\mu_E = \frac{\text{velocity of light in vacuo}}{\text{velocity of }E\text{-ray in a direction perpendicular to optic axis}}$$

For a **negative** crystal (e.g., calcite), the velocity of E-ray perpendicular to optic axis is highest and so, $\mu_E < \mu_O$.

For a **positive** crystal (e.g., quartz), the velocity of E-ray perpendicular to optic axis is the lowest and so, $\mu_E > \mu_O$.

24.9.1 Determination of μ_O and μ_E

As shown in Fig. 24.9, the uniaxial crystal prism ABC cut with optic axis perpendicular to the edge, is mounted on the prism table of the spectrometer so that O-image and E-image of the slit are seen by refraction through the prism. Each image is adjusted in succession by rotating the prism to its position of minimum deviation for O-ray and E-ray respectively. The angle of the prism A is determined by the usual method and then μ_E and μ_O are computed from

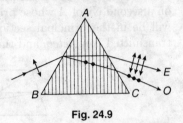

Fig. 24.9

$$\mu_E = \frac{(A + \delta_E)/2}{\sin A/2} \tag{24.6}$$

and $$\mu_O = \frac{\sin(A + \delta_O)/2}{\sin A/2}. \tag{24.7}$$

24.10 Nicol's Prism

A Nicol's prism, made out of a calcite crystal, is used both for the production and analysis of plane polarized light.

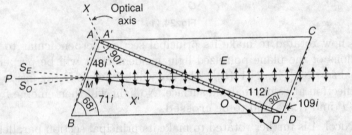

Fig. 24.10

$ABCD$ is a calcite crystal having a length to width ratio as $3:1$. The end faces AB and CD are properly grounded to make the angles in the principal section $68°$ and $112°$ in place of $71°$ and $109°$ respectively. The crystal is cut into two along the plane $A'D'$ perpendicular to both the principal section and the end faces. The two surfaces are polished to make them *optically flat* and then cemented together by using Canada balsam, a transparent liquid with index $\mu = 1.55$ for sodium light. The crystal is then enclosed in a tube blackened inside.

Action

Let a ray PM of unpolarized light almost parallel to BD' be incident on the face $A'B$. It splits into two refracted rays, MO and ME, inside the crystal. Both these rays are plane polarized. The O-ray has vibrations perpendicular to the principal section of the crystal and E-ray has vibrations in the principal section.

The refractive index of Canada balsam μ_C lies between μ_E and μ_O, i.e., $\mu_E < \mu_C < \mu_O$ ($\mu_E = 1.486$, $\mu_O = 1.658$). As a result, when O-ray reaches the balsam layer, it passes from a denser to a rarer medium. As the length of the crystal is large, the O-ray is usually incident at the calcite-balsam surface at an angle greater than its critical ($69°$). Hence it is totally reflected and is finally absorbed by the tube that encloses the crystal. On the other hand, the E-ray is transmitted by the calcite-balsam surface to emerge from the Nicol as plane polarized light with vibrations parallel to the principal section.

24.10.1 Nicol Prism as Polarizer and Analyzer

If an unpolarized ray is incident on a Nicol P, the emergent ray is plane polarized with vibrations in the principal section of P [Fig. 24.11(a)]. If this emergent ray falls on a second Nicol A whose principal section is parallel to that of P, the vibrations will be in the principal section of A. The ray, behaving as E-ray in it, will be transmitted *completely* and the intensity of the emergent light will be a *maximum*.

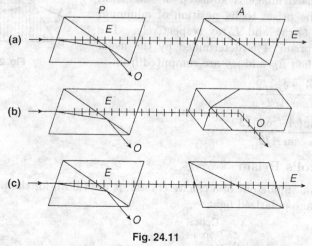

Fig. 24.11

If A is now rotated to make its principal section perpendicular to that of P, the vibrations of the plane polarized light incident on it will be perpendicular to its principal section [Fig. 24.11(b)]. The ray will behave as O-ray inside A and lost by *total* reflection at calcite-balsam surface. No light will then emerge from A, and the Nicols P and A are said to be **crossed**.

If the Nicol A is further rotated to make its principal section parallel to that of P, the intensity of the emergent light will be *maximum* again [Fig. 24.11(c)]. Thus, if the given light on viewing through a rotating Nicol shows intensity variation with *zero minimum*, then the given light is *plane polarized*. Nicol P is called the *polarizer* while the Nicol A is known as the *analyzer*.

A Nicol prism works when the incident beam is either *slightly convergent or slightly divergent* and *cannot* be used in highly convergent or divergent beams.

24.11   Wollaston Prism

Nicol prism is unsuitable to use with UV-light as the Canada balsam layer absorbs such radiation. Also, it is desirable sometimes to have both O-rays and E-rays widely separated. For this *Wollaston prism* is appropriate.

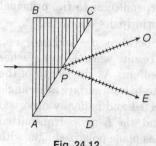

Fig. 24.12

It cosists of two right-angled prisms ABC and ADC of quartz cemented together with glycerine or castor oil (Fig. 24.12). The prism ABC has its optic axis parallel to the face AB while the second prism ADC is cut with its optic axis perpendicular to that of the first. The incident ray entering normally to the surface AB travels perpendicular to optic axis. As a result, O-rays and E-rays travel in the same direction but with different velocities. At the entry into the second prism, the roles of O-ray and E-ray are interchanged. The O-ray now becomes E-ray and conversely. Both the rays are thus deviated and dispersed causing greater separation between them.

24.12 Malus Law

It states that if a **completely** plane polarized light is incident on an analyzer, the intensity of the emergent light varies as the square of the cosine of the angle between the planes of transmission of the polarizer and the analyzer.

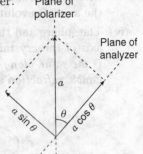

Fig. 24.13

Let a be the amplitude of light transmitted by the polarizer, and θ be the angle between the planes of transmission of the polarizer and the analyzer (Fig. 24.13). This plane polarized light is incident on the analyzer. Resolving amplitude a into two components, parallel and perpendicular to the plane of transmission of analyzer, we have

parallel component $= a \cos \theta$,

perpendicular component $= a \sin \theta$.

Out of the two components, only the parallel one, $a \cos \theta$, will be transmitted by the analyzer. Hence the intensity of light emerging from the analyzer is

$$I_\theta = a^2 \cos^2 \theta = I \cos^2 \theta, \tag{24.8}$$

where $I = a^2$, the intensity of incident plane polarized light. Eq. (24.8) is the **Malus law**.

Special cases

If the polarizer and analyzer are parallel to each other, $\theta = 0°$ or $180°$. Then,

$$I_\theta = I. \tag{24.9}$$

If on the other hand, the polarizer and the analyzer are perpendicular to each other, $\theta = 90°$. Then,

$$I_\theta = 0. \tag{24.10}$$

24.12.1 Experimental Verification of the Law

A beam of unpolarized light is passed through a pair of polaroids (a polarizer and an analyzer). The emergent beam is then passed into a photoelectric cell to measure the light intensity. With the light beam as axis, the analyzer is rotated and the *orientation* corresponding to *maximum* intensity of emergent beam is marked as $\theta = 0$. The intensities I_θ for various values of θ, relative to the above orientation, are next measured *photoelectrically*.

A plot of I_θ against $\cos^2 \theta$ is made. The graph so obtained is found to be a *straight line* which verifies Malus law.

24.13 Huygens Theory of Double Refraction

According to Huygens wave theory, each point on a wavefront is the source of new disturbance and sends secondary wavelets. Huygens original theory cannot explain double refraction in uniaxial crystals, and so he extended his theory of secondary wavelets to explain the phenomenon of double refraction. **Salient features** of his extended theory are :

(i) When a wavefront is incident on a doubly refracting crystal, every point on the crystal becomes the origin of *two wavefronts*, one the *ordinary* and the other *extraordinary rays* to account for the two types of rays.

(ii) Ordinary wavefront corresponds to ordinary rays obeying the laws of refraction and have the *same velocity in all directions* and thus the ordinary *wavefront* is *spherical*.

(iii) Extraordinary wavefront corresponds to extraordinary rays which do not obey the laws of refraction and have different velocities in different directions. Thus extraordinary wavefront is an ellipsoid of revolution, with optic axis as the axis of revolution.

(iv) The sphere and the ellipsoid touch each other at points that lie on the optic axis of the crystal as the *velocity of the ordinary and the extraordinary ray is the same along the optic axis*. Thus the uniaxial crystals do *not* show any *double refraction* along the optic axis.

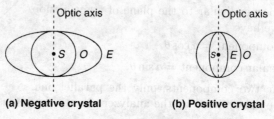

(a) Negative crystal   **(b) Positive crystal**

Fig. 24.14

(v) In **negative crystals** (like calcite and tourmaline), the ellipsoid lies outside the sphere (*S* being the source) [Fig. 24.14(a)]. This implies that in such crystals, the *extraordinary wavefront travels faster* than the ordinary wavefront except along the optic axis.

(vi) In **positive crystals** (like quartz and ice), the sphere lies outside the ellipsoid [Fig. 24.14(b)]. This implies that in such crystals the *ordinary wavefront travels faster* than the extraordinary wavefront except along the optic axis.

24.14   Dichroism and Polaroids

Some doubly-refracting crystals show the property of absorbing one of the doubly-refracting rays strongly and allowing the other to pass through with low loss. This phenomenon of selective absorption of light rays is known as **dichroism** and the crystals are called **dichroic.** Tourmaline is an example of such a crystal. It absorbs ordinary ray much more strongly than the extraordinary.

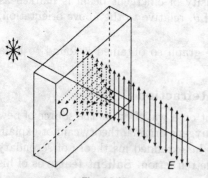

Fig. 24.15

When a ray of unpolarized light is passed on a tourmaline plate, it splits into two plane polarized ray—the *O*-ray and the *E*-ray (Fig. 24.15). The *O*-ray is completely absorbed by the plate, but the *E*-ray gets transmitted. Thus the emergent light is plane polarized.

A **polaroid** has a large polarizing film mounted between two glass sheets. The film is a thin sheet of nitro-cellulose packed with ultramicroscopic crystals. They act together as a single crystal of large dimensions. Such crystals are highly dichroic. They completely absorb one of the doubly- refracted beams within a thickness of 0.13 mm. Thus, if a beam of unpolarized light passes through the polaroid film, the emergent light is plane polarized. This can be verified by using a second polaroid.

Large-sized polaroids are manufactured from polyvinyl alcohol film by *stretching* it 3 to 8 times its original length. This makes them doubly-refracting. The film is then impregnated with iodine when it becomes *dichroic*. These are known as **H-polaroids.** If the stretched film is heated instead of iodine impregnation, it becomes strongly dichroic, dark and stable and it is called **K-polaroid.**

If two pieces of polaroids are *parallel*, the light transmitted by the first is also transmitted by the second. If they are crossed, there is a perfect extinction of light. This is shown in Fig. 24.16(a) and (b).

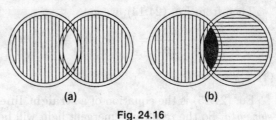

(a)   **(b)**

Fig. 24.16

Polaroids are cheaper than Nicols and they are used in the laboratory for *production* and *analysis* of plane polarized light. Polaroids are also used in *sun-glasses*.

24.15 Elliptically and Circularly Polarized Light

We assume that a plane polarized monochromatic light wave be incident *normally* on a *calcite crystal cut with its optic axis parallel to its faces*. Let A be the amplitude of incident vibration that makes an angle θ with the optic axis, so that the vibration is along PA, as shown in Fig. 24.17.

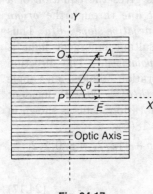

Fig. 24.17

Entering in the crystal at P, the light will break into (i) ordinary waves of amplitude $A\sin\theta$ with vibrations normal to the optic axis and (ii) extraordinary waves of amplitude $A\cos\theta$ with vibrations along the optic axis. The O- and E-waves will move in the crystal in the *same direction* but with *separate velocities* so that on emergence from the crystal of thickness d, a path-difference $d(\mu_o - \mu_e)$ is produced where μ_o is the refractive index of O-ray, and μ_e that of E-ray, for the crystal. As calcite is a *negative* crystal, $\mu_o > \mu_e$ and so the phase difference,

$$\delta = \frac{2\pi}{\lambda}d(\mu_o - \mu_e). \qquad (24.11)$$

Hence, the equation of the E- and O-waves are written as

$$x = A\cos\theta\sin(\omega t + \delta) = a\sin(\omega t + \delta) \qquad (24.12)$$

$$y = A\sin\theta\sin\omega t = b\sin\omega t, \qquad (24.13)$$

where ω is the frequency of vibrations.

From Eqs. (24.12) and (24.13), we get

$$\frac{x}{a} = \sin(\omega t + \delta) = \sin\omega t\cos\delta + \cos\omega t\sin\delta$$

$$= \frac{y}{b}\cos\delta + \sqrt{1 - \frac{y^2}{b^2}}\sin\delta, \text{ [using Eq. (24.13)]}$$

or, $\left(\dfrac{x}{a} - \dfrac{y}{b}\cos\delta\right)^2 = \left(1 - \dfrac{y^2}{b^2}\right)\sin^2\delta$

or, $\dfrac{x^2}{a^2} + \dfrac{y^2}{b^2} - \dfrac{2xy}{ab}\cos\delta = \sin^2\delta,$ (24.14)

which is the *general equation* of an **ellipse.**

Special cases.

    Case 1. If $\delta = 0,\ 2\pi,\ 4\pi,\ldots,$ we get, $\sin\delta = 0$ and $\cos\delta = 1.$

Then from Eq. (24.14), we get

$$\dfrac{x^2}{a^2} + \dfrac{y^2}{b^2} - \dfrac{2xy}{ab} = 0 \quad \text{or,} \quad \left(\dfrac{x}{a} - \dfrac{y}{b}\right)^2 = 0 \quad \text{or,} \quad \dfrac{x}{a} - \dfrac{y}{b} = 0$$

or, $y = \dfrac{b}{a}x.$ (24.15)

    Eq. (24.15) is the equation of a **straight line** through the *origin* with a *positive slope* b/a. So the resultant emergent light will be *plane polarized* with *vibrations* in the *same plane* as the *original incident light* [Fig. 24.18(a)].

    Case 2. If $\delta = \pi,\ 3\pi,\ 5\pi,\ldots,$ etc., we have $\sin\delta = 0$ and $\cos\delta = -1.$

Then from Eq. (24.14), we get

$$\dfrac{x^2}{a^2} + \dfrac{y^2}{b^2} + \dfrac{2xy}{ab} = 0 \quad \text{or,} \quad \dfrac{x}{a} + \dfrac{y}{b} = 0$$

or, $y = -\dfrac{b}{a}x.$ (24.16)

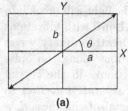
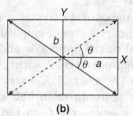

(a)   **(b)**

Fig. 24.18

This gives the equation of a *straight line* through the *origin* with a *negative slope* $-b/a$. Thus the resultant emergent light is *plane polarized*. The direction of vibration makes an angle $2\tan^{-1}(b/a) = 2\theta$ with incident light vibration. This is shown in Fig. 24.18(b).

    Case 3. If $\delta = \pi/2,\ 3\pi/2,\ 5\pi/2,\ldots,$ etc., i.e., $\delta = (2n+1)\pi/2,\ n = 0,1,2,\ldots,$ $\sin\delta = 1,\ \cos\delta = 0$ and Eq. (24.14) becomes

$$\dfrac{x^2}{a^2} + \dfrac{y^2}{b^2} = 1.$$ (24.17)

    Eq. (24.17) is the equation of a *symmetrical ellipse* with major axis and minor axis coinciding with the co-ordinate axes. Then the emergent light will be *elliptically polarized* (Fig. 24.19). The axes of the ellipse are along and perpendicular to the optic axis. For values of δ other than an integral multiple of π, the ellipse is rotated with respect to X- and Y-axes.

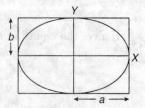

Fig. 24.19

    Case 4. If $\delta = \pi/2$ or, $3\pi/2$ and $\theta = 45°$, then incident light makes an angle $45°$ with optic axis, and we can write,

$$a = A\cos 45°;\ \ b = A\sin 45°, \quad \text{i.e.,} \quad a = b.$$

Hence, from Eq. (24.17), we get

$$x^2 + y^2 = a^2.$$ (24.18)

    This represents the equation of a *circle* and the emergent light will be *circularly polarized.*

24.16 Quarter-wave Plate

A plate of a doubly-refracting crystal of such a thickness so as to produce a path difference of $\lambda/4$ or a phase difference of $\pi/2$ between the ordinary and extraordinary waves is known as a **quarter-wave plate.** This is also called $\lambda/4$-*plate*.

Let us consider a plane parallel plate that can be obtained by cutting a doubly-refracting crystal with faces parallel to optic axis. A beam of light of wavelength λ be incident normally on it, so that the beam breaks up into O- and E-waves, both travelling along the same path perpendicular to the faces but with different velocities.

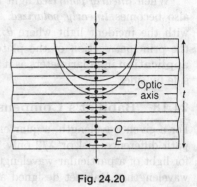

Fig. 24.20

For a **negative** crystal (e.g., calcite), E-wave moves faster than O-wave so that $\mu_o > \mu_e$, where μ_o is the principal index of the crystal for O-waves μ_e that for E-waves. If t be the thickness of the plate, then the path difference between the two waves on emergence is given by

$$\Delta = (\mu_o - \mu_e)t. \tag{24.19}$$

According to the definition of the quarter-wave plate, $\Delta = \lambda/4$.

$$\therefore \quad (\mu_o - \mu_e)t = \frac{\lambda}{4}$$

or, $\quad t = \dfrac{\lambda}{4(\mu_o - \mu_e)}.$ $\tag{24.20}$

If the crystal is positive (e.g., quartz), $\mu_e > \mu_o$ and so

$$t = \frac{\lambda}{4(\mu_e - \mu_o)}. \tag{24.21}$$

Therefore, a plate of thickness given by Eq. (24.20) or (24.21) acts as a *quarter-wave plate* for a given λ. With the *change in* λ, the *thickness* of the quarter-wave plate *will also be changed*.

Applications

Quarter-wave plates are used to produce *circularly* and *elliptically* polarized light. When used in conjunction with a Nicol, it becomes an analyzer and can *analyse* polarized light.

24.17 Half-wave Plate

A doubly-refracting plate of a crystal of such a thickness so as to produce a path difference $\lambda/2$, or a phase difference of π between the ordinary and extraordinary waves is known as a **half-wave plate** (or $\lambda/2$-*plate*).

If t be the thickness of a half-wave plate, then by definition, we have for a **negative** crystal (e.g., calcite)

$$(\mu_o - \mu_e)t = \frac{\lambda}{2}$$

or, $\quad t = \dfrac{\lambda}{2(\mu_o - \mu_e)}.$ $\tag{24.22}$

Similarly, for a **positive** crystal (e.g., quartz),

$$t = \frac{\lambda}{2(\mu_e - \mu_o)}. \tag{24.23}$$

When *linearly polarized* light is passed through a $\lambda/2$-plate, the emergent light also becomes *linearly polarized*. The direction of its vibration is inclined at 2θ with the incident light where θ is the angle between the incident vibration and the principal section of the plate. A half-wave plate thus finds very important **application** in polarimeters as it divides the field of view into two halves presenting side by side.

24.18   Babinet's Compensator

For a given wavelength, a quarter-wave plate or a half-wave plate produces a fixed path difference $\lambda/4$ or $\lambda/2$ only between the O-rays and the E-rays. It is useful for light of a particular wavelength and different plates are to be used for different wavelengths. Babinet designed a *compensator* which can be used for any desired path difference. This optical device is useful to produce and analyse elliptically polarized light.

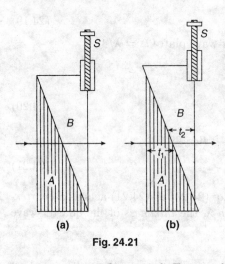

Fig. 24.21

Construction

It consists of two wedges A, B of quartz crystal, having equal small acute angles. They are placed with their hypotenuse-planes in contact for forming a rectangular block [Fig. 24.21(a)]. Of the wedges, the left one is cut with its optic axis perpendicular to the refracting edge, and the *right one* with its *optic axis parallel* to it. One of the wedges is fixed in position and the other one can be slid in its own plane by a micrometer screw S as shown in Fig. 24.21(b).

Theory

If plane polarized light falls normally on the first wedge A with its plane of vibration inclined at an angle θ with the optic axis, it breaks up into O-ray and E-ray, where E-ray moves slower than O-ray. After entering into the second wedge B, the O-ray becomes the E-ray and conversely. Thus the two components interchange their velocities in transit from one wedge to the other and as a matter of fact each wedge cancels the effect of the other.

If t_1, t_2 be the thicknesses of the wedges traversed by a ray and μ_e and μ_o be the indices of quartz for the E-ray and O-ray respectively, then the path difference introduced between the components by the first wedge,

$$\Delta_1 = t_1(\mu_e - \mu_o). \tag{24.24}$$

Similarly, the path difference introduced by the second wedge,

$$\Delta_2 = t_2(\mu_o - \mu_e). \tag{24.25}$$

Hence the resultant path difference,

$$\Delta = \Delta_1 + \Delta_2 = (\mu_e - \mu_o)(t_1 - t_2). \tag{24.26}$$

At the *centre* of the Babinet's compensator, $t_1 = t_2$, i.e., $\Delta = 0$. Thus the emergent light is *plane polarized* in the original plane.

On either side of the centre, the value of Δ gradually increases and depending on the values of $(t_1 - t_2)$ the emergent light will be polarized.

Uses of Babinet's Compensator

As the path difference and so the phase difference, of any desired value can be obtained at the centre of the compensator, we may get linearly, circularly or elliptically polarized light with the help of the compensator. It can be used also in the analysis of elliptically polarized light by proper calibration. It can be used to find some features of elliptically polarized light as stated below :

(i) Phase difference between its two components O and E,

(ii) Position of the major and minor axes, and

(iii) Ratio of the axes.

24.19   Circularly and Elliptically Polarized Light : Experimental Set-up

(a) Circularly polarized light : It is the resultant of two waves of equal amplitudes, vibrating at right angles to each other with a phase difference of $\pi/2$ or a path difference of $\lambda/4$. This can be obtained with the help of a *quarter-wave plate*.

The **experimental set-up** is shown in Fig. 24.22. A parallel beam of monochromatic light is incident on a Nicol prism N_1. The emergent light from N_1 is plane polarized. A second Nicol prism N_2 is placed at a certain distance in a *crossed position* relative to N_1 so that *no light is transmitted by N_2*.

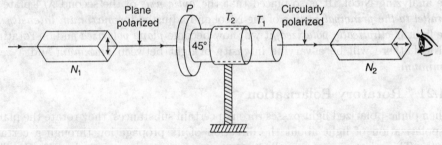

Fig. 24.22

Then a $\lambda/4$-plate P mounted on a tube T_1, the circumference of which is graduated in degrees. It is introduced between the Nicols N_1, N_2 and held *normal* to the incident beam. When $\lambda/4$-plate is placed between N_1 and N_2, there may be some light in the field of view of N_2. The $\lambda/4$-plate is now rotated till the field of view of N_2 becomes again dark. In this position, the *vibrations of light incident on $\lambda/4$-plate are parallel to its optic axis*. Also both E- and O-waves travel in the same direction but with different velocities. The $\lambda/4$-plate is now rotated through $45°$ with its optic axis to ensure that the amplitudes of E-wave and O-wave are same and also a *phase difference $\pi/2$* has been introduced between the two waves. Thus the resultant beam emerging out of the $\lambda/4$-plate will be **circularly polarized.**

(b) Elliptically polarized light : It is the resultant of two waves of *unequal amplitudes* vibrating at right angles to each other with a phase difference of $\pi/2$ (i.e., a path difference of $\lambda/4$).

A parallel beam of monochromatic light is incident on the Nicol prism N_1 and then the outgoing plane polarized light falls on the second Nicol N_2 in *crossed* position with N_1. Thus the field of view of N_2 is dark. The quarter-wave plate is then interposed between the Nicols and held normal to the incident beam. The field of view may now be bright again, due to interposition of $\lambda/4$-plate. The quarter-wave plate is rotated till the field of view is again dark. In this position, vibrations of light incident on quarter-wave plate are parallel to the optic axis of the plate and hence perpendicular to N_2.

The quarter-wave plate is rotated further so that the vibration of light incident on it makes an angle *other than* 45°. This ensures the amplitudes of ordinary and extraordinary rays *unequal* and thus the resulting light is **elliptically polarized.**

24.20   Detection of Circularly and Elliptically Polarized Light

(a) Detection of circularly polarized light : When the circularly polarized light is seen through a rotating Nicol, it exhibits no variation in intensity and hence resembles unpolarized light. In order to detect if the given light is circularly polarized or not, it is first passed through a quarter-wave plate with its *optic axis in any position.* The light that will emerge out of the quarter-wave plate will become *plane polarized* which is next examined by using a Nicol prism. If the Nicol, on rotation reveals a variation in intensity with *zero minimum*, then the original light is *circularly polarized.*

(b) Detection of elliptically polarized light : In order to detect if the light emerging out of the $\lambda/4$-plate is elliptically polarized or not, it is examined with a rotating Nicol and the Nicol is adjusted to the position of *maximum intensity*. Then a second quarter-wave plate is interposed between the first quarter-wave plate and the analyzing Nicol. It is so placed that the *optic axis* of the second $\lambda/4$-plate is *parallel to the principal section* of the Nicol and adjusted for *maximum intensity*. If the light is *elliptically polarized,* it will now become *plane polarized* and on rotating a Nicol, there will be a varying intensity of light between *maximum* and a *zero minimum.*

24.21   Rotatory Polarization

When plane-polarized light passes through certain substances, they rotate the plane of polarization of light about the direction of its propagation through a certain angle. This phenomenon is called *rotatory polarization or optical rotation*. The substances which rotate the plane of polarization are known as *optically active* and the property is the *optical activity*. Optically active substances include crystals (e.g., quartz), liquids (e.g., turpentine oil), organic substances in solution, etc. Optically active substances are of two types. Those which rotate the plane of polarization *clockwise* when looking *against* the direction of light are known as *dextro-rotatory* or *right-handed,* while those that rotate the plane of polarization *anticlockwise* on looking *against* the light are known as *laevo-rotatory* or *left-handed.* Quartz is a good example which occurs in both the forms.

Experimental detection

If plane-polarized light emerging from the Nicol N_1 is examined by passing through another Nicol N_2 *at cross* with N_1, the field of view is found to be totally dark (Fig. 24.23). If now a plate of quartz crystal C, cut with *optic axis perpendicular to its face* be interposed between N_1 and N_2 so that light is incident normally on C, then some light passes through N_2. In order to cut off the light completely, N_2 is to be *rotated* again through a certain angle which depends on the thickness of C. It proves that light emerging from quartz still remains plane-polarized but its plane of polarization has been rotated by the plate by a certain angle and so quartz is an optically active substance.

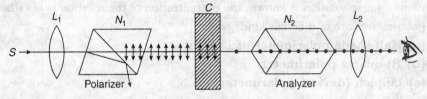

Fig. 24.23

24.22 Specific Rotation

Through some careful experiments on the phenomenon of optical rotation, Biot established the following laws :

(i) For a given wavelength, the *angle of rotation* of the plane of polarization is *directly proportional* to the *length* of the active substance *traversed*.

(ii) The *angle of rotation* for a given path length for *solutions* and *vapour* is *proportional* to the *concentration of the solution and vapour*.

(iii) The rotation produced by *a number of active substances* is equal to the *algebraic sum* of the *individual rotations*. The anticlockwise and clockwise rotations are to be taken with opposite signs.

(iv) The *angle of rotation* θ is nearly *inversely proportional* to the *square of the wavelength* λ. For quartz, this can be expressed as

$$\theta = A + B/\lambda^2, \tag{24.27}$$

where A and B are constants.

This indicates that if plane-polarized white light with vibration along AA, as shown in Fig. 24.24, be incident normally on a quartz plate, the different colours will be rotated by different angles and the field of view will appear coloured. The phenomenon is called **rotatory dispersion.**

(v) The *angle of rotation* of the plane of polarization further depends on the temperature of the active substance.

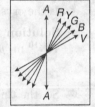

Fig. 24.24

From a consideration of the above characteristics, we may define **specific rotation** in the following way :

The specific rotation (S) of an optically active substance at a given temperature T and for a given wavelength λ of light may be defined as the rotation in degrees produced by one decimetre length of the substance in solution when its concentration is 1 g per cc.

Let θ be the rotation in degrees by l decimetre length of a solution and C be the concentration of the solution in g/cc. Then we can write,

$$(S)_\lambda^T = \frac{\theta}{l \times C} = \frac{\text{rotation in degrees}}{\text{length in decimetre} \times \text{concentration in g/cc}}.$$

The product of the specific rotation and the molecular weight of an active substance is called **molecular rotation.**

24.23   Polarimeter

It is an optical instrument used to measure the optical rotation of optically active substances. When used to find the optical rotation of sugar solution and to estimate the quantity of sugar in the solution, it is called a *saccharimeter*. When the specific rotation of sugar solution is known, the concentration of the solution is obtained.

Polarimeters are of different kinds, viz.,

(a) **Half-shade polarimeter of Laurent,**

(b) **Bi-quartz polarimeter,**

(c) **Lippich (device) polarimeter.**

In all the types, the *basic polarimeter* is *identical*. It is only to know exactly the correct position for complete darkness. Different attachments are used for the purpose, e.g., half-shade device in Laurent's half-shade polarimeter, bi-quartz arrangement in bi-quartz polarimeter, etc.

Examples

1. Calculate the thickness of a quarter-wave plate for light of wavelength 5893 Å. Given, $\mu_o = 1.544$ and $\mu_e = 1.553$.

   Solution : Given, $\lambda = 5893$ Å $= 5893 \times 10^{-10}$ m, $\mu_o = 1.544$ and $\mu_e = 1.553$. As $\mu_e > \mu_o$, the $\lambda/4$-plate is of a *uniaxial positive* crystal.

   Therefore, the thickness, $t = \dfrac{\lambda}{4(\mu_e - \mu_o)} = \dfrac{5893 \times 10^{-10}}{4(1.553 - 1.544)}$

   $$= \dfrac{5893 \times 10^{-10}}{4 \times 0.009} = \mathbf{0.1637 \times 10^{-4}\ m}.$$

2. Calculate the thickness of a half-wave plate for sodium light, given $\mu_o = 1.54$ and the ratio of velocity of ordinary and extraordinary components is 1.007. Is the crystal positive or negative?

   Solution : Given, λ = wavelength of sodium light = 5893 Å = 5893 × 10^{-10} m, $\mu_o = 1.54$. Again, $1.007 = v_o/v_e = \mu_e/\mu_o$.

   $\therefore \quad \mu_e = \mu_o \times 1.007 = 1.54 \times 1.007 = 1.551$

   So, the thickness of the $\lambda/2$-plate,

   $$t = \dfrac{\lambda}{2(\mu_e - \mu_o)} = \dfrac{5893 \times 10^{-10}}{2 \times (1.551 - 1.540)} = \mathbf{0.2679 \times 10^{-4}\ m}.$$

   As $\mu_e > \mu_o$, the crystal is positive.

3. Calculate the thickness of a half-wave plate for light of wavelength $\lambda = 5000$ Å; $\mu_o = 1.544$ and $\mu_e = 1.533$.

   Solution : Given, $\lambda = 5000$ Å $= 5000 \times 10^{-10}$ m; $\mu_e = 1.533$, $\mu_o = 1.544$.

   So, the thickness, $t = \dfrac{\lambda}{2(\mu_o - \mu_e)} = \dfrac{5000 \times 10^{-10}}{2(1.544 - 1.533)} = \mathbf{0.227 \times 10^{-4}\ m}.$

4. A beam of plane polarized light of wavelength 6000 Å is incident on a thin quartz-plate cut with faces parallel to the optic axis. Calculate the minimum thickness of the plate which introduces a phase difference of 60° between the O-rays and the E-rays. Given, $\mu_e = 1.553$, $\mu_o = 1.544$.

Solution : We know that a phase difference of 360° corresponds to a path difference of λ.

So the phase difference of 60° $\equiv$ a path difference $(\lambda/360) \times 60$ or, $\lambda/6$.

Hence, $t(\mu_e - \mu_o) = \lambda/6 \Rightarrow t = \dfrac{\lambda}{6(\mu_e - \mu_o)}$

$$= \dfrac{6000 \times 10^{-10}}{6 \times (1.553 - 1.544)} = \mathbf{0.111 \times 10^{-5}\ m}.$$

5. A beam of linearly polarized light is changed into a circularly polarized light by passing it through a slice of crystal 0.003 cm thick. Find the difference in the indices of two rays in the crystal, assuming it to be the minimum thickness that will produce the effect and that the wavelength is 6×10^{-7} m.

Solution : Given, $\lambda = 6 \times 10^{-7}$ m; $t = 0.003$ cm $= 3 \times 10^{-5}$ m. As a linearly polarized light changes into a circularly polarized one, the crystal plate has a thickness equal to that of a quarter-wave plate.

Hence, $t = $ minimum thickness of plate $= \dfrac{\lambda}{4(\mu_e \sim \mu_o)}$.

As we do not know whether the crystal is positive or negative, we use the difference sign ($\sim$) in the above formula.

$$\therefore \quad \mu_e \sim \mu_o = \dfrac{\lambda}{4t} = \dfrac{6 \times 10^{-7}}{4 \times 3 \times 1^{-5}} = \mathbf{0.005}.$$

6. In the above example, Ex. 5, calculate the minimum thickness of the plate for which the ordinary and the extraordinary waves will combine to produce a plane polarized light.

Solution : The ordinary and extraordinary waves will combine to form a plane polarized light on emergence from the plate under reference, only if the plate introduces a phase difference of π, i.e., a path difference of $\lambda/2$.

Let t be the required *minimum* thickness. Then according to the condition of the problem,

$$t(\mu_e - \mu_o) = \lambda/2$$

or, $t = \dfrac{\lambda}{2(\mu_e - \mu_o)} = \dfrac{6000 \times 10^{-10}}{2(1.553 - 1.544)}$

$$= \dfrac{6000}{2 \times 0.009} \times 10^{-10} = \mathbf{0.33 \times 10^{-5}\ m}.$$

7. Calculate the thickness of a quartz half-wave plate for the line 6563 Å for which the extraordinary and ordinary refractive indices are $\mu_e = 1.55085$ and $\mu_o = 1.54184$. **[C.U. 1997]**

Solution : As quartz is a positive crystal, $\mu_e > \mu_o$. Hence, if t be the thickness of the half-wave plate, we have

$$t = \dfrac{\lambda}{2(\mu_e - \mu_o)} = \dfrac{6563 \times 10^{-8}}{2(1.55085 - 1.54184)} = \dfrac{6563 \times 10^{-8}}{2 \times 0.00901} = \mathbf{3.64 \times 10^{-3}\ cm}.$$

8. Calculate the thickness of quarter-wave plate of quartz with $\lambda = 5.8 \times 10^{-7}$ m; $\mu_e = 1.553$ and $\mu_o = 1.544$. **[C.U. 1985]**

Solution : For a quarter-wave plate of quartz, we can write,

$$t = \frac{\lambda}{4(\mu_e - \mu_o)} = \frac{5.2 \times 10^{-7}}{4(1.553 - 1.544)} = \frac{5.9 \times 10^{-7}}{4 \times 0.009} = \mathbf{1.64 \times 10^{-5}\ m}.$$

9. A polarizer and an analyzer are oriented so that maximum amount of light is transmitted. To what fraction of its maximum value is the intensity of the transmitted light reduced when the analyzer is rotated through 60°?

   Solution : If I be the maximum intensity of the transmitted light, then according to the law of Malus we have

   $$I_1 = I \cdot \cos^2\theta = I \cdot (\cos 60°)^2 = \frac{1}{4}I.$$

   $$\therefore \quad \frac{I_1}{I} = \frac{1}{4} = \mathbf{0.25}.$$

10. A tube 20 cm long filled with a solution of cane sugar placed in the path of a polarized light, gives an optical rotation of 11°. Find the strength of the solution if the specific rotation of cane sugar is 66°. **[N.B.U. 2001]**

    Solution : We have $[S]_t^\lambda = \dfrac{10\theta}{l \cdot C}$. Here, $[S]_t^\lambda = 66°$; $l = 20$ cm; $\theta = 11°$.

    $$C = \frac{10 \times 11}{20 \times 66} = \frac{1}{12} = 0.0833$$

    $$\therefore \quad C = \mathbf{8.33\%}.$$

11. Two polaroids are adjusted so as to obtain maximum intensity. Through what angle should one polaroid be rotated to reduce the intensity to (i) half and (ii) one-fourth.

    Solution : From Malus law, we have $I_1 = I_0 \cos^2\theta$ or, $I_1/I_0 = \cos^2\theta$.

    (i) When $I_1/I_0 = 1/2$, $\cos^2\theta = 1/2$

    or, $\qquad \cos\theta = \pm 1/\sqrt{2}$ or, $\theta = \pm 45°; \pm 135°$.

    (ii) When $I_1/I_0 = 1/4$, $\cos^2\theta = 1/4$ or, $\cos\theta = \pm 1/2$

    or, $\qquad \theta = \pm 60°, \pm 120°$.

    Hence, the required angles of rotation are $\pm \mathbf{45°}, \pm \mathbf{135°}$ and $\pm \mathbf{60°}, \pm \mathbf{120°}$.

12. The refractive indices of calcite and Canada balsam are 1.658 and 1.550 respectively for ordinary ray. Calculate the maximum possible inclination with Canada balsam surface so that the ordinary ray is still quenched.

    Solution : We have $\mu_o = 1.658$ and $\mu_b = 1.550$. If C be the critical angle when ordinary ray proceeds from calcite towards balsam, then

    $$\sin C = \frac{1.550}{1.658} = 0.935 \implies C = 69.2°.$$

    So, O-ray if incident on balsam layer at an angle not exceeding 69.2° will not be quenched. Hence, required maximum possible inclination $= 90° - 69.2° = \mathbf{20.8°}$.

13. The critical angle of light in a certain substance is 45°. What is the polarizing angle?

Solution : The incident light moves in the denser medium. Let μ be the refractive index of the rarer (second) medium and C be the critical angle. Then we have

$$\mu = \sin C = \sin 45° = 1/\sqrt{2} = 0.707.$$

If ϕ be the polarizing angle, then using Brewster's law, we get

$$\tan \phi = \mu \quad \text{or,} \quad \phi = \tan^{-1} \mu = \tan^{-1}(0.707) = \mathbf{35.26°}.$$

14. A solution of camphor in alcohol in a tube 25 cm long is found to affect the rotation of the plane of vibration of light passing through it by 36°. What must be the density of camphor in g/cc of solution? Specific rotation of camphor is $+56°$.

Solution : Given, rotation $\theta = 36°$, sp. rotation $S = +56°$, l = length of solution = 25 cm = 2.5 decimetre.

If C be the concentration in g/cc, then

$$C = \frac{\theta}{S \times l} = \frac{36}{56 \times 2.5} = \mathbf{0.257 \ g/cc}.$$

Hence, density of camphor = 0.257 g/cc = $\mathbf{0.257 \times 10^3 \ kg/m^3}$.

15. The rotation in the plane of polarization ($\lambda = 5893$ Å) in a certain substance is 10° per cm. Calculate the difference between the refractive indices for right-handed and left-handed circularly polarized light in the substance.

Solution : If t cm be the thickness of the substance and μ_R and μ_L the indices for right and left circularly polarized light in it, then the rotation θ in the plane of polarization is

$$\theta = \frac{\pi}{\lambda}(\mu_R \sim \mu_L)t \quad \text{or,} \quad \mu_R \sim \mu_L = \frac{\theta}{t} \cdot \frac{\lambda}{\pi}.$$

In this case, $\theta/t = 10°/$ cm $= (10 \times 2\pi/360)$ rad/cm; $\lambda = 5893 \times 10^{-8}$ cm.

Therefore, $\mu_R \sim \mu_L = \dfrac{10 \times 2\pi}{360} \times \dfrac{5893 \times 10^{-8}}{3.142} = 409 \times 10^{-7}$.

16. The plane of polarization of plane polarized light is rotated through 6.5° in passing through a length of 2.0 decimetre of sugar solution of 5% concentration. Calculate the specific rotation of the sugar solution.

Solution : Given, $\theta = 6.5°$, $l = 2.0$ decimetre, $C = 5\% = 0.05$ g/cc. Therefore, the specific rotation,

$$S = \frac{\theta}{l \times C} = \frac{6.5°}{2.0 \text{ dm} \times 0.05 \text{ g/cc}} = 65° \ (\text{dm})^{-1} \ (\text{g/cc})^{-1}.$$

17. A 20 cm long tube is filled with a solution of 15 g of cane sugar in 100 cc of water. Find the angle of rotation of the plane of polarization of a beam of plane-polarized light when it passes through the solution. Specific rotation for cane sugar = 65.5° per dm per g/cc.

Solution : We have the specific rotation,

$$S = \frac{\theta}{l \times C} \Rightarrow \theta = S \times l \times C.$$

In this case, $S = 66.5° \ (\text{dm})^{-1} \ (\text{g/cc})^{-1}$; $C = \dfrac{15}{100}$ g/cc;

$$l = 20 \text{ cm} = 2.0 \text{ dm}.$$

$$\therefore \quad \theta = 66.5° \times 2.0 \times (15/100) = 20°.$$

18. A certain length of 5% solution causes an optical rotation of 20°. How much length of 10% solution of the same substance will cause rotation of 35°?

Solution : If S be the specific rotation of the solution, l_1 the length of 5% solution causing 20° optical rotation and l_2 the length of 10% solution causing 35° optical rotation, then

$$S = \frac{\theta_1}{l_1 \times C_1} = \frac{\theta_2}{l_2 \times C_2} \Rightarrow \frac{20°}{l_1 \times 5\%} = \frac{35°}{l_2 \times 10\%}$$

$$\therefore \quad l_2 = \frac{5\% \times 35°}{10\% \times 20°} l_1 = \frac{7}{8} l_1.$$

Questions

Essay-type

1. Describe a method of polarizing a beam of light by reflection.

[C.U. 1920; N.B.U. 2001]

2. Write a short essay on polarization of light.

3. Explain the principle and working of Biot's polariscope. What is Malus' law?

[N.B.U. 1982; C.U. 2004]

4. State Brewster's law. Show that the angles of incidence and refraction are complementary when maximum polarization is obtained by reflection at a plane glass surface.

5. Enumerate the steps you would follow to investigate qualitatively a beam of light for polarization characteristics. The beam may contain **(a)** unpolarized and plane-polarized light, **(b)** unpolarized and elliptically polarized light and **(c)** circularly polarized light only.

6. Give an account of Huygens theory of double refraction in a uniaxial crystal. What are positive and negative crystals? Name a crystal of each type.

7. Describe the construction of a Nicol prism and explain how it acts as **(a)** a polarizer and **(b)** an analyzer. [C.U. 1999; B.U. 2004; Tripura 1990]

8. Describe the construction and action of a Nicol prism. [C.U. 1963, '67, '87]

9. Describe an arrangement for determining accurately the optical activity of liquids. To what practical uses does its study lead?

10. Describe a half-shade polarimeter and explain the action of its optical parts.

11. What is optical activity? State with example the classification of optically active substances. [C.U. 2001]

12. Describe Laurent's half-shade polarimeter. In what respect is a bi-quartz better than a half-shade plate?

13. What is Babinet's compensator? Explain how this can be used to produce **(i)** circularly polarized, **(ii)** elliptically polarized beams.

14. Show that a beam of plane-polarized light can be regarded as being composed of two equal and opposite circularly polarized lights.

Short Answer-type

15. What is plane of polarization and in which of the types of waves—longitudinal and transverse—can it occur?

16. Explain the terms :

    (a) Polarized light;   **(b)** Plane of polarization ;

    (c) Extraordinary ray;   **(d)** Optic axis.   **[C.U. 1985]**

17. Distinguish between polarized and unpolarized light.   **[N.B.U. 2001]**

18. State Brewster's law. Prove that when light strikes a plane parallel glass plate at the polarizing angle, refracted beam also falls on the second surface at its polarizing angle.   **[C.U. 1999]**

19. What are half-wave and quarter-wave plates?   **[C.U. 1999]**

20. What is doubly refracting crystal? What is the difference between ordinary and extraordinary rays? Distinguish between positive and negative crystals.

21. Two polarizing sheets initially have their polarization directions parallel. Through what angle ‚must one sheet be turned so that the intensity of transmitted light is reduced to a third of the original intensity?

22. What is optical activity? Define specific rotation for both solids and solution.   **[C.U. 2001, '03]**

23. What is elliptically polarized light? Can its transmission be prevented by an analyzer?

24. What are polaroids? Mention some of the uses of polaroids.

25. What is a half-shade plate? What is the difference between a half-shade plate and a bi-quartz plate?

Review Questions

26. What is meant by an elliptically and a circularly polarized light?

27. How are eliptically and circularly polarized light produced light experimentally?

28. How would you analyse plane polarized, circularly polarized and the elliptically polarized light?

29. How would you distinguish between elliptically polarized light and a mixture of plane polarized and unpolarized light?

30. How is circularly polarized light distinguished from the unpolarized light?

31. How can you convert **(a)** elliptically polarized light into circularly polarized light and **(b)** plane polarized light into circularly polarized light?

32. Give the theory and construction of a quarter-wave plate.

33. What is meant by elliptically and circularly polarized light?

34. How can you convert plane polarized light into a circularly polarized light?

35. What is the nature of the emergent light when circularly polarized light is passed through **(a)** a quarter-wave plate and **(b)** a half-wave plate?

36. How will you detect plane polarized light from partially polarized light?

37. "A rotation Nicol fails to distinguish between circularly polarized and unpolarized lights." Explain this and discus how to distinguish between the two.

38. "A rotating Nicol fails to distinguish between elliptically polarized and partially polarized light." Explain this and discuss how to distinguish between the two.

39. If you are given a quarter-wave plate, a half-wave plate and a simple glass plate, how will you proceed to distinguish them from each other?

40. "Polarization requires that vibrations are transverse"—comment on the statement.

41. What do you understand by the following terms—

(a) polarization of light, (b) plane of vibration and (c) plane of polarization?

42. Light waves can be polarized but sound waves cannot. Why?

43. Explain the terms : optic axis, principal plane, uniaxial crystal, positive crystal and negative crystal.

44. State and prove Brewster's law. State and explain Malus law.

45. What is dichroism? What are polaroids? Give some of their applications. What is meant by H-polaroid?

46. What is birefringence? Explain double refraction and ordinary and extraordinary rays.

47. Write a few lines on Wollaston prism.

48. What is the greatest importance of polarization ?

49. What do you conclude about the nature of light from polarization ?

50. Explain what do you understand by the principal refractive index.

51. What is the difference between positive and negative crystals?

Numerical Problems

52. Refractive index of glass is 1.5. Calculate the Brewster's angle for it. Also calculate the angle of refraction.   [N.B.U. 2000]

[**Ans.** 56°; 33°30′]

53. Calculate the polarizing angle for diamond surface, if the angle of refraction of a beam of light through it is 12° when the incident beam makes an angle of 60°.   [**Ans.** 76.5]

54. The angle of refraction of an unpolarized beam of light, incident at a polarizing angle on a glass block is 32.5°. Calculate the refractive index of glass.

[K.U. 2003]

[**Ans.** 1.57]

55. It is found that when light is incident on a glass block, the reflected beam is completely plane polarized when the angle of incidence is 57°. What is the refractive index of glass?   [**Ans.** 1.54]

56. Light reflected from a smooth ice surface, is found to be completely polarized. Find the angle of incidence of light, if the refractive index of ice is 1.309.

[C.U. 2005]

[**Ans.** 52°36′ (approx.)]

57. Determine the Brewster's angle for glass of refractive index 1.5 immersed in water of refractive index 1.33.   [**Ans.** 48.5°]

58. The refractive index of glass is 1.5. Calculate Brewster's angle for it. Also calculate the angle of refraction. [**Ans.** 56.3°; 33.7°]

59. The angle of polarization is found to be 62°24′ with a slab of flint glass. What is the refractive index of flint glass? [**Ans.** 1.9128]

60. The critical angle for refraction for a transparent substance to air is 40°. Calculate the polarizing angle of the substance. [**Ans.** 57.3°]

61. Two Nicol prisms are so arranged that the amount of light transmitted through them is maximum. What will be the percentage reduction in intensity of incident light when the analyzer is rotated through

(a) 30°, **(b)** 45°, **(c)** 60° and **(d)** 90°? [**Ans.** 25%, 50%, 75%, 100%]

62. If the angle between a polarizer and an analyzer is 60°, what will be the intensity of light transmitted having I_0 as the original intensity of the incident light?

63. The polarizing angle of a medium is 60°. What is the critical angle for it? [**Ans.** 25°16′]

64. An analyzing Nicol examines two adjacent plane polarized beams of light A and B with their planes of polarization at right angles to each other. In one position of the analyzer, the beam B shows zero intensity. A rotation by 30° from this position shows the beams to be matched (i.e., equal). What is the intensity ratio of the beams? [**Ans.** 1 : 3]

65. The critical angle of a transparent crystal for green light is found to be 24.4°. Find the angle of polarization . [**Ans.** 65°50′]

66. At what angle the light should be incident on a glass plate ($\mu = 1.5697$) to get a plane polarized light by reflection. [**Ans.** 57°30′]

67. Determine the wavelength of light used when a quarter-wave plate of thickness 1.2×10^{-5} cm is used for detection. Given, $\mu_o = 1.65$ and $\mu_e = 1.64$. Is the crystal plate positive? [**Ans.** 4800 Å; No]

68. Calculate the thickness of a quartz plate for C-line of wavelength 6563 Å. Given, $\mu_o = 1.5418I$. Is the crystal positive? [**Ans.** 3.63×10^{-5}m; Yes]

69. Calculate the thickness of a **(i)** a quarter-wave plate and **(ii)** a half-wave plate, given that $\mu_e = 1.5333$, $\mu_o = 1.544$ and $\lambda = 5000$ Å.
[**Ans.** 1.136×10^{-5}m; 2.272×10^{-5} m]

70. A plane polarized beam of light is incident on a quartz plate cut with faces parallel to the axis. Find the least thickness for which the O-ray and the E-ray will combine to form plane polarized light. Given, $\mu_o = 1.5442$ and $\mu_e = 1.5533$ and $\lambda = 5000$ Å. [**Ans.** 2.748×10^{-5} m]

71. The faces of a quartz plate are parallel to the optic axis of the crystal. What is the thinnest possible plate that would make the ordinary and the extraordinary rays of $\lambda = 5890$ Å, a half-wave apart on their exit? What multiple of this thickness would give the same result? Given, $\mu_e = 1.553$ and $\mu_o = 1.544$. [**Ans.** 3.27×10^{-5} m; n-multiples, whose $n = 1, 3, 5$, etc.]

72. Plane polarized light of wavelength 6000 Å is incident on a thin quartz plate cut with faces parallel to the optic axis. Calculate the ratio of the intensities of the O-ray and the E-ray if the plane of vibration of two incident lights makes an angle of 30° with optic axis. Given, $\mu_o = 1.544$, $\mu_e = 1.53$.

[**Ans. 3 : 1**]

73. Calculate the thickness of a crystal sheet required for making a quarter-wave plate for $\lambda = 5460$ Å. The indices of refraction of the ordinary and the extraordinary rays in the crystal are 1.586 and 1.592.

[**Ans.** 2.275×10^{-4} m]

74. A 10 cm long tube containing 20% sugar solution produces an optical rotation of 13.2°. Find the specific rotation. [**Ans. 66°**]

75. A 20 cm long glass tube is filled with solution of sugar, containing 20 g of sugar in 100 ml of water. The plane of polarized light, passing through the solution, in rotated through 26.2°. Find specific rotation of sugar.

[**Ans. 65.5°**]

76. A 22 cm long tube containing 88 cc of sugar solution produces an optical rotation of 9.9° when placed in a polarimeter. If the amount of sugar in the solution is 6 g, find the specific rotation. [**Ans. 66°**]

77. For a given wavelength, one millimetre of quartz cut perpendicular to the optic axis rotates the plane of polarization by 20°. Find for what thickness will no light of this wavelength be transmitted when the quartz piece is interposed between a pair of parallel Nicols. [**Ans. 4.5 mm**]

78. On putting a polarimeter tube 25 cm long containing sugar solution of unknown strength, the plane of polarization is rotated through 10°. Find the strength of sugar solution. Specific rotation of sugar is 60°/dm/unit concentration. [**Ans. 6.67%**]

79. Calculate the required thickness of a quartz crystal whose faces are perpendicular to the optic axis in order to produce a rotation of 43.5° for $\lambda = 5893$ Å. The specific rotation in quartz for this wavelength is 21.72°/mm. [**Ans. 2.00 mm**]

80. The refractive indices of quartz for right-handed and left-handed circularly polarized sodium light propagating along the optic axis are 1.54420 and 1.54427 respectively. Calculate the specific rotation of quartz. Take $\lambda = 6 \times 10^{-5}$ cm. [**Ans. 21°/mm**]

81. The indices of refraction of quartz for right-handed and left-handed circularly polarized light of $\lambda = 7620$ Å are 1.53914 and 1.53920 respectively. Calculate the rotation of plane of polarization of the light in degrees produced by a plate 0.5 mm thick. [**Ans. 7.1°**]

82. Calculate the specific rotation of sugar solution if the plane of polarization is rotated by 13.2°. The length of the tube containing sugar solution is 20 cm and 5 g of sugar is dissolved in 50 cc of water. [**Ans.** $66°$ $(dm)^{-1}$ $(g/cc)^{-1}$]

83. A sugar solution in a tube of length 20 cm produces an optical rotation of 13°. The solution is then diluted to one-third of its previous concentration. Find the optical rotation produced by 30 cm long tube containing the diluted solution. [**Ans. 6.5°**]

84. A tube of sugar solution 20 cm long is placed between crossed Nicols and illuminated with light of wavelength 6×10^{-5} cm. If the optical rotation produced is 13° and the specific rotation $S = 65°$/dm/g/cm³, determine the strength of the solution. [**Ans. 10%**]

Chapter 25
Spectroscopy

25.1 Introduction

We need to have some knowledge of the nature of light so that the behaviour of prisms and lenses can be clearly understood. As all monochromatic light are coloured, white light which has no colour must be a compound one. Light from the sun, and various other common white lights, like carbon arc light, gas light, electric incandescent light 'show similarity in their composition and they are found to contain practically all types of monochromatic light. Spectroscopy is an analysis of electromagnetic spectrum by wavelength or frequency.

25.2 Newton's Experiment on Sunlight

The fact that the light coming from the sun is of composite character was first demonstrated by Newton in 1676.

In performing the experiment a narrow beam of sunlight was admitted into a darkened room through a narrow slit in a shutter (Fig. 25.1). It is then allowed to fall on a glass prism with its refracting edge parallel to the slit. Instead of a white image of the slit, Newton found a coloured band of seven different colours, on the screen placed in the path of the emergent rays. This coloured band is known as *spectrum* and

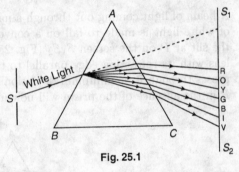

Fig. 25.1

consists of **violet, indigo, blue, green, yellow, orange** and **red** colours. Of these, the violet is the most deviated and red the least. This phenomenon of breaking up of white light into several constituent colours is called *Dispersion*.

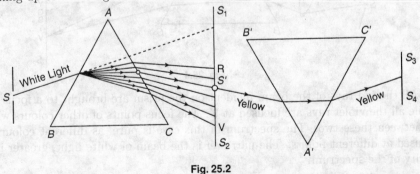

Fig. 25.2

Taking one of the constituents in the emergent beam and allowing it to be deviated by a second prism (Fig. 25.2), Newton observed that no further dispersion of different colours can be produced.

601

25.3   Impure and Pure Spectrum

The spectrum ordinarily produced by a prism is impure since in it the different constituent colours overlap each other. The spectrum in which there is overlapping of different colours is known as **impure spectrum.** A spectrum in which there is no overlapping of constituent colours and in which these colours are distinctly separated, is known as a **pure spectrum.**

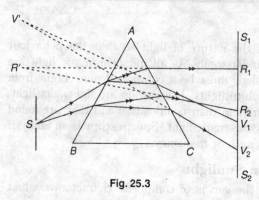

Fig. 25.3

In Fig. 25.3, a broad beam of light from source S is shown. Two extreme rays fall on the prism ABC and these rays produce two separate spectra R_1V_1 and R_2V_2. They overlap each other and thus the spectrum becomes impure. If the slit S be very narrow, the width of the incident beam diminishes reducing the width of R_1V_1 and R_2V_2. Then the spectrum will nearly pure with very little overlapping.

25.4   Methods of Producing Pure Spectra

A beam of light coming out through a narrow slit S illuminated by a strong source of white light is made to fall on a convex achromatic lens L to form an image of the slit at P on the screen S_1S_2 (Fig. 25.4). A prism ABC is kept in front of the lens with its refracting edge parallel to the slit. As a result the mean ray (yellow) passes through it at minimum deviation. Each ray which would have converged to P in the absence of the prism will now undergo both deviation and dispersion.

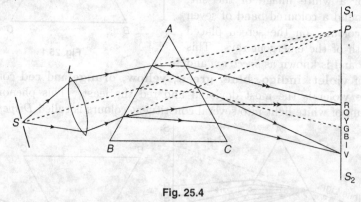

Fig. 25.4

All the red rays of the beam incident on the prism are brought to a focus at R while all the violet rays are focused at V. The focus points of other colours will be in between these two. The spectrum in this case is pure, as different colours are focused at different points. The narrower is the beam of white light, greater is the purity of the spectrum.

In a modified method the achromatic lens is placed between the screen and the prism (Fig. 25.5). The prism is then adjusted for minimum deviation of the mean ray. The dispersed beam of violet rays appears to diverge from a point V', the virtual image of the slit produced by the violet rays. The whole beam is brought to a focus at V on the screen. The beam of red rays emerging from the prism appear to diverge from R' is focused at R on the screen. Rays of other colours appear to diverge in between V' and R' and are focused by the lens at intermediate points between V and R on the screen. The spectrum RV thus obtained is pure without overlapping.

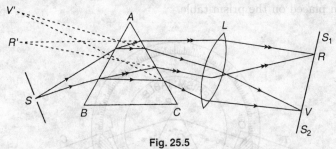

Fig. 25.5

25.4.1 Ideal Arrangement to Produce Pure Spectrum

An achromatic convex lens L_1 is placed at a distance equal to the focal length of the lens from the slit S illuminated by white light. The emergent parallel rays are received by the prism which is placed in the position of minimum deviation. The dispersed rays coming out of the prism will proceed in parallel directions. A second achromatic lens L_2 is kept beyond the prism to bring different groups of parallel rays to different foci, violet at V and red at R. The focus points of other colours are in between them and thus a real pure spectrum is formed on the screen.

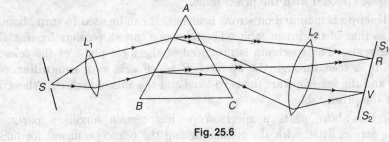

Fig. 25.6

In order to produce pure spectrum the following conditions should be satisfied :

(i) The slit should be narrow.

(ii) An achromatic convex lens should be placed between the slit and the prism, so that the slit is at the principal focus of the lens and a parallel emergent beam may fall on the prism.

(iii) The prism should be kept in the position of minimum deviation for the mean ray.

(iv) An achromatic convex lens should be kept beyond the prism to bring the coloured rays to different foci forming a real, pure spectrum on a screen.

25.5 Spectroscope

It is an instrument used for the production and study of different spectra. A spectroscope is shown in Fig. 25.7. It has the following essential parts :

(a) The **Collimator**, (b) The **Prism Table** and (c) The **Telescope**.

The *collimator* consists of metal tube with a convex achromatic lens facing the prism table. At the other end of the tube there is a small metal tube with a vertical slit of adjustable width. The small tube can be slided within the outer tube by rack and pinion screw. Thus the distance between the slit and the lens can be altered. The slit is illuminated by the source of light to be studied. It should be at the focal plane of the lens, so that the collimator can produce a parallel beam to be received by the prism placed on the prism table.

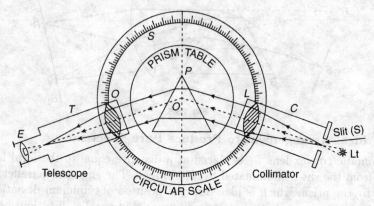

Fig. 25.7

The **prism table** is a thick metal disc. It is provided with levelling screws, to turn about a vertical axis. The prism table is attached with verniers moving along a circular scale co-axial with the prism table.

The **telescope** is mounted on strong bearings. It can be used to turn about the same axis as that of the prism table. The telescope carries verniers moving along the circular scale. The spectrum is produced at the focal plane of the telescope objective. It is seen through the eyepiece E which acts as a **magnifier.** The collimator and the telescope are made co-axial and the axis of each cuts the axis of rotation of the prism table.

Besides the above parts a spectroscope has certain auxiliary parts, like (i) levelling screws fitted with the collimator and the telescope meant for making their axis horizontal, (ii) three levelling screws beneath the supporting base of the instrument for making the axis of rotation of the telescope and the prism table vertical, (iii) three levelling screws below the prism table to make the prism table horizontal, (iv) fixing screws to fix the prism table or the telescope at any required position and (v) screws called *tangent screws* to permit slow motion of the telescope or the prism table after they have been fixed in certain position.

The spectrometer and spectroscope are essentially similar apparatus and each is referred to as spectroscope. A spectrometer have a graduated circular scale and when there is no such scale a spectrometer is called a *spectroscope*. A spectrometer is employed for measurement of refractive index than for the investigation of different spectra which is done by a spectroscope.

25.6   Infrared and Ultraviolet Spectra

The portion of the spectrum beyond the visible red is significant for its *heating effect* and is called the *infrared* spectrum. This was discovered by *Herschel* in 1800 by keeping a delicate thermometer with a blackened bulb in this region. The rise in temperature indicated the absorption of heat. Later, the region has been thoroughly investigated by *Langley* by using a delicate instrument called **Bolometer.** As glass is a good absorbent of these rays, prisms of rock-salt or flour-spar are used for studying this region of the spectrum. As infrared rays penetrate the atmosphere, they are used for photographing of landscapes and objects situated a great distance away.

The portion of the spectrum beyond the visible violet is called the *ultraviolet* spectrum. The wavelengths in this region are too short to excite the nerves of the eye but are capable of decomposing silver salts of photographic emulsions. This was first noted by Scheel. As glass absorbs ultraviolet rays, the glass prism and lenses of the collimator and telescope of the ordinary spectrometer may be replaced by prism and lenses of *quartz* for studying the ultraviolet spectrum. Ultraviolet waves have a penetrating influence and are used in medicine. They cause certain substances like quinine, paraffin oil, etc. to fluoresce and they can ionise gases.

25.7 The Complete Spectrum

The radiation from the sun and other sources is not limited to the region of visible spectrum whose wavelengths range only about 7×10^{-5} cm for the extreme red to about 3.9×10^{-5} cm for the extreme violet. The infrared radiation has been detected and studied up to wavelengths as long as 10^{-2} cm, while radiations beyond the visible violet have been studied up to wavelengths as short as 10^{-6} cm.

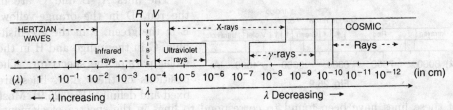

Fig. 25.8

Beyond ultraviolet radiations, another shorter radiation (X-rays) has been found. These X-rays consist of wavelengths ranging from 10^{-7} cm to 10^{-9} cm. Again beyond X-rays, radiations known as γ-rays are emitted by radioactive atoms have been detected and they have wavelengths as short as 10^{-10} cm. The cosmic rays discovered by *Millikan* were supposed to originate from the birth of helium and some other atoms in celestial bodies in space at exceedingly low pressure and temperature have the shortest wavelength of about 2×10^{-12} cm.

Beyond infrared radiations, electromagnetic Hertzian waves known as *radio waves* of wavelengths ranging from 10^{-1} cm to 10^{-7} cm have been found, which are produced by oscillations of electricity in the transmitting aerial. These waves show the phenomena of polarization, interference, reflection, refraction, etc. The radiations are all alike in nature but they differ in their wavelengths only. Gradation of wavelength is shown in Fig. 25.8.

25.8 Absorption of Light

If light is allowed to fall on the surface of a transparent substance, part of the light is reflected, part is absorbed, and the rest is transmitted unchanged. The amount of light reflected or absorbed depends on the substance itself over which it falls. Lamp black and platinum black do not reflect any light, neither they transmit it, but they absorb waves of all lengths, except the very longest. This type of absorption is known as **general absorption.** On the other hand, certain substances instead of absorbing the whole amount of light falling on them, absorb a part and the amount of this absorption is different for different wavelengths. This type of absorption is known as **selective absorption.**

To find the nature of absorption, a beam of white light is passed through the given substance and the transmitted light is observed by a spectroscope. When the substance shows selective absorption, i.e., if it absorbs light of one wavelength more strongly than other, the spectrum will be crossed by a number of dark lines corresponding to the colours which have been absorbed.

25.9   Fraunhofer Lines

If we carefully investigate the solar spectrum, we will find that a large number of dark lines cross the whole length of the spectrum. The existence of these dark lines were first noticed by *Wollaston* in 1802, but *Fraunhofer* made a very systematic study of these lines. He mapped them and denoted these marked lines by several letters such as A, *a*, B, C, D, E, *b*, F, G, H. These lines are known as **Fraunhofer lines.** Fraunhofer counted in the spectrum more than 600 dark lines. They are more or less distinct but distributed irregularly from the extreme red to the extreme violet colour.

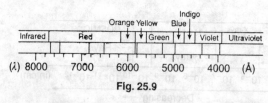

Fig. 25.9

The lines A, B and C are in the red, D in the orange-yellow, E in the green, F in the greenish-blue, G in the indigo and H in the violet part of the spectrum. The positions of these dark lines are fixed and definite (Fig. 25.9). Most of these lines have been found to correspond to lines in the spectra of elements present in earth. As a result we can conclude that the substances or elements whose bright lines correspond on position to the dark lines in the solar spectrum compose the outer atmosphere of the sun. An interpretation of the dark lines was first given by *Kirchhoff* who from several experiments concluded that the vapour of an element absorbs those light waves which it would emit if it were incandescent.

The sun is assumed to consist of an incandescent solid or liquid nucleus surrounded by a cooler envelope where vapours of all terrestrial elements are present. The inner nucleus is called **photosphere** and the surrounding cooler envelope is the **chromosphere.** In *Kirchhoff's law,* white light emitted by the sun is robbed in passing the enveloping layer, of those waves which correspond to the waves the element would emit if they were incandescent. Due to the absorption of these waves, dark lines are produced.

25.10   Different Types of Spectra

There are two types of spectra : (a) Emission spectra and (b) Absorption spectra.

(a) **Emission spectra :** If a body is heated to incandescence, the spectrum produced by it is called an *Emission spectrum.*

Emission spectra may be divided into three classes :

(i) **Continuous spectrum :** It is an unbroken band of light where all the spectral colours are present. Electric light, luminous bunsen flame and white hot solid body give rise to this type of spectrum.

(ii) Line spectrum : It consists of a number of bright lines separated by dark spaces. Such a spectrum is obtained from vapours or gases of elementary substances in the incandescent state, each giving its characteristic lines.

A bit of metallic salt (e.g., NaCl) when introduced into a colourless bunsen flame it gives rise to this kind of spectrum. A vacuum tube containing a gas and made luminous by an electric discharge with an induction coil also gives rise to a number of isolated bright lines. The colour and position of these lines will differ for different gases. Fig. 25.10 shows emission spectral lines of *Hydrogen, Helium, Mercury* and *Sodium*.

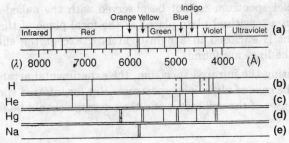

Fig. 25.10

(iii) Band or fluted spectrum : It consists of a number of luminous bands sharply defined at one edge and shading off gradually at the other edge.

It is seen that each fluting consists of a large number of lines at the bright end and more widely spaced at the other. Chemical compounds (like Cyanogen) give rise to fluted spectra while simple substances give line spectra. Antimony Fluoride gives a band spectrum. Gases whose molecules contain more than one atom give a band spectrum.

(b) Absorption spectra : It is not a continuous spectrum but a spectrum of all colours crossed by a number of dark bands called *absorption bands*.

If we examine the light coming out from the sun, the spectrum obtained is a continuous spectrum crossed by a number of dark lines. Further, when white light be passed through a piece of red glass and examined, the spectrum of the transmitted light consists of the red portion only, there being *dark bands* in the remaining portion. These are known as *absorption bands*.

25.11 Stellar Spectra and Doppler's Principle

The spectra of some stars resemble in appearance the solar spectrum. They contain a number of dark lines corresponding to a number of elements present in the earth, while others are closely allied to the fluted spectra of some of the elements. The spectra of nebulae consist of bright lines and resemble the spectrum formed by an incandescent gas. Thus nebulae are purely masses of incandescent gases. The star *Orionis* gives a continuous spectrum with narrow hydrogen lines, while the star *Ceti* gives a spectrum of bright lines and flutings.

If the source be made to move with a high velocity, the spectral line will be displaced either towards the violet or towards the red end of the spectrum, depending on the direction of motion of the source. This displacement in spectral lines in the case of spectra of stars and other celestial bodies is noticed and explained by a principle known as *Doppler's principle*.

Huggins observed that the F line of Hydrogen in the spectrum of Sirius is slightly shifted towards the red end of the spectrum. It indicates that the star **Sirius** is moving away from the earth with a certain velocity, usually of the order of 29 miles per sec.

25.12   Study of Ultraviolet and Infrared Spectra

In order to study the ultraviolet part of the spectrum, the glass prism and lenses of the collimator and the telescope of an ordinary spectrometer must be replaced by prism and lenses of *quartz*, as glass absorbs ultraviolet rays.

The ultraviolet spectrum cannot be observed with the naked eye and so it is photographed on a sensitised plate placed at the focal plane of the telescope. The whole instrument is enclosed in a light-tight box, except the slit. The plate is developed and the lines are found.

For investigating the infrared spectrum, the experimental arrangement is made the same as in the case of ultraviolet spectrum. But for infrared spectrum the glass prism and the lenses of the collimator and the telescope should be made of *rock-salt* or *fluor-spar*.

25.13   Importance of Spectrum Analysis

All elementary substances either in gaseous or in vapour state under suitable stimulus produce their own peculiar spectrum. As for example, lithium gives a red line; hydrogen gas one violet line, one green line and three red lines; sodium only two yellow lines. One can detect an element by its own characteristic spectrum even if it be present in small quantities. A mixture will produce a spectra of its ingredients. The identification of substances by studying their spectra is called *spectrum analysis* and provides information about stars, nebulae and other heavenly bodies. It has a great importance in chemical investigations and in detecting the purity of unknown samples.

25.14   Fluorescence

This phenomenon is observed in many substances. It becomes luminous when light of certain wavelengths falls on the substance. The name comes from fluor-spar, the substance which first showed this peculiar emission of light.

This phenomenon is noticed largely in many of the aniline dyes, like *eosine, fuchsine, fluorescin* and also in *sulphate of quinine* and *paraffin oil*. The fluorescence is most brilliant at the surface of incidence of the white light. The brilliancy gradually diminishes with the thickness of the solution through which the light has passed. The phenomenon of fluorescence can be applied to the study of the ultraviolet region of the spectrum.

If a spectrum is projected on fluorescent substances, the blue fluorescent light is emitted by the parts of the surfaces on which the blue, violet and ultraviolet portions of the solar spectrum falls. Stokes investigated the solar spectrum in this way and mapped the positions of the principal **Fraunhofer lines** in it.

Fluorescent powders are used with mercury vapour lamps to convert the intense ultraviolet light into visible violet.

25.15   Phosphorescence

Many substances continue to emit light if placed in a dark room after being exposed to light of short wavelengths. This phenomenon is known as *phosphorescence*.

Diamond, barium and strontium, sulphides of calcium are prominent amongst the phosphorescent substances. The *ultraviolet* light is most active in producing phosphorescence.

The term phosphorescence appears to be misleading, as the glow emitted by *phosphorous* is due to slow chemical action while the glow of a phosphorescent substance is not due to chemical action but is due to fluorescence which persists after the removal of the exciting light.

25.16 Calorescence

The action is just converse to that which occurs in the case of fluorescence. The absorption by a body of radiation of one wavelength and its consequent emission of radiation of shorter wavelength is known as *calorescence*.

Tyndall showed that if the **infrared** rays from an electric arc are allowed to pass through a solution of iodine in carbon bisulphide, the luminous rays would be absorbed and the transmitted infrared rays when focused on a piece of paper or a cigar will burst into flame.

25.17 Luminescence

The process of light production depending on temperature radiation is known as *incandescence*. With the increase of temperature there is an increase in radiation in the visible region. But this process has a certain upper limit.

Luminescence is the process wherein the chemical or electrical energy is directly transformed into light, i.e., without passing through the intermediate form of heat as in the case of flame or mercury arc lamp. The method is adopted for general illumination. The neon lamp comes under this group of light producing agents. The temperature inside a vacuum discharge tube is confined between 30 °C and 40 °C and as such this process of light emission is different from that of temperature radiation.

A few types of luminescence are mentioned below :

(i) **Photoluminescence :** It is due to the action of light—phosphorescence and fluorescence come under this group. The emission of light from a Welsbach mantle is partly an actual heat radiation and partly phosphorescence.

(ii) **Electroluminescence :** This is produced in a vacuum discharge tube. The glow in the body of the tube is due to the impact of negatively charged ions or electrons on the neutral gas molecules. If pressure is very low, the parts of the walls of the tube hit by the ions begin to glow. Many crystals glow under the influence of radiations from radioactive substances.

(iii) **Triboluminescence :** This is due to mechanical factors like friction, percussion and cleavage. This type of luminescence occurs when quartz crystals are rubbed together, a lump of sugar-candy is crushed, or a thick mica sheet is cleaved.

25.18 Scattering of Light and Colour of the Sky

When light falls on small particle of a body whose size is small in comparison to the wavelength of the incident light, the particle takes up energy from the incident light and radiates it in different directions. This process is called *scattering of light*. Light of shorter waves are scattered more than the lights of longer waves. Sunlight falling on the molecules of air or dust particles is scattered in all directions. As blue light has shorter wavelength, it is scattered more than the long wave light at the red end. Therefore, the scattered light consists mainly of blue colour. It is this blue light which reaches our eyes from the sky and gives us an impression of blue colour of the sky.

The cause of red colour of rising and setting sun can also be interpreted in a similar way. At the time of sunrise or sunset the rays of the sun have to travel through a longer path of a atmospheric air loaded with dust particles. So more and more shorter waves (e.g., blue, violet) are scattered away, and ultimately the longer red waves are transmitted to us. As a result the sun appears red at sunrise and at sunset.

Questions

Essay-type

1. Describe the various forms of spectra that may be obtained, illustrating each type by an example.

2. Describe a spectrometer and explain the working and adjustment in detail.

3. What is Doppler effect? Discuss two astrophysical evidences of the effect?
[C.U. 1970]

4. Give a general account of solar spectrum pointing out the peculiarities observed in it. Explain how the study of the spectrum enables us to draw conclusions regarding the presence of some familiar elements in the sun. Suggest a simple laboratory experiment for demostrating the essential validity of the explanation.
[C.U. 1967]

5. What are infrared and ultraviolet rays? What are their applications?

6. Write a short account of the contribution of spectroscopy to astrophysics.

7. Describe the general pattern of spectra of light obtained from the following sources :

    (i) An incandescent solid,

    (ii) A discharge tube containing a gas at low pressure.
[C.U. 1971]

8. What are the significances of the Fraunhofer lines in the spectra of celestial bodies? Describe an arrangement for the demonstration of these lines in the laboratory.

Short Answer-type

9. Enumerate the different adjustments necessary for observing a pure spectrum by the spectrometer.

10. What would be the nature of spectra of light from (i) the sun, (ii) an electric bulb, (iii) a neon lamp, (iv) sodium salt in bunsen flame?

11. What are the significance of Fraunhofer lines in the spectra of celestial bodies?

12. What is Kirchhoff's law concerning the absorption spectra?

13. "Line spectra are characteristic of elementary state of a substance"—explain.

14. The red line of hydrogen spectrum of a star is found shifted towards the red end of the spectrum from its usual position. Is the star approaching to or receding from the earth?
[C.U. 1984]

15. Are all the Fraunhofer lines due to absorption of light by the sun's atmosphere?

16. Write short notes on :

   (i) Different methods of exciting substances,

   (ii) Blue of the sky,   **(iii)** Tyndall effect.

17. Obtain an expression for the change of wavelength of light emitted by a moving star due to Doppler effect.

18. What are the wavelength ranges of infrared and ultraviolet spectrum?

Chapter 26

Laser, Holography, Optical Fibres and Other Optical Phenomena

26.1 Introduction

Einstein in 1917 first predicted the fact that there should be two kinds of emissions, viz., spontaneous and stimulated. He suggested that both the emissions are required for getting the Planck's radiation law. The phenomenon of stimulated emission was first used by Townes in 1954 for constructing a microwave amplifier device called 'maser.' In 1958, Schawlow and Townes extended the 'maser' principle to the optical frequencies which led to the device called 'LASER' (an acronym for *light amplification by stimulated emission of radiation*). In 1960, Maiman first successfully demonstrated the operation of a 'LASER ' device using ruby crystal. Since then the laser action has been noted in a wide variety of materials including semiconductors, dyes, liquids, ionized gases, etc.

The present-day light-wave communication had its birth in 1960s. The first successful demonstration of the ruby laser in 1960 and then a demonstration of laser operation in 1962 were the early stepping stones. In the year 1966, an evolution of fibre technology was taking place, though at that time the existing fibres had a loss even more than 1000 dB/km. Research workers at Corning Glass Works in 1970 first produced the fibre with a loss below 20 dB/km. Since then fibre technology has advanced to the point of fabricating fibre with a loss less than 0.5 dB/km.

26.2 Einstein's Coefficients

In 1970, Einstein predicted that there are two kinds of emissions. The first one is called *spontaneous emission* while the other is known as stimulated emission which is caused by the presence of the light radiation of the proper frequency. We have discussed below Einstein's coefficients and also presented the original argument of Einstein which led to a relation between these coefficients. It has also been established how a light beam gets amplified in the presence of population inversion.

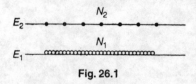

Fig. 26.1

Let us assume that N_1 and N_2 are two numbers of atoms per unit volume in levels 1 and 2 respectively. As shown in Fig. 26.1, these levels correspond to energies E_1 and E_2. An atom in the lower energy level absorbs radiation and thereby gets excited to the level E_2. The process of excitation occurs in the presence of radiation only and is known as absorption. The rate of absorption depends on the density of radiation at a particular frequency separating the two levels.

If ω represents the frequency, then

$$\omega = \frac{E_2 - E_1}{\hbar}.$$

(26.1)

In this case, the absorption process depends on the energy density of radiation at that frequency. These energy density may be represented by $u(\omega)$ and is defined such that $u(\omega)d\omega$ represents the radiation energy per unit volume in the frequency interval ω to $\omega + d\omega$.

The rate of absorption is proportional to N_1 and also to $u(\omega)$. Hence, the number of absorptions per unit volume can be written as

$$N_1 B_{12} u(\omega),$$

where $B_{12} =$ the coefficient of proportionality.

Next, let us consider the reverse process, viz., the emission of radiation at a frequency ω when the atom de-excites from E_2 to E_1. Einstein postulated that in an excited level an atom makes a radiative transitions to a lower energy level either through spontaneous emission or through stimulated emission. In spontaneous emission, the probability per unit time of the atom making a downward transition does not depend on the energy density of the radiation field but it depends only on the levels involved in the transition. Thus the rate of spontaneous emissions to the lower energy levels can be represented by

$$N_1 A_{21},$$

where $A_{21} =$ coefficient of proportionality.

For stimulated emission, the rate of transition to the lower energy levels is directly proportional to the energy density of the radiation at a frequency ω. So the rate of stimulated emission is represented by

$$N_2 B_{21} u(\omega).$$

The quantities A_{21}, B_{12} and B_{21} are called Einstein's coefficients.

The above coefficients are determined by the atomic system. The number of upward transitions at thermal equilibrium must be equal to the number of downward transitions. Hence, at thermal equilibrium, we may write,

$$N_1 B_{12} u(\omega) = N_2 A_{21} + N_2 B_{21} u(\omega) \tag{26.2}$$

or,
$$u(\omega) = \frac{A_{21}}{\left(\frac{N_1}{N_2}\right) B_{12} - B_{21}} \tag{26.3}$$

From Boltzmann's law, we can write the following expressions for the ratio of populations of two levels at temperature T:

$$\frac{E_2 - E_1}{k_B T} \quad [k_B = \text{Boltzmann's constant}]$$

$$\frac{N_1}{N_2} = e = e^{\frac{\hbar\omega}{k_B T}}. \tag{26.4}$$

By Eqs. (26.3) and (26.4) we have

$$u(\omega) = \frac{A_{21}}{B_{12} e^{\frac{\hbar\omega}{k_B T}} - B_{21}}. \tag{26.5}$$

Again, according to Planck's law, the energy density of radiation is given by

$$u(\omega) = \frac{\hbar\omega^3}{\pi^2 C^3} \cdot \frac{1}{e^{\frac{\hbar\omega}{k_B T}} - 1}. \tag{26.6}$$

Again, from Eq. (26.5),

$$u(\omega) = \frac{A_{21}}{B_{21}} \cdot \frac{1}{B_{21}\left(\frac{e^{\hbar\omega/k_B T}-1}{B_{21}}\right)}$$

$$= \frac{A_{21}}{B_{21}} \cdot \frac{1}{\left(e^{\hbar\omega/k_B T} - 1\right)}. \tag{26.7}$$

Comparing Eqs. (26.6) and (26.7) we get

$$B_{12} = B_{21} = B \quad \text{and} \quad \frac{\hbar\omega^3}{\pi^2 C^3} = \frac{A_{21}}{B_{21}}. \tag{26.8}$$

It is thus seen that the probabilities of stimulated absorption and stimulated emission are same. The ratio of the A and B coefficients is represented in the above equation. At thermal equilibrium, the ratio of the number of spontaneous to stimulated emission is expressed as

$$\frac{A}{Bu(\omega)} = e^{\hbar\omega/k_B T} - 1 \quad \text{[using Eq. (26.6)]}. \tag{26.9}$$

Thus at thermal equilibrium for

$$\omega \ll \frac{k_B T}{\hbar},$$

the number of stimulated emissions exceeds the number of spontaneous emissions. Again, for

$$\omega \gg \frac{k_B T}{\hbar},$$

the number of spontaneous emissions far exceeds the number of stimulated emissions.

For normal optical sources, $T \sim 10^3$ K and

$$\frac{k_B T}{\hbar} \sim \frac{1.38 \times 10^{-23}(\text{J/K}) \times 10^3(\text{K})}{1.054 \times 10^{-34}(\text{J sec})} = 1.3 \times 10^{14} \text{ sec}^{-1}.$$

Since for optical regions $\omega \sim 4 \times 10^{15}$ per second, at optical frequency the emission is mainly due to the spontaneous transitions and, therefore, the emission from usual light sources is incoherent.

26.3   Ruby Laser

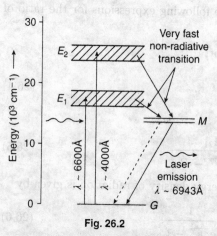

Fig. 26.2

It was the first laser operated successfully by Maiman in 1960. It has a single crystal of ruby whose ends are flat. One of the ends is completely silvered while the other is partially silvered and thus the two ends form a resonant cavity. Ruby is an aluminium oxide with some of the Al atoms replaced by chromium (about 0.05%). The energy levels of the chromium ion are presented in Fig. 26.2. The states E_1 and E_2 have very short lifetime ($\leq 10^{-9}$ second) while the metastable state M has a longer lifetime ($\sim$ milliseconds). The ruby crystal is placed inside a flash lamp which is connected to a capacitor as shown in Fig. 26.3. The capacitor discharges a few thousand joules of energy in a few milliseconds. This causes a power output from the flash lamp of a few megawatts order and a part of this energy is absorbed by the chromium ions resulting an excitation to the energy level inside the bands E_1 and E_2. Transitions to E_1 and E_2 are caused by the radiation of wavelengths ~ 6600 Å and ~ 4000 Å respectively.

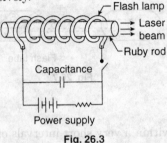

Fig. 26.3

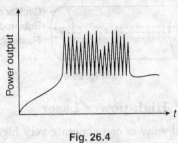

Fig. 26.4

Chromium ions make a 'fast non-radiative transition from the excited to the metastable state. They lead to a state of population inversion between M and G. Once a state of population inversion is achieved lasing action maybe triggered by spontaneously emitted photons.

The flash lamp operation provides a pulse output of the laser. As soon as the flash lamp stops operating, the population in the upper level is depleted and lasing action stops till the arrival of the next flash of the lamp. Even in the short period in which the ruby is lasing one may see that emission is measured as spikes of high intensity emissions as shown in Fig. 26.4. This phenomenon is known as *spiking of the laser*. Such spiking occurs due to the following mechanism :

As soon as the flash lamp power attains the threshold level, the laser oscillation sets in and depletes most atoms in the upper level to a stage when the laser action ceases. In this way the laser emission lasts for a few microseconds during which the flash lamp again pumps the ground state atoms to the upper level and thus further laser oscillation begins. The process repeats itself till the flash lamp power falls below the threshold value and the lasing action stops.

Alternative methods for pumping may also be employed. Fig. 26.5 exhibits an optical pumping scheme in which the laser rod and the flash lamp coincides with the focal lines of a cylindrical reflector of an elliptical cross-section. The property

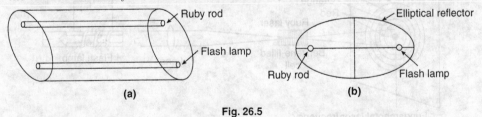

Fig. 26.5

of an elliptical reflector is that all the energy emerging from one of its foci after reflection from the reflecting surface focuses to the other focus. As a result an efficient transfer energy occurs from the flash lamp to the laser rod.

The efficiency of pumping the lasers is increased by using the following two methods : (i) The flash tube and the ruby rod may be mounted closely near the central axis of a circular mirror (Fig. 26.6). Due to this arrangement a major portion of the radiated light comes back to the centre of the cylinder giving light illumination. (ii) To increase the efficiency further, a cylindrical mirror with elliptical contours may be used (Fig. 26.7). At one focus F_1 of the ellipse the flash lamp is placed while at the other focus F_2 the laser rod is kept. The light which radiates from one focus strikes the mirror and thereby it reflects to the other focus. Thus most of the light from flash lamp reaches the laser rod at the other focus.

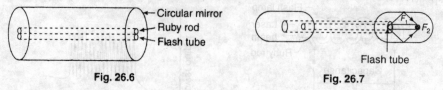

Fig. 26.6   **Fig. 26.7**

26.4   High-power Laser

The ruby lasers can generate very high power within a very short intervals of time. An important technique used for producing high-power lasers is called *Q-spoiling*. Between one end of the ruby rod and the mirror a fast-acting shutter is interposed. As the mirror at one end is obstructed, the internal reflections between the two mirror surfaces cannot take place. For most of the pumping cycle, the shutter is kept in closed positions permitting no laser action to take place. Consequently, many atoms are raised to an excited level.

Next, the shutter is quickly opened allowing the laser action to proceed. The energy built up within the rod is mainly emitted in one tremendous burst. The enormous energies (millions of watts) such achieved have been used to burn holes in diamonds and in about six-millimetre thick steel girders.

26.5   Raman Laser

A method of changing the laser frequencies was developed by E. J. Woodbury. A beam of ruby laser light was made to pass through a vessel containing benzene. Additional wavelengths were produced on either side of 6943 Å wavelength of the ruby laser. This is shown in Fig. 26.8. Like the main beam, the additional wavelengths were also highly parallel and coherent.

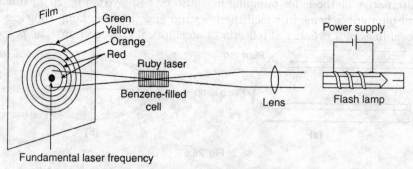

Fig. 26.8

It was noted that the frequency shifts were equal to the multiples of natural vibration frequency of benzene molecule. A change in the frequency of light owing to the vibrational frequencies of a substance is known as the *Raman effect*. In Raman laser, the intensities of the new wavelengths were half of the main beam.

The Raman laser provides a valuable method for getting information about the natural vibrational frequencies of many molecules.

26.6 Applications of Laser

(i) Medical uses : Lasers have been successfully utilised in the treatment of detached retinas. Ophthalmologists find the possibility of using the laser as an improved tool for microsurgery and vision research. Lasers also show great promise in cancer treatment.

(ii) Applications in military : Owing to the high amount of energy which the laser can concentrate, it can be used as 'death-ray' type of incendiary weapon for use against enemy missiles. However, the technology required for the purpose is not yet well developed. Presently, the laser system can put out energy of the order of 1500 joules. By proper lens system, if that intensity is concentrated, it could set on fire inflammable material situated at a distance of two miles or 3.2 kilometres long.

(iii) Uses in science : Laser has been used to repeat Michelson-Morley experiment showing that the velocity of light is constant and hence it proved the Einstein's theory of relativity. Using gas lasers many experiments were performed by various scientists and some valuable results were achieved.

The use of lasers in computers is being investigated for various potential applications, e.g., to transmit an entire memory bank from one computer to another.

26.7 Holography

In 1948, the principle of Holography was laid down by Gabor. But its practical importance was not noted until the lasers arrived in 1960. Before the advent of

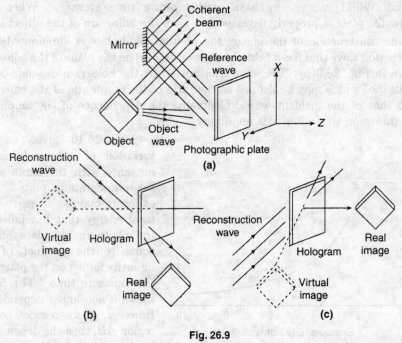

Fig. 26.9

laser, the method of in-lying holography as proposed by Gabor was employed. In fact, he showed that one can record both amplitude and phase of a wave by using interferometric principle. In such a method, coherent reference wave is added to the wave coming out from the object and the resulting interference pattern is recorded. This interference pattern is the characteristic of the object and is known as the *hologram.* The term hologram means a total recording, i.e., a record of both the amplitude and phase. When the wave is viewed the effect is such as would be the case if the object is still in position though the object may not be present there. This is because during reconstruction the object wave is itself emerging from the hologram, one has all the effects of the dimensionality at the time of viewing such a wave.

26.7.1 The Underlying Principle

Let us consider a simple configuration of taking a hologram and examine how the object wave may be reconstructed. The experimental set-up is shown in Fig. 26.9(a) where part of a coherent beam of light is made to fall on a plane mirror and the remaining part is allowed to illuminate the object whose hologram is to be recorded. The light scattered from the object falls on a photographic plate in addition to the reference wave as shown. The photographic plate records the resulting interference pattern which is developed and forms the hologram.

Let us assume that the photographic plate corresponds to the X-Y plane. Let $O(x,y)$ represents the field at the photographic plate due to the object wave and $R(x,y)$ the field due to the reference wave. The resultant field on the photographic plate is then given by

$$U(x,y) = O(x,y) + R(x,y). \tag{26.10}$$

The photographic plate only responds to the intensity variation. These may be given by

$$I(x,y) = |O(x,y)|^2 + |R(x,y)|^2 + O(x,y)R^*(x,y) + O^*(x,y)R(x,y). \tag{26.11}$$

In Eq. (26.11) above, we have carried out a time average. When this photographic plate is properly developed, it gives the hologram of the object.

To the construction of the image, the photographic plate is illuminated by a reconstruction wave that has a field distribution $R(x,y)$ on the plane of the hologram as shown in Fig. 26.9(b). The wave transmitted by the hologram depends on its transmittance which may be defined as the ratio of the amplitude of the emergent wave to that of the incident wave. Generally, the dependence of the amplitude transmittance on the intensity is non-linear.

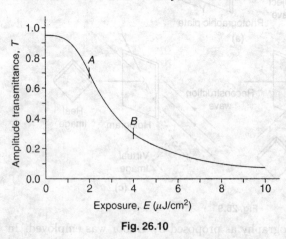

Fig. 26.10

Fig. 26.10 gives us the variation of amplitude transmittance with the exposure of the photographic plate. The exposure may be defined as the total energy that has fallen on the photographic plate and is equal to the product of the intensity falling on the plate and the exposure time. The figure shows a non-linear dependence. However, if we restrict to the region AB, then the dependence is almost linear. If we assume that the amplitude transmittance T is linearly related to the intensity incident during exposure I, then we can write,

$$T = I. \tag{26.12}$$

Therefore, the amplitude transmittance T of the developed transparency will be

$$T(x,y) = |O(x,y)|^2 + |R(x,y)|^2 + O(x,y)R^*(x,y) + O^*(x,y)R(x,y). \qquad (26.13)$$

If we illuminate the transparency into the reference wave $R(x,y)$, then the field $\phi(x,y)$, emerging from the hologram can be expressed as

$$\phi(x,y) = T(x,y)R(x,y) = [|O(x,y)|^2 + |R(x,y)|^2]R(x,y) + O(x,y)|R^*(x,y)|^2$$
$$+ O^*(x,y)R(x,y)R(x,y). \qquad (26.14)$$

Assuming the referring wave as a plane wave with its propagation vector using in the X-Z plane, we have

$$R(x,y) = R_0 e^{-ikx \sin\theta}, \qquad (26.15)$$

where $k \sin\theta$ and $k \cos\theta$ represent the X and Z component of k. Thus we have

$$\phi(x,y) = [|O(x,y)|^2 + R_0^2]R_0 e^{-ikx\sin\theta} + O(x,y)R_0^2 + R_0^2 O^*(x,y) \cdot e^{-ikx\sin\theta}. \qquad (26.16)$$

In Eq. (26.16), the first term on the right-hand side corresponds to a wave propagating in the direction of the reference wave with an amplitude distorted wave, the second term is proportional to the object wave $O(x,y)$, the effect of viewing this wave will be the same as the effect of viewing the object itself. The last term is proportional to $O^*(x,y)$ which is the conjugate of the object wave. It produces a real image lying in the opposite side of the hologram [Fig. 26.9(b)].

If the hologram is illuminated by a wave such that the field distribution is $R^*(x,y)$, then

$$\phi(x,y) = [|O(x,y)|^2 + R_0^2]R^*(x,y) + O(x,y)R^*(x,y) + O^*(x,y)R_0^2 \qquad (26.17)$$

It may be noted that since holography is an interference phenomenon, the radiation must satisfy certain coherence requirements for forming good holograms.

26.7.2 Applications of Holography

Holography was invented in an effort with a view to increase the resolving power of microscope. With the advent of laser, many diverse applications have emerged, some of which are :

  (i) three-dimensional reconstruction,

  (ii) interferometer,

  (iii) microscopy, and

  (iv) imaging through aberrating media.

26.8   Classification of Optical Fibres

Optical fibres (light guides) are classified : (i) in terms of the refractive index profile of the core and (ii) whether single-mode fibre or multimode fibre are propagating in the guide. When the core, made of a high-silica content glass or multicomponent glass, has a uniform refractive index n_1, it is called a *step-index fibre*, while if the core has a gradually decreasing refractive index from the centre toward the core-cladding interface, then the fibre is called a *graded-index fibre*.

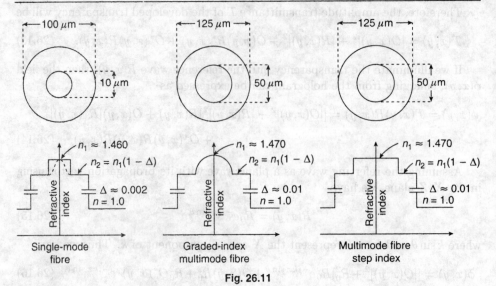

Fig. 26.11

Fig. 26.11 shows dimensions and refractive indices for frequently used telecommunication fibres while Fig. 26.12 provides some advantages, constraints and applications for the three different types of fibre.

	Single-mode fibre	Graded-index multimode fibre	Multimode fibre step index
	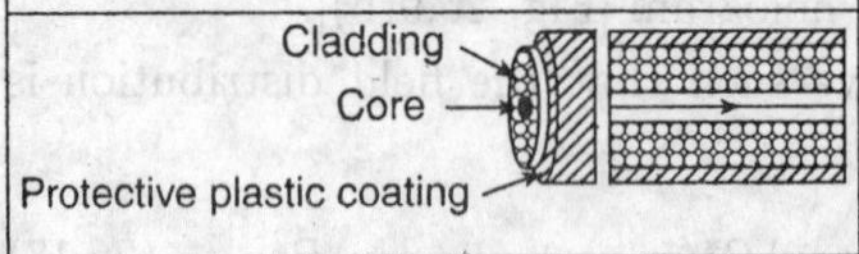 Cladding Core Protective plastic coating		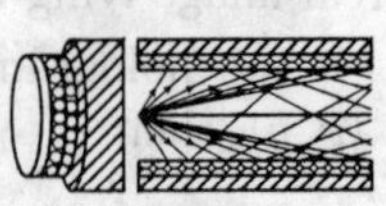
Source	Requires laser	Laser or LED	Laser or LED
Bandwidth	Very very large > 3 GHz-km	Very large 200 MHz to 3 GHz-km	Large < 200 MHz-km
Splicing	Very difficult due to small care	Difficult but doable	Difficult but doable
Example of application	Submarine cable system	Telephone trunk between central offices	Data links
Cost	Less expensive	Most expensive	Least expensive

Fig. 26.12

A single-mode fibre is used for the case when the transmission medium has a very high bandwidth. A graded-index multimode fibre is used for intermediate bandwidth between 200 MHz and 2 GHz-km while a step-index multimode fibre is used for lower bandwidth in the transmission system.

26.9 Fabrication

Fibres used for communication are constructed from material systems which must satisfy the following requirements :

(i) The dielectric materials used must have low loss (< 10 dB/km) in the infrared region of the optical spectrum.

(ii) The dielectric material must be capable of being drawn into a fibre.

(iii) The dielectric material in the core must have a greater refractive index than the cladding material.

(iv) In order to get a high-bandwidth fibre, the materials used must be capable of producing a graded refractive index profile in the core of the fibre.

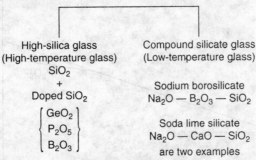

High-silica glass
(High-temperature glass)
SiO_2
+
Doped SiO_2

$$\left[\begin{array}{c} GeO_2 \\ P_2O_5 \\ B_2O_3 \end{array}\right]$$

Compound silicate glass
(Low-temperature glass)

Sodium borosilicate
$Na_2O - B_2O_3 - SiO_2$

Soda lime silicate
$Na_2O - CaO - SiO_2$
are two examples

Fig. 26.13

The above requirements limit the field of dielectric material systems to glasses and plastics. Two types of glass systems are used in general. This is shown in Fig. 26.13. The first type consists of glasses produced by a deposition process. The vapour phase reaction of oxygen with mixtures of compounds like $SiCl_4$, $GeCl_4$, BCl_3 and $POCl_3$ produces an ultrapure glass rod known as *preform*. The preform has a doped silica core and a pure silica (SiO_2) cladding. The concentration of the dopants GeO_2, P_2O_5 and B_2O_3 is radially varied to get the desired variation of the refractive index of the core. The preforms are pulled into fibres at high temperatures (typically 2000 °C). The resultant fibres are then referred to as 'high-silica' fibres. Such fibres are mostly used in optical telecommunication systems. The other type of glass system is constructed by pure powdered raw materials that are processed using classical glass-making techniques for producing compound silicate glasses. By means of this technique, the two glasses (core and cladding) of different chemical compositions are separately melted at relatively low temperatures (850 °C to 1100 °C) and fed into two concentric crucibles with a hole at the bottom through which a fibre is pulled. The fibres thus constructed are known as 'multicomponent glass' fibres.

26.9.1 Preform Fabrication Techniques

In these techniques pure silica (SiO_2) is used as a base material and a small amount of dopants is added to it for changing its refractive index sufficiently to allow a waveguide to be formed. In a typical vapour phase reaction, chloride precursors like $SiCl_4$, $GeCl_4$, $POCl_3$ and BCl_3 undergo a high-temperature oxidation resulting oxides of silicon and dopant elements as given below :

$$SiCl_4 + O_2 \rightarrow SiO_2 + 2Cl_2$$

$$GeCl_4 + O_2 \rightarrow GeO_2 + 2Cl_2$$

$$2POCl_3 + \tfrac{3}{2}O_2 \rightarrow P_2O_5 + 3Cl_2$$

$$2BCl_3 + \tfrac{3}{2}O_2 \rightarrow B_2O_3 + 3Cl_2$$

In the above chemical reactions the dopant materials GeO_2 and P_2O_5 increase the refractive index of silica but B_2O_3 reduces it as shown in Fig. 26.14. Dopants like phosphorus and boron are used as fining agents. Those are thus used to lower the fusion temperature and the viscosity of the deposited glass and hence making it more homogeneous.

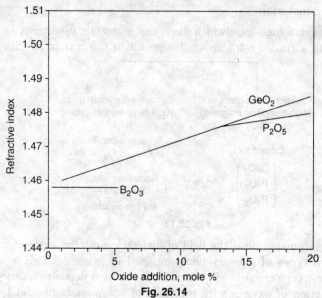

Fig. 26.14

For fabricating preforms, two different processes are employed in general. These are (i) the inside deposition processes and (ii) the outside deposition processes. The inside and outside refer to the general environment in which the glass materials are deposited. Deposition in an inside process occurs on the inside surface of a fused silica tube while in the outside process the materials are deposited onto an external target surface directly called a *bait rod*. The commonly used inside process is the modified chemical vapour deposition (MCVD) process while the outside processes belong to the (a) lateral deposition and (b) vapour-phase axial deposition (VAD).

26.10   Transmission Loss Measurements

We know that various absorption and scattering losses will contribute to the total transmission loss of an optical fibre. The transmission loss is determined by measuring the total power at the two points in the fibre by a length L. The attenuation of a fibre of length L is given by the expression,

$$A = 10 \log \left(\frac{P_{NE}}{P_{FE}} \right) \text{dB}, \qquad (26.18)$$

where P_{FE} is the power at the output or far end of the fibre and P_{NE} is the power at the near end of the fibre. When a fibre is excited with its EMD (equilibrium mode distribution), the attenuation constant α is defined as

$$\alpha = \frac{A}{L} = \frac{10}{L} \log \left(\frac{P_{NE}}{P_{FE}} \right) \frac{\text{dB}}{\text{m}}, \qquad (26.19)$$

where L represents a length independent steady-state loss.

26.11   Scattering and Absorption Loss Measurements

In order to measure the scattering loss of a fibre, the light scattered from a short length of fibre is collected and then compared with the light travelling in the fibre core. The following equation is used to measure the scattering loss :

$$\alpha_{sc} = \frac{4.34 \times 10^5}{l} \cdot \frac{P_{sc}}{P_{tot}} \frac{\text{dB}}{\text{km}}, \tag{26.20}$$

where P_{sc} is the scattered power, P_{tot} is the power transmitted in the core and l is the length of the fibre.

The absorption loss can be determined from the difference between its total and scattering loss.

26.12 Non-destructive Loss Measurements

When a fibre is packaged with a connector on its end, a non-destructive loss measurement is required.

The insertion loss (IL) is given by

$$\text{IL} = 10 \log \frac{P_{in}}{P_{out}} \text{ dB}, \tag{26.21}$$

where P_{in} is the input power by inserting a short length fibre and P_{out} is the output power after removing the fibre.

26.13 Bandwidth Measurements

Characteristics of a fibre are given in terms of its power transfer function $H(\omega)$ or in terms of its impulse response $h(t)$ where $H(\omega)$ and $h(t)$ are Fourier transform of the form

$$H(\omega) = \int_{-\infty}^{\infty} h(t) e^{-j\omega t} dt \tag{26.22}$$

$$h(t) = \frac{1}{2\pi} \int_{-\infty}^{\infty} H(\omega) e^{j\omega t} d\omega, \tag{26.23}$$

where ω is the radian base-band frequency of the envelope of the modulated optical carrier.

In the time domain, the shape of the impulse response is characterized by its r.m.s. pulse-width (2σ) given by

$$\sigma^2 = \frac{1}{P} \int_{-\infty}^{\infty} h(t) t^2 dt - \tau^2, \tag{26.24}$$

where $\tau = \dfrac{1}{P} \displaystyle\int_{-\infty}^{\infty} h(t) t \, dt$ and $P = \displaystyle\int_{-\infty}^{\infty} h(t) dt,$

τ and P are respectively the pulse delay and the energy in $h(t)$.

26.14 Time Domain Measurements

A narrow pulse having optical power $f(t)$ is used to excite a fibre and an output voltage $g(t)$ is produced. The output voltage $g(t)$ is a distorted version of the input signal $f(t)$.

The detected output pulses through the full length of the fibre $g_1(t)$ and through a short length of the fibre $g_0(t)$ are measured. The corresponding Fourier transform is

$$G(\omega) = \sum_{n=0}^{N-1} g(nT) e^{-j\omega nT}, \tag{26.25}$$

where $g(nT)$ is the digitized samples of $g(t)$ for each time interval T. Then the frequency response of the fibre is calculated as

$$H(\omega) = \frac{G_1(\omega)}{G_0(\omega)}. \tag{26.26}$$

26.15   Frequency Domain Measurements

Here the fibre mode is considered to be independent base-band channels so that Fourier transform of the impulse response yields

$$H(\omega) = |H(\omega)|e^{-j\omega\tau_0}e^{j\theta(\omega)}$$

$$= \sum_{v=1}^{N} |C_v|^2 e^{-j\omega\tau}v\Delta t, \tag{26.27}$$

where, $H(\omega) = $ complex power transfer function, $|C_v|^2 = $ output power in the vth mode, $\tau_0 = $ average delay common to all modes, $\omega = $ base-band frequency.

26.16   Fibre Characteristics

Three mechanisms are there which can cause delay distortion and hence limit the bandwidth of a fibre. These are : (i) modal delay distortion, (ii) chromatic (material) dispersion and (iii) waveguide dispersion.

In the case of a multimode fibre, the group velocities of the propagating modes are nearly equalized if the fibre profile shape parameter α has an optimum value α_0 which depends on both the glass composition and wavelength. When $\alpha = \alpha_0$, the minimum r.m.s. pulse spreading σ_m that can occur per unit length of the fibre is given by

$$\sigma_m \approx 0.14\Delta^2 \mu s/km. \tag{26.28}$$

So when $\Delta = 1\%$, $\sigma_m \approx 14$ ps/km.

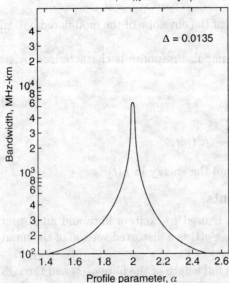

Fig. 26.15

The relationship between the bandwidth (BW) of a fibre and its r.m.s. impulse response width σ is expressed as

$$BW \approx \frac{180}{\sigma}, \tag{26.29}$$

where the bandwidth is in gigahertz-kilometres and σ in picoseconds per kilometre. Fig. 26.15 exhibits a sharp peak in the bandwidth at the optimum value $\alpha = \alpha_0$.

Delay distortion due to chromatic dispersion is caused by the change of refractive index of the glass with wavelength and the relative bandwidth of the source. The total r.m.s. pulse spreading σ_t, can be expressed as

$$\sigma_t \approx (\sigma_m^2 + \sigma_c^2)^{1/2}, \tag{26.30}$$

where $\sigma_m = $ pulse spreading due to modal delay distortion, $\sigma_c = $ r.m.s. chromatic pulse spreading.

In the region where chromatic dispersion approaches to zero, σ_c will be minimum but not exactly equal to zero owing to the finite line width of the source. The bandwidth of a fibre excited with LED source of spectral width $\frac{\lambda^2}{40}\mu$m in the zero chromatic dispersion region of the fibre is shown in Fig. 26.16.

The waveguide dispersion, associated with the guidance effects of the fibre structure, is important only in single-mode fibres. For a given single-mode fibre design, if Δ is increased or the core radius is decreased, it increases the zero material dispersion wavelength.

The maximum theoretical band-width and the largest measured band-width to date, for single-mode and the

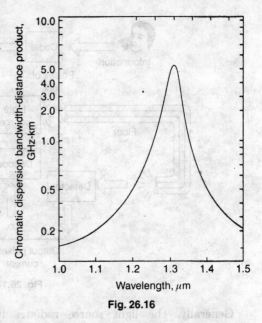

Fig. 26.16

graded-index multimode Ge-P-SiO$_2$ fibres are given in Table 26.1. For all source-fibre communications, the table gives an optimistic upper bound for the bandwidths.

Table 26.1 : Best bandwidth results in Ge-P-SiO$_2$ core fibres

Wave-length	Source Type	r.m.s. $\Delta\lambda$, nm	σ_c ps/km	Single-mode fibres Theore-tical BW GHz-km	Single-mode fibres Largest measured BW	Graded-index multimode fibres $\Delta \approx 1\%$ Theore-tical BW GHz-km	Graded-index multimode fibres $\Delta \approx 1\%$ Largest measured BW	σ_t ps/km
850 nm	LED	18	†	†	†	0.1	0.07	1720
850 nm	Laser	0.6	57	3.2	3.3	3.1	3.1	58
1300 nm	LED	42	†	†	†	3.5	7.0††	52
1300 nm	Laser	1.5	1.5	120	92	13	6.5	14

† Low coupling efficiency rules out LED as a source with single-mode fibres.

†† This exceeds the theoretical bandwidth value.

26.17 Fibres in Communication System

In order to understand how fibres are used in a communication system, we consider Fig. 26.17 as a simple example of a telephone conversation being transmitted over an optical communication system. The system consists of a light-emitting diode or of a transmitter in the form of a semiconductor laser which is modulated by an information-bearing signal.

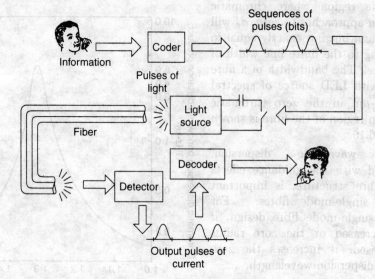

Fig. 26.17

Generally, the light source radiates in the near-infrared portion of the electromagnetic spectrum as shown in Fig. 26.18. The receiver system has a PIN or *avalanche photodiode* (APD) which converts the optical signal into an information-bearing electrical signal. The electrical signal is then demodulated for producing the audio signal heard in the telephone.

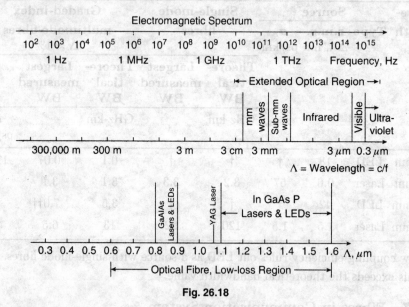

Fig. 26.18

Due to low-loss and wide-bandwidth capabilities, optical fibres are utilized where twisted wire pairs or coaxial cables are used as the transmission medium in a communication system. Some of the attractive features of optical fibre transmission are : (i) low loss and high bandwidth, (ii) small size and bending radius, (iii) light weight, (iv) non-conductive, non-radiative and non-inductive character, and (v) capability of providing natural growth.

To appreciate the low-loss and wide-bandwidth capabilities, we have shown the signal attenuation versus frequency curve for three different media in Fig. 26.19. Optical fibres have a flat transfer function beyond 100 MHz. The small size, small bending radius of a few centimetres and light weight of optical fibres and cables are important in aircrafts, ships, etc., where space is at a premium. As the optical fibres are dielectric waveguides, so they can avoid many problems like the radiative interference, ground loops. Furthermore, the loss of the optical fibre is a constant as can be found for the three digital-transmission rates considered in Table 26.2, viz., 1.544, 6.312 and 44.736 Mb/second. A comparison of the growth capability of different transmission media is made in the Table 26.2.

It is interesting to note that the optical fibre system could be used at all bit rates and can naturally grow to satisfy system needs. The loss of the metallic transmission lines, on the other hand, increases with the increase of the transmission rates and so limits their use at the higher bit rates.

Table 26.2 : A comparison of the growth capability of different transmission media

Transmission media	Loss in dB/km at half bit rate frequency (digital transmission rates)		
	T_1 (1.544 Mb/sec)	T_2 (6.312 Mb/sec)	T_3 (44.736 Mb/sec)
26-Gauge twisted wire pair	24	48	128
19-Gauge twisted wire pair	10.8	21	56
0.375-in diameter	2.1	4.5	11
Low-loss optical fibre	3.5	3.5	3.5

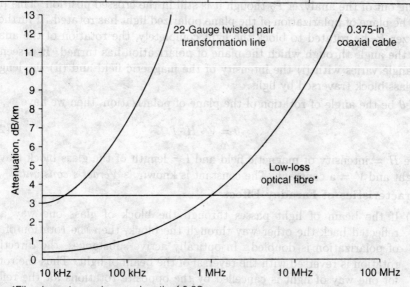

*Fibre loss at a carrier wavelength of 0.82 mm

Fig. 26.19

26.18   Some Optical Phenomena

Light being an electromagnetic wave, electric field and magnetic field have significant effects on light. Faraday, Kerr, Zeeman, Stark and others discovered several important magneto-optical and electro-optical effects as discussed below.

26.18.1   Faraday Effect

If a plane polarized beam is allowed to pass through a glass block, no change takes place in its plane of polarization as under ordinary circumstances glass is not optically active. But Faraday in 1864, observed that if the glass block is kept in a strong magnetic field, the block temporarily acquires the property of optical activity and rotates the plane of polarization of plane polarized light. This phenomena is called *Faraday effect.*

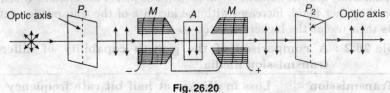

Fig. 26.20

Let us consider an unpolarized beam incident normally on a Nicol prism P_1 (Fig. 26.20). After emerging, it becomes plane polarized with vibrations parallel to the optic axis of the Nicol P_1. The beam is next passed through a hole bored along the axis of an electromagnet (M-M) to fall on the analyzing Nicol P_2. A is a glass block kept in the space between the pole pieces of the electromagnet. When no current passes through the electromagnet and the optic axes of the crystals P_1 and P_2 are parallel to each other, then full strength of light will emerge from the analyzing Nicol P_2. The analyzer is then rotated and keep it in a crossed position with respect to the polarizing Nicol P_1. At that condition no light will emerge from the Nicol P_2. Next the magnetic field is applied on the glass block A by sending strong current through the electromagnet. It will be observed that some light is coming out of the analyzer P_2 though it is still in the crossed position. This proves that the plane of polarization of the plane polarized light has rotated. If further the analyzer P_2 be rotated to block the light completely, the rotation of the analyzer gives the angle through which the plane of polarization has turned. It is seen that this angle varies with (i) the intensity of the magnetic field and (ii) the length of the glass block traversed by light.

If θ be the angle of rotation of the plane of polarization, then we have

$$\theta = V \cdot H \cdot l, \tag{26.31}$$

where H = intensity of magnetic field and l = length of the glass block traversed by light and V = a constant. The constant is known as *Verdet's constant.*

Characteristics of Faraday Effect

(i) If the beam of light passes through the block of glass one way and is reflected back the other way through the block, then the rotation of plane of polarization is doubled. In optically active substances, the direction of rotation is reversed with the reversal of the beam of light. Thus the rotation for one way of light is cancelled by the opposite rotations for the reflected way. This is, in fact, the basic difference between ordinary optical activity and optical activity induced by magnetic field. If a beam of light be sent to-and-fro along the direction of lines of force through the glass block, the rotation is largely amplified owing to repeated reflections.

(ii) The rotation of plane of polarization is seen to be greatest if light travels along the lines of force of the magnetic field. It becomes least or zero if light travels perpendicular to the lines of force of the magnetic field.

(iii) When the current flows in a clockwise direction through the electromagnet, the rotation of plane of polarization is also clockwise or right-handed. On the other hand, if the current through the electromagnet is anti-clockwise, the rotation is also anti-clockwise or left-handed.

26.18.2 Kerr Effect

Kerr in 1876 discovered an electro-optical effect. In general, glass is isotropic, but if a piece of glass is kept between the plates of a capacitor on which an electric field is applied, the piece becomes doubly refracting. If a ray of light is allowed to pass through the piece, it splits up into E-ray and O-ray which travel with different velocities. One of the components is polarized with its plane of vibration along the direction of the electric field, while the other has its plane of vibration perpendicular to the field. The two components travelling in an electric field of length l and of strength E have a path-difference of n wavelength introduced between them. This is expressed as $n = KlE^2$, where K is the Kerr constant for the substance used. Nitro-benzene shows strong Kerr effect for which the value of K is 2.7×10^{-8}. A capacitor having nitro-benzene placed between its plates produces a Kerr cell. When such a cell is placed between two crossed Nicols, it will not pass any light in the absence of an electric field. But when the field is applied, nitro-benzene behaves like a doubly refracting crystal and so passes a certain amount of light through the Nicols. This behaviour of a Kerr cell is used for finding the velocity of light.

26.18.3 Zeeman Effect

Zeeman in 1896 showed that if the emitting atoms are placed in a magnetic field, the spectral line emitted by excited atoms splits up into a doublet or a triplet. This magneto-optical effect of splitting a spectral line by the application of a magnetic field is known as *Zeeman effect*. If a sodium source is placed in a strong magnetic field and the spectral line be examined by a high resolution spectroscope, it is seen that each spectral line is split into two or more components. If light is examined at right angles to the direction of the magnetic field, then the original line splits into three components. Out of these, one line remains in the same position as the original line and the other two lines go on the two sides. If the two outer lines are examined by a Nicol prism as an analyzer, they are found to be polarized at right angles to the original line. The effect is called *transverse Zeeman effect* [Fig. 26.21(a)].

When observations are taken along the direction of magnetic field by boring an axial hole in the pole-pieces of the electromagnet, it is seen that there is no line in the position of the original spectral line but only two outer lines are present. The lines are seen to be circularly polarized in opposite directions [Fig. 26.21(b)]. This effect is called *longitudinal*

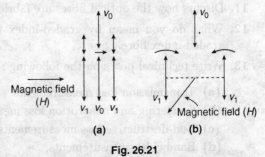

Fig. 26.21

Zeeman effect. Both these effects are noticed when a strong magnetic field is applied and are generally called *normal Zeeman effect.* If on the other hand, a weak magnetic field is applied to split the spectral lines, many additional lines can be seen and the effect is then called *anomalous Zeeman effect.*

Using Fig. 26.22, the Zeeman effect can be demonstrated in a laboratory. The normal Zeeman effect can be suitably explained by Lorentz electron theory or more precisely by using quantum mechanics.

26.18.4 Stark Effect

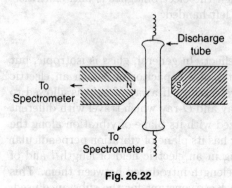

Fig. 26.22

Stark in 1913 showed that if the spectral lines are subjected to strong electric field instead of magnetic field, similar splitting of lines occurs. This phenomenon is called *Stark effect.* Like Zeeman effect, the Stark effect can also be classified into *transverse* and *longitudinal* effects depending on whether the direction of observation is at right angles to or parallel to the direction of the applied electric field. Stark effect can be explained suitably by using quantum theory.

Questions

Essay-type

1. Explain what are meant by Einstein's coefficients.

2. Make a discussion on optical resonator and ruby laser.

3. What are the applications of lasers?

4. Write a note on holography. Derive the principle of holography.

5. Show mathematically that the probabilities of stimulated absorption and stimulated emission are same.

6. What is an optical resonator? Give the principle of general spherical resonators.

7. Analyse geometrically the principle of an optical resonator.

8. Discuss how the efficiency of pumping the lasers is increased.

9. What do you mean by high power laser? Explain briefly the Raman laser.

10. Explain mathematically the condition for laser action in semiconductor.

11. Discuss how the optical fibres are fabricated.

12. What do you mean by graded-index fibre? Make WKBJ analysis of the graded-index fibre.

13. Write technical notes on the following :

    (a) Transmission loss measurements,

    (b) Scattering and absorption loss measurements,

    (c) Non-destructive loss measurements,

    (d) Bandwidth measurements,

(e) Time domain measurements,

(f) Frequency domain measurements,

(g) Faraday effect and Kerr effect,

(h) Zeeman effect and Stark effect.

Short Answer-type

14. Draw the energy levels of the chromium ion.

15. What are the uses of semiconductor lasers?

16. Classify the different types of optical fibres.

17. What is meant by step-index fibre? Give the fields in the core and cladding of the step-index fibre.

18. What are important fibre characteristics?

19. How are fibres used in communication system?

20. What are the characteristics of Faraday effect?

Chapter 27
Special Theory of Relativity

27.1 Introduction

The origin of the special theory of relativity is present in the electromagnetism. Since its publication by Einstein in 1905, the special theory of relativity has occupied a common place in physics and is employed for the consideration of precise atomic phenomena, in high-energy physics and in nuclear physics. Now the special theory is believed to apply to all forms of interaction except large-scale gravitational phenomena. In modern physics, it serves as a touch stone for the possible forms of interaction between fundamental particles.

27.2 Propagation of Light in Free Space

One of the outstanding conclusions of Maxwell's theory of electromagnetic field was the propagation of e.m. waves in accordance with the ordinary laws of wave motion. This propagation in free space would take place with a fixed velocity c whose numerical magnitude as obtained by Weber and Kohlrausch came out to be 3.1×10^{10} cm/sec approximately. Within the limits of experimental error, this value is the same as the speed of light obtained by Fizeau a few years earlier.

Fizeau, in 1851, determined the effect of the motion of the medium of propagation on the speed of light. If c' represents the speed of light in the laboratory system and v the speed of the medium in the laboratory, then

$$c' = \frac{c}{n} \pm v, \tag{27.1}$$

where $\frac{c}{n}$ is the speed of light in the medium itself, n being the refractive index. The two motions are taken to be parallel or antiparallel. The actual result was, however, somewhat different from that expressed in Eq. (27.1) and can be written as

$$c' = \frac{c}{n} \pm v \left(1 - \frac{1}{n^2}\right). \tag{27.2}$$

The elastic-solid theory of light demands an all-pervading medium for the propagation of light waves through it. The high value of the velocity of light can be explained if the elasticity of the medium is considered very large and also its density be very small. But these are quite abnormal properties which have nothing in common with the ordinary matter. Therefore, the medium is a hypothetical one and is called the *aether*.

In order to study the existence of aether, a good number of experiments have been performed. The experimental results of Fizeau and also of Airy on the aberration of stars led to the conclusion that the all-pervading aether must be stationary. Hence, it can be used as an absolute frame of reference.

27.3   Michelson-Morley's Experiment

The purpose of the famous experiment of Michelson and Morley was to examine the motion of the earth with respect to the stationary aether or the *absolute velocity* of the earth.

Apparatus

It is well known that in Michelson's interferometer two rays of light travel after reflection and transmission from a half-silvered mirror in two different directions at right angles to each other. These are then reflected again and retrace their paths to recombine and interfere. The optical arrangement of Michelson and Morley apparatus is shown in Fig. 27.1.

It consists of two plane mirrors M_1 and M_2 and a half-silvered glass plate G set in a manner as shown. S is a source of light from which a beam is rendered parallel by a lens.' By the half-silvered divider plate G, the beam is divided in two parts. The reflected part travels along the path AM_1 and after reflection from M_1 it retraces its path. After refraction at G it then reaches to the observing telescope T. The transmitted beam through the plate G traverses in the path AM_2 perpendicular to AM_1 through the compensatory plate C. By reflection at the mirror M_2 normally it retraces its path and, as before, after reflection at G it goes to the telescope T. The

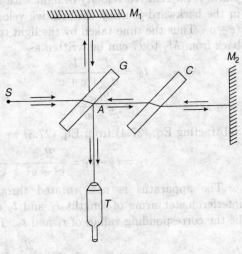

Fig. 27.1

path difference along AM_1 and AM_2 produces interference fringes as viewed by the telescope. Any alteration of the difference of path causes a shift of these fringes from a measurement of which the alteration in the path difference can be calculated.

Theory

Let us assume that the arm A_2M_2 of the interferometer is kept in the direction of velocity v of the earth while the arm A_1M_1 is in the perpendicular direction (Fig. 27.2). With the movement of the apparatus and the earth, a stream of aether current flows whose direction is parallel to A_2M_2.

Let A_1 be the position of the glass plate at any instant τ_1 when a pulse moves in the direction M_1. After reflection at M_1 when the pulse returns at the instant τ_2, the glass plate has moved to the A_2 position, say. Thus during this time the pulse moves over the distance $A_1M_1A_2$ with velocity c and the glass plate moves the distance

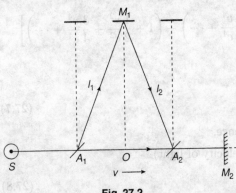

Fig. 27.2

A_1A_2 with velocity v. Let the interval $(\tau_2 - \tau_1)$ is equal to t_1. Then we can write,

$$t_1 = \frac{A_1M_1 + M_1A_2}{c} = \frac{A_1A_2}{v} \quad \text{or,} \quad \frac{2A_1M_1}{c} = \frac{2A_1O}{v}$$

or, $\quad \dfrac{2\sqrt{l_1^2 + (A_1O)^2}}{c} = \dfrac{2A_1O}{v} \quad$ or, $\quad \dfrac{l_1^2 + (A_1O)^2}{c^2} = \dfrac{(A_1O)^2}{v^2}$

or, $\quad (A_1O)^2 \left[\dfrac{1}{v^2} - \dfrac{1}{c^2}\right] = \dfrac{l_1^2}{c^2} \quad$ or, $\quad A_1O = \dfrac{l_1 v}{\sqrt{c^2 - v^2}}$.

$$\therefore \quad t_1 = \frac{2A_1O}{v} = \frac{2l_1}{\sqrt{c^2 - v^2}}. \tag{27.3}$$

Next, let l_2 be the distance of the mirror M_2 from the glass plate. In the forward journey, the relative velocity of light with respect to the mirror M_2 is $(c - v)$ while in the backward journey the relative velocity of light with respect to the glass is $(c + v)$. Thus the time taken by the light to move from the glass plate G to M_2 and back from M_2 to G can be written as

$$t_2 = \frac{l_2}{c - v} \frac{l_2}{c + v}$$
$$= \frac{2l_2 c}{c^2 - v^2}. \tag{27.4}$$

Subtracting Eq. (27.4) from Eq. (27.3) we get

$$\tau_1 = t_2 - t_1 = \frac{2l_2 c}{c^2 - v^2} - \frac{2l_1}{\sqrt{c^2 - v^2}}. \tag{27.5}$$

The apparatus is now rotated through $90°$ so that the position of the interferometer arms of lengths l_1 and l_2 are interchanged. Then, let t_1' and t_2' be the corresponding values of t_1 and t_2. Then we have

$$\tau_2 = \frac{2l_2}{\sqrt{c^2 - v^2}} - \frac{2l_1 c}{c^2 - v^2}. \tag{27.6}$$

Therefore, in the two orientations of the apparatus, the change in time retardation is given by

$$\tau_2 - \tau_1 = 2(l_1 + l_2)\left[\frac{c}{c^2 - v^2} - \frac{1}{\sqrt{c^2 - v^2}}\right]$$

$$= 2(l_1 + l_2)\left[\frac{c}{c^2\left(1 - \frac{v^2}{c^2}\right)} - \frac{1}{c\sqrt{1 - \frac{v^2}{c^2}}}\right]$$

$$= \frac{2(l_1 + l_2)}{c}\left[\left(1 + \frac{v^2}{c^2} + \frac{v^4}{c^4} + \cdots\right) - \left(1 + \frac{1}{2}\frac{v^2}{c^2} + \frac{3}{4}\frac{v^4}{c^4} + \cdots\right)\right]$$

$$= \frac{2(l_1 + l_2)}{c} \cdot \frac{1}{2}\frac{v^2}{c^2}$$

$$= \frac{(l_1 + l_2)v^2}{c^3}. \tag{27.7}$$

Hence, the corresponding path difference,

$$\Delta = (\tau_1 - \tau_2) \times c \quad \text{(where } c = \text{velocity of light)}$$

$$= (l_1 + l_2)\frac{v^2}{c^2}. \tag{27.8}$$

The theoretical result of the shift is about two-fifths of a fringe width. Careful experiment could not show any fringe shift formed by the interferometer. Thus the experiment proves that the aether is not dragged with matter when it moves through the aether.

27.4   Lorentz-Fitzgerald Contraction

The discrepancy found in Michelson's experimental values with those expected according to the idea of absolute space as distinct from the frame of reference moving with the earth was explained by Lorentz and Fitzgerald. For a suitable explanation of the null result of the Michelson-Morley's experiment, Fitzgerald suggested that the dimensions of the apparatus are changed as it is rotated through a right angle. In Fig. 27.1, let us therefore assume that at the rotated position l_1' and l_2' are the altered lengths of the arms AM_1 and AM_2, respectively.

Now in the initial position the time of retardation is expressed as

$$\tau_1 = 2 \left[\frac{l_2 c}{c^2 - v^2} - \frac{l_1}{\sqrt{c^2 - v^2}} \right] \quad \text{[by Eq. (27.5)]}.$$

In the rotated position by replacing l_1 by l_1' and l_2 by l_2' we can get the time of retardation, using Eq. (27.6). This can be written as

$$\tau_2 = 2 \left[\frac{l_2'}{\sqrt{c^2 - v^2}} - \frac{l_1' c}{c^2 - v^2} \right].$$

For the null result, we have $\tau_1 = \tau_2$

or, $\qquad \dfrac{l_2 c}{c^2 - v^2} - \dfrac{l_1}{\sqrt{c^2 - v^2}} = \dfrac{l_2'}{\sqrt{c^2 - v^2}} - \dfrac{l_1' c}{c^2 - v^2}$

or, $\qquad \dfrac{l_2'}{\sqrt{c^2 - v^2}} - \dfrac{l_2 c}{c^2 - v^2} = \dfrac{l_1' c}{c^2 - v^2} - \dfrac{l_1}{\sqrt{c^2 - v^2}}. \qquad (27.9)$

Relation (27.9) will be true, if

$$\frac{l_2 c}{l_2'} = \frac{c^2 - v^2}{\sqrt{c^2 - v^2}} = \sqrt{c^2 - v^2}$$

or, $\qquad \dfrac{l_2}{l_2'} = \sqrt{1 - \dfrac{v^2}{c^2}}. \qquad (27.10)$

Also, $\qquad \dfrac{l_1' c}{l_1} = \dfrac{c^2 - v^2}{\sqrt{c^2 - v^2}}$

or, $\qquad \dfrac{l_1'}{l_1} = \sqrt{1 - \dfrac{v^2}{c^2}}. \qquad (27.11)$

Eqs. (27.10) and (27.11) indicate that either arm of the interferometer contracts in the ratio $1 : \sqrt{1 - \frac{v^2}{c^2}}$.

27.5   Einstein's Postulates

Einstein, in 1905, successfully enunciated two postulates for explaining the discrepancies between the experimental observations and the prevailing ideas on relative motion and coordinate transformation. The two postulates of Einstein are stated below :

(1) It is impossible by any experimental technique to detect uniform motion of a body through free space or through any aether-like medium which might be assumed to pervade it.

(2) The velocity of light in free space is same for all inertial observers, independent of the relative velocity of the source of light and the observer.

It is clear that the first postulate is just an alternative way of asserting that the laws of physics are covariant in respect of all inertial systems of reference. Because if this were not so, then it would be possible to differentiate the various systems.

The second postulate also follows from a common sense. In a material medium, the velocity of waves is determined by its elasticity and density. The velocity of the source of light and the observer has the effect of changing the apparent length of the waves, but it does not alter the velocity of waves through the medium. This principle is known as the principle of constancy of the velocity of light.

It was observed that the above two postulates of Einstein remove the difficulties in explaining different experimental observations related to the velocity of light. The postulates also suitably explained the so-called emission theories where the light waves were assumed to be associated with the source of emission.

27.6   Newtonian Principle of Relativity : Galilean Transformation

The mechanical laws of Newton can be expressed as the proportional relationship between the force vector **k** and the acceleration by an equation,

$$\mathbf{k} = m\frac{d^2\mathbf{r}}{dt^2}. \tag{27.12}$$

Eq. (27.12) is satisfied in all systems and moving relatively to each other with a uniform motion. This is quite evident if we consider the transformation relationship for the two systems moving in the X-direction with a uniform relative motion, as

$$\left.\begin{array}{l} x' = x - vt \\ y' = y \\ z' = z \\ \text{and} \quad t' = t. \end{array}\right\} \tag{27.13}$$

The above transformation relationships are known as the Galilean transformations. With a constant value for v in relations (27.13), the primary dynamical relationship (27.12) is satisfied in any two systems moving relative to each other. This characteristic behaviour is called as the *Newtonian principle of relativity*. Alternatively, this can be stated in the form that all inertial frames are equivalent for the purpose of dynamical laws.

On the consideration of composition of velocities, the Galilean transformation gives us different laws of propagation of light in two systems which have a relative velocity between them. Therefore, if we assume the velocity of light in the co-ordinate system (x, y, z), then the law for the propagation of light may be put as

$$x^2 + y^2 + z^2 - (ct)^2 = 0. \tag{27.14}$$

When the Galilean transformation is applied in the primed system, the law is evidently changed as

$$x'^2 + y'^2 + z'^2 - (ct')^2 = 0. \tag{27.15}$$

It indicates that the law of propagation of light is not invariant to Galilean transformation.

Michelson-Morley experiment, in fact, tells us that the velocity of light remains invariant in the systems moving with a uniform relative velocity. Or, in other words, the laws expressed in Eqs. (27.14) and (27.15) should be identical in the form as

$$x^2 + y^2 + z^2 - c^2t^2 = x'^2 + y'^2 + z'^2 - c^2t'^2 = 0. \tag{27.16}$$

We may thus conclude that the speculated ether frame does not provide any preferential velocity of light over other frames of reference.

27.7 Lorentz Transformations

Let us assume that there be two rectangular systems of co-ordinates employed by the two systems S and S'. The axes of the S-system are parallel to the corresponding axes of the S'-system and that their relative motion is confined in the direction of one of the axes, say the X(or X')-axis. As shown in Fig. 27.3, let the speed of motion of S'-system with respect to S-system is equal to v. Let the two origins O and O' coincide at $t = 0$.

An observer in the S-system finds that the disturbance created at O has spread over a sphere of radius,

$$r = (x^2 + y^2 + z^2)^{\frac{1}{2}} \text{ in time } t.$$

So the velocity of light measured in the S-system is

$$r = ct$$

or, $\quad x^2 + y^2 + z^2 - c^2t^2 = 0. \tag{27.17}$

By the principle of constancy of velocity of light, we can say that the observer in the S'-system finds that in time t' the disturbance at O' has spread over a sphere of radius r', so that

$$r' = ct'$$

or, $\quad x'^2 + y'^2 + z'^2 - c^2t'^2 = r. \tag{27.18}$

Eqs. (27.17) and (27.18) must be equivalent.

Since the velocity v is considered along the X-direction, we may put,

$$y = y' \quad \text{and} \quad z = z'.$$

Subtracting Eq. (27.18) from Eq. (27.17) we get

$$x^2 - c^2t^2 = x'^2 - c^2t'^2. \tag{27.19}$$

Now, if the co-ordinates of the point P for the S- and S'-systems are (x, y, z) and (x', y', z') respectively, then the distance $O'P$ measured along the x-axis from the S-system is $(x - vt)$. Let the distance $O'P$ measured along the x-axis from the S'-system is x', when we get

$$x' = k(x - vt). \qquad (27.20)$$

Again, the distance OP measured from the S'-system is $(x' + vt')$. Then the distance OP measured from the S-system can be written as

$$x = k'(x' + vt'), \qquad (27.21)$$

where k and k' are undetermined multipliers.

If we eliminate x' between Eqs. (27.20) and (27.21), we get

$$\frac{t'}{k} = t - \frac{x}{v}\left(L - \frac{1}{kk'}\right). \qquad (27.22)$$

Putting the value of x' from Eq. (27.20) and t' from Eq. (27.21) in Eq. (27.19) we get

$$k^2(x^2 + v^2t^2 - 2xvt)$$

$$- k^2c^2\left[t^2 + \frac{x^2}{v^2}\left(1 - \frac{l}{kk'}\right)^2 - \frac{2xt}{v}\left(1 - \frac{1}{kk'}\right)\right] = x^2 - c^2t^2. \qquad (27.23)$$

Equating the coefficient of x^2, t^2 and x, t from both sides of Eq. (27.23) and substituting $\beta = \frac{v}{c}$, we get

$$k^2 - \frac{k^2c^2}{v^2}\left(1 - \frac{1}{kk'}\right) = 1$$

or, $$\beta^2\left(1 - \frac{1}{k^2}\right) = \left(1 - \frac{1}{kk'}\right)^2. \qquad (27.24a)$$

Also, $k^2v^2 - k^2c^2 = -c^2$

or $$\frac{1}{k^2} = 1 - \beta^2 \qquad (27.24b)$$

and $$-2k^2v + \frac{2k^2c^2}{v}\left(1 - \frac{1}{kk'}\right) = 0$$

or, $$\frac{1}{kk'} = 1 - \beta^2. \qquad (27.24c)$$

From Eqs. (27.24b) and (27.24c), we have

$$k = k' = \frac{1}{\sqrt{1 - \beta^2}}. \qquad (27.25)$$

If we now substitute the values of k and k' in Eqs. (27.20) and (27.22), we get

$$\left.\begin{array}{l} x' = \dfrac{x - vt}{\sqrt{1 - \beta^2}} \\[4mm] \text{and} \quad t' = \dfrac{t - \frac{vx}{c^2}}{\sqrt{1 - \beta^2}}. \end{array}\right\} \qquad (27.26)$$

These equations along with the equations $y = y'$ and $z = z'$ constitute the special Lorentz transformation formulae. From the very structure of Eq. (27.26), one can easily feel how intimately the space and time co-ordinates are mixed up.

Solving for x, y, z and t we also have the reverse relationship in the form

$$\left.\begin{array}{l} x = \dfrac{x' + vt'}{\sqrt{1 - \beta^2}} \\[3mm] y = y', \ z = z' \\[3mm] \text{and} \quad t = \dfrac{t' + \frac{vx'}{c^2}}{\sqrt{1 - \beta^2}}. \end{array}\right\} \tag{27.27}$$

We may thus generally conclude that the change of space co-ordinates involves a corresponding change in the time co-ordinates. Or, in other words, space and time are connected to each other. This, however, does not agree with the Newtonian and Galilean conception of space and time which assumed in the development of mechanics that time and space are absolute entities independent of each other. According to their conception, space is a fixed standard of reference while time always flows uniformly without reference to anything else. It may be mentioned in this connection that if we take the velocity of light to be infinity, then the relativistic space and time agree with the Newtonian space and time.

27.8 Contraction Simultaneity and Time Dilatation

The relative character of simultaneity of events in various inertial frames, the time dilatation and the Lorentz contraction may now be explored by relations derived from the Lorentz transformation which is a consequence of Einstein's postulate.

By the term length of any line of a body, we mean the distance between two points in space occupied by two end points of the line at any instant or simultaneously. Let us assume that a rod is lying at rest in the S'-system along the x'-axis, the co-ordinates of the end points of the rod being x_1' and x_2'. Now to find the length of the rod measured from the S-system, we may proceed in the following way :

From Eq. (27.21), we get

$$\begin{aligned} x_2 - x_1 &= k[(x_2' - x_1') + v(t_2' - t_1')] \\ &= k[l' + v(t_2' - t_1')] \quad \text{(putting, } x_2' - x_1' = l'\text{).} \end{aligned} \tag{27.28}$$

Also we have

$$\left.\begin{array}{l} y_2 - y_1 = y_2' - y_1' \\[2mm] \text{and} \quad z_2 - z_1 = z_2' - z_1' \end{array}\right\} \tag{27.29}$$

and from Eq. (27.27),

$$\begin{aligned} t_2 - t_1 &= k\left[(t_2' - t_1') + \dfrac{v}{c^2}(x_2' - x_1')\right] \\ &= k\left[(t_2' - t_1') + \dfrac{vl'}{c^2}\right]. \end{aligned} \tag{27.30}$$

As the rod is supposed to be measured from the S-system, the two ends of the rod are to be read simultaneously. Thus we have $t_2 = t_1$. Therefore, Eq. (27.30) reduces to

$$t_2' - t_1' = -\dfrac{vl'}{c^2}. \tag{27.31}$$

Putting this value in Eq. (27.28), we get

$$x_2 - x_1 = k\left(l' - \dfrac{v^2 l'}{c^2}\right)$$

or, $l = kl'(1 - \beta^2)$ $\left(\text{where } \beta = \dfrac{v}{c} \right)$

$$= \frac{l' \cdot (1 - \beta^2)}{\sqrt{1 - \beta^2}}$$

$$= l'\sqrt{1 - \beta^2}. \tag{27.32}$$

We thus find that the apparent length of a rod of velocity v moving with respect to a frame of reference at rest is smaller than its length at rest. This is true for whether the body is moving towards or away from the frame at rest. When the rod is kept perpendicularly to the direction of motion, then the length of the rod remains unchanged.

Eq. (27.32) above gives us the Lorentz contraction. Following the contraction of length, there would be a contraction in volume which is obtained by using the relation

$$V = V'\sqrt{1 - \beta^2}, \tag{27.33}$$

where V' is the rest volume measured in a frame where both the body and the observer are relatively at rest.

To discuss the problem of simultaneity, it is required to be more clear about its significance. If we consider two events to take place in an inertial frame Σ, with co-ordinates (x, y, z, t) their points of occurrence may differ as (x_1, y_1, z_1) and (x_2, y_2, z_2) with the times of occurrence different from each other $(t_1 \neq t_2)$ or the same $(t_1 = t_2)$. When the times of occurrence of the events are identical, we consider the events to be simultaneous in the Σ-frame.

Now, it would appear from Eq. (27.30) that two instants of time which are simultaneous in the S'-system are not so when measured from the S-system. If two instants t'_2 and r'_1 are considered simultaneous, then $t'_2 - t'_1 = 0$. Then Eq. (27.30) becomes

$$t_2 - t_1 = k\frac{vl'}{c^2}$$

or, $\Delta t = \dfrac{vl'}{c^2\sqrt{1 - \beta^2}}.$ \hfill (27.34)

This indicates that the two events which are simultaneous in the S'-system moving with a velocity v with respect to the S-system are not simultaneous if observed from the S-system.

Let us next assume that the events are occurring at regular intervals $\Delta t'$ at a fixed point x' in the S'-system which is moving with velocity v with respect to S-system. In this case, $l' = 0$ and so when measured from the S-system, the corresponding time would be

$$\Delta t = \frac{\Delta t'}{\sqrt{1 - \beta^2}}. \tag{27.35}$$

Eq. (27.35) is called the *Einstein's time dilatation*.

27.9   Addition Theorem of Velocities

The addition theorem of velocities is derived on the basis of the Lorentz transformations. The theorem reveals one why the velocity of light c is not changed in various relatively moving co-ordinate frames.

To establish the theorem, let us consider two co-ordinate frames Σ and Σ', where the frame Σ' is moving relatively forward direction of the x-axis with a uniform velocity v. We also assume that a point associated with the Σ' frame has a velocity $\mathbf{u}'$ with its components $u'x$, $u'y$ and $u'z$. Using the relations of Lorentz transformation the components of $\mathbf{u}$ in the Σ-frame may be correlated with those of Σ'-frame. We thus have,

$$u_x = \frac{dx}{dt} = \frac{d}{dt}\left[\frac{x' + vt'}{\sqrt{1-\beta^2}}\right]$$

$$= \frac{1}{\sqrt{1-\beta^2}}\left[\frac{dx'}{dt'}\frac{dt'}{dt} + v\frac{dt'}{dt}\right]. \tag{27.36}$$

Again, $\dfrac{dt}{dt'} = \dfrac{d}{dt'}\left[\dfrac{t' + v\frac{x'}{c^2}}{\sqrt{1-\beta^2}}\right]$

$$= \frac{1}{\sqrt{1-\beta^2}}\left[1 + v\frac{u'_x}{c^2}\right] \quad \left(\text{putting, } u'_x = \frac{dx'}{dt'}\right)$$

or, $\qquad \dfrac{dt'}{dt} = \sqrt{1-\beta^2}\left[\dfrac{1}{1 + v\frac{u'_x}{c^2}}\right]. \tag{27.37}$

Eq. (27.36) can now be rewritten as

$$u_x = \frac{dt'}{dt}\cdot\frac{1}{\sqrt{1-\beta^2}}\left[u'_x + v\right]$$

$$= \frac{u'_x + v}{1 + v\frac{u'_x}{c^2}} \quad \text{[by Eq. (27.37)]}. \tag{27.38}$$

The interrelations between the other components of $\mathbf{u}$ in the two frames can then be obtained as

$$u_y = \frac{dy}{dt} = \frac{dy}{dt'}\frac{dt'}{dt}$$

$$= u'_y\frac{\sqrt{1-\beta^2}}{1 + v\frac{u'_x}{c^2}} \tag{27.39}$$

and $\quad u_x = \dfrac{dz}{dt} = \dfrac{dz}{dt'}\dfrac{dt'}{dt}$

$$= u'_x\frac{\sqrt{1-\beta^2}}{1 + v\frac{u'_x}{c^2}}. \tag{27.40}$$

Eqs. (27.38), (27.39) and (27.40) give us the laws to be satisfied for the addition of velocities.

27.9.1 Velocity of Light, Maximum Velocity

If two velocities, each of which is less than the velocity of light, are superposed, then it is not possible to get a velocity higher than that of light. Let v' be the velocity of a body with respect to S'-system which relative to S-system moves with a velocity v. We assume that both the velocities v and v' are less than the velocity of light c. We then have

$$\frac{v}{c} < 1 \quad \text{or,} \quad \beta < 1 \quad \text{and} \quad \frac{v'}{c} < 1 \quad \text{or,} \quad \beta' < 1.$$

Therefore, we can write,

$$(1 - \beta)(1 - \beta') > 0 \quad \text{or,} \quad 1 - (\beta + \beta') + \beta\beta' > 0$$

$$\text{or,} \quad (1 + \beta\beta') > (\beta + \beta') \quad \text{or,} \quad \frac{\beta + \beta'}{1 + \beta\beta'} < 1$$

$$\text{or,} \quad \frac{\frac{1}{c}(v + v')}{1 + v\frac{v'}{c^2}} < 1 \quad \text{or,} \quad \frac{v + v'}{1 + v\frac{v'}{c^2}} < c.$$

If the S'-system moves with a velocity c and if the body moves with a velocity v' with respect to S'-system, then the velocity of the body with respect to S-system is

$$\frac{c + v'}{1 + c\frac{v'}{c^2}} = c.$$

Also, if $v' = c$, then again the velocity of the body with respect to S-system is c. Hence, we can conclude that the velocity of a body can never exceed the velocity of light.

27.9.2   Dragging of Light by a Moving Medium

An immediate consequence of the velocity-addition theorem is an explanation of the experimental results of Fizeau is 1851.

The experiment that was performed by Fizeau was on the velocity of light in a medium of refractive index n which itself was moving in the form of water through a tube. Then by definition of refractive index, the velocity of light in the medium is $\frac{c}{n}$, where c is the velocity of light in free space. But a stationary observer in the laboratory finds that the velocity of light is neither equal to $\frac{c}{n}$ nor equal to the sum of the velocities of light and the medium but is determined by the relation,

$$u = \frac{c}{n} + av, \tag{27.41}$$

where $a = \left(1 - \frac{1}{n^2}\right)$ and is called the *dragging coefficient*. The above relation is obtained by applying the velocity-addition theorem in the following way :

Let us assume that the water is moving with a velocity u along the x-direction. The velocity of light associated with Σ'-frame, with respect to the flowing water is taken as u'_x, where $u'_x = \frac{c}{n}$. The observer stationed in the laboratory is required to find the velocity u_x of light passing through the flowing medium. With the help of velocity-addition relationship, we have

$$u_x = \frac{u'_x + v}{1 + v\frac{u'_x}{c^2}} = \frac{\frac{c}{n} + v}{1 + \frac{v}{c^2} \cdot \frac{c}{n}} \quad \left(\text{putting } u'_x = \frac{c}{n}\right)$$

$$= \frac{\frac{c}{n} + v}{1 + \frac{v}{cn}}$$

$$\text{or,} \quad u_x = \frac{c}{n} + v\left(1 - \frac{1}{n^2}\right) \quad \text{(neglecting the second order term).} \tag{27.42}$$

A correction is further required in equation (27.42) on account of the Doppler effect. The additional term so required when included the expression becomes

$$u_x = \frac{c}{n} + v\left(1 - \frac{1}{n^2} - \frac{\lambda}{n}\frac{dn}{d\lambda}\right). \tag{27.43}$$

This correction is worked out on account of the dispersive nature of the medium where the Doppler effect would produce a change of wavelength in the moving medium. The correction was verified by Zeeman in 1914.

27.10 Doppler Effect and Aberration of Light

Applying the Lorentz transformation relation, one can obtain the relativistic Doppler effect for the propagation of light waves in different frames of reference as well as the aberration of light from the stars. For the purpose, let us consider a source of light S' at rest in the Σ' frame sending out spherical waves. In this frame, the wave equation can be written in the standard form as

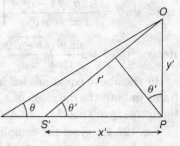

Fig. 27.4

$$S' = A' \exp\left[2\pi i v'\left(t' - \frac{r'}{c}\right) + i\delta'\right]. \quad (27.44)$$

Let an observer at O is at rest in the Σ-frame where the spherical wave is supposed to meet (Fig. 27.4). The co-ordinates of O in the Σ-frame are (x, y) and in the Σ'-frame (x', y'). The direction of relative velocity v between the frames is along the x- and x'-axis. The ray frame S' to O makes an angle θ' with the x'-axis, so that we have

$$r' = x' \cos\theta' + y' \sin\theta'. \quad (27.45)$$

Substituting the value of r' in Eq. (27.44), we get

$$S' = A' \exp\left[2\pi i v'\left(t' - \frac{x' \cos\theta' + y' \sin\theta'}{c}\right) + i\delta'\right].$$

Again, for the stationary observer in the Σ-frame, the light is considered to be coming from a point source in its own system and therefore its wave equation can be expressed as

$$S = A \exp\left[2\pi i v\left(t - \frac{x \cos\theta + y \sin\theta}{c}\right) + i\delta\right]. \quad (27.46)$$

Since the phase in the waveform of expression is invariant to transformation of co-ordinates, we may write,

$$\exp 2\pi i v'\left(t' - \frac{x' \cos\theta' + y' \sin\theta'}{c}\right) = \exp 2\pi i v\left(t - \frac{x \cos\theta + y \sin\theta}{c}\right). \quad (27.47)$$

The co-ordinates in Eq. (27.47) are correlated by the Lorentz transformation. We may therefore write,

$$2\pi i v'\left(\frac{t - \frac{vx}{c^2}}{\sqrt{1 - \beta^2}} - \frac{x - vt \cos\theta'}{c\sqrt{1 - \beta^2}} - \frac{y \sin\theta'}{c}\right)$$

$$= 2\pi i v\left(\frac{t - x \cos\theta + y \sin\theta}{c}\right). \quad (27.48)$$

Equating the coefficients of t, x and y from the above relations, we get

$$v = \frac{v'(1 \pm \beta \cos\theta')}{\sqrt{1 - \beta^2}}. \quad (27.49)$$

$$\left.\begin{array}{l}\cos\theta = \dfrac{\cos\theta' \pm \beta}{1 \pm \beta\cos\theta} \\[4mm] \text{and} \quad \sin\theta = \dfrac{\sin\theta'\sqrt{1-\beta^2}}{1 \pm \beta\cos\theta'}.\end{array}\right\} \tag{27.50}$$

Hence, $\quad \tan\theta = \dfrac{\sin\theta'\sqrt{1-\beta^2}}{\cos\theta' \pm \beta}. \tag{27.51}$

In the above equations for incorporating the effect of the relative motion of Σ-frame in both the direction of x, +ve and −ve signs both have been included before the terms involving β.

Eq. (27.49) gives the complete expression for the relativistic Doppler effect. It is seen from the equation that for $\cos\theta' = 0$, i.e., when the light source moves at right angles to the direction from which it is observed, we have

$$v = \frac{v'}{\sqrt{1-\beta^2}}. \tag{27.52}$$

Then the Doppler effect persists unlike the non-relativistic case.

Aberration of Stars

The two relations of Eq. (27.50) determine the aberration of light from the stars. We know that the earth suffers a reversal of the direction of motion in every six months. So the displacement of the apparent position of the stars which are sending light to the earth reverses in the course of the year. This phenomenon was discovered by Bradley in 1728 and is known as the *aberration of stars*.

When the star in its Σ'-frame is overhead, the magnitude of the aberration from the relationship between the cosine terms in Eq. (27.50), we then have

$$\theta' = \frac{\pi}{2}.$$

$\therefore \quad \cos\theta = \pm\dfrac{v}{c}. \tag{27.53}$

27.11   Geometrical Representation of Relativistic Motion

We have found that the fundamental principle of the theory of relativity can be expressed in the form

$$x^2 + y^2 + z^2 - c^2t^2 = x'^2 + y'^2 + z'^2 - c^2t'^2.$$

If we put $\tau = ict$ and $\tau' = ict'$, then the above equation becomes

$$x^2 + y^2 + z^2 + \tau^2 = x'^2 + y'^2 + z'^2 + \tau'^2. \tag{27.54}$$

The expression for both sides of Eq. (27.54) has a significant implications on a geometrical basis if we restrict to two- or three-dimensional space. In plane geometry, for two rectangular systems (x, y) and (x', y') with the same origin, we have the representation of the vector $\mathbf{A}$ from the origin in the form,

$$\mathbf{A}^2 = x^2 + y^2 = x'^2 + y'^2. \tag{27.55}$$

A similar type of representation can also be extended to the three- or four-dimensional rectangular co-ordinate frames by the relation,

$$S^2 = x^2 + y^2 + z^2 + \tau^2 = x'^2 + y'^2 + z'^2 + \tau'^2. \tag{27.56}$$

The four-dimensional space with co-ordinates x, y, z and t is called the *four-dimensional world*. If the world line element is denoted by ds, then we have

$$ds^2 = dx^2 + dy^2 + dz^2 + d\tau^2 = dx'^2 + dy'^2 + dz'^2 + d\tau'^2. \qquad (27.57)$$

For further development of the geometrical idea, we may consider

$$v^2 = \left(\frac{dx}{dt}\right)^2 + \left(\frac{dy}{dt}\right)^2 + \left(\frac{dz}{dt}\right)^2,$$

so that we have

$$\left(\frac{ds}{dt}\right)^2 = v^2 - c^2. \qquad (27.58)$$

Hence, $\qquad \dfrac{dt}{ds} = \dfrac{1}{ic} \dfrac{1}{\sqrt{1-\beta^2}}. \qquad (27.59)$

Further, $\cos(ds, x) = \dfrac{dx}{ds} = \dfrac{dx}{dt}\dfrac{dt}{ds}$

$$= \frac{v_x}{ic\sqrt{1-\beta^2}} \qquad (27.60)$$

and $\qquad \cos(ds, \tau) = \dfrac{d\tau}{ds} = ic\dfrac{dt}{ds}$

$$= \frac{1}{\sqrt{1-\beta^2}}. \qquad (27.61)$$

The relation in equation (27.60) under the imposed conditions would satisfy the following :

$$\cos(ds, x) = \cos(ds, y) = \cos(ds, z) = 0, \ \cos(ds, \tau) = 1.$$

27.12 Minkowski Space

The world line element in the four-dimensional space is written as

$$ds^2 = dx^2 + dy^2 + dz^2 + d\tau^2.$$

This can be rewritten, in terms of the real quantities, as

$$ds^2 = dx_1^2 + dx_2^2 + dx_3^2 - dx_4^2, \qquad (27.62)$$

where instead of $\tau = ict$ we have put $x_4 = ct$. The co-ordinates x_1, x_2, x_3 here stand for x, y and z.

If we put $s = is_t$, then we can write,

$$ds_t^2 = dx_4^2 - (dx_1^2 + dx_2^2 + dx_3^2). \qquad (27.63)$$

Now, the equations for the variation of the time co-ordinates with s are written in the form,

$$\frac{dt}{ds} = \frac{1}{ic}\sqrt{1-\beta^2} \qquad (27.64)$$

$$\frac{dt}{ds_t} = \pm\frac{1}{c\sqrt{1-\beta^2}}$$

or, $\qquad \dfrac{dx_4}{ds_t} = \dfrac{1}{\sqrt{1-\beta^2}}. \qquad (27.65)$

In Eq. (27.65) we have kept only the positive sign to assure that s_t increases with time. Again, the co-ordinates x_1, x_2, x_3, x_4 enable us to rewrite the Lorentz transformation as

$$\left.\begin{aligned} x_1' &= \frac{x_1 - \beta x}{\sqrt{1 - \beta^2}} \\ x_2' &= x_2, \; x_3' = x_3 \\ x_4' &= \frac{x_4 - \beta x_1}{\sqrt{1 - \beta^2}}. \end{aligned}\right\} \tag{27.66}$$

The space generally represented by the real co-ordinates x_1, x_2, x_3 and x_4 is known as *Minkowski space*. The imaginary character of the four-dimensional space due to the mutually perpendicular co-ordinates x, y, z, τ thus eliminated.

The peculiarities in the four-vector S and S_t give us to divide the Minkowski space as the spatial and temporal regions. The two relations determining the four vectors s and s_t can be considered as

$$s^2 = x_1^2 + x_2^2 + x_3^2 - x_4^2$$

and $\quad s_t^2 = x_4^2 - (x_1^2 + x_2^2 + x_3^2)$.

In a reference system which is moving with the point at the origin, we have x_1, x_2, x_3 as zero and so

$$s_t^2 = x_4^2 = (ct_0)^2. \tag{27.66a}$$

In view of Eqs. (27.65) and (27.66a) the local and the proper times may be interrelated as

$$\frac{dt}{dt_0} = \frac{1}{\sqrt{1 - \beta^2}}. \tag{27.67}$$

27.12.1   Minkowski Space and Lorentz Transformation

We can express x_1' and x_4' in the form

$$\left.\begin{aligned} x_1' &= ax_1 + bx_4 \\ x_4' &= cx_1 + dx_4 \end{aligned}\right\}. \tag{27.68}$$

For the point $x_1' = 1$ and $x_4' = 0$ we have in view of the constructional procedure the relations,

$$\left.\begin{aligned} x_1^2 - x_4^2 &= +1 \\ x_4 &= \beta x_1 \end{aligned}\right\}. \tag{27.69}$$

Hence, we get

$$\left.\begin{aligned} x_1 &= \frac{1}{\sqrt{1 - \beta^2}} \\ \text{and} \quad x_4 &= \frac{\beta}{\sqrt{1 - \beta^2}}. \end{aligned}\right\} \tag{27.70}$$

From equations (27.68), we get

$$\left.\begin{aligned} x_1' = 1 &= \frac{a}{\sqrt{1 - \beta^2}} + \frac{b\beta}{\sqrt{1 - \beta^2}} \\ x_4' = 0 &= \frac{c}{\sqrt{1 - \beta^2}} + \frac{d\beta}{\sqrt{1 - \beta^2}} \end{aligned}\right\}. \tag{27.71}$$

In a similar way, for the point $x_1' = 0$ and $x_4' = 1$, the co-ordinates x_1 and x_4 satisfy the relations,

$$\left.\begin{array}{c} x_1^2 - x_4^2 = -1 \\ x_1 = \beta x_4 \end{array}\right\} . \tag{27.72}$$

Hence, we get

$$\left.\begin{array}{c} x_4 = \dfrac{1}{\sqrt{1 - \beta^2}} \\[3mm] x_1 = \dfrac{\beta}{\sqrt{1 - \beta^2}} \end{array}\right\} . \tag{27.73}$$

As before, we have

$$\left.\begin{array}{c} x_1' = 0 = \dfrac{a\beta}{\sqrt{1 - \beta^2}} + \dfrac{b}{\sqrt{1 - \beta^2}} \\[3mm] x_4' = 1 = \dfrac{c\beta}{\sqrt{1 - \beta^2}} + \dfrac{d}{\sqrt{1 - \beta^2}} \end{array}\right\} . \tag{27.74}$$

Solving Eqs. (27.71) and (27.74), we get

$$\left.\begin{array}{c} a = d = \dfrac{1}{\sqrt{1 - \beta^2}} \\[3mm] b = c = -\dfrac{\beta}{\sqrt{1 - \beta^2}} \end{array}\right\} . \tag{27.75}$$

Putting these values of a, b, c and d we get from Eq. (27.68) the Lorentz transformation relations,

$$\left.\begin{array}{c} x_1' = \dfrac{x_1 - \beta x_4}{\sqrt{1 - \beta^2}} \\[3mm] x_4' = \dfrac{x_4 - \beta x_1}{\sqrt{1 - \beta^2}} \end{array}\right\} . \tag{27.76}$$

27.13 Variation of Mass with Velocity

In dynamical relations, velocity, momentum and force are the fundamental entities. We know that the usual velocity and momentum are determined by differentiating with respect to time. According to the theory of relativity, a time scale is specific for a particular frame. We are, therefore, required to extend the conception to four-dimensional space.

As regards the spatial four-vector, we can take the world line element ds with components dx_1, dx_2, dx_3 and dx_4 or $d\tau$. We may now define a four-dimensional velocity q by the relation,

$$q = \frac{ds}{dt_0}, \tag{27.77}$$

whose components are

$$\frac{dx}{dt_0}, \frac{dy}{dt_0}, \frac{dz}{dt_0} \quad \text{and} \quad ic\frac{dt}{dt_0}.$$

It is possible to correlate the four-dimensional and three-dimensional velocity components by using the relationship between the proper time t_0 and the local time

t. We thus have

$$q_x = \frac{dx}{dt_0} = \frac{dx}{dt}\frac{dt}{dt_0}$$

$$= \frac{v_x}{\sqrt{1-\beta^2}}. \qquad (27.78a)$$

Similarly, $q_y = \dfrac{v_y}{\sqrt{1-\beta^2}} \qquad (27.78b)$

and $\qquad q_z = \dfrac{v_z}{\sqrt{1-\beta^2}}. \qquad (27.78c)$

For the fourth component q_τ, we have

$$q_\tau = \frac{ic}{\sqrt{1-\beta^2}}; \quad q_4 = \frac{c}{\sqrt{1-\beta^2}}. \qquad (27.78d)$$

The above components define the four-velocity q as

$$q = (q_x^2 + q_y^2 + q_z^2 + q_\tau^2)^{\frac{1}{2}} = [(v^2 - c^2)/(1-\beta^2)]^{\frac{1}{2}}$$

or, $\qquad q = ic. \qquad (27.79)$

The four-velocity q can alternately be defined by using the relation,

$$q = \frac{ds}{ds_t} = i \qquad (27.80)$$

in view of the relation, $s_t = ct_0$.

Next, let us define the force $\mathbf{K}$ in three dimensions as the rate of change of momentum in the form,

$$\mathbf{K} = \frac{d}{dt}(m\,v)$$

or, $\qquad K_x = \dfrac{d}{dt}(mv_x), \qquad (27.81)$

where m is the mass and v the three-dimensional velocity. Changing to four-vector relationship, the four-force $\mathbf{P}$ can be written in the form,

$$\left.\begin{aligned} \mathbf{P} &= \frac{d}{dt_0}(m_0 q) \\ \text{or,} \quad P_x &= \frac{d}{dt_0}(m_0 q_x) \end{aligned}\right\} \qquad (27.82)$$

where like m_0, t_0 is a four-dimensional invariant.

In view of the interrelationship between t and t_0, viz., $dt = \dfrac{dt_0}{\sqrt{1-\beta^2}}$, the x and τ components of $\mathbf{P}$ can then be expressed as

$$P_x = \frac{1}{\sqrt{1-\beta^2}}\frac{d}{dt}\left(\frac{m_0 v_x}{\sqrt{1-\beta^2}}\right) \qquad (27.83)$$

$$P_\tau = \frac{1}{\sqrt{1-\beta^2}}\frac{d}{dt}\left(\frac{m_0 ic}{\sqrt{1-\beta^2}}\right). \qquad (27.84)$$

Comparing Eqs. (27.83) and (27.81), we get

$$P_x = \frac{1}{\sqrt{1-\beta^2}}K_x, \qquad (27.85)$$

where m in Eq. (27.81) is determined by the relation,

$$m = \frac{m_0}{\sqrt{1 - \beta^2}} \qquad (27.86)$$

by comparing Eqs. (27.81) and (27.83).

Eq. (27.86) indicates that the mass m of a body is not constant in all frames of reference but it depends on the velocity of the frame in which the body is placed. It may, however, be pointed out that in most of the terrestrial observations the magnitude of β is extremely small and so for all practical purposes the effect of the change of mass is undetectable. For that reason, in order to solve the usual dynamical problems we may proceed with the idea of constancy of mass.

27.13.1 Transverse and Longitudinal Mass

In non-relativistic case, the resultant force can be defined as the product of mass of the body and its acceleration vectorially. But in relativistic case, there is one fundamental difference. In this case, the force vector and the acceleration vector may not be even parallel to each other. This arises because of the presence of the factor $\sqrt{1 - \frac{v^2}{c^2}}$ in the expression for momentum.

The net force $\mathbf{K}$ can be expressed as

$$\mathbf{K} = \frac{d\mathbf{P}}{dt} = \frac{d}{dt}\left(\frac{m_0 \mathbf{v}}{\sqrt{1 - \frac{v^2}{c^2}}} \right)$$

$$= \frac{m_0}{\sqrt{1 - \frac{v^2}{c^2}}}\mathbf{v} + \frac{m_0(\mathbf{v} \cdot \dot{\mathbf{v}})/c^2}{\sqrt{\left(1 - \frac{v^2}{c^2}\right)^3}}\mathbf{v}. \qquad (27.87)$$

Eq. (27.87) shows that the force $\mathbf{K}$ is not simply parallel to $\dot{\mathbf{v}}\left(= \frac{dv}{dt}\right)$, the acceleration; rather it is the sum of two vectors. One of the vectors which is parallel to a $\dot{\mathbf{v}}$ arises due to the change in the velocity of the body while the other vector parallel to $\mathbf{v}$ arises due to the change in the mass of the body consequent upon the change in magnitude of its velocity as a result of acceleration.

When the force acts in an arbitrary direction, it can be resolved into the longitudinal and transverse directions. The Eq. (27.87) can thus be transformed into two relations as :

(i) When the acceleration of the body is perpendicular to its velocity, we have

$$\mathbf{K}_t = \frac{m_0}{\sqrt{1 - \frac{v^2}{c^2}}}\dot{\mathbf{v}}, \qquad (27.88)$$

where the coefficient of $\dot{\mathbf{v}}$ is referred to as the *transverse* mass of the body.

(ii) When the acceleration of the body is either parallel or anti-parallel to its velocity, we have

$$\mathbf{K}_l = \frac{m_0}{\sqrt{\left(1 - \frac{v^2}{c^2}\right)^3}}\dot{\mathbf{v}}, \qquad (27.89)$$

where the coefficient of $\dot{\mathbf{v}}$ is referred to as the *longitudinal* mass of the body.

Here both the masses appear as the *effective* mass of the body when subjected to a transverse or a longitudinal acceleration respectively.

27.14   Mass-Energy Equivalence

In order to establish the relationship between the mass and the energy content of
a body either in the moving or in the stationary condition, let us study the scalar
product of the three-dimensional force and the velocity $\mathbf{K} \cdot \mathbf{v}$ in relation to the four-
dimensional force and velocity $\mathbf{P} \cdot \mathbf{q}$. Now, the rate at which work is done by a force
$\mathbf{K}$ acting on a body which moves with an instantaneous velocity $\mathbf{v}$ is expressed by
the formula,

$$\frac{dW}{dt} = \mathbf{K}\mathbf{v}. \tag{27.90}$$

On the other hand, if we put the explicit form of $\mathbf{P}$ and set the scalar product
with $\mathbf{q}$, we get

$$\mathbf{P} \cdot \mathbf{q} = P_r q_r + P_\tau q_\tau \tag{27.91}$$

expressing the x, y, z components together as the r-component.

Again, the four-force $\mathbf{P}$ is written in the form,

$$\mathbf{P} = \frac{d}{dt_0}(m_0 \mathbf{q}).$$

$$\therefore \quad \mathbf{P}\mathbf{q} = \frac{d}{dt_0}(m_0 \mathbf{q})\mathbf{q} = \frac{1}{2}\frac{d}{dt_0}(m_0 q^2) = -\frac{1}{2}\frac{d}{dt_0}(m_0 c^2) \quad \text{(putting } q = ic)$$

$$= 0.$$

Hence Eq. (27.91) can be written as

$$P_r q_r + P_\tau q_\tau = 0. \tag{27.92}$$

To simplify the above equation, we utilise the relations given below :

$$P_r = \frac{d}{dt_0}(m_0 q_r) = \frac{1}{\sqrt{1 - v^2/c^2}}K$$

$$P_\tau = \frac{d}{dt_0}\left(\frac{m_0 ic}{\sqrt{1 - v^2/c^2}}\right) = \frac{1}{\sqrt{1 - v^2/c^2}}\frac{d}{dt}\left(\frac{m_0 ic}{\sqrt{1 - v^2/c^2}}\right) \tag{27.93}$$

$$q_r = \frac{\mathbf{v}}{\sqrt{1 - v^2/c^2}}$$

$$q_\tau = \frac{ic}{\sqrt{1 - v^2/c^2}}.$$

Then we get

$$P_r q_r = \frac{\mathbf{K} \cdot \mathbf{v}}{(1 - v^2/c^2)}$$

and $$P_\tau q_\tau = -\frac{d}{dt}\left(\frac{m_0 c^2}{\sqrt{1 - v^2/c^2}}\right) \Big/ (1 - v^2/c^2). \tag{27.94}$$

Substituting the values of $P_r q_r$ and $P_\tau q_\tau$ in equation (27.92), we get

$$\mathbf{K} \cdot \mathbf{v} = \frac{d}{dt}\left(\frac{m_0 c^2}{\sqrt{1 - v^2/c^2}}\right)$$

or, $$\frac{dW}{dt} = \frac{d}{dt}\left(\frac{m_0 c^2}{\sqrt{1 - v^2/c^2}}\right) \left(\because \frac{dW}{dt} = \mathbf{K} \cdot \mathbf{v}\right). \tag{27.95}$$

By integrating over time from the initial to the final state of motion, we obtain the kinetic energy as

$$W = \frac{m_0 c^2}{\sqrt{1 - v^2/c^2}} \bigg|_0^v = \left[\frac{m_0}{\sqrt{1 - v^2/c^2}} - m_0 \right] c^2$$

$$= (m - m_0)c^2, \tag{27.96}$$

where m is the relativistic mass of the body.

Eq. (27.96) thus reveals that the kinetic energy acquired by a body is directly proportional to the change in the mass of the body brought about by its motion. In the formula, mc^2 is the total energy of the body when moving with a velocity v and $m_0 c^2$ is the rest energy. The kinetic energy W is thus the difference between the total energy and the rest energy, i.e.,

$$W = E - E_0, \tag{27.97}$$

where $E = mc^2.$ (27.98)

Eq. (27.98) is the famous relation constituting a remarkable conclusion of the special theory of relativity. The changes in the kinetic energy of the body with changes in its mass are, therefore, connected by the linear relationship in the form,

$$\Delta E = \Delta mc^2 \tag{27.99}$$

or, $\Delta m = \dfrac{\Delta E}{c^2}.$ (27.100)

Eq. (27.100) gives the principle of the mass-energy equivalence. It indicates that a loss of energy by radiation is equivalent to a loss of mass. The above relation thus suggests that on account of the enormous amount of radiation the loss of mass of the sun or of the stars is worth consideration.

27.15   Relativistic Formula for Kinetic Energy

The relativistic formula for kinetic energy is written as

$$T = mc^2 - m_0 c^2 = \frac{m_0 c^2}{\sqrt{1 - v^2/c^2}} - m_0 c^2$$

$$= m_0 c^2 \left(\frac{1}{\sqrt{1 - v^2/c^2}} - 1 \right). \tag{27.101}$$

Thus it is different from the expression $\frac{1}{2} m_0 v^2$ obtained in classical mechanics. The difference becomes more prominent when v is comparable to the velocity of light c.

At low speeds, $v \ll c$; the relativistic expression then reduces to the classical one. This can be established in the following way :

Expanding $1/\sqrt{1 - v^2/c^2}$, i.e., $(1 - v^2/c^2)^{-1/2}$ binomially and keeping only the first two terms (since $c \gg v$), we get from Eq. (27.101),

$$T = m_0 c^2 \left\{ \left(1 + \frac{v^2}{2c^2} + \cdots \right) - 1 \right\}$$

$$\simeq \frac{1}{2} m_0 v^2, \tag{27.102}$$

the Eq. (27.102) represents the classical expression for the kinetic energy.

27.15.1   Proof of an Important Relation

$$\sqrt{1 - \frac{u'^2}{c^2}} = \frac{\sqrt{\left(1 - \frac{v^2}{c^2}\right)\left(1 - \frac{u^2}{c^2}\right)}}{1 - \frac{v}{c^2}u_x}$$

Proof :   Let u and u' be the velocities of a particle in S- and S'-frames respectively. Then from velocity addition theorem, we can write,

$$u'_x = \frac{u_x - v}{1 - \frac{v}{c^2}u_x}; \quad u'_y = \frac{u_y\sqrt{1 - v^2/c^2}}{1 - \frac{v}{c^2}u_x}; \quad u'_z = \frac{u_z\sqrt{1 - v^2/c^2}}{1 - \frac{v}{c^2}u_x}, \qquad (27.103)$$

where u_x, u_y, u_z and u'_x, u'_y, u'_z are the component velocities.

$$\therefore \quad u'^2 = u'^2_x + u'^2_y + u'^2_z = \frac{(u_x - v)^2 + (u^2_y + u^2_z)(1 - v^2/c^2)}{(1 - u_x v/c^2)^2}, \text{ using Eq. (27.103)}.$$

$$\therefore \quad \frac{u'^2}{c^2} = \frac{\left(\frac{u_x}{c} - \frac{v}{c}\right)^2 + \left(\frac{u^2}{c^2} - \frac{u^2_x}{c^2}\right)\left(1 - \frac{v^2}{c^2}\right)}{\left(1 - \frac{u_x v}{c^2}\right)^2}, \quad (\because \; u^2_y + u^2_z = u^2 - u^2_x)$$

$$1 - \frac{u'^2}{c^2} = \frac{\left(1 - \frac{u_x v}{c^2}\right)^2 - \left(\frac{u_x}{c} - \frac{v}{c}\right)^2 - \left(\frac{u^2}{c^2} - \frac{u^2_x}{c^2}\right)\left(1 - \frac{v^2}{c^2}\right)}{\left(1 - \frac{v}{c^2}u_x\right)^2}$$

$$= \frac{\left(1 + \frac{v^2}{c^4}u^2_x - \frac{2u_x v}{c^2}\right) - \left(\frac{u^2_x}{c^2} + \frac{v^2}{c^2} - \frac{2u_x v}{c^2}\right) - \left(\frac{u^2}{c^2} - \frac{u^2 v^2}{c^4} - \frac{u^2_x}{c^2} + \frac{v^2 u^2_x}{c^4}\right)}{\left(1 - \frac{v}{c^2}u_x\right)^2}$$

$$= \frac{\left(1 - \frac{v^2}{c^2}\right) - \frac{u^2}{c^2}\left(1 - \frac{v^2}{c^2}\right)}{\left(1 - \frac{v}{c^2}u_x\right)^2} = \frac{\left(1 - \frac{v^2}{c^2}\right)\left(1 - \frac{u^2}{c^2}\right)}{\left(1 - \frac{v}{c^2}u_x\right)^2}.$$

Hence, $\sqrt{1 - \frac{u'^2}{c^2}} = \dfrac{\sqrt{\left(1 - \frac{v^2}{c^2}\right)\left(1 - \frac{u^2}{c^2}\right)}}{1 - \frac{v}{c^2}u_x}.$ \hfill (27.104)

27.16   Transformation Formulae for Momentum, Energy and Force

Momentum

When a particle of mass m moves with velocity **u**, its momentum is $\mathbf{p} = m\mathbf{u}$. Thus the components of momentum in S-frame are :

$$p_x = mu_x = \frac{m_0 u_x}{\sqrt{1 - u^2/c^2}}; \quad p_y = mu_y = \frac{m_0 u_y}{\sqrt{1 - u^2/c^2}}; \quad p_z = mu_z = \frac{m_0 u_z}{\sqrt{1 - u^2/c^2}},$$

where u_x, u_y, u_z represent the component velocities.

Now, the momentum components in S'-frame can be written as

$$p'_x = \frac{m_0 u'_x}{\sqrt{1 - u'^2/c^2}}; \quad p'_y = \frac{m_0 u'_y}{\sqrt{1 - u'^2/c^2}}; \quad p'_z = \frac{m_0 u'_z}{\sqrt{1 - u'^2/c^2}}.$$

$$\therefore \quad p'_x = \frac{m_0}{\sqrt{1 - u'^2/c^2}}u'_x = \frac{m_0\left(1 - \frac{v}{c^2}u_x\right)}{\sqrt{(1 - v^2/c^2)(1 - u^2/c^2)}} \times \frac{u_x - v}{\left(1 - \frac{v}{c^2}u_x\right)},$$

transforming u'_x and using Eq. (27.104),

$$= \frac{m_0 u_x - m_0 v}{\sqrt{1 - v^2/c^2}\sqrt{1 - u^2/c^2}} = \frac{p_x}{\sqrt{1 - v^2/c^2}} - \frac{m_0 c^2 (v/c^2)}{\sqrt{(1 - u^2/c^2)(1 - v^2/c^2)}}$$

$$= \frac{p_x - (v/c^2)E}{\sqrt{1 - v^2/c^2}} \quad (\because \ E = mc^2 = m_0 c^2 / \sqrt{1 - u^2/c^2}).$$

Again, we have

$$p_y' = \frac{m_0}{\sqrt{1 - u'^2/c^2}} u_y' = \frac{m_0}{\sqrt{1 - u'^2/c^2}} \times u_y \frac{\sqrt{1 - v^2/c^2}}{\left(1 - \frac{v}{c^2}u_x\right)},$$

transforming u_y'; using Eq. (27.104),

$$= \frac{m_0 \left(1 - \frac{v}{c^2}u_x\right)}{\sqrt{\left(1 - \frac{u^2}{c^2}\right)\left(1 - \frac{v^2}{c^2}\right)}} \times u_y \frac{\sqrt{1 - v^2/c^2}}{\left(1 - \frac{v}{c^2}u_x\right)} = \frac{m_0}{\sqrt{1 - \frac{u^2}{c^2}}} u_y = p_y.$$

Similarly, $p_z' = p_z$.

Thus, the transformation formulae for momentum are written as

$$p_x' = \frac{p_x - \frac{v}{c^2}E}{\sqrt{1 - v^2/c^2}}; \ p_y' = p_y; \ p_z' = p_z;$$

the inverse : $p_x = \dfrac{p_x' + \frac{v}{c^2}E}{\sqrt{1 - v^2/c^2}}; \ p_y = p_y'; \ p_z = p_z'.$

Energy

The energy E of a particle of mass m' in S'-frame is written as

$$E' = m'c^2 = \frac{m_0 c^2}{\sqrt{1 - u'^2/c^2}} = \frac{m_0 c^2 \left(1 - \frac{v}{c^2}u_x\right)}{\sqrt{(1 - v^2/c^2)(1 - u^2/c^2)}}$$

$$= \frac{\frac{m_0 c^2}{\sqrt{1 - u^2/c^2}} - \frac{m_0 u_x}{\sqrt{1 - u^2/c^2}}v}{\sqrt{1 - v^2/c^2}}$$

$$= \frac{E - vp_x}{\sqrt{1 - v^2/c^2}}; \text{ the inverse relation is : } E = \frac{E' + vp_x'}{\sqrt{1 - v^2/c^2}}.$$

Force

We consider a particle of mass m under the action of a force **F** and having a momentum **p** in an inertial frame-S.

$$\therefore \quad \mathbf{F} = \frac{d\mathbf{p}}{dt}; \ F_x = \frac{dp_x}{dt}, \ F_y = \frac{dp_y}{dt}, \ F_z = \frac{dp_z}{dt},$$

where F_x, F_y, F_z and p_x, p_y, p_z are the components of force and momentum respectively.

The corresponding values in S'-frame, moving relative to S-frame with a constant velocity v along X-axis, are expressed as

$$\mathbf{F}' = \frac{d\mathbf{p}'}{dt'}; \ F_x' = \frac{dp_x'}{dt'}, \ F_y' = \frac{dp_y'}{dt'}, \ F_z' = \frac{dp_z'}{dt'}.$$

But the transformation equations for momentum give

$$p_x' = \frac{p_x - \frac{v}{c^2}E}{\sqrt{1 - v^2/c^2}}, \ p_y' = p_y, \ p_z' = p_z; \text{ also, } t' = \frac{t - \frac{v}{c^2}x}{\sqrt{1 - v^2/c^2}}.$$

$$\therefore \ F'_x = \frac{dp'_x}{dt'} = \frac{dp'_x}{dt} \cdot \frac{dt}{dt'} = \frac{\frac{dp_x}{dt} - \frac{v}{c^2}\frac{dE}{dt}}{\sqrt{1 - v^2/c^2}} \cdot \frac{\sqrt{1 - v^2/c^2}}{1 - \frac{v}{c^2}\frac{dx}{dt}}$$

$$= \frac{F_x - \frac{v}{c^2}\frac{dE}{dt}}{1 - \frac{v}{c^2}u_x} \qquad \left(\because \ \frac{dx}{dt} = u_x\right). \tag{27.105}$$

Now, from Dirac equation we have

$$E^2 = p^2c^2 + m_0^2c^4 = (\mathbf{p \cdot p})c^2 + m_0^2c^4$$

$$\text{or,} \ \ 2E\frac{dE}{dt} = \left(2\mathbf{p} \cdot \frac{d\mathbf{p}}{dt}\right)c^2 = 2mc^2(\mathbf{u \cdot F}) = 2E(\mathbf{u \cdot F}) \ [\because \ \mathbf{p} = m\mathbf{u}; \ \mathbf{F} = d\mathbf{p}/dt]$$

$$\therefore \ \ \frac{dE}{dt} = \mathbf{u \cdot F} = \dot{u}_x F_x + u_y F_y + u_z F_z.$$

Substituting the value of dE/dt in Eq. (27.105), we get

$$F'_x = \frac{F_x - \frac{v}{c^2}(u_x F_x + u_y F_y + u_z F_z)}{1 - \frac{v}{c^2}u_x} = \frac{F_x\left(1 - \frac{v}{c^2}u_x\right) - \frac{v}{c^2}(u_y F_y + u_z F_z)}{1 - \frac{v}{c^2}u_x}$$

$$= F_x - \frac{v/c^2}{1 - \frac{v}{c^2}u_x}(u_y F_y + u_z F_z). \tag{27.106}$$

Further, $F'_y = \dfrac{dp'_y}{dt'} = \dfrac{dp'_y}{dt} \cdot \dfrac{dt}{dt'} = \dfrac{dp_y}{dt} \cdot \dfrac{\sqrt{1 - v^2/c^2}}{1 - \frac{v}{c^2}u_x} = \dfrac{F_y\sqrt{1 - v^2/c^2}}{1 - \frac{v}{c^2}u_x}.$ (27.107)

In a similar way,

$$F'_z = \frac{F_z\sqrt{1 - v^2/c^2}}{1 - \frac{v}{c^2}u_x}. \tag{27.108}$$

Eqs. (27.106), (27.107) and (27.108) constitute the transformation relations for the components of the forces.

If the velocity of the particle $v = u_x$, $u_y = 0 = u_z$, the transformation equations for force can be written as

$$F'_x = F_x; \ \ F'_y = \frac{F_y}{\sqrt{1 - v^2/c^2}}; \ \ F'_z = \frac{F_z}{\sqrt{1 - v^2/c^2}}. \tag{27.109}$$

27.17   Some Important Relativistic Formulae

The following relativistic formulae are frequently used in nuclear and elementary particle physics :

(i) $v = pc/\sqrt{p^2 + m_0^2c^2}$

(ii) $E = \sqrt{p^2c^2 + m_0^2c^4} = c\sqrt{p^2 + m_0^2c^2}$

(iii) $p = m_0c\left(\dfrac{1}{1 - v^2/c^2} - 1\right)^{1/2}$

(iv) $1 + \dfrac{T}{m_0c^2} = \dfrac{1}{\sqrt{1 - v^2/c^2}} = \sqrt{1 + \dfrac{p^2}{m_0^2c^2}}.$

Proof of Relation (i) : The momentum p of a particle of mass m, moving with a velocity v is given by

$$p = mv = \frac{m_0 v}{\sqrt{1 - v^2/c^2}} \qquad \text{(where } m_0 = \text{rest mass)}$$

or, $\quad p^2 = \dfrac{m_0^2 v^2}{(1 - v^2/c^2)} = \dfrac{m_0^2 v^2 c^2}{c^2 - v^2}$.

$\therefore \quad p^2 c^2 - p^2 v^2 = m_0^2 v^2 c^2 \quad$ or, $\quad p^2 c^2 = v^2 (p^2 + m_0^2 c^2)$.

$\therefore \quad v = \dfrac{pc}{\sqrt{p^2 + m_0^2 c^2}}$.

Proof of Relation (ii) : The momentum p of a body is given by

$$p = mv = \frac{m_0 v}{\sqrt{1 - v^2/c^2}}$$

$\therefore \quad p^2 c^2 + m_0^2 c^4 = \dfrac{m_0^2 v^2 c^2}{1 - v^2/c^2} + m_0^2 c^4 = m_0^2 c^4 \left(\dfrac{v^2}{c^2 - v^2} + 1 \right) = m_0^2 c^4 \dfrac{c^2}{c^2 - v^2}$

$$= m_0^2 c^4 \frac{1}{1 - v^2/c^2} = m^2 c^4 = E^2 \quad (\because \ E = mc^2).$$

$\therefore \quad E^2 = p^2 c^2 + m_0^2 c^4 = c^2 (p^2 + m_0^2 c^2). \hfill (27.110)$

$\therefore \quad E = \sqrt{p^2 c^2 + m_0^2 c^4} = c\sqrt{p^2 + m_0^2 c^2}. \hfill 27.111)$

The relations (27.110) and (27.111) connecting the total energy and the momentum reveal that a particle with no rest mass ($m_0 = 0$) can still have a momentum

$$p = \frac{E}{c} = mc$$

as in the case of a photon or a neutrino.

Eq. (27.111) is known as the **Dirac equation** in quantum mechanics.

At high speeds, E_0 is small in comparison to T and from Eq. (27.110), $E \simeq T \simeq pc$. Particles are then said to be in *extreme relativistic* region.

Proof of Relation (iii) : We have

$$p = mv = \frac{m_0 v}{\sqrt{1 - v^2/c^2}} = m_0 c \frac{v}{\sqrt{c^2 - v^2}} = m_0 c \sqrt{\frac{v^2}{c^2 - v^2}} = m_0 c \sqrt{\frac{v^2 - c^2 + c^2}{c^2 - v^2}}$$

$$= m_0 c \sqrt{\frac{c^2}{c^2 - v^2} - 1}.$$

$\therefore \quad p = m_0 c \sqrt{\dfrac{1}{1 - v^2/c^2} - 1}. \hfill (27.112)$

Proof of Relation (iv) : We can write the kinetic energy as

$$T = mc^2 - m_0 c^2 = \frac{m_0 c^2}{\sqrt{1 - v^2/c^2}} - m_0 c^2 \quad \text{or,} \quad \frac{T}{m_0 c^2} = \frac{1}{\sqrt{1 - v^2/c^2}} - 1.$$

$\therefore \quad 1 + \dfrac{T}{m_0 c^2} = \dfrac{1}{\sqrt{1 - v^2/c^2}}. \hfill (27.113)$

But, from Eq. (27.112), we have

$$\frac{p^2}{m_0^2 c^2} = \frac{1}{1 - v^2/c^2} - 1.$$

$\therefore \quad 1 + \dfrac{p^2}{m_0^2 c^2} = \dfrac{1}{1 - v^2/c^2}. \hfill (27.114)$

Combining Eqs. (27.113) and (27.114) we get,

$$1 + \frac{T}{m_0 c^2} = \frac{1}{\sqrt{1 - v^2/c^2}} = \sqrt{1 + \frac{p^2}{m_0^2 c^2}}. \tag{27.115}$$

The other useful result that follows from the first equality of (27.115) is

$$\frac{v^2}{c^2} = 1 - \frac{1}{(1 + T/m_0 c^2)^2}. \tag{27.116}$$

Again, we have

$$\frac{E}{E_0} = \frac{mc^2}{m_0 c^2} = \frac{m}{m_0}.$$

$$\therefore \qquad E = \frac{m}{m_0} E_0. \tag{27.117}$$

Eq. (27.117) allows a rapid computation of the mass-increase of a particle at a particular energy.

Examples

1. Find the speed of a spacecraft whose clock runs 1 second slow per hour relative to a clock on the earth.

   Solution : Here, the proper time interval on the earth, $t_0 = 3600$ sec,

   the time interval in the moving frame, $t = 3601$ sec.

   Now, we have

   $$t = \frac{t_0}{\sqrt{1 - \frac{v^2}{c^2}}} \quad \text{or,} \quad \sqrt{1 - \frac{v^2}{c^2}} = \frac{t_0}{t} \quad \text{or,} \quad \frac{v^2}{c^2} = 1 - \frac{t_0^2}{t^2}$$

   $$\text{or,} \quad v = c\sqrt{1 - \frac{t_0^2}{t^2}} = (3 \times 10^8 \text{ m/sec})\sqrt{1 - \left(\frac{3600 \text{ sec}}{3601 \text{ sec}}\right)^2} = \mathbf{7.1 \times 10^6 \text{ m/sec}}.$$

2. What is the mass of an electron whose velocity is 0.990. (Given, $m_0 = 9.1 \times 10^{-31}$ kg)

   Solution : Here, $v = 0.99c$ or, $\dfrac{v}{c} = 0.99$

   or, $\dfrac{v^2}{c^2} = 0.98$ and $m_0 = 9.1 \times 10^{-31}$ kg.

   Now, we have

   $$m = \frac{m_0}{\sqrt{1 - \frac{v^2}{c^2}}} = \frac{9.1 \times 10^{-31}}{\sqrt{1 - 0.98}} = \mathbf{64 \times 10^{-31} \text{ kg}}.$$

3. A stationary body explodes into two fragments of rest mass 1 kg that move apart at speeds of 0.6c. Calculate the rest mass of the original body.

   Solution : The total energy of the original body must be equal to the sum of the energies of the fragments. So we can write,

   $$m_0 c^2 = \frac{m_{01} c^2}{\sqrt{1 - \frac{v_1^2}{c^2}}} + \frac{m_{02} c^2}{\sqrt{1 - \frac{v_2^2}{c^2}}} \quad \text{or,} \quad m_0 = \frac{2 \times 1}{\sqrt{1 - (0.6)^2}} = \mathbf{2.5 \text{ kg}}.$$

4. A radioactive nucleus decays into equal fragments, the velocity of each of which is $0.6c$ with respect to centre of mass. If the original nucleus is travelling at $0.5c$ and the fragments separate along the line of motion, then find the velocity of each fragment as seen by a stationary observer.

Solution : Let S and S' are two inertial frames at rest with respect to the observer and the centre of mass respectively, and the nucleus decays into two equal parts A and B which have equal but opposite velocity u. In the reference frame S', the event A has the co-ordinates $(t', -ut')$ and those of $B(t', ut')$ while in the reference frame-S, their co-ordinates are respectively $(t, u_A t)$ and $(t, u_B t)$.

Now, between the two frames of reference, the transformations are

$$x = \frac{x' + vt'}{\sqrt{1 - \frac{v^2}{c^2}}} = \gamma(x' + vt') \quad \text{and} \quad t = \frac{t' + \frac{vx'}{c^2}}{\sqrt{1 - \frac{v^2}{c^2}}} = \gamma\left(t' + v\frac{xc'}{c^2}\right),$$

where $\gamma = \dfrac{1}{\sqrt{1 - \frac{v^2}{c^2}}}$.

For fragment A,

$$x' = -ut'.$$

$$\therefore \quad x = \gamma t'(-u + v) \quad \text{and} \quad t = \gamma t'\left(1 - \frac{uv}{c^2}\right).$$

$\therefore$ the velocity of A, $u_A = \dfrac{x}{t} = \dfrac{v - u}{1 - u\frac{v}{c^2}}$.

For fragment B,

$$x' = ut'.$$

$\therefore$ the velocity of B, $u_B = \dfrac{u + v}{1 + u\frac{v}{c^2}}$

Now, we have

$$u = 0.6c \quad \text{and} \quad v = 0.5c.$$

$$\therefore \quad u_A = -\frac{0.1}{0.2}c = \mathbf{-0.143c} \quad \text{and} \quad u_B = \frac{1.1}{1.3}c = \mathbf{+0.846c}.$$

5. An observer on the earth (assumed to be an inertial frame) finds that a spaceship A receding away from him at 2×10^8 m/sec and overtaking a spaceship B receding at 1.5×10^8 m/sec.

Determine the relative velocity of :

    (i) spaceship B as observed by A,

    (ii) spaceship A as observed by B

and (iii) spaceship B relative to spaceship A as observed by an observer on the earth.

Solution : From the velocity transformation equation, we have

$$u' = \frac{u - v}{1 - u\frac{v}{c^2}}.$$

(i) In this case, $v = 2 \times 10^8$ m/sec, $u = 1.5 \times 10^8$ m/sec, $c = 3 \times 10^8$ m/sec. Putting these values we get $u' = -0.75 \times 10^8$ **m/sec.**

(ii) In this case, we interchange the velocity symbols and hence we get

$$u = 2 \times 10^8 \text{ m/sec}, v = 1.5 \times 10^8 \text{ m/sec}, c = 3 \times 10^8 \text{ m/sec}.$$

$\therefore$ $u' = + 0.75 \times 10^8$ **m/sec.**

(iii) In this case, we take the difference of two velocities observed from the earth.

$\therefore$ $u' = (1.5 - 2.0) \times 10^8$ m/sec $= -0.5 \times 10^8$ **m/sec.**

6. At what speed an electron will move in order to double its rest mass? (Given that $c = 3 \times 10^8$ m/sec.)

Solution : We have $m = \dfrac{m_0}{\sqrt{1 - \frac{v^2}{c^2}}}$.

Here, $\dfrac{m}{m_0} = 2$, $c = 3 \times 10^8$ m/sec.

$\therefore$ $\dfrac{m}{m_0} = 2 = \dfrac{1}{\sqrt{1 - \frac{v^2}{c^2}}}$ or, $1 - \dfrac{v^2}{c^2} = \dfrac{1}{4}$ or, $\dfrac{v^2}{c^2} = 1 - \dfrac{1}{4} = \dfrac{3}{4} = 0.75$

$\therefore$ $v^2 = 0.75c^2$ or, $v = c\sqrt{0.75} = 3 \times 10^8 \times 0.866 = \mathbf{2.598 \times 10^8}$ **m/sec.**

7. With what energy electron can be accelerated to in a cyclotron for the relative increase in the mass of the particles not to exceed 5%?

Solution : We have the kinetic energy, $E = m_0 c^2 \left(\dfrac{1}{\sqrt{1 - \frac{v^2}{c^2}}} - 1 \right)$

$$= c^2 \left(\dfrac{m_0}{\sqrt{1 - \frac{v^2}{c^2}}} - m_0 \right)$$

$$= c^2 (m - m_0)$$

or, $\dfrac{E}{m_0} = c^2 \dfrac{m - m_0}{m_0} = c^2 k$ (say),   where $k = \dfrac{m - m_0}{m_0}$.

$\therefore$ $E = m_0 c^2 k$.

Here, $k = 5\% = 0.05$.

$\therefore$ for electron, $E = 2.56 \times 10^{-2}$ MeV.

8. If (x, y, z, t) be the co-ordinates of an event in S-system and $(x', y'z', t')$ be those of the same event in S'-system which moves relative to S-system with a uniform velocity v along x-direction, show that $ds^2 = dx^2 + dy^2 + dz^2 - c^2 dt^2$ is invariant under Lorentz transformation.

Solution : Using Lorentz transformation formulae, we have

$$dx = \dfrac{dx' + vdt'}{\sqrt{1 - v^2/c^2}}; \quad dy = dy'; \quad dz = dz'; \text{ and}$$

$$dt = \dfrac{dt' + (v/c^2)dx'}{\sqrt{1 - v^2/c^2}}; \text{ the velocity } v = \text{constant.}$$

$$\therefore \quad ds^2 = dx^2 + dy^2 + dz^2 - c^2 dt^2$$

$$= \left(\frac{dx' + vdt'}{\sqrt{1 - v^2/c^2}}\right)^2 + dy'^2 + dz'^2 - c^2 \left(\frac{dt' + (v/c^2)dx'}{\sqrt{1 - v^2/c^2}}\right)^2$$

$$= \frac{1}{1 - v^2/c^2} \left\{ dx'^2 + v^2 dt'^2 + 2vdx'dt' - c^2 dt'^2 - \frac{v^2}{c^2}dx'^2 - 2vdx'dt \right\}$$
$$+ dy'^2 + dz'^2$$

$$= \frac{dx'^2(1 - v^2/c^2)}{1 - v^2/c^2} + dy'^2 + dz'^2 - \frac{c^2 dt'^2(1 - v^2/c^2)}{1 - v^2/c^2}$$

$$= dx'^2 + dy'^2 + dz'^2 - c^2 dt'^2 = ds'^2.$$

Hence, ds^2 **is invariant under Lorentz transformation**.

9. An experimenter intends to study a beam of π-mesons of velocity $0.9c$. How far can he place his apparatus from the target where π-mesons are produced and still expect to get sufficient number of π-mesons?

Solution : Taking relativistic time-dilation into consideration,

$$\Delta t = \frac{\Delta t'}{\sqrt{1 - v^2/c^2}} = \frac{\Delta t'}{\sqrt{1 - 0.9^2}} = 2.3\Delta t'.$$

As $\Delta t'$ is the time-interval measured by an observer moving with π-mesons, it is the rest life-time. So in the *laboratory frame*, the mean life is given by

$$\Delta t = 2.3\Delta t' = 2.3 \times 2 \times 10^{-8} = 4.6 \times 10^{-8} \text{ sec.}$$

So, the average distance travelled by the particles in this time is

$$\Delta x = v \cdot \Delta t = 0.9c \times \Delta t = 0.9 \times 3 \times 10^8 \times 4.6 \times 10^{-8} \text{ m} = 12.42 \text{ m.}$$

10. An electron of rest mass 9.1×10^{-31} kg is moving with a speed $0.99c$. What is its total energy? Find the ratio of Newtonian kinetic energy to the relativistic kinetic energy. $c = 3.0 \times 10^8$ m/sec.

Solution : The mass of electron corresponding to velocity $v = 0.99c$ is written as

$$m = \frac{m_0}{\sqrt{1 - 0.99^2}} = \frac{9.1 \times 10^{-31}}{0.141} = 64.54 \times 10^{-31} \text{ kg.}$$

Therefore, total energy of electron,

$$E = mc^2 = 64.54 \times 10^{-31} \times (3.0 \times 10^8)^2 = 5.81 \times 10^{-31} \text{ J.}$$

Now, Newtonian kinetic energy $= \frac{1}{2}m_0 v^2$ and the relativistic K.E. $= mc^2 - m_0 c^2$.

So, the required ratio $= \dfrac{\frac{1}{2}m_0 v^2}{mc^2 - m_0 c^2} = \dfrac{m_0}{2(m - m_0)}\left(\dfrac{v}{c}\right)^2$

$$= \frac{9.1 \times 10^{-31}}{2(64.54 - 9.1) \times 10^{-31}} \times (0.99)^2 = 0.08.$$

11. A certain quantity of ice at $0\,°C$ melts into water at $0\,°C$, and thereby gains 1 kg mass. Find its initial mass.

Solution : Since $E = mc^2 = 1 \times (3 \times 10^8)$ J. Let m be the initial mass of ice in kg. The gain in energy per kg of ice at $0\,^\circ$C melting into water at $0\,^\circ$C $= 80 \times 1000$ cal $= 80 \times 1000 \times 4.18$ J.

If m kg be the required quantity of ice, then we can write,

$$80 \times 1000 \times 4.18m = (3 \times 10^8)^2$$

$$m = \frac{9 \times 10^{16}}{80 \times 1000 \times 4.18} = \mathbf{2.69 \times 10^{11}} \text{ kg}.$$

12. The rest mass of electron is 9.11×10^{-31} kg. What is its momentum according to relativistic mechanics when it is moving down the axis of a linear accelerator tube at a speed of 0.4c relative to the accelerator tube.

    Solution : The relativistic momentum, $p = \dfrac{m_0 v}{\sqrt{1 - v^2/c^2}}$.

    So, the required momentum of the electron is

    $$p = \frac{9.11 \times 10^{-31} \times 0.4c}{\sqrt{1 - 0.4^2}} = 9.11 \times 10^{-31} \times 0.4 \times 3 \times 10^8/0.917$$

    $$= 1.19 \times 10^{-22} \text{ kg m/sec}.$$

13. The half-life of a particular particle as measured in the laboratory comes out to be 4.0×10^{-8} sec when its speed is $0.80c$ and 3.0×10^{-8} sec when the speed is $0.60c$. Find its actual life-time.

    Solution : The half-life of a moving particle appears lengthened to a stationary observer due to time dilation. If t_0 be the actual half-life in the frame of reference of the particle and t that measured by a stationary observer, then we have

    $$t = \frac{t_0}{\sqrt{1 - v^2/c^2}} \;\Rightarrow\; 4.0 \times 10^{-8} = \frac{t_0}{\sqrt{1 - 0.80^2}} = \frac{t_0}{0.6}.$$

    Further, $3.0 \times 10^{-8} = \dfrac{t_0}{\sqrt{1 - 0.60^2}} = \dfrac{t_0}{0.8}.$

    We thus get $t_0 = 2.4 \times 10^{-8}$ sec.

14. What will be the period of 'seconds' pendulum measured by an observer moving at a speed of 0.80c?

    Solution : If T_0 be the period of 'seconds' pendulum as measured by an observer at rest, then the same would be T to the moving observer. Therefore, we have

    $$\text{time dilation, } T = \frac{T_0}{\sqrt{1 - v^2/c^2}} = \frac{2}{\sqrt{1 - 0.80^2}} = \frac{2}{0.6} = \mathbf{3.33} \text{ sec}.$$

    (as $T_0 = 2$ sec, by definition).

15. A rocket is travelling towards the moon with a velocity 0.6c. When half-way to the moon, it fires a message rocket back towards the earth with a velocity 0.8c relative to the primary rocket. What is the velocity of the message rocket as seen by a terrestrial observer? Neglect the recoil effect.

    Solution : By velocity addition theorem, we get

    $$v = \frac{(0.6 - 0.8)c}{1 - 0.8 \times 0.6} = \frac{-0.2c}{1 - 0.48} = \frac{-0.2c}{0.52} = \mathbf{-0.385c}.$$

    The negative sign shows that the rocket is coming towards the earth.

16. The average life-time of a neutron is 15 min. It disintegrates spontaneously into an electron, a proton and a neutrino. If the distance of the sun from the earth is 11×10^{10} m, find the average minimum velocity with which a neutron must leave the sun so as to reach the earth before breaking up.

Solution : Let v be the required velocity of the neutron. The time t_1 for the neutron to reach the earth from the sun before it decays is

$$t_1 = \frac{11 \times 10^{10} \text{ m}}{v}.$$

Again, if t_0 be the life-time of neutron at rest, then the average life-time of a 'moving' neutron, as measured by a terrestrial observer, is

$$t = \frac{t_0}{\sqrt{1 - v^2/c^2}} = \frac{15 \times 60 \text{ sec}}{\sqrt{1 - v^2/(3 \times 10^8)^2}}$$

$$\therefore \quad \frac{11 \times 10^{10}}{v} = \frac{15 \times 60}{\sqrt{1 - v^2/(9 \times 10^{16})}} \quad (\because t_1 \text{ must equal } t)$$

$$\Rightarrow \quad \frac{121 \times 10^{20}}{v^2} = \frac{225 \times 3600}{1 - v^2/(9 \times 10^{16})}.$$

$$\therefore \quad v = 1.132 \times 10^8 \text{ m/sec}.$$

17. A burst of 10^4 π^+-mesons travels in a circular path of radius 20 m at a speed $v = 0.99c$. The proper mean life of π^+-mesons is 2.5×10^{-8} sec. How many mesons survive when the burst returns to the point of origin? How many would be left in a burst that had remained at rest at the origin for the same period of time?

Solution : Length of the circular path $= 2\pi \times 20 = 40\pi$ m. If T be the time as observed in laboratory, frame for a π^+-meson to travel the circular path with a velocity $0.99c$, then

$$T = \frac{40\pi}{0.99 \times 3 \times 10^8} = 4.23 \times 10^{-7} \text{ sec}.$$

If T_0 be the corresponding time in a frame in which π^+-meson is at rest, then we have

$$T = T_0/\sqrt{1 - v^2/c^2}$$

$$\Rightarrow T_0 = \sqrt{1 - v^2/c^2} T = \sqrt{(1 - 0.99^2)} \times 4.23 \times 10^{-7} \text{ sec} = 0.5967 \times 10^{-7} \text{ sec}.$$

Proper mean life of π^+-meson $= 2.5 \times 10^{-8}$ sec. So the decay constant

$$\lambda = \frac{1}{\text{mean life}} = \frac{1}{2.5 \times 10^{-8}} = 4 \times 10^7.$$

(a) If N mesons survive, out of $N_0 = 10^4$, after the burst returns to the point of origin, we can write,

$$\frac{N}{N_0} = e^{-\lambda T_0} \quad \text{or,} \quad \frac{N_0}{N} = e^{\lambda T_0} = e^{4 \times 10^7 \times 0.5967 \times 10^7} = e^{2.387} = 10.88.$$

$$N = N_0/10.88 = 10^4/10.88 = \mathbf{920}.$$

(b) If the burst was at the origin, $T_0 = T = 4.23 \times 10^{-7}$ sec, then we have

$$\frac{N_0}{N} = e^{4 \times \times 10^{-7} \times 4.23 \times 10^{-7}} = e^{16.93} = 2.25 \times 10^7.$$

$$\therefore \quad N = \frac{N_0}{2.25 \times 10^7} = \frac{10^4}{2.25 \times 10^7} \ll 1.$$

$\therefore$ No π^+-mesons would practically survive.

18. A beam of μ-mesons, produced at a height of 20 km in the atmosphere, travels downwards with a velocity of $0.99c$. If 99% of the original mesons decay before reaching the earth's surface, find the mean life-time of the μ-mesons.

Solution : If T be the time, as observed by a terrestrial observer, for a μ-meson to travel over 20 km with a velocity $0.99c$, then we have,

$$T = \frac{20 \times 10^3}{0.99 \times 3 \times 10^8} = 67.34 \times 10^{-6} \text{ sec.}$$

Again, if T_0 be the corresponding time in the rest frame of μ-meson,

$$T = \frac{T_0}{\sqrt{1 - v^2/c^2}} \quad \Rightarrow \quad T_0 = T\sqrt{1 - v^2/c^2} = T\sqrt{1 - 0.99^2}.$$

$$\therefore \quad T_0 = 67.34 \times 10^{-6} \times 0.141 = 9.495 \times 10^{-6} \text{ sec.}$$

During this time T_0, 99% of mesons decay. If λ be the decay constant of μ-mesons, we have

$$N = N_0 e^{-\lambda T_0} \quad \text{or,} \quad \lambda T_0 = \ln \frac{N_0}{N} = \ln \frac{100}{1} = \ln 100.$$

$$\therefore \quad \lambda = \frac{\ln 100}{T_0} = \frac{2.303 \times 2}{9.495 \times 10^{-6}} \text{ sec}^{-1}.$$

So, the mean life-time,

$$\tau = \frac{1}{\lambda} = \frac{9.495 \times 10^{-6}}{2.303 \times 2} = \mathbf{2.06 \times 10^{-6}} \text{ sec.}$$

19. Express the relativistic expression of the second law of motion in terms of rest mass and velocity of a particle.

Solution : From Newton's second law of motion, we have

$$\vec{F} = \frac{d}{dt}(m\vec{v}) = m\frac{d\vec{v}}{dt} + \vec{v}\frac{dm}{dt}, \quad \text{where } m = m_0/\sqrt{1 - v^2/c^2}.$$

For a force acting along $+X$-direction, we obtain

$$F_x = \frac{d}{dt}(mv_x) = \frac{d}{dt}\left\{ \frac{m_0 v_x}{\sqrt{1 - v_x^2/c^2}} \right\}$$

$$= \frac{m_0}{\sqrt{1 - v_x^2/c^2}} \frac{dv_x}{dt} + \frac{m_0(v_x^2/c^2)}{(1 - v_x^2/c^2)^{3/2}} \frac{dv_x}{dt}$$

$$= \frac{m_0}{(1 - v_x^2/c^2)^{3/2}} \frac{dv_x}{dt}, \quad \text{on simplification.}$$

20. A body of mass m_0 at rest breaks up spontaneously into two parts, having rest masses m_{01} and m_{02} and speeds v_1 and v_2 respectively. Show that

$$m_0 > m_{01} + m_{02}.$$

Solution : The total energy of the body at rest $= m_0 c^2$, the rest-mass energy. It breaks up into two moving parts. The total energies are

(i) $\dfrac{m_{01} c^2}{\sqrt{1 - v_1^2/c^2}}$ and   (ii) $\dfrac{m_{02} c^2}{\sqrt{1 - v_2^2/c^2}}$.

Now, the mass-energy conservation principle provides

$$m_0 c^2 = \frac{m_{01} c^2}{\sqrt{1 - v_1^2/c^2}} + \frac{m_{02} c^2}{\sqrt{1 - v_2^2/c^2}} > (m_{01} c^2 + m_{02} c^2).$$

$$(\because \ \sqrt{1 - v_1^2/c^2} < 1)$$

$$\therefore \quad m_0 > m_{01} + m_{02}.$$

21. Show that the Fresnel's drag coefficient follows from the relativity theory as a direct consequence of the velocity transformation equation.

Solution : Let us take water medium, at rest in S'-system and consider propagation of light through the medium along x'-axis (Fresnel's experiment).

$$\therefore \quad u_x' = c', \text{ the speed of light in water.}$$

From the velocity addition theorem, we have

$$u_x = \frac{u_x' + v}{1 + u_x' v/c^2} \simeq (c' + v)\{1 - (c'/c)^2 v/c'\}$$

$$\simeq (c' + v)(1 - v/n^2 c') \text{ (where } n = \text{refractive index of water} = c/c').$$

22. Show that the space interval $x^2 + y^2 + z^2$ is not invariant under Lorentz transformations while the space-time interval $x^2 + y^2 + z^2 - c^2 t^2$ is invariant.

Solution : Let (x, y, z) be the co-ordinates of a fixed point in space in the S-frame and the co-ordinates of the same point in S'-frame which is moving with a uniform velocity v along X-axis are (x', y', z'). According to Lorentz transformation, we then have

$$x' = k(x - vt)$$
$$y' = y$$
$$z' = z.$$

Therefore, $x'^2 + y'^2 + z'^2 = k^2(x - vt)^2 + y^2 + z^2$, which is clearly not invariant.

As time in the two frames is related by the equation,

$$t' = k\left(t - \frac{v}{c^2} \cdot x\right),$$

then

$$x'^2 + y'^2 + z'^2 - c^2 t'^2 = k^2(x - vt)^2 + y^2 + z^2 - c^2 k^2 \left(t - \frac{v}{c^2} x\right)^2$$

$$= k^2(x^2 - 2xvt + v^2 t^2) + y^2 + z^2 - c^2 k^2 \left(t^2 - \frac{2vtx}{c^2} + \frac{v^2}{c^4} x^2\right)$$

$$= y^2 + z^2 + k^2 \left(x^2 - 2xvt + v^2 t^2 - c^2 t^2 + 2vtx - \frac{v^2}{c^2} x^2\right)$$

$$= y^2 + z^2 + k^2 \left[x^2 \left(1 - \frac{v^2}{c^2}\right) - c^2 t^2 \left(1 - \frac{v^2}{c^2}\right)\right]$$

$$= y^2 + z^2 + k^2 \left[x^2 \left(1 - \frac{v^2}{c^2}\right) - c^2 t^2 \left(1 - \frac{v^2}{c^2}\right)\right]$$

$$= y^2 + z^2 + k^2 \left(1 - \frac{v^2}{c^2}\right)(x^2 - c^2 t^2)$$

$$= y^2 + z^2 + x^2 - c^2 t^2 \left[\because \ k = \frac{1}{\sqrt{1 - \frac{v^2}{c^2}}}\right].$$

This shows that the **space-time interval is invariant under Lorentz transformation**.

23. A wrist-watch keeps correct time on earth. It is worn by an astronaut leaving the earth in a space-craft with constant velocity of 5×10^7 m-sec^{-1}. How much slow will the watch appear to be in a day to an observer on the earth?

Solution : According to relativistic time dilation formula, we have

$$t = \frac{t_0}{\sqrt{1 - v^2/c^2}}.$$

In the present problem, $v = 5 \times 10^7$ m-sec^{-1} and $t = 24$ hours.

$$\therefore \quad 24 = \frac{t_0}{\sqrt{1 - \left(\frac{5 \times 10^7}{3 \times 10^8}\right)^2}} = \frac{t_0}{\sqrt{1 - \frac{25}{900}}}$$

$$\therefore \quad t_0 = 24 \left(1 - \frac{25}{900}\right)^{1/2} \text{ hours} = 24 \left(1 - \frac{1}{2} \times \frac{25}{900}\right) \text{ hours}$$

$$= 24 - \frac{24 \times 25}{2 \times 900} \text{ hours} = (24 - 0.33) \text{ hours}.$$

Thus, the watch will appear to be 0.33 hour = 19.8 minutes **slow** in a day.

24. A rod of length 1 metre moves past an observer standing on the ground with a velocity 3×10^7 m-sec^{-1} along the direction of its length. What is the apparent length of the rod with respect to the observer?

Solution : We have $l = l_0\sqrt{1 - v^2/c^2}$; here, $l_0 = 1$ m, $v = 3 \times 10^7$ m-sec^{-1}, $c = 3 \times 10^8$ m-sec^{-1}.

$$\therefore \quad l = 1 \times \sqrt{1 - \left(\frac{3 \times 10^7}{3 \times 10^8}\right)} = 1 \times \frac{\sqrt{99}}{10} = 0.995 \text{ metre.}$$

25. A radioactive nucleus of half-life 1 μsec moves through the laboratory at 2.7×10^{10} cm/sec. What will be its half-life as measured by an observer in the laboratory? Velocity of light in air = 3×10^{10} cm/sec.   **[C.U. 2000]**

Solution: There will be dilation of half-life as the nucleus is in motion relative to the observer.

The apparent time dilation, $t = \dfrac{t_0}{\sqrt{1 - v^2/c^2}}$.

Given, $t_0 = 1$ μsec. $v = 2.7 \times 10^{10}$ cm/sec and $c = 3 \times 10^{10}$ cm/sec.

$$\therefore \quad t = \frac{1\,\mu\text{sec}}{\sqrt{1 - \left(\frac{2.7 \times 10^{10}}{3 \times 10^{10}}\right)^2}} = \frac{1\,\mu\text{sec}}{\sqrt{1 - 0.81}} = 2.29 \ \mu\text{sec.}$$

So, the half-life of the nucleus as measured by the observer is **2.29 μ sec**.

26. Calculate the amount of energy associated with one atomic mass unit in electron-volt. Avogadro number = 6.023×10^{23} and 1 MeV = 1.6×10^{-13} joule.

Solution : We have 1 a.m.u. $= \dfrac{1}{N_a}$ g $= \dfrac{1}{N_a \times 10^3}$ kg $= \dfrac{1}{6.023 \times 10^{23} \times 10^3}$ kg

$$= 1.66 \times 10^{-27} \text{ kg.}$$

According to mass-energy equivalence, we can write,

$$E = mc^2 = 1.66 \times 10^{-27} \times (3 \times 10^8)^2 \text{ joule} \quad [c = 3 \times 10^8 \text{ m-sec}^{-1}]$$

$$= \frac{1.66 \times 10^{-27} \times (3 \times 10^8)^2}{1.6 \times 10^{-13}} \text{ MeV} = \textbf{933.75 MeV}.$$

27. A particle is at rest at the origin. A force F starts acting on it at $t = 0$. Find the speed of the particle at t.

Solution : Let v be the speed of the particle at t. Given that the initial momentum of the particle is zero. The final momentum of the particle $= \frac{m_0 v}{\sqrt{1 - v^2/c^2}}$.

Hence, change of momentum $= \frac{m_0 v}{\sqrt{1 - v^2/c^2}}$.

Therefore, $\frac{m_0 v}{\sqrt{1 - v^2/c^2}} = F.t$ or, $m_0^2 v^2 = F^2 t^2 - \frac{F^2 t^2}{c^2} v^2$

or, $\qquad v^2 \left[m_0^2 + \frac{F^2 t^2}{c^2} \right] = F^2 t^2.$

$\therefore \qquad v = \frac{F \cdot t \cdot c}{(m_0^2 c^2 + F^2 t^2)^{1/2}}.$

Questions

Essay-type

1. Describe the apparatus of Michelson-Morley's experiment. Explain the theory of it.

2. Critically discuss the Lorentz-Fitzgerald contraction.

3. What are the postulates of Einstein's theory of relativity? What are its immediate consequences?

4. Establish the special Lorentz transformation formulae. Justify the statement, "Space and time are connected to each other."

5. Show that the apparent length of a rod moving with respect to a frame of reference at rest is less than its length at rest.

6. Explain what is meant by Einstein's time dilatation.

7. Give the addition theorem of velocities and show that the velocity of light is the maximum velocity.

8. Compare the frequency of the relativistic Doppler effect with the non-relativistic one and discuss it briefly.

9. Establish the relations which determine the aberration of light from the stars.

10. Calculate the relative velocity between two frames of reference in the light of the geometrical representation of Minkowski space.

11. In accordance with the relativistic mechanics, find an expression for the momentum of a body.

12. What do you mean by longitudinal and transverse inertial masses of a body? Find expressions for them.

13. What is meant by mass-energy equivalence? Establish the principle.

14. Write down the postulates of Einstein's special theory of relativity. Derive relativistic velocity addition theorem. **[C.U. 2005]**

15. State the basic postulates of Einstein's special theory of relativity. Hence deduce Lorentz transformation equations. **[C.U. 2000, '02, '03]**

16. On the basis of Lorentz transformation, discuss the following :

    (i) Length contraction and (ii) Time dilation. **[C.U. 2000]**

17. Deduce the theorem of velocity addition based on the special theory of relativity. How does it lead to the postulate that the velocity of light is the same for all observers regardless of their relative motion.

18. Defining force as the rate of change of momentum and kinetic energy as the work done by the force that generates the velocity v of a particle from rest, show by direct evaluation that the kinetic energy of moving particle is given by $(m - m_0)c^2$, where m_0 is the rest mass. Assume that $m = m_0\sqrt{1 - v^2/c^2}$. **[C.U. (Hons.) 1982]**

19. Establish Einstein's mass-energy relationship. Explain its significance.

20. Derive the formula for relative variation of mass with motion. Briefly explain its significance.

21. Describe Michelson-Morley experiment. Explain the significance of the results of the experiment. **[K.U. 2002]**

22. Starting from the relation of variation of mass with velocity, establish the equivalence relation of mass and energy. **[C.U. 2001; Burd. U. 2004]**

23. Show that the rest mass of a particle moving with the speed of light is zero.

24. Write down the space-time transformation equations of Lorentz in special theory of relativity. Establish the 'Einstein time dilation' with their help. **[B.U. 2003]**

25. Using Lorentz transformation equations, show that the time measured by an observer moving with uniform velocity will appear dilated to a stationary observer. **[K.U. 2001]**

26. Write down the expressions of the length contraction and time dilation as derived from the Lorentz transformation equation. **[C.U. 2000, '04]**

27. Write down the space-time Lorentz transformation in relativity. **[B.U. 2002]**

Short Answer-type

28. "The speculated a ether frame does not provide any preferential velocity of light over other frames of reference." Justify.

29. What do you mean by aberration of stars?

30. What is meant by effective mass of the body?

31. What is the conclusion you can draw from the experimental results on the aberration of stars.

32. What is proved from Michelson-Morley's experiment?

33. What is meant by Lorentz-Fitzgerald contraction?

34. Write down the two postulates of Einstein related to the discrepancies between the experimental observations and the prevailing ideas on relative motion and co-ordinate transformation.

35. The speed of light in glass is 2×10^8 m-sec^{-1}. Does it violate the second postulate of special relativity? [C.U. 2001]

36. What do you mean by inertial and non-inertial frames of reference? In which frame are the laws of Newtonian mechanics applicable?

37. Why the period of a clock that is moving relative to an observer is longer than the period when it is measured by a stationary observer?

38. Length of a rod is measured less when it is moving parallel to its length than the length when at rest with respect to an observer. Explain.

39. What were the difficulties is physics which led to the concept of relativity?

40. Write the relationship between total energy and momentum of a body. Hence, show that the relativistic expression of kinetic energy of a moving body reduces to the classical expression when the velocity of the body is extremely small compared to the velocity of light.

41. An observer sees two events to be simultaneous but another observer reports the same to be not simultaneous. Under what circumstances is it possible? Explain.

42. Discuss briefly the concepts of length, mass and time according to (i) classical mechanics and (ii) relativistic mechanics.

43. Show that the limit of maximum velocity in this universe is the velocity of light.

44. Show that a moving clock runs slow. [N.B.U. 2005]

45. Deduce the formula for addition of velocities in relativistic mechanics. Show that the addition of any velocity with the velocity of light in vacuum nearly reproduces the velocity of light in vacuum. [N.B.U. 2005]

46. What will be the resultant of two parallel and unidirectional velocities according to (i) classical mechanics and (ii) relativistic mechanics?

Numerical Problems

47. Electrons from an electron-gun escapes with speeds which are about 98% of the speed of light. Prove that to a stationary observer, these electrons appear to have a mass five times their rest mass.

48. What is the error involved in calculating the kinetic energy according to the classical expression when the body is moving with a speed equal to half the speed of light? [Ans. 20%]

49. With what velocity should a bullet travel so that its total energy becomes exactly twice its rest mass energy? [Ans. $\frac{\sqrt{3}}{2}c$]

50. With what velocity should a space-craft travel so that everyday spent on it may correspond to 3 days on the earth's surface? $c = 3 \times 10^8$ m-sec^{-1}
[Ans. 2.83×10^8 m sec^{-1}]

51. A particle has a rest mass of 2.5×10^{-25} kg. Find its total energy (i) when the particle is at rest and (ii) when the particle has a velocity of $0.9c$. Express your answer in MeV. [Ans. (i) 10^4, (ii) 32.25×10^4]

52. Find the velocity at which the mass of a particle becomes double its rest mass. [**Ans.** 2.598×10^8 m sec^{-1}]

53. Two particles approach each other with a speed of $0.9c$. What is their relative speed? [**Ans.** $0.9945c$]

54. Calculate the ratio of the mass of an electron to its rest mass when it is moving with a kinetic energy of 20 MeV. Rest mass is energy of electron = 0.51 MeV. [**Ans.** 40.21]

55. A hypothetical train moving with a speed of $0.6c$ passes by the platform of a small station. An observer on the platform notes that the length of the train is just equal to the length of the platform which is 200 m. Find **(i)** the rest length of the train and **(ii)** the length of the platform as measured by an observer in the train. [**Ans.** (i) 250 m, (ii) 160 m]

56. A radioactive nucleus of half-life 1 μsec moves through the laboratory at 2.7×10^{10} cm/sec. What will be its half-life as measured by an observer in the laboratory? Velocity of light in air = 3×10^{10} cm/sec. [**C.U. 2000**]
[**Ans.** 2.3 μ sec (nearly)]

57. Calculate the increase in mass when a body of rest mass = 1 kg is raised through 2 metres near the earth's surface. [**Ans.** 2.18×10^{-16} kg]

58. How much energy (in joule) will be produced on complete combustion of 1 g of $_{92}U^{255}$, assuming that 0.1% of mass is converted into energy? [**Ans.** 9×10^{10} joules]

59. What is the increase in mass of 120 kg of copper of specific heat capacity 0.389 J kg^{-1} K^{-1}, if its temperature is raised by 100 °C? [**Ans.** 5.196×10^{-11} kg]

60. Muons have a life-time of 2.2×10^{-6} sec in its rest frame. If their velocity with respect to the laboratory frame is $0.998c$, then how far can they travel in laboratory frame before decay? [**N.B.U. 2005**]
[**Ans.** 104.22×10^2 m]

61. The interval between two events on a spaceship resting on the earth is 3 seconds. What will be the interval between the same two events when the spaceship is moving with a velocity $0.8c$? [**Ans.** 5 sec]

62. Two identical balls of mass m_0 move towards each other with equal velocity u. They collide elastically and stick together after collision. Show that the rest mass is not conserved in the case.

63. P and Q are two neutrons approaching each other along a straight line. Each has a constant speed BC as measured in the laboratory. If M_n represents the neutron mass and $\beta = \frac{v}{c}$, then show that the total energy of the neutron Q as observed in the rest frame of neutron P is

$$(1 + \beta^2)(1 - \beta^2)^{-1} M_n c^2.$$

64. A space-probe travelling directly away from the earth contains a transmitter radiating at a constant frequency of 10^9 c/sec. The frequency reaching the earth can be measured with an accuracy of ± 1 c/sec. At what speed relative to the earth will the relativistic Doppler shift differ measurably from the expected? [**Ans.** $v = 1.9 \times 10^4$ m/sec]

65. An excited atom of mass m_0 is at rest in a certain system of reference. It emits a photon, thereby losing an internal energy equal to ΔE. Making due allowance for the recoil of the atom, show that the exact frequency of the emitted photon is

$$\gamma = \frac{\Delta E}{h}\left(1 - \frac{1}{2}\frac{\Delta E}{m_0 c^2}\right).$$

66. A meson of mass π comes to rest and disintegrates into a lighter meson of mass μ and a neutrino of mass ν. Show that the total energies of the product particles are $\frac{\pi^2 + \mu^2 - \nu^2}{2\pi}c^2$ and $\frac{\pi^2 - \mu^2 + \nu^2}{2\pi}c^2$ respectively.

67. Show that if the variation of mass with velocity is taken into account, the kinetic energy of a particle of rest mass m_0 and moving with a velocity v is given by

$$T = m_0 c^2\left[\left(1 - \frac{v^2}{c^2}\right)^{-1/2} - 1\right],$$

where c is the velocity of light in vacuo.

68. Establish the relation (Dirac equation)

$$E^2 = p^2 c^2 + m_0^2 c^4$$

for a particle of rest mass m_0, momentum p and total energy E.

69. Prove that if a unidirectional force F acts on a particle of rest mass m_0, which is at rest initially, the latter acquaires a velocity,

$$v = cFt/\sqrt{m_0^2 c^2 + F^2 t^2}$$

after a tme t. Show that if t is small, the above expression reduces to the classical result. What is the velocity when $t \to \infty$?

70. Establish the following relations, the symbols having their usual meanings.

(a) $1 + \dfrac{T}{m_0 c^2} = \sqrt{1 + p^2/m_0^2 c^2} = 1/\sqrt{1 - v^2/c^2}$

(b) $(E/m_0 c^2)^2 = 1 + (p/m_0 c)^2$

(c) $\dfrac{v}{c} = \sqrt{1 - \dfrac{1}{(T/m_0 c^2 + 1)^2}}.$

71. A rocket 10 m long is flying at 300 m/sec. How much shorter will it appear to be to an observer on the ground? How long will it take for the pilot's watch to lose 1 μ sec with respect to the clock of a ground observer?

72. Calculate the length and orientation of a rod length 5 m in a frame which is moving with a velocity $0.6c$ in a direction making an angle 30° with the rod. **[Ans. 4.27 m; 35°45′]**

73. A man on the moon observes two spaceships coming towards him from opposite directions at speeds of $0.8c$ and $0.9c$ respectively. What is the relative velocity of two spaceships as measured by an observer on either of them?

74. What is the mean life of a burst of π^+-mesons travelling with $\beta = 0.73$ (proper mean life-time, $T_0 = 2.5 \times 10^{-8}$sec). What is the distance travelled at this velocity during one mean life?

75. Two electron beams travel along the same straight line but in opposite directions with velocities $0.9c$ relative to the laboratory frame. Find the relative velocity of electrons according to Newtonian mechanics. What will be the velocity measured by an observer moving with one of the electron beams?   [**Ans.** $1.8c$; $0.994c$]

76. An electron moves with a velocity 0.6×10^{10} cm/sec. Calculate its mass ($m_0 = 9 \times 10^{-28}$ g). Calculate the wavelength of radiation emitted by the annihilation of an electron with a positron, each of rest mass 9.1×10^{-28} g.

77. The rest mass of electron is 9.028×10^{-28} g. Find the energy equivalent in eV. The atomic mass of unit is 1.6550×10^{-24} g. Find the energy equivalent in eV.   [**Ans.** 0.508 MeV; 931 MeV]

78. Calculate (a) the effective mass of a photon of wavelength 1A, (b) the momentum of a proton having kinetic energy 1 BeV.
[**Ans.** 2.21×10^{-32} kg; 9.045×10^{-19} N.sec]

79. Atomic particles in the form of a beam have a velocity 98% of the velocity of light. What is the relativistic mass of an atomic particle as compared with its rest mass?   [**Ans.** $5m_0$]

80. Prove that under Lorentz transformation the four dimensional volume '$dxdydzdt$' is invariant.

81. Show that if T is the kinetic energy of a particle and p its momentum, its rest mass is given by $m_0 = (p^2c^2 - T^2)/2Tc^2$.

82. Two lumps of clay, each of rest mass m_0, collide head-on at $\frac{4}{5}c$ and stick together. Calculate the mass of the composite lump. Comment on the result obtained.   [**Ans.** $10m_0/3$]

83. If $\gamma = 1/\sqrt{1 - v^2/c^2} = 1/\epsilon(\epsilon \gg 1)$, show that (i) $\beta = 1 - \epsilon^2/2$ and (ii) $K/E = 1 - \epsilon$, where $\beta = v/c$, K and E are kinetic and total energies of a particle.

Review Short Questions on *Physical Optics*
(with Answers)

Wave Nature of Light

1. *Mention the different theories of light in the order of discovery.*

Ans. The theories of light in the order of discovery are : (i) Corpuscular theory, (ii) Wave theory, (iii) Electro-magnetic theory and (iv) Quantum theory.

2. *State Huygens' principle.*

Ans. Huygens' principle may be stated as follows : In a wavefront each point becomes an independent source of disturbance which originates a secondary wave or wavelet. The wavelets touch a spherical surface having its centre at the source and this spherical surface will be the new wavefront whose particles are also in the same phase of vibration.

3. *What relation you notice between a ray and wavefront?*

Ans. A ray is a straight line and this becomes perpendicular to the wavefront.

4. *'The laws of refraction cannot be explained from the wave theory'—whether the statement is true or false?*

Ans. False; the laws can be explained from the wave theory.

5. *What is the physical significance of the refractive index according to the wave theory?*

Ans. According to the wave theory, the refractive index of the second medium with respect to the first medium is equal to the ratio of the velocity of light in the first medium to that in the second medium.

If the two media are represented by a and b and whose corresponding velocities are V_a and V_b, then

$$_a\mu_b = \frac{V_a}{V_b},$$

where $_a\mu_b$ is the refractive index of the medium b with respect to the medium a.

6. *What will be the optical path in a medium?*

Ans. If light travels in a medium of refractive index μ with a velocity V, then the time required to traverse a distance S is given by

$$t = \frac{S}{V}.$$

But since the velocity of light in vacuum is c, we have

$$\mu = \frac{c}{V}.$$

$$\therefore \quad t = \frac{\mu S}{c}.$$

Thus in vacuum the light in time t travels a distance

$$\left(\frac{\mu S}{c}\right) \times c = \mu.$$

The quantity μS is the optical path of light in a medium of refractive index μ.

Interference of Light

7. *What is interference of light?*

Ans. In interference of light equispaced bright and dark bands are formed by the superposition of waves from two sources having a constant phase relationship between them.

8. *What are the conditions necessary for producing interference of light?*

Ans. (i) There must be two sources of light and these must emit continuous waves of same wavelength and periodic time.

(ii) At the start the wave trains should have either the same phase or some constant difference in phase.

(iii) The two sources should be narrow and very close to each other.

(iv) The amplitude of the two waves should be same.

9. *What do you mean by coherent sources?*

Ans. By the term coherent sources we mean the two sources which are derived from the same source.

10. *How can you obtain two coherent sources of light?*

Ans. Two coherent sources of light can be obtained in the following manner :

(i) An illuminated narrow slit and its virtual image are formed by reflection. This is applied in the experiment of *Lloyd's single mirror.*

(ii) Two virtual images formed by reflection due to the same source (illuminated narrow slit). This is applied in the experiment of *Fresnel's double mirror.*

(iii) Two virtual images formed by refraction due to the same source (illuminated narrow slit). This is applied in the experiment of *Fresnel's biprism.*

(iv) By division of amplitude of a wavefront in two parts by either reflection or refraction or by the both. The two parts are later combined to form interference of light. This is applied in the experiment of *Michelson's Interferometer* and also in *Newton's ring.*

11. *How are the conditions of interference of light fulfilled in the case of biprism?*

Ans. In the experiment of biprism the virtual sources are formed from the same source due to refraction through the two halves of the biprism. So the waves which appear to diverge from two virtual sources produce interference of light.

12. *What is the nature of the biprism fringes in space? Why we get straight fringes on the screen?*

Ans. In space the biprism fringes are hyperboloids of revolution with the two virtual sources as foci.

We get straight fringes on the screen because it is held parallel to the line joining the two virtual sources.

13. *In the experiment of biprism, would you require an extended or a narrow source?*

Ans. A narrow source is required since it will produce distinct fringes. An extended source will not produce any fringe.

14. *Are the biprism fringes localised or non-localised?*

Ans. The biprism fringes can be found by holding the screen anywhere in the region where the waves from the two virtual sources superpose. Thus the biprism fringes are non-localised in nature.

15. *What will happen if the slit is illuminated by white light? Explain.*

Ans. The central fringe will be white and all other fringes will be coloured.

The distance of the nth fringe x_n from the central one can be expressed as

$$x_n = \frac{D}{d}n\lambda.$$

When $n = 0$ for the central fringe, we have, $x_n = 0$ for all wavelengths due to which the central band is white.

For other fringes red with greater wavelength will be in the outermost position and violet with smaller wavelength will be in the innermost position forming a coloured appearance of the fringes.

16. *Do you desire to get the values of d_1 and d_2 nearly equal or widely different?*

Ans. Nearly equal values are desired.

17. *Why is the plane face of biprism directed towards the slit?*

Ans. If the plane face of the biprism is directed towards the slit then an almost equal increments of deviation occur due to refraction at the two faces of the prism. As a matter of fact the fringes will be narrow.

18. *What will happen if the acute angles of the biprism are increased?*

Ans. When α is increased, d also increases by the relation,

$$d = 2a(\mu - 1)\alpha.$$

Again, we have

$$\beta = \frac{D}{d}\lambda,$$

where β is the fringe width.

Thus we find that with the increase of d, the value of β decreases.

19. *What will happen when the slit is made horizontal and the edge of the prism is kept (a) horizontal and (b) vertical?*

Ans. (a) When the slit and the edge of the prism are made horizontal the fringes will extend along the vertical line and so the distance between two consecutive fringes cannot be measured by the eyepiece.

(b) When the slit is made horizontal the source extends along the breadth. As a result fringes will shift laterally by which they will disappear.

20. *Can you perform the biprism experiment with a convex lens of any focal length?*

Ans. The focal length of the convex lens f is to be selected in such a manner that the condition $D > 4f$ is satisfied, where D is the distance between the slit and the eyepiece.

21. *What will happen when the distance between the slit and the eyepiece is increased?*

Ans. The fringe width β will be increased for an increase of the distance D between the slit and the eyepiece.

22. *How does interference occur in Newton's ring?*

Ans. In Newton's ring the two waves produced by reflection from the front and back surface of the air film are originated from the same wavefront. Thus the condition of coherency is satisfied and so they produce interference.

23. *What will happen when light is employed?*

Ans. A smaller number of rings will be seen and these will be coloured.

24. *Where are the rings produced?*

Ans. The rings are produced in the air film enclosed between the lens and the glass plate.

25. *Is the central ring bright or dark?*

Ans. The central ring with reflected light is dark. This is due to the change of phase of π be reflection from the glass plate (denser medium).

26. *What happens if an illuminated slit is used instead of an extended source?*

Ans. Only a part of the rings will be observed.

27. *What will happen when the air film is replaced by a liquid film?*

Ans. The rings will contact.

28. *Can one measure the refractive index of a liquid by using your apparatus?*

Ans. The refractive index of the liquid can be measured simply by enclosing the liquid between the lens and the glass plate.

29. *Are the rings equispaced?*

Ans. The rings are not equispaced. With the increase of the diameter of the rings the width decreases.

30. *Is it possible to see the central spot bright?*

Ans. When the rings are observed with transmitted light the central spot would be bright.

31. *How do Newton's rings differ from biprism fringes?*

Ans. (i) An extended source is required for Newton's experiment while for biprism experiment a narrow source is required.

(ii) Interference fringes produced in Newton's rings are based on the division of amplitude while those produced by biprism are based on the division of wavefront.

Diffraction of Light

32. *What is meant by diffraction of light?*

Ans. The bending of light waves round the edge of an opaque obstacle resulting a rapid diminution in the intensity of light within its geometrical shadow is called the diffraction of light.

33. *Is the phenomenon of diffraction consistent with the principle of rectilinear propagation of light?*

Ans. No; the phenomenon of diffraction is not consistent with the principle of rectilinear propagation of light.

34. *What are the different types of diffraction?*

Ans. There are two main types of diffraction phenomena.

These are : (i) Fresnel's diffraction and (ii) Fraunhofer's diffraction.

35. *What is the difference between the Fresnel and Fraunhofer classes of diffraction?*

Ans. In Fresnel diffraction phenomena both the source and the point of observation are very near to the diffraction obstacle. On the other hand, in Fraunhofer diffraction phenomena those are at infinite distance from the diffraction obstacle.

36. *Give examples of Fraunhofer type of diffraction.*

Ans. Fraunhofer type of diffraction is noticed in (i) plane diffraction grating and (ii) concave reflection grating.

37. *What happens when the incident light is white?*

Ans. For a white incident light the central fringe will also be white. On either side, however, a few coloured fringes will be observed.

38. *What differences you notice between the diffraction and interference of light?*

Ans.

Diffraction	*Interference*
(i) Diffraction fringes are produced by the interaction of light waves coming from same wavefront.	(i) Interference fringes are produced by the interaction of light waves coming from different wavefronts originated from the same source.
(ii) All the bright bands have not identical intensity.	(ii) All the bright bands have identical intensity.
(iii) Diffraction fringes do not have the same width.	(iii) Interference fringes may or may not have the same width.
(iv) Minimum light intensity regions are not perfectly dark.	(iv) Minimum light intensity regions are perfectly dark.

39. *What will you do to increase the angular widths of diffraction and interference fringes?*

Ans. If θ and ϕ represent the angular separations between two successive dark bands of diffraction pattern and also two successive dark bands of interference pattern respectively, then

$$\theta = \frac{\lambda}{a} \quad \text{and} \quad \phi = \frac{\lambda}{(a+b)},$$

where a is the width of the slit and b the width of the opaque space.

Now, to increase θ of diffraction dark bands a should be made smaller while to increase ϕ of interference fringes $(a+b)$ should be made smaller. But in the second case the number of interference fringes in the central bright diffraction band will decrease.

40. *What is the effect of widening the slit?*

Ans. With the increase of the width of the slit the angle of diffraction gradually decreases and ultimately the bands disappear but diffraction is obtained at the two edges of the rectangular aperture.

41. *What will be the change in the nature of the fringes when the distance between the opaque space is increased?*

Ans. If the slit width is not changed then the diffraction system will remain same but the member of interference fringes will be increased.

42. *What will happen if the two slits are joined together?*

Ans. In that case it will behave like a single slit of width $2a$, a being the width of each slit. As a result the diffraction bands come closer but the interference pattern disappears completely.

43. *What will happen if the width of the collimator slit is made greater?*

Ans. With the increase of the width of the collimator slit the interference fringes will be indistinct and ultimately for a certain width the fringes disappear.

44. *When a given order bright fringe of interference pattern will be missing?*

Ans. If the condition for minimum of the diffraction pattern due to a single slit and the condition for maximum of the interference pattern due to double slit are both satisfied for the same value of θ then a given order of interference maxima will be missing.

45. *What is the practical importance of the interference pattern due to double slit?*

Ans. It is applied to find the angular width of a star.

46. *What is meant by diffraction grating?*

Ans. Diffraction gratings can be constructed by drawing equidistant parallel rulings on a glass plate by using diamond point.

47. *How is the replica grating constructed?*

Ans. Replica grating is constructed by pouring a thin layer of colloidal solution on the original grating. After evaporation of the solution a film is produced on the grating surface which when stripped from the grating and thereby mounted between glass plates, forms the replica grating.

48. *What do you mean by grating element and corresponding points?*

Ans. If the width of the slit and the opaque of a grating is represented by a and b respectively then $(a + b)$ is termed as the grating element. The two points in the consecutive slits separated by a distance $(a + b)$ are known as the corresponding points.

49. *What will happen if the number of rulings per cm is (i) decreased, (ii) increased?*

Ans. (i) When the number of rulings per cm is decreased one can obtain several order numbers separated by a small angle.

(ii) When the number of rulings is increased, a few order number of bands separated by a large angle are found.

50. *What will happen if the total width of the grating is increased but the number of rulings are kept constant?*

Ans. Sharpness of principal maxima will increase causing an increase of the resolving power of the grating. However, the dispersion will remain same.

51. *What do you mean by 'Ghost line'?*

Ans. If the distance between two consecutive slits is not constant and the rulings are not parallel, near the real spectral lines additional lines are found. These additional lines are known as 'Ghost lines.'

52. *What will you do if unequal number of principal maxima are noted on two sides of the central maximum?*

Ans. The position of the source is to be adjusted until the number of bands on both sides become equal and equally bright.

53. *What happens in the spectra when the incident light is not strictly monochromatic?*

Ans. The two lines of wavelengths very close to each other will be more and more resolved as one goes to the higher orders.

54. *What happens when the slit is illuminated by electric lamp?*

Ans. In that case the central band will be white and for the other bands we get spectra of which red will be in the outermost position and violet in the innermost position.

55. *What happens when the ruled surface of the grating is directed towards the collimator?*

Ans. The angle θ, in this case, will be due to both diffraction and refraction since the incident rays will be first diffracted at the ruled surface and then again they will be refracted by the glass surface. Thus the angle θ will not be due to diffraction alone.

56. *What is reflection grating and what is its utility?*

Ans. Reflection grating has no absorption of light as occurs in transmission grating. These are more suitably used for studying extreme ultraviolet light.

57. *How does a grating spectrum differ from a prismatic spectrum?*

Ans. (i) The degree of purity and the resolving power of a grating is far greater than that of the prism.

(ii) For a grating spectrum, $d\theta/d\lambda$ is nearly constant, i.e., the spectrum is normal. For a prismatic spectrum it is not so; $d\theta/d\lambda$ is far greater towards the violet than the red.

(iii) Dispersion does not depend on the material of the grating but it depends on the order number and the number of rulings per cm but for prismatic spectrum the dispersion depends on the material of the prism.

Polarization of Light

58. *What is meant by polarized light?*

Ans. When all the rays of a beam of light vibrate in a definite direction on a plane drawn perpendicularly to the beam, then the light is said to be polarized.

59. *What do you mean by double refraction?*

Ans. If an unpolarized ray is made to fall on a crystal of Iceland spar, it is refracted into two rays. One of these rays obeys the laws of refraction and is known as *ordinary ray* while the other ray does not obey those laws in general and is known as *extraordinary ray*. Both of these rays are plane polarized; the vibration of the ordinary ray is perpendicular to the principal section and that of the extraordinary ray is in the principal section. This phenomena in which one incident ray is refracted into two rays is called double refraction or birefringence. The crystals which exhibit such phenomenon are known as doubly refracting crystals.

60. *Define the terms : (i) Optic axis and (ii) Principal section.*

Ans. (i) *Optic axis*—It is the direction of the crystal along which no double refraction of the ray takes place due to identical properties of the ordinary and the extraordinary ray.

(ii) *Principal section*—It is the section of the crystal by a plane which passes through the optic axis of the crystal and is at right angle to its two opposite refracting faces.

61. *What is meant by plane of polarization?*

Ans. It is a plane drawn at right angles to the direction of vibration of the polarized light.

62. *What are 'optically active substances'?*

Ans. The substances which rotate the plane of polarization after passing light through it are known as optically active substances.

63. *How does the optical activity depend on the wavelength?*

Ans. The rotation is proportional approximately to the inverse square of the wavelength of light.

64. *What do you mean by 'rotatory dispersion'?*

Ans. The phenomenon of the variation of rotation with the λ of light used is called the rotatory dispersion.

65. *How can you define specific rotation for pure liquids and pure solids?*

Ans. Specific rotation (S) for pure liquids may be defined as :

$$S = \frac{\text{rotation per decimetre}}{\text{density of liquid}}.$$

On the other hand, specific rotation for a pure solid is the rotation produced by the solid of 1 mm thick.

66. *Following Fresnel, how is the plane of polarization explained?*

Ans. Fresnel showed that a plane polarized light is resolved into two equal and opposite circularly polarized lights which move with an unequal speed inside the substance. After emergence, a phase difference occurs between the two emergent circular vibrations. At a certain angle these will combine to form a linear vibration.

67. *State Malus law.*

Ans. The law may be stated as follows : 'The intensity of the incident ray is equal to the sum of the intensities of the transmitted rays.'

68. *What is Nicol's prism.*

Ans. The prism is called so after the name of its designer William Nicol. It is an optical device constructed from a doubly refracting crystal known as calcite. Nicol's prism is used for production and analysis of polarized light.

69. *Mention different methods of producing plane polarized light.*

Ans.   By the following methods plane polarized light can be produced successfully :

(i) By reflection from transparent substance (e.g., glass) at the polarizing angle.

(ii) By double refraction through a doubly refracting crystal (e.g., Iceland spar).

70. *What is a quarter-wave plate?*

Ans.   A crystal plate which produces a phase difference of $\frac{\pi}{2}$ between the ordinary and extraordinary rays is called the quarter-wave plate.

If d be the thickness of such a plate then the path difference δ between the ordinary and extraordinary rays is given by

$$\delta = d(\mu_o - \mu_e),$$

where μ stands for refractive index.

For a quarter-wave plate,

$$\delta = \frac{\lambda}{4}.$$

So by the above equations, we get

$$\frac{\lambda}{4} = d(\mu_o - \mu_e) \quad \text{or,} \quad d = \frac{\lambda}{4(\mu_o - \mu_e)}.$$

For a positive crystal (e.g., quartz), $\mu_o < \mu_e$ and then

$$d = \frac{\lambda}{4(\mu_e - \mu_o)}.$$

Spectroscopy

71. *What are the constituents of white light? How did Newton prove it?*

Ans. The white light consists of seven colours such as violet, indigo, blue, green, yellow, orange and red.

The composite character of white light was first performed by Newton. A narrow beam of sunlight is allowed to fall on a prism. He found that a coloured band of seven different colours is produced on the screen. In this way Newton proved the composite nature of white light.

72. *What is Newton's disc?*

Ans. It is nothing but a disc divided into seven radial segments and each segment is pointed with different colours of the white light. This disc can be rotated at any speed.

73. *What is the difference between impure spectrum and pure spectrum?*

Ans. The spectrum in which there is overlapping of different colours is called an impure spectrum.

A spectrum in which there is no overlapping of different colours and the colours are distinctly separated is known as pure spectrum.

74. *Mention the names of different parts of a spectrometer.*

Ans. The different parts of spectometer are

(i) Telescope, (ii) Prism-table and (iii) Collimeter.

75. *Discuss the differences between Infrared rays and Ultraviolet rays.*

Ans.

Infrared rays	*Ultraviolet rays*
(i) The portion of the spectrum beyond the visible red is known as infrared region.	(i) The portion of the spectrum beyond the violet is known as ultraviolet region.
(ii) Infrared region has wavelength in the range 7800 Å to 0.04 cm.	(ii) Ultraviolet region has wavelength in the range 3900 Å to 150 Å.
(iii) Heating effect of this region is most effective.	(iii) Heating effect is practically nil.
(iv) Chemical effect is practically nil.	(iv) Chemical effect is present.
(v) Infrared rays can penetrate the atmosphere and are used for photographing of landscapes.	(v) Ultraviolet rays have a very penetrating influence and are used in medicine.

76. *Discuss graduation of wavelengths for complete spectrum.*

Ans.

Region of spectrum	Wavelength range
(i) Visible spectrum	(i) 7×10^{-5} cm to $3\cdot9 \times 10^{-5}$ cm
(ii) Infrared	(ii) 7.8×10^{-5} cm to 4×10^{-2} cm
(iii) Ultraviolet	(iii) 3.9×10^{-5} cm to 15×10^{-7} cm
(iv) X-rays	(iv) 10^{-7} cm to 10^{-9} cm
(v) λ-rays	(v) 10^{-10} cm
(vi) Radio waves	(vi) 10^{-1} cm to 10^{-7} cm

77. *What do you mean by general absorption and selective absorption?*

Ans. The amount of light reflected or absorbed depends on the substance over which it is incident. Certain substances do not reflect and transmit light but totally absorb light of all wavelengths. This type of absorption is known as general absorption.

Certain substances absorb a part of the light incident on them depending on the wavelengths. This type of absorption is known as selective absorption.

78. *What are Fraunhofer's lines in a solar spectrum? Explain their origin.*

Ans. Fraunhofer found that a large number of lines exist in the solar spectrum. He marked these lines by A, B and C in the red, D in the orange-yellow, E in the green, F in the greenish-blue, G in the indigo and H in the violet part of the spectrum. These lines are called Fraunhofer's lines.

The explanation of the dark lines was given by Kirchhoff. According to him, white light emitted by the sun when passed through the envelopping layer, those waves which corresponds to the waves of the enveloping elements, are absorbed. The absorption of these waves causes the dark lines in the solar spectrum.

79. *What are different kinds of spectra?*

Ans. There are mainly two kinds of spectra. Emission spectra and absorption spectra.

Emission spectra may be divided into three characteristics, viz., (i) Continuous spectrum, (ii) Line spectrum and (iii) Band spectrum.

80. *What would be the nature of spectra produced by (a) an electric lamp, (b) a sodium lamp, (c) a neon lamp and (d) the sun?*

Ans.

(a) Electric lamp	(a) Continuous spectra
(b) Sodium lamp	(b) Line spectra
(c) Neon lamp	(c) Line spectra
(d) The sun	(d) Absorption spectra

81. *State Doppler's principle and give some of its astrophysical applications.*

Ans. When a source of waves is moving through a stationary medium, the waves sent in the direction of motion of the source become shorter while those sent in the opposite direction become larger then the waves from a stationary source. This principle is known as Doppler's effect.

Applications : (i) Rotation of the sun, (ii) temperature of stars and (iii) motion of a planet are determined by applying Doppler's principle.

82. *What is the scattering of light? What is Rayleigh scattering law?*

Ans. When light falls on small particles whose size is smaller than the wavelength of the incident light, the particle radiates incident light in different direction. This phenomena is known as scattering.

Rayleigh law of scattering states that the intensity of scattered light varies inversely to the fourth power of the wavelength of the incident light.

83. *How will you explain (a) blue of the sky; (b) red colour of the rising and the setting sun?*

Ans. Sunlight falls on the air molecules or dust particles and is scattered in all directions. Blue light has shorter wavelength and so is scattered much more than the red light. The scattered light consists mainly of blue colour and the sky appears blue.

At the times of sunrise and sunset shorter waves are scattered away and finally red waves are transmitted to us and as a result of these transmission the sun appears red.

84. *Discuss the dependence of the visual sensation on colours and wavelengths.*

Ans. The various colours and their approximate wavelengths on visual sensation are given below :

Colour	Wavelength
Violet	4300 Å
Blue	4800 Å
Green	5300 Å
Yellow	5800 Å
Orange	6300 Å
Red	6800 Å

Miscellaneous Questions on Physical Optics

85. *Water of deep lake looks blue'.—Explain why.*

Ans. There occurs a scattering of sunlight by water molecules in the clear water of deep lake. The intensity of scattering of blue light is greater than that of red light due to the sun. An observer, therefore, looks blue light mainly from the water surface.

86. *The rising or the setting sun appears red—why?*

Ans. We know that the intensity of scattering is inversely proportional to the fourth power of the wavelength. The rays of light from the rising or the setting sun goes through the longest path in the atmosphere. At such times the blue-violet light of shorter wavelengths are mainly scattered away in different directions while the red light of longest wavelength is least scattered. Hence the rising or the setting sun for an observer appears red.

87. *Wavelengths of light coming from distant stars appear to be increased or decreased—why?*

Ans. When with a high speed a star moves away from the earth, the light coming from it undergoes an apparent increase in wavelength by Doppler effect.

On the other hand, if a star moves towards the earth the light undergoes a decrease in wavelength.

88. *Why is only red light used in the dark room for developing negative of a photographic film?*

Ans. Since the chemical effect of red light is negligible so it does not affect the photographic film. If during developing the photographic film is exposed to white light or to any other colour of light except red, the negative film is affected and the photograph is spoiled. That is why red is only used.

89. *How is the phase difference related to the path difference for a wavelength λ?*

Ans. If ϕ represents the phase difference and x is the path difference, then

$$\phi = \frac{2\pi}{\lambda} x.$$

90. *Will the velocity of light in a denser medium be greater than, equal to or less than that in a rarer medium and why?*

Ans. Velocity of light is less in a denser medium than that in a rarer medium. We know that,

$$_r\mu_d = \frac{\text{velocity of light in a rarer medium}(v_r)}{\text{velocity of light in a denser medium}(v_d)} > 1,$$

where $_r\mu_d$ is the refractive index of a denser medium with respect to rarer medium.

$\therefore \quad v_d < v_r$

91. *How is the refractive index of medium 2 with respect to medium 1 is related to the wavelengths of a particular light in the two particular media?*

Ans. If λ_1 is the wavelength of medium 1 and λ_2 is that of the medium 2 and n is the frequency of the particular light, then

$$_1\mu_2 = \frac{v_1}{v_2} = \frac{n\lambda_1}{n\lambda_2} = \frac{\lambda_1}{\lambda_2}$$

92. *Out of the two colours red and blue, which has the greater velocity through glass?*

Ans. Since $\frac{v_r}{v_b} > 1$, so the velocity of red light through glass is greater than that of blue light.

93. *What is meant by dual nature of light?*

Ans. In order to explain interference, diffraction, polarization, etc., the wave theory of light is applied while for explaining black body radiation, line spectra, photoelectric effect, etc., the quantum theory is applied. It means light has dual nature—sometimes wave and sometimes quanta.

94. *'Interference fringes are not contrary to conservation of energy.'—Justify the statement.*

Ans. It can be established that the average intensity of light for a dark and a bright band is identical with the intensity under generally illuminated condition. Hence interference fringes are not contrary to conservation of energy.

95. *Can you obtain interference of a monochromatic light coming from two independent sources?*

Ans. No interference pattern is obtained.

96. *Why are Newton's rings so named?*

Ans. Since these fringes are in the form of concentric circles, these are called rings. These rings were first observed by Sir Issac Newton and hence these are called Newton's rings after his name.

97. *Where are the fringes formed?*

Ans. In Newton's rings, the fringes are formed in the air-film, between the glass plate and the lens.

98. *Write down the factors on which the diameters of the rings depend.*

Ans. If D_n be the diameter of the nth ring, then calculations show, $D_n^2 = \frac{4Rn\lambda}{\mu}$.

Therefore, the diameters of the Newton's rings depend upon (i) the refractive index (μ) of the medium enclosed between the lens and the plate, (ii) the radius of curvature (R) of the spherical surface of the lens, (iii) the wavelength λ of light used.

99. *If instead of a plane glass plate a plane mirror is used, what change is observed?*

Ans. Here no fringes will be visible and only uniform illumination is observed. When a plane mirror is used no part of the light will be transmitted through it. Hence the reflected part and the transmitted part will superimpose on each other and uniform illumination is observed.

100. *How do you measure the radius of curvature of the lens?*

Ans. The radius of curvature of the lens is measured either by Boy's method or by a spherometer.

101. *Is the central spot bright or dark?*

Ans. In reflected light the central spot should be dark. Newton's rings in reflected light are formed as a result of interference between the rays reflected directly from the upper surface of the air-film between the lens and the plate. The total path difference between the two interfering rays is $2\mu t \cos\theta \pm \frac{\lambda}{2}$, where θ is the angle of refraction in the film of thickness t. At the point of contact $t = 0$ and here the total path difference $= \lambda/2$. So at the point of contact, the two interfering rays are in opposite phase and they produce zero intensity and hence the central spot is dark.

But in actual practice, the point of contact between the lens and the plate is not perfect due to the presence of dust particles and roughness of glass surfaces. Hence in general, the central spot is diffused.

102. *Can you obtain a central bright spot in the reflected rays also?*

Ans. If Newton's rings are obtained by using a crown glass lens placed on the flint glass plate with a small quantity of oil of sassafras between them, the centre of the ring system is bright. This is because, the oil of sassafras is optically denser than crown glass but rarer than flint glass. Therefore, the reflection at the upper and lower surface of the film takes place under similar condition, i.e., from rarer to denser medium. Thus a phase change of π occurs at both reflections. Hence the phase-difference between the interfering rays at the point of contact is zero and the central spot appears bright.

103. *Why are the fringes circular?*

Ans. The wedge-shaped film is formed in the air film between the convex lens and the glass plate. The locii of constant path difference are different circles with the point of contact as the centre. Hence the fringes are concentric circular fringes.

104. *Why an extended source is necessary for this experiment?*

Ans. In order to obtain interference due to the whole wedge-shaped film, the whole film is to be illuminated.

105. *What will be the nature of the fringes if the light is allowed to fall obliquely on the air-film?*

Ans. In this case, the path difference at any point decreases and hence the diameter of each ring pattern increases.

106. *What are the nature of the fringe pattern if white light is used instead of a monochromatic light?*

Ans. The central pattern is diffused, and the colour of the first order fringe will be violet, since $D_n \alpha \sqrt{\lambda}$. With increasing thickness, the colour of fringes will change from violet to red. After 8 to 10 coloured fringes uniform illumination, owing to overlapping of all the colours, is observed.

107. *What are the nature of the fringe patterns if observations are made in transmitted light?*

Ans. In transmitted system we get bright centre, instead of dark. Owing to no excess path difference ($\lambda/2$) introduced in transmitted system, the intensity of the two systems of rings will be complementary to each other. If the intensity of the nth order fringe for the reflected system is bright, then the intensity of that nth order in transmitted light will be dark. Also the intensity of the fringe system in transmitted light will be much poorer than that obtained in reflected light.

108. *What will happen if in Newton's ring experiment, instead of an extended source of monochromatic light, an illuminated narrow slit is used?*

Ans. In this case complete rings are not obtained, only small parts of the ring may be formed.

109. *Is the width of each Newton's ring same?*

Ans. No; with the increase of diameter the width of Newton's ring gradually decreases.

110. *What is the basic difference in the conditions of formation of Newton's rings and of interference fringes by Fresnel's biprism?*

Ans. For Newton's rings an extended source is required while for fringes by biprism an illuminated narrow slit is necessary. Newton's rings are produced on the division of amplitude of waves while fringes by biprism are formed on the division of wavefront.

111. *What will be the effect on fringes if one-half of the biprism is covered?*

Ans. When one-half of the biprism is covered, interference fringes are not formed. In fact, there will be a general illumination on the screen for the light emerging from the uncovered half of the prism.

112. *How will the pattern of diffraction bands be changed if one of the slits of a double slit is covered?*

Ans. In that case it will behave as a single slit. So the interference bands that are formed on the diffraction bands by a double slit is not obtained. If one slit is covered only the diffraction bands will remain.

113. *If the screen (or the micrometer eyepiece) be replaced by a photographic plate what will be the nature of the pattern of the photographic plate?*

Ans. At the centre of the photographic plate some closely spaced fringes will be observed. These fringes are due to the interference. At the edge of the pattern, some wide fringes will be seen. These wider bands are due to the diffraction produced by the vertices of the biprism and are of similar nature of those produced by the diffraction effect due to a straight edge. Hence, the edge of the biprism also produces diffraction bands.

114. *Suppose that in Young's experiment, the angle between the extreme rays is made very large, (i.e., the separation between the two slits is increased). Will there be any interference pattern on the screen?*

Ans. As the double slit no longer produces two temporal coherent sources, no pattern is seen. Hence, as the slit separation is gradually increased, the visibility of the fringes gradually decreases. For a large separation the visibility is zero, i.e., the fringe system disappears.

115. *What kind of coherence is needed in the biprism experiment?*

Ans. Here, temporal coherence is necessary to observe the fringes.

116. *What do you mean by microwaves? State whether any special arrangement is needed to produce coherent sources in order to observe interference pattern with microwaves.*

Ans. Radio waves of a few centimetres wavelength belong to microwaves. Generally, radio waves have frequency lying within 10^5 to 10^9 cycles per second. Radio waves are produced by radio frequency oscillator and the phase of such waves may be treated as constant during the time of observation. Therefore, two independent microwave sources having the same amplitude and frequency may be treated as two coherent sources to produce sustained interference pattern.

117. *What is the position of micrometer eyepiece for the measurement of d_1 and d_2? Will values of d_1 and d_2 be nearly equal or not, for accurate measurement of d?*

Ans. The values of d_1 and d_2 must be measured with the *same* value of $a+b$ (i.e., D) as is used in the fringe-width (β) measurement. Also, during the experiment the distance between the source-slit and the biprism should be kept unaltered. For accurate measurements of d_1 and d_2, the position of the lens should be adjusted in such a way that the values of d_1, and d_2 are nearly equal. This will introduce the minimum error in the measurement.

118. *Why no fringe is seen when the angle between the slit S and the edge of the prism is not very small?*

Ans. In biprism experiment a single source on the slit 'S' produces approximately straight line fringes parallel to the edge of the biprism. Hence, if the illuminated narrow slit S is not parallel to the edge of the biprism, then the relative positions of the fringes produced by the neighbouring points on S are slightly displaced laterally. Thus the maxima produced by two neighbouring points of S are not in coincidence. Therefore, the contrast between the maxima and minima of the fringe pattern is reduced. Other points on S reduce the visibility of the pattern further and so if the angle between S and the refracting edge of the biprism is large, no fringe is observed and we get uniform illumination.

119. *In your experiment the slit S is in vertical plane. What will you observe if the slit S be made horizontal?*

Ans. As discussed in the answer of the previous question the lateral shift of the different fringes produced by different points on S are so large that complete uniform illumination is seen.

120. *What will you observe when the refracting edge of the biprism and the illuminated slit are both kept in the same horizontal plane? Assume that all other adjustments are properly done.*

Ans. In the case the equispaced fringes are horizontal and hence the fringe-width cannot be measured by the micrometer supplied. If the micrometer eyepiece can be moved in a direction perpendicular to the optical bench, then the width can be measured. Of course, using a photographic plate the photograph of the pattern can be obtained.

121. *What is the limiting distance up to which fringes can be seen?*

Ans. There is no mathematical relation relating distance of observation and the visibility of the fringes. Of course, at a smaller distance the visibility of the fringes is large. But as the distance of the screen from the coherent sources is increased, the contrast of bright and dark fringes gradually decreases and finally fringe system disappears.

122. *State whether any focusing arrangement is necessary to observe the interference pattern in the biprism experiment.*

Ans. If the beams of interfering rays from the coherent sources subtend a very small angle to any point on the plane of observation no focusing arrangement is needed. But, if the angle is large, focusing arrangement is necessary. Hence to observe the interference pattern using extended source certain type of focusing arrangement is needed.

123. *What happens if the emitted lights from the coherent sources are of different frequencies?*

Ans. Here the phenomenon similar to that of formation of beats in sound will occur. Therefore, the resultant intensity at any points of observation will be alternately minimum and maximum as time passes. Hence, if the two frequencies differ by a large amount, no fringe will be seen.

124. *Why the coherent sources should be monochromatic?*

Ans. We know that the fringe width is given by $\beta = \frac{D\lambda}{d}$. Hence, if the wavelengths emitted by two coherent sources differ, then the fringe widths will be different for each wavelength. As a result of this, the positions of higher order maximum for a particular order number will be different for different wavelengths although the position of the central maximum remains the same. Thus the contrast of the fringe pattern tends towards the minimum as the difference in wavelength is gradually increased.

125. *What do you mean by coherent and non-coherent beams of light?*

Ans. If the phase difference between the waves which is superimposed in space or elsewhere is constant during the period normally covered by the observation, the sources emitting the wave are said to be coherent.

If the phase difference between the two beams is not constant but changes in an irregular way and also changes many times during the shortest period of observation, the beams are said to be non-coherent.

126. *Can a coherent source be exactly realised in practical situation?*

Ans. No. The term coherent is actually an ideal concept and can never be exactly realised in practice. This is, because, the coherence of a particular wave or wave-trains describes the accuracy with which it can be represented by a pure sine-wave. If the frequency of the perfectly monochromatic waves remains exactly the same, then the waves can be treated as coherent. Actually in strictest sense, infinitely long wave-trains are always completely coherent.

127. *Which kind of wave groups can be treated as coherent ones?*

Ans. A set of wave groups whose properties are not actually the same may be treated as coherent provided the differences of disturbances produced due to superimpositions are very very small. The deviations owing to departure from a pure sine-wave do not produce appreciable effects under ordinary conditions of observations. Actually we are dealing with partially coherent waves under existing experimental conditions.

128. *What do you mean by partially coherence, temporal coherence and spatial coherence?*

Ans. If the wave groups apparently appear to be pure sine-waves during the limited time of observations, the wave-trains are said to be in temporal coherence. On the other hand, if the wave groups behave as coherrent, when observations are confined to a limited space, the waves are said to be in spatial coherence.

129. *Which property of the light waves governs the degree of coherence?*

Ans. The photon populations characterise the degree of coherence. If all the photons emitted by a source are in the same phase (i.e. have the same energy, the same state of polarization and are moving in the same direction), then the source is said to be coherent in this strictest sense. For non-coherent or incoherent source, the photon energies are distributed irregularly over different states.

130. *Explain the term coherence time and coherence length.*

Ans. Let us consider a wave represented by

$$y = a\sin(\omega t + \delta),$$

where a is the amplitude, ω is the angular frequency and δ represents the phase. Since no light source can produce perfect sinusoidal variation over an infinite time and over all space, hence we shall introduce the term coherence time denoted by T_C. This coherence time indicates the average time for which the wave can be treated as a pure sine-wave. Also l, the spatial dimension through which the wave may be treated as a perfectly monochromatic one, is given by

$$l = T_c \times c = \frac{T_c}{T}\lambda,$$

where c is the velocity of light and T is the time period. Let us consider a sodium discharge tube producing two coherent sources. Let coherence length be about 3 cm. Hence, the coherence time

$$T_c = l/c \approx 10^{-10} \text{ sec.}$$

Hence, sodium lamp can be treated perfectly as a temporal coherent source for about 10^{-10} sec. Also, the number of oscillations produced during 10^{-10} sec is

$$\frac{T_c}{T} = \frac{l/c}{\lambda/c} = l/\lambda = 6 \times 10^4 \text{ cycles.}$$

131. *How coherence length is related with coherence time for coherent and non-coherent sources?*

Ans. If path differences produced by two coherent sources is related with coherence time (T_c) by the equation $L \ll T_c c$, then the sources are said to be coherence because in the above case definite phase relationship exists between the two coherent sources. Hence, the similar parts of the same wave-train superimpose at the point of observation. In this case, distinct interference fringes can be obtained. But if $L \gg T_c c$, the two interfering sources behave as non-coherent because no definite phase relationship exists between the two interfering beams. In this case no fringe is observed.

132. *In biprism experiment with monochromatic light no fringe pattern is seen if the width of the slit is made broad. Lack of what type of coherency is responsible for it?*

Ans. When the slit is made broad the monochromatic source lacks spatial coherence. A broad vertical slit may be imagined to consist of a large number of very narrow slits placed side by side. Since ordinary light lacks spatial coherence, hence each slit produces interference fringes that are displaced from those produced by the other nearly elementary slits. Hence, the average effect due to superimposition of the pattern owing to lack of spatial coherence gives rise to the uniform illumination.

133. *In holography where interference is produced by a laser beam, what type of coherence are needed?*

Ans. In holography, the monochromatic laser beams used must possess both the temporal and spatial coherence for the production of interference fringes.

134. *Explain it quantitatively.*

Ans. When the slit is narrow we get complete coherence in the strictest sense. In this case the emitted radiations are approximately due to one particular set of excited atoms. But when the slit is made very broad, the interfering beams pass from the state of coherence to the state of incoherence. When the slit is made *not very wide*, the emerging beams are *partially coherent*. For a broad slit the emitted radiations are due to set of excited atoms which are independent of one another, and hence the phases of the interfering beams emerging from the slit are completely uncorrelated. Hence the interference are always occuring between any two individual point sources of the slit, but the aggregate effect of all interfering point sources in space is uniform illumination.

135. *If the eyepiece is replaced by the photographic plate, what is the effect?*

Ans. Photograph of interference fringes will be obtained.

136. *Will the photograph can indicate anything about the phases of the beams?*

Ans. Photographic plate cannot give any information about the phase difference. This is because, photographic plate is only sensitive to the intensity of the resultant interfering waves. Hence the photograph can give an idea only about the amplitude. But no information about relative phase differences can be obtained.

137. *Which kind of intensity, electric or magnetic, is responsible for producing interference pattern?*

Ans. Interference is produced due to superposition of electric waves with each other; of course, the magnetic vectors also superimpose with one another during interference. But since the retina of the eye is only sensitive to electric vector and hence it is customary to assume that the electric vector is responsible to produce interference, diffraction and polarization. In this sense, the magnetic vector is less important.

Therefore, the amplitude of the light wave generally indicates the *electric vector* associated with the *incoming* wave. Also electric vector only affects the photographic plate but not the magnetic vector.

138. *Discuss the shape of the fringe.*

Ans. The nature of the shape of the fringe depends on (i) the distance of screen and (ii) on the relative position of the screen with respect to the sources.

If the screen is very close to the coherent sources the fringe-width is very very small and hence nearly uniform illumination is observed. If the screen or the micrometer eyepiece is too far from the sources the illumination is too poor to measure the fringe-width.

In between these two positions there is a considerable range where distinct fringe-pattern can be photographed or viewed through the micrometer eyepiece.

Actually the fringes are formed on a set of surfaces of constant phase difference. If the coherent sources can be regarded as point sources, these surfaces of constant phase differences are hyperboloids. The fringes observed are due to the intersections of these hyperboloids with the plane of observations. If the position of the screen is parallel to the line joining coherent sources S_1 and S_2, nearly straight line fringes are observed. These fringes are parallel to the length of the slits.

If the position of the screen is perpendicular to the line joining the coherent sources S_1 and S_2, then alternative bright and dark concentric circular fringes are obtained. The common centre of the concentric circles is at the point of intersection of the produced $S_1 S_2$ line with the screen.

139. *Mention the adjustments necessary for working with a spectrometer.*

Ans. The following adjustments must be made:

(i) The axes of the telescope and the collimator must intersect the vertical axis of the instrument.

(ii) The eyepiece should be focused on the cross-wires.

(iii) The telescope must be focused for parallel rays.

(iv) The collimator must be focused for parallel rays.

(v) The optical axes of the collimator and the telescope must be perpendicular to the axis of rotation of the telescope which in a good spectrometer must coincide with the axis of rotation of the prism table.

(vi) The prism table should be mechanically and optically levelled so that the refracting surface of the prism must be parallel to the axis of rotations.

140. *Why the above adjustments are necessary?*

Ans. To get a pure spectrum and to bring the spectrum in the centre of the field of view of the telescope, the above adjustments are necessary.

141. *Describe the construction of the collimator.*

Ans. The collimator consists of a long tube carrying an adjustable vertical slit at one end and a collimating lens at the other end. The position of the slit can be changed in inward or in outward direction by rack and pinion arrangement. The width of the slit, can also be adjusted. The function of the collimator is to obtain parallel pencil of rays from the discharge tube (or source of light) placed in front of the vertical slit. The convex lens used in a collimator is actually an achromatic doublet. The focal length of the lens is smaller than the length of the collimator tube.

142. *Describe the construction of the telescope.*

Ans. It is an astronomical telescope. It consists of two convex lenses placed co-axially at the two ends of brass tube. Actually, the objective is an achromatic doublet, and the eyepiece is of Ramsden type. [For further discussions, see oral questions on telescope and microscope.]

143. *What is the distance of the slit from the collimating lens and that of the cross-wires from the telescope objective after focusing for parallel rays is completed?*

Ans. The distance of the slit from the collimating lens is equal to the first focal length of the lens. So after refraction from the collimating lens, the parallel rays emerge from it. This is because, ultimately the slit has been adjusted in the first focal plane of the collimator. The position of the cross-wire is in the *second focal plane* of the telescope objective. Also the position of the cross-wire is at the *first focal plane* of the Ramsden eyepiece of the telescope. This is because the parallel rays are brought to the second focal plane of the telescope objective, and finally viewed by the eyepiece.

144. *Will the adjustments for focusing for parallel rays be same for all persons or will vary from individual to individual?*

Ans. The adjustments will vary from individual to individual. The spectrum and also the image of the cross-wire seen through the eyepiece are formed at the far point of the observer's eye. But since the far point of the eye varies from individual to individual, hence the adjustment performed by one will not suffice for all. Also the image should be seen without any strain on the eye. This is also one of the causes of variation from individual to individual. Hence the collimator and telescope cannot be permanently set for parallel rays.

145. *Why are two verniers provided in the spectrometer?*

Ans. If the axis of rotation of the prism table and the telescope coincides, then the readings from the two verniers should differ by 180°. If the axis of rotation does not coincide, one vernier will give a greater value than the true value, while the other vernier will give a lesser value than the true value. The mean of the two values eliminates the error arising out of the non-coincidence of the axis of rotation.

146. *Point out the essential difference between a spectrometer and spectrograph.*

Ans. The spectral lines may only be observed by using a spectrometer. A spectrograph is provided with a photographic camera instead of a simple telescope, so that we may take a permanent photographic record of the spectral lines with the aid of this instrument. But only observations and measurements of spectral lines of different sources are possible with a spectrometer.

147. *Sometimes the reflected image of the slit from the prism is seen directly by nacked eye, but by bringing the telescope the image is not observed. Give reasons.*

Ans. This is due to the fact that the prism table is not properly levelled and hence the reflected image is either shifted to downward or upward direction of the field of view of the telescope.

148. *Is the optical levelling using one prism remains unaltered if the prism is replaced by another?*

Ans. No. Because, the optical parallelism of the base of two prisms is generally not of the same order.

149. *What is meant by the angle of deviation?*

Ans. The angle made between the direction of the incident ray on one refracting face of a prism and the direction of the emergent ray coming out of the second refracting face of the prism is known as the angle of deviation of the ray.

150. *What are the governing factors of the angle of deviation produced by a prism?*

Ans. The main factors controlling the angle of deviation produced by a prism are (i) the refracting angle of the prism, (ii) the refractive index of the material of the prism, (iii) the angle of incidence of the ray of light for which the angle of deviation is concerned, and (iv) the colour of the light used.

151. *What is the effect of the length of the base of the prism on the angle of deviation of a given ray produced by the prism?*

Ans. The angle of deviation of a ray produced by the prism does not depend at all on the length of the base of the prism. Consequently, there is no effect on the angle of deviation of a ray if the length of the base of the prism is altered.

152. *Then why the prisms of larger base are manufactured?*

Ans. Prisms of larger base have higher resolving power. To obtain the distinctly separated lines for wavelengths having very small difference between them by the prism, (i.e., to increase the resolving power of the prism), the length of its base is increased.

153. *State the relation between the wavelength of light and the refractive index of the material of the prism, when the experiment is performed far from the absorbtion band.*

Ans. The refractive index of the material of a prism corresponding to the light of a particular wavelength decreases with increase in the wavelength of that light. These two quantities are, however, related between themselves according to Cauchy's relation which is

$$\mu = A + \frac{B}{\lambda^2} + \frac{C}{\lambda^4} + \cdots,$$

where A, B, C are constants of diminishing magnitudes. So we may neglect the terms occurring after the second one when Cauchy's relation reduces to this form,

$$\mu = A + \frac{B}{\lambda^2}. \text{ Here, } \frac{d\mu}{d\lambda} \text{ is a negative quantity.}$$

The equation gives the required relation for normal dispersion.

154. *What do you mean by anomalous dispersion?*

Ans. In the absorbtion region, $\frac{d\mu}{d\lambda}$ is a positive quantity, and hence higher wavelengths will be deviated to maximum extent than those of lower ones.

155. *Do the light rays of different colours have the same velocity inside a prism?*

Ans. Though light of different colours, i.e., of different wavelengths have the same velocity in air medium, their velocities decrease by different amounts for different colours. When they travel into a refractive medium like a glass prism, the velocity of the violet rays travelling through a glass prism decreases to a greater extent than that of the red rays. Consequently, the refractive index of glass for violet colour is greater than that for red one. This is the basic principle of the production of spectrum by a prism.

156. *How anomalous dispersion can be observed?*

Ans. Iodine vapour placed inside a thin walled glass prism exhibits anomalous dispersion in white light.

157. *Why a prism is set into minimum deviation position?*

Ans. There are certain advantages of the minimum deviation position of a prism. They are the following :

(i) In this position, the rays of light appear to diverge from the same point after refraction through the prism. The image is, therefore, the brightest and in focus in this case. The rays are mostly concentrated after suffering the minimum deviation.

(ii) The magnification is unity due to the fact that object and the image are equidistant from the prism.

(iii) We get a pure spectrum in this position of the prism.

(iv) The position can be easily arranged without causing much error in practice.

(v) There are possibilities of least errors if one take readings for measurements in this position.

158. *How the necessary arrangements are made in order to get a pure spectrum?*

Ans. The essential arrangements for production of a pure spectrum are the following :

(i) A narrow slit is placed near the source of the light.

(ii) The illuminated slit is placed at the focal plane of a convex lens so that a parallel pencil of light is incident on one refracting face of the prism.

(iii) The prism should be placed at its minimum deviation position with respect to the light of a particular wavelength used in experiment. This edges should be parallel to the slit.

(iv) Another convex lens is used to focus the rays of different colours to different foci.

(v) The observations should be made with the help of an eyepiece.

All these conditions required may very easily be obtained with the help of a spectrometer.

159. *What is the reason behind the fact that we get a bright and distinct spectrum in the minimum deviation position of a prism?*

Ans. At a minimum deviation position of a prism, the object distance (u) and the image distance (v) both measured from the prism is the same and, therefore, the magnification ($m = v/u$) is unity in this case.

Again, the rays of different wavelengths, after refraction through the prism, appear to diverge from the same point which is fixed for a particular wavelength. So we get a bright and distinct spectrum, in the minimum deviation position of a prism.

160. *State whether the angle of minimum deviation remains the same or not if during experiment the prism is immersed in water (or in glycerine).*

Ans. It will change, and the angle of minimum deviation will diminish. This is because the relative refractive index of glass (or glycerine) in air is greater than that of glass in water, i.e.,

$$_\omega\mu^g = \frac{_a\mu^g}{_a\mu^\omega} = \frac{1.5}{1.33} = \frac{9}{8} = 1.12.$$

161. *State how μ of any liquid can be determined.*

Ans. This can be done by enclosing the liquid in a hollow thin glass prism.

162. *What are the different methods for exciting substances whose spectra are to be obtained?*

Ans. There are four principal methods of exciting a substance, e.g., a Bunsen flame, the electric arc, the electric spark and the discharge tube.

163. *Discuss the excitation by a Bunsen flame.*

Ans. Excitation by a Bunsen flame is suitable for a few substances that can easily volatilise. Such substances are salts of sodium, potassium, lithium, rubidium, thallium, calcium, caesium, barium and storntium. Generally a small loop at the end of a piece of platinum wire is made and the loop is cleaned by dipping it in hydrochloric acid and heating it in the flame. The loop is then dipped in the salt and is placed into the outer surface of the Bunsen flame. However, the salts generally burn out quickly and is necessary to have constant supply of the salt into the loop.

164. *What is the fundamental principle of excitation and emission of light?*

Ans. The atom is excited when it absorbs energy from a suitable external source. On excitation, electrons from lower energy levels jump to higher energy states. But the excited electrons tend to jump to the lower states within 10^{-8} sec or less. During such transitions from higher states to lower states, the line spectra originate according to the Bohr quantum condition.

165. *What are various methods for excitation of an atom?*

Ans. Different methods of excitations of atoms are the following :

(i) By collisions with atoms or electrons, (ii) by absorbtion of energy from thermal sources, (iii) by absorbtion of radiation, (iv) high frequency electrodeless discharge.

166. *How is light produced in a gaseous discharge tube?*

Ans. The light produced in a gaseous discharge tube is the result of excitation of gaseous atoms. The atoms, on colliding with electrons emitted from the cathode, absorb energy and are excited to some higher energy states for about 10^{-8} sec or less. After this time they come back to the lower energy states and hence the absorbed energy is emitted as light radiation.

167. *Explain the working of the lamp.*

Ans. When the electrodes E_1 and E_2 are connected to a leak transformer, a starting voltage of about 440 volts is generated. This is done with the help of a step-up auto-transformer generally known as a leak transformer. This voltage initiates a discharge in the neon.

The heat of neon discharge gradually vaporises the sodium. The voltage across the terminal very soon drops to about 170 volts. The lamp now begins to emit lines, characteristic of sodium. As the ionisation potential of sodium is much less than that of neon, hence a lesser potential difference is needed to operate the lamp.

168. *How does the neon help in maintaining the discharge?*

Ans. When the lamp is switched on, the starting voltage of about 440 volts excites the neon gas. Since the filaments E_1 and E_2 are coated with barium oxide, at first barium oxide supplies plenty of electrons to carry the discharge and so red light is first emitted. After 5 to 10 minutes, the voltage drops to about 170 volts. So sodium vapour is excited as its excitation voltage is low. The temperature and vapour pressure of sodium increases and so sodium emits its own spectrum in partnership with neon. Since the voltage drops, hence Na only emits light. This is because the excitation voltage of Na is much lower than that required for Ne. Thus Ne performs the role of catalyst.

169. *Why in a sodium vapour lamp, the characteristic lines of neon are not emitted?*

Ans. The relative concentration of neon atom to sodium atom is approximately 8000 : 1. Though the number of neon atoms are much larger, yet owing to the presence of leak transformer the voltage drops to 170 volts. But this voltage is too low to excite neon atoms. Also neon atoms loose much of their energy during collision with sodium atoms, and so neon atoms do not acquire sufficient energy for their excitation. For this reason, no lines of neon are observed.

170. *Why the* Hg *vapour lamp cannot be immediately started again once the lamp is switched off?*

Ans. The Hg vapour must condense at first so that the starting electrode can function again.

171. *What do you mean by emission spectrum?*

Ans. When a body is heated to such an extent that it emits light, it is said to be incandescent. The spectrum given out by the body in this state is known as emission spectrum.

172. *Classify emission spectra.*

Ans. Emission spectra may be divided into three characteristic classes as discussed below:

(1) **Continuous spectrum:** This type of spectrum consists of unbroken luminous bands showing all the colours from red to violet and contains rays of all refrangibilities. Such a spectrum depends on the temperature of the source and is given out by electric lamp, lime light, coal gas flame, etc. Liquids and gases under great pressure also give continuous spectra. It is easy to obtain continuous spectra for incandescent solids.

(2) **Line spectrum:** Such a spectrum given out by incandescent vapours of elementary substances consists of bright lines separated from one another by dark spaces. According to the characteristic appearance of the lines, the spectra of most of the elements have been classed as principal, sharp, diffuse and fundamental series.

(3) **Fluted or band spectrum:** It consists of a number of broad, luminous bands, sharply defined at one edge and gradually shading off at the other. It is given by elements or compounds in their molecular state, e.g., cyanogen. Such spectra are characteristics of the molecule, depending on the method of excitation. Band spectra are due to excited states of the molecules. Energy of the molecule can have only discrete values called energy states. When a molecule jumps from higher energy (E_2) to lower energy (E_1), the frequency of the band is given by $h\nu = E_2 - E_1$.

173. *How absorption spectrum is obtained?*

Ans. It may be obtained by passing a continuous spectrum through a transparent coloured substance when some of the constituent rays are absorbed and the rest is transmitted through it. This type of spectrum is then found to be devoid of some colours absorbed by the absorbent. Solar spectrum provides an example of absorbtion spectrum. If a transparent substance is placed in front of white light, and if the substance absorbs some of the constituent rays, then the final spectrum is devoid of absorbed colours and we get absorbtion spectrum. Each substance has its own absorbtion spectrum by which it can be identified.

174. *Define dispersive power of the material of a prism.*

Ans. It is defined to be the ability of the material of the prism to disperse the constituent colours of the incident polychromatic light.

Mathematically it is given by the ratio of the angular separation or the dispersion between the violet and red rays and the deviation of the mean yellow line lying between them. Thus,

$$\omega = \frac{D_v - D_r}{D_y}.$$

175. *What are the main factors controlling the dispersive power?*

Ans. The following two factors control the dispersive power, viz., (i) the wavelength of the colour concerned and (ii) the material of the prism used.

176. *What is the expression for dispersive power which has been accepted internationally?*

Ans. The internationally accepted expression for dispersive power is $\omega = \frac{\mu_F - \mu_C}{\mu_D - 1}$. Here μ_F, μ_C and μ_D represent the refractive indices of the material of the prism for F- and C-lines of hydrogen spectrum and the D-line of the sodium spectrum, respectively.

177. *On what factors does the value of refractive index (r.i.) and dispersive power depend?*

Ans. The dispersive power directly depends on the refractive index. The refractive index of a substance is different for light of different colours. Even for a given substance, for a given colour, the value of refractive index depends upon the physical conditions under which the determination is made. Actually, the refractive index determined by the usual experimental methods is the relative refractive index with respect to air. The absolute value of r.i. μ_0 with respect to vacuum is given by $\mu_0 = \mu \cdot \mu_a$, where μ is the experimentally determined value, and μ_a is the r.i. of air. Both μ_0 and μ_a depend on temperature, and μ_a is also affected by pressure. Hence, it is evident that the experimentally determined value of μ is correct only for that temperature and pressure when the experiment is done. Hence, during recording, the temperature and pressure should be stated. Also, according to Gladstone and Dale's law the value of $(\mu - 1)$ is proportional to the density of the gas. For solid, the formula giving the variation of μ with temperature and pressure is complicated.

178. *What is the reason behind the selection of only the F, C and D lines for this purpose?*

Ans. Their choice is based on the fact that the F- and C-lines occur in the blue ($\lambda = 4861\text{Å}$) and red ($\lambda = 6563\text{Å}$) region respectively of the hydrogen spectrum while the D-line of sodium occurs in the yellow ($\lambda = 5893\text{Å}$) region of its spectrum. Therefore, they cover the visible region of the spectrum to which human eyes are most sensitive.

179. *Can you distinguish between the prisms of crown glass and flint glass?*

Ans. Yes, as the prism of flint glass have a greater dispersive power than that made of crown glass, they may be distinguished easily by visualising the spectrum produced by each of them using a polychromatic light. The separation between the spectral lines produced by a prism of flint glass will be greater compared to that produced by a prism made of crown glass due to the higher dispersive power of the former.

180. *Will you prefer a prism made of flint glass or, that made of crown glass?*

Ans. A prism of flint glass has higher dispersive power than that of crown glass. Consequently, it gives higher resolutions of the spectral lines produced by it. A flint glass prism will, therefore, be preferred for the experimental measurement of dispersive power.

181. *Give the definition of normal spectrum.*

Ans. It is defined to be that spectrum in which the angular separation between the spectral lines corresponding to any two wavelengths varies directly with the difference between those two wavelengths.

182. *Will the relative positions of different colours in the prism and grating spectra be the same?*

Ans. No, the relative positions of different colours are not same in the two spectra. In the prism spectrum of white light, red occurs nearest to the line of incidence and the violet to the furthest end while in grating spectrum the positions are just reversed.

183. *A Nicol prism is rotated about a light ray falling normally on it. What will be the effect if the light is (i) plane polarized, (ii) elliptically polarized and (iii) circularly polarized?*

Ans. (i) If the light is plane polarized, its intensity will vary twice between the maximum and zero values.

(ii) If the light is elliptically polarized, its intensity will vary twice between the maximum and a certain minimum values.

(iii) If the light is circularly polarized, its intensity will remain unchanged.

184. *What is the result of sending an elliptically polarized light through a $(\lambda/4)$ plate?*

Ans. If an elliptically polarized light is made to pass through a $(\lambda/4)$ plate, it will emerge as plane polarized light.

Electronics

Chapter 28

Vacuum Tubes, Semiconductor Diodes and Transistors

28.1 Introduction

Vacuum tubes ushered in the age of electronics. Nowadays though vacuum tubes have been upstaged by solid-state devices, like diodes, transistors and integrated circuits, they are still used in various electronic equipments. Of course, vacuum tubes have undergone many changes since the introduction of the Fleming valve. The early tubes were physically large and complicated in operation while modern production have transformed these into small in size with high efficiency.

A P-N junction is known as a *semiconductor diode*. This is also called a crystal diode as it is grown out of a crystal. The action of a P-N junction can be considered as the basis of the working of all semiconductor devices.

The bipolar transistor can be viewed as two-junction diodes kept back-to-back and sharing a common impurity material. Therefore, the transistor theory depends heavily on the semiconductor principles. The N-regions of a transistor have mostly conduction band electrons while the P-regions have mostly holes. For that reason, a junction transistor is also termed as a bipolar transistor.

The theory of the junction transistor was first worked out by Shockley in 1949 while the first transistor was produced in 1951, after two years of the development of the theory. In the field of electronics, the impact of the transistor is enormous. In fact, the transistor has led to all kinds of recent inventions like integrated circuits, optoelectronic devices and microprocessors.

28.2 Classification of Vacuum Tubes

Vacuum tubes are classified in a number of ways as discussed below :

(i) Depending on the number of electrodes : (a) Diode has two electrodes : anode and cathode. (b) Triode has three electrodes : anode, cathode and control grid. (c) Tetrode has four electrodes : anode, cathode, control grid and screen grid. (d) Pentode has five electrodes : anode, cathode, control grid, screen grid and suppressor grid. Similarly, hexode has six electrodes, heptode has seven electrodes, and so on.

(ii) Depending on the presence or absence of gas : (a) High vacuum tubes : After mounting of the electrodes in the tube envelope, the gas is removed from the electron tube with a vacuum pump of the order of 10^{-8} atmosphere. (b) Gas tubes : After evacuation an inert gas is inserted within the tube envelope.

(iii) Depending on the type of cathode used : (a) Thermoionic tubes : In these tubes cathode is heated for emission of electrons. (b) Electron multiplier tubes : Electron emission at a number of electrodes, called *dynodes*, takes place due to secondary emission. (c) Cold cathode tubes : Electron emission is obtained by high field. (d) Phototubes : Cathode emits electrons when light falls on it.

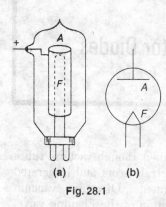

(a)   **(b)**

Fig. 28.1

28.3 Diode Valve

The term 'di-ode' means two electrodes. The valve consists essentially of a cathode which serves as an emitter of electrons surrounded by a plate or anode which acts as a collector of electrons. Both the electrodes of the valve are sealed inside an evacuated glass or metallic envelope. The emitter may be either directly or indirectly heated type. A diagram of the directly heated diode is shown in Fig. 28.1(a) and its schematic symbol in Fig. 28.1(b). In the figure, F is the filament surrounded by a hollow cylinder A, known as the anode. The anode is usually made of nickel, molybdenum, graphite, iron, etc.

28.3.1 Operation

From the basic law of electricity, we know that like charges repel and unlike charges attract each other. Electrons emitted from the cathode surface may be either attracted to or repelled from the anode depending on whether the anode is charged positively or negatively. When the anode A is kept at a positive potential relative to the filament F by means of a high tension battery as shown in Fig. 28.2(a), electrons are able to move from cathode to anode owing to an attractive effect of the electrons and the valve is said to conduct. But, if A is maintained at a negative potential relative to F, as shown in Fig. 28.2(b), no electrons would reach at A due to the repulsive effect on them and so the valve would not conduct. Thus the anode current flows in a diode only when the anode is made positive with respect to filament. No current flows when the anode is negative with respect to filament.

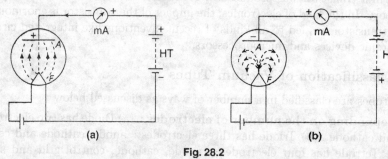

(a)   **(b)**

Fig. 28.2

28.3.2 Characteristic Curves

The curves obtained on plotting anode current along the y-axis against anode voltage along the x-axis is called the current-voltage characteristics of a diode. Since current and voltage involved pertain to the tube alone, irrespective of the associated circuits, the characteristics thus obtained usually referred to as 'static characteristics'. Fig. 28.3 illustrates a circuit for determining the static characteristic curves of a directly heated diode. In the figure, the anode A is kept at a positive potential relative to F by

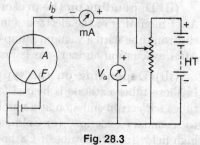

Fig. 28.3

means of a HT battery. The anode current i_b is read on the milliammeter in the circuit.

The anode voltage e_b is gradually increased in regular steps, and at each step, the anode current i_b is recorded keeping the filament current constant. The observations are repeated for different values of filament current. For static characteristic curves, the anode current is then plotted against anode voltage as shown in Fig. 28.4.

The nature of the curve may be explained easily. The number of electrons reaching the anode depends on the electrostatic field round the filament. When e_b is zero, the electrons emitted at F will be attracted back to F again. So, no anode current i_b is obtained. Next, when e_b is made positive, some electrons will reach A and the electrostatic field round the filament is determined by the anode potential e_b. In practice, for any given value of anode voltage, a balance is

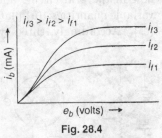

Fig. 28.4

reached at a certain value of anode current when the number of electrons emitted become equal to the numbers collected by the anode. It may be mentioned here that at very high anode voltage, oxide-coated cathodes may become damaged because of abnormally large emission. Generally, electron tubes are operated in the space charge limited (low e_b) region.

28.4 Triode Valve

The triode valve, as the name implies, contains three electrodes : a cathode of either filament or indirectly heated type, a control grid and an anode. The grid was first introduced in 1907 by Lee de Forest. It is usually made by a spiral of fine wire placed between the cathode and anode, usually close to the cathode.

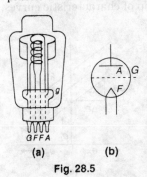

(a)   **(b)**

Fig. 28.5

The components of a triode valve and its schematic symbol are shown in Fig. 28.5. The filament is made by a fine tungsten wire, the two terminals of which are sealed in a glass base g and finally connected to two long pins (F, F). Around this filament, the grid made by molybdenum wire is situated in the form of spiral as shown; the interspaces between the turns of which are sufficiently wide so that electrons can flow easily through them. The grid is sealed to the base and connected to a pin G attached to it. Next, the anode which is a nickel cylinder is constructed surrounding the grid. This is supported on the base by two wires, one of which is connected to A attached to the base. The whole arrangement, viz., the filament, grid and the anode, is enclosed in a glass casing which is evacuated to a pressure of about 10^{-6} mm.

28.4.1 Function of Control Grid

Since the control grid is usually placed close to the cathode, the potential applied to the grid has a greater effect on the electric field inside the tube. The grid, therefore, has a controlling effect on the plate current. The control grid in operation is kept at a negative potential with respect to the cathode. As a result, it does not draw any current and consume power.

As the voltage applied to the grid is made gradually negative, the space current also reduces. Ultimately, a certain value is reached when the space current and hence the plate current becomes zero. Such a grid voltage at which plate current vanishes is known as 'cut-off grid voltage'.

28.4.2 Characteristic Curves

When the grid potential is made negative relative to the cathode, electrons do not flow in the grid circuit and hence $i_c = 0$. In a triode valve then we have three variable quantities: (a) plate current (i_b), (b) plate voltage (e_b) and (c) grid voltage (e_c). Accordingly, three types of characteristics are there : (a) plate current vs.

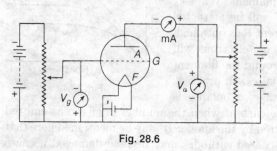

plate voltage characteristics or 'plate characteristics'; (b) plate current-grid voltage characteristics or 'mutual characteristics', also known as 'transfer characteristics' and (c) plate voltage-grid voltage characteristics or 'constant current characteristics.' This is further known as 'amplification charac-teristics'.

Fig. 28.6

Since the characteristics refer to the tube alone without any allied circuit, the curves such obtained are known as *static characteristic curves*. The basic circuit diagram for finding the static characteristic of a triode is given in Fig. 28.6.

Plate characteristics : When the grid voltage e_c is made constant and the plate voltage e_b is varied, the plate current i_b will also change. The curve connecting plate current (i_b) with the plate voltage (e_b) is called the plate characteristic curve corresponding to that e_c. If e_c is changed to different values, and i_b and e_b are altered, we may get different characteristic curves. A group of characteristic curves, such obtained, has been shown in Fig. 28.7(a).

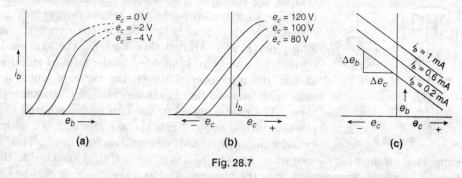

Fig. 28.7

Mutual characteristics : For a fixed anode voltage (e_b), if e_c is varied and the corresponding i_b is noted, we may draw (i_b-e_c) curve as shown in Fig. 28.7(b). The curves such obtained are known as *mutual characteristics* of a triode valve. When the grid voltage is increased on the positive side, each of these curves will first run parallel and finally approach the saturation value. The mutual characteristics are curved at their lower part and fairly straight and parallel for major portions.

Amplification characteristics : The amplification characteristics or the constant current characteristics of a triode are shown in Fig. 28.7(c). These may be obtained from the plate characteristics by drawing horizontal line for constant plate current and grid voltage at each intersection.

28.4.3 Valve Constants

The design factors of a valve are summarized by a series of numbers, called the *valve constants*. Valve manufacturers publish a manual in which these constants are listed along with the characteristic curves and other ratings for each valve. The three most important constants of a valve are : (i) the anode slope resistance or the a.c. plate resistance, (ii) the transconductance or the mutual conductance, and (iii) the amplification factor.

(i) Plate resistance (r_p) : This is defined as the ratio of a small change in plate voltage to the corresponding change in plate current, when the grid voltage is kept constant. Mathematically,

AC Plate resistance,

$$r_p = \frac{\delta e_b}{\delta i_b} = \frac{\Delta e_b}{\Delta i_b}, \quad e_c = \text{constant}, \tag{28.1}$$

where Δe_b = a small change in plate voltage,

Δi_b = a small change in plate current.

Since r_p is a ratio of two small quantities, it is correctly called 'incremental plate resistance' or the 'dynamic plate resistance'. Again, as it represents the slope of anode characteristic, it is also known as *'anode slope resistance'*.

The a.c. plate resistance differs from the d.c. plate resistance which is the ratio of the plate voltage to plate current, i.e., e_b/i_b. The d.c. plate resistance is also known as the 'static plate resistance' of the valve. The unit of plate resistance is ohm.

(ii) Transconductance (g_m) : This is defined as the ratio of a small change in plate current to the corresponding change in control grid voltage, when the plate voltage is kept constant. Mathematically,

Transconductance,

$$g_m = \frac{\delta i_b}{\delta e_c} = \frac{\Delta i_b}{\Delta e_c}, e_b = \text{constant}, \tag{28.2}$$

where Δi_b = a small change in plate current,

Δe_b = a small change in grid voltage.

Since the transconductance relates a quantity on the plate side to a quantity on the grid side, it is also called *'mutual conductance'*. The unit of mutual conductance is expressed in mho (ohm spelled backward).

(iii) Amplification factor (μ) : This is defined as the ratio of a small change in plate voltage to the corresponding change in grid voltage, when the plate current is kept constant. Mathematically,

Amplification factor,

$$\mu = \frac{\delta e_b}{\delta e_c} = \frac{\Delta e_b}{\Delta e_c}, i_b = \text{constant} \tag{28.3}$$

where Δe_b = a small change in plate voltage,

Δe_c = a small change in grid voltage.

To determine the amplification factor it is, therefore, required to change the plate voltage by a certain amount, record the change in plate current and then change the grid voltage by an amount just to attain the previous value of the plate current.

28.4.4   Relation between r_p, g_m and μ

We can write the mathematical form of the amplification factor as

$$\mu = \frac{\delta e_b}{\delta e_c} = \frac{\delta e_b}{\delta i_b} \times \frac{\delta i_b}{\delta e_c}$$

$$= r_p \times g_m. \tag{28.4}$$

That is, the amplification factor is equal to the product of plate resistance and mutual conductance. The three valve constants are thus interrelated in accordance with their definition.

28.5   Electron Emission

Electrons perform a certain amount of work to escape from the surface of emitter. To do this work, energy is imparted to them from some external sources such as heat energy, kinetic energy of electric charges, energy stored in electric or magnetic fields and the light energy. Accordingly, the emission of electrons from a metallic surface is classified as follows :

(i) Thermionic (Primary) emission : If electrons are emitted from a metal by supplying thermal energy, the process is called *thermionic emission.* The number of electrons released depends on temperature. At a given temperature, the thermionic emission current density is obtained by an equation known as *Richardson's equation.*

(ii) Secondary emission : When electrons at a high speed suddenly strike a metallic surface, some will collide directly with free electrons on the metal surface and project them outward. The electrons freed in this manner are called secondary emission.

(iii) Field emission : The presence of strong electric field set up by a high positive voltage outside the emitter surface may cause electron emission from it. The stronger the field applied, the greater will be the field emission from the cold emitter surface.

(iv) Photoelectric emission : In this process, light energy called *quanta* falling upon the emitter is transferred to the free electrons within the metal and speeds them up sufficiently to eject from the surface. The number of electrons emission will depend on the intensity of the beam falling upon the metallic surface.

Out of the four methods of emission discussed above, the thermionic emission is the most vital one and most commonly used in electron tubes.

28.6   Thermionic Emitters

Thermionic emitters are of two different types : (i) *directly heated emitter* or *filamentary emitter* and (ii) *indirectly heated emitter* or *oxide-coated emitter.*

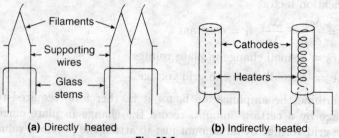

(a) Directly heated   **(b) Indirectly heated**

Fig. 28.8

In the direct heating, the electric current is applied directly to a wire called *filament* which itself serves as electron emitter, while in indirect heating, electric current is applied to a separate heater located inside a cylindrical cathode that serves as emitter. The arrangement of these two different types of heating is shown in Fig. 28.8. Both alternating or direct current can be used in either methods of heating. Two important directly heated emitters are (a) tungsten emitter and (b) thoriated tungsten emitter. Indirectly heated cathodes always use oxide-coated emitters. Receiving tubes are, in general, indirectly heated types.

28.7 Space Charge

For simplicity, let us consider a vacuum diode consisting of an emitter called *cathode* and a collector of electrons called *anode*. At low temperatures, there is no emission of electrons from the cathode surface and hence anode current is zero. As the temperature is raised to emit electrons from the cathode, and the anode is disconnected from a source of potential, electrons from the emitter form a cloud in the space. This atmosphere of thermoelectrons that is formed in the interelectrode space between cathode and plate is known as the *space charge*. Since it is made up of electrons, this atmosphere constitutes a negative charge that has a repelling effect on the electrons being emitted from the cathode. So the effect of the negative space charge alone is to force the emitted electrons back into the cathode by a considerable amount and prevent others from reaching the plate.

However, the space charge does not act alone. It is counteracted by the positive plate which attracts electrons through the space charge. When the plate voltage is low, only those electrons which are nearest to the plate are attracted to it and constitute a small plate current. With the increase of plate voltage, a greater number of electrons is attracted towards the plate and eventually a point is reached when all the electrons emitted from the cathode are attracted to the plate overcoming the effect of space charge completely. With further increase of plate voltage there will be no further increase of current. The current is then temperature-controlled. The total number of electrons emitted by an emitter is always same at a given operating temperature and is determined by using Richardson's equation.

28.8 Preparation of Semiconductor Materials

To use germanium and silicon in diodes, those are required to purify to a very high degree. Out of the two, it is easier to purify germanium than silicon.

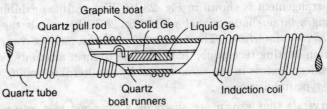

Fig. 28.9

Commercially, germanium is obtained as germanium dioxide (GeO_2). It is reduced to germanium powder at $650\,°C$ in a controlled atmosphere of hydrogen. In an inert gas atmosphere, if it is heated above the melting point ($936\,°C$), the material can be obtained in polycrystalline form. Further, purification is made by the process of zone melting which is based on the principle that when a molten semiconductor solidifies slowly, most of the impurities remain in liquid phase. These will be swept to the end which solidifies last. The semiconductor bar to be refined is kept in a graphite boat and then slowly pulled through a series of induction-heating coils. The arrangement is shown in Fig. 28.9. When the bar is moved slowly from right to left along the quartz tube having a few induction-coil heating zones, the impurities will remain in the liquid zone. These are concentrated finally at the right end of the bar which may be cut off to reject. The molten zones are removed with a speed of one-half to several tenths of a cm per minute so that the impurities are not trapped in the recrystallizing solid interface. To increase the impurity of the desired degree, the process is repeated several times.

Silicon has favourable semiconductor characteristics up to about 200 °C. This is in contrast to germanium which fails as a semiconductor above 100 °C. But due to great solubility of other materials in silicon, its purification is too difficult and expensive. By the action of chlorine on a heated mixture of silica (sand) and carbon, one can get silicon tetrachloride. This is then reduced with zinc, followed by hydrogen and other reducing agents to a purity of 99.9%. At the end of chemical purification, a zone refining process is applied to reduce the impurities to 1 part in 10^{10} or less.

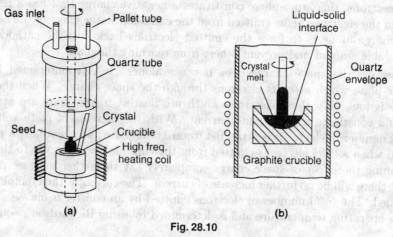

Fig. 28.10

In order to fabricate diodes (or transistors), large single crystals are used which are grown by touching a small seed crystal to the surface of molten semiconductor material and then withdrawing it slowly as new lattice crystals. A typical crystal-growing arrangement is shown in Fig. 28.10. Fig. 28.10(a) exhibits the apparatus for growing a large single crystal while Fig. 28.10(b) reveals the cross-section of the crystal melt interface. The temperature of the melt is controlled accurately by induction-heating technique. It is possible to form alternate regions of N- and P-type semiconductors in the same crystal by an alternate doping of the melt with N- and P-type impurities.

The crystals thus grown are sliced by a diamond saw into small wafers, the surface of each of which is polished and etched with acids.

28.9   Preparation of P-N Junctions

The P-N junctions are prepared by a transition from P- to N-type to occur within a single crystal. Junctions are generally made by three different means. These are : (i) the grown-junction method, (ii) the alloy-junction method and (iii) the diffused-junction method.

(i) Grown junctions : In this method, first of all, the germanium (or the silicon) crystal is doped with a very small quantity of P-type impurity. Then an N-type impurity is added at an appropriate instant in sufficient quantity. Thus a single crystal with a junction between P- and N-material is prepared. Junctions formed in this way have a relatively gradual transition from P to N and are classified generally as 'graded' junctions.

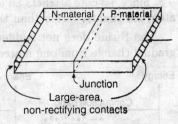

Fig. 28.11

After the preparation of the crystal, it is cut into rods along its length, the surface of each of the rod is polished and etched. The rod is then mounted and sealed in an enclosure. Fig. 28.11 shows the geometry of a rod containing a grown junction.

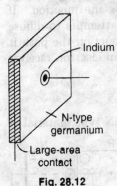

Fig. 28.12

(ii) Alloy junctions : The fused or alloy junctions are mostly used because of its simplicity. First of all a wafer to be used for the base is selected and the surface treated. A piece of material of opposite impurity is kept on the surface and the wafer is heated. For N-type germanium, a pallet or dot of indium may be used to form the junction. For the purpose, the temperature is raised to about 900 °C for a minute or so. Due to heating, the indium pallet melts and dissolves the germanium to form an alloy. When the heating is completed, the liquid begins to solidify. The junction thus produced has a very narrow transition from N- to P-type. This is usually classified as 'abrupt' junction and it depends upon the time-temperature cycle to a great extent. The structure of the junction is represented in Fig. 28.12.

(iii) Diffused junctions : In this technique, one surface of a slab of material of the type to be used for the base is exposed to a gaseous impurity of opposite type. The slab is next heated to a high temperature. The gaseous impurity diffuses slowly into the surface whose concentration is the highest at the surface and decreases exponentially inwards. Under the surface, a P-N junction is thus formed directly. The structure of

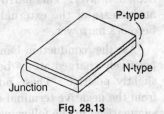

Fig. 28.13

the junction is shown in Fig. 28.13. This method is found to be very useful for making solar cells.

28.10 The Energy Hill

The energy-band diagram, before the diffusion of the electrons across the junction,

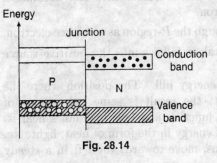

Fig. 28.14

is shown in Fig. 28.14. Under such condition, the P-side has many holes in the valence band and the N-side has many electrons in the conduction band. But it is interesting to see from the figure that the P-bands are slightly higher than the N-bands. The reason for this is very simple. We know that the P-side has trivalent atoms with a core of charge of +3 and the N-side has pentavalent atoms with a core of charge of

+5. Since +3 core attracts an electron less than +5 core, so the orbits of a trivalent atom are slightly larger than those of a pentavalent atom.

The P-side does not suddenly end where the N-side begins; rather, there is a gradual change from one material to the other. This is shown in Fig. 28.15(a).

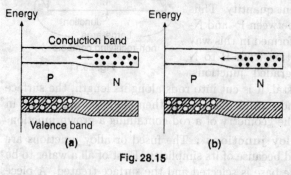

Conduction band

P   N

Valence band

(a)   (b)

Fig. 28.15

The nature of the energy diagram when the equilibrium is attained has been presented in Fig. 28.15(b). The bottom of each P-band is still with the top of the N-band indicating that electrons on the N-side no longer have enough energy to get across the junction. If an electron attempts to diffuse across the junction the path it must travel looks like a hill, known as the *energy hill*. Unless an electron receives energy from outside, it will not be able to climb this energy hill.

28.11   Forward Bias

If the negative terminal of a d.c. source is connected across the N-type material of a diode and the positive terminal to the P-type, then the connection is called *forward-bias arrangement*. Such an arrangement has been shown in Fig. 28.16. Here the d.c. source sets up an electric field which opposes the field of the depletion layer. Thus it pushes electrons and holes towards the junction and hence deionizes the edges of the depletion layer. This narrows the depletion layer. With an increase of the external voltage, the depletion layer becomes narrower.

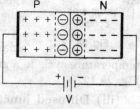

Fig. 28.16

As the conduction-band electrons move toward the junction, they leave positively charged atoms behind. Therefore, the right end of the crystal becomes slightly positive. These positively charged atoms pull electrons into the crystal from the negative terminal of the d.c. source. What happens to an electron can be summarized in the following few steps (Fig. 28.17) :

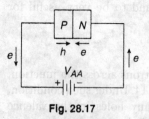

Fig. 28.17

(i) After leaving the negative terminal of the d.c. source, it enters the right end of the crystal.

(ii) It moves through the N-region as a conduction-band electron.

(iii) Near the junction, it recombines and becomes a valence electron.

(iv) It moves through the P-region as a valence electron.

(v) After leaving the left end of the crystal, it follows into the positive source terminal.

A forward bias arrangement lowers the energy hill. The position where the recombination takes place is not important; the result is same. A stream of conduction band electrons goes towards the junction and falls into holes near it. When an electron falls into a hole, it gives off energy in the form of heat, light, etc. The captured electrons, now valence electrons, move towards the left in a steady stream through the holes in the P-region. Thus a continuous flow of electrons through the diode is achieved.

28.12   Reverse Bias

If the positive terminal of a d.c. source is connected across the N-type material of a diode and the negative terminal to the P-type, then the connection is called *reverse-bias arrangement.* Such an arrangement has been shown in Fig. 28.18. Here the field produced by the external source is in the same direction as the depletion layer field. So the holes and electrons move towards the ends of the crystal, i.e., away from the junction.

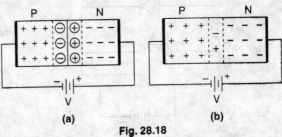

Fig. 28.18

The fleeing electrons leave positive ions behind and the holes leave negative ions resulting the depletion layer wider. The newly produced ions enhance the difference of potential across the depletion layer. The wider the depletion layer, the greater is the potential difference. The depletion layer will not grow further when the potential difference becomes equal to the applied reverse voltage.

Even after the depletion layer settles down, a few minority carrier exists on both sides of the junction, most of which recombine with the majority carriers. However, inside the depletion layer, these may live for a long time to get across the junction. As a matter of fact, a small current flows in the external circuit. This idea can be explained by considering Fig. 28.18(b). As soon as an electron-hole pair is created inside the depletion layer, the depletion layer field pushes the electron to the right forming one electron to leave the right end of the crystal. The hole in the depletion layer is, on the other hand, pushed to the left. Due to this extra hole on the P-side, one electron enters the left end of the crystal and falls into the hole. As the thermal energy produces electron-hole pairs near the junction continuously, a small current always flows in the external circuit. This reverse current caused by the minority carriers is known as the *saturation current.* The saturation current becomes approximately double for each 10 °C rise in temperature.

Since the energy gap between the valence band and the conduction band is greater in silicon than in germanium, the thermal energy produces fewer minority carriers in silicon diodes than in the latter. This indicates that with the same junction area, a silicon diode has smaller saturation current than a germanium diode.

The greater is the value of the reverse voltage, the steeper is the energy hill. When a conduction-band electron is made to fall down, this hill can attain a high velocity.

28.13   Circuit Symbol of a Semiconductor Diode

The circuit symbol of a semiconductor diode is shown in Fig. 28.19. The terminal marked cathode is connected to N-type material, while that marked anode is connected to P-type. It may, therefore, be pointed out that to make a forward-bias arrangement the negative terminal of the battery must be connected to the cathode and the positive to the anode.

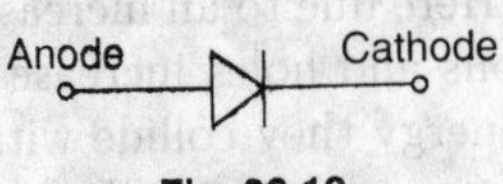

Anode   Cathode

Fig. 28.19

28.14   Characteristics of a Semiconductor Diode

In order to use the P-N junction as a circuit element, a study of its current-voltage characteristic for both forward and reverse condition is required. The circuit diagrams for studying the forward and reverse characteristics of the diode are shown in Fig. 28.20(a) and 28.20(b) respectively.

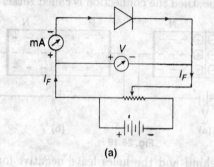

(a)

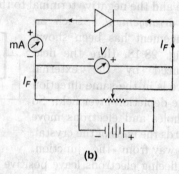

(b)

Fig. 28.20

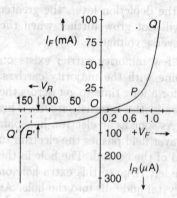

Fig. 28.21

For studying the forward characteristic of the diode, the forward voltage is increased from zero at suitable regular steps and the corresponding current is recorded by the milliammeter. On the other hand, for studying the reverse characteristic of the diode the reverse voltage is increased from zero at suitable regular steps and the corresponding current is measured by a micro-ammeter. The nature of the curve obtained by considering both forward and reverse characteristics is shown in Fig. 28.21. From the curve the following important conclusions can be drawn :

Forward characteristic

(i) The forward characteristic does not show a straight line nature indicating that a semiconductor diode is a nonlinear conductor of electricity.

(ii) If the applied forward voltage V_F is less than the internal potential barrier V_0 of the diode, then I_F becomes zero. For germanium diode V_0 is approximately 0.3 V, while for silicon diode it is nearly 0.7 V at 25 °C. When $V_0 > V_F$, the potential barrier prevents holes from P-region and electrons from N-region to flow across the depletion region in the opposite directions. But when $V_F > V_0$, a small current flows as represented by OP in the figure. The forward voltage for which the forward current just starts is known as the *break-point voltage*. It is also called as the threshold, cut-in or the offset voltage. This threshold voltage becomes equal to the potential barrier of the diode.

(iii) With a further increase of the forward voltage, the current is sharply increased as represented by the steep part PQ of the curve. Here due to an increase of the forward bias voltage, the speed of the flow of electrons and holes increases. During the movement of the electrons with higher kinetic energy they collide with crystal atoms. As a result some covalent bonds of the atoms are broken and pairs of electron and hole are created causing an increase of the forward current.

Again, with the increase of the forward current the heating effect in the crystal increases. As the generation of pairs of electron and hole depends on temperature, a rise of temperature causes a further increase in the current. When V_F is sufficiently large in comparison to V_0; the value of I_F rises exponentially with V_F.

Reverse characteristic

(i) With an increase of the reverse voltage V_R the reverse current I_R increases and attains the maximum value I_0. With a further increase of V_R, the I_R becomes almost independent of V_R up to a certain critical value. This value of I_R is known as the *reverse saturation current*. This is also called as *leakage current* which is due to a few minority carriers.

(ii) When V_R is increased to the critical value corresponding to the point P' in the figure, the reverse current rapidly increases due to the breakdown of the junction. The critical value of the reverse voltage is known as the *turnover voltage*. Beyond this voltage the junction is said to be in the breakdown region.

28.14.1 Static and Dynamic Resistance of a Semiconductor Diode

The static resistance can be defined as the resistance offered by the diode when a steady direct current passes through it. Thus the static resistance R of the diode is the ratio of the applied voltage V to the steady current I. Mathematically,

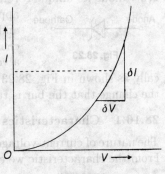

$$R = \frac{V}{I}. \qquad (28.5)$$

If the forward current flowing through a diode changes about its some average value, then the dynamic resistance r_f can be defined as

Fig. 28.22

$$r_f = \frac{\text{small change in applied voltage}}{\text{corresponding small change in diode current}}$$

$$= \frac{\delta V}{\delta I}. \qquad (28.6)$$

The values of δV and δI are obtained from the curve as shown in Fig. 28.22. Sometimes, r_f is also called as the *incremental resistance*.

28.15 Current-Voltage Equation of a Semiconductor Diode

If I represents the diode current in amperes and I_0 the reverse saturation current at a temperature T K, then the current-voltage characteristic of a semiconductor diode can be written as

$$I = I_0(e^{qV/nkT} - 1), \qquad (28.7)$$

where q is the electronic charge and k the Boltzmann constant; V represents the potential difference in volts which is positive for forward bias and negative for reverse bias. In the equation, the value of n is 1 for germanium and 2 for silicon. When V is positive the forward current is provided by the equation, while for a negative V it gives the reverse current.

For a large forward bias voltage, $e^{qV/nkT} \gg 1$ and then the forward current I_F can be written as

$$I_F = I_0 e^{qV/nkT}. \qquad (28.8)$$

Eq. (28.8) indicates that at a constant junction temperature the forward current exponentially increases with the forward voltage.

Again, under reverse-bias condition V is negative and so Eq. (28.7) can be written as

$$I_R = I_0 \left(\frac{1}{e^{qV/nkT}} - 1 \right). \tag{28.9}$$

For a large reverse-bias voltage,

$$e^{qV/nkT} \gg 1.$$

$$\therefore \quad I_R = -I_0. \tag{28.10}$$

Eq. (28.10) shows that the reverse current is independent of the applied voltage.

28.16   Zener Diode

A junction diode is operated suitably by using forward-bias arrangement. In zener diode its unique reverse-bias characteristic provides some important different applications. By adjusting the concentration of acceptor and donor impurity atoms near the junction the characteristic beyond the turnover voltage becomes nearly a vertical line, A zener diode can be represented symbolically as shown in Fig. 28.23. The symbol is similar to that of a crystal diode with the change that the bar is turned into the letter Z.

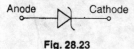

Fig. 28.23

28.16.1   Characteristics of Zener Diode

The nature of current-voltage characteristic of the zener diode is shown in Fig. 28.24. From the characteristic we can draw the following important conclusions :

(i) When the diode is operated under forward-bias condition, it behaves like a closed switch and then with an increase in applied voltage the forward current increases. Under forward-bias condition it thus acts like an ordinary P-N junction diode.

(ii) When the diode is reverse-biased a small reverse current, called the *saturation current,* flows through it. This current is found to be fairly constant until a certain critical voltage is attained. This voltage is known as the *turnover voltage.* Beyond this voltage the reverse current is increased sharply to a high value. In this region, since a small voltage change alters the current considerably the effective resistance in the P-N junction also changes dramatically.

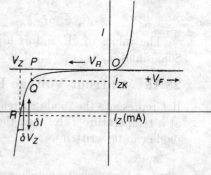

Fig. 28.24

28.16.2   Some Terms Related to Zener Diode

(i) Breakdown voltage : It is the reverse voltage corresponding to the point Q just beyond the curvature of the characteristic. In the figure, the voltage corresponding to the point P represents the breakdown voltage.

(ii) Breakdown current : The reverse current corresponding to the breakdown voltage is called the breakdown current I_{ZK}.

(iii) Zener voltage : It is the reverse voltage at some value of the zener current I_Z. On the linear portion of the reverse characteristic, it corresponds to a suitable R. The zener voltage is represented by V_Z in the figure.

(iv) Zener dynamic impedance : The zener dynamic impedance r_Z can be defined as the ratio of a small change in the zener voltage V_Z to the corresponding small change in the zener current I_Z. Mathematically,

$$r_z = \frac{\delta V_Z}{\delta I_Z} \tag{28.11}$$

In practice, r_z may vary from a low value to a large value depending on the operating current and the particular zener diode used. The above equation can be rewritten as

$$\delta V_Z = r_z \delta I_Z \tag{28.12}$$

When the zener diode characteristic is exactly vertical, then

$$\delta V_Z = 0$$

and so $r_z = 0$.

28.17 Applications of Zener Diode

Zener diode is used conveniently as a regulator in power supply. A zener regulator circuit for explanation is shown in Fig. 28.25. In the circuit, the input is a d.c. voltage whose voltage variations are to be regulated. The input voltage is obtained from the output of a power supply. Across the input voltage, the anode of the diode is connected to the negative point and the cathode to the positive. That is, the zener is reverse-connected. If the input voltage V_{in} is greater than the zener votage V_Z (i.e., $V_{in} > V_Z$), it conducts and draws a relatively large zener current through the series resistance R_S. Across the output, there is a load resistor R_L, as shown, so that the total current through R_S is the sum of the zener diode and the load currents. If the input voltage is increased, the current through both the zener diode and the load will also increase. The zener diode resistance, however, decreases simultaneously causing an increase of the voltage drop across R_S. As a result, across the zener regulator a substantially constant output voltage is obtained within a fraction of a volt even when the input voltage is varied over a range of several volts.

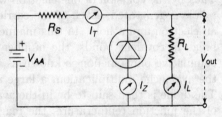

Fig. 28.25

In order to analyse the circuit of Fig. 28.25 which contains linear (resistors) and nonlinear (zener diode) elements apply Ohm's and Kirchhoff's laws.

Let us consider the operation of the circuit when the voltage source V_{AA} is constant but the load current I_L varies. Let a constant output voltage V_{out} is required across the load. The two currents $I_Z = V_{out}/R_Z$ (R_Z = zener resistance) and $I_L = V_{out}/R_L$ combine to form the total current I_T. Thus we can write,

$$I_T = I_Z + I_L. \tag{28.13}$$

The voltage across R_S is equal to the product of I_T and R_S.

i.e., $$V_{R_S} = I_T \times R_S. \tag{28.14}$$

But, $$V_{AA} = V_{R_S} + V_{out}. \tag{28.15}$$

So, if V_{AA} remains constant and it is necessary that V_{out} remains constant, then V_{R_S} must also remain constant. Therefore, the total current flowing in the circuit I_T must remain fixed despite variations in load current. This is accomplished only by compensating changes in I_Z, where

$$I_Z = I_T - I_L, \tag{28.16}$$

supposing I_T is a constant and I_L can vary.

If the regulator circuit is properly designed, the increased voltage across R_S, ΔV_{R_S} should be approximately equal to the increased supply voltage ΔV_{AA}, and V_{out} would drop back to its original value. Similarly, a decrease in V_{AA} would result a decrease in I_Z and hence in I_T.

28.18 Breakdown Mechanisms of Semiconductor Diodes

We know that the reverse current of a P-N junction, under reverse-bias condition, is due to the movement of electrons from the P-region and holes from the N-region of the semiconductor across the depletion region. With the increase of the reverse voltage a minority electron passing through the depletion region gains high kinetic energy from the applied voltage. This electron when collides with a crystal atom, an electron in a covalent bond may acquire high energy to be free from the bond. In this manner the covalent bond is broken and a pair of electron and hole is created. Thus by the collision of one electron with a crystal atom, a pair of an electron and a hole is generated. Each of the carriers, by the same process, generates a pair of an electron and a hole. In this manner by the process of collision and subsequent break of covalent bonds, the number of free electrons and holes increases. This cumulative phenomenon is known as the *avalanche multiplication*. As a result of the avalanche multiplication, a large reverse current passes through the junction. The diode is then said to be in the avalanche breakdown region. With an increase of the junction temperature, the magnitude of the avalanche breakdown voltage increases.

Let the P-region of a P-N junction diode has very large concentration of acceptor impurity atom and N-region of donor impurity atom. With an increase of its reverse voltage the reverse current increases rapidly when the junction breaks down. Such a breakdown at low reverse voltage is not simply due to the avalanche multiplication of electron-hole pairs but by an electric field of high magnitude which exerts a large force on valence electrons (of silicon atoms) in the depletion region. The process of removal of electrons from the valence-band to the conduction-band with the help of a strong electric field in an insulator was first proposed by C. Zener in 1934 and hence it is called *zener breakdown* or *zener effect*. It has been found that the zener breakdown of an insulator occurs for an electric field of about 2×10^7 V/m.

28.19 Advantages of Semiconductor Diodes over Vacuum Diodes

The controlling function of a vacuum tube is similar to that of a semiconductor but it is rapidly replacing vacuum tubes because of added advantages. Some of which are :

(i) Semiconductor is solid. Therefore, there is a little chance of vibration as in vacuum tube.

(ii) Little power is required for a semiconductor and also it radiates less heat than in a tube.

(iii) They do not need time for warm up and so operate immediately with the application of power.

(iv) A semiconductor does not undergo any chemical deterioration which occurs in a tube cathode.

(v) A semiconductor is small in size and light in weight.

(vi) Junction diodes can be operated either at low or high voltages depending on the current and voltage ratings.

(vii) It is physically very strong and it has a long operating life.

28.20   The Junction Transistor

The junction transistor consists of a silicon (or germanium) single crystal of two P-N junctions formed among the three layers–base (B), emitter (E) and the collector (C). Junction transistors can be classified into two main groups, viz., N-P-N and P-N-P. This classification depends on the impurity elements used for the construction of emitter, base and collector.

Fig. 28.26(a) illustrates the physical construction of an N-P-N junction transistor while Fig. 28.26(b) is for the P-N-P type. In the figure, the constructions of (a) the grown junction transistor, (b) alloy junction transistor and (c) planar-type double diffused transistor are shown. Physically, the base is narrower than the emitter or the collector. The relative size of the emitter in comparison to the collector depends on the type of transistor and also on its application.

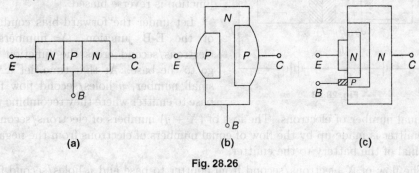

(a)   (b)   (c)

Fig. 28.26

28.21   Operation of a Transistor

In order to explain the operation of a transistor, let us first consider a P-N-P type which is like two P-N junction diodes placed back-to-back. At each junction a depletion region is there which gives rise to an internal potential barrier.

In Fig. 28.27, two batteries are connected in a manner, as shown. As the C-B junction is reversed bias, the width of the depletion region increases at the junction and the majority carriers, i.e., electrons are blocked in the base.

Let under the forward-bias condition of the E-B junction, X numbers of holes/second cross the junction and go to the base. At that time, let y numbers of electrons/second, which are very small in

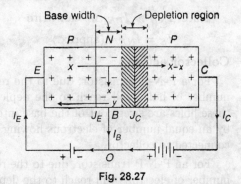

Fig. 28.27

number, flow from base to emitter where they recombine with equal number of holes. The loss of $(X + y)$ numbers of holes/second in the emitter is made up by the flow of equal number of electrons from the emitter to the positive terminal of the battery connected to it.

The flow of x holes/second from emitter to base and y electrons/second from base to emitter produce the emitter current I_E, where

$$I_E = I_{PE} + I_{NE} \tag{28.17}$$

Here, I_{PE} = current due to flow of holes

and I_{NE} = current due to flow of electrons.

Since $I_{PE} \gg I_{NE}$, we can write,

$$I_E = I_{PE} \quad \text{(approx.).} \tag{28.18}$$

Next, let us consider an N-P-N transistor where two P-N junction diodes are kept back-to-back with their P-regions as common. A depletion region is there at each of the junction which produces an internal potential barrier.

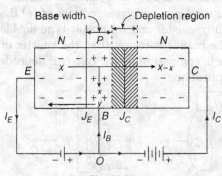

Fig. 28.28

For the transistor action, the circuit arrangement is made by connecting the two batteries as shown in Fig. 28.28. In the figure, the emitter-base junction is forward biased while the collector-base junction is reverse biased.

Let under the forward-bias condition of the E-B junction, X numbers of electrons/second cross the junction and go to the base. At that time, let a very small number, y holes/second flow from base to emitter where they recombine with an equal number of electrons. The loss of $(X + y)$ numbers of electrons/second in the emitter is made up by the flow of equal numbers of electrons from the negative terminal of the battery to the emitter.

The flow of X electrons/second from emitter to base and y holes/second from base to emitter produces the emitter current I_E, where

$$I_E = I_{NE} + I_{PE} \tag{28.19}$$

Here, I_{NE} = current due to flow of electrons

and I_{PE} = current due to flow of holes.

Since $I_{NE} \gg I_{PE}$, we can write,

$$I_E = I_{NE} \quad \text{(approx.)} \tag{28.20}$$

Collector action

For a P-N-P transistor, due to the recombination process in the base, $(X - x)$ number of holes will reach to the depletion region. By the reverse-bias voltage, these holes are swept out of the base into the collector where these are neutralized by an equal number of electrons flowing from the negative terminal of the battery connected to collector.

For an P-N-P transistor, due to the recombination process in the base, $(X - x)$ number of electrons will reach to the depletion region. By the reverse-bias voltage, these electrons are swept out of the base into the collector wherefrom these are attracted by the positive terminal of the battery connected to collector.

28.22 Current Amplification Factors

The characteristics of a bipolar transistor are described in terms of current. At the transistor electrodes, the magnitudes of current are related by the equation

$$I_E = I_B + I_C. \tag{28.21}$$

The above equation indicates that there are two current amplification factors for the static (d.c.) currents and two for small changes in the currents.

Definition of Amplification Factors

(i) **Static current amplification factor (α_{dc})** : For a transistor with common base configuration, it is defined as the ratio of static (d.c.) collector current I_C to the static emitter current I_E at a constant collector voltage with respect to base. Mathematically, we can write,

$$\alpha_{dc} = \left(\frac{I_C}{I_E}\right)_{V_{CB}=\text{constant}} \tag{28.22}$$

α_{dc} is also known as the *static forward current transfer ratio* or the *d.c. current gain* for the common base configuration.

(ii) **Static current amplification factor (β_{dc})** : For a transistor with common emitter configuration, it is defined as the ratio of static collector current I_C to the static base current I_B at a constant collector voltage with respect to emitter. Mathematically, we can write,

$$\beta_{dc} = \left(\frac{I_C}{I_E}\right)_{V_{CE}=\text{constant}} \tag{28.23}$$

β_{dc} is also known as the *static forward current transfer ratio* or the *d.c. current gain* for the common emitter configuration.

Relation between α_{dc} and β_{dc}

We know that,

$$I_E = I_B + I_C.$$

Dividing both sides by I_C, we get

$$\frac{I_E}{I_C} = \frac{I_B}{I_C} + 1$$

or, $$\frac{1}{\alpha_{dc}} = \frac{1}{\beta_{dc}} + 1. \tag{28.24}$$

From Eq. (28.24), we get

$$\alpha_{dc} = \frac{\beta_{dc}}{1 + \beta_{dc}} \tag{28.25}$$

or, $$\beta_{dc} = \frac{\alpha_{dc}}{1 - \alpha_{dc}}. \tag{28.26}$$

(iii) **Small-signal current amplification factor (α)** : For a transistor with common base configuration, it is defined as the ratio of the small change in the collector current to the corresponding small change in the emitter current when collector voltage is kept constant with respect to the base. Thus,

$$\alpha = \left(\frac{\delta I_C}{\delta I_E}\right)_{V_{CB}=\text{ constant}} \qquad (28.27)$$

(iv) Small-signal current amplification factor (β) : For a transistor with common emitter configuration, it is defined as the ratio of a small change in the collector current to the corresponding small change in the base current when the collector voltage is kept constant with respect to the emitter. Thus,

$$\beta = \left(\frac{\delta I_C}{\delta I_B}\right)_{V_{CE}=\text{constant}} \qquad (28.28)$$

Relation between α and β

We have, $I_E = I_B + I_C$ or, $\delta I_E = \delta I_B + \delta I_C$.

Dividing both sides by δI_C,

$$\frac{\delta I_E}{\delta I_C} = \frac{\delta I_B}{\delta I_C} + 1$$

or, $$\frac{1}{\alpha} = \frac{1}{\beta} + 1 \qquad (28.29)$$

From Eq. (28.29) we get,

$$\alpha = \frac{\beta}{1+\beta}$$

or, $$\beta = \frac{\alpha}{1-\alpha}. \qquad (28.30)$$

It is seen from above that as α approaches towards unity, β becomes increasingly larger. For a transistor whose α is 0.98, β becomes 49 while an α of 0.99 gives β of 99. So, during the performance of the experiment α should be measured very accurately for avoiding formula error in β.

It has been noted from experimental data that the values of α_{dc} and α are very nearly equal.

28.23   Transistor Leakage Currents

It can be classified as (i) collector-to-base leakage current (I_{CB0}), (ii) collector-to-emitter leakage current (I_{CE0}) and (iii) emitter-to-base leakage current (I_{EB0}).

(i) If the emitter is open-circuited and the collector-base junction is reversed biased [Fig. 28.29(a)], a small collector current called as the *collector-to-base leakage current* (I_{CB0}) flows. In the symbol I_{CB0}, the subscript CB shows a collector-base current while the subscript 0 indicates that the current in the third electrode (viz., the emitter, E) is zero. In transistor-biasing circuits, the current I_{CB0} has high importance.

When the emitter current is zero, the transistor is said to be off and in this condition, the leakage current continues to flow. For the common base configuration of the transistor with the emitter-base junction forward biased and the collector-base junction reverse biased, the part of the emitter current which reaches the collector is $I_C - I_{CB0}$. Thus, when the leakage current is taken into account, we can define α as,

$$\alpha = \frac{I_C - I_{CB0}}{I_E}$$

or, $\qquad\qquad I_C = \alpha I_E + I_{CB0}.$ $\qquad\qquad\qquad\qquad$ (28.31)

Putting $I_E = I_C + I_B$,

$\qquad\qquad I_C = \alpha(I_C + I_B) + I_{CB0}$

or, $\qquad\qquad (1 - \alpha)I_C = \alpha I_B + I_{CB0}$

or, $\qquad\qquad I_C = \left(\dfrac{\alpha}{1 - \alpha}\right) I_B + \left(\dfrac{1}{1 - \alpha}\right) I_{CB0}.$ $\qquad$ (28.32)

But we have $\beta = \dfrac{\alpha}{1 - \alpha}.$

$\therefore\qquad\qquad \beta + 1 = \dfrac{\alpha}{1 - \alpha} + 1 = \dfrac{1}{1 - \alpha}$

Hence from Eq. (28.32), we get

$\qquad\qquad I_C = \beta I_B + (\beta + 1)I_{CB0}$ $\qquad\qquad\qquad$ (28.33)

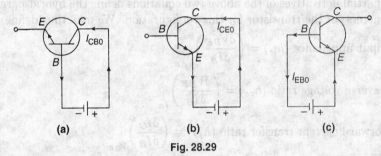

Fig. 28.29

(ii) If the base is open-circuited and the collector is reverse biased with respect to emitter [Fig. 28.29(b)], a small collector current called as the *collector-to-emitter leakage current* (I_{CE0}) flows.

For the common emitter configuration of the transistor with the emitter-base junction forward biased and the collector-base junction reverse biased, the part of the emitter current which reaches the collector is $I_C - I_{CE0}$. Thus, when the leakage current is taken into account, we can define β as

$\qquad\qquad \beta = \dfrac{I_C - I_{CE0}}{I_B}$

or, $\quad I_C = \beta I_B + I_{CE0}$ $\qquad\qquad\qquad\qquad\qquad$ (28.34)

Substituting the value of I_C from Eq. (28.33), we have

$\qquad\qquad \beta I_B + (\beta + 1)I_{CB0} = \beta I_B + I_{CE0}$

or, $\quad I_{CE0} = (\beta + 1)I_{CB0}.$ $\qquad\qquad\qquad\qquad\qquad$ (28.35)

Eq. (28.35) shows that the collector-emitter leakage current in common emitter configuration is $(\beta + 1)$ times greater than that in common base configuration.

(iii) If the collector is open-circuited and the emitter-base junction is reverse biased [Fig. 28.29(c)], a small emitter current called as the *emitter-to-base leakage current* (I_{EB0}) flows.

28.24   Transistor Characteristics

For the common-emitter configuration of a transistor, I_B and V_{CE} are taken as independent variables. Since V_{BE} is a function of I_B and V_{CE} and also I_C is another function of I_B and V_{CE}, we can write the functional equations as

$$V_{BE} = f(I_B, V_{CE}) \tag{28.36}$$

and $\quad I_C = f(I_B, V_{CE}). \tag{28.37}$

If a curve represents the variations of the dependent variable V_{BE} or I_C with one of the two independent variables, then the curve is called the *characteristic of the transistor*.

Expanding Eqs. (28.36) and (28.37) by Taylor's theorem and neglecting higher orders, we can write,

$$dV_{BE} = \left(\frac{\delta V_{BE}}{\delta I_B}\right)_{V_{CE}} dI_B + \left(\frac{\delta V_{BE}}{\delta V_{CE}}\right)_{I_B} dV_{CE} \tag{28.38}$$

$$dI_C = \left(\frac{\delta I_C}{\delta I_B}\right)_{V_{CE}} dI_B + \left(\frac{\delta I_C}{\delta V_{CE}}\right)_{I_B} dV_{CE}. \tag{28.39}$$

The partial derivatives of the above two equations define the hybrid-parameters (h-parameters) of the transistor for this configuration. We may thus define :

(i) Input impedance $(h_{ie}) = \left(\dfrac{\delta V_{BE}}{\delta I_B}\right)_{V_{CE}}$

(ii) Reverse voltage ratio $(h_{re}) = \left(\dfrac{\delta V_{BE}}{\delta I_B}\right)_{I_B}$

(iii) Forward current transfer ratio $(h_{fe}) = \left(\dfrac{\delta I_C}{\delta I_B}\right)_{V_{CE}}$

(iv) Output admittance $(h_{oe}) = \left(\dfrac{\delta I_C}{\delta V_{CE}}\right)_{I_B}$.

Similarly, for the common base configuration of a transistor, I_E and V_{CB} are taken as independent variables. Since V_{EB} is a function of I_E and V_{CB} and also I_C is a function of I_E and V_{CB}, we can write,

$$V_{BE} = f(I_E, V_{CB}) \tag{28.40}$$

$$I_C = f(I_E, V_{CB}). \tag{28.41}$$

Each of the above equations represents two sets of characteristic curves. Expanding Eqs. (28.40) and (28.41) by Taylor's theorem and neglecting higher orders, we have

$$dV_{EB} = \left(\frac{\delta V_{EB}}{\delta I_E}\right)_{V_{CB}} dI_E + \left(\frac{\delta V_{EB}}{\delta V_{CB}}\right)_{I_E} dV_{CB} \tag{28.42}$$

$$dI_C = \left(\frac{\delta I_C}{\delta I_E}\right)_{V_{CB}} dI_E + \left(\frac{\delta I_C}{\delta V_{CB}}\right)_{I_E} dV_{CB}. \tag{28.43}$$

The partial derivatives of the above two equations define the h-parameters of the transistor for the common base configuration. We may thus define :

(i) Input impedance $(h_{ib}) = \left(\dfrac{\delta V_{EB}}{\delta I_E}\right)_{V_{CB}}$

(ii) Reverse voltage ratio $(h_{rb}) = \left(\dfrac{\delta V_{EB}}{\delta V_{CB}}\right)_{I_E}$

(iii) Forward current transfer ratio $(h_{fb}) = \left(\dfrac{\delta I_C}{\delta I_E}\right)_{V_{CB}}$

(iv) Output admittance $(h_{ob}) = \left(\dfrac{\delta I_C}{\delta V_{CB}}\right)_{I_E}$

28.24.1 Characteristics with Common Emitter Configuration

The circuit diagram for determining the static characteristics under common emitter configuration of a P-N-P junction transistor is shown in Fig. 28.30. It is seen that a forward bias is applied to the emitter junction while a reverse bias to the collector junction.

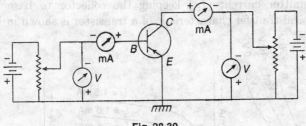

Fig. 28.30

(a) **Input characteristics :** Values of base current (I_B) are plotted against base to emitter voltage (V_{BE}) for a fixed V_{CE}. The nature of the curves obtained for different sets of V_{CE} is shown in Fig. 28.31.

(b) **Output characteristics :** Values of collector current (I_C) are plotted against collector to emitter voltage (V_{CE}) for a fixed I_B. The nature of the curves obtained for different sets of I_B. is shown in Fig. 28.32.

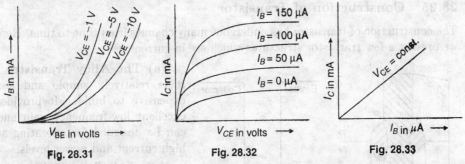

Fig. 28.31   **Fig. 28.32**   **Fig. 28.33**

(c) **Transfer characteristics :** Values of collector current (I_C) are plotted against the base current (I_B) for fixed V_{CE}. The characteristic is shown in Fig. 28.33.

28.24.2 Characteristics with Common Base Configuration

The circuit diagram for studying the characteristics under common base configurations of a P-N-P junction transistor is shown in Fig. 28.34.

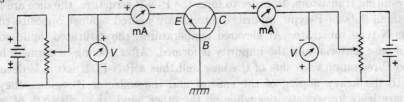

Fig. 28.34

(a) Input characteristics : The curve obtained by plotting emitter current (I_E) against the emitter to base voltage (V_{EB}) keeping the collector to base voltage (V_{CB}) as parameter is called the *input characteristic of a transistor.* Typical input characteristic of a transistor is shown in Fig. 28.35.

(b) Output characteristics : The curve obtained on plotting collector current (I_C) against the collector to base voltage (V_{CB}) keeping the emitter current (I_E) as parameter is the *output characteristics of a transistor.* Typical characteristic curves such obtained are shown in Fig. 28.36.

(c) Transfer characteristics : Values of collector current (I_C) are plotted against the emitter current (I_E) keeping the collector to base voltage (V_{CB}) constant. Typical transfer characteristic of a transistor is shown in Fig. 28.37.

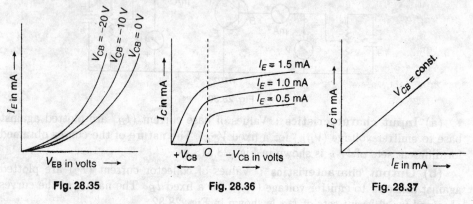

| Fig. 28.35 | Fig. 28.36 | Fig. 28.37 |

28.25   Construction of Transistor

The construction of transistor has undergone many changes from time to time. Here we present a few transistor structures which are in current use.

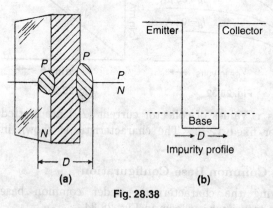

Fig. 28.38

(a) The Alloy Transistor : It is relatively simple and less expensive to build. It provides excellent low-frequency gain and can be designed for operating at high current and power levels.

A typical alloy transistor and its impurity profile are shown in Fig. 28.38(a) and (b). It begins with a very lightly doped N-type crystal. The crystal is sectioned into small, thin dice which are employed as the base regions of the resulting transistors. In order to form the P-N-P structure, the dice are heated and small dots of P-type impurity material are melted against opposite surfaces of the N-type substrate. At elevated temperatures, the saturated liquid solution of the base material and the impurity is formed. After cooling, it forms a heavily doped P-region on each side of the base and thus a P-N-P structure is developed. Due to the heavy doping of the emitter and the collector P-regions, they have comparatively low resistivities while on the other hand, the resistivity of original base region remains high.

Analysing its electrical characteristics, it is seen that it should have a high gain, low emitter and collector resistances and high avalanche breakdown voltage of the collector junction. Here the current gain is high due to the high ratio of base to emitter resistivities.

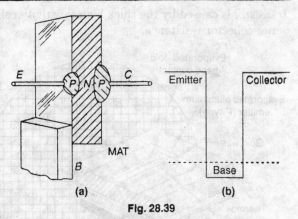

(a)

(b)

Fig. 28.39

Alloy transistors are, in general, low-frequency devices. An improvement in the original alloy process is made later on, resulting in devices called *microalloy transistors*. Fig. 28.39(a) shows its construction detail while 28.39(b) shows impurity profile of typical MAT structure. In the process, the pits are etched into each surface of the original base die leaving a thin membrane of N-type material which serves as the base region.

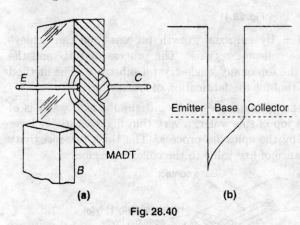

(a)

(b)

Fig. 28.40

Further improvements in the alloy transistor have been achieved by combining the alloy process with that of solid state diffusion. By controlling the surface impurity concentration and the diffusion time any desired impurity profile for an alloy transistor is possible to obtain. The structure thus obtained is referred to as microalloy diffused transistor (MADT). The MADT construction and impurity profile is shown in Fig. 28.40(a) and (b). For such transistors, the punch-through voltage is considerably increased.

(b) The Mesa Transistor : With the development of the mesa structure, an important breakthrough in high-frequency transistor design came. As shown in Fig. 28.41, in the mesa transistor fabrication process, the originally grown crystal is lightly doped. The crystal rod is then sliced into thin wafer into which an opposite polarity impurity is now diffused. Thus we get a two-layer wafer forming a P-N (or N-P) junction.

The emitter junction is produced on the base layer by the vacuum evaporation or diffusion. At the same time, a base-contact stripe is cross-evaporated on to the base layer for each transistor. The wafer is next heated. As a result the stripes alloy into the base layer for forming the necessary junction. Since the collector of the transistor is of highest resistivity material, so the depletion layer of the junction spreads into the collector rather than the base region.

The gain of a mesa transistor is very high due to the extremely narrow base widths obtainable with the diffusion process. The main disadvantage of a mesa transistor is caused by the thick high resistivity collector region which increases the series collector resistance.

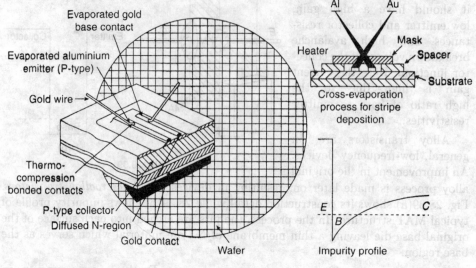

Fig. 28.41

(c) The Epitaxial Mesa : By epitaxial growth process, one can achieve extremely high resistivity active collector regions. The process permits and the growing of a crystalline film on the top of any single-crystal substrate. The method provides an extremely valuable tool for the fabrication of transistors.

As shown in Fig. 28.42 in the epitaxial mesa, the initial substrate wafer is of low-resistivity material. On the top of this wafer, a very thin high-resistivity layer of the same impurity is grown by the epitaxial process. The thick low-resistivity layer beneath adds series resistance of low value to the collector region.

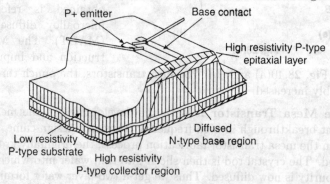

Fig. 28.42

The drawbacks in the above process have been eliminated by the *epitaxial planar transistor*. In this process, the collector-base junction is buried under a layer of silicon dioxide.

The epitaxial planar transistor (Fig. 28.43) also begins with a low-resistivity substrate. It is capped by a thin high-resistivity layer of epitaxial material of same impurity. On top of this structure is grown a thin film of SiO_2 while the base region is formed within the epitaxial collector by diffusing impurities of opposite conductivity into the collector region.

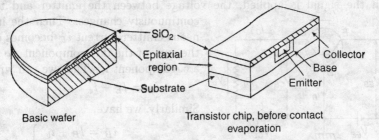

Fig. 28.43

(d) The Annular Transistor : Annular process is the most recently developed transistor structure. In the annular structure, an inversion layer is introduced into the collector material under SiO$_2$ (Fig. 28.44). The other transistor parameters are designed for compensating the channel characteristics. The channel is aborted by a shallow moat of low-resistivity P-type material. It surrounds the base and terminates the collector-base junction at the top surface of the wafer.

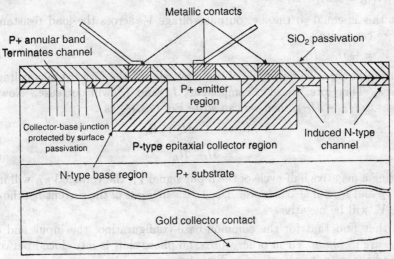

Fig. 28.44

The annular transistor combines the high voltage advantage of the mesa structure and the low leakage advantage of the planar-type structure. Such structures provide greater parameter stability and better long-term reliability. It is suitable also for the applications of integrated circuit.

28.26 Basic Circuits for Transistor Amplifier

The basic circuits for transistor amplifiers are : (i) Common-base configuration, (ii) Common-emitter configuration and (iii) Common-collector configuration. Here the term common is applied by considering the terminal of the transistor common to both input and output terminals.

(i) Common-base configuration : The basic circuit diagram for an N-P-N transistor is shown in Fig. 28.45. In the figure, the base is the common terminal connected to the earth. The input signal V_s is applied between the emitter and the base while the output V_o is found across the load R_L. V_{EE} and V_{CC} are the two supplies.

When the signal is applied, the voltage between the emitter and the base

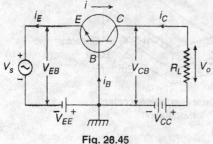

Fig. 28.45

continuously changes. Then the instantaneous emitter current i_E becomes equal to the sum of the d.c. component I_E and the a.c. component i_e. Thus we can write,

$$i_E = I_E + i_e \qquad (28.44)$$

Similarly, we have,

$$\left.\begin{array}{c} i_B = I_B + i_b \\ \text{and} \quad i_C = I_C + i_c \end{array}\right\} . \qquad (28.45)$$

The d.c. collector to base voltage V_{CB} and the d.c. collector current I_C is related by the equation,

$$V_{CB} = V_{CC} - I_C \cdot R_L. \qquad (28.46)$$

If there is a small change in V_{CB} due to a small change in I_C, we have

$$\delta V_{CB} = -\delta I_C \cdot R_L. \qquad (28.47)$$

But this is equal to the a.c. output voltage V_o across the load resistance R_L. Hence we can write,

$$V_o = -\delta I_C \cdot R_L. \qquad (28.48)$$

During the positive half-cycle of the input signal, the forward bias voltage V_{EB} decreases. Therefore, the d.c. components I_E and I_C will decrease. Now, if I_C decreases to $(I_C - \delta I_C)$, then we can write Eq. (28.48) as

$$V_o = -(-\delta I_C) \cdot R_L$$

$$= \delta I_C \cdot R_L. \qquad (28.49)$$

During a negative half-cycle of the input signal V_s, the voltage V_{EB} will increase and so I_E and I_C will also increase. Due to the increase of the current I_C, the output voltage V_o will be negative.

We thus find that for the common-base configuration, the input and output voltages are in phase. Or in other words, no phase shift is introduced between the input and the output voltages of such configuration.

(ii) Common-emitter configuration : The basic circuit diagram using an N-P-N transistor is shown in Fig. 28.46. In the figure, the input signal V_s is applied between the base and the emitter while the output voltage V_o is obtained across the load resistance R_L. Here the emitter is the common terminal connected to the ground. V_{BB} is the base-bias voltage and V_{CC} is the collector supply voltage.

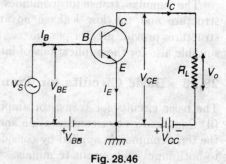

Fig. 28.46

The d.c. collector to emitter voltage V_{CE} and the d.c. collector current I_C are related by the equation,

$$V_{CE} = V_{CC} - I_C \cdot R_L. \qquad (28.50)$$

If there is a small change in V_{CE} due to a small change in I_C, we have

$$\delta V_{CE} = -\delta I_C \cdot R_L. \qquad (28.51)$$

But this is equal to the a.c. output voltage across the load resistance R_L. Hence, we can write,

$$V_o = -\delta I_C \cdot R_L. \tag{28.52}$$

During the positive half-cycle of V_s, the forward bias voltage V_{BE} increases. Therefore, the d.c. components I_E and I_C will increase. Now, if I_C increases to $(I_C + \delta I_C)$, then the output voltage V_o decreases. on the other hand, during the negative half-cycle of the input signal, V_{BE} will decrease and so I_E and I_C will decrease. Due to the decrease of the collector current I_C, the output voltage V_o will be positive.

We thus conclude that for the common-emitter configuration, the input and output voltages are 180° out of phase.

(iii) Common-collector configuration : The basic circuit diagram using an N-P-N transistor is shown in Fig. 28.47. In the figure, the collector is the common terminal connected to the earth. The input signal V_s is applied between the base and the collector while the output voltage V_o is obtained across the load R_L. Here V_{BB} is the base-bias voltage while V_{EE} is the emitter supply voltage.

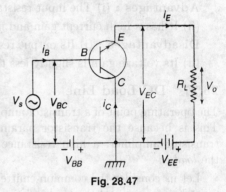

Fig. 28.47

The d.c. emitter to collector voltage V_{EC} and the d.c. emitter current I_E is related by the equation,

$$V_{EC} = -V_{EE} + I_E \cdot R_L. \tag{28.53}$$

If there is a small change in V_{EC} due to a small change in I_E, we have

$$\delta V_{EC} = -\delta I_E \cdot R_L. \tag{28.54}$$

But this is equal to the a.c. output voltage V_o across the load resistance R_L. Hence, we can write,

$$V_o = -\delta I_E \cdot R_L. \tag{28.55}$$

During the positive half-cycle of the input signal, the forward bias of the transistor increases. Therefore, the d.c. components I_E will increase. If I_E increases to $(I_E + \delta I_E)$, then V_o will increase. Hence, we can conclude that for a common-collector transistor amplifier there is no phase shift between the input and the output voltage.

28.26.1 Advantages and Disadvantages of CB, CE and CC Amplifiers

CB Amplifier

Advantages : (i) A transistor of CB configuration can operate at a higher frequency than in CE configuration.

(ii) A transistor in CB connection is not so sensitive to variations in the transistor parameters as in the case of a CE connection.

Disadvantages : (i) For a CB amplifier, the current gain is less than unity while the voltage gain is high. Therefore, the power gain of this amplifier is not high enough. It is nearly equal to the value of voltage gain.

(ii) In order to couple one CB stage to another, it is required to use a step-down matching transformer.

CE Amplifier

Advantages : (i) Among the three configurations, it provides the highest power gain.

(ii) Its input and output impedances are not widely differed. Consequently, it can be connected in cascade easily and there is no need of matching the input and output impedances with transformers.

(iii) It has a good current and voltage gain.

Disadvantages : (i) Its frequency response is inferior to that of the CB and CC amplifiers. This is due to the large effective input capacitance.

CC Amplifier

Advantages : (i) The input resistance of CC amplifier is high.

(ii) It has a high current gain and moderate power gain.

Disadvantages : (i) Its output resistance is low.

(ii) Its voltage gain is slightly less than unity.

28.27   DC Load Line

The operating point of a transistor amplifier shifts owing to changes in temperature. This is because the transistor parameters are functions of temperature. In a transistor amplifier, a high resistance is included at the output which is called the *load*.

Let us consider the common-emitter amplifier of Fig. 28.46. When the emitter resistance is zero and the load resistance is R_L, we have

$$V_{CE} = V_{CC} - I_C \cdot R_L$$

or,
$$I_C = \left(-\frac{1}{R_L}\right) V_{CE} + \frac{V_{CC}}{R_L}. \tag{28.56}$$

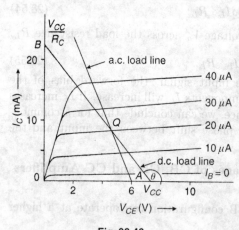

Fig. 28.48

If now I_C is plotted against V_{CE} for a particular value of I_B, we may get the output characteristics of the transistor as shown in Fig. 28.48. For given values of R_L and V_{CC}, two points $A(V_{CC},0)$ and $B\left(0,\frac{V_{CC}}{R_L}\right)$ are located on the axes of V_{CE} and I_C respectively. The two points A and B are next joined to get the load line AB. The point of intersection Q of this line with the output characteristics for known value of I_B is called the *operating point* under quiescent condition, i.e., under zero signal condition for given values of I_B, R_L and V_{CC}. The operating point represents the required d.c. base current I_B, the d.c. collector current I_C and the d.c. collector to emitter voltage V_{CE} in the active region of the characteristics.

It is thus seen that the load line AB passes through the points :

A, where $I_C = 0$ and $V_{CE} = V_{CC}$

B, where $I_C = \dfrac{V_{CC}}{R_L}$ and $V_{CE} = 0$.

The slope of the load line is written as

$$\tan \theta = -\frac{1}{R_L}.$$

(28.57)

28.27.1 AC Load Line

For all practical amplifiers, the load is not a pure resistance in general. The a.c. load in such a case is found by the equivalent impedance considering all the circuit components in the emitter-to-collector circuit.

The a.c. load line has also been shown in Fig. 28.48 above. It is to be noted from the figure that the a.c. load line also passes through he operating point.

28.28 Transistor Biasing

In order to provide distortionless amplification, the base of a transistor must be biased properly so that the input signal operates over the linear portion of the characteristics of the transistor. The manner of transistor biasing determines the output signal it will produce for a given input signal.

28.28.1 Fixed Bias Circuit

In Fig. 28.49, the arrangement of a fixed bias circuit is shown. Here both for the collector and the base, there is a common d.c. supply voltage V_{CC}. The base resistance R_B should be such that a constant base current I_B flows through it. The base current I_B can be written as

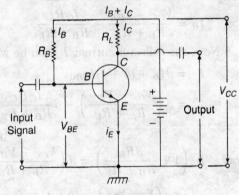

$$I_B = \frac{V_{CC} - V_{BE}}{R_B}$$

(28.58)

Fig. 28.49

In Eq. (28.58), since $V_{CC} \gg V_{BE}$, so change in V_{BE} will cause little effect on I_B. Thus for a constant V_{CC} and R_B the base current I_B is constant in this circuit. That is why it is named as fixed bias circuit.

The collector current in the circuit is given by

$$I_C = \beta I_B + (\beta + 1) I_{CB0}$$

$$= \frac{\beta (V_{CC} - V_{BE})}{R_B} + (\beta + 1) I_{CB0}$$

(28.59)

(putting the value of I_B).

Differentiating Eq. (28.59) with respect to I_{CB0}, we have

$$\frac{\partial I_C}{\partial I_{CB0}} = \beta + 1$$

or, the stability factor, $S = \beta + 1$.

(28.60)

Since β is sufficiently large, so the stability of the circuit is poor. For that reason this circuit is not used in general for biasing the base.

28.28.2 Collector-to-Base Bias Circuit

In Fig. 28.50, the arrangement of a collector-to-base bias, i.e., a grounded emitter

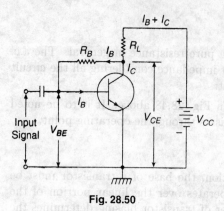

Fig. 28.50

circuit with feedback resistor is shown. Here the bias voltage is taken from the collector of the transistor instead of taking from the collector supply voltage V_{CC}. If I_C tends to increase, the voltage drop across R_L increases reducing the collector to emitter voltage V_{CE} and hence the base current I_B. Thus the decrease in I_B will try to compensate the increase in I_C and thereby a greater stability is attained.

Considering Fig. 28.50, we have

$$V_{CE} = V_{BE} + I_B R_B \qquad (28.61)$$

and $\quad V_{CE} + (I_C + I_B) R_L = V_{CC}. \qquad (28.62)$

Substituting the value of V_{CE} from Eq. (28.61) in Eq. (28.62), we get

$$V_{BE} + I_B R_B + (I_C + I_B) R_L = V_{CC}$$

or, $\quad I_B(R_B + R_L) = (V_{CC} - V_{BE}) - I_C R_L$

or, $\quad I_B = \dfrac{V_{CC} - V_{BE}}{R_B + R_L} - \dfrac{I_C R_L}{R_B + R_L}. \qquad (28.63)$

Now, the collector current I_C can be written as

$$I_C = \beta I_B + (\beta + 1) I_{CB0}$$

$$= \beta \left(\frac{V_{CC} - V_{BE}}{R_B + R_L} \right) - \beta \frac{I_C R_L}{R_B + R_L} + (\beta + 1) I_{CB0}$$

(putting the value of I_B)

or, $\quad I_C \left(1 + \dfrac{\beta R_L}{R_B + R_L} \right) = \beta \left(\dfrac{V_{CC} - V_{BE}}{R_B + R_L} \right) + (\beta + 1) I_{CB0}$

or, $\quad I_C = \dfrac{\beta \left(\frac{V_{CC} - V_{BE}}{R_B + R_L} \right) + (\beta + 1) I_{CB0}}{1 + \frac{\beta R_L}{R_B + R_L}}. \qquad (28.64)$

Differentiating Eq. (28.64) with respect to I_{CB0}, we have

$$S = \frac{\partial I_C}{\partial I_{CB0}} = \frac{(\beta + 1)}{1 + \frac{\beta R_L}{R_B + R_L}} \qquad (28.65)$$

$$= \frac{(\beta + 1)(R_B + R_L)}{R_B + (\beta + 1) R_L}. \qquad (28.66)$$

Eq. (28.66) indicates that the stability of this circuit is better than that of the fixed bias circuit.

Equation (28.65) can alternatively be written as

$$S = \frac{\beta + 1}{1 + \frac{\beta}{1 + \frac{R_B}{R_L}}}. \qquad (28.67)$$

It is seen from above that when $\frac{\beta}{1+\frac{R_B}{R_L}}$ is large, S is small. In other words, the stability can be improved by making R_L large or R_B small.

Disadvantages

This biasing circuit has the following disadvantages :

(i) Since R_B is connected to the collector, so the amplified a.c. signal present at the collector will be feedback to the input. As a result, the a.c. input decreases which in turn reduces the a.c. output. To avoid this the collector-to-base bias circuit is arranged in such a way that only the d.c. changes at the collector will be feedback and not the a.c. changes.

(ii) In this arrangement, the collector current must be greater than $(\beta + 1)I_{CBO}$.

28.28.3 Emitter Bias Circuit

In Fig. 28.51, the arrangement of the emitter-resistor and potential-divider circuit is shown.

The biasing circuit agrees well all the necessary conditions and hence it is almost universally used. In the figure, a common power supply V_{CC} has been used so that both the base and the collector terminals receive a d.c. negative voltage with respect to the emitter. Resistors R_1 and R_2 constitute a voltage divider on the base while R_L serves the purpose of a load resistance. To stabilize the amplifier and to protect the

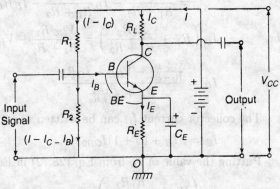

Fig. 28.51

transistor against run-away, a form of compensation is required to use, known as *bias stabilization*. The effect of the resistor R_E connected to the emitter leg is to compensate any slight increase in collector current due to the variation of transistor characteristics. In fact, an increase in collector current causes an increased voltage drop across R_E. This voltage is in opposition to the forward bias in the base-emitter circuit and hence reduces the base current which in turn reduces the collector current. R_E is thus utilized for balancing the tendency of the collector current to increase in value by providing negative d.c. feedback. In a circuit, the values of R_E and R_L are chosen simply by considering the supply voltage and the required operating point.

In order to calculate the stability factor for the circuit, we may proceed in the following way :

If V_{BE} represents the base-emitter voltage, then we can write,

V_{BE} = p.d. between base and ground − p.d. between emitter and ground

$$= V_{B0} - I_E R_E \tag{28.68}$$

Now, we have

$$V_{B0} = (I - I_C - I_B)R_2$$
$$= (I - I_C)R_2 - I_B R_2. \tag{28.69}$$

Again, $(I - I_C)R_1 + (I - I_C - I_B)R_2 = V_{CC}$

or, $\qquad (I - I_C)(R_1 + R_2) = V_{CC} + I_B R_2$

or, $\qquad I - I_C = \dfrac{V_{CC}}{R_1 + R_2} + \dfrac{I_B R_2}{R_1 + R_2}.$ $\qquad\qquad$ (28.70)

Putting the above value of $(I - I_C)$ in Eq. (28.69),

$$V_{B0} = \frac{V_{CC}R_2}{R_1 + R_2} + \frac{I_B R_2^2}{R_1 + R_2} - I_B R_2$$

$$= \frac{V_{CC}R_2}{R_1 + R_2} - I_B \frac{R_1 R_2}{R_1 + R_2}. \qquad\qquad (28.71)$$

Hence from Eq. (28.68),

$$V_{BE} = \frac{V_{CC}R_2}{R_1 + R_2} - I_B \frac{R_1 R_2}{R_1 + R_2} - I_E R_E$$

$$= \frac{V_{CC}R_2}{R_1 + R_2} - I_B \frac{R_1 R_2}{R_1 + R_2} - I_B R_E - I_C R_E \text{ (putting } I_E = I_B + I_C)$$

or, $\qquad I_B \left(R_E + \dfrac{R_1 R_2}{R_1 + R_2} \right) = \dfrac{V_{CC}R_2}{R_1 + R_2} - V_{BE} - I_C R_E$

or, $\qquad I_B = \dfrac{\frac{V_{CC}R_2}{R_1+R_2} - V_{BE} - I_C R_E}{R_E + \frac{R_1 R_2}{R_1 + R_2}}.$ $\qquad\qquad$ (28.72)

The collector current I_C can be written as

$$I_C = \beta I_B + (\beta + 1)I_{CB0}. \qquad\qquad (28.73)$$

Putting the value of I_B from Eq. (28.72) in Eq. (28.73) and simplifying, we get

$$I_C \left(R_E + \frac{R_1 R_2}{R_1 + R_2} \right)$$

$$= \beta \left(\frac{V_{CC}R_2}{R_1 + R_2} - V_{BE} - I_C R_E \right) + (\beta + 1)I_{CB0} \left(R_E + \frac{R_1 R_2}{R_1 + R_2} \right)$$

or, $\qquad I_C = \left[(\beta + 1)R_E + \dfrac{R_1 R_2}{R_1 + R_2} \right]$

$$= \beta \left(\frac{V_{CC}R_2}{R_1 + R_2} - V_{BE} \right) + (\beta + 1)I_{CB0} \left(R_E + \frac{R_1 R_2}{R_1 + R_2} \right)$$

or, $\qquad I_C = \dfrac{\beta \left(\frac{V_{CC}R_2}{R_1+R_2} - V_{BE} \right) + (\beta + 1)I_{CB0} \left(R_E + \frac{R_1 R_2}{R_1+R_2} \right)}{(\beta + 1)R_E + \frac{R_1 R_2}{R_1+R_2}}$

$$= \frac{\frac{\beta}{\beta+1} \left(\frac{V_{CC}R_2}{R_1+R_2} - V_{BE} \right) + I_{CB0} \left(R_E + \frac{R_1 R_2}{R_1+R_2} \right)}{R_E + \left(\frac{1}{\beta+1} \right) \frac{R_1 R_2}{R_1+R_2}}. \qquad (28.74)$$

Since $\left(\frac{1}{\beta+1} \right)$ is a large quantity, so the second term in the denominator can be ignored compared with R_E. Also, if

$$R_E \gg \frac{R_1 R_2}{R_1 + R_2},$$

then
$$I_C = \frac{1}{R_E}\left(\frac{\beta}{\beta+1}\right)\left(\frac{V_{CC}R_2}{R_1+R_2} - V_{BE}\right) + I_{CB0} \tag{28.75}$$

Differentiating Eq. (28.75) with respect to I_{CB0} we may get the stability factor. Thus,

$$S = \frac{\delta I_C}{\delta I_{CB0}} = \frac{R_E + \frac{R_1 R_2}{R_1+R_2}}{R_E + \left(\frac{1}{\beta+1}\right)\frac{R_1 R_2}{R_1+R_2}}. \tag{28.76}$$

The above equation indicates that, if $R_E \gg \frac{R_1 R_2}{R_1+R_2}$, then the stability factor approaches towards unity, a maximum stability for the circuit.

Advantages

The emitter bias circuit has the following advantages :

(i) It requires only one d.c. supply battery.

(ii) Several combinations of the potential divider resistances R_1 and R_2 are possible.

(iii) The collector current I_C can be reduced to the collector-base leakage current I_{CB0}.

(iv) Emitter bias circuit gives a stable position of the operating point.

Examples

1. Determine the amplification factor of a triode valve if its plate resistance is 20000 Ω and the mutual conductance is 3 mA/volt.

   Solution : We have, the amplification factor, $\mu = r_p \times g_m$.

   Here, $r_p = 20000\ \Omega = 20 \times 10^3\ \Omega$

   and $g_m = 3$ mA/volt $= 3 \times 10^{-3}$ mho.

   $\therefore \quad \mu = 20 \times 10^3 \times 3 \times 10^{-3} = \mathbf{60}$.

2. Find the mutual conductance of a triode if its anode slope resistance be 10000 Ω and the amplification factor 20.

   Solution : Here, $r_p = 10000\ \Omega = 10 \times 10^3\ \Omega$

   and $\mu = 20$.

   $\therefore$ mutual conductance, $g_m = \frac{\mu}{r_p} = \frac{20}{10 \times 10^3} = \mathbf{2 \times 10^{-3}}$ **mho**.

3. In a triode valve, the output current is 5 mA with an anode potential of 220 volts and a grid potential of -3 volts. When the anode potential is increased to 260 volts, the current rises to 7 mA. A change of grid potential to -4 volts restores the current to its original value. Calculate the valve constants.

   Solution : Here, change in anode potential, $\Delta e_b = 260 - 220 = 40$ volts,

   change in anode current, $\Delta i_b = 7 - 5 = 2$ mA

   and change in grid potential, $\Delta e_c = 4 - 3 = 1$ volt.

Now, the amplification factor, $\mu = \dfrac{\Delta e_b}{\Delta e_c} = \dfrac{40}{1} = 40$;

the anode resistance, $r_p = \dfrac{\Delta e_b}{\Delta i_b} = \dfrac{40}{2 \times 10^{-3}} = 20 \times 10^3 \ \Omega = \mathbf{20 \ k\Omega}$

and   the transconductance, $g_m = \dfrac{\Delta i_b}{\Delta e_c} = \dfrac{2 \times 10^{-3}}{1} = 2 \times 10^{-3}$ A/volt

$$= \mathbf{2 \times 10^{-3} \ mho.}$$

4. A certain triode passes a plate current of 5 mA at plate voltage of 180 volts and grid voltage of −3 volts. If the grid voltage is changed to −5 volts, the plate current falls to 3 mA. The plate current is restored to 5 mA if the voltage is raised to 200 volts. Determine the value of the amplification factor of the valve. Find also the a.c. plate resistance and the mutual conductance.

Solution : Here, change in plate voltage, $\Delta e_b = 200 - 180 = 20$ volts,

change in plate current, $\Delta i_b = 5 - 3 = 2$ mA

and   change in grid voltage, $\Delta e_c = 5 - 3 = 2$ volts.

Now, $\mu = \dfrac{\Delta e_b}{\Delta e_c} = \dfrac{20}{2} = 10$,

$r_p = \dfrac{\Delta e_b}{\Delta i_b} = \dfrac{20}{2 \times 10^{-3}} = 10000 \ \Omega = 10 \ k\Omega$

and $g_m = \dfrac{\Delta i_b}{\Delta e_c} = \dfrac{2 \times 10^{-3}}{2} = 1.0$ mA/volt $= 10^{-3}$ mho.

5. The current in a triode is given by the following relation : $i_b = 0.003(e_b + 10e_c)^2$, where plate current i_b is in mA, plate voltage e_b and grid voltage e_c are in volts. Calculate the mutual conductance of the triode at grid voltage of zero and plate voltage of 150 volts.

Solution : We have, $i_b = 0.003(e_b + 10e_c)^2 \times 10^{-3}$ A

For a constant e_b,

$$\frac{di_b}{de_c} = 0.003 \frac{d}{de_c}(e_b + 10e_c)^2 \times 10^{-3} = 2 \times 0.003(e_b + 10e_c)10 \times 10^{-3}$$

$$= 0.06(e_b + 10e_c) \times 10^{-3}.$$

Now, when $e_b = 150$ volts and $e_c = 0$ volt, the mutual conductance,

$$g_m = \frac{di_b}{de_c} = 0.06(150 + 0) \times 10^{-3} \text{ A/volt}$$

$$= 9 \times 10^{-3} \text{ A/volt} = \mathbf{9 \ mA/volt.}$$

6. The following observations in the table are taken for drawing the mutual characteristic curves of a triode :

Grid voltage, in volts	0	−2	−4	−6
Plate current in mA for plate voltage of 120 volts	14	8	3.2	0.8
Plate current in mA for plate voltage of 80 volts	8	3.2	0.6	0

Draw the mutual characteristic curves and find the values of r_p, g_m and μ.

Solution : The mutual characteristic curves are drawn in Fig. 28.52.

From Fig. 28.52 between points P
and Q,

$$\Delta i_b = 14 - 8 = 6 \text{ mA}$$

and $\Delta e_b = 120 - 80 = 40$ volts.

So at $e_c = 0$ volt,

the dynamic plate resistance,

$$r_p = \frac{\Delta e_b}{\Delta i_b}, \ (e_c = 0)$$

$$= \frac{40}{6 \times 10^{-3}} = \textbf{6666 ohms}.$$

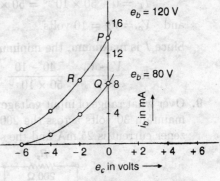

Fig. 28.52

Again, between points P and R,

$$\Delta e_c = 0 - (-2) = 2 \text{ volts}$$

and $\Delta i_b = 14 - 8 = 6$ mA.

So the mutual conductance, $g_m = \dfrac{\Delta i_b}{\Delta e_c}, \ (e_b = 120 \text{ volts})$

$$= \frac{6 \times 10^{-3}}{2} = 3 \times 10^{-3} \text{ mho}.$$

Now, the amplification factor,

$$\mu = r_p \times g_m = \frac{40}{6 \times 10^{-3}} \times 3 \times 10^{-3} = \textbf{20}.$$

7. A silicon diode for which the reverse saturation current is 10 μA is conducting
   1 ampere at 300 K. Determine the forward voltage drop across it.

   Solution : We have, $I = I_0(e^{qV/2kT} - 1)$.

   Here, $I = 1$ ampere, $I_0 = 10 \ \mu$A $= 10 \times 10^{-6} = 10^{-5}$ A

   and $T = 300$ K.

   Now we can write,

   $$\frac{I}{I_0} + 1 = e^{qV/2kT} \quad \text{or,} \quad \frac{qV}{2kT} = \log_e \left(\frac{I}{I_0} + 1 \right)$$

   or, $V = \dfrac{2kT}{q} \times 2.303 \log_{10} \left(\dfrac{I}{I_0} + 1 \right)$

   $$= \frac{2 \times 1.38 \times 10^{-23} \times 300}{1.6 \times 10^{-19}} \times 2.303 \log_{10} \left(\frac{1}{10^{-5}} + 1 \right)$$

   $$= \frac{2 \times 1.38 \times 3 \times 2.303 \times 5 \times 10^{-2}}{1.6} = \textbf{0.59 volt}.$$

8. A 10-volt zener diode along with a series resistance is connected across a 40-
   volt supply. Calculate the minimum value of the resistance required, if the
   maximum zener current is 50 mA.

   Solution : Here we have

   $$V = 40 \text{ volts}, \ I_Z = 50 \text{ mA} = 50 \times 10^{-3} \text{ A},$$

$$I_T = 0 + 50 \times 10^{-3} = 50 \times 10^{-3} \text{ A}$$

and $V_o = V_Z = 10$ volts.

Since I is maximum, the minimum value of the resistance required is

$$R = \frac{V - V_0}{I_T} = \frac{40 - 10}{50 \times 10^{-3}} = \mathbf{600 \ \Omega}.$$

9. Over what range of input voltage will the zener regulating circuit of Fig. 28.53 maintain 30 volts across the 2000 ohms resistor? Given that the maximum zener current is 25 mA and the source resistance $R_s = 200$ ohms.

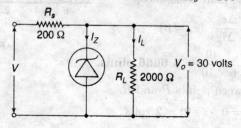

Fig. 28.53

Solution : Here, $V_o = V_Z = 30$ volts, $R_L = 2000 \ \Omega$, $R_s = 200 \ \Omega$,

$$(I_Z)_{\text{max}} = 25 \text{ mA} = 25 \times 10^{-3} \text{ A}$$

and $(I_Z)_{\text{min}} = 0$.

The load current,

$$I_L = \frac{30}{2000} = 15 \times 10^{-3} \text{ A}.$$

Now, the supply voltage V can be written as

$$V = V_o + R(I_Z + I_L).$$

Case I : When $I_Z = 0$,

$$V = 30 + 200 \times 15 \times 10^{-3} = 30 + 3 = 33 \text{ volts}.$$

Case II : When $I_Z = 25 \times 10^{-3}$ A,

$$V = 30 + 200(25 + 15)10^{-3} = 38 \text{ volts}.$$

Therefore, when the supply voltage changes from 33 volts to 38 volts, the value of V_o will be **30 volts**.

10. Determine the conductivity and resistivity at 300 K of pure germanium assuming that at the above temperature the concentration of carriers is $2.5 \times 10^{13}/\text{cm}^3$ for Ge and taking the carrier mobilities to be 3600 cm^2/volt-second for electrons and 1700 cm^2/volt-second for holes. Given that, electronic charge $= 1.602 \times 10^{-19}$ coulomb.

Solution : We know that, conductivity, $\sigma = nq(\mu_e + \mu_h)$.

Here, $n = 2.5 \times 10^{13}/\text{cm}^3$, $q = 1.602 \times 10^{-19}$ coulomb

$$\mu_e = 3600 \text{ cm}^2/\text{volt-second}, \ \mu_h = 1700 \text{ cm}^2/\text{volt-second}.$$

$\therefore$ $\sigma = 2.5 \times 10^{13} \times 1.602 \times 10^{-19}(3600 + 1700) = 0.0212$ mho/cm.

Again we know,

resistivity, $\rho = \dfrac{1}{\sigma} = \dfrac{1}{0.0212} = 47.2$ ohms-cm.

11. If at 300 K the concentration of carriers is $1.6 \times 10^{10}/\text{cm}^3$ for silicon and the carrier mobilities to be 1500 cm^2/volt-second for electrons and 500 cm^2/volt-second for holes, find the resistivity of pure silicon at that temp. of 300 K. Assume the charge of electron = 1.602×10^{-19} coulomb.

Solution : We have, conductivity, $\dot{\sigma} = nq(\mu_e + \mu_h)$.

Here, $n = 1.6 \times 10^{10}/\text{cm}^3$, $q = 1.602 \times 10^{-19}$ coulomb

$\mu_e = 1500$ cm^2/volt-second, $\mu_h = 500$ cm^2/volt-second.

$\therefore \quad \sigma = 1.6 \times 10^{10} \times 1.602 \times 10^{-19}(1500 + 500) = 5.12 \times 10^{-6}$ mho/cm.

So the required resistivity,

$$\rho = \frac{1}{\sigma} = \frac{1}{5.12 \times 10^{-6}} = 195.300 \text{ ohms-cm.}$$

12. A crystal diode with internal resistance $R_f = 20 \ \Omega$ is used for half-wave rectification. If the applied voltage $v = 50 \sin \omega t$ and load resistance $R_L = 800 \ \Omega$, calculate the values of (i) I_m, I_{rms}, I_{dc}, (ii) a.c. power input and d.c. power output, (iii) d.c. output voltage, (iv) efficiency of rectification.

Solution : We have $v = 50 \sin \omega t$.

$\therefore$ maximum voltage, $V_m = 50$ V.

Also, $R_f = 20 \ \Omega$ and $R_L = 800 \ \Omega$.

(i) $I_m = \dfrac{V_m}{R_f + R_L} = \dfrac{50}{20 + 800} = 0.061$ A = **61 mA**.

$I_{rms} = \dfrac{I_m}{2} = \dfrac{61}{2} = \textbf{30.5 mA}.$

$I_{dc} = \dfrac{I_m}{\pi} = \dfrac{61}{\pi} = \dfrac{61}{3.14} = \textbf{19.4 mA}.$

(ii) a.c. power input $= (I_{rms})^2 (R_f + R_L) = \left(\dfrac{30.5}{1000}\right)^2 (20 + 800) = \textbf{0.763 watt}.$

d.c. power output $= I_{dc}^2 \times R_L = \left(\dfrac{19.4}{1000}\right)^2 \times 800 = \textbf{0.301 watt}.$

(iii) d.c. output voltage $= I_{dc} \cdot R_L = 19.4 \times 800$ volts = **15.52 volts**.

(iv) Efficiency of rectification,

$$\eta = \frac{0.301}{0.763} \times 100\% = \textbf{39.5\%}.$$

13. If the applied input a.c. power to a half-wave rectifier is 100 watts and the d.c. output power obtained is 45 watts, find the efficiency of the rectifier.

Solution : We have the efficiency of the rectifier

$$= \frac{\text{d.c. output power}}{\text{a.c. input power}} = \frac{45}{100} = 0.45 = 45\%.$$

14. A 150 V (r.m.s.) is applied to the primary of a step-up transformer having the turn ratio $\frac{N_2}{N_1} = 4$. The transformer is having a centre tap and it is used for full-wave rectification with two diodes and with a load resistance of 1 kΩ. Determine the d.c. output voltage. (Neglect the voltage drop across the diodes.)

Solution : Here we have, $2V_m = 4 \times 150\sqrt{2} = 848.4$ volts,

$V_m = 424.2$ volts, $R_L = 1$ k$\Omega = 1000$ Ω.

$$I_{dc} = \frac{2I_m}{\pi} = \frac{2}{\pi}\left(\frac{V_m}{R_L}\right) = \frac{2 \times 424.2}{3.14 \times 1000} = 270.2 \times 10^{-3} \text{ A}.$$

$\therefore$ $V_{dc} = I_{dc} \times R_L = 270.2 \times 10^{-3} \times 1000 = 270.2$ volts.

15. A 10 V zener diode along with a series resistance is connected across a 40 V supply. Calculate the minimum value of the resistance required, if the maximum zener current is 50 mA.

Solution : We have $V = 40$ volts

$$I_Z = 50 \text{ mA} = 50 \times 10^{-3} \text{ A}$$

$$I_T = 0 + 50 \times 10^{-3} = 50 \times 10^{-3} \text{ A}$$

$$V_o = V_Z = 10 \text{ volts}.$$

Since I is maximum, the minimum value of the resistance required is

$$R = \frac{V - V_o}{I_T} = \frac{40 - 10}{50 \times 10^{-3}} = \textbf{600 } \boldsymbol{\Omega}.$$

16. A stabilized voltage of 12 V across a load whose current varies from 5 mA to 35 mA with an unregulated d.c. supply of 18 V is to be obtained with a zener diode of zener voltage 12 V and $I_Z = 20$ mA. Calculate the value of the current limiting resistance required for the same and the power dissipated in the resistance.

Solution : Here, $V = 18$ volts, $I_Z = 20$ mA, $I_L = \frac{1}{2}(5 + 35) = 20$ mA

$\therefore$ $I_T = I_L + I_Z = 20 + 20 = 40$ mA $= 40 \times 10^{-3}$ A

and $V_o = V_Z = 12$ volts.

$\therefore$ the current limiting resistance,

$$R = \frac{V - V_o}{I_T} = \frac{18 - 12}{40 \times 10^{-3}} = \textbf{150 } \boldsymbol{\Omega}.$$

The power dissipated in the resistance,

$$P = I_T^2 R = (40 \times 10^{-3})^2 \times 150 = \textbf{0.24 watt}.$$

17. If the output voltage across the zener is 50 volts with a load resistance of 10 kΩ, find the load current. If the total current in the circuit is 14 mA, then what value of current will pass through the zener?

Solution : We have $V_Z = 50$ volts, $R_L = 10$ kΩ.

$\therefore$ $I_L = \frac{50 \text{ volts}}{10 \text{ k}\Omega} = 5$ mA.

Now, $I_T = I_L + I_Z$ or, $I_Z = I_T - I_L = 14 - 5$ ($\because I_T = 14$ mA)

$= \textbf{9 mA}.$

18. If a transistor is connected in a common-base configuration, what a.c. collector current will flow when an a.c. current of 2 mamp flows through the emitter? Assume the collector potential to be constant and β of the transistor $= 60$.

Solution : Here, $\beta = 60$, $\partial I_E = 2$ mA.

Now, $\beta = \dfrac{\alpha}{1 - \alpha}$ or, $60 = \dfrac{\alpha}{1 - \alpha}$ or, $61\alpha = 60$ or, $\alpha = \dfrac{60}{61}$.

By definition,

$$\partial I_C = \alpha \times I_E = \frac{60}{61} \times 2 = 1.967 \text{ A.}$$

19. The common-base current gain in an N-P-N transistor is 0.98. The reverse saturation current $I_{CBO} = 12.5\ \mu$A. Determine the base and the collector current for an emitter current of 2 mA.

Solution : Here, $\alpha = 0.98$

$$I_{CBO} = 12.5\ \mu\text{A} = 12.5 \times 10^{-3}\ \text{mA}$$

and $I_E = 2$ mA.

Now, we have

$$I_C = \alpha I_E + I_{CBO} = 0.98 \times 2 + 12.5 \times 10^{-3} = 1.97 \text{ mA.}$$

Again, $I_E = I_B + I_C$ or, $I_B = I_E - I_C = (2 - 1.97)$ mA $= 30\ \mu$A.

20. A given transistor has $\alpha = 0.98$. The transistor is connected with its emitter grounded. If the base current is changed by 0.2 mA, calculate the change in collector current.

Solution : We know that, $\beta = \dfrac{\alpha}{1 - \alpha}$.

Here, $\alpha = 0.98$.

$\therefore \qquad \beta = \dfrac{0.98}{1 - 0.98} = 49$.

Now, $\beta = \dfrac{\Delta I_C}{\Delta I_B}$.

$\therefore \qquad \Delta I_C = \beta \times \Delta I_B = 49 \times 0.2$ $\quad (\because\ \Delta I_B = 0.2 \text{ mA})$

$\qquad\qquad = 9.8$ mA.

21. In a common base configuration with a base current of 0.05 mA, the emitter current is 1 mA. Calculate the value of the collector current.

Solution : We have, $I_E = I_B + I_C$.

Here, $I_B = 0.05$ mA, $I_E = 1$ mA.

So the collector current, $I_C = I_E - I_B = 0.95$ mA.

22. A given transistor has $\beta = 60$. If it is connected in a grounded base configuration, what theoretical a.c. collector current will flow when an a.c. current of 2 mA flows through the emitter? Assume the collector potential to be constant.

Solution : Here, $\beta = 60$, $\Delta I_E = 2$ mA

$\therefore \qquad \beta = \dfrac{\alpha}{1 - \alpha}$

$\qquad 60 = \dfrac{\alpha}{1 - \alpha}$ or, $61\alpha = 60$,

$$\therefore \qquad \alpha = \frac{60}{61}.$$

Now, $\Delta I_C = \alpha \times \Delta I_E = \dfrac{60}{61} \times 2 = 1.967$ mA.

23. Current amplification factor of a common-base configuration is 0.88. Find the value of the base current, when the emitter current is 1 mA.

Solution : If only d.c. values are considered, then

$$\alpha = \frac{I_C}{I_E}.$$

Here, $\alpha = \dfrac{I_C}{I_B} = 0.88$ and $I_E = 1$ mA.

$\therefore \qquad I_C = 0.88 \times 1 = 0.88$ mA

Now using the relation,

$$I_E = I_B + I_C \quad \text{or,} \quad I_B = I_E - I_C = 1 - 0.88 = 0.12 \text{ mA.}$$

24. In a common-base configuration, the voltage drop across a 2.2 kΩ resistor which is connected in the collector is 2.2 V. Calculate the value of the base current (given, $\alpha = 0.9$.).

Solution : We have $I_C = \dfrac{2.2}{2.2} = 1$ mA

and $\alpha = \dfrac{I_C}{I_E} = 0.9$, i.e., $I_E = \dfrac{I_C}{I_\alpha} = \dfrac{1}{0.9} = 1.1$.

Using the relation,

$$I_E = I_B + I_C,$$

we have $I_B = I_E - I_C = 1.1 - 1 = 0.1$ mA.

25. A transistor is connected in CE configuration. The voltage drop across 5 kΩ resistance which is connected in the collector circuit is 5 V. If α of the transistor is 0.998, calculate the base current.

Solution : Here, $R_L = 5$ kΩ, $V_{RL} \doteq 5$ V and $\alpha = 0.998$.

Since $I_C R_L = V_{RL}$,

$$\therefore \qquad I_C = \frac{V_{RL}}{R_L} = \frac{5}{5} = 1 \text{ mA} = 10^{-3} \text{ A.}$$

Now, the current gain β is given by

$$\beta = \frac{\alpha}{1 - \alpha} = \frac{0.998}{1 - 0.998} = 499.$$

$$\therefore \qquad I_B = \frac{I_C}{\beta} = \frac{10^{-3}}{499} = 2 \times 10^{-6} \text{ A} = 2 \ \mu\text{A.}$$

26. If the base current of a transistor is 20 μA, find the value of the emitter current. (Given, $\beta = 50$.)

Solution : Here, $I_B = 20 \ \mu$A $= 0.02$ mA and $\beta = 50$.

Now, $\beta = \dfrac{I_C}{I_B}$ or, $I_C = \beta I_B = 50 \times 0.02 = 1$ mA.

Using the relation, $I_E = I_B + I_C$,

we get $I_E = 0.02 + 1 = 1.02$ mA.

Questions

Essay-type

1. How vacuum tubes can be classified?

2. Describe a diode valve. What are the static characteristics of a diode?

3. Describe the construction of a triode valve. Clearly indicate the function of a control grid.

4. Describe an experimental arrangement for obtaining the characteristic curves of a triode valve and of calculating from them the amplification factor and the internal resistance of the triode. What do these constants signify?

5. Establish a mathematical relation between μ, r_p and g_m of a triode valve.

6. Explain the four different methods for the emission of electrons from a metallic surface.

7. What are the two different types of thermionic emitters? Explain.

8. What is meant by space charge? Explain clearly.

9. Discuss how the semiconductor materials are prepared.

10. Explain how the P-N junctions are prepared by grown junction, alloy junction and diffused junction method.

11. What do you mean by the terms depletion layer and barrier potential of a P-N junction diode?

12. Find an expression for the electric field and potential in the depletion region.

13. Explain what you mean by forward-bias and reverse-bias arrangement of a diode.

14. What are meant by energy hill and surface leakage current?

15. Find an expression for total current in a semiconductor.

16. Explain the forward and reverse characteristics of a semiconductor diode.

17. Define the static and dynamic resistance of a semiconductor diode. Write down the current-voltage equation of a semiconductor diode.

18. What is a zener diode? Explain its characteristic. What are the applications of a zener diode?

19. Define the following terms : (i) Zener voltage, (ii) Breakdown voltage and Breakdown current, (iii) Zener dynamic impedance.

20. Discuss the breakdown mechanisms of semiconductor diodes.

21. What are the advantages of a semiconductor diode over the vacuum diode?

22. What is a dipolar transistor?

23. What is meant by a junction transistor?

24. Explain clearly the operation of a transistor.

25. Define α and β of a transistor. Find a relation between them.

26. Discuss the characteristics of a transistor with (i) common-emitter configuration and (ii) common-base configuration.

27. Discuss briefly the different techniques for the construction of transistor.

28. Show neatly the basic circuits for transistor amplifiers with different configurations and explain those.

29. Indicate clearly the relative advantages and disadvantages of CB, CE and CC amplifiers.

30. Explain mathematically the d.c. and a.c. load line.

31. Mention the important factors responsible for the shift of the operating point of a transistor.

32. What is meant by the biasing of a transistor? Discuss the advantages of emitter-bias circuit over the others.

33. Explain with suitable circuit diagrams the different types of biasing of a dipolar transistor.

Short Answer-type

34. How would you proceed to obtain characteristic curve of a diode? What do you learn from characteristic?   [B.U. 1994]

35. What do you understand by the term 'detection of electromagnetic wave'?

36. Describe the construction of a diode and explain how it can be used as a half-wave and full-wave rectifier.   [C.U. 1971; B.U. 1991]

37. Explain the dynamic characteristics of a triode valve. What do you mean by a load line? State its importance.

38. Give the classification of amplifiers, pointing out the conditions of operation. Explain the use of each class.

39. Explain how a triode can be used as an amplifier.   [C.U. 1993]

40. Describe the use of a triode as an oscillation generator.

41. Define valve constants and show how these are interrelated.

                                          [Vid. U. 2005; B.U. 1992]

42. Draw the circuit diagram of a bridge rectifier and explain its principle of action. How does a capacitor act as a filter?   [C.U. 2000, '03, '05]

43. What is zener voltage? Explain the use of a zener diode in the stabilization of voltage.   [C.U. 2004]

44. How can you obtain a semiconductor diode? What is the nature of the characteristic of such a diode?

45. What do you mean by semiconductor? Describe how P-type and N-type crystals are formed. Show how P-N junction acts like a rectifier.

                                          [C.U. 1993; B.U. 2004]

46. What are (i) input characteristics, (ii) output characteristics and (iii) transfer characteristics in the case of a transistor? How can you draw these characteristics for (a) grounded base and (b) grounded emitter configurations?

47. What is a transistor? What are the similarities between a transistor and a triode valve? What are the advantages of transistors over vacuum tubes?

48. Draw and explain the output characteristic curve for a transistor in CE configuration.   [C.U. 2004]

49. Derive the relation between the collector current (I_C) and the base current (I_B) of a transistor of CE mode.   [C.U. 2000]

50. Define α and β of a transistor, and find the relation between them.

                                          [C.U. 2001, '03, '05]

51. What do you mean by **(i)** positive feedback and **(ii)** negative feedback?

52. What is a zener diode? Draw its symbol. Draw with proper explanation, the equivalent circuit of an ideal zener in the breakdown region.

53. Draw the circuit diagram of a common-emitter type amplifier using an n-p-n transistor. Name each element of the circuit properly. **[C.U. 2002]**

54. Explain how zener diode maintains constant voltage across a load.
  [N.B.U. 2005]

55. Draw a circuit diagram of a CE mode P-N-P transistor and state different current elements. Plotting static input and output characteristics of such a transistor, show the active, saturation and cut-off region. **[B.U. 2003]**

56. Draw a simple circuit diagram of a CE mode P-N-P transistor amplifier and explain how voltage amplification is obtained with it. **[B.U. 2002, '04]**

57. For a P-N-P transistor in CE mode, what are input and output characteristics? Draw the characteristics and also draw the required circuit diagram to get them. How can you calculate the values of α and β from these characteristics? **[B.U. 2005]**

58. Draw the circuit diagram for studying the static characteristic curves of a P-N-P transistor in common-emitter mode, and draw the input and output characteristic curves. In the output characteristic curves, indicate different regions of operation. **[N.B.U. 2005]**

59. Draw the output characteristic curves of a transistor in CE mode for at least three different base currents. In the curve indicate different region of operation. **[N.B.U. 2002]**

60. The resistance of a pure metal increases with the increase of temperature but the resistance of a semiconductor diminishes with the rise of temperature. Why is this difference?

61. What is the difference between an intrinsic crystal and an extrinsic crystal?

62. Why does a junction diode behave differently when the potential difference across it is reversed?

63. Explain, in terms of the movement of carriers, why the resistance of junction diode is low in one direction and high in the reverse direction.

64. What is special about the application of zener diode?

65. What is zener potential? **[C.U. 2003]**

66. Write short notes on : **(i)** Triode as a rectifier, **(ii)** Zener diode, **(iii)** Common-emitter type amplifier, **(iv)** Positive and negative feedback, **(v)** Load line.

67. When examining a circuit diagram, how is it possible to tell whether a transistor is N-P-N or P-N-P?

68. Can the barrier voltage of a junction diode be measured with a voltmeter?

69. What are majority and minority carriers in **(i)** P-type and **(ii)** N-type semiconductors? Name two P-type and N-type dopants of an elemental semiconductor (Si). **[Vid. U. 2005]**

70. How are d.c. and a.c. resistance of a diode mathematically defined?

71. How is the a.c. resistance of a diode calculated from its characteristics?
  [B.U. 2005]

72. How would you connect a battery with a semiconductor diode to get (i) forward bias and (ii) reverse bias?

73. What are the mechanism in which a diode breakdown takes place? Mention the similarities between a transistor and a vacuum triode.

74. For a typical transistor the collector current is 0.98 times the emitter current. Calculate the current amplification factor for the transistor in CE mode.
                                                                          [N.B.U. 2001]

75. How does a depletion region form in a P-N junction? What happens to this region when the junction is forward and reverse biased?   [N.B.U. 2001]

76. A triode has the following characteristics : $\mu = 20$; a.c. resistance, $R_a = 12$ kΩ and the load in the plate circuit, $R = 28$ kΩ. Find the voltage amplification.
                                                                          [Vid. U. 2005]

Numerical Problems

77. If the anode current of a triode valve is changed from 9 to 14 mA, the anode potential changes from 80 to 120 volts. Determine the valve constants if the changes above are obtained for a change of grid potential by 2 volts.
         [**Ans.** $r_p = 6666$ ohms, $g_m = 3 \times 10^{-3}$ mho, $\mu = 20$]

78. Calculate the plate resistance of a valve whose mutual conductance is 1.5 mA/volt and the amplification factor is 30.   [**Ans.** 20000 ohms]

79. The anode-voltage/anode-current characteristic of a certain diode is given by the following figures :

Voltage (in volts)	0	5	10	15	20	25	30	35
Current (in mA)	0	3.1	8.9	17.0	26.8	38	51.4	66

Plot the dynamic characteristic curve if the load has a resistance of 2500 Ω. Hence find the load current and the voltage across the load when the supply voltage is 50 volts.   [**Ans.** 14.5 mA, 36.25 volts]

80. In tests on a certain thyratron, with a steady value of negative grid voltage applied to the valve the anode voltage was gradually raised until the valve conducted. The corresponding grid and anode voltages at the point of conduction were :

Grid voltage (in volts)	−8.7	−8.0	−7.0	−6.0	−5.0	−4.0	−3.0	−2.0	−1.0	−0.5
Anode voltage (in volts)	191	176	152	131	109	88	66	46	34.2	33.8

Plot the control characteristic and estimate the control ratio over the portion of the graph which is approximately linear.   [**Ans.** 21.8]

81. In a triode a current of 6 mA was found with the following values of plate voltage and grid voltage :

Plate voltage e_b (in volts)	140	80	40	220	300	380
Grid voltage e_c (in volts)	0	+4	+8	−4	−8	−12

Draw the amplification characteristic and hence deduce the amplification factor of the valve at zero grid voltage.   [**Ans.** $\mu = 17.5$]

82. A d.c. supply voltage to two valves is 400 volts. A resistance of 10 kΩ is connected between the mains and the anode of the first valve while a resistance of 5 kΩ is connected between the two anodes. Determine the currents that will flow through each valve. Given that the effective resistances of the first and the second valves are 15 kΩ and 13 kΩ respectively.

[**Ans.** 12.63 mA, 10.53 mA]

83. The plate current of a triode valve is represented by the equation,

$$i_b = 0.003(e_b + 10e_c)^2, \quad \text{where } i_b \text{ is in mA and } e_b, e_c \text{ are in volts.}$$

Establish the relation $\mu = r_p \times g_m$ between the three coefficients of a triode at grid voltage of zero volt and plate voltage of 150 volts.

84. If the output voltage across the zener is 50 volts with a load resistance of 10 kΩ, find the load current. If the total current in the circuit is 14 mA, then what value of current will pass through the zener? [**Ans.** 5 mA, 9 mA]

85. A stabilized voltage of 12 volts across a load whose current varies from 5 mA to 35 mA with an unregulated d.c. supply of 18 volts is to be obtained with a zener diode of zener voltage 12 volts and $I_Z = 20$ mA. Calculate the value of current limiting resistance required for the same and the power dissipated in the resistance. [**Ans.** 150 Ω, 0.24 watt]

86. The intrinsic resistivity of Ge at 27 °C is 0.47 ohm-m, and the electron and hole mobilities are 0.38 m^2/volt-second and 0.18 m^2/volt-second. Calculate the intrinsic carrier density n_i at the given temperature.

[**Ans.** 2.37×10^{19} m^{-3}]

87. Find the concentration of atoms (atoms/m^3) in germanium and silicon. At. wt. of Ge = 72.6, at. wt. of Si = 28.1, Avogadro's number = 6.02×10^{26} per k-mole, density of Ge = 5.32×10^3 kg/m^3 and density of Si = 2.33×10^3 kg/m^3. [**Ans.** 4.41×10^{28} atoms/m^3, 5.0×10^{28} atoms/m^3]

88. Find the value of β if **(i)** $\alpha = 0.98$, **(ii)** $\alpha = 0.99$. [**Ans.** (i) 49; (ii) 100]

89. A germanium transistor has a collector cut-off current $I_{CBO} = 14$ μA at room temperature and $\beta = 50$. It is used in common-emitter amplifier.

(a) Calculate the collector current when the base current is 0.2 A.

(b) Assuming β does not change with temperature, calculate the new collector current if the temperature of the transistor rises through 50 °C.

[**Ans.** (a) 10.714 mA; (b) 32.848 mA]

90. It is required to set the operating point by biasing with feedback resistor at $I_C = 1$ mA, $V_{CE} = 8$ volts. If $\beta = 100$, $V_{CC} = 12$ volts, $V_{BE} = 0.3$ volt, how will you do it? [**Ans.** $R_B = 770$ kΩ]

91. In a CE transistor amplifier circuit, the bias is provided by emitter resistor and potential divider arrangement. The various parameters are $R_L = 1$ kΩ, $R_E = 2$ kΩ, $R_1 = 10$ kΩ, $R_2 = 5$ kΩ, $V_{CC} = 12$ V and $\beta = 100$.

Find **(i)** the co-ordinates of the operating point and **(ii)** the stability factor.

[**Ans.** (i) Co-ordinates are $I_C = 1.65$ mA, $V_{CC} = 7.05$ V; (ii) 2.62]

Chapter 29

Amplifiers and Oscillators

29.1 Introduction

For all practical purposes, in electronic circuits it is necessary to amplify signals of small amplitudes for getting the desired output voltage with a minimum distortion. The ratio of output to input, i.e., the gain of a single stage amplifier is often found to be insufficient and hence in most of the cases several amplifier stages are connected in cascade for amplifying the input signal successively by different stages. There are several ways for coupling one amplifier stage to the other, viz., (i) direct coupling, (ii) resistance-capacitance coupling, (iii) inductance-capacitance coupling and (iv) transformer coupling. Out of these, the resistance-capacitance coupled amplifiers are widely used in present days.

An oscillator may be defined as an active device that generates sinusoidal or other repetitive waveforms. Important characteristics of an oscillator are its frequency and amplitude stability, harmonic content and output power. One group of oscillators is known as *sinusoidal* (or *harmonic*) *oscillators* as they are characterized by the generation of sinusoidal waveform of definite frequency. Relaxation oscillators, on the other hand, are active devices which generate non-sinusoidal waveforms like square and sawtooth waveforms. Oscillators can further be classified as negative impedance or feedback oscillators which make use of an active device that possesses a negative impedance over a range of its operating characteristics.

Although an oscillator is required, in general, for producing a single frequency, non-linearities are sometimes present in the oscillator circuit and these give rise to other frequencies known as harmonics. Depending on the particular use an oscillator may be classified as class A, AB, B or C. For high quality laboratory instruments, oscillators are operated in class A condition while for transmitters when efficiency is of greatest importance, class C operation might be used.

29.2 Classification of Amplifiers

Amplifiers may be classified in a variety of ways as discussed below :

(a) According to the type of load used, amplifiers are classified as : (i) untuned amplifiers and (ii) tuned amplifiers.

Untuned amplifiers are again divided into two groups. These are audio frequency (up to about 15 kHz) and video frequency (up to a few MHz) amplifiers.

The tuned amplifiers, also referred to as radio frequency amplifiers, are used to amplify an electrical signal containing a radio frequency (a frequency above 30 kHz).

(b) According to the number of stages and methods of coupling, amplifiers are classified as: (i) single-stage amplifiers and (ii) cascade amplifiers.

A single-stage amplifier is suitable for cases where small amplification is necessary while in a cascade amplifier considerable amount of gain is achieved.

Depending on the method of coupling, cascade amplifiers may again be divided as Resistance-Capacitance(R-C)-coupled amplifier, Transformer-coupled amplifier, Direct-coupled or DC amplifier and LC-coupled amplifier.

(c) According to the choice of the operating point of the vacuum tube, amplifiers are classified as (i) Class A, (ii) Class AB, (iii) Class B and (iv) Class C amplifiers.

In a class A amplifier, the grid bias and the input signal are so adjusted that the plate current flows during the entire cycle of the input signal. A class AB amplifier is designed such that the plate current flows for more than half but less than the complete cycle of the input voltage. A class B amplifier is designed to have its grid bias almost equal to the cut-off voltage so that the plate current flows for half the a.c. cycle while in a class C amplifier, the plate current flows over less than the half period of the input signal. In all the above classes of amplifiers, a subscript 1 is added to letter (or letters) to indicate that the grid current does not flow during any part of the input cycle (e.g., class A_1), while a subscript 2 is given to indicate that the grid current flows during a part of the input cycle (e.g., class A_2).

29.3   Single-stage Voltage Amplifier (Untuned Class A_1)

The basic circuit of a single-stage untuned class A_1 amplifier using a triode is shown in Fig. 29.1. The resistor R_g between the grid and the cathode is the grid leak resistor and Z_L is the load impedance which is, in general, complex. If an alternating voltage is applied between the grid and the cathode of the tube, an amplified voltage is obtained across Z_L and thus it acts as a voltage amplifier.

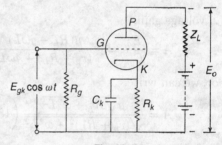

Fig. 29.1

Let us assume that R_g is very large and also C_k is so large in comparison to the cathode resistor R_k that its reactance may be neglected. Then we can draw, as shown in Fig. 29.2, the a.c. equivalent circuit of the amplifier valid for linear class A_1 operation. It should be noted that the equivalent circuit may be drawn by (i) eliminating all d.c. voltage and current sources, (ii) considering only a.c. or incremental values of currents and voltages, and (iii) replacing the tube by a current or voltage generator.

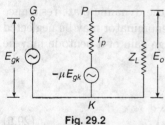

Fig. 29.2

Let us consider a source supplying grid potential of r.m.s. value E_{gk} so that the equivalent voltage generator generates a voltage of value μE_{gk}. The total impedance in the plate circuit then becomes $(r_p + Z_L)$, where r_p is the series resistance.

The r.m.s. value of the a.c. plate current I_p is given by

$$I_p = \frac{\mu E_{gk}}{(r_p + Z_L)}. \tag{29.1}$$

This current I_p flowing through the load impedance Z_L produces the output voltage between the plate and the cathode. Let it be denoted by E_o, where

$$E_o = -I_p Z_L$$

$$= -\frac{\mu E_{gk}}{(r_p + Z_L)} \cdot Z_L \text{ [from equation (29.1)]} \tag{29.2}$$

$\therefore$ complex voltage gain, $A = \dfrac{\text{complex output voltage}}{\text{complex input voltage}}$

$$= \frac{E_o}{E_{gk}} = -\frac{\mu Z_L}{(r_p + Z_L)}. \tag{29.3}$$

In equation (29.3), A is a complex quantity since the load impedance Z_L is a complex factor, in general, containing both resistive and reactive parts. We may consider three special cases as below :

Case 1 : Z_L complex inductive

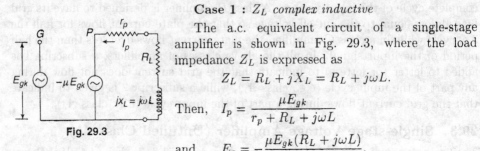

Fig. 29.3

The a.c. equivalent circuit of a single-stage amplifier is shown in Fig. 29.3, where the load impedance Z_L is expressed as

$$Z_L = R_L + jX_L = R_L + j\omega L.$$

Then, $\quad I_p = \dfrac{\mu E_{gk}}{r_p + R_L + j\omega L}$

and $\quad E_o = -\dfrac{\mu E_{gk}(R_L + j\omega L)}{(r_p + R_L) + j\omega L}.$

$\therefore$ voltage gain,

$$A = \frac{E_o}{E_{gk}} = -\frac{\mu(R_L + j\omega L)}{(r_p + R_L) + j\omega L}, \tag{29.4}$$

or, we can write,

$$A = \frac{\mu\sqrt{R_L^2 + \omega^2 L^2}}{\sqrt{(r_p + R_L)^2 + \omega^2 L^2}}\left(180° + \tan^{-1}\frac{\omega L}{R_L} - \tan^{-1}\frac{\omega L}{r_p + R_L}\right)$$

$$= G\angle\theta, \tag{29.5}$$

where G is the magnitude of the gain and θ is the phase angle.

Here, the phase angle $\theta = 180° + \tan^{-1}\dfrac{\omega L}{R_L} - \tan^{-1}\dfrac{\omega L}{r_p + R_L}.$

It is interesting to consider here the same problem in the case of a pentode amplifier and also its advantages over a triode. Since the dynamic plate resistance r_p of a pentode is very large in Eq. (29.3), Z_L in the denominator may be neglected compared with r_p. Therefore, the expression for voltage gain of a pentode may be written as

$$A = -\frac{\mu Z_L}{r_p}$$

$$= -g_m Z_L \quad \left(\because \frac{\mu}{r_p} = g_m\right). \tag{29.6}$$

This means that the voltage gain in a pentode may be increased simply by increasing the load impedance.

In the construction of a pentode, as we know, a suppressor grid is inserted between the screen grid and the plate, which is usually connected directly to the cathode. The suppressor is thus kept at a substantial negative potential relative to the plate to eliminate the effects of secondary emission. As a matter of fact, with increasing plate voltage the plate current rises smoothly from zero up to the maximum value for each control grid voltage. Moreover, the presence of suppressor grid increases the shielding action between the plate and the control grid and, therefore, reduces the grid to plate capacitance. As a result, the amplification of a pentode becomes extremely high even 1000–2000 for specially designed tubes. In spite of such a high μ, pentode as an amplifier is very stable in operation because of its low capacitance between the control grid and the plate.

Besides, pentodes are also used as a wideband amplifier or video amplifier in radar and television circuits. For amplifying pulses, it becomes necessary to amplify over a very wide frequency range. The pentode is then designed specially, keeping spacing between the control grid and the cathode small and also by keeping the pitch of the control grid wires small.

Case 2 : Z_L *purely resistive*

We have $Z_L = (R_L + jX_L)$.

For pure resistive load, $X_L = 0$.

$\therefore \qquad Z_L = R_L$.

Then, $\qquad I_p = \dfrac{\mu E_{gk}}{(r_p + R_L)} \quad$ and $\quad E_o = I_p \cdot R_L = -\dfrac{\mu E_{gk} R_L}{(r_p + R_L)}$.

$\therefore$ voltage gain,

$$A = \frac{E_o}{E_{gk}} = -\frac{\mu R_L}{(r_p + R_L)} \tag{29.7}$$

or, $\qquad A = \dfrac{\mu R_L}{r_p + R_L}(\cos 180° + j \sin 180°) = \left|\dfrac{\mu R_L}{r_p + R_L}\right| \angle 180°$

$$= G\angle\theta, \tag{29.8}$$

where G is the magnitude of the gain and θ is the phase shift of the plate voltage with respect to the grid voltage.

Case 3 : Z_L *purely inductive*

In this case, $R_L = 0$.

$\therefore \qquad Z_L = 0 + jX_L = 0 + j \cdot \omega L$.

Then, $I_p = \dfrac{\mu E_{gk}}{r_p + j\omega L} \quad$ and $\quad E_o = -I_p \cdot j\omega L = -\dfrac{\mu E_{gk}}{r_p + j\omega L} \cdot j\omega L$.

$\therefore$ voltage gain $= \dfrac{E_o}{E_{gk}} = -\dfrac{\mu}{1 + \frac{r_p}{j\omega L}} \tag{29.9}$

$$= \frac{\mu}{\sqrt{1 + \left(\frac{r_p}{\omega L}\right)^2}}\left(270° - \tan^{-1}\frac{\omega L}{r_p}\right)$$

$$= G\angle\theta, \tag{29.10}$$

where the phase angle is $\left(270° - \tan^{-1}\dfrac{\omega L}{r_p}\right)$.

29.4 Distortion in Amplifiers

The amplified output in an ideal amplifier is the enlarged version of the input signal. But in practice, a difference is noticed always between the output and input waveforms. The amplifier is then said to have a distortion. The three main types of distortions are the amplitude distortion, frequency distortion and phase distortion.

Amplitude distortion

This distortion is caused by non-linear operation, such as plate current cut-off and grid current flow. This distortion results when harmonic frequencies not present in the input signal appear in the output.

Frequency distortion

This distortion is caused by the amplifier coupling elements when signals of different frequencies are amplified separately. In general, both amplitude and frequency distortions may be present simultaneously in an amplifier.

Phase distortion

This distortion is due to the unequal delay of different audio frequencies by phase shifts in the amplifier coupling elements.

29.5 RC-coupled Amplifier

The resistance-capacitance coupled amplifier, as the name implies, consists of a load

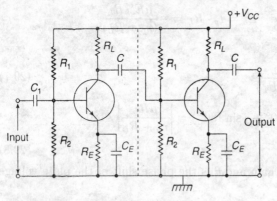

Fig. 29.4

resistance R_L and a coupling capacitance C as shown in Fig. 29.4. The output of the first stage is fed to the input of the second stage of the amplifier through the coupling condenser C. Besides coupling this condenser also presents the d.c. component of the output of the first stage to reach the input of the second stage. It is hence known as the blocking condenser. The biasing of the circuit is made by the emitter resistance R_E and two other resistances R_1 and R_2. The capacitor C_E connected in parallel to R_E is large so that its reactance $1/\omega C_E$ is small.

The voltage gain of the amplifier depends on the frequency range over which it operates. The entire frequency range of the amplifier can be well divided into three ranges :

(i) **Mid-frequency range :** In this range the voltage gain is almost constant and is not effected due to the changes of the capacitance in the circuit. Here the reactance $\frac{1}{\omega C}$ of the coupling capacitor is small and can be ignored. The mid-frequency range equivalent circuit is shown in Fig. 29.5. For the mid-frequency range the output resistance

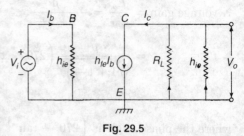

Fig. 29.5

$(1/h_{oc})$, the feedback voltage $(h_{re}V_o)$, the output resistance of the input voltage source, the capacitors C_E and C are dropped in the equivalent circuit.

The output resistance of the first stage is the equivalent resistance Z which can be found by considering the parallel combination of R_L and h_{ie}. Thus we have

$$\frac{1}{Z} = \frac{1}{R_L} + \frac{1}{h_{ie}}$$

or, $\quad Z = \dfrac{h_{ie}R_L}{h_{ie} + R_L}.$ $\hfill$ (29.11)

So the r.m.s. voltage V_o across Z is written as

$$V_o = -h_{je}I_b Z.$$ $\hfill$ (29.12)

Again, the r.m.s. input voltage V_i is given by

$$V_i = -I_b h_{ie}.$$ $\hfill$ (29.13)

$\therefore$ the voltage gain,

$$(A_v)_{\text{mid}} = \frac{V_o}{V_i} = -\frac{h_{fe}I_b Z}{I_b h_{ie}} = -\frac{h_{fe}Z}{h_{ie}}$$

$$= -\frac{h_{fe}}{h_{ie}}\left(\frac{h_{ie}R_L}{h_{ie}+R_L}\right) \text{ [putting the value of } Z]$$

$$= -\frac{h_{fe}R_L}{h_{ie}+R_L}.$$ $\hfill$ (29.14)

The negative sign in equation (29.14) indicates that the phase shift of the voltage gain is $180\,^{\circ}$. The magnitude of the gain is

$$|(A_v)_{\text{mid}}| = \frac{h_{fe}R_L}{h_{ie}+R_L}.$$ $\hfill$ (29.15)

(ii) Low-frequency range : The equivalent circuit of the low-frequency range is shown in Fig. 29.6. The r.m.s. input voltage V_i is given by

$$V_i = I_b h_{ie}.$$ $\hfill$ (29.16)

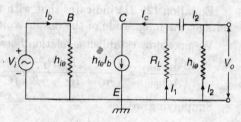

Fig. 29.6

To find the output voltage let us first calculate the output impedance Z due to the parallel combination of R_L and $\left(h_{ie} + \dfrac{1}{j\omega C}\right)$. Thus we have

$$\frac{1}{Z} = \frac{1}{R_L} + \frac{1}{h_{ie}+\frac{1}{j\omega C}} = \frac{1}{R_L} + \frac{1}{h_{ie}+\frac{j}{\omega C}} = \frac{h_{ie}R_L - \frac{j}{\omega C}}{R_L\left(h_{ie}-\frac{j}{\omega C}\right)}.$$

$$\therefore \quad Z = \frac{R_L\left(h_{ie}-\frac{j}{\omega C}\right)}{h_{ie}+R_L-\frac{j}{\omega C}}.$$ $\hfill$ (29.17)

If the r.m.s. value of the current through h_{ie} and C is I_2 then the p.d. between the emitter and collector along h_{ie} and C = p.d. across the load impedance Z.

i.e., $\quad I_2\left(h_{ie} - \dfrac{j}{\omega C}\right) = h_{fe}I_b Z$

or, $\quad I_2 = \dfrac{h_{fe}I_b Z}{h_{ie}-\frac{j}{\omega C}}.$ $\hfill$ (29.18)

Hence the output voltage V_o across h_{ie} is given by

$$V_o = I_2 h_{ie}$$

$$= -\frac{h_{fe}I_b Z h_{ie}}{h_{ie}-\frac{j}{\omega C}}.$$ $\hfill$ (29.19)

So the voltage gain,

$$(A_v)_{\text{low}} = \frac{V_o}{V_i} = -\frac{h_{fe}Z}{h_{ie} - j/\omega C}$$

$$= \frac{h_{fe}R_L}{h_{ie} + R_L + j2\pi f C_d h_{ie} R_L} \quad \text{(putting the value of } Z\text{)}$$

$$= -\frac{h_{fe}R_L}{h_{ie} + R_L - j/2\pi f C}. \tag{29.20}$$

The magnitude of the voltage gain,

$$|(A_v)_{\text{low}}| = \frac{h_{fe}R_L}{\sqrt{(h_{ie} + R_L)^2 + \left(\frac{1}{2\pi f C}\right)^2}} \tag{29.21}$$

and the phase angle ϕ_L is given by

$$\phi_L = 180° + \phi_L,$$

where $\phi_L = \tan^{-1}\left(\frac{1/2\pi f C}{h_{ie} + R_L}\right)$

$$= \tan^{-1}\left[\frac{1}{2\pi f C(h_{ie} + R_L)}\right]. \tag{29.22}$$

Equation (29.21) indicates that with the decrease of the frequency of the input voltage, the magnitude of the output voltage decreases in the low-frequency range. We may now establish a relation between $(A_v)_{\text{low}}$ and $(A_v)_{\text{mid}}$. We have

$$\frac{(A_v)_{\text{low}}}{(A_v)_{\text{mid}}} = \left(\frac{h_{fe}R_L}{h_{ie} + R_L - j/2\pi f C}\right)\left(\frac{h_{ie} + R_L}{h_{fe}R_L}\right).$$

Simplifying we get

$$(A_v)_{\text{low}} = \frac{(A_v)_{\text{mid}}}{1 - \frac{1}{2\pi f C(h_{ie} + R_L)}}. \tag{29.23}$$

So the magnitudes of the gains are related by the equation,

$$|(A_v)_{\text{low}}| = \frac{|(A_v)_{\text{mid}}|}{\sqrt{1 + \left\{\frac{1}{2\pi f C(h_{ie} + R_L)}\right\}}}. \tag{29.24}$$

The above equation shows that

$$|(A_v)_{\text{low}}| < |(A_v)_{\text{mid}}|.$$

(iii) **High-frequency range :** The equivalent circuit for the high-frequency range is shown in Fig. 29.7. By considering the figure, we have

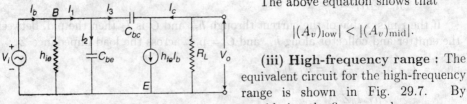

Fig. 29.7

$$I_1 = I_2 + I_3. \tag{29.25}$$

Again, the input voltage V_i is given by,

$$V_i = \frac{I_2}{j\omega C_{be}}$$

or, $I_2 = j\omega C_{be}V_i$ (29.26)

Also we have

$$V_o = -I_c R_L. \tag{29.27}$$

If we now apply Kirchhoff's law to the circuit containing C_{be}, R_L and C_{be}, we get

$$\frac{I_3}{j\omega C_{bc}} - I_c R_L - \frac{I_2}{j\omega C_{be}} = 0 \quad \text{or,} \quad \frac{I_3}{j\omega C_{bc}} + V_o - V_i = 0$$

or, $$I_3 = j\omega C_{bc}(V_i - V_o). \tag{29.28}$$

Putting the values of I_2 and I_3 in equation (29.22), we get

$$I_1 = j\omega C_{be}V_i + j\omega C_{bc}(V_i - V_o) = j\omega V_i \left[C_{be} + \left(1 - \frac{V_o}{V_i}\right) C_{bc} \right].$$

But, $$\frac{V_o}{V_i} = -\frac{h_{fe}R_L}{h_{ie}}.$$

$$\therefore \qquad I_1 = j\omega V_i \left[C_{be} + \left(1 + \frac{h_{fe}R_L}{h_{ie}}\right) C_{bc} \right]$$

$$= j\omega V_i C_d, \tag{29.29}$$

where $$C_d = C_{bc} + \left(1 + \frac{h_{fe}R_L}{h_{ie}}\right) C_{bc}. \tag{29.30}$$

Equation (29.19) indicates that the capacitors C_{be} and C_{bc} may be replaced by a single capacitance C_d across the input resistance h_{ie}. Again, we find that the capacitance C_{be} of the reverse bias collector-base junction is multiplied by $\left(1 + \frac{h_{fe}}{h_{ie}}R_L\right)$. This increased capacitance of the collector-base junction is known as the Miller

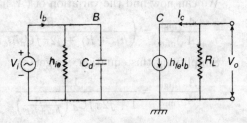

Fig. 29.8

effect. The equivalent circuit at high frequencies can thus be alternately drawn in a manner as shown in Fig. 29.8. Here the capacitance C_d has been included in the circuit replacing C_{be} and C_{bc}.

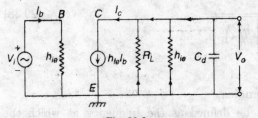

Fig. 29.9

In order to calculate the voltage gain in the high-frequency range, let us consider the equivalent circuit of Fig. 29.9.

The r.m.s. input voltage V_i is given by

$$V_i = I_b h_{ie}. \tag{29.31}$$

In this case the equivalent impedance Z of the parallel combination is obtained from

$$\frac{1}{Z} = \frac{1}{R_L} + \frac{1}{h_{ie}} + \frac{1}{\frac{1}{j\omega C_d}} = \frac{1}{R_L} + \frac{1}{h_{ie}} + j\omega C_d$$

$$Z = \frac{h_{ie} R_L}{h_{ie} + R_L + j\omega C_d h_{ie} R_L}. \tag{29.32}$$

The r.m.s. value of the output voltage V_o across Z is

$$V_o = -h_{fe} I_b Z. \tag{29.33}$$

Hence the voltage gain in the high frequency gain,

$$(A_v)_{\text{high}} = \frac{V_o}{V_i} = -\frac{h_{fe}Z}{h_{ie}} = -\frac{h_{fe}}{h_{ie}} \left(\frac{h_{ie}R_L}{h_{ie} + R_L + j\omega C_d h_{ie} R_L} \right)$$

$$= -\frac{h_{fe}R_L}{h_{ie} + R_L + j\omega C_d h_{ie} R_L}$$

$$= -\frac{h_{fe}R_L}{h_{ie} + R_L + j2\pi f C_d h_{ie} R_L}. \tag{29.34}$$

The magnitude of the voltage gain is

$$|(A_v)_{\text{high}}| = \frac{h_{fe}R_L}{\sqrt{(h_{ie} + R_L)^2 + (2\pi f C_d h_{ie} R_L)^2}} \tag{29.35}$$

and the phase angle

$$\phi = 180^\circ - \theta_H,$$

where $\theta_H = \tan^{-1}\left(\frac{2\pi f C_d h_{ie} R_L}{h_{ie} + R_L} \right). \tag{29.36}$

Equation (29.35) indicates that in the high-frequency range as the frequency of the input voltage increases, the magnitude of the voltage gain diminishes.

We can now find the variation of $(A_v)_{\text{high}}$ with $(A_v)_{\text{mid}}$. We have

$$\frac{(A_v)_{\text{high}}}{(A_v)_{\text{mid}}} = \left(\frac{h_{fe}R_L}{h_{ie} + R_L + j2\pi f C_d h_{ie} R_L} \right) \left(\frac{h_{ie} + R_L}{h_{fe}R_L} \right).$$

Simplifying this equation, we get

$$\frac{(A_v)_{\text{high}}}{(A_v)_{\text{mid}}} = \frac{1}{1 + j2\pi f C_d \left(\frac{h_{ie}R_L}{h_{ie}+R_L} \right)}$$

or, $\quad (A_v)_{\text{high}} = \dfrac{(A_v)_{\text{mid}}}{1 + j2\pi f C_d \left(\frac{h_{ie}R_L}{h_{ie}+R_L} \right)}. \tag{29.37}$

Thus the magnitudes of the gains are related by

$$|(A_v)_{\text{high}}| = \frac{|(A_v)_{\text{mid}}|}{\sqrt{1 + \left[2\pi f C_d \left(\frac{h_{ie}R_L}{h_{ie}+R_L} \right) \right]^2}}. \tag{29.38}$$

$$\therefore \quad |(A_v)_{\text{high}}| < |(A_v)_{\text{mid}}|.$$

Lower and Upper Cut-off Frequencies

The lower cut-off frequency can be defined as the frequency at which the magnitude of the voltage gain in the low-frequency range falls to 0.707 or $\frac{1}{\sqrt{2}}$ value of the magnitude in the mid-frequency range. Mathematically,

$$|(A_v)_{\text{low}}| = \frac{|(A_v)_{\text{mid}}|}{\sqrt{2}}.$$

To obtain an expression for the lower cut-off frequency f_1 let us substitute $f = f_1$ and $|(A_v)_{\text{low}}| = \frac{|(A_v)_{\text{mid}}|}{\sqrt{2}}$. Hence from equation (29.24),

$$\frac{|(A_v)_{\text{mid}}|}{\sqrt{2}} = \frac{|(A_v)_{\text{mid}}|}{\sqrt{1 + \frac{1}{2\pi f_1 C(h_{ie}+R_L)}}}.$$

From this, after simplification, we get

$$f_1 = \frac{1}{2\pi C(h_{ie} + R_L)}.$$ (29.39)

Again, the upper cut-off frequency f_2 can be defined as the frequency at which the magnitude of the voltage gain in the high-frequency range falls to 0.707 or $\frac{1}{\sqrt{2}}$ value of the magnitude in the mid-frequency range. Mathematically,

$$|(A_v)_{high}| = \frac{|(A_v)_{mid}|}{\sqrt{2}}.$$

To obtain an expression for f_2, let us put $f = f_2$ in equation (29.38). Then we get

$$\frac{|(A_v)_{mid}|}{\sqrt{2}} = \frac{|(A_v)_{mid}|}{\sqrt{1 + \left[2\pi f_2 C_d \left(\frac{h_{ie} R_L}{h_{ie} + R_L}\right)\right]^2}}.$$ (29.40)

After simplification, we get

$$f_2 = \frac{1}{2\pi C_d} \left(\frac{h_{ie} + R_L}{h_{ie} R_L}\right)$$

$$= \frac{1}{2\pi C_d} \left(\frac{1}{h_{ie}} + \frac{1}{R_L}\right).$$ (29.41)

The above discussion suggests that the voltage gain of the RC-coupled transistor amplifier is independent of frequency and diminishes at both the high and the low frequencies. A variation of the ratio of voltage gain to mid-frequency gain is plotted against frequency in Fig. 29.10. In the figure, the frequency range from f_1 to f_2 is called the *bandwidth* of the amplifier. In Fig. 29.11, the variation of the total phase shift between the input and the output voltages has been plotted with frequencies.

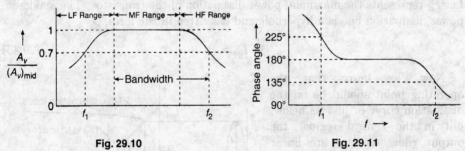

Fig. 29.10   Fig. 29.11

29.6   Power Amplifiers

A Power amplifier is nothing but a frequency converter which changes d.c. power into a.c. power according to the relation :

d.c. power input = a.c. power output + losses.

Power amplifiers are operated as class A, class B, class AB or class C. In transistor circuits, however, class A and class B push-pull power amplifiers are commonly used.

A transistor suitable for power amplifier is called a *power transistor*. It has the following two basic differences with other transistors : (i) The emitter and base layers are heavily doped in a power transistor and also the contact area between base layers and base leads is in ring form so that the area is increased. As a matter of fact, the ohmic resistance between the emitter and base is very low so that it requires a low input power. (ii) In a power transistor, the area of the collector region is large and it is attached to a metallic heat sink. Consequently, the heat generated is quickly removed.

29.7 Transformer-coupled Class *A* Power Amplifiers

In class *A* power amplifier, the load is always coupled to the collector circuit by using a transformer. High impedance primary of the output transformer is connected to the collector circuit while the low impedance secondary is connected across the voice coil of the speaker. If R_L denotes the impedance of the speaker, then following the theory of an ideal transformer, the a.c. load impedance in the collector is written as

$$R'_L = \frac{R_L}{n^2}, \qquad (29.42)$$

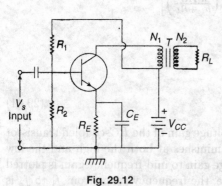

Fig. 29.12

where $n = \frac{N_2}{N_1}$; N_1 and N_2 are respectively the number of turns of the primary and the secondary of the transformer.

The circuit diagram of a transformer-coupled class *A* power amplifier is shown in Fig. 29.12. The resistances R_1 and R_2 make the potential divider arrangement for forward biasing. C_E is the bipass capacitor and R_E is the emitter resistor. The output transformer T, in the figure, is a step-down transformer.

29.7.1 Operation

Let P_d represents the maximum power dissipation of the transistor. The maximum power dissipation line is a hyperbola and is written in the form,

$$V_C I_C = P_d. \qquad (29.43)$$

Now, we know that the operating point should be on the dissipation curve or just its below, but in the central region, the output characteristics are linear and uniformly spaced. We thus choose the operating point Q as shown in Fig. 29.13. If V_{CC} is the collector supply voltage, then the equation of the d.c. load line is

$$V_{CE} = V_{CC}. \qquad (29.44)$$

The slope of the dynamic load line is $-\frac{1}{R_L}$. As shown, the load line is drawn through the operating point and it determines the maxi-

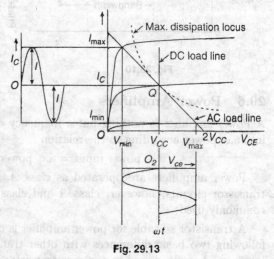

Fig. 29.13

mum and minimum a.c. collector current as denoted by I_{max} and I_{min} respectively. The corresponding values of the collector voltage V_{max} and V_{min} with respect to the emitter are also shown.

When the signal is zero, let I_C be the quiescent collector current. Then the d.c. power supplied by the source of the collector supply voltage is expressed as

$$P_d = V_{CC} I_C. \tag{29.45}$$

Let I and I' represent respectively the peak value of current in the positive and negative directions. If I_{rms} denotes the a.c. collector current, then the a.c. output power is given by

$$P_o = I_{rms} V_{rms} \quad \text{(where } V_{rms} \text{ is the r.m.s., a.c. collector voltage)}$$
$$= I_{rms}^2 R_L'. \tag{29.46}$$

Again, from the figure, we have

$$I = I_{max} - I_C \quad \text{and} \quad I' = I_C - I_{min}.$$

If the distortion is small, then

$$I = I' \quad \text{or,} \quad I_{max} - I_C = I_C - I_{min}$$

or,
$$2I_C = I_{max} + I_{min}$$

$$\therefore \quad I_C = \frac{I_{max} + I_{min}}{2}. \tag{29.47}$$

Similarly, we can show that,

$$V_{CC} = \frac{V_{max} + V_{min}}{2}. \tag{29.48}$$

The average peak value of the current is

$$I_m = \frac{I + I'}{2} = \frac{(I_{max} - I_C) + (I_C - I_{min})}{2} = \frac{I_{max} - I_{min}}{2}.$$

So we get

$$I_{rms} = \frac{I_{max} - I_{min}}{2\sqrt{2}}. \tag{29.49}$$

Similarly, $V_{rms} = \dfrac{V_{max} - V_{min}}{2\sqrt{2}}.$ \hfill (29.50)

Substituting equation (29.47) and (29.48) in equation (29.45), we get

$$P_d = \frac{1}{4}(I_{max} + I_{min})(V_{max} + V_{min}). \tag{29.51}$$

Again, putting the values of I_{rms} and V_{rms} from equations (29.49) and (29.50) in equation (29.46), we get

$$P_o = \frac{1}{8}(I_{max} - I_{min})(V_{max} - V_{min}). \tag{29.52}$$

Hence by equation (29.51) and (29.52) we can conclude that

$$P_o < P_d.$$

The power difference is dissipated at the collector junction. If that power dissipated is denoted by P_C, then

$$P_C = P_d - P_o. \tag{29.53}$$

29.7.2 Efficiency

The efficiency of the power amplifier is defined as the ratio of the a.c. power output to the d.c. power input. We may thus write the efficiency η as

$$\eta = \frac{P_o}{P_d} = \frac{4(I_{max} - I_{min})(V_{max} - V_{min})}{8(I_{max} + I_{min})(V_{max} + V_{min})}$$

$$= \frac{(I_{max} - I_{min})(V_{max} - V_{min})}{2(I_{max} + I_{min})(V_{max} + V_{min})}. \tag{29.54}$$

Equation (29.54) indicates that the efficiency of the amplifier is less than 50%. When the operating point moves from I_{max} to zero current, one can get the maximum efficiency. Under this condition, $I_{min} = 0$ and $V_{min} = 0$. Then we have

$$\eta_{max} = \frac{I_{max}V_{max}}{2I_{max}V_{max}} = \frac{1}{2} \text{ or } 50\%.$$

For practical purposes, the efficiency is noted to be much smaller than the above theoretical value. In general, it becomes about 40%.

29.8   Theory of a Feedback Amplifier

A feedback amplifier, an internal amplifier and a feedback network are shown in Fig. 29.14. In the figure, V_i is the input voltage and V_o be the output voltage. The

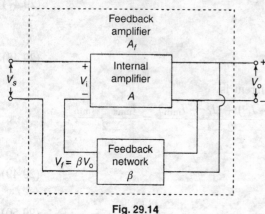

Fig. 29.14

ratio of V_o to V_i is the transfer gain of the amplifier without feedback and is represented by the symbol A. The feedback network extracts a part of the voltage $V_f(= \beta V_o)$ from the output voltage which is then added to or subtracted from the externally applied signal voltage V_s. The input to the basic amplifier thus becomes either $(V_s + V_f)$ or $(V_s - V_f)$. In the first case, the feedback is said to be positive and in the second case it is negative.

The transfer gain A without feedback is expressed as

$$A = \frac{V_o}{V_i} \tag{29.55}$$

Let us consider the case of negative feedback. We have in this case

$$V_i = V_s - V_f. \tag{29.56}$$

By equations (29.55) and (29.56) we can write,

$$V_o = AV_i = A(V_s - V_f). \tag{29.57}$$

The feedback ratio β can be defined as

$$\beta = \frac{V_f}{V_o}$$

or, $V_f = \beta V_o.$ \hfill (29.58)

Substituting the above value of V_f in equation (29.57), we get

$$V_o = A(V_s - \beta V_o) \quad \text{or,} \quad V_o(1 + A\beta) = AV_s$$

or, $\quad \dfrac{V_o}{V_s} = \dfrac{A}{1 + A\beta}.$ $\hspace{6cm}$ (29.59)

The overall gain with feedback A_f of the amplifier is the ratio of the output voltage V_o to the signal voltage V_s. So equation (29.59) can be written as

$$A_f = \frac{A}{1 + A\beta}. \hspace{4cm} (29.60)$$

The gain A_f with feedback is called as the closed-loop gain. In absence of the feedback the gain is A and is called the *open-loop gain*. The factor $(-A\beta)$ is known as the loop gain, loop transmission, feedback factor or the return ratio. When it is subtracted from 1 we get $(1 + A\beta)$ which is called the return difference.

Equation (29.60) above leads to the following different cases :

Case 1. If $|1 + A\beta| > 1$, then $|A_f| < |A|$ and the feedback is negative.

Case 2. If $|1 + A\beta| < 1$, then $|A_f| > |A|$ and the feedback is positive.

Case 3. If $|1 + A\beta| = 0$, then $|A_f| = \infty$ and so the amplifier is now capable of sustaining an output even if its input is zero. Or in other words, the amplifier then behaves as an oscillator.

It may be noted here that the overall gain of an amplifier increases with positive feedback arrangement. So there is a great chance of oscillations to occur. That is why the positive feedback is accompained by instability and is undesirable, in general.

29.8.1 Transfer Gain for Positive Feedback

In this case, we have

$$V_i = V_s + V_f. \hspace{5cm} (29.61)$$

$\therefore \quad V_o = AV_i = A(V_s + V_f)$ $\hspace{4.5cm}$ (29.62)

$$= A(V_s + \beta V_o) \text{ [by Eq. (29.58)]}$$

or, $\quad V_o(1 - A\beta) = AV_s \quad$ or, $\quad \dfrac{V_o}{V_s} = \dfrac{A}{1 - A\beta}.$

$\therefore \quad A_f = \dfrac{A}{1 - A\beta}.$ $\hspace{6cm}$ (29.63)

Eq. (29.63) shows that the voltage gain of the amplifier is changed by a factor $(1 - A\beta)$ when positive feedback is introduced.

Basic Assumptions

The above calculations of the transfer gain of the amplifier with feedback are made on the basis of the following assumptions :

(i) The ratio of the feedback voltage to the output voltage is not dependent on the load resistance.

(ii) The input signal is transmitted to the output through the amplifier and not through the feedback network.

(iii) The feedback signal is transmitted from the output to the input through the feedback network and not through the amplifier.

29.9 Effects to Feedback

Let us discuss the effects of feedback on the characteristics of an amplifier. The amplifier characteristics are the gain, dynamic range, input and output impedances, frequency and phase response and the output noise level.

   (i) **Voltage gain :** The gain of an amplifier with feedback can be expressed as

$$A_f = \frac{A}{1 - A\beta}.$$

Let the internal gain of the amplifier A be very large. Then,

$$A\beta \gg 1.$$

$$\therefore \quad A_f \approx \frac{A}{A\beta} \approx \frac{1}{\beta}. \tag{29.64}$$

Eq. (29.64) shows that the gain of the amplifier with feedback depends on the properties of the feedback network only. Feedback network, in general, consists of resistors and capacitors. So the gain of the feedback amplifiers becomes more stable and it does not change with transistor parameters.

   (ii) **Stabilization of gain :** We have

$$A_f = \frac{A}{1 - A\beta}.$$

Taking log of both sides,

$$\log_e A_f = \log_e A - \log_e (1 - A\beta). \tag{29.65}$$

Differentiating Eq. (29.65) with respect to A,

$$\frac{1}{A_f} \frac{dA_f}{dA} = \frac{1}{A} + \frac{1}{1 + A\beta}\beta = \frac{1}{A(1 - A\beta)}$$

or,
$$\frac{dA_f}{A_f} = \frac{dA}{A}\left(\frac{1}{1 - A\beta}\right). \tag{29.66}$$

The voltage gain sensitivity S_f of the amplifier with feedback is written as

$$S_f = \frac{dA_f}{A_f}. \tag{29.67}$$

Thus, we can write,

$$S_f = \frac{S}{1 - A\beta}, \tag{29.67a}$$

where S = voltage gain sensitivity without feedback = $\frac{dA}{A}$.

For negative feedback β is negative.

$$\therefore \quad S_f = \frac{S}{[1 + |\beta||A|]}. \tag{29.68}$$

Since $[1 + |\beta||A|] > 1$,

$$\therefore \quad S_f < S.$$

So the negative feedback decreases the gain sensitivity of the amplifier. That means it improves the gain stability.

   (iii) **Reduction in distortion :** Let D be the distortion generated in the final stage of an amplifier. The output voltage E_o including distortion is then written as

$$E_o = V_o + D. \tag{29.69}$$

So the input voltage V_i at the input terminals is

$$V_i = V_s + \beta E_o \tag{29.70}$$

$$= V_s + \beta(V_o + D). \tag{29.71}$$

But, $A = \dfrac{V_o}{V_i}$ or, $V_i = \dfrac{V_o}{A}$.

$$\therefore \quad \frac{V_o}{A} = V_s + \beta(V_o + D) \quad \text{or,} \quad V_o\left(\frac{1}{A} - \beta\right) = V_s + \beta D.$$

$$\therefore \quad V_o = \left(\frac{A}{1 - \beta A}\right)V_s + \left(\frac{A}{1 - \beta A}\right)\beta D. \tag{29.72}$$

Putting this value of V_o in equation (28.70), we get

$$E_o = \left(\frac{A}{1 - \beta A}\right)V_s + \left(\frac{A}{1 - \beta A}\right)\beta D + D = \left(\frac{A}{1 - \beta A}\right)V_s + \frac{D}{1 - \beta A}$$

$$= \left(\frac{A}{1 - \beta A}\right)V_s + D_f. \tag{29.73}$$

The second term on the r.h.s. of Eq. (29.73) gives the distortion D_f with feedback. Thus, we have

$$D_f = \frac{D}{1 - \beta A}. \tag{29.74}$$

In Eq. (29.74), if β is negative and A is large, then D_f will be much less than D. Therefore, the negative feedback reduces the amplitude distortion in the same magnitude as the gain.

(iv) **Change in input impedance** : Let Z_i be the input impedance of the amplifier without feedback and Z_{if} is the input impedance of the feedback. If I_1 be the input current flowing through Z_i and Z_{if} in series, then

$$Z_i I_1 = V_i \tag{29.75}$$

and $Z_{if} I_1 = V_s$. $\tag{29.76}$

We can further write,

$$V_i = V_s + \beta V_o$$

or, $V_s = V_i - \beta V_o$ $\tag{29.77}$

and $\left.\begin{array}{c} A = \dfrac{V_o}{V_i} \\[2mm] A = \dfrac{V_o}{V_s} \end{array}\right\}.$ $\tag{29.78}$

Dividing Eq. (29.76) by Eq. (29.75), we get

$$\frac{Z_{if}}{Z_i} = \frac{V_s}{V_i} = \frac{V_i - \beta V_o}{V_i} = 1 - \beta\frac{V_o}{V_i} = 1 - \beta A$$

or, $Z_{if} = (1 - \beta A)Z_i$. $\tag{29.79}$

For negative feedback, β is negative. So we can write,

$$Z_{if} = [1 + |\beta|A]Z_i. \tag{29.80}$$

The above equation shows that $Z_{if} > Z_i$.

To obtain Z_{if} in terms of A we may proceed in the following way :

$$\frac{Z_{if}}{Z_i} = \frac{V_s}{V_i} = \frac{V_s}{V_s + \beta V_o}.$$

$$\therefore \quad Z_{if} = \frac{Z_i}{1 + A_f \beta}. \tag{29.81}$$

(v) Change in output impedance : In order to calculate the output impedance of an amplifier with feedback, the input source V_s is reduced to zero and a voltage source of e.m.f. V_o is connected to the output terminals (Fig. 29.15). With $V_i = 0$, the input voltage at the input terminals is βV_o. Due to this input voltage, the output voltage becomes $\beta V_o A$. If I_o be the current applied, then

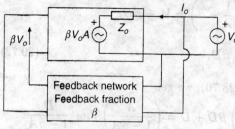

Fig. 29.15

$$I_o = \frac{V_o - \beta V_o A}{Z_o}$$

$$= \frac{V_o(1 - \beta A)}{Z_o}. \tag{29.82}$$

The effective output impedance with feedback,

$$Z_{of} = \frac{V_o}{I_o}$$

$$= \frac{Z_o}{1 - \beta A}. \tag{29.83}$$

[by equation (29.82)]

For negative feedback, β is negative.

$$\therefore \quad Z_{of} = \frac{Z_o}{1 + |\beta| A}. \tag{29.84}$$

So the negative feedback reduces the output impedance by the same factor as the voltage gain.

(vi) Improvement of bandwidth : If feedback is applied to an amplifier, then the lower cut-off frequency and the upper cut-off frequency may be considered in the following way :

(a) Lower cut-off frequency : The voltage gain at a frequency f of an RC-coupled amplifier is written as

$$A_l = \frac{A_m}{1 - j\frac{f_1}{f}}, \tag{29.85}$$

where f_1 is the lower cut-off frequency and A_m is the voltage gain in the mid-frequency range.

The voltage gains with feedback in the low-frequency and mid-frequency range are respectively expressed as

$$A_{if} = \frac{A_l}{1 - \beta A_l} \tag{29.86}$$

and $\quad A_{mf} = \frac{A_m}{1 - \beta A_m}. \tag{29.87}$

Putting the value of A_l from Eq. (29.85) in Eq. (29.86), we get

$$A_{lf} = \frac{\frac{A_m}{1-j\frac{f_1}{f}}}{1 - \beta\left(\frac{A_m}{1-j\frac{f_1}{f}}\right)} = \frac{A_m}{1 - j\frac{f_1}{f} - \beta A_m}$$

$$= \left(\frac{A_m}{1 - \beta A_m}\right)\frac{1}{1 - j\frac{f_1}{f(1-\beta A_m)}}$$

$$= \frac{A_{mf}}{1 - j\frac{f_1'}{f}}, \quad \text{[by Eq. (29.87)]} \tag{29.88}$$

where $\quad f_1' = \dfrac{f_1}{1 - \beta A_m}$.

f_1' represents the lower cut-off frequency of the amplifier with feedback. For negative feedback β is negative and hence,

$$f_1' < f_1,$$

i.e., the negative feedback decreases the lower cur-off frequency.

(b) Upper cut-off frequency : The voltage gain in the high-frequency range of an RC-coupled amplifier is written as

$$A_h = \frac{A_m}{1 + j\frac{f}{f_2}}, \tag{29.89}$$

where f_2 is the upper cut-off frequency.

The voltage gain with feedback in the mid-frequency and the high-frequency range of an amplifier is given by

$$A_{hf} = \frac{A_h}{1 - \beta A_h} \tag{29.90}$$

and $\quad A_{mf} = \dfrac{A_m}{1 - \beta A_m}$. $\tag{29.91}$

Putting the value of A_h from Eq. (29.89) in Eq. (29.90), we get

$$A_{hf} = \frac{\frac{A_m}{1+j\frac{f}{f_2}}}{1 - \beta\left(\frac{A_m}{1+j\frac{f}{f_2}}\right)} = \frac{A_m}{1 + j\frac{f}{f_2} - \beta A_m}$$

$$= \left(\frac{A_m}{1 - \beta A_m}\right)\frac{1}{1 + j\frac{f}{f_2(1-\beta A_m)}}$$

$$= \left(\frac{A_{mf}}{1 + j\frac{f}{f_2'}}\right), \quad \text{[by Eq. (29.91)]} \tag{29.92}$$

where $\quad f_2' = f_2(1 - \beta A_m)$. $\tag{29.93}$

Eq. (29.93) represents the upper cut-off frequency of an amplifier for a feedback arrangement. For a negative feedback, β is negative and so

$$f_2' < f_2.$$

The improvement in bandwidth with feedback is shown in Fig. 29.16.

(vii) Reduction in noise : The output of a transistor amplifier can be considered as the sum of the noise voltage N and the output signal. If feedback is applied, then the noise voltage N_f can be obtained in a similar way as in the case of distortion. We may thus write,

$$N_f = \frac{N}{1 - \beta A}. \qquad (29.94)$$

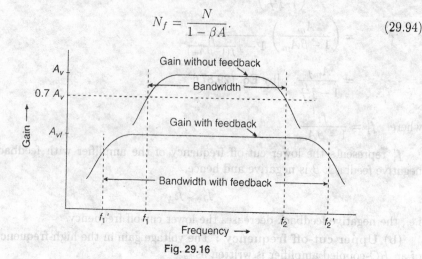

Fig. 29.16

29.10   Conditions for Oscillation

Before attaining the steady state, an oscillator must build up oscillations. For the oscillations to be self-sustaining the following items are required :

  (i) an amplifying device,

  (ii) regenerative feedback,

  (iii) some circuit non-linearity, and

  (iv) some energy storage system.

  Basically, the four-terminal or feedback oscillator is a regenerative feedback amplifier. Positive feedback results when the feedback factor βA is positive and less than unity. If βA is increased to unity, the gain with feedback becomes infinite and then the amplifier functions as an oscillator. The condition $\beta A = 1$ is known as the *Barkhausen criterion* and this is true at a single and precise frequency at which the feedback signal appearing at the input is exactly in phase with the input signal. Oscillations occur even if $\beta A > 1$ and the amplitude of oscillation increases without limit. For all practical purposes, non-linearity limits the theoretically infinitive gain to some finite value for both $\beta A = 1$ and $\beta A > 1$.

29.11   LC Oscillatory Circuit

A fundamental oscillatory circuit is the LCR circuit. In Fig. 29.17(a), R_s is the series resistance while in Fig. 29.17(b), R_p is the parallel resistance connected with L and C as shown.

  We may now define resonance as a condition in which the current and voltage in a reactive circuit are in phase with each other. If the resistance R_s becomes zero, then the resonant frequency f_0 can be defined as

$$f_0 = \frac{1}{2\pi\sqrt{LC}}. \qquad (29.95)$$

But in practice, R_s is not zero and so the above equation is expressed in a modified form as

$$f_0 = \frac{1}{2\pi\sqrt{LC}}\left[\frac{1}{\sqrt{1 + (R_s^2/\omega_0^2 L^2)}}\right].\qquad(29.96)$$

The fact that some resistance is present in the circuit we mean that some of the energy stored in the reactive elements is dissipated as heat in R_s. The quality factor Q can be defined as

$$Q_s = \frac{\text{enegy stored in system}}{\text{energy dissipated per cycle}}$$

$$= \frac{X_L}{R_s} = \frac{\omega_o L}{R_s}.\qquad(29.97)$$

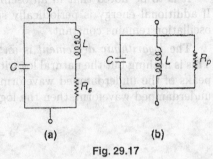

(a)   **(b)**

Fig. 29.17

If we consider Fig. 29.17(b), then we can write,

$$R_p = \omega_o L Q_p$$

or, $\quad Q_p = \dfrac{R_p}{\omega_o L}.\qquad(29.98)$

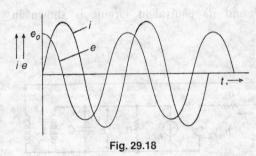

Fig. 29.18

Fig. 29.18 shows that if some initial energy is given in an ideal LC circuit, it will oscillate indefinitely at the resonance frequency as given by Eq. (29.95). The analysis of the circuit with an initial current I_0 in the inductor involves a differential equation, the solution of which leads to three possible conditions. The oscillatory or underdamped condition results, when

$$\frac{L}{C} < 4R_p^2.\qquad(29.99)$$

In Fig. 29.19(a), the current in the circuit for the undamped condition is shown. If i be the current, then

$$i = I_0\epsilon^{-\alpha t}\cos\omega t,\qquad(29.100)$$

where I_0 = initial current in L, damping factor, $\alpha = -\frac{1}{2R_pC}$ and frequency,

$$\omega = \sqrt{\frac{1}{LC} - \frac{1}{4R_p^2 C^2}}.\qquad(29.101)$$

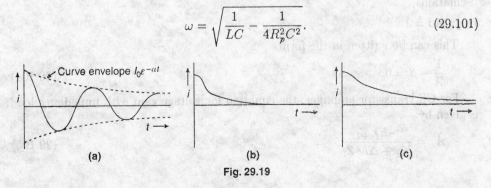

(a)   **(b)**   **(c)**

Fig. 29.19

When $L/C = 4R_p^2$, we get the critical damping. The critically damped circuit does not oscillate but within a very short time it dissipates the circuit energy.

If $L/C > 4R_p^2$, the overdamped condition shown in Fig. 29.19(c) results.

It is to be noted that in an oscillator the underdamped condition is desirable. If additional energy is periodically supplied to the circuit, then the amplitude of oscillation remains constant.

The *logarithmic decrement* is an important factor in many oscillator circuits. This is nothing but the natural logarithm of the ratio of amplitudes of two successive peaks of the underdamped waveform. If i_1 and i_2 are the successive peaks of the underdamped waveform, then the logarithmic decrement δ is given by

$$\delta = \ln\left(\frac{i_1}{i_2}\right). \qquad (29.102)$$

In terms of the Q of the circuit, δ can alternately be expressed as

$$\delta = \frac{\pi}{Q_p}. \qquad (29.103)$$

29.12   Tuned Collector Oscillator

A transistor-tuned collector oscillator and its equivalent circuit is shown in Fig. 29.20(a) and (b) respectively.

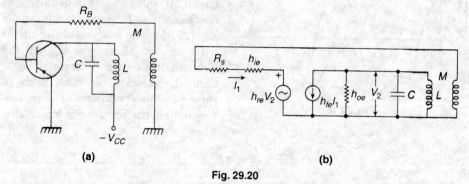

Fig. 29.20

The output of the tuned tank circuit is magnetically coupled to a secondary winding. The voltage developed across the output is fed back to the input base lead through a series resistor R_s.

The Barkhausen criterion must be satisfied as a condition for sustained oscillations,

i.e., $A\beta = 1$.

This can be written in the form,

$$\frac{1}{A} - \beta = 0. \qquad (29.104)$$

For CE transistor amplifier, the equation for voltage gain with impedance load is given by

$$A_v = \frac{-h_{fe}Z_l}{h_{ie} + \Delta h^e Z_l}. \qquad (29.105)$$

Having satisfied the condition that R_p prevents loading the tank circuit, we can write to a good approximation

$$\beta = \frac{-j\omega M I_1}{(R + j\omega L)I_1}$$

$$= \frac{-j\omega M}{R + j\omega L}. \qquad (29.106)$$

By Eqs. (29.104), (29.105) and (29.106), we get

$$h_{ie}R\omega C + j(\omega^2 LC - 1)h_{ie} - j\Delta h^e R + \omega L\Delta h^e - \omega M h_{fe} = 0. \qquad (29.107)$$

In an equation of the form $X + iY = 0$, it is required to set the reals equal to zero and the imaginaries equal to zero. Equating the imaginaries of equation (29.107) to zero

$$\omega^2 LCh_{ie} - h_{ie} - \Delta h^e R = 0 \qquad (29.108)$$

Solving for ω, we get

$$\omega = \frac{1}{\sqrt{LC}}\left[1 + \frac{\Delta h^e R}{h_{ie}}\right]^{1/2}. \qquad (29.109)$$

Thus, we find that the frequency of oscillation depends on the tank-circuit values and the transistor parameters. Since the value of Δh is small and also for a high Q-coil the coil resistance is small. So the frequency of oscillation is close to the natural frequency of the resonant circuit.

Again, equating the real part to zero, we have

$$\omega(h_{ie}RC + L\Delta h^e - M h_{je}) = 0$$

Since $\omega \neq 0$,

$$\therefore \qquad h_{ie}RC + L\Delta h^e - M h_{fe} = 0$$

or, $\qquad M = \dfrac{h_{ie}RC}{h_{fe}} + \dfrac{L\Delta h^e}{h_{fe}}. \qquad (29.110)$

The above equation gives us a relation between circuit and transistor values that should exist for oscillations to begin.

29.13 Frequency Stability

Changes in transistor parameters, power supply voltages and in the passive circuit elements cause a change from the required frequency value. This change is called as the *drift*. In general, both active and passive oscillator circuit parameters change due to temperature and aging. The variations of temperature of transistor parameters cause a very great problem. Use of emitter resistor stabilizes the operating point against changes in transistor parameters or bias voltages. Additional stabilization can also be realized using a thermistor (R_{th}) in the base bias network of the oscillator. This is shown in Fig. 29.21. The thermistor R_{th}, a temperature sensitive resistance with negative temperature coefficient, tends to reduce the base-forward bias with increasing temperature.

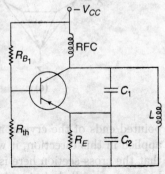

Fig. 29.21

For the compensation of the temperature, semiconductor diodes are also very useful. For a good frequency stability, a piezoelectric crystal is used as the frequency-determining element.

29.14 Push-pull Oscillators

Some oscillators can be readily converted to push-pull operation. The output power with a push-pull connection is increased and harmonics are decreased. A Hartley oscillator might be connected in push-pull. the feedback is achieved by capacitive coupling from the plate tank back to the input. The 180° phase shift can be obtained by tapping to opposite sides of the tank. For high frequencies the push-pull connection is found to be useful.

29.15 Crystal Oscillators

A crystal oscillator is one where piezoelectric crystal is used as the frequency-determining component. The crystal takes the place of the inductor in the parallel resonant LC circuit and has the property that its resonant frequency is relatively constant.

Certain natural crystals like quartz, tourmaline and rochelle salts exhibit a piezoelectric effect. When a voltage is applied to the faces of a piezoelectric crystal, the shape of the crystal is distorted. If an alternating voltage is applied to the faces of a piezoelectric crystal, it produces mechanical vibration showing a maximum amplitude at the natural resonant frequency of the crystal.

29.15.1 Quartz Crystal and Its Characteristics

In Fig. 29.22(a), we have illustrated the form of the natural quartz crystal while in Fig. 29.22(b), the relation between the various axes is shown. The axis joining the

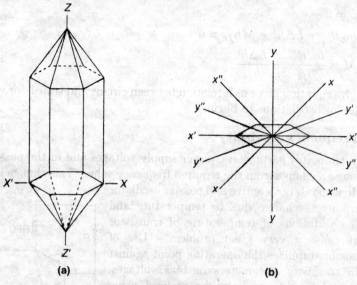

(a)   (b)

Fig. 29.22

pointed ends of the crystal is called the *Z-axis* or the *optical axis*. If any stress is applied in this direction, it will not produce a piezoelectric effect. It may be noted that the cross-section here is hexagonal in shape. Axes through the corners of the hexagon are called *electrical axes* and are labelled x, x' and x''. On the other hand, the three axes perpendicular to the faces of the crystal are known as the *mechanical axes* and are labelled y, y' and y''.

If a section is cut from the crystal in such a manner that the flat sides of longer dimension are perpendicular to one of the electrical axes, mechanical stresses along the edges in the y-direction will produce an electric potential in the direction of X-axis. This section as shown in Fig. 29.23(a) is referred to as an X-cut. Again, when the direction of cut is changed by 30° so that the flat side

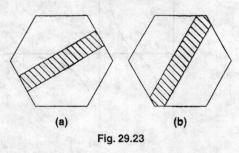

(a)   (b)

Fig. 29.23

is perpendicular to the mechancial axis, then the section as revealed in Fig. 29.23(b) is called a Y-*cut*. A mechanical force applied to the flat sides in the y-direction produces an electric potential across the edges.

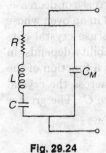

Fig. 29.24

Electrical equivalent circuit of a quartz or other piezoelectric crystal is shown in Fig. 29.24. The crystal is represented by a series resonant circuit LCR shunted by a capacitance C_M. The inductance L represents the electrical equivalent of crystal mass, C is the electrical equivalent of crystal compliance and R is an equivalent of the internal friction of the crystal structure. The shunt capacitance C_M represents the capacitance between the mounting electrodes with the crystal as a dielectric. The circuit of Fig. 29.24 has two resonant frequencies. One of the frequencies f_1 can be expressed as

$$f_1 = \frac{1}{2\pi\sqrt{LC}}. \tag{29.111}$$

At this series resonant frequency, the crystal impedance presented to the circuit is very low.

An electrical equivalent circuit of a crystal at frequency greater than the series resonant frequency is shown in Fig. 29.25. In the circuit, L_x represents the equivalent inductance of the series arm. The resonant frequency f_2 can be obtained by using the equation,

$$f_2 = \frac{1}{2\pi}\sqrt{\frac{C}{C_M(LC-1)}}. \tag{29.112}$$

At frequencies below f_1, the crystal is capacitive. With typical crystals, the difference between f_1 and f_2 is very small. The resonant frequencies are inversely proportional to the thickness of the cut. If t represents the thickness in centimetres, then

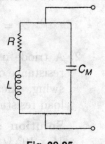

Fig. 29.25

$$f_1 = \frac{k}{t} \text{ kHz}, \tag{29.113}$$

where k has different values for the different cuts.

Variation of reactance of a crystal with frequency is shown in Fig. 29.26(a) while Fig. 29.26(b) illustrates the low impedance at series resonance f_1 and high impedance at parallel resonance f_2.

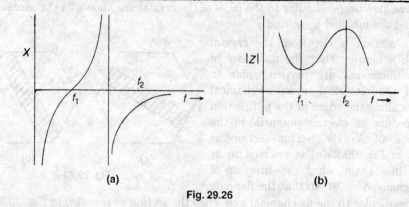

Fig. 29.26

With the variation of temperature, the resonant frequency of a quartz crystal is affected, causing minute changes in dimensions, compliance and density. With an increase of temperature, the frequency of oscillation may either increase or decrease. One of the methods of frequency stabilization is to keep the crystal in an oven whose temperature is properly regulated. An alternative method is to use crystal cuts whose temperature coefficient approaches zero. The frequency stability depends, in fact, on the amplitude of mechanical vibrations. This vibration is a function of the current through the crystal whose flow depends on the voltage across the crystal and the ratio of mounting capacitance C_M to internal capacitance C. The greater is the amplitude of vibration, the poorer is the frequency stability.

Examples

1. A 12 AU7 triode used as an amplifier has an amplification factor of 20 and a.c. plate resistance of 12 kΩ. Calculate the voltage gain of the amplifier for a load resistance of 18 kΩ.

Solution : Here, $\mu = 20$, $r_p = 12$ kΩ and $R_L = 18$ kΩ.

Now, voltage gain,

$$A = \frac{\mu R_L}{r_p + R_L} = \frac{20 \times 18}{12 + 18} = 12.$$

2. A triode used as amplifier has an amplification factor of 20 and a.c. plate resistance of 10 kΩ. If the signal voltage applied to the grid has a 3-volt peak swing, calculate the value of the load current and the output voltage. The load resistance is 15 kΩ.

Solution : Here, $\mu = 20$, $r_p = 10$ k$\Omega = 10 \times 10^3$ Ω, $R_L = 15$ k$\Omega = 15 \times 10^3$ Ω, $E_s = 3$ volts.

Now, the load current,

$$I_p = \frac{\mu \frac{E_s}{\sqrt{2}}}{r_p + R_L} = \frac{20 \times 3 \times 0.707}{(10 + 15) \times 10^3} = 1.69 \times 10^{-3} \text{ A}$$

and the output voltage,

$$E_o = I_p \times R_L = 16.9 \times 10^{-3} \times 15 \times 10^3 = 253.5 \text{ volts}.$$

3. A triode valve used as an amplifier has $\mu = 15$ and $r_p = 12$ kΩ. If the anode load consists of a resistance and inductance of values 20 kΩ and 7500 μH

respectively, calculate the voltage gain of the amplifier. Given that the input voltage has a frequency of 600 kHz.

Solution : Here, $\mu = 15$, $r_p = 12$ k$\Omega = 12 \times 10^3 \,\Omega$, $R_L = 20$ k$\Omega = 20 \times 10^3 \,\Omega$, $L = 7500 \,\mu$H $= 75 \times 10^{-4}$ H, $f = 600$ kHz $= 600 \times 10^3$ Hz.

Now, voltage gain, $A = \dfrac{\mu Z_L}{r_p + Z_L}$,

where $Z_L = \sqrt{R_L^2 + X_L^2} = \sqrt{R_L^2 + (2\pi f L)^2}$

$$= \sqrt{(20 \times 10^3)^2 + (2 \times 3.14 \times 600 \times 10^3 \times 75 \times 10^{-4})^2} = 34653 \,\Omega.$$

$\therefore \qquad A = \dfrac{15 \times 34653}{12000 + 34653} = \mathbf{11.14}.$

4. A transistor having $h_{ie} = 1100$ ohms, $h_{re} = 2.5 \times 10^{-4}$, $h_{fe} = 50$ and $h_{oe} = 25$ micromhos is connected as a common emitter amplifier with the load resistance $R_L = 1000$ ohms. Calculate the current gain and the input impedance.

Solution : Here, $h_{ie} = 1100$ ohms $= h_{11}$, $h_{re} = 2.5 \times 10^{-4} = h_{12}$, $h_{fe} = 50 = h_{21}$, $h_{oe} = 25$ micromhos $= 25 \times 10^{-6}$ mho $= h_{22}$ and $R_L = 1000$ ohms.

Now, current gain,

$$A_i = \frac{h_{21}}{h_{22} R_L + 1} = \frac{50}{25 \times 10^{-6} \times 10^3 + 1} = \frac{50}{1.025} = 48.8.$$

Input impedance,

$$R_{\text{in}} = \frac{\Delta h R_L + h_{11}}{h_{22} R_L + 1},$$

when $\Delta h = h_{11} h_{22} - h_{12} h_{21}$

$$= 1000 \times 25 \times 10^{-6} - 2.5 \times 10^{-4} \times 50 = 150 \times 10^{-4}.$$

$\therefore \qquad R_{\text{in}} = \dfrac{150 \times 10^{-4} \times 10^3 + 1100}{1.025} = \dfrac{1115}{1.025} = \mathbf{1088 \text{ ohms}}.$

5. A junction transistor has the following specifications : $h_{ib} = 40$ ohms, $h_{rb} = 4 \times 10^{-4}$, $h_{fb} = -0.98$ and $h_{ob} = 10^{-6}$ mho. Calculate the maximum available power gain of the transistor.

Solution : The power gain,

$$A_p = -\frac{h_{21}^2 R_L}{(R_L \Delta h + h_{11})(1 + h_{22} R_L)} = -\frac{h_{21}^2}{\left(\Delta h + \frac{h_{11}}{R_L}\right)(1 + h_{22} R_L)}.$$

For maximum power gain we differentiate A_p with respect to R_L and equate the result to zero. Thus,

$$\frac{dA_p}{dR_L} = -h_{21}^2 \frac{(\Delta h + h_{11}/R_L)h_{22} - (1 + h_{22} R_L)h_{11}/R_L^2}{[(\Delta h + h_{11}/R_L)(1 + h_{22} R_L)]^2} = 0$$

or, $\left(\Delta h + \dfrac{h_{11}}{R_L}\right) h_{22} = \dfrac{h_{11}}{R_L^2} + \dfrac{h_{11} h_{22}}{R_L}$

or, $R_L^2 = \dfrac{h_{11}}{\Delta h \cdot h_{22}}.$

So the maximum power gain,

$$A_{p_{max}} = -\frac{h_{21}^2}{\left[\Delta h + h_{11}\left(\frac{\Delta h h_{22}}{h_{11}}\right)^{1/2}\right]\left[h_{22}\left(\frac{h_{11}}{\Delta h h_{22}}\right)^{1/2} + 1\right]}$$

$$= -\frac{h_{21}^2(\Delta h)^{1/2}}{(\Delta h)^{1/2}[(\Delta h)^{1/2} + (h_{11}h_{22})^{1/2}][(h_{11}h_{22})^{1/2} + (\Delta h)^{1/2}]}$$

$$= -\frac{h_{21}^2}{[(\Delta h)^{1/2} + (h_{11}h_{22})^{1/2}]^2}$$

In the given problem,

$$h_{ib} = 40 \text{ ohms} = h_{11}, \quad h_{rb} = 4 \times 10^{-4} = h_{12}$$

$$h_{fb} = -0.98 = h_{21}, \quad h_{ob} = 10^{-6} \text{ mho} = h_{22}$$

Here, $\Delta h = h_{11}h_{22} - h_{12}h_{21} = 40 \times 10^{-6} - 4 \times 10^{-4} \times 0.98 = 432 \times 10^{-6}$.

$$\therefore \quad A_{p_{max}} = -\frac{(-0.98)^2}{[(432 \times 10^{-6})^{1/2} + (40 \times 10^{-6})^{1/2}]^2} = \mathbf{-1307}.$$

So the maximum power gain is **1307**.

6. The voltage gain of a transistor amplifier is 50. Its input and output resistances are 1 kΩ and 40 kΩ respectively. If the amplifier is provided with 10% negative voltage feedback in series with the input, then **calculate** the voltage gain, input resistance and the output impedance.

Solution : We have $A_f = \dfrac{A}{1 - A\beta}$

Here, $A = 50$, $\beta = -\dfrac{10}{100} = -0.1$.

$$\therefore \quad A_f = \frac{50}{1 - (50 \times -0.1)} = \frac{50}{6} = 8.3.$$

Input impedance with feedback,

$$Z_{if} = Z_f(1 - A\beta) = 1[1 - (50 \times -0.1)] \quad (\because Z_f = 1 \text{ k}\Omega)$$

$$= 6 \text{ k}\Omega.$$

Output impedance with feedback,

$$Z_{of} = \frac{Z}{1 - A\beta} = \frac{40}{1 - [50 \times (-0.1)]} = \frac{40}{6} = \mathbf{6.6 \text{ k}\Omega}.$$

7. Find the component values of a Colpitts oscillator at 1 MHz using a transistor having the following parameters : $h_{ie} = 1.8$ kΩ, $h_{oe} = 18$ μmhos, $h_{re} = 1.8 \times 10^{-4}$, $h_{fe} = 90$ (given, $C_1 = 0.5$ μF).

Solution : We have $\Delta h^e = h_{ie}h_{oe} - h_{fe}h_{re}$

$$= (1.8 \times 10^3)(18 \times 10^{-4}) - (1.8 \times 10^{-4})(9 \times 10^{-1})$$

$$= 16.2 \times 10^{-3}.$$

Now, $C_2 = \dfrac{\Delta h_e}{h_{fe}}C_1 = \dfrac{16.2 \times 10^{-3}}{90}(0.5 \times 10^{-6}) = 0.9 \times 10^{-9}$ F.

Again, the inductance can be obtained from

$$L = \frac{1}{\omega^2}\left(\frac{C_1 + C_2}{C_1 C_2}\right) = \frac{1}{(2\pi \times 10^6)^2}\left(\frac{0.5 + 0.0009}{0.5 \times 0.0009}\right)$$

$$= 0.284 \times 10^{-4} \text{H}.$$

8. A transistor RC oscillator has the following circuit values : $C = 0.01\ \mu\text{F}$, $R = 4.7$ kΩ and $R_L = 2.2$ kΩ. Calculate the frequency of oscillation and h_{fe} required.

Solution: The frequency of oscillation,

$$f = \frac{1}{2\pi C\sqrt{4RR_L + 6R^2}}$$

$$= \frac{1}{2\pi(1 \times 10^{-2})(10^6)[4 \times 4.7 \times 10^3 \times 2.2 \times 10^3 + 6(4.7 \times 10^3)^2]^{1/2}}$$

$$= 1200 \text{ Hz}.$$

Again, $h_{fe} = 23 + \dfrac{29R}{R_L} + \dfrac{4R_L}{R} = 23 + 29\left(\dfrac{4.7}{2.2}\right) + 4\left(\dfrac{2.2}{4.7}\right) \cong \mathbf{87}.$

Questions

Essay-type

1. What are amplifiers? How are they classified?

2. Describe with circuit diagram the operation of a single-stage voltage amplifier. Find its voltage gain.

3. Obtain expressions for voltage gain of an untuned class A_1 amplifier when **(i)** Z_L is purely resistive, **(ii)** Z_L is purely inductive and **(iii)** Z_L is complex inductive.

4. What is meant by distortion in amplifiers? Define the three main types of distortions.

5. How are the amplifiers classified? Explain graphically how class A, class B, class AB and class C amplifiers work.

6. Draw the circuit diagram of an RC-coupled amplifier and explain it. Find expressions of voltage gain for **(i)** mid-frequency, **(ii)** low-frequency and **(iii)** high-frequency range of the amplifier. Calculate the values for lower and upper cut-off frequencies.

7. What is meant by power amplifier. Describe the operation of a transformer-coupled class A power amplifier and hence calculate its efficiency.

8. Discuss the working of a push-pull amplifier. Calculate the efficiency, dissipation and maximum power output of the amplifier.

9. Explain the term feedback. Find out an expression for the gain of an amplifier with feedback. What are the advantages of negative feedback?

10. Derive an expression for the voltage gain of an amplifier using feedback. Discuss the effect of negative feedback on **(i)** distortion, **(ii)** input impedance and **(iii)** output impedance.

11. Explain the nature of feedback in an emitter follower circuit. What are the advantages of this circuit? Can this circuit be used as a voltage amplifier?

12. Discuss mathematically the various effects of negative feedback amplifier.

13. What are the important characteristics of an oscillator?

14. What is the Barkhausen criterion?

15. What conditions must be satisfied to have self-sustained oscillations?

16. What is the piezoelectric effect?

17. What important natural crystals reveal piezoelectricity?

18. How does the resonant frequency vary with crystal thickness?

19. How does a Pierce oscillator operate?

Numerical Problems

20. A two-stage common-emitter RC-coupled amplifier is constructed using transistor. The h-parameters and the internal capacitances are :

$$h_{fe} = 600, \quad h_{ie} = 10 \text{ k}\Omega, \quad C_{bc} = 2.5 \text{ pF}, \quad C_{be} = 9 \text{ pF}.$$

Determine the lower and upper cut-off frequencies when the coupling capacitance is 0.5 μF and the load resistance is 10 kΩ. [**Ans.** 16 Hz, 26 kHz]

21. A class A power amplifier uses a transformer as a coupling device. The turn ratio of the transformer is 10 and the secondary load is 10 ohms. Calculate the maximum power output when the zero signal collector current is 100 mA.

[**Ans.** 5 watts]

22. In a common-base configuration, the emitter current is 1 mA. Find the base current when the collector current is 0.96 mA. [**Ans.** 0.4 mA]

23. In a transistor circuit, if the emitter current and collector current are respectively 1 mA and 0.9 mA, determine the value of base current.

[**Ans.** 0.1 mA]

24. If $\alpha = 0.99$, then what is the value of β? [**Ans.** 100]

25. In a transistor with $\beta = 45$, the voltage across 5 kΩ resistance which is connected in the collector circuit is 5 volts. Calculate the value of the base current. [**Ans.** 0.022 mA]

26. Find the value of β if $\alpha = 0.98$. [**Ans.** 49]

27. A change of 200 mV in base-emitter voltage causes a change of 50 μA in the base current. Determine the input resistance of the transistor. [**Ans.** 4 kΩ]

28. For a single-stage transistor amplifier, the collector load is 1.5 kΩ and the input resistance is 0.5 kΩ. If the current gain is 40, find the voltage gain of the amplifier. [**Ans.** 120]

29. It is required to set the operating point by biasing with feedback resistor at $I_C = 1$ mA, $V_{CE} = 8$ V. If $\beta = 100$, $V_{CC} = 12$ V, $V_{BE} = 0.3$ V, how will you do it? [**Ans.** $R_B = 770$ kΩ]

30. A CE transistor amplifier is biased by the collector-to-base bias method using $R_B = 100$ kΩ. If $V_{CC} = 25$ V, $R_L = 1$ kW and $\beta = 200$, find the co-ordinates of the operating point. [**Ans.** $I_C = 16.2$ mA, $V_{CE} = 8.8$ V]

31. A CE transistor amplifier using emitter resistor and potential-divider circuit has the following parameters :

$$V_{CC} = 15 \text{ V}, \quad R_L = 470 \ \Omega, \quad R_1 = 4 \text{ k}\Omega, \quad R_2 = 1 \text{ k}\Omega \text{ and } R_E = 220 \ \Omega.$$

Assuming the transistor to be of silicon, calculate the operating point.

[**Ans.** $I_C = 10.5$ mA, $V_{CE} = 7.75$ V]

32. The change in gain of an amplifier without feedback is $\pm 10\%$. If 20 dB negative feedback is introduced, what will be the change of gain in percentage? Assuming the internal amplifier gain to be 1000, calculate the feedback ratio and the overall gain of the amplifier. [**Ans.** $\pm 1\%, 9 \times 10^{-3}, 100$]

33. The voltage gain of a transistor amplifier is 80 and its input resistance is 2.2 kΩ. If the amplifier is modified to provide 10% negative voltage feedback, find the voltage gain and the input resistance with feedback.

[**Ans.** 8.89, 19.8 kΩ]

34. A transistor RC oscillator has the values $C = 0.001$ μF, $R = 18$ kΩ and $R_L = 4.7$ kΩ. Compute the frequency of oscillation and value of h_{fe} required of the transistor. [**Ans.** $f = 3.3$ kHz, $h_{fe} = 135$]

35. If $C = 0.015$ μF, $R = 100$ kΩ and if $C = 0.005$ μF and $R = 10$ kΩ, find the frequency of oscillation of a Wien bridge oscillator.

[**Ans.** $f = 106$ Hz, $f = 3180$ Hz]

Chapter 30
Cathode-Ray Oscillograph

30.1   Introduction

Nowadays perhaps all of us are familiar with at least one type of cathode-ray tube used in the television picture tube known as *kinescope*. However, cathode-ray tubes are of many types, sizes and shapes. The modern cathode-ray tube is, in fact, an important modification of the Crookes tube discovered in 1879.

The CR tube is now widely used in laboratory to study the electric circuit phenomena, It is also extensively used as a viewing device for the reception of radar signals and television images. The CR tube is, in general, used in an assemblage of apparatus called a *cathode-ray oscillograph;* the essential components of which are : (i) cathode-ray tube, (ii) deflection voltage amplifiers, (iii) power supplies and (iv) time base circuit.

30.2   Construction

A cathode-ray tube, as shown in Fig. 30.1, has the following main components :

(i) The electron gun for producing and focusing the emitted electrons in a narrow beam, (ii) a deflection system, for deflecting the electron beam either electrostatically or magnetically, and (iii) a fluorescent screen, upon which the electron beam impinges to create a visible light spot.

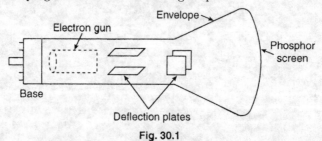

Fig. 30.1

A tube base is there to which connections from the elements inside the tube are made. The components of a CR tube are mounted carefully inside a highly evacuated glass envelope.

30.3   Electron Gun

In an electrostatically focused CR tube, as illustrated in Fig. 30.2, the electron gun consists of (a) an indirectly heated cathode, (b) a control grid, (c) an accelerating electrode, (d) a first focusing anode and (e) a second, or final accelerating anode.

The cylindrical cathode is usually coated with barium and strontium oxides for providing a plentiful supply of electrons. By a tungsten heater wire this cathode is indirectly heated. The control grid is a cylinder with a tiny aperture at its centre and is kept enveloping the cathode. Adjacent to the control grid there are first and second anodes, followed by the accelerating grid, which are also cylindrical in shape with small apertures at the centre.

The indirectly heated cathode emits a stream of electrons whose density is controlled by the bias voltage applied between the control grid and the cathode. In order to focus the beam of electrons properly, the voltage applied on the first anode is utilized. The second anode which is kept at a high positive d.c. voltage relative to the cathode, accelerates the electron beam.

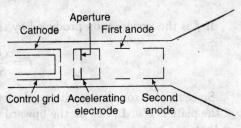

Fig. 30.2

The anode potentials in a CR tube are adjusted by considering the required beam power. The first anode is always kept at an appreciably lower potential than the second one. In television camera tube of iconoscope type the first anode potential is of the order of 300 volts while that of the second anode potential is 1000 volts.

30.4 Fluorescent Screen

If the beam of electrons coming from the electron gun is not deflected, it would form a luminous spot of light at the centre of the fluorescent screen. Though the control grid is usually used to control the intensity of this spot, but it is also dependent on the fluorescent material. The fluorescent material coated inside the tube is termed as phosphor. Some commonly used phosphors are : zinc silicate, zinc oxide, zinc sulphide, etc.

30.5 Deflection Sensitivity

The beam of electrons in a CR tube is deflected by two different means : (i) electrostatically and (ii) magnetostatically.

Electrostatic deflection

The electrostatic deflection sensitivity is the amount of deflection of electron spot produced on the screen when a voltage of one volt from a d.c. source is applied to the deflection plates. The unit of deflection sensitivity is then expressed in inch/volt or mm/volt.

The geometry of the electrostatic deflection system is shown in Fig. 30.3. In the

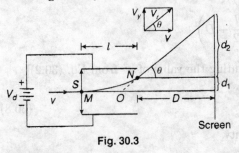

Fig. 30.3

figure, V_d is the potential applied between two plates, each of lengths l and spacings S. Let the plates be kept at a distance D from the screen and on entering the deflection plates let an electron move with a velocity v.

Then we have

$$\frac{1}{2}m_e v^2 = Q_e V_a, \qquad (30.1)$$

where m_e = mass of an electron, Q_e = its charge and V_a = final anode voltage.

From equation (30.1), we get

$$v^2 = \frac{2Q_e}{m_e} V_a. \qquad (30.2)$$

The electrons during its movement are attracted towards the positive plate with a force F, where

$$F = \frac{Q_e V_d}{S}. \tag{30.3}$$

If f is the acceleration produced by the force F, then

$$f = \frac{Q_e \cdot V_d}{S \cdot m_e}. \tag{30.4}$$

Since an electron moves with a velocity v, the time required to traverse the fields of the plate is l/v. Let v_y be the upward velocity attained in this time interval l/v, so that

$$v_y = \frac{l}{v} \cdot f = \frac{l}{v} \cdot \frac{Q_e \cdot V_d}{S \cdot m_e}. \tag{30.5}$$

From the point of entrance to the point of leaving, i.e., from M to N, the electrons move in a curved path. Let d_1 be the vertical displacement during this period. Then,

$$d_1 = \frac{1}{2} f \left(\frac{l}{v}\right)^2$$

$$= \frac{1}{2} \frac{Q_e \cdot V_d}{S \cdot m_e} \frac{l^2}{v^2}. \tag{30.6}$$

After emerging from the field of deflection plates, let the electron beam make an angle θ. Then,

$$\tan \theta = \frac{v_y}{v} = \frac{d_2}{D}$$

i.e., $$d_2 = \frac{v_y}{v} \cdot D$$

$$= \frac{1}{v^2} \cdot \frac{Q_e \cdot V_d}{S \cdot m_e} \cdot D \quad \text{[using equation (30.5)]} \tag{30.7}$$

Knowing d_1 and d_2 from Eqs. (30.6) and (30.7), we can now calculate the total deflection d. Thus,

$$d = d_1 + d_2 = \frac{Q_e \cdot V_d}{S \cdot m_e} \frac{l}{v^2} \left(\frac{l}{2} + D\right)$$

$$= \frac{Q_e \cdot V_d}{S \cdot m_e} \frac{l}{v^2} \cdot L \quad \left(\text{where } L = \frac{l}{2} + D\right)$$

$$= \frac{Q_e \cdot V_d}{S \cdot m_e} \cdot \frac{l \cdot m_e}{2 Q_e \cdot V_a} \cdot L \quad \text{[substituting the value of } v^2 \text{ from Eq. (30.2)]}$$

i.e., $$d = \frac{lL}{2S} \cdot \frac{V_d}{V_a}. \tag{30.8}$$

Now by definition, deflection sensitivity,

$$S_e = \frac{d}{V_d}$$

$$= lL/2SV_a. \tag{30.9}$$

For a given CR tube, l, L and S are fixed and so varying the voltage applied to the plates, V_d, or the final anode voltage V_a, one may alter the deflection spot d. It is also seen from Eq. (30.9) that the deflection sensitivity is inversely proportional to the final anode voltage.

Magnetostatic deflection

The magnetic deflection sensitivity is defined as the amount of deflection of electron spot produced when one milli-ampere current flows through the deflection coil. The unit of deflection sensitivity is then expressed in inch/mA or mm/mA. In this system the magnetic field is produced by passing current through the coil, as in Fig. 30.4, whose axis is kept normal to the direction of the electron beam.

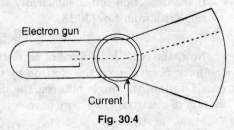

Electron gun

Current

Fig. 30.4

The configuration of the magnetic deflection system is shown in Fig. 30.5. As shown in the figure, the electron travels in an arc MN of a circle inside the magnetic field and thereafter it moves in a straight line. Thus, the total deflection of the spot can be divided into two parts : (i) deflection within the magnetic field, d_1 and (ii) deflection outside the field, d_2.

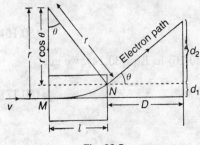

Fig. 30.5

Let in the direction of electron beam, θ be the angular change in passing through the magnetic field and also let the electron move in a circle of radius r inside the field, so that

$$d_1 = r - r\cos\theta = r - r\sqrt{1 - \sin^2\theta}$$

$$= r - r\sqrt{1 - \frac{l^2}{r^2}} \quad \left(\because \sin\theta = \frac{l}{r}\right)$$

$$= r\left(1 - \sqrt{1 - \frac{l^2}{r^2}}\right)$$

or, $\dfrac{d_1}{r} = \dfrac{r - \sqrt{r^2 - l^2}}{r}$ or, $r - d_1 = \sqrt{r^2 - l^2}$

or, $r^2 - 2rd_1 + d_1^2 = r^2 - l^2$ or, $(2r - d_1)d_1 = l^2$. $\qquad$ (30.10)

In Eq. (30.10), we may neglect d_1^2 comparing $2rd_1$ and hence we have

$$2rd_1 = l^2$$

i.e., $d_1 = \dfrac{l^2}{2r}$. $\qquad$ (30.11)

Again, from Fig. 30.5, we get

$$\frac{d_2}{D} = \tan\theta$$

or, $d_2 = D\tan\theta = D\dfrac{\sin\theta}{\cos\theta} = D\dfrac{\sin\theta}{\sqrt{(1 - \sin^2\theta)}} = D\dfrac{l/r}{\sqrt{1 - \frac{l^2}{r^2}}}$

or, $d_2 = \dfrac{Dl}{\sqrt{(r^2 - l^2)}}$. $\qquad$ (30.12)

Therefore, the total displacement,

$$d = d_1 + d_2$$

$$= \frac{l^2}{2r} + \frac{Dl}{\sqrt{(r^2 - l^2)}}. \tag{30.13}$$

If the deflection coil is sufficiently short, so that l is small in comparison to r, we can write from Eq. (30.13),

$$d = Dl/r. \tag{30.14}$$

Now, the centrifugal force of an electron is given by $m_e v^2/r$, which is equal to the force F exerted on the electron by the magnetic field. Since in the case under consideration, the angle between the direction of magnetic flux and direction of motion of electrons is $90°$, we have

$$F = HQ_e v \sin 90°$$

$$= HQ_e v, \tag{30.15}$$

where H is the magnetic flux density.

Now, as discussed above, we may write,

$$\frac{m_e v^2}{r} = HQ_e v$$

i.e., $$r = \frac{m_e v}{HQ_e}. \tag{30.16}$$

Substituting the value of r from equation (30.16) in Eq. (30.14), we get

$$d = Dl \cdot \frac{HQ_e}{m_e v}, \tag{30.17}$$

so that the magnetic deflection sensitivity,

$$S_m = \frac{d}{H} = Dl \cdot \frac{Q_e}{m_e} \cdot \frac{1}{v}. \tag{30.18}$$

Using Eq. (30.2), this may be expressed alternatively in terms of final anode potential V_a as

$$S_m = Dl \frac{Q_e}{m_e} \sqrt{\frac{m_e}{2Q_e V_a}}$$

$$= Dl \sqrt{\frac{Q_e}{2m_e V_a}}. \tag{30.19}$$

Eq. (30.19) shows that the deflection sensitivity is directly proportional to the square root of the ratio of the charge to mass of an electron but inversely proportional to the square root of the final anode potential.

30.6   Power Supply

In a CR tube, the final anode potential is generally of the order of 1000 to 2000 volts. In television and radar circuits, however, much higher anode potentials are required and so the power supply in such cases must be designed accordingly.

In practice, the final anode is often kept at the earth potential while a negative voltage is applied to the other electrode of the CR tube. This avoids the danger of electrical shock which may come if the final anode is kept at a high positive voltage as this terminal is frequently required to be handled during the study of waveforms, etc., using a CRO.

30.7   Time Base or Sweep Circuits

On the front panel of a cathode-ray oscillograph, there are various d.c. voltage controls which are named as : (i) focus control, (ii) intensity control, (iii) horizontal position control and (iv) vertical position control. Using these controls, the beam is first focused to a spot and then it can be placed at any desired position on the screen.

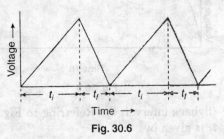

Fig. 30.6

In addition to all these d.c. voltage controls, a source of sweep voltage is internally provided. The waveform of this sweep generator output is of the shape of saw-tooth, as shown in Fig. 30.6, and so this voltage is termed as *saw-tooth voltage*. As seen from the figure, the voltage during each cycle increases linearly with time up to t_i and then falls to zero in a shorter time t_f. Using a switch the saw-tooth generator may be connected to the horizontal deflecting plates. In the most common form, since the deflection of the spot in the horizontal direction (or vertical or sometimes circular) is proportional to time, it is called *time base*, and the retracing time t_f is known as the *flyback time*. Some common types of time base circuits are : (i) Neon time base, (ii) Puckle's hard valve time base, (iii) Thyratron time base, etc. Out of these the neon time base is discussed in the next subsection.

30.7.1   Neon Time Base

The property of neon tube is applied in a neon time base circuit. It has been found that a neon tube conducts at a definite potential called the *striking potential*. But, if that potential is gradually reduced, a stage is reached called *extinguishing potential*, when the conduction by ionisation ceases.

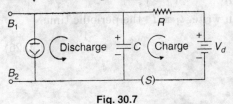

Fig. 30.7

This behaviour is important in the operation of neon time base. A basic neon time base circuit is shown in Fig. 30.7. In the figure, a voltage source V_d is connected with a high resistance R and a capacitor C. When the battery circuit is made on, the voltage V_c across the capacitor increases exponentially with time by a relation,

$$V_c = V_d(1 - \epsilon^{-t/CR}),\tag{30.20}$$

where t is the time in seconds.

Neglecting smaller terms we can write,

$$V_c = \frac{V_d t}{CR}.\tag{30.21}$$

Eq. (30.21) shows that the voltage across the condenser V_c is approximately proportional to the time. The value of V_c depends on the time constant CR of the charging circuit. When the value of CR is low, the rate of charging becomes more

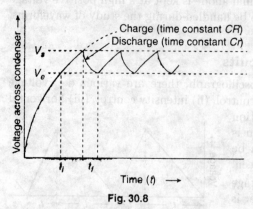

Fig. 30.8

rapid. At the striking potential, neon tube starts to conduct and its resistance decreases to a very small value, say r ohms. The condenser C then discharges exponentially through the neon tube with a time constant Cr. The charging and discharging curves of a condenser is shown in Fig. 30.8. Since the value of r is small, the discharge of condenser becomes more rapid.

The time period T of a neon time base potential is the sum of time of charge t_i, and time of discharge (flyback interval) t_f. Referring to Fig. 30.8, the extinguishing potential V_e at time t_i is given by

$$V_e = V_d(1 - \epsilon^{-t_i/CR}) \qquad (30.22)$$

or,
$$\frac{V_e}{V_d} = 1 - \epsilon^{-t_i/CR}$$

or,
$$\epsilon^{-t_i/CR} = 1 - \frac{V_e}{V_d} = \frac{V_d - V_e}{V_d} \qquad (30.23)$$

and the striking potential V_s at time t_f is

$$V_s = V_d(1 - \epsilon^{-t_f/CR}) \qquad (30.24)$$

or,
$$\epsilon^{-t_f/CR} = 1 - \frac{V_s}{V_d} = \frac{V_d - V_s}{V_d}. \qquad (30.25)$$

Dividing Eq. (30.23) by Eq. (30.30), we get

$$\epsilon^{(t_f-t_i)/CR} = \frac{V_d - V_e}{V_d - V_s} \quad \text{or,} \quad \frac{t_i}{CR} = \log_\epsilon \frac{V_d - V_e}{V_d - V_s}.$$

Since t_f is small compared to t_i, we can write, $t_i \simeq T$, the periodic time.

Hence, $T = CR \log_\epsilon \dfrac{V_d - V_e}{V_d - V_s}$ \hfill (30.26)

or, the frequency, $f = \dfrac{1}{T}$

$$= \frac{1}{CR \log_\epsilon \frac{V_d - V_e}{V_d - V_s}}. \qquad (30.27)$$

It may be noted here that the sweep-voltage curve departs considerably from linearity in a neon time base circuit. This is achieved by utilizing the constant current property of a pentode.

30.8   Frequency and Phase Measurements

If suitable alternating voltages are applied to the two sets of deflection plates of a CRO, various patterns may be obtained on the screen in the form of closed loop or straight line. These figures are known as 'Lissajous Figures'. If v_x and v_y are the two instantaneous voltages applied to the x and y plates, we can write,

$$v_x = V_x \sin \omega_x t \qquad (30.28)$$

and $v_y = V_y \sin(\omega_y t + \alpha)$, \hfill (30.29)

where V_x and V_y are the voltage amplitudes; ω_x, ω_y are the angular frequencies and α is the phase angle for v_y voltage. By adjusting all these parameters the so-called 'Lissajous Figures' are obtained on the screen. Some typical conditions are discussed below.

Condition 1

When $\omega_x = \omega_y$ and $\alpha = 0$,

then equations (30.28) and (30.29) reduce to

$$v_y = \frac{V_y}{V_x} v_x, \qquad (30.30)$$

which is the equation of a straight line passing through the origin in Fig. 30.9(a).

Condition 2

When $\omega_x = \omega_y$ and $\alpha = \frac{\pi}{2}$,

then the Eqs. (30.28) and (30.29) reduce to

$$\frac{v_x^2}{V_x^2} + \frac{v_y^2}{V_y^2} = 1, \qquad (30.31)$$

which is the equation of an ellipse as shown in Fig. 30.9(b).

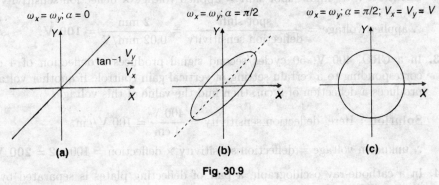

Fig. 30.9

Condition 3

When $\omega_x = \omega_y$, $\alpha = \frac{\pi}{2}$ and $V_x = V_y = V$,

then the Eqs. (30.28) and (30.29) reduce to

$$v_x^2 + v_y^2 = V^2, \qquad (30.32)$$

which is the equation of a circle as shown in Fig. 30.9(c).

In order to measure the frequencies of an alternating voltage, it is applied to one set of deflection plates while at the other set sinusoidal voltage is applied from a variable frequency standard oscillator which is properly calibrated. The oscillator is allowed to work for sometime to get a stabilized temperature and then the frequency of this oscillator is altered until a single loop stationary pattern is obtained. Now, the frequency of the oscillator voltage is noted from the calibrated dial of the oscillator which is equal to the frequency of the alternating voltage applied.

To measure relative phase angle of two alternating voltages of identical amplitude and frequency, they are

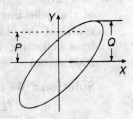

Fig. 30.10

applied to the x and y deflection plates of a CRO. Usually, an ellipse is obtained on the screen from which values of P and Q are noted, as illustrated in Fig. 30.10, and then the phase angle α is calculated by using the relation,

$$\alpha = \sin^{-1}(P/Q). \tag{30.33}$$

Examples

1. If the deflection sensitivity of a cathode-ray tube is 0.01 mm/V, calculate the shift produced in the spot when 300 V is applied to the vertical plates.

   Solution : Since the voltage is applied only to the vertical plates, so the spot will be shifted vertically.

   Now, spot shift = applied voltage × deflection sensitivity

   $$= 300 \times 0.01 = \textbf{3 mm}.$$

2. The deflection sensitivity of a cathode-ray tube is 0.02 mm/V, when an unknown voltage is applied to the horizontal plates, the spot shifts 2 mm horizontally. Determine the value of the unknown voltage.

   Solution : We know, spot shift = applied voltage × deflection sensitivity

   $$\therefore \text{ applied voltage} = \frac{\text{spot shift}}{\text{deflection sensitivity}} = \frac{2 \text{ mm}}{0.02 \text{ mm/V}} = \textbf{100 V}.$$

3. In a CRO, 400 V, 50 cycles/second signal produces a deflection of 4 cm corresponding to a certain setting of vertical gain control. If another voltage produces a deflection of 2 cm, then find the value of this voltage.

   Solution : Here, deflection sensitivity $= \dfrac{400 \text{ V}}{4 \text{ cm}} = 100 \text{ V/cm}.$

   $\therefore$ unknown voltage = deflection sensitivity × deflection $= 100 \times 2 = \textbf{200 V}.$

4. In a cathode-ray oscillograph, a pair of deflecting plates is separated by a distance of 0.5 cm. If the distance of the fluorescent screen from the centres of the plates is 36 cm, find the deflection sensitivity for a final anode voltage of 1000 volts.

   Solution : We have the deflection sensitivity, $S_e = \dfrac{lL}{2SV_a}.$

   Here, $l = 2.0$ cm, $S = 0.5$ cm, $L = 36$ cm, $V_a = 1000$ volts.

   $$\therefore \quad S_e = \frac{2 \times 36}{2 \times 0.5 \times 1000} \text{ cm/volt} = \textbf{0.072 cm/volt}.$$

5. In a cathode-ray oscillograph, the spacing of the plates is 0.5 cm, the length of the deflecting plates is 2.0 cm and the distance of the screen from the centre of the plates is 12 cm. Find the value of the displacement produced by a deflecting voltage of 30 volts. (Given that the final anode voltage = 2000 volts.)

   Solution : We have

   $$\frac{d}{V_d} = \frac{lL}{2SV_a} \quad \text{or,} \quad d = \frac{lL}{2SV_a} \cdot V_d.$$

Here, $l = 2.0$ cm, $S = 0.5$ cm, $L = 12$ cm, $V_d = 30$ volts, $V_a = 2000$ volts

$\therefore \qquad d = \dfrac{2 \times 12 \times 30}{2 \times 0.5 \times 2000}$ cm $= \mathbf{0.36}$ **cm**.

6. In a CRT having electric deflection system, the deflection plates are 2 cm long and have a uniform spacing of 4 mm between them. The fluorescent screen is 25 cm away from the centre of the deflection plates. If the potential of the final anode is 2000 V, find the deflection sensitivity in mm/volt.

Solution : Here we have

$l = 2$ cm $= 2 \times 10^{-2}$ m, $S = 4$ mm $= 4 \times 10^{-3}$ m

$L = 25$ cm $= 25 \times 10^{-2}$ m, $V_a = 2000$ V.

$\therefore$ deflection sensitivity,

$$S_e = \frac{lL}{2SV_a} = \frac{2 \times 10^{-2} \times 25 \times 10^{-2}}{2 \times 4 \times 10^{-3} \times 2000}$$

$$= 3.125 \times 10^{-4} \text{ m/V} = \mathbf{0.3125 \ mm/V}.$$

7. In a cathode-ray oscillograph, a sinusoidal voltage $30 \sin 2\pi \times 100\,t$ is applied to the Y-deflection plates and the time base voltage is applied to the X-deflection plates. What should be the frequency of the time base if two complete sine waves are required to be seen on the screen?

If the above time base voltage is required to get from a neon time base, find approximately the value of the charging resistance that should be used. It is given that,

supply voltage to the time base $= 200$ volts d.c., striking voltage $= 170$ volts, extinguishing voltage $= 140$ volts, and charging capacitor $= 0.02$ μF.

Solution : Here, periodic time of the sine wave $= \dfrac{1}{100}$ second.

So, to get two complete sine waves, the periodic time of time base

$$= 2 \times \frac{1}{100} \text{ second} = \frac{1}{50} \text{ second.}$$

$\therefore$ the frequency, $f = 50$ Hz.

Again, we have

$$f = \frac{1}{CR \log_e \frac{V_d - V_e}{V_d - V_s}}.$$

Putting the values given,

$$50 = \frac{1}{R \times 0.02 \times 10^{-6} \times 2.3 \log_{10} \frac{200-140}{200-170}}$$

$$= \frac{10^6}{R \times 0.046 \times \log_{10} 2}$$

or, $\quad R = \dfrac{10^6}{50 \times 0.046 \times \log_{10} 2} = 1.442 \times 10^6 \ \Omega = \mathbf{1.442 \ M\Omega}.$

Questions

Essay-type

1. What are the uses of a cathode-ray oscillograph? What are its essential components?

2. Describe briefly the construction of a cathode-ray tube.

3. Obtain expressions for the electrostatic and magnetic deflection sensitivities of a CR tube.

4. What is a sweep circuit? Explain its function.

5. Define 'time base' and 'flyback time'. Give names of some common time base circuits.

6. Discuss briefly with necessary diagrams the operation of a neon time base circuit.

7. Neglecting the flyback period, obtain an expression for the frequency of a neon time base.

8. What are 'Lissajous Figures'? How are these obtained on the screen?

9. How can the frequency and phase be determined experimentally?

Numerical Problems

10. In a cathode-ray oscillograph, the pair of deflecting plates is 2 cm long and separated by a distance of 0.5 cm. The distance of the screen from the centre of the plate is 9 cm. Calculate the deflection sensitivity in cm/volt for an anode voltage of 500 volts.   [**Ans.** 0.036 cm/volt]

11. A cathode-ray tube has a magnetic deflection field of flux density 10.35×10^{-5} weber/sq. metre and the distance from the end of the field to the screen is 24 cm. If the length of the field along the axis is 4 cm, calculate the final anode voltage in volts to produce a deflection of 1.2 cm on the screen.

[**Ans.** 600 volts]

12. In a CR tube with electric deflection system, the deflection plates are 2 cm long and have a uniform spacing of 4 mm between them. The fluorescent screen is kept at a distance of 25 cm away from the centre of the deflection plates. Determine the deflection sensitivity in mm/volt, if final anode potential is (i) 100 volts and (ii) 3500 volts. [**Ans.** (i) 0.625 mm/V, (ii) 0.1785 mm/V]

13. The deflection plates in a CR tube are 3 cm long and are separated by a distance of 0.5 cm. The distance of the screen from the centre of the plates is 24 cm and the potential of the final anode is 1200 volts. If a voltage of 40 volts is applied between the deflection plates, then determine (i) the velocity of the electrons on reaching the screen, (ii) time taken by an electron to travel through the deflection plates and (iii) deflection sensitivity.

[**Ans.** (i) 20.65×10^6 m/sec, (ii) 1.46 nsec, (iii) 0.6 mm/V]

14. In a cathode-ray oscillograph, the pair of deflecting plates is 2 cm long and separated by a distance of 0.5 cm. The distance of the screen from the centre of the plate is 9 cm. Calculate the deflection sensitivity in cm/volt for an anode voltage of 500 volts.   [**Ans.** 0.036 cm/volt]

15. A cathode-ray tube has a magnetic deflection field of flux density 10.35×10^{-5} weber/sq. metre and the distance from the end of the field to the screen is 24 cm. If the length of the field along the axis is 4 cm, calculate the final anode voltage in volts to produce a deflection of 1.2 cm on the screen.

[**Ans.** 600 volts]

16. In a CR tube with magnetic deflection system, the screen is 26 cm away from the centre of the deflection coils. The length of the uniform magnetic field along the axis is 4 cm. If a deflection of 2 cm is required on the screen, find the amount of magnetic flux density required for the final anode voltage of 1500 volts. Calculate also the deflection sensitivity.

[**Ans.** 2.51×10^{-4} weber/m^2; 79.9 m/(weber/m^2)]

17. In a CR tube, kept with its axis vertical, the final anode voltage is 1000 volts and the screen is at a distance of 20 cm from it. Determine the deflection of the spot on the screen due to the earth's magnetic field, horizontal component being 2.5×10^{-5} weber/m^2. [**Ans.** 4.68 mm]

18. A cathode-ray tube employs a magnetic field which runs for a distance of 3.5 cm along the axis and is placed 26 cm from the screen. Calculate the magnetic flux density required to produce a deflection 1.6 cm on the screen using the final anode voltage of 450 volts. [**Ans.** 1.258×10^{-4} weber/m^2]

Chapter 31
Radio Communication

31.1 Introduction

Our music or speech is usually in the form of low-frequency waves lying in the audio frequency range of 0–15 kHz approximately which cannot be transmitted directly at a long distance. For transmission of intelligence or message from one place to

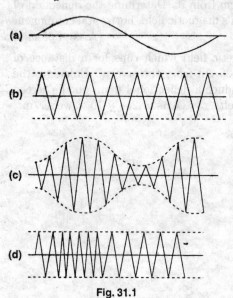

Fig. 31.1

another we have to take the help of high-frequency or radio-frequency waves. Such a process of raising the frequency of the intelligence or the message by superposition over high-frequency voltage is known as *modulation*. Or, briefly, we may define modulation as a process of superposing information on a radio-carrier wave. Thus it is seen that the process of modulation arose due to the human desire to establish communication over a long path. On the other hand, the reverse process of translating back the information from the radio wave to the original frequency is called *demodulation* or *detection*.

To illustrate the phenomena more explicitly, let us consider the waveforms of Fig. 31.1. Here Fig. 31.1(a) reveals the electrical equivalent of a single musical tone which is simply an a.c. sine wave of the corresponding frequency while an RF carrier wave of constant amplitude and frequency is shown in Fig. 31.1(b). In Fig. 31.1(c), the RF carrier is being amplitude-modulated by the AF wave so that the amplitudes of both the half cycles vary in accordance with the audio signal. In (d) of Fig. 31.1 finally, the frequency of the carrier is varied according to the amplitude of the AF signal. Note that if the positive amplitude of the audio wave is higher, the greater is the frequency of the RF carrier.

In 1865, Prof. C. Maxwell, an English scientist, first predicted the existence of the electromagnetic (radio) waves which was later verified by a German scientist H. Hertz in 1887 using a simple transmitter and a detector. A more sophisticated communication system for a distance of about 2 miles sent out the first radio telegraphy messages in 1896. Continued research on the science of radio communication system was started from 1901, but the progress was very slow and erratic until the invention of the crystal detector and the triode valve by Lee de Forest in 1907.

Present radio communication system consists of either modulation of radio waves by speech or music, called *radio telephony* or *continuous radio waves* (CW) with a telegraphic code, known as *radio telegraphy*.

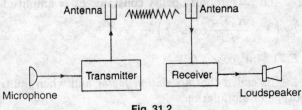

Fig. 31.2

The basic elements of a radio communication system are shown in Fig. 31.2. The elements are : (i) a microphone or a telegraph key to control the radio waves, (ii) a transmitter for generation of radio waves, (iii) a transmitting antenna and a receiving antenna, (iv) a radio receiver to select, amplify and demodulate the information present in radio waves, and (v) a loudspeaker or a headphone to convert the electrical waves into sound.

31.2 Types of Modulation

The equation of an alternating voltage may be accurately written as

$$e = A_m \cos\theta, \tag{31.1}$$

where A_m is the amplitude and

$$\theta = \int \omega dt + \phi \quad \left(\because \text{ angular velocity } \omega = \frac{d\theta}{dt} \right).$$

So we can write equation (31.1) as

$$e = A_m \cos\left(\int \omega dt + \phi \right), \tag{31.2}$$

where the constant of integration ϕ is the phase angle.

Eq. (31.2) clearly shows that the a.c. wave has two parameters which may be varied or modulated. These parameters are (i) the amplitude and (ii) the angle, causing the following two basic types of modulation :

(a) Variation of amplitude A_m with time, giving the amplitude modulation (AM),

(b) Variation of the angle with time, giving the angle modulation which has two subgroups, viz. (i) variation of $\int \omega dt$ with time resulting frequency modulation (FM) and (ii) variation of ϕ, the phase angle, with time resulting phase modulation (PM).

31.3 Analysis of Modulation

(a) **Amplitude Modulation :** For this case, the angular velocity ω is a constant factor at ω_c, where ω_c is the so-called carrier frequency. Eq. (31.2) can then be written as

$$e = A_m \cos(\omega_c t + \phi). \tag{31.3}$$

Let the signal or the modulating voltage is expressed as

$$e_m = E_m \cos\omega_m t, \tag{31.4}$$

where E_m is the amplitude and ω_m is the angular frequency of the signal.

Now, the amplitude A_m should vary as

$$A_m = E_c + K_a E_m \cos \omega_m t$$

(K_a = proportionality constant, E_c = amplitude of the carrier)

$$= E_c \left(1 + \frac{K_a E_m}{E_c} \cos \omega_m t \right)$$

$$= E_c (1 + m_a \cos \omega_m t), \tag{31.5}$$

where $m_a = \frac{K_a E_m}{E_c}$ is called the *modulation factor* and when multiplied by 100, it gives the percentage of modulation.

The complete expression for the amplitude-modulated voltage is now written as

$$e = E_c (1 + m_a \cos \omega_m t) \cos \omega_c t. \tag{31.6}$$

The constant phase term ϕ has been neglected here as it has no importance in this process.

(b) **Frequency Modulation :** For this case, the angular velocity ω may be expressed as

$$\omega = \omega_0 + K_f E_m \cos \omega_m t, \tag{31.7}$$

where the centre frequency, $f_0 = \frac{\omega_0}{2\pi}$ and K_f = degree of frequency variation.

Use of Eq. (31.2) then gives,

$$e = E_c \sin \int (\omega_0 + K_f E_m \cos \omega_m t) dt + \phi$$

or, $$e = E_c \sin \left(\omega_0 t + \frac{K_f E_m}{\omega_m} \sin \omega_m t \right). \tag{31.8}$$

The integration constant ϕ is again dropped as a constant angle.

The frequency-modulated voltage in Eq. (31.8) can alternately be written as

$$e = E_c \sin(\omega_0 t + \delta \sin \omega_m t), \tag{31.9}$$

where $\delta = \frac{K_f E_m}{\omega_m}$ is called the *deviation ratio*.

(c) **Phase Modulation :** For this case, ω is a constant factor at ω_0. Eq. (31.2) then gives the form,

$$e = E_c \sin(\omega_0 t + \psi), \tag{31.10}$$

where the angle ψ may be given time variation as

$$\psi = \psi_0 + K_p E_m \cos \omega_m t. \tag{31.11}$$

Here K_p relates the phase angle variation with the signal amplitude and is called *proportionality constant*.

From equation (31.10) substituting the value of ψ we have

$$e = E_c \sin(\omega_0 t + \psi_0 + K_p E_m \cos \omega_m t). \tag{31.12}$$

Neglecting the constant phase angle ψ_0, the general expression for a phase-modulated voltage is written as

$$e = E_c \sin(\omega_0 t + \psi_d \cos \omega_m t). \tag{31.13}$$

In Eq. (31.13), $\psi_d = K_p E_m$ is called the *phase deviation*. It is interesting to note that the expressions for frequency and phase modulations obtained in Eqs. (31.9) and (31.13) differ in the coefficients δ and ψ_d and also in a $90°$ shift in the modulation phase angle.

31.4 Sidebands and Energy Consideration

Both amplitude and frequency modulation systems serve well the basic function of communication. However, AM is more widely used due to its greater power output, simplicity of operation, etc. We shall here confine our attention only to the case of amplitude modulation.

We have found that the equation for an amplitude-modulated wave may be written as

$$e = E_c(1 + m_a \cos \omega_m t) \cos \omega_c t,$$

where $\quad \cos \omega_m t \cos \omega_c t = \dfrac{1}{2}[\cos(\omega_c + \omega_m)t + \cos(\omega_c - \omega_m)t].$

$\therefore \qquad e = E_c \cos \omega_c t + \dfrac{m_a E_c}{2}[\cos(\omega_c + \omega_m)t + \cos(\omega_c - \omega_m)t]. \qquad (31.14)$

Eq. (31.14) shows that in an amplitude-modulated wave there are altogether three frequencies. The first one is the original carrier frequency ω_c while the other two are the algebraic sum and difference of the carrier and modulation frequencies known as the *upper side frequency* and *lower side frequency* respectively. The width $\Delta\omega$ of the modulated wave is, therefore, given by

$$\Delta\omega = (\omega_c + \omega_m) - (\omega_c - \omega_m)$$

$$= 2\omega_m. \qquad (31.15)$$

Thus we see that the required bandwidth for transmission of an amplitude-modulated signal is twice the highest modulating frequency.

Again, from Eq. (31.14), it appears that for both the sidebands the amplitude is $m_a/2$ times the carrier amplitude. Since power is directly proportional to the square of the voltage, we have

$$\text{carrier power} = \frac{KE_c^2}{2} = P_c$$

and total sideband power $= 2\dfrac{Km_a^2 E_c^2}{8} = \text{carrier power} \times \dfrac{m_a^2}{2}.$

$\therefore$ total power in a modulated wave = carrier power + total sideband power

$$= \frac{KE_c^2}{2}\left(1 + \frac{m_a^2}{2}\right)$$

$$= P_c\left(1 + \frac{m_a^2}{2}\right). \qquad (31.16)$$

31.5 Radio Transmitters

Radio transmitters may be broadly classified according to the (a) type of modulation used, (b) carrier frequency involved and (c) service processes involved.

According to modulation : There are amplitude, frequency and phase modulation transmitters.

According to carrier frequency : Long, medium and short wave transmitters, VHF and UHF transmitters and microwave transmitters.

According to service processes : Radio broadcast, radio telephone and telegraph, television, radar and navigational transmitters.

31.5.1 AM Radio Transmitter

An AM radio transmitter using modulation at high carrier power level is discussed here briefly.

A block diagram of the transmitter is given in Fig. 31.3, which consists essentially (i) a master oscillator, (ii) a number of frequency multipliers, (iii) several power amplifiers and (iv) modulating system.

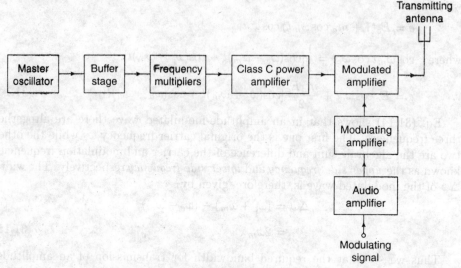

Fig. 31.3

The master oscillator generates oscillation at a desired frequency which is kept constant within a very close limit. If the frequency of the oscillator becomes less than the desired carrier frequency of the transmitter the frequency multiplier stages, called *harmonic generators*, are used to get it. In order to isolate the harmonic generators from the master oscillator, a buffer stage is used as shown, so that the variation of load, if any, may not affect the oscillator.

The RF voltage thus generated by the oscillator has a low power which is raised to a sufficiently high value by a chain of class *C* amplifiers and is then modulated by using usually series plate modulation of high efficiency. At low power levels, however, grid bias modulation and suppressor grid modulation are also used sometimes.

The modulating amplifier, generally a class *B* pushpull type, feeds audio power into the modulated amplifier which is finally connected to the transmitting antenna, as shown.

31.6 Antenna

We have already seen that in order to radiate or receive electromagnetic waves successfully an antenna is required. The antenna, popularly known as *aerial*, is a system of elevated conductors. A transmitting antenna radiates power from a transmitter in all directions or in some definite directions while a receiving antenna intercepts a part of that electromagnetic energy travelling through the atmosphere.

From the famous Maxwell's theory, we know that the accelerated electric charges (i.e., electrons) always radiate energy in the form of electromagnetic waves whose electric and magnetic fields travel at right angles to each other. The orientation of the electric field with respect to earth is called *polarisation*. Accordingly, if the plane of the electric field is oriented horizontally, it is said to be horizontally polarised while if the field is vertical with respect to earth, the wave is said to be vertically polarised. Obviously, the wave polarisation is basically a function of the antenna orientation.

31.7 Receiving Antenna

In principle, the design and shape of both the transmitting and receiving antennas are same. However, because of space restrictions, the receiving antenna has usually a convenient length or loop of wire in practice.

31.7.1 Characteristics

Characteristics of an ideal receiving antenna are : (i) it receives all the desired signal efficiently, (ii) it has an omnidirectional characteristic for long, medium and short wave receptions while for VHF and UHF reception directional properties are utilized, (iii) with change of signal frequency, it has small variation of terminal impedance and (iv) it should minimise interference effect due to house wiring, etc., and also fading characteristics.

31.7.2 Classification

The receiving aerials may be either indoor or outdoor type. The indoor aerial has a comparatively poor pick-up and its terminal impedance has large resistive and capacitive components. The outdoor aerials are of the following types : (a) vertical aerial, (b) inverted-L aerial, (c) T-aerial and (d) dipole aerial.

Vertical aerial

It is easy to construct. This aerial receives only vertically polarized transmission and so minimizes distortion and fading which may be caused by obliquely, circularly or elliptically polarized transmission. Hence for reception of medium and long waves it is often preferred to inverted-L aerial.

Inverted-L aerial

It has a long horizontal top with a vertical lead-in wire. The horizontal top influences both the terminal impedance and total induced voltage in the aerial. The horizontal portion also adds a capacitance between the top of the vertical section and the earth. This capacitance for a vertically polarized incident wave becomes more effective for the voltage induced in the vertical section.

The disadvantage of the aerial is that it collects both horizontally and vertically polarized components of the incident electromagnetic wave. The components, as a result, get a random phase relation and so tend to cause distortion and fading.

T-aerial

The operation of the T-aerial is little different from that of an inverted-L aerial. The horizontal section, divided into two parts, in a T-aerial serves as a capacitor to the earth and thus increases the effective height. The balanced horizontal top is used to cancel the horizontally polarized wave coming at right angles to the aerial top. As far as other directions are concerned, the horizontally polarized wave will provide sufficiently less pick-up in comparison to an inverted-L aerial.

It is to be noted that both the T- and inverted-L aerials are used mainly for medium- and long-wave reception but are not suitable enough for short-waves. At short-wave reception, when the aerial length becomes approximately $\lambda/4$, it forms resonance which causes serious mistuning and damping in the first tuned circuit.

Dipole aerial

The dipole aerial consists of two equal lengths of open wire connected to the receiver by a feeder. The two wires are at 180° with each other and they are kept in the same plane.

Reflectors and directors may be used in a dipole aerial to increase the directivity. The reflector is made slightly longer than the dipole and is usually spaced $\lambda/4$ from the dipole and parallel while the director is made slightly shorter than the dipole and spaced $\lambda/8$ apart and parallel.

To increase the impedance of the dipole, it is folded. A folded dipole, in fact, has an impedance four times greater than that of a simple dipole.

The aerial described above is very useful for short-wave reception. Since in a short-wave communication, the radio waves coming from the ionosphere has an appreciable horizontally polarized component which induces the desired voltage in the horizontal dipole. Besides, when erected horizontally, the aerial is balanced to the earth and so cancelling the local interference effect.

31.8   Propagation of Electromagnetic Waves

We know that the radio frequency energy in the form of electromagnetic waves travels outward from a transmitting antenna with a velocity of 186 000 miles per second. These waves can easily penetrate non-metallic objects but are little influenced by the disturbed weather, like rain, snow, etc. They are supposed to travel best in a free space or in a vacuum and no medium is necessary for its propagation.

Several ways are there for the propagation of electromagnetic waves from a transmitting to a receiving antenna. The most important of these are : (i) ground or surface wave, (ii) space or tropospheric wave and (iii) sky wave.

In ground-wave propagation, the electromagnetic waves are guided by the surface of the earth and follow a curved surface from the transmitting to the receiving antenna. Obviously, the propagation in this case is controlled by the radio frequency characteristics of the ground, like conductivity, dielectric constant, etc. Ground-wave propagation is utilized suitably in the MF band (300 kHz–3000 kHz) where field intensities are obtained up to a distance of a few hundred miles and the vertical antenna radiates in all directions equally. So this wave has practical importance for local radio broadcasts.

In space-wave propagation, the e.m. waves travel within the first 10 miles over the earth's surface, i.e., in the earth's troposphere either directly through the space or after reflection from the ground. Space-wave propagation becomes important in the VHF band from 30 MHz.

With contributions from the ground-reflected wave, TV and FM signals are transmitted in this way. UHF transmission also takes place by utilizing the space wave.

In sky-wave propagation, the e.m. waves come to the receiving antenna by reflection from the ionized upper atmosphere known as ionosphere. Obviously, the propagation in this case is controlled by the reflecting property of the ionized upper atmosphere which has erratic changes with night and day atmospheric conditions and seasons. The sky-wave propagation is the primary method of short-wave communication around the world.

31.8.1 The Ionosphere

It is well known by now that the layers of ionized particles, called collectively as the *ionosphere*, are created due to various strong radiations coming from the sun. During day time, both electrons and ions are formed at different heights about 60 km above the ground while at night they recombine. In Fig 31.4, the variations of electron density with height at day and night time are shown by solid and dotted lines respectively. The figure shows that during day time D-, E-, F_1- and F_2-layers are formed while at night the D-layer is absent, and the F_1- and F_2-layers merge together to create a night time F-layer. Above the F_2-layer, the electron density decreases exponentially with height, as shown.

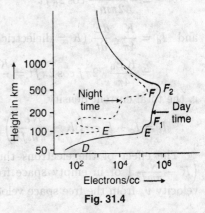

Fig. 31.4

The maximum electron densities and the corresponding heights of different ionospheric layers are required to know for a successful design of the communication link. A close observation of Fig. 31.4 reveals that during day time, D- and E-layers are situated at 60 km and 100 km respectively whose corresponding electron densities are 10^4 and 10^5 electrons/cc. The height of the F_1-layer is about 200 km with an electron density of twice the E-layer, while the F_2-layer is situated at about 300 km with a maximum electron density of 10^6 electrons/cc. At night, the electron density of the E-layer decreases by a factor of 10 from its day-time value. For the F-layer also which is formed by the combination of F_1- and F_2-layers at such times it decreases by the same factor from the value of the F_2-layer.

31.8.2 Basic Equation of Electromagnetic Wave

Let us consider after Eccles and Larmor the basic equation of an electromagnetic wave that travels through an ionized medium containing N electrons per cc each of charge e and m. We shall neglect here the effect of collision and also assume the absence of any external magnetic field.

Let the electric field of fluctuating intensity associated with the e.m. wave is

$$E = E_0 \sin \omega t$$

$$= E_0 \sin 2\pi ft \quad (\because \text{ angular frequency, } \omega = 2\pi f), \tag{31.17}$$

where E_0 is the amplitude of the wave and f is its frequency.

The electron will vibrate under the action of the electric field whose equation of motion is

$$m\frac{dv}{dt} = E_0 e \sin 2\pi ft.$$

Integrating, $v = -\dfrac{E_0 e}{2\pi mf} \cos 2\pi ft,$ \hfill (31.18)

where the constant of integration is made zero by a proper choice of the phase.

The motion of electrons produces a conduction current density I_c and a displacement current density I_d, where

$$I_c = Nev$$

[N = number of free electrons per unit volume at any point in the medium]

$$= -\frac{E_0 Ne^2}{2\pi mf} \cos 2\pi ft \tag{31.19}$$

and $\quad I_d = \dfrac{K}{4\pi} \cdot \dfrac{dE}{dt}$ (K = dielectric constant of the medium)

$$= \frac{KE_0}{4\pi} \cdot 2\pi f \cos 2\pi ft = \frac{KE_0}{2} f \cos 2\pi ft. \tag{31.20}$$

∴ the total current density,

$$I_t = I_c + I_d = \left(K - \frac{Ne^2}{\pi mf^2}\right) \frac{E_0 f}{2} \cos 2\pi ft. \tag{31.21}$$

The effect of the electrons thus reduces the dielectric constant from K to $\left(K - \frac{Ne^2}{\pi mf^2}\right)$ or in empty space from unity to $\left(1 - \frac{Ne^2}{\pi mf^2}\right)$ and alters the phase velocity v_p from the free space velocity c by

$$v_p = \frac{c}{\sqrt{1 - \frac{Ne^2}{\pi mf^2}}}. \tag{31.22}$$

The refractive index of the ionized layer is then given by

$$\mu = \frac{c}{v_p} = \sqrt{1 - \frac{Ne^2}{\pi mf^2}}. \tag{31.23}$$

If the wave is incident vertically on the ionized layer, then the angle of incidence $\phi_0 = 0$ and so the condition of total reflection is

$$\sin \phi_0 = \sin 0 = 0 = \sqrt{1 - \frac{Ne^2}{\pi mf^2}}$$

or, $\quad N = \dfrac{\pi mf^2}{e^2}. \tag{31.24}$

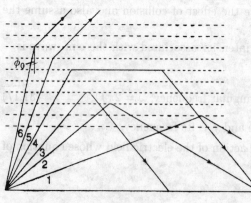

Fig. 31.5

Next, in order to explain the 'skip distance' and the 'maximum usable frequency', let us consider Fig. 31.5, where ray paths have been drawn for different angles of incidence ϕ_0. When ϕ_0 is relatively large (ray 1), the condition $\mu = \sin \phi_0$ is satisfied and the refractive index becomes slightly less than unity. Under such conditions, the wave returns to the earth after slight penetration of the ionized layer. But as ϕ_0 is decreased more and more (rays 2, 3 and 4), λ must be progressively smaller to return the wave and the penetration into the layer will be deeper. With further decrease of ϕ_0, the maximum electron density will be unable to reflect the wave and thus penetration occurs (rays 5, 6). Therefore, we see that as ϕ_0 decreases, the distance from the transmitter to the point where a ray returns to the ground first decreases (rays 1, 2) until we arrive at the angle of incidence ϕ_0 at which the distance becomes minimum (ray 3). This distance is called the 'skip distance' and the corresponding frequency of the sky wave is termed as the 'maximum usable frequency'(MUF). An ionospheric layer will, therefore, be unable to return a sky wave if the frequency of transmission becomes greater than the maximum usable frequency for that receiving point.

31.8.3 Fading

The signals received by a radio receiver depend on the ionospheric characteristics which are again influenced by night and day, seasons of the year and atmospheric conditions. The intensity of any signal coming after reflections from the ionosphere is often fluctuating in nature. The phenomenon of fluctuating field intensity is called *fading*. Fading is mostly occurred on short-wave band but also noticed sometimes on higher bands. The fluctuations in signal strength at a receiver may be due to several reasons :

(i) Fading may occur on short-wave band when radio waves after reflections from the ionospheric layers reach at a common receiving point. The field strength at the receiver at such times is the vector sum of the field intensities by the two rays. Most severe fading is noticed when the component intensities are of the same order.

(ii) Fading may occur due to interference between the direct ground wave and the indirect reflected wave received simultaneously at the receiver.

(iii) Since the variation in the length of the ray path through the ionosphere is a function of frequency, the carrier wave and the sideband components may combine differently causing a frequency distortion. This is known as *selective fading*.

31.9 Radio Receivers

A radio receiver picks up any RF signal through a receiving antenna and then recovers from it the original modulating signal. Radio receivers may be broadly classified as : (a) Amplitude Modulation (AM) broadcast receivers, (b) Frequency Modulation (FM) broadcast receivers, (c) Television (TV) receivers, (d) Radar receivers, (e) Communication receivers and (f) Code receivers.

The essential functions of a radio receiver are (i) to extract the desired RF signal from the electromagnetic waves, (ii) to amplify the RF signal, (iii) to demodulate the RF signal for getting back the original modulating voltage and (iv) to feed the modulating voltage in an indicator, like loudspeaker, etc., for receiving the original programme.

31.9.1 Broadcast Receivers

Both AM and FM broadcast receivers are usually used in home for entertainment purposes. The following characteristics of a broadcast receiver are of primary importance :

(i) **Adaptability to different aerials :** A receiver is to be designed in such a manner so that it can be applied to any type of aerial.

(ii) Operational simplicity : Since broadcast receivers are used by listeners with little technical knowledge, a simplicity of operation is desired. A receiver in its most elementary form, has therefore three controls. These are band switch, tuning control and volume control.

(iii) Good fidelity : Good fidelity of a receiver means a uniform frequency response over the entire audio frequency band. For an AM receiver the maximum modulating frequency is 5 kHz while for an FM receiver this is 15 kHz and so the latter gives a better fidelity.

(iv) Average sensitivity : The term sensitivity of a receiver is defined as the minimum input voltage necessary for producing a standard output voltage. A receiver should have reasonably high sensitivity to achieve good response over the low and medium strength signals. However, it should not be high enough since it will then pick up even the undesired disturbances.

(v) Good selectivity : By the term selectivity of a radio receiver is meant its ability to differentiate a desired signal of a particular frequency from other unwanted signals of slightly different in frequencies. Good selectivity depends on the sharpness of the resonance curves of different tuned circuits used in the receiver.

31.9.2   Types of AM Receivers

Depending on the techniques of operation, radio receivers are classified into two types. These are (i) straight receivers, which operate in a straight manner without frequency conversion and (ii) superheterodyne receiver, which convert AF signals to standard intermediate frequency before detection.

31.9.3   Straight Receivers

Let us first consider the operation of a simple crystal receiver which illustrates the basic principle of radio reception. A schematic diagram of the receiver is shown in hlFig. 31.6.   The electromagnetic waves radiated by the radio transmitters are picked up by the receiving antenna which is coupled to the L-C tank circuit through a step-up RF transformer where some amplification takes place. The tank circuit serves the purpose of signal selection which is rectified by a crystal of silicon (or carborundum, etc.) for converting

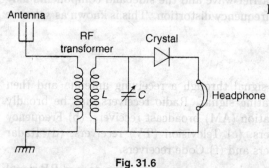

Fig. 31.6

the oscillatory current into unidirectional current. Finally, it acts on the diaphragm of the headphone and produces sound.

The crystal receiver has drawbacks of poor sensitivity and selectivity. Improvement in sensitivity is made by substituting the crystal by a vacuum tube. A typical vacuum tube receiver of this type is shown in Fig. 31.7. The vacuum tube along with $R_g C_g$ combination and bypass capacitor C_p removes the remaining RF components and keeps them out of the headphone. Though the sensitivity of this receiver is high enough but selectivity is considerably low which may be increased by using one or more tuned RF amplifier stages. Amplification in this manner to the tuned RF stages is called *tuned radio frequency amplification* and the receiver is called 'TRF receiver'. A block diagram of a TRF receiver is shown in Fig. 31.8. It has several stages of RF amplification with tuned tank circuit at the input of each stage, an AM detector and one or more AF amplifiers which are finally connected

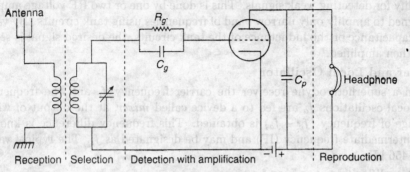

Fig. 31.7

to a loudspeaker. One major limitation here is that the selectivity of the receiver varies sufficiently with the variation of the signal frequency. With the increase of the frequency the selectivity is found to decrease. It may be noted that the TRF receiver though has enough selectivity but if too many tuned RF stages are used, the circuit becomes too selective and then reduces the fidelity of the receiver.

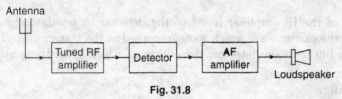

Fig. 31.8

31.9.4 Superheterodyne Receiver

Major Armstrong invented the superheterodyne receiver during the First World War. In this receiver all incoming carrier frequencies are converted to a fixed lower value, called the *intermediate frequency*, at which the amplifier circuits can operate with maximum stability, sensitivity and selectivity. Such conversion to the intermediate frequency (IF) is made by beating or heterodyning the carrier frequency against a locally generated frequency.

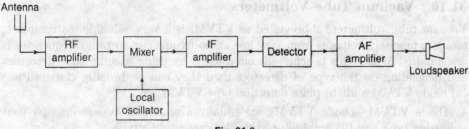

Fig. 31.9

A block diagram of the basic superheterodyne circuit is shown in Fig. 31.9. Functions of different stages are discussed below :

Antenna

It receives all the electromagnetic waves and the voltages so induced are communicated to the receiver input where a parallel tuned circuit responds only to voltage at the desired carrier frequency.

RF Amplifier

The voltage developed across the capacitor of the input tuned circuit needs to amplify for detecting weak signals. This is done by one or two RF voltage amplifiers designed to amplify only narrow band of frequencies using tank circuits. By varying the capacitance or the inductance of the tank circuits, the desired signal is selected and then amplified.

Mixer and Local Oscillator

In a superheterodyne receiver the carrier frequency f_c and the frequency of the local oscillations f_o are fed to a device called *mixer*, at the output of which a voltage of frequency $(f_c - f_o)$ is obtained. This frequency difference is known as the intermediate frequency (IF) and may be designated as f_i. The typical value of f_i is 456 kHz.

IF Amplifier

It consists of one or more stages of tuned voltage amplifier designed to amplify only a narrow band of frequencies around a fixed centre frequency. Since this centre frequency has a value intermediate between the radio and audio frequencies, the amplifier is designated as an IF amplifier. Most of the receiver amplifications and selectivity are provided by this IF amplifier.

Detector

Output of the IF amplifier is fed to the detector to separate the modulating signal from the carrier wave which was superposed at the transmitter. The detector is usually a linear diode detector, the output of which gives the audio frequency signal.

AF Amplifier

Since the audio frequency signal obtained at the output of the detector is of insufficient amplitude, it is fed to the AF amplifier to provide additional amplification. Generally, one stage of audio voltage amplifier is applied followed by one or more stages of audio power amplifier.

Loudspeaker

Through an impedance-matching transformer, the audio output voltage is fed to a loudspeaker which reproduces the original programme.

31.10   Vacuum Tube Voltmeters

Vacuum tube voltmeter, abbreviated as VTVM, is a very valuable instrument to measure precisely voltages from very low audio frequencies to radio frequencies of few hundred MHz. This is achieved conveniently by using vacuum tube detectors, and depending on the type of detectors used they can be broadly classified as : (a) diode VTVM and (b) plate detection type VTVM.

Diode VTVM—Diode VTVMs are usually available in two forms: (i) 'peak indicating type and (ii) amplifier-rectifier average reading type.

In the peak indicating type VTVM, similar to the diode detector shown in Fig. 31.10, the rectified d.c. voltage across CR_L combination is a measure of the peak amplitude of the input signal voltage. The average d.c. current flowing through R_L may be measured by connecting a sensitive current meter in series with it. The sensitivity of the VTVM is increased by amplifying the d.c. voltage developed across R_L. The sensitivity of the VTVM corresponds to a full-scale deflection with only a fraction input voltage. Signals up to several hundred MHz can be measured by such instrument. However, the only drawback is that it is very inconvenient to construct amplifiers with good gain and stability.

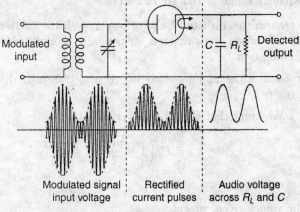

Modulated signal   Rectified   Audio voltage
input voltage   current pulses   across R_L and C

Fig. 31.10

In the average reading type VTVM, the a.c. signal to be measured is first applied and then it is rectified. The output thus obtained becomes proportional to the average amplitude of the signal and hence it is so named. The sensitivity of the VTVM depends on the gain of the amplifier which is stabilized by making negative feedback. The frequency range of the instrument is rather limited.

Plate detection type VTVM

The principle of this VTVM is similar to that of anode bend detectors. If the tube in Fig. 31.11 is biased to near cut-off value, there will be a small plate current in absence of any input signal. Under such condition, if the voltage to be measured is applied at the input, the average plate current increases as recorded by a current meter connected in the plate circuit. Signals of radio frequency ranges can be measured accurately by such instruments.

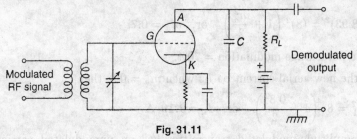

Fig. 31.11

Examples

1. The tuned circuit of an oscillator in an amplitude-modulated transmitter employs a 50-μH coil and a 0.001-μF capacitor. If the oscillator output is modulated up to 10000 c/s, what is the frequency range occupied by the carrier and sidebands?

Solution : Here, $L = 50 \ \mu\text{H} = 50 \times 10^{-6} \ \text{H}$

$$C = 0.001 \ \mu\text{F} = 0.001 \times 10^{-6} \ \text{F}$$

$$\therefore \quad f_c = \frac{1}{2\pi\sqrt{(LC)}} = \frac{1}{2\pi\sqrt{(50 \times 10^{-6} \times 0.001 \times 10^{-6})}} = 712 \ \text{kHz}.$$

So the sidebands are of frequencies $= 712 \pm 10$ kHz

or, the frequency range $= $ **702 to 722 kHz**.

2. A certain transmitter radiates 9 kW of power with the carrier unmodulated and 10.125 kW when the carrier is sinusoidally modulated. Calculate the depth of modulation.

If another audio wave modulated to 40% is also transmitted, determine the radiated power.

Solution : We know that the total power radiated

$$= P_c \left(1 + \frac{m_a^2}{2} \right),$$

where $P_c = $ carrier power.

Putting the values given, we get

$$10.125 = 9 \left(1 + \frac{m_a^2}{2} \right) \quad \text{or,} \quad m_a = 0.5.$$

$\therefore$ radiated power $= 9 \left[1 + \dfrac{(0.5)^2}{2} + \dfrac{(0.4)^2}{2} \right] = $ **10.845 kW**.

3. The aerial current of a transmitter is 8 A when the carrier only is transmitted, but it increases to 8.93 A when the carrier is sinusoidally modulated. Find the percentage modulation.

Determine the aerial current when the depth of modulation is 0.8.

Solution : Total power radiated $=$ carrier power $\left(1 + \dfrac{m_a^2}{2} \right)$.

Putting the values, we have

$$(8.93)^2 = (8)^2 \left(1 + \frac{m_a^2}{2} \right) \quad \text{or,} \quad m_a = 0.7.$$

$\therefore$ the percentage modulation $= 70\%$.

Let the new aerial current be I_1; when $m_a = 0.8$, then

$$I_1^2 = 8^2 \left(1 + \frac{0.8^2}{2} \right) \quad \text{or,} \quad I_1 = \textbf{9.19 A}.$$

4. An amplitude-modulated transmitter has an unmodulated carrier output power of 20 kW and can be modulated by a sinusoidal modulating voltage to a maximum depth of 60% without resulting in overloading. If the maximum modulation index is rectified to 40%, calculate the value to which unmodulated carrier power may be increased without causing overloading.

Solution : We have modulated carrier power, $P = P_c \left(1 + \dfrac{m_a^2}{2} \right)$.

Here, $P_c = 20$ kW, $m_a = 60\%$.

So, the maximum power which may be handled by the transmitter is

$$P = 20 \left(1 + \frac{0.6^2}{2} \right) = 23.6.$$

The increased unmodulated carrier power is then given by

$$23.6 = P'_c \left(1 + \frac{0.4^2}{2}\right) = P'_c \times 1.08.$$

$$\therefore \quad P'_c = \frac{23.6}{1.08} = \textbf{21.85 kW}.$$

5. For an ionospheric layer, the electron density varies with thickness as $N = N_0(1+0.02t)$ m^{-3}; where t is the thickness of the layer in kilometres measured from the bottom of the layer and $N_0 = 10^{11}$ m^{-3}. The layer starts at a height of 100 km above the ground. If a radio wave of frequency 3 MHz is incident vertically on this layer, find the height of the portion of the layer above the ground which will reflect the wave downward.

Solution : We have electron density,

$$N = \frac{f_c^2}{81} = \frac{(3 \times 10^6)^2}{81} = 1.11 \times 10^{11} \text{ m}^{-3}.$$

The corresponding thickness of the layer is obtained from

$$N = N_0(1 + 0.02t) \quad \text{or,} \quad 1.11 \times 10^{11} = 10^{11}(1 + 0.02t)$$

or, $t = 5.5$ km.

$\therefore$ the height of the portion of the layer above the ground is $h = 100 + 5.5 = $ **105.5 km**.

6. An e.m. wave is incident at an angle of 50° on an ionospheric layer with peak electron density of 7×10^{11} per m^3. Calculate the maximum frequency for which the wave will be received at the skip distance. Find the skip distance if the virtual height of reflection is 200 km.

Solution : We have $f_c = 9\sqrt{N_m} = 9\sqrt{7 \times 10^{11}} = 7.53$ MHz.

Again, $f = f_c \sec \phi = 7.53 \times 10^6 \sec 50° = 11.7$ MHz.

Skip distance $= 2$ (virtual height) $\tan \phi = 2 \times 200 \times \tan 50° = $ **477 km**.

Questions

Essay-type

1. What are modulation and demodulation? Classify their different types and explain.

2. What are the basic elements of a radio communication system?

3. What are the different types of radio transmitter you know? With a block diagram briefly explain an AM radio transmitter.

4. What is an antenna? Mention the important characteristics of an ideal receiving antenna.

5. Explain briefly the following :

   (a) Vertical aerial, (b) Inverted-L aerial, (c) T-aerial and (d) Dipole aerial.

6. How electromagnetic waves are propagated from a transmitting to a receiving antenna? Discuss briefly.

7. Write a note on the 'Ionosphere' explaining its different layers and the corresponding electron densities.

8. Establish the basic equation of electromagnetic wave. Explain, what is meant by 'skip distance' and 'MUF'.

9. How radio receivers can be classified? What are its essential functions? Mention the important characteristics of broadcast receivers.

10. Explain with circuit diagram, the operation of a straight receiver. What are its limitations?

11. With a suitable block diagram, discuss the different parts of a superheterodyne receiver.

Numerical Problems

12. A radio telephone transmitter using amplitude modulation has an unmodulated carrier output power of 20 kW and can be modulated to a maximum depth of 80% by a sinusoidal modulating voltage without causing overloading. Find the value to which unmodulated carrier power may be increased without resulting in overloading if the maximum permitted modulation index is restricted to 60 per cent. [**Ans. 22.38 kW**]

13. A sinusoidal carrier voltage of frequency 1 MHz and amplitude 80 V is amplitude-modulated by a sinusoidal voltage of frequency 6 kHz producing 40% modulation. Determine the frequency and amplitude of each sideband. [**Ans. 1006 kHz; 994 kHz; 16 volts**]

14. An amplitude-modulated amplifier drives an aerial. The r.m.s. aerial current before and after modulation is 5 A and 5.9 A respectively. Find the percentage modulation. If the unmodulated carrier power fed to the aerial is 2 kW, calculate the modulated carrier power. [**Ans. 80.31%; 2645 kW**]

15. Design an oscillator-tuned circuit containing only two present components for a receiver covering the frequency band 550 to 1500 kHz which has to be ganged with a signal circuit containing a 156-μH inductance coil. The intermediate frequency is 465 kHz.

　　　　[**Ans.** Padding capacitance = 288 pF; Tuning inductance = 117.3 μH]

16. The frequency-modulated wave, resulting from modulation by an audio-frequency wave of frequency $f_a = 5000$ c/s, has a frequency deviation of 50 kHz. If this wave when radiated produces an unmodulated field of 1 mV/m at a certain point, what is the strength of the carrier and the sidebands at the same point when the wave is modulated?

　　　[**Ans.** Carrier 240 μV/m; Sidebands 50 μV/m, 260 μV/m, 50 μV/m, etc.]

Chapter 32

Boolean Algebra and Logic Circuits

32.1 Introduction

A complete system of formal logic was constructed by Aristotle (384–322 BC). Mathematicians, for centuries afterward, attempted unsuccessfully to solve the logic problems using conventional algebra. George Boole (1815–1864) was the first who in 1854 developed a mathematical system of logic to arrive at a conclusion. His new system was not our familiar algebra but an algebra of logic. For example, according to him, $A + A = A$ and not $2A$ as in our known algebra. Boole's work remained in the realm of philosophy until 1938 when C. E. Shannon used Boole's algebraic system for solving relay logic problems.

32.2 Development of Boolean Algebra

Boolean algebra is considered as a system of mathematical logic which differs from both ordinary algebra and the binary number system. As for example, in Boolean, $1 + 1 = 1$ while in binary arithmetic the result is 10. Thus, Boolean algebra, though there are certain similarities, is a unique system.

In the Boolean system, there are two constants, viz., 0 and 1. There are no fractional or negative numbers. In fact, every number is expressed either by 0 or by 1. Thus, if $x = 1$, then $x \neq 0$ and if $x = 0$, then $x \neq 1$. The system of Boolean algebra is applied to the solution of electronic circuit involving only two possible states. The objectives of the use of Boolean algebra to any logic circuit are : (i) to simplify the procedure required in solving logical problems and (ii) to simplify any circuit to its fewest components necessary to perform the function.

32.3 AND, OR and NOT Operators

(a) **AND operator :** The AND function is defined in Boolean algebra by use of the dot and so it is similar to multiplication in ordinary algebra. As for example, $A \cdot B = C$ means that if A is true and B is true, then C will be true; otherwise, C will be false. There are four different combinations of A and B as shown in Table 32.1.

Table 32.1 : AND Functions

$A \cdot B = C$
$0 \cdot 0 = 0$
$0 \cdot 1 = 0$
$1 \cdot 0 = 0$
$1 \cdot 1 = 1$

It is to be noted that only when both A and B are 1, the output C will be 1. AND gates may have any number of inputs, Fig. 32.1 shows a four-input AND gate and its associated truth table.

805

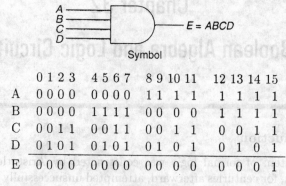

Symbol

	0 1 2 3	4 5 6 7	8 9 10 11	12 13 14 15
A	0 0 0 0	0 0 0 0	1 1 1 1	1 1 1 1
B	0 0 0 0	1 1 1 1	0 0 0 0	1 1 1 1
C	0 0 1 1	0 0 1 1	0 0 1 1	0 0 1 1
D	0 1 0 1	0 1 0 1	0 1 0 1	0 1 0 1
E	0 0 0 0	0 0 0 0	0 0 0 0	0 0 0 1

Truth Table

Fig. 32.1

AND laws

Considering the AND gate and its meaning, the following three Boolean algebraic laws can be verified :

$$A \cdot 1 = A \tag{32.1}$$

$$A \cdot 0 = 0 \tag{32.2}$$

$$A \cdot A = A \tag{32.3}$$

Let us consider Eq. (32.1) and apply it to a two-input AND gate as shown in Fig. 32.2. If $A = 0$ and the other input is 1, then the output will give zero [Fig. 32.2(a)]. But if $A = 1$ and the other input is also 1, then the output is 1 [Fig. 32.2(b)]. Hence the output is always equal to the A input.

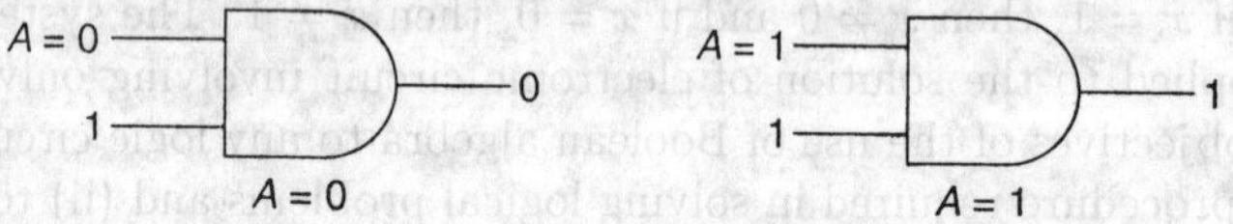

A = 0 ———
1 ——— 0
A = 0

A = 1 ———
1 ——— 1
A = 1

(a)   **(b)**

Fig. 32.2

Let us now consider Eq. (32.2) and apply it to a two-input gate as shown in Fig. 32.3. It is found that if A becomes 0 or 1, the output will always be 0. Next we consider Eq. (32.3) and its realization in Fig. 32.3. It is seen that the output always takes the value of A.

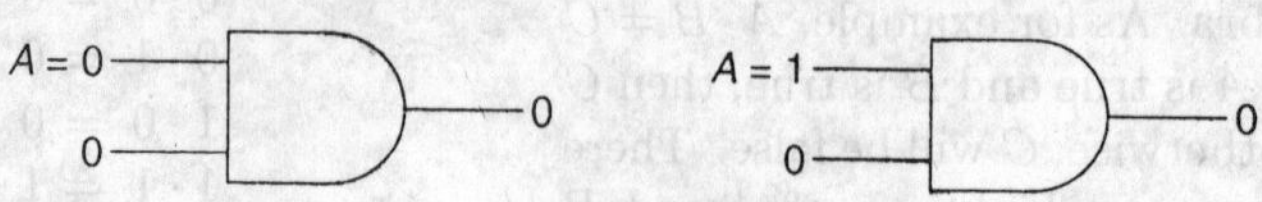

A = 0 ———
0 ——— 0

A = 1 ———
0 ——— 0

Verifying $A \cdot 0 = 0$

Fig. 32.3

Table 32.2 : OR Functions

$A + B = C$
$0 + 0 = 0$
$0 + 1 = 1$
$1 + 0 = 1$
$1 + 1 = 1$

(b) OR operator : The OR operator is indicated by a plus (+) sign. Thus, $A + B = C$ means that if A is true or B is true, then C will be true; otherwise (i.e., when both A and B are false), C will be false. There are four possible combinations as indicated in Table 32.2.

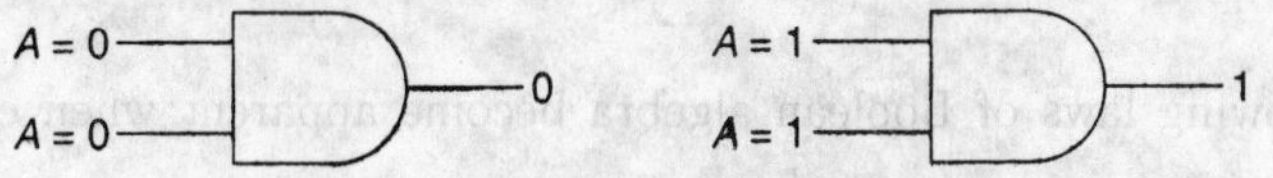

Verifying $A \cdot A = A$

Fig. 32.4

It may be noted that 1 appears at the output in three of the four cases. The OR gate may have any number of inputs. A four-input OR gate along with its truth table is shown in Fig. 32.5.

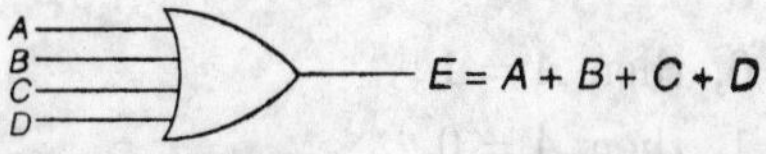

The OR operator discussed above is called an *inclusive OR*, as it includes the case when both inputs are true. In fact, whenever an OR function is mentioned, then inclusive OR is meant.

$E = A + B + C + D$

Symbol

	0 1 2 3	4 5 6 7	8 9 10 11	12 13 14 15
A	0 0 0 0	0 0 0 0	1 1 1 1	1 1 1 1
B	0 0 0 0	1 1 1 1	0 0 0 0	1 1 1 1
C	0 0 1 1	0 0 1 1	0 0 1 1	0 0 1 1
D	0 1 0 1	0 1 0 1	0 1 0 1	0 1 0 1
E	0 1 1 1	1 1 1 1	1 1	1 1 1 1

Truth table

Fig. 32.5

The other type of OR function is known as the *exclusive OR*. Fig. 32.6 reveals the symbol and truth table for an exclusive OR gate. If either of the inputs but not both is true, then the output is true; otherwise, the output is false.

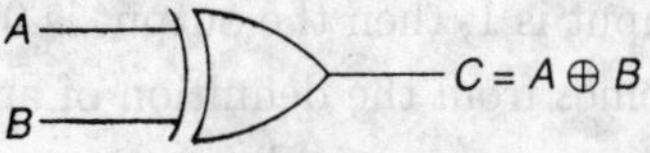

OR laws

$C = A \oplus B$

Symbol

Fig. 32.6

	0 1 2 3
A	0 0 1 1
B	0 1 0 1
C	0 1 1 0

Truth table

There are several OR laws which can be verified by studying the OR gate. These are given below :

$$A + 1 = A \qquad (32.4)$$
$$A + 0 = 0 \qquad (32.5)$$
$$A + A = A \qquad (32.6)$$

The two possible cases of Eq. (32.4) are presented in Fig. 32.7. If A is taken as either 0 or 1, the output is always 1. Eq. (32.5) is established by means of Fig. 32.8. If $A = 0$, the

Verifying $A + 1 = 1$

Fig. 32.7

output is 0 and if $A = 1$, the output is 1. Thus, the output assumes the value of A. Eq. (32.6) is next established by using Fig. 32.9. With A set to 0, the output is 0 and with A set to 1, the output is 1. Therefore, the output always equals A.

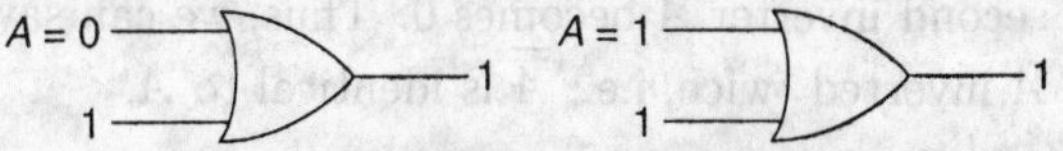

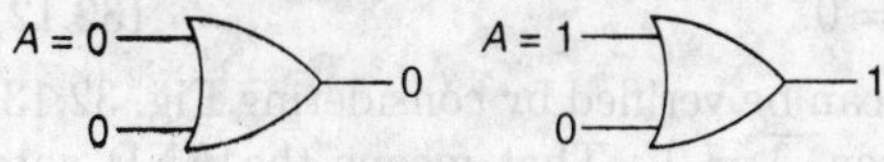

Verifying $A + 0 = A$

Fig. 32.8

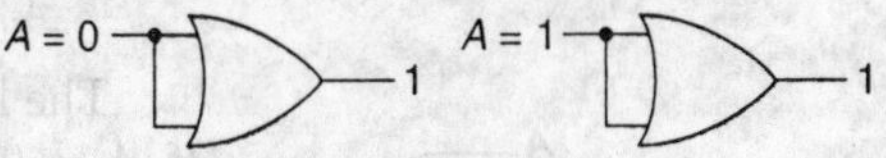

Verifying $A + A = A$

Fig. 32.9

(c) **NOT operator :** The NOT operator is used to change the sense of an argument. The logic diagrams for the NOT operator are called *inverters*. With truth table, the inverters are shown in Fig. 32.10. The circles in the figure represents the inversion and the triangle an amplifier.

NOT laws

The following laws of Boolean algebra become apparent when examining the inverter :

$$\bar{0} = 1 \tag{32.7}$$

$$\bar{1} = 0 \tag{32.8}$$

If $\bar{A} = 0$, then $A = 1$. $\tag{32.9}$

If $\bar{A} = 1$, then $A = 0$. $\tag{32.10}$

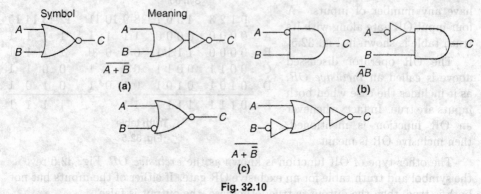

Fig. 32.10

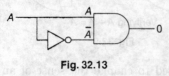

Fig. 32.11

The above equations can be verified by considering Fig. 32.11. If the input is 0, then the output is 1 and if the input is 1, then the output is 0.

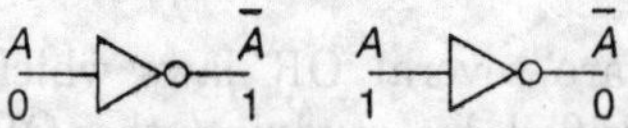

Another law that comes from the definition of an inverter is

$$\bar{\bar{A}} = A. \tag{32.11}$$

This law can be established by considering Fig. 32.12. If $A = 0$ appears at the input of the first inverter, then $\bar{A} = 1$ and so the output of the second inverter $\bar{\bar{A}}$ becomes 0. Thus, we can say that A inverted twice, i.e., $\bar{\bar{A}}$ is identical to A.

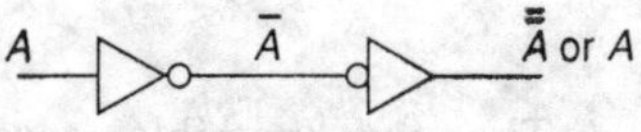

Fig. 32.12

32.4   Laws of Boolean Algebra

The Boolean algebra is a mathematical system. There are some fundamental laws of this algebra which are used to build a workable framework. Some of these laws have already been given in Eqs. (32.1) to (32.11). Others are given below :

(a) An important AND law : The law is expressed mathematically in the form

$$A \cdot \bar{A} = 0. \tag{32.12}$$

Fig. 32.13

The law can be verified by considering Fig. 32.13. If $A = 0$, then $\bar{A} = 1$. That means the AND gate would have a 0 on one input and 1 on the other, resulting a 0 at the output. Similarly, if $A = 1$, then $\bar{A} = 0$ and so the output of the AND gate becomes 0. Hence, we can say that $A\bar{A} = 0$.

(b) An important OR law : The law is given below :

$$A + \bar{A} = 1. \tag{32.13}$$

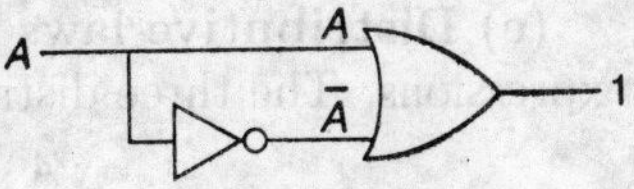

The law is verified by considering Fig. 32.14. If $A = 1$, then $\overline{A} = 0$ and so $A + \overline{A} = 1 + 0 = 1$.

Again, if $A = 0$, then $\overline{A} = 1$ and so $A + \overline{A} = 0 + 1 = 1$.

Fig. 32.14

We can hence write that $A + \overline{A} = 1$.

(c) Commutative laws : The laws permit the change in position of an AND or OR variable :

$$A + B = B + A \qquad (32.14)$$

$$A \cdot B = B \cdot A. \qquad (32.15)$$

To verify the law given in Eq. (32.14), we may consider as follows :

	0	1	2	3
A	0	0	1	1
B	0	1	0	1
$A+B$	0	1	1	1
$B+A$	0	1	1	1

Again, to verify the law given in Eq. (32.15), we may proceed in the following way :

	0	1	2	3
A	0	0	1	1
B	0	1	0	1
$A \cdot B$	0	0	0	1
$B \cdot A$	0	0	0	1

Thus, by perfect induction the above laws can be verified.

(d) Associative laws : These laws permit the grouping of variables. The laws are :

$$A + (B + C) = (A + B) + C \qquad (32.16)$$

$$A \cdot (B \cdot C) = (A \cdot B) \cdot C \qquad (32.17)$$

(i) The law as expressed in Eq. (32.16) can be established in the following way :

	0	1	2	3	4	5	6	7
A	0	0	0	0	1	1	1	1
B	0	0	1	1	0	0	1	1
C	0	1	0	1	0	1	0	1
$(A+B)$	0	0	1	1	1	1	1	1
$(B+C)$	0	1	1	1	0	1	1	1
$(A+B)+C$	0	1	1	1	1	1	1	1
$A+(B+C)$	0	1	1	1	1	1	1	1

(ii) Further, the associative law of Eq. (32.17) can be established in the following manner :

	0	1	2	3	4	5	6	7
A	0	0	0	0	1	1	1	1
B	0	0	1	1	0	0	1	1
C	0	1	0	1	0	1	0	1
$(A \cdot B)$	0	0	0	0	0	0	1	1
$(B \cdot C)$	0	0	0	1	0	0	0	1
$(A \cdot B) \cdot C$	0	0	0	0	0	0	0	1
$A \cdot (B \cdot C)$	0	0	0	0	0	0	0	1

(e) Distributive laws : These laws permit the factoring or multiplying out of expressions. The three distributive laws given below will be considered :

$$A \cdot (B + C) = (A \cdot B) + (A \cdot C) \tag{32.18}$$

$$A + (B \cdot C) = (A + B) \cdot (A + C) \tag{32.19}$$

$$A + (\overline{A} \cdot B) = A + B \tag{32.20}$$

(i) To verify the law given in Eq. (32.18), we may proceed in the following way :

	0	1	2	3	4	5	6	7
A	0	0	0	0	1	1	1	1
B	0	1	1	1	0	0	1	1
C	0	1	0	1	0	1	0	1
$(B + C)$	0	1	1	1	0	1	1	1
$(A \cdot B)$	0	0	0	0	0	0	1	1
$(A \cdot C)$	0	0	0	0	0	1	0	1
$A \cdot (B + C)$	0	0	0	0	0	1	1	1
$(A \cdot B) + (A \cdot C)$	0	0	0	0	0	1	1	1

It is thus seen that the left-hand side of the identity is the same as the right-hand side.

(ii) The Boolean law given in Eq. (32.19) can be proved in the following way :

$$A + (B \cdot C) = A + BC$$
$$= A \cdot 1 + BC \quad [\because A \cdot 1 = A]$$
$$= A(1 + B) + BC \quad [\because B + 1 = 1 \text{ and } B + 1 = 1 + B]$$
$$= A + AB + BC$$
$$= A(1 + C) + AB + BC \quad [\because 1 + C = 1]$$
$$= AA + AC + AB + BC \quad [\because A \cdot A = A]$$
$$= A(A + C) + B(A + C) = (A + B)(A + C).$$

(iii) The Boolean law of Eq. (32.20) is proved below :

$$A + \overline{A}B = A \cdot 1 + \overline{A} \cdot B \quad [\because A \cdot 1 = A]$$
$$= A(1 + B) + \overline{A}B \quad [\because 1 + B = 1]$$
$$= A \cdot 1 + AB + \overline{A}B = A + AB + \overline{A}B \quad [\because A \cdot 1 + A]$$
$$= A + BA + B\overline{A} \quad [\because A \cdot B = B \cdot A]$$
$$= A + B(A + \overline{A}) = A + B \cdot 1 \quad [\because 1 = A + \overline{A}]$$
$$= A + B \quad [\because B \cdot 1 = B]$$

$$\therefore \quad A + \overline{A}B = A + B.$$

32.5   de Morgan's Theorem

The de Morgan's theorem is one of the most powerful identities used in Boolean algebra. It can provide the following two tools to the designer :

(i) It permits to remove the individual variables from under a NOT sign.

As for example, $\overline{A + BC}$ can be transformed into $\overline{A}(\overline{B} + \overline{C})$.

(ii) It permits to transform from a sum-of-products form to a product-of-sums form.

As for example, $A\overline{B}C + AB\overline{C}$ can be transformed into

$$(\overline{A} + B + \overline{C})(\overline{A} + \overline{B} + C).$$

The theorem is expressed by the following identity :

$$\overline{A} \cdot \overline{B} = \overline{A + B} \qquad (32.21)$$

The identity can be verified below. Fig. (32.15) compares the logic required for each :

	0	1	2	3
A	0	0	1	1
B	0	1	0	1
$\overline{A}$	1	1	0	0
$\overline{B}$	1	0	1	0
$\overline{A} \cdot \overline{B}$	1	0	0	0
$A + B$	0	1	1	1
$\overline{A + B}$	1	0	0	0

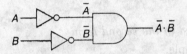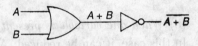

Fig. 32.15

It may be noted that the basic logic function involved can be either an AND gate or an OR gate depending on what is available to the designer.

Demorganization

Although the above identity represents the de Morgan's theorem, the transformation can be made more conveniently by going through three different steps :

(i) Complement the entire function,

(ii) Change all the ANDs to ORs and all the ORs to ANDs,

(iii) Complement each of the individual variables.

The above procedure is called *demorganization*. An example is given below :

Example : Demorganize the function $\quad \overline{A\overline{B} + C}$

Given	$\overline{A\overline{B} + C}$
Complement function	$A\overline{B} + C$
Change operators	$(A + \overline{B})(C)$
Complement variables	$(\overline{A} + B)(\overline{C})$

An alternative method of performing demorganization is

"Break the line, change the sign"

(itty bitty ditty)

Example : Demorganize $A + \overline{BC}$.

First, we break the line between B and C, and change the operation sign from that of ANDing to that of ORing. This gives

$$A + \overline{BC} = A + \overline{B} + \overline{C}.$$

The second method is used particularly in multiple levels of transformation.

32.6   Reducing Boolean Expressions

As all the logic operators represent a corresponding element of hardware, the designer must reduce all the Boolean equations to a simplified form for minimizing cost. The following procedure can be employed, in general, for such reduction :

(i) Multiply all the variables required to remove parentheses.

(ii) Look for the identical terms. One of these can be dropped using Eq. (32.12).

(iii) Look for a variable and its negation in the same term. This term can be dropped. As for example,

$$BB\overline{B}C = 0 \cdot C = 0.$$

(iv) Look for pairs of terms which are identical except for one variable.

(a) *When one variable is missing*

In this case, the larger term can be dropped. As for example,

$$ABCD + ABD = ABD(C + 1)$$
$$= ABD \cdot 1 \quad [\because \ C + 1 = 1]$$
$$= ABD.$$

(b) *When one variable is present but negated in the second term*

In this case, it can be reduced. As for example,

$$ABCD + A\overline{B}CD = ACD(B + \overline{B})$$
$$= ACD \cdot 1 \quad [\because \ B + \overline{B} = 1]$$
$$= ACD.$$

32.6.1   AND Circuit and Its Truth Table

An AND circuit is shown in Fig. 32.16(a) while Fig. 32.16(b) gives its symbolic representation. This is a simple logic circuit using diodes. In such a circuit, both the inputs must be UP level to produce an UP level at the output. In the figure, D_1 and D_2 are two diodes, each receives an independent input signal voltage (+ 20 V or −20 V) through S_1 and S_2 respectively.

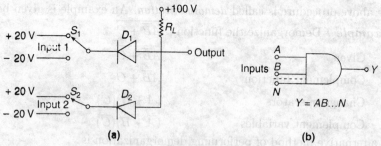

Fig. 32.16

Fig. 32.17

To understand the operation of an AND circuit, let us consider first the simple circuit diagram of Fig. 32.17. As shown, when the switch S_1 is in −20 V position, circuit is completed from the −20 V source through diode D_1 and resistor R_L to the +100 V source. Under such condition, since D_1 is forward biased, it conducts. As the forward resistance of D_1 is low compared with the load resistance, a negligible voltage drop appears across D_1. Therefore, with respect to common ground the output level exhibits -20 V. Similarly, when the switch is placed in the $+20$ V position, output voltage exhibits $+20$ V.

The use of one diode in a circuit is, therefore, just to transfer either input level to the output. That is why with only one diode and one input, the circuit has little value as a logic circuit. When the second diode and input are included as in Fig. 32.16(a), a real AND logic circuit is formed.

Let us now consider the circuit of Fig 32.16(a). When both S_1 and S_2 are at -20 V position, the output is -20 V. But if S_1 is placed in the $+20$ V position and S_2 in the -20 V position, the output remains at -20 V, since the diode D_2 has a -20 V level on its cathode. Diode D_1 is cut off because its cathode is $+20$ V and is more positive than its anode. D_1 is thus reverse biased. If next the switches S_1 and S_2 are both set in $+20$ V position, the output gives $+20$ V.

From the measurement of the output of an AND circuit we can, therefore, draw the following logical conclusions :

(i) If the output is UP, then both the inputs must be UP.

(ii) If the output is DOWN, then either or both the inputs must be DOWN.

Truth Table

Usually, the logic of digital circuits is given in the form of a truth table. A digital UP state is represented in convention by the binary 1 while a DOWN state by the binary number 0. All the necessary conditions in a two-input AND circuit are then given in Table 32.3.

Table 32.3 : AND Truth Table

Inputs		Output
A	B	Y
0	0	0
1	0	0
0	1	0
1	1	1

32.6.2   OR Circuit and Its Truth Table

The OR circuit is another logic circuit. Such a circuit provides an UP level at the output when any one of its inputs has an UP level. It is, however, similar to the AND circuit with a difference that the polarity of the diodes is reversed and the load resistance R_L is connected to the negative voltage source. Fig. 32.18(a) shows an OR circuit while Fig. 32.18(b) is its symbolic representation.

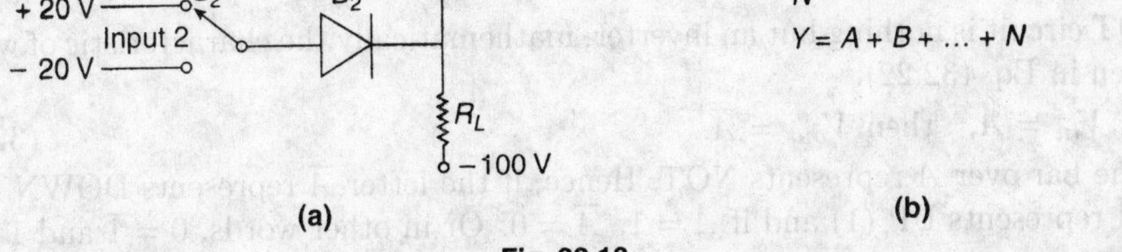

Fig. 32.18

To understand the operation of an OR circuit, for the time being, let us consider that only the diode D_1 is present in the circuit of Fig. 32.18(a). When the input to D_1 is -20 V, the diode becomes forward biased since the anode is less negative than the cathode which is connected through the load resistor to the -100 V source. The diode D_1 thus conducts and it acts as a low resistance switch. A very small voltage, therefore, drops across D_1 as compared to that across R_L. The output level so exhibits -20 V. Similarly, when the switch S_1 is placed to $+20$ V position, the output will exhibit $+20$ V.

Now, if both the diodes are connected and the inputs are at -20 V position, the output is -20 V. But, if either D_1 or D_2 has $+20$ V on its input, the output is $+20$ V.

From the measurement of the output of an OR circuit we can, therefore, draw the following logical conclusions :

(i) If the output is DOWN, then both the inputs must be DOWN.

(ii) If the output is UP, then either or both the inputs must be UP.

Truth Table

All the possible conditions in a two-input OR circuit are given in Table **32.4**.

Table 32.4 : OR Truth Table

Inputs		Output
A	B	Y
0	0	0
1	0	1
0	1	1
1	1	1

32.6.3   Combined AND-OR Circuits

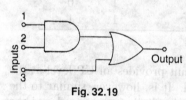

Fig. 32.19

In computer technology sometimes a combination of AND and OR circuits is used to perform complex logical operations. A simple example of it in the form of block diagram is shown in Fig. 32.19. Analysis shows that an UP level on inputs 1 and 2 will produce an UP level, on input 3 alone produces an UP level at the output.

32.6.4   AND and OR Gates

AND and OR circuits are also known as *Gates*. In digital electronics, a gate is a circuit which has two or more inputs and one output. The natures of the gate and input combinations determine the output, i.e., either UP (1) or DOWN (0).

32.6.5   NOT Circuit

A NOT circuit is nothing but an inverter, mathematically the characteristic of which is given in Eq. (32.22).

If $V_{in} = A$, then $V_{out} = \overline{A}$.   (32.22)

The bar over A represents NOT. Hence, if the letter $\overline{A}$ represents DOWN level (0), $\overline{A}$ represents UP (1) and if $A = 1$, $\overline{A} = 0$. Or in other words, $\overline{0} = \overline{1}$ and $1 = 0$.

Fig. 32.20 shows a NOT circuit and its symbolic representation. In the grounded emitter configuration in Fig. 32.20(a), the output is taken from the collector. When no signal is applied at the input, the transistor is cut off and the output is at V_{cc}, i.e., it is UP. On the other hand, when a positive pulse is applied to the base, the transistor conducts and the collector voltage drops. Thus for a positive input, the output goes DOWN. We can, therefore, conclude that in a NOT circuit, the output is present when an input is not applied. Similarly, an output signal is not present when an input signal is applied.

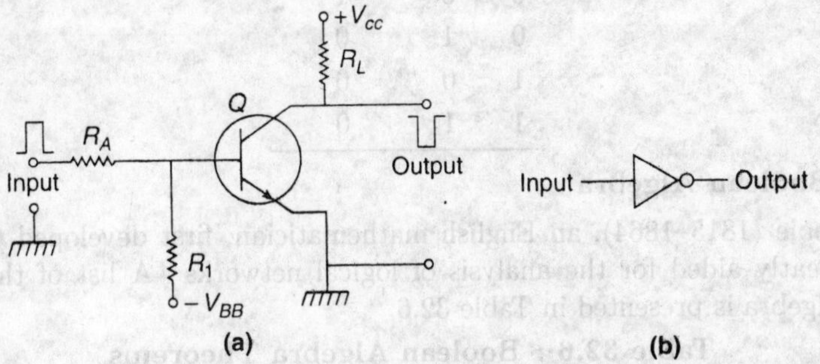

Fig. 32.20

32.6.6 NOR Gate and its Truth Table

The NOR gate is a combination of NOT and OR logic, the characteristic of which is that the output is produced without application of signal to input A, or to input $B, \ldots$, or to input N, or to any combination of inputs. Fig. 32.21(a) is a NOR gate with two inputs while Fig. 32.21(b) is its logic symbol.

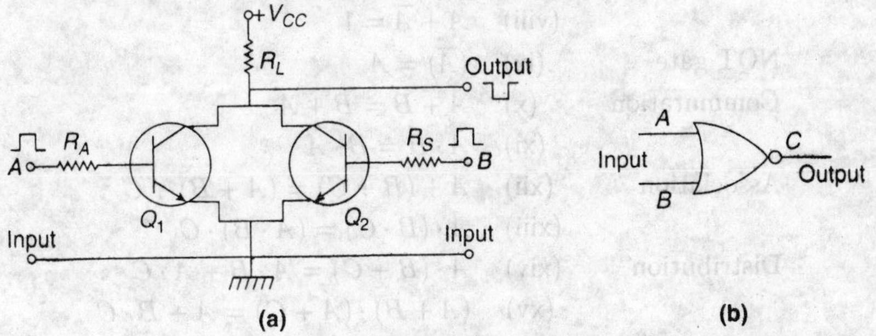

Fig. 32.21

Let us consider the basic circuits of Q_1 and Q_2. When the input signal is absent, both the bases are returned to ground through the input circuits (not shown in the figure). So, Q_1, and Q_2 are cut off for lack of forward bias. The output, common to both Q_1 and Q_2, taken from the collector resistor R_L is, therefore, equal to $+V_{CC}$ when no input signal is present on A or on B. If a positive pulse is applied at input A or B or both, Q_1 or Q_2 or both respectively conduct and a negative pulse appears at the output. The output is, therefore, DOWN. So we have an effect of an inverter (NOT) and an OR circuit in the operation of this gate, mathematically, which can be expressed as

$$\overline{A + B} = V_{out}$$

or, $\overline{A} \cdot \overline{B} = V_{out}.$ (32.23)

Truth Table

All the possible conditions in a two-input NOR gate are given in Table 32.5.

Table 32.5 : NOR Truth Table

Inputs		Output
A	B	Y
0	0	1
0	1	0
1	0	0
1	1	0

32.6.7 Boolean Algebra

George Boole (1815–1864), an English mathematician, first developed the logical algebra greatly aided for the analysis of logical networks. A list of theorems in Boolean algebra is presented in Table 32.6.

Table 32.6 : Boolean Algebra Theorems

AND gate	(i)	$0 \cdot A = 0$
	(ii)	$1 \cdot A = A$
	(iii)	$A \cdot A = A$
	(iv)	$A \cdot \overline{A} = 0$
OR gate	(v)	$0 + A = A$
	(vi)	$1 + A = 1$
	(vii)	$A + A = 1$
	(viii)	$A + \overline{A} = 1$
NOT gate	(ix)	$(\overline{A}) = A$
Commutation	(x)	$A + B = B + A$
	(xi)	$A \cdot B = B \cdot A$
Association	(xii)	$A + (B + C) = (A + B) + C$
	(xiii)	$A \cdot (B \cdot C) = (A \cdot B) \cdot C$
Distribution	(xiv)	$A \cdot (B + C) = A \cdot B + A \cdot C$
	(xv)	$(A + B) \cdot (A + C) = A + B \cdot C$
Absorption	(xvi)	$A + A \cdot B = A$
	(xvii)	$A \cdot (A + B) = A$
de Morgan's	(xviii)	$(\overline{A + B}) = \overline{A} \cdot B$
theorems	(xix)	$\overline{A \cdot B} = \overline{A} + B$

The equations above may be proved by considering the definitions or truth tables or the behaviour of the circuits discussed earlier. In the table, the de Morgan's theorems are interesting enough showing a useful relation between AND and OR functions.

The theorems of Boolean algebra are utilized to simplify digital logic networks in a similar way as the mathematical logic is utilized for manipulating ordinary algebraic expressions.

32.7 Binary Operation of a System

The binary system of arithmetic has only two possible states to represent all quantities. These two states are either 0 (zero) or 1 (one). Since 0 and 1 can be easily represented by two-state digital circuits, the binary operation finds wide use in computer technology. Thus, a hole in a card can represent a binary 1 while no hole is a binary 0. Similarly, the magnetic flux of a magnetic material can represent 1 in one direction and 0 in the opposite direction. In a computer, to transmit digits from one part to another, a binary 1 can be represented by a positive level and a binary 0 by a negative level or vice versa. Various designations are used, in general, for the two quantized states of a binary system, the most common of which are given in Table 32.7.

Table 32.7 : Binary-state Terminology

	1	2	3	4	5	6	7
One state	True	Closed	High	Up	Off	Yes	1
Other state	False	Open	Low	Down	On	No	0

In logic, a statement may be either true or false which is the notation under 1. Similarly, a switch may be either closed or open as shown under notation 2 and so on.

A binary digit (either 0 or 1) is called *a bit* and a group of bits having a significance is called *a code, word* or *byte*.

32.7.1 Binary Numbers

For explaining the binary numbers, let us start with the familiar decimal system based on the use of 10 digits. Consider, as an example, the meaning of the decimal number 634 which can be written as follows :

$$634 = (6 \times 10^2) + (3 \times 10^1) + (4 \times 10^0) = 600 + 30 + 4.$$

It is seen, therefore, that in a number the individual digits represent coefficients for the increasing powers of 10. The farthest digit to the right is the coefficient of the 0th power, the next is the coefficient of the 1st power and so on. In general, any decimal number can be represented by the equation,

$$Y = d_n \times r^n + d_{n-1} \times r^{n-1} + \cdots + d_1 \times r^1 + d_0 \times r^0, \tag{32.24}$$

where Y is the entire number, d_n is the nth digit from the point and r is the radix or base. This equation can also be applied to the binary system as discussed below :

Since only two digits (0 and 1) are available in a binary system, the individual digits represent the coefficients of powers of 2 rather than 10 as in the decimal system. The binary number 10111, as an example, may be solved as follows :

$$Y = d_4 \times r^4 + d_3 \times r^3 + d_2 \times r^2 + d_1 \times r^1 + d_0 \times r^0$$

$$= 1 \times 2^4 + 0 \times 2^3 + 1 \times 2^2 + 1 \times 2^1 + 1 \times 2^0 = 16 + 0 + 4 + 2 + 1 = 23$$

or, arithmetically we can write, $10111_2 = 23_{10}$.

This means the binary number 10111 represents the same quantity as the decimal number 23. A short list of decimal-binary equivalents is given in Table 32.8.

Table 32.8 : Equivalent Numbers

Decimal notation	Binary notation	Decimal notation	Binary notation
0	0000	6	0110
1	0001	7	0111
2	0010	8	1000
3	0011	9	1001
4	0100	10	1010
5	0101		

32.7.2 Decimal to Binary Conversion

The order of a binary number is designated as 1, 2, 4, 8, 16, 32, 64, 128, 256, etc., and not as unit, tens, hundreds, thousands, etc., as in the decimal system. There are two methods for converting a decimal to a binary number.

In the first method, a table of powers of 2 is utilized (Table 32.9). The decimal number to be evaluated is taken and the largest power of 2 from the table is noted without exceeding the original number. Then subtract the table-oriented number from the original number and repeat the process for the remainder until it becomes zero. Next, add the binary numbers obtained from the Table to get the answer.

Table 32.9 : Power of 2

2^n	n
1	0
2	1
4	2
8	3
16	4
32	5
64	6
128	7
256	8
512	9
1024	10
...	...

In the second method of converting decimal to binary, the number is successively divided by 2 and its remainders recorded. The final binary result is obtained by reading the remainders from the bottom to the top.

32.7.3 Binary Addition

Addition of binary numbers is very simple. The addition of two binary numbers A and B can be done by using the Table 32.10. The Table shows all the possible combinations of A and B.

Table 32.10 : Truth Table for Addition

Inputs		Sum	Carry
A	B		
0	0	0	0
0	1	1	0
1	0	1	0
1	1	0	1

A digit, in the fourth entry of Table 32.9, is carried by shifting it to the next position to the left.

Binary numbers can also be subtracted, multiplied and divided using similar rules as applied for addition.

32.8 Conversion of Real Number

If we consider a decimal number system, the digits after the decimal point have weights as explained below :

$$0.627 = 0.6 + 0.02 + 0.007$$
$$= 6 \times 10^{-1} + 2 \times 10^{-2} + 7 \times 10^{-2}.$$

Again, if we consider a binary system, the weights of binary bits after the binary point are as follows :

$$0.1011 = 1 \times 2^{-1} + 0 \times 2^{-2} + 1 \times 2^{-3} + 1 \times 2^{-4}$$
$$= 1 \times \frac{1}{2} + 0 \times \frac{1}{4} + 1 \times \frac{1}{8} + 1 \times \frac{1}{16}$$
$$= 0.5 + 0 + 0.125 + 0.0625$$
$$= 0.6875 \text{ (decimal)}.$$

Example : Convert the binary real number 1011.011 to its decimal equivalent.

Solution : The given binary real number has two parts—an integer part and a fraction. The decimal equivalent is to be expressed as both the integer and the fraction, and thereby they are to be added to convert the binary one to the decimal real number. Now we can write,

$$1011.011 = (1 \times 2^3 + 0 \times 2^2 + 1 \times 2^1 + 1 \times 2^0) + (0 \times 2^{-1} + 1 \times 2^{-2} + 1 \times 2^{-3})$$
$$= (8 + 0 + 2 + 1) + \left(0 \times \frac{1}{2} + \frac{1}{4} + \frac{1}{8}\right)$$
$$= 11 + (0 + 0.25 + 0.125)$$
$$= 11.375 \text{ (decimal real number)}.$$

32.9 Conversion of Decimal Fraction to Binary Fraction

It is obtained by using the technique of successive multiplication by 2. In this technique, the integer part is noted down after each multiplication and the new fraction obtained is used for multiplication.

Example : Convert 50.7 (decimal) to its binary equivalent.

Solution : For this decimal real number, its binary equivalent is obtained separately for the integer and the fraction.

We first convert the decimal number 50 to binary number in the following way :

Binary number	Remainder
2 | 50	
2 | 25	0 (LSB)
2 | 12	1
2 | 6	0
2 | 3	0
2 | 1	1
0	1 (MSB)

$\therefore$ 50 (decimal) = .110010 (binary).

Next, we convert 0.7 (decimal) to its binary fraction in the following way :

Fraction	Fraction ×2	Remainder fraction	Integer
0.7	1.4	0.4	1 (MSB)
0.4	0.8	0.8	0
0.8	1.6	0.6	1
0.6	1.2	0.2	1
0.2	0.4	0.4	0
0.4	0.8	0.8	0
0.8	1.6	0.6	1 (LSB)
—	—	—	—
—	—	—	—
—	—	—	—

We find that the fraction has not become zero and the process will continue. So, we have taken an approximation in this case. We have taken here 7 binary bits after the binary point. The result is 0.7 (decimal) = 0.1011001 (binary), combining the above two steps, we have,

   50.7 (decimal) = 110010.1011001 (binary).

Examples

1. Solve the Boolean expression $C = A + B$ for the following inputs : $A = 0$, $B = 0$; $A = 1$, $B = 0$; $A = 1$, $B = 1$.

Soltion : When $A = 0$ and $B = 0$, then $C = 0 + 0 = 0$

When $A = 1$ and $B = 0$, then $C = 1 + 0 = 1$

When $A = 1$ and $B = 1$, then $C = 1 + 1 = 1$

2. Using Boolean algebra, verify the following :

(a) $\overline{A + B} + \overline{A + \overline{B}} = A$

(b) $AB + AC + B\overline{C} = AC + B\overline{C}$

(c) $\overline{AB + BC + CA} = \overline{AB} + \overline{BC} + \overline{CA}$

(d) $(A + B)(B + C)(C + A) = AB + BC + CA$

(e) $(A + B)(\overline{A} + C) = AC + \overline{A}B$

(f) $AB + \overline{BC} + A\overline{C} = AB + \overline{BC}$

(g) $A + \overline{A}B = A + B$

(h) $A(\overline{A} + B) = AB$

(i) $AB + \overline{A}C = (A + C)(\overline{A} + B)$

(j) $ABC + AB\overline{C} = AB$

Solution : (a) $\overline{A + B} + \overline{A + \overline{B}} = (\overline{\overline{A}} \cdot \overline{B}) + (\overline{\overline{A}} \cdot \overline{\overline{B}})$ [using de Morgan's law]

$$= (A\overline{B}) + AB = A(B + \overline{B})$$

$$= A \cdot 1 \ [\because \ B + \overline{B} = 1]$$

$$= A.$$

(b) $AB + AC + B\overline{C} = AB(C + \overline{C}) + A\overline{C} + B\overline{C} \ [\because \ C + \overline{C} = 1]$

$$= ABC + AB\overline{C} + AC + B\overline{C}$$

$$= ABC + AC + AB\overline{C} + B\overline{C} \quad \text{[rearranging terms]}$$

$$= AC(B+1)B\overline{C}(A+1)$$

$$= AC + B\overline{C} \quad [\because \; B+1 = 1, \; A+1 = 1]$$

(c) $\overline{AB + BC + CA} = (\overline{A} + \overline{B})(\overline{B} + \overline{C})(\overline{C} + \overline{A})$ [using de Morgan's law]

$$= (\overline{B} + \overline{A})(\overline{B} + \overline{C})(\overline{A} + \overline{C})$$

$$= (\overline{B} + \overline{A}\,\overline{C})(\overline{A} + \overline{C}) \quad [\because \; (A+B)(A+C) = A + BC]$$

$$= \overline{B}\,\overline{A} + \overline{B}\,\overline{C} + \overline{A}\,\overline{A}\,\overline{C} + \overline{A}\,\overline{C}\,\overline{C}$$

$$= \overline{A}\overline{B} + \overline{B}\overline{C} + \overline{A}\overline{C} + \overline{A}\overline{C} \quad [\because \; \overline{A}\,\overline{A} = \overline{A}, \; \overline{C}\,\overline{C} = \overline{C}]$$

$$= \overline{A}\overline{B} + \overline{B}\overline{C} + \overline{A}\overline{C} \quad [\because \; \overline{A}\overline{C} + \overline{A}\overline{C} = \overline{A}\overline{C}]$$

(d) $(A + B)(B + C)(C + A) = (B + A)(B + C)(C + A) = (B + AC)(C + A)$

$$= BC + AB + ACC + AAC$$

$$= BC + AB + AC + AC = BC + AB + AC.$$

(e) $(A + B)(\overline{A} + C) = AA + AC + AB + BC = 0 + AC + \overline{A}B + BC$

$$= AC + \overline{A}B + BC(A + \overline{A}) \quad [\because \; A + \overline{A} = 1]$$

$$= AC + \overline{A}B + ABC + \overline{A}BC$$

$$= (AC + ABC) + \overline{A}B + \overline{A}BC$$

$$= AC(1 + B) + \overline{A}B(1 + C)$$

$$= AC + \overline{A}B \quad [\because \; 1 + B = 1, \; 1 + C = 1].$$

(f) $AB + \overline{B}\,\overline{C} + A\overline{C} = AB + \overline{B}\,\overline{C} + A\overline{C}(B + \overline{B})$

$$= AB + \overline{B}\,\overline{C} + AB\overline{C} + A\overline{B}\,\overline{C}$$

$$= AB + AB\overline{C} + \overline{B}\,\overline{C} + A\overline{B}\,\overline{C}$$

$$= AB(1 + \overline{C}) + \overline{B}\,\overline{C}(1 + A)$$

$$= AB + \overline{B}\,\overline{C}.$$

(g) $A + \overline{A}B = A(B + \overline{B}) + \overline{A}B \quad [\because \; B + \overline{B} = 1]$

$$= AB + A\overline{B} + \overline{A}B$$

$$= AB + A\overline{B} + AB + \overline{A}B \quad [\because \; AB + AB = AB]$$

$$= A(B + \overline{B}) + B(A + \overline{A}) = A \cdot 1 + B \cdot 1 = A + B.$$

(h) $A(\overline{A} + B) = A\overline{A} + AB = 0 + AB \quad [\because \; A\overline{A} = 0]$

$$= AB.$$

(i) Here r.h.s. $= (A + C)(\overline{A} + B) = AA + AB + C\overline{A} + BC$

$$= AB + \overline{A}C + BC \quad [\because \; A\overline{A} = 0]$$

$$= AB + \overline{A}C + BC(A + \overline{A}) = AB + \overline{A}C + ABC + \overline{A}BC$$

$$= AB + ABC + \overline{A}C + \overline{A}BC = AB(1 + C) + \overline{A}C(1 + B)$$

$$= AB + \overline{A}C \quad [\because \; 1 + C = 1, \; 1 + B = 1]$$

$$= 1 \; \text{l.h.s.}$$

(j) $ABC + AB\overline{C} = AB(C + \overline{C}) = AB \cdot 1 \;\; [\because \; C + \overline{C} = 1]$

$\qquad\qquad\qquad = AB.$

3. An AND gate is followed by a NOT gate. Using two inputs A and B, find the Boolean expression of the output C.

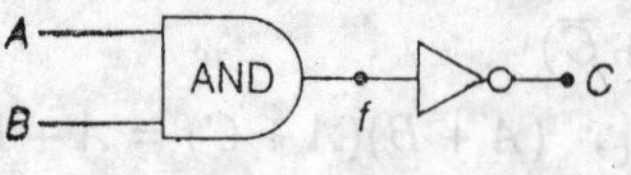

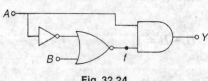

Fig. 32.22

Solution : The logic circuit where the AND gate is followed by a NOT gate is shown in Fig. 32.22.

Since A and B are the two inputs of the AND gate, its output $f = AB$. This output f is the input to the NOT circuit.

So, the output of the NOT circuit,

$$C = \overline{f} = \overline{A \cdot B} = \overline{A} + \overline{B}.$$

4. Explain how an OR gate may be constructed with AND and NOT gates.

Solution : The logic circuit for the purpose is drawn in Fig. 32.23. If A and B are the two inputs applied to the two inputs of the NOT gate, then the output will be,

$$C = \overline{A} \quad \text{and} \quad D = \overline{B}.$$

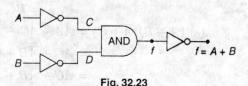

Fig. 32.23

If C and D are the two inputs of the AND gate, then its output,

$$Y = C \cdot D = \overline{A} \cdot \overline{B}.$$

If a NOT gate is followed by this AND gate, then

$$f = \overline{Y} = \overline{C \cdot D} = \overline{\overline{A} \cdot \overline{B}} = A + B.$$

In this way, an OR gate may be constructed with AND and NOT gates.

5. A logic circuit is given in Fig. 32.24. Change it into a simpler form.

Fig. 32.24

Solution : In Fig. 32.24, A is the input to the NOT and the AND gate. So A and B are the inputs to the OR circuit. The output of the OR gate is thus,

$$f = \overline{A} + B$$

This output f thus becomes another input to the AND gate.

The Boolean expression for the output of the AND gate is given by

$$Y = A(\overline{A} + B) = A\overline{A} + AB$$

$$= AB \;\; [\because \; A\overline{A} = 0].$$

A ○——⟍
Inputs   ⟍ ——○ $Y (= AB)$
B ○——⟋

Fig. 32.25

Now, if A and B are the two inputs of an AND gate, then its output becomes $Y = AB$. Thus, the above logic circuit can be represented in a simplified form as shown in Fig. 32.25.

6. Reduce the following expressions :

(a) $\overline{\overline{AB} + \overline{A} + AB}$ \qquad (b) $\overline{\overline{A\overline{B} + ABC} + A(B + A\overline{B})}$

(c) $AB + \overline{AC} + A\overline{B}C(AB + C)$

Solution : (a) $\overline{\overline{AB} + \overline{A} + AB} = \overline{\overline{A} + \overline{B} + \overline{A} + AB}$ (Demorganize AB)

$$= \overline{\overline{A} + \overline{B} + AB} \quad \text{(Reduce)}$$

$$= \overline{\overline{A} + \overline{B} + A} \quad \text{(Reduce)}$$

$$= \overline{A + \overline{A} + \overline{B}} \quad \text{(Rearrange)}$$

$$= \overline{1 + \overline{B}} \quad \text{(Reduce)}$$

$$= \overline{1} \quad \text{(Reduce)}$$

$$= 0 \quad \text{(Convert)}.$$

(b) $\overline{\overline{A\overline{B} + ABC + A(B + A\overline{B})}}$

$$= \overline{\overline{A(\overline{B} + BC) + A(B + A\overline{B})}} \quad \text{(Factor)}$$

$$= \overline{\overline{A(\overline{B} + C) + A(B + A)}} \quad \text{(Reduce)}$$

$$= \overline{\overline{A\overline{B} + AC + AA + AB}} \quad \text{(Multiply)}$$

$$= \overline{\overline{A\overline{B} + AC + A}} \quad \text{(Reduce)}$$

$$= \overline{(\overline{A} + B)(\overline{A} + \overline{C}) + A} \quad \text{(Demorganize } A\overline{B} + AC)$$

$$= \overline{\overline{A}\,\overline{A} + \overline{A}\,\overline{C} + \overline{A}B + B\overline{C} + A} \quad \text{(Multiply)}$$

$$= \overline{\overline{A} + \overline{A}\,\overline{C} + \overline{A}B + B\overline{C} + A} \quad \text{(Reduce)}$$

$$= \overline{\overline{A}(1 + \overline{C} + B) + B\overline{C} + A} \quad \text{(Factor)}$$

$$= \overline{\overline{A} + B\overline{C} + A} \quad \text{(Reduce)}$$

$$= \overline{1} \quad \text{(Reduce)}$$

$$= 0 \quad \text{(Convert)}$$

(c) $AB + \overline{AC} + A\overline{B}C(AB + C)$

$$= AB + \overline{AC} + AAB\overline{B}C + A\overline{B}CC \quad \text{(Multiply)}$$

$$= AB + \overline{AC} + A\overline{B}C \quad \text{(Reduce)}$$

$$= AB + \overline{A} + \overline{C} + A\overline{B}C \quad \text{(Demorganize } \overline{AC})$$

$$= AB + \overline{C} + \overline{A} + A\overline{B}C \quad \text{(Rearrange)}$$

$$= AB + \overline{C} + \overline{A} + \overline{B}C \quad \text{(Reduce)}$$

$$= A + AB + \overline{C} + \overline{B}C \quad \text{(Rearrange)}$$

$$= \overline{A} + B + \overline{C} + \overline{B} \quad \text{(Reduce)}$$

$$= 1 \quad \text{(Reduce)}.$$

Questions

Essay-type

1. Name the three Boolean operators.

2. Give an example of a truth function using **(i)** an AND function, **(ii)** an OR function and **(iii)** a NOT function.

3. What down the laws of Boolean algebra.

4. State and prove de Morgan's theorem. What is meant by demorganization?

5. Discuss how a Boolean expression can be reduced.

6. Prove that, $AB + BC + C\overline{A} = AB + C\overline{A}$

Short Answer-type

7. Express the following decimal numbers in binary form :

   (a) 125   (b) 53   (c) 25   (d) 129   (e) 15.005   [C.U. 2000]
   [**Ans.** (a) 1111101 (b) 110101 (c) 11001 (d) $(10000001)_2$ (e) $(111.0000001+)_2$]

8. What is the difference between decimal system and binary system?

9. What are the digits in binary system?   [B.U. 2005]

10. (a) Explain the rules for binary addition and subtraction.

    (b) Explain the rule for obtaining binary equivalent of a negative decimal number. Apply the rule to get the binary equivalent of $(-19)_{10}$.

                                                              [**Ans.** $(101100)_2$]

11. Find the decimal equivalents of the following binaries :

    (a) 11011101   (b) 100001   (c) 111   (d) 11001011   [C.U. 2000]
                              [**Ans.** (a) 211 (b) 33 (c) 0.875 (d) $(202)_{10}$]

12. Define an OR gate and give its truth table. State the Boolean identities for it.

13. Define an AND gate and give its truth table. State the Boolean identities for the gate. Give an electrical circuit explaining the gate.

14. Find the results of :

    (a) $110111 + 11011$ (b) $11001.101 + 11101.11$

    (c) $1100 - 1011$ (d) $.111 - .101$

                [**Ans.** (a) 1010010 (b) 110111.100 (c) 0001 (d) .010]

15. Draw the circuit symbols of NOT, OR and AND gates.

16. Explain the following statements :

    (a) If $A = 1$, $B = 1$, $C = 1$, $Y = 1 + 1 + 1 = 1$.

    (b) If $A = 1$, $B = 1$, $C = 0$, $Y = 1 \cdot 1 \cdot 0 = 0$.

17. Define a NOT gate and give its truth table. Why is it called an inverter?

18. State de Morgan's theorem.   [C.U. 2000, '05; N.B.U. 2005]

19. Draw the circuit diagram of an 'OR' gate using discrete components and write down the truth table.   [C.U. 2000]

20. Perform the binary addition corresponding to the decimal addition. $2 + 2 = 4$.

21. State and prove de Morgan's theorems.

22. Sketch a basic NAND and a NOR gate. Write their truth table. [C.U. 2005]

23. (i) Convert the decimal number 23 to binary number.

    (ii) $10010 - 1001 =$? (numbers are binary).   [C.U. 2005]

                                        [**Ans.** (i) 1011.1 (ii) 01001]

24. (i) Convert decimal number 145.26 to binary number.

(ii) Convert binary number 11101 to decimal number.

(iii) Add binary numbers 100001 and 11101. **[B.U. 2005]**

[Ans. (i) $(101001)_2$ (ii) $(31)_{10}$ (iii) 111110]

25. Construct a digital half-adder circuit using logic gates and explain its action. Why is it called half-adder? **[B.U. 2002]**

26. Solve the Boolean expression, $C = A + B$, for the following inputs : $A = 0$, $B = 0$; $A = 1$, $B = 0$; $A = 1$, $B = 1$. **[Ans.** 0, 1, 1]

27. Show how you can form an AND gate and an OR gate from NAND gates. Verify with appropriate truth tables. **[C.U. 2001, '03]**

28. Write down the circuit symbol and truth table of AND gate. **[B.U. 2003]**

29. Draw the circuit diagram of a diode AND gate having three input terminals. Write down its truth table. **[C.U. 2002]**

30. Sketch the diagram of a basic AND gate with two diodes and explain its action. **[N.B.U. 2005]**

31. "NAND gate and NOR gate are called universal gates." Prove the above statement by constructing AND gate, OR gate and NOT gate using only NAND gates. **[B.U. 2004]**

32. Is is possible to get AND gate by using a few NOR gates? How? **[C.U. 2005]**

33. How can a NAND gate be used as a NOT gate? **[N.B.U. 2005]**

Numerical Problems

34. Reduce the following Boolean expression :

(a) $AABC$, (b) $ABBBC$, (c) $ABBCCC$,

(d) $A \cdot 1 \cdot 4$, (e) $A \cdot A \cdot A \cdot \overline{A}$.

[Ans. (a) ABC, (b) ABC, (c) ABC, (d) A, (e) 0]

35. Reduce the following Boolean expressions :

(a) $AA + BB$, (b) $BC + B\overline{B}C$, (c) $A\overline{A} + BBB$.

[Ans. (a) $A + B$, (b) BC, (c) B]

36. Reduce the following Boolean functions :

(a) $A + \overline{A}\,\overline{B} + AB$, (b) $A\overline{B} + \overline{A}B + AB + \overline{A}\,\overline{B}$,

(c) $A\overline{B}D + AB\overline{D} + \overline{B}\,\overline{D}$, (d) $(AB + C)(AB + D)$.

[Ans. (a) $A + B$, (b) 1, (c) $A\overline{B} + \overline{B}\,\overline{D}$, (d) $AB + CD$]

37. Reduce the following Boolean expressions :

(a) $A + \overline{B}C(A + \overline{B}C)$, (b) $C(\overline{ABC} + A\overline{B}C)$, (c) $\overline{ABC + \overline{AB} + BC}$

[Ans. (a) A, (b) $\overline{A}C + \overline{B}C$, (c) $\overline{A}\,\overline{B}$]

38. Without reducing, convert the following expressions to AND/OR/invert logic :

(a) $AB + C(\overline{A} + B)$, (b) $\overline{A}\,\overline{B} + A + \overline{B + C}$, (c) $A\overline{B} + \overline{A}\,\overline{B}$.

[Ans. It is given in Fig. 32.26 below]

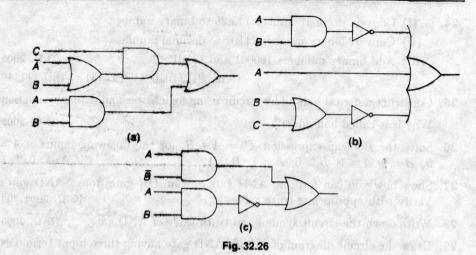

Fig. 32.26

39. Assuming lines A and B are expressed in negative logic, draw the logic diagram for AB in AND /OR/invert logic.   [**Ans.** It is given in Fig. **32.27** below]

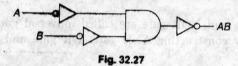

Fig. 32.27

Review Short Questions on *Electronics*
(with Answers)

Vacuum Tubes

1. *What are the values of charge, mass and radius of an electron?*

Ans. The values of charge, mass and radius of an electron are given below :

Electronic charge $(Q_e) = 4.803 \times 10^{-10}$ e.s.u.

Electronic rest mass $(m_e) = 9.109 \times 10^{-31}$ kilogram.

Electronic radius $(r_e) = 2.817 \times 10^{-15}$ metre.

2. *What are the different processes of electron emission from a metallic surface?*

Ans. The emission of electrons from a metallic surface is classified as follows :
(i) Thermionic emission, (ii) Secondary emission, (iii) Field emission and (iv) Photo-electric emission.

3. *What is meant by thermionic emission?*

Ans. If electrons are emitted from a metal by supplying thermal energy, the process is called thermionic emission. The number of electrons released depends on temperature. At a given temperature the thermionic emission current density is obtained by an equation known as Richardson's law.

4. *What is the relation between thermionic current density and temperature, as given by Richardson?*

Ans. The thermionic current density (J) is related to the temperature (T) by a relation,

$$J = AT^2 \epsilon^{-b/T}$$

where A and b are constants.

5. *What are the different types of thermionic emitters?*

Ans. Thermionic emitters are of two different types. These are : (i) directly heated emitter or filamentary emitter and (ii) indirectly heated emitter or oxide-coated emitter.

6. *What is space charge?*

Ans. The atmosphere of thermoelectrons that is formed in the interelectrode space between cathode and plate is known as the space charge.

7. *How vacuum tubes can be classified?*

Ans. Vacuum tubes are classified in a number of ways :

(i) Depending on the number of electrodes, e.g., diode, triode, tetrode, pentode, etc.

(ii) Depending on the presence or absence of gas, e.g., high vacuum tubes and gas tubes.

(iii) Depending on the type of cathode use, e.g., thermionic tubes, electron multiplier tubes, cold cathode tubes and photo-tubes.

8. *How many electrodes are sealed in a diode valve?*

Ans. The term diode means two electrodes. The valve consists essentially of a cathode which serves as an emitter of electrons surrounded by a plate or an anode which acts as a collector of electrons. Both the electrodes of the valve are sealed inside an evacuated glass or metallic envelope.

9. *What are the static characteristics of a diode?*

Ans. The curves obtained on plotting anode current along the *y*-axis against the anode voltage along the *x*-axis is called the current-voltage characteristic of a diode. Since current and voltage involved pertain to the tube alone, irrespective of the associated circuits, the characteristics thus obtained usually referred to as 'static characteristics'.

10. *Indicate the function of the control grid of a triode.*

Ans. Since the control grid is usually placed close to the cathode, the potential applied to the grid has a greater effect on the electric field inside the tube. The grid, therefore, has a controlling effect on the plate current. The control grid in operation is kept at a negative potential with respect to the cathode. As a result, it does not draw any current and consume power.

11. *In a triode valve how many variable quantities are there?*

Ans. In a triode valve we have three variable quantities. There are : (i) plate current, (ii) plate voltage and (iii) grid voltage.

12. *What are the different characteristics of a triode?*

Ans. Three types of characteristics are there : (a) plate current-plate voltage characteristics, or 'plate characteristics'; (b) plate current-grid voltage characteristics or 'mutual characteristics'; this is also known as transfer characteristics; (c) plate voltage-grid voltage characteristics or 'constant current characteristics'. This is further known as 'amplification characteristics'.

13. *What do you mean by valve constants?*

Ans. The design factors of a valve are summarized by a series of numbers, called the valve constants.

14. *What are the important constants of a valve?*

Ans. The three most important constants of a valve are :

(i) the anode slope resistance or the a.c. plate resistance,

(ii) the transconductance or the mutual conductance, and

(iii) the amplification factor.

15. *Define Plate Resistance, Transconductance and Amplification Factor of a valve.*

Ans. Plate Resistance—This is defined as the ratio of a small change in plate voltage to the corresponding change in plate current when the grid voltage is kept constant.

Mathematically, plate resistance r_p is given by

$$r_p = \left(\frac{\delta e_b}{\delta i_b} \right)_{e_c = \text{constant}}$$

Transconductance—This is defined as the ratio of a small change in plate current to the corresponding change in control grid voltage when the plate voltage is kept constant.

Mathematically, transconductance g_m is given by

$$g_m = \left(\frac{\delta e_b}{\delta e_c} \right)_{i_b = \text{constant}}$$

Amplification Factor—This is defined as the ratio of a small change in plate voltage to the corresponding change in grid voltage when the plate current is kept constant.

Mathematically, amplification factor μ is given by

$$\mu = \left(\frac{\delta e_b}{\delta e_c}\right)_{i_b = \text{constant}}$$

16. *What is the relation between r_p, g_m and μ of a valve?*

Ans. The amplification factor (μ) is equal to the product of plate resistance (r_p) and mutual conductance (g_m) of a valve. Mathematically,

$$\mu = r_p \times g_m.$$

17. *What are the functions of screen grid?*

Ans. The screen grid of a tetrode valve has two important functions. First, it being maintained at a positive potential, helps to overcome the space charge effect and hence increases the plate current and mutual conductance. Secondly, when the valve is used as an amplifier, the screen grid eliminates the evil effect of interelectrode capacitance between the control grid and the anode.

18. *What are the functions of suppressor grid?*

Ans. The secondary electrons emitted by the anode are repelled by the negative suppressor grid and are driven back to the plate again. In this fashion the grid eliminates the effect of secondary electrons and hence the plate current rises smoothly with the increase of plate voltage.

The addition of suppressor grid also increases the shielding action between the plate and the control grid, and thus reduces the grid to plate capacitance.

Cathode-ray Oscillograph

19. *What is a cathode-ray oscillograph?*

Ans. The cathode-ray tube is used generally in an assemblage of apparatus called a cathode-ray oscillograph; the essential components of which are : (i) cathode-ray tube, (ii) deflection voltage amplifiers, (iii) power supplies and (iv) time base circuit.

20. *What are the main components of a cathode-ray tube?*

Ans. A cathode-ray tube has the following main components : (i) the electron gun, (ii) a deflection system and (iii) a fluorescent screen. A tube base is there to which connections from the elements inside the tube are made. The components of a CR tube are mounted carefully inside a highly evacuated glass envelope.

21. *What is the utility of the electron gun in a CR tube?*

Ans. The electron gun is used for producing and focussing the emitted electrons in a narrow beam.

22. *What are the different parts of an electron gun?*

Ans. The electron gun consists of (i) an indirectly heated cathode, (ii) a control grid, (iii) an accelerating electrode, (iv) a first focussing anode and (v) a second, or final accelerating anode.

23. *What is phosphor? Give names of some commonly used phosphor.*

Ans. The fluorescent material coated inside the tube is termed as phosphor. Some commonly used phosphors are : zinc silicate, zinc oxide, zinc sulphide, etc.

24. *Define electrostatic and magnetostatic deflection sensitivity.*

Ans. Electrostatic deflection—The electrostatic deflection sensitivity is the amount of deflection of electron spot produced on the screen when a voltage of one volt from a d.c. source is applied to the deflection plates. The unit of deflection sensitivity is then expressed in inch/volt or, mm/volt.

Magnetostatic deflection—The magnetostatic deflection sensitivity is defined as the amount of deflection of electron spot produced when one milliampere current flows through the deflection coil. The unit of deflection sensitivity is then expressed in inch/mA or, mm/mA.

25. *How are the two anodes a CR tube utilized?*

Ans. In order to focus the beam of electrons properly, the voltage applied on the first anode is utilized. The second anode which is kept at a high positive d.c. voltage relative to the cathode, accelerates the electron beam.

26. *How the deflection spot in an electrostatic deflection varies with the final anode voltage?*

Ans. We have, the deflection sensitivity,

$$S_d = \frac{d}{V_d} = \frac{lL}{2SV_a}.$$

For a given CR tube l, L and S are fixed and so varying the voltage applied to the plates, V_d, or the final anode voltage V_a, one may alter the deflection spot d. The equation shows that the deflection spot varies inversely with the final anode voltage.

Rectifiers and Filters

27. *What is a rectifier?*

Ans. A rectifier provides a substantially one-way path for the flow of electric current. That is a rectifier changes a.c. into pulsating d.c. by eliminating the negative half-cycles. This is called a unidirectional characteristic or unilateral conduction. The diode is admirably suited for rectification as it permits current to flow in one direction only.

28. *Why is rectification required?*

Ans. Power companies generally supply a.c. power because it can be easily generated and also economical to transmit. On the other hand, d.c. supply usually serves the power requirements for various electronic devices. This demands a rectification of a.c. into d.c. voltages and currents.

29. *What are the different types of diode used for rectification?*

Ans. The diode used for rectification may be : (i) electron tubes of the vacuum or gas-filled type, (ii) metallic type like copper oxide or selenium rectifiers and (iii) crystals or semiconductors made of germanium or silicon. Nowadays selenium rectifiers or crystal diodes are widely used in various electronic circuits as no filament supply is required there and so they have become increasingly popular in the field of radio and television receivers, in particular.

30. *How many types of rectifiers are there?*

Ans. Rectifiers may be broadly put into two categories depending on the period of conduction. These are (a) Half-wave rectifier and (b) Full-wave rectifier.

31. *Define (i) Half-wave and (ii) Full-wave Rectifier.*

Ans. (i) Half-wave Rectifier—A half-wave rectifier (one-diode) converts the applied alternating voltage to a pulsating voltage using half-cycle of the applied voltage. That is the conduction takes place during one half cycle only.

(ii) Full-wave Rectifier—A full-wave rectifier (two-diode) converts the applied alternating voltage to a pulsating voltage using full cycle of the applied voltage. That is the conduction takes place by the one rectifier element during one half and by the other element during the other half cycle.

32. *Write down the expressions for currents and voltages of the two rectifiers.*

Ans. If I_m represents the maximum current, E_m the maximum voltage and R_a be the resistance connected in series with the load R_l, then we have,

(i) DC or average value of current

$$(I_{dc})_{H.W.} = \frac{I_m}{\pi} = \frac{E_m}{\pi(R_a + R_l)}$$

$$(I_{dc})_{F.W.} = \frac{2I_m}{\pi} = \frac{2E_m}{\pi(R_a + R_l)}$$

(ii) RMS value of current

$$(I_{rms})_{H.W} = \frac{I_m}{2} \qquad (I_{rms})_{F.W.} = \frac{I_m}{\sqrt{2}}$$

(iii) DC or average voltage across the load

$$(E_{dc})_{H.W.} = \frac{E_m}{\pi\left(1 + \frac{R_a}{R_l}\right)} \qquad (E_{dc})_{F.W.} = \frac{2E_m}{\pi\left(1 + \frac{R_a}{R_l}\right)}$$

(iv) RMS value of the voltage across the load

$$(E_{rms})_{H.W.} = \frac{E_m}{2\left(1 + \frac{R_a}{R_l}\right)} \qquad (E_{rms})_{F.W.} = \frac{E_m}{\sqrt{2}\left(1 + \frac{R_a}{R_l}\right)}$$

33. *Define ripple factor and form factor.*

Ans. We know that the rectified output is unidirectional in nature. But because of the continuous changes in amplitudes or pulsations the current is not a direct one (d.c.), rather these pulsations contain both d.c. and a.c. components.

The ripple factor, denoted by γ, may be defined as,

$$\gamma = \frac{\text{effective value of the a.c. components of current (or voltage)}}{\text{d.c. value of current (or voltage)}} = \frac{I_{ac}}{I_{dc}}$$

$$= \sqrt{\left(\frac{I_{rms}}{I_{dc}}\right)^2 - 1} = \sqrt{F^2 - 1}$$

where $F = \dfrac{I_{rms}}{I_{dc}}$ is called the form factor.

34. *Show that the ripple factor for a full-wave rectifier is small in comparison to a half-wave rectifier.*

Ans. We have, the ripple factor, $\gamma = \sqrt{F^2 - 1}$

For a half-wave rectifier,

$$(F)_{H.W.} = \frac{I_m/2}{I_m/\pi} = \frac{\pi}{2} = 1.57$$

$$\therefore \quad (\gamma)_{H.W.} = \sqrt{(1.57)^2 - 1} = 1.21$$

and for a full-wave rectifier,

$$(F)_{\text{F.W.}} = \frac{I_m/\sqrt{2}}{2I_m/\pi} = \frac{\pi}{2\sqrt{2}} = 1.11$$

$$\therefore \quad (\gamma)_{\text{H.W.}} = \sqrt{(1.11)^2 - 1} = 0.48$$

It thus appears that the ripple factor for a full-wave rectifier is small in comparison to half-wave rectifier.

35. *What do you mean by the efficiency of the rectifier?*

Ans. The efficiency of the rectifier, denoted by η, may be defined as,

$$\eta = \frac{\text{d.c. output power}}{\text{a.c. input power}} = \frac{P_{\text{dc}}}{P_{\text{ac}}}$$

For a half-wave rectifier, $(\eta)_{\text{H.W.}} = \dfrac{0.406}{1 + \frac{R_a}{R_L}}$

and for a full-wave rectifier, $(\eta)_{\text{F.W.}} = \dfrac{0.812}{1 + \frac{R_a}{R_L}}$

36. *Make a comparative study of half-wave and full-wave rectifier.*

Ans. We may compare a half-wave rectifier with a full-wave rectifier by considering the following important points :

(i) Ripple factor of a half-wave rectifier is greater than that of a full-wave rectifier.

(ii) Rectifier efficiency of a full-wave rectifier is greater than that of a half-wave rectifier.

(iii) Half-wave rectifier has a low transformer efficiency and a low output voltage than that of a full-wave rectifier.

(iv) In half-wave rectification current through the secondary of a transformer flows in the same direction while in full-wave rectification equal currents flow in the opposite direction through the centre-tapped secondary.

(v) Half-wave rectifier has low cost in comparison to a full-wave rectifier.

37. *What is a filter?*

Ans. The output voltage obtained by using a rectifier circuit includes ripple which must be minimized to use it as a d.c. source. The required smoothing action is achieved by filter networks. Choke, capacitor and resistor are usually filter elements.

38. *What are the functions of a bleeder resistor?*

Ans. The bleeder has the following important functions :

(i) It helps to maintain a constant output voltage by drawing a minimum current at all times.

(ii) When the receiver tubes or other loads in the circuit are heating up, the bleeder resistor maintains a minimum load across the rectifier. Without the bleeder resistor, there would be an initial high voltage surge as soon as the rectifier is turned on which might damage the circuit.

(iii) After the rectifier has been turned off, the bleeder discharges the capacitors and thus helps to prevent dangerous shocks.

39. *What are the different types of filter?*

Ans. Filters are broadly classified as : choke input filter and capacitor input filter. In a choke input filter, since the first component of the filter circuit is a choke coil connected in series with the rectifier output, it is so named. In a capacitor input filter similarly the first component is a shunt capacitor connected across the rectifier.

40. *Make a comparative study of the two filters.*

Ans.

Choke Input Filter	*Capacitor Input Filter*
(i) DC output here has not attained the peak value of pulsation.	(i) For the same AC input the output voltage attains a comparatively higher value.
(ii) The output voltage changes very little with the changes of the load current.	(ii) The output voltage rapidly falls with an increase of load current.
(iii) It provides a good voltage regulation.	(ii) The voltage regulation is considerably poor.

Amplifiers

41. *What is the function of an amplifier?*

Ans. The function of an amplifier is to increase the level of the current, voltage or power at its output.

42. *What do you mean by the gain of an amplifier?*

Ans. The amount of the increase of the level of the current (or voltage or power) is called the amplification or gain of the amplifier.

43. *What is meant by the cascade amplifier?*

Ans. If a number of amplifiers are connected in series so that the output of one becomes input to the next, then the early stages build up the voltage to a high level while the last stage builds up the power to a level suitable for operating a speaker or other similar devices. This amplifier is known as a cascade amplifier.

44. *How are the amplifiers classified?*

Ans. Amplifiers are classified in a number of ways. These are : (i) according to the type of load used, (ii) according to the number of stages and methods of coupling and (iii) according to the choice of the operating point of the vacuum tube.

45. *Give names of different types of amplifiers according to the load used.*

Ans. Examples according to the type of load used are untuned amplifiers (i.e., audio frequency and video frequency amplifiers) and tuned amplifiers (also referred to as radio frequency amplifiers).

46. *What is meant by distortion in amplifiers?*

Ans. The amplified output in an ideal amplifier is the enlarged version of the input signal. But in practice, a difference is noticed between the output and input waveforms. The amplifier is then said to have a distortion. The three main types of distortions are the amplitude distortion, frequency distortion and phase distortion.

47. *What do you mean by feedback in amplifiers?*

Ans. The term feedback means transferring a portion of the output energy of any device to its input. If the feedback voltage in an amplifier adds to the input signal voltage, it increases the amplification of the amplifier and it is called a positive or regenerative feedback. On the other hand, if the feedback voltage subtracts from the input signal voltage, the amplification decreases and the feedback is called a degenerative feedback.

Radio Communication

48. *Define the terms modulation and detection.*

Ans. For transmission of intelligence or message from one place to another, we have to take the help of high frequency or radio frequency waves. Such a process of raising the frequency of the intelligence or message by superposition over a high frequency voltage is known as modulation. Or, briefly we may define modulation as a process of superposing information on a radio carrier wave. The reverse process of translating back the information from the radio wave to the original frequency is called demodulation or detection.

49. *What are the basic elements of a radio communication system?*

Ans. The basic elements of a radio communication system are : (i) a microphone or a telegraph key to control the radio waves, (ii) a transmitter for generation of radio waves, (iii) a transmitting antenna and a receiving antenna, (iv) a radio receiver to select, amplify and demodulate the information present in radio waves and (v) a loudspeaker or a headphone to convert the electrical waves into sound.

50. *What are the essential parts of an AM radio transmitter?*

Ans. An AM radio transmitter consists essentially of (i) a master oscillator, (ii) a number of frequency multipliers, (iii) several power amplifiers and (iv) modulating system.

51. *What is a radio receiver?*

Ans. A radio receiver picks up any RF signal through a receiving antenna and then recovers from it the original modulating signal.

52. *How are the radio receivers classified?*

Ans. Radio receivers may be, broadly classified as : (a) Amplitude Modulation (AM) broadcast receivers, (b) Frequency Modulation (FM) broadcast receivers, (c) Television (TV) receivers, (d) Radar receivers, (e) Communication receivers and (f) Code receivers.

53. *Mention the essential functions of a radio receiver.*

Ans. The essential functions of a radio receiver are : (i) to extract the desired RF signal from the electromagnetic waves, (ii) to amplify the RF signal, (iii) to demodulate the RF signal for getting back the original modulating voltage and (iv) to feed the modulating voltage in an indicator like loudspeaker, etc., for receiving the original programme.

54. *What are the important characteristics of a broadcast receiver?*

Ans. The following characteristics of a broadcast receiver are of primary importance : (i) Adaptability to different aerials, (ii) Operational simplicity, (iii) Good fidelity, (iv) Average sensitivity and (v) Good selectivity.

Semiconductors

55. *What are the advantages of a semiconductor over a vacuum tube?*

Ans. The following are the main advantages of a semiconductor over a vacuum tube :

(i) Semiconductor is solid. Therefore, there is a little chance of vibration as in vacuum tube.

(ii) Little power is required for a semiconductor and also it radiates less heat than in a tube.

(iii) They do not need time for warm up and so operate immediately with the application of power.

(iv) A semiconductor does not undergo any chemical deterioration which occurs in a tube cathode.

(v) A semiconductor is small in size and light in weight.

56. *How can a semiconductor be identified from a conductor and an insulator?*

Ans. A conductor and an insulator are first distinguished by their extreme values of electrical conductivity. A conductor has a conductivity of 10^4 to 10^6 ohm^{-1} cm^{-1} while the conductivity of an insulator is less than 10^{-6} ohm^{-1} cm^{-1}. Moreover, the conductivity of a conductor decreases with the increase of its temperature while that for an insulator increases slightly with increasing temperature. In addition to conductors and insulators, there is a class of solids with intermediate values of electrical conductivity in the range 10^{-6} to 10^3 ohm^{-1} cm^{-1} and whose conductivity increases more strongly with increasing temperature. Such solids are called semiconductors.

57. *What is meant by 'current carriers'?*

Ans. In vacuum tubes, negatively charged electrons are considered as the 'current carriers'. In order to explain current flow in semiconductor diodes and transistors, this concept must be modified by the addition of positive charge carriers known as 'holes', which have mass, mobility and velocity. Current flow in semiconductors is thus carried on by the flow of both negative charges (free electrons) and positive charges (holes). Holes are usually attracted by free electrons and when they combine, the free electron 'fills' the hole neutralizing its charge. When this happens the hole and free electrons both are lost as current carriers and form new current carrier at other points in the semiconductor.

58. *Explain how P-type and N-type semiconductors are formed?*

Ans. Impurity like arsenic or antimony (pentavalent atoms) increases the conductivity of silicon, which has four valance electrons in its outer shell, by increasing the number of negative charge carriers. Silicon which has been doped here with arsenic or antimony is designated as '*N*-type'. Similarly, impurity like indium or gallium (trivalent atoms) increases the conductivity of silicon by increasing the number of positive charge carriers. For this reason, silicon which has been doped with indium or gallium is called '*P*-type'.

59. *How is a junction diode formed?*

Ans. When *P*-type and *N*-type silicons are joined together, a junction diode is formed. The diode thus created has a characteristic to pass current in one direction readily but not in the other.

60. *What do you mean by 'forward-bias' and 'reverse-bias' arrangement?*

Ans. When the positive terminal of a battery is connected to P-type and negative battery terminal to N-type of a diode, it is called 'forward-bias' and the diode is said to have a low forward resistance.

If the polarities of the battery are reversed, no combination of free electrons and holes takes place and the arrangement is called 'reverse-bias' condition.

61. *What is a zener diode?*

Ans. We know that a junction diode is operated suitably by using forward-bias arrangement. In zener diode, its unique reverse-bias characteristic provides some important applications from those of the crystal diode. Manufacturers supply a specification sheet for each type of zener diode. The breakdown voltage in a diode mainly depends on the material used in its construction.

The zener diode is used conveniently as a regulator in power supply.

Transistors

62. *Broadly classify the different types of transistors.*

Ans. Transistors are of many types which may be broadly classified as :

(i) Depending on the basic materials from which they are formed (e.g., silicon and germanium transistors).

(ii) Depending on the number of elements used (e.g., triode and tetrode transistors).

(iii) Depending on the ability to dissipate power (i.e., from low power to high power).

(iv) Depending on the process of construction (e.g., planar transistors, point contact transistors).

63. *Discuss how the leads of a transistor can be identified.*

Ans. The emitter, base and collector leads of a transistor can be conveniently identified by the following two ways :

(i) The central lead corresponds to the base. The spacing between the emitter lead and the base lead is less than the spacing between the base lead and the collector lead.

(ii) If the leads are along the circumference of a circle, then the centre one is called base. The emitter and the collector leads are then identified by reading clockwise from the base. In such reading first comes the collector and then the emitter.

The collector lead can also be identified by a dot which is pointed on the body of the transistor close to the collector.

64. *Define α and β of a transistor.*

Ans. α is defined as the ratio of the change in collector current (ΔI_C) to the change in emitter current (ΔI_E) when the collector voltage (V_{CB}) is maintained at a constant value. Mathematically, this can be expressed as,

$$\alpha = \left(\frac{\Delta I_C}{\Delta I_E} \right)_{V_{CB}=\text{constant}}$$

β is defined as the ratio of the change in collector current (ΔI_C) to the change in base current (ΔI_B) when the collector voltage (V_{CE}) is kept constant.

Mathematically, this can be expressed as,

$$\beta = \left(\frac{\Delta I_C}{\Delta I_B}\right)_{V_{CE}=\text{constant}}$$

65. *What is the relation between currents in the elements of a transistor?*

Ans. The relationship between currents in the elements of a transistor is expressed as,

$$I_E = I_B + I_C$$

where I_E is the emitter current and I_B, I_C are the base current and collector current respectively.

66. *What is the relation between α and β of a transistor?*

Ans. The relation between α and β of a transistor can be written as,

$$\beta = \frac{\alpha}{1-\alpha} \quad \text{or,} \quad \alpha = \frac{\beta}{1+\beta}.$$

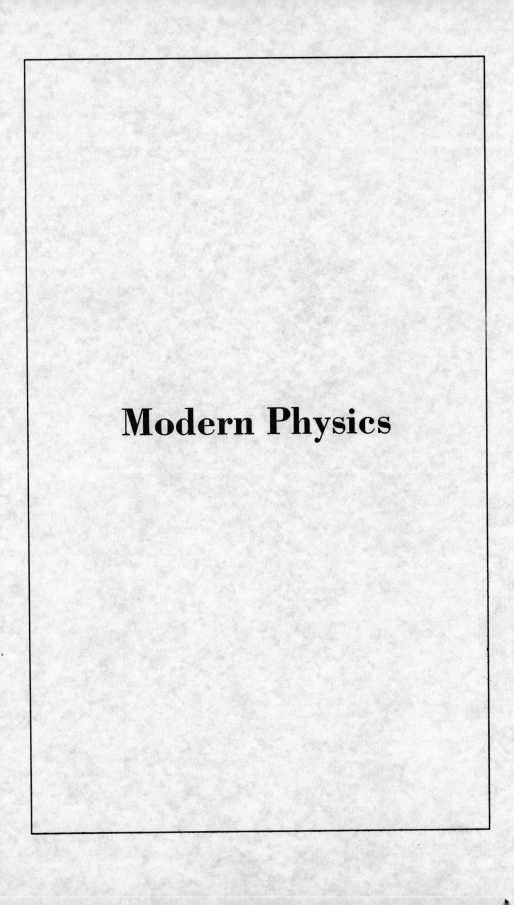

Modern Physics

Chapter 33
Cathode Rays and Positive Rays

33.1 Introduction

Modern Physics deals with various phenomena based on the atomicity of matter and radiations of all types including radiant heat and light. The atomicity of matter was explained by Dalton as far back as 1803. Later, Prout concluded that different kinds of atoms are built up of hydrogen atoms. Mendeleeff's discovery of periodic table suggested subatomic constituent components of atom. According to him, it was propounded that properties of elements are periodic functions of their atomic weights. The measurement of charge carried by the process of electrolysis was a step forward at atomicity of electricity. The study of the discharge of electricity through rarefied gases by Thomson, Rutherford and Millikan may be regarded as the starting point of the modern atomic physics which led to the discovery of electron. The experimental works of Thomson, Aston, Bainbridge on positive rays established the existence of a type of subatom called *proton* which was identified as the nucleus of hydrogen atom. Rutherford's investigations on radioactive elements suggested that an atom is composed of a massive nucleus around which the electrons revolve.

The discovery that both matter and electricity are of atomic nature was the origin of Planck's quantum theory. The discovery of isotopes, X-rays and ordinary optical spectra have given information about the structure of atom. The domain of Modern Physics became widened during the last half century. Einstein's theory of relatively led to the discovery of Einstein's mass-energy equivalence. The dual nature, i.e., wave and corpuscular nature of electron was then established. The nuclear fission and fusion of elements of radioactive type on which atom and hydrogen bombs are based, are great inventions undoubtedly. The discovery of the existence of highly penetrating radiations called *cosmic rays* in the outer spaces, was a further step in throwing new light on the structure and behaviour of nucleus.

33.2 Electrical Conduction through Gases

At normal pressure and temperature, gases are poor conductors of electricity. Normal air behaves as a perfect insulator of electricity. For that reason, a charged gold-leaf electroscope should retain its charge for an infinitely long time. With a most perfect insulation of a charged electroscope, Rutherford and Wilson found a gradual leakage of charge. This fact was attributed to the existence of some agents, like cosmic rays, radioactive radiations, etc., in the atmospheric air which produced charged ions in the neutral air particles all round the gold leaves. The splitting of neutral atoms into electrically charged components both positive and negative type are called *ions* and the process said to be *ionization*. The agents which split up the neutral atoms into ions are known as *ionizing agents*.

33.3 Ionization of Gas

The process of breaking-up of neutral gas atoms into positively and negatively charged particles is known as *ionization*. The opposite charges are equal in amount.

In ionization, one or more electrons are removed from the atom. The atom is then left behind with a net positive charge and it called *positive ion*. This net positive charges are same as the total negative charges of the electrons removed. The electron removed from the atom may remain alone or may be attached to a neutral atom. In this way, the electron also forms a negative ion. The electrons in an atom are strongly bound by an attractive force to the nucleus. So in order to remove the electron and to ionize a gas, a definite amount of energy is necessary which differs for different gases. It is larger for inert gases like helium and neon than for hydrogen and oxygen, as the binding force in the atoms is higher for helium and neon than for hydrogen and oxygen.

33.4   Methods of Producing Ionization

Ionization may be produced by different methods, some of which are as follows :

(i) By radioactive radiations like α-, β- and γ-rays : This can be verified by putting a small quantity of a radioactive substance near a charged electroscope and observing the collapse of the leaves of the electroscope.

(ii) By electro-magnetic radiations of short wavelength (shorter than wavelengths of visible light) : These are ultra-violet light ($\lambda = 3200$ A.U.), X-rays ($\lambda = 0.5$ A.U.), γ-rays ($\lambda = 0.05$ A.U.) and cosmic rays ($\lambda = 0.00005$ A.U.).

The shorter wavelength radiation has greater energy and so they have greater ionizing power.

(iii) By flames and heat : Gases in the vicinity of flames become ionized and thus behave as conductor of electricity. If gases are heated to a very high temperature, molecules collide with one another with high velocity. Electrons are then ejected and gases become ionized.

When a charged gold-leaf electroscope is exposed to ultra-violet light, X-rays or radioactive radiations, the electroscope is found to lose charge slowly.

The various agents utilized to produce ionization are known as *ionizing agents*.

33.5   Ionization Current

If the two electrodes, one maintained at positive potential and the other at negative potential by a battery, are placed in a space containing gaseous ions, the positive ions will go towards the negative electrode, and the negative ions towards the positive electrode. This movement of the oppositely charged ions produces the *ionization current*.

A simple device called *ionization chamber* can be used for the study of ionization produced in a gas by an ionizing agent. The ionization chamber consists of an airtight metal box connected to earth to serve the purpose of shielding the parallel plate electrodes A and B, placed inside the chamber, from stray electric field (Fig. 33.1). At one side of the box, there is a window of thin aluminium sheet transparent to the ionizing rays entering from

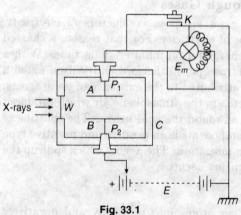

Fig. 33.1

outside. The plates are attached to two wires to pass out through non-conducting plugs P_1, P_2 fitted with the box. The box is filled with the experimental gas at a definite pressure. The plate A is connected to one pair of quadrant of a low-capacity electrometer E_m, whose other pair is earthed. A high tension battery with a potential divider is used to apply a known positive potential to the plate B, the negative terminal of the battery being earthed. Then having the adjacent quadrants short-circuited by the key K the plate A is first earthed. The electrometer needle then exhibits no deflection as both the pairs of quadrants are at zero potential. Next, if after opening the key K, the ionizing rays are allowed to enter the chamber, the potential of A and the attached electrometer changes gradually due to the ionic charges acquired by A. The deflection of electrometer needle is increased at a steady rate. This gives a measure of the increase in the potential of A per second which can be expressed as dv/dt.

Let C be the combined capacity of the electrometer and the plate-systems A-B, then charge q and potential v are related by the equation,

$$q = Cv. \tag{33.1}$$

So the ionization current,

$$i = \frac{dq}{dt} = C \cdot \frac{dv}{dt}. \tag{33.2}$$

Further v being proportional to the deflection θ, we can write,

$$v = C'\theta \text{ (where } C' \text{ is a constant).} \tag{33.3}$$

Hence, $\dfrac{dv}{dt} = C'\dfrac{d\theta}{dt}$. Therefore, $i = CC' \cdot \dfrac{d\theta}{dt} = K\dfrac{d\theta}{dt}$. $\tag{33.4}$

Eq. (33.4), shows that the ionization current is proportional to the steady rate of increase of electrometer deflection.

33.5.1 Relation between Ionization Current and Applied Voltage

If the potential difference between the plates A and B be gradually increased, the ionization also increases. A graph plotted with values of i against the applied voltage V shows that up to certain value of V the current increases linearly with the applied voltage (Fig. 33.2). This is represented by straight portion OA where Ohm's law is obeyed. As the voltage is increased in steps, the rate of increase of current slows down, as shown by the portion AB. When the applied voltage attains a certain value at B, the current is found to remain constant. This constant value is maintained even when the applied voltage is further increased. This constant current is known as

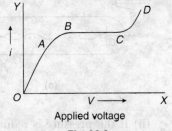

Applied voltage

Fig. 33.2

the *saturation current*. This is indicated by the horizontal portion BC. When the applied voltage is further increased beyond C, the current increases more rapidity until it causes a spark between the plates. This is represented by CD in the graph.

In course of experiment, when a potential difference is set up between the plates, the positive and the negative ions move towards the negative and the positive plate respectively. For initial low voltage, most ions recombine to form neutral atoms and cannot go to the plates. With the increase of applied voltage the ions move more and more quickly and a larger number of ions go to the opposite plates before recombination can occur. The current thus increases and the process continues until the applied voltage becomes so large that all the ions formed per second by the ionizing agent attain the respective plates before recombination can take place. At this stage the current is the saturation current. Further increase in applied voltage cannot produce any increase in current as there will be no more free ions reaching the plates in a second.

When the applied voltage is increased beyond the critical value C, the ions formed between the plates move so fast that they produce fresh ions by impact or collision with other neutral atoms of the gas. This causes a rapid increase of ionization current as indicated by CD in the graph. Finally, the conductivity of the gas becomes so high that the ions shoot out from one electrode to the other and a spark passes in between them. The difference of potential between the electrodes to start the discharge is known as the spark-potential. It is independent of the metal of the electrodes, but depends on the distance between the electrodes and also on the pressure of the gas between them. The minimum potential difference required to set up between the electrodes to cause ionization of gas in between them by electric discharge is the ionization potential.

The value of the saturation voltage depends on (i) the distance apart of the electrodes, (ii) the pressure of the gas and (iii) the intensity of ionization in the gas.

33.6 Phenomena of Discharge through Gases at Low Pressure

The phenomena of discharge in a gas at low pressure can be done by taking a glass tube containing the gas. The tube is fitted with two electrods, cathode C and anode A at its ends and has a side tube having a stopcock. The side tube is connected with a high vacuum pump to produce low pressure. When the terminals of the electrodes are connected to the secondary terminals of an induction coil, no spark discharge occurs at ordinary pressure of the air in the tube. The following situation will arise corresponding to different pressures :

(i) At a pressure of about 20 mm of mercury, a faint discharge with cracking sound occurs. If there is some reduction of pressure, the cracking sound ceases.

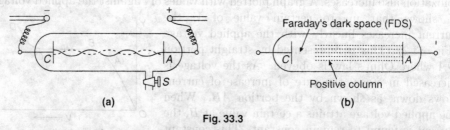

(a)   (b)

Fig. 33.3

(ii) If the pressure is reduced to about 10 mm of mercury, a spark in the form of a streak of light of pink colour extends from cathode to anode along a zigzag tortuous path [Fig. 33.3(a)].

(iii) When a pressure of about 1 mm of mercury is applied, a column of beautiful crimson colour, called *positive column*, is seen to extend from the cathode to the anode [Fig. 33.3(b)]. Close to the cathode, a short dark space separates the cathode from the positive column. This dark space is known as the *Faraday's Dark Space*. The cathode itself is found to cover by a thin glow, called the *Negative Glow* [Fig. 33.4(a)].

(iv) With a further reduction of pressure, the negative glow is found to detach itself from the cathode and a second dark space, called the *Crookes' Dark Space*, appears between the negative glow and the cathode which itself emits a glow called *Cathode Glow*. If the pressure is reduced to 0.1 mm of mercury, the same appearance continues in the tube except that the positive column splits up into alternate dark and bright bands called *Striations* which become fewer when the pressure is further reduced [Fig. 33.4(b)].

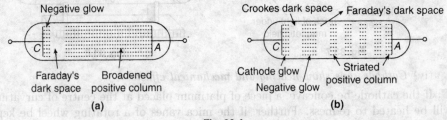

Negative glow

Faraday's dark space Broadened positive column

(a)

Crookes dark space Faraday's dark space

Cathode glow Striated positive column

Negative glow

(b)

Fig. 33.4

(v) With further reduction of pressure, the Crookes' dark space rapidly increases in size and the negative glow moves almost to the anode and the striated positive column almost disappears.

(vi) At a pressure between 0.01 mm and 0.02 mm of mercury, the Crookes' dark space alone fills the whole tube and the glow inside the tube completely disappears. The portion of glass wall opposite to the cathode and near the anode emits a glow, yellowish green or bluish according to the composition of the glass.

The glow emitted from the wall is owing to the impingement on the wall, of an invisible stream of charged particles moving with high velocity. These moving charged particles emanating from the cathode are known as *Cathode Rays*.

33.7 Properties of Cathode Rays

(i) *Cathode rays travel in straight lines and cast shadows of objects.*

This can be demonstrated by placing a mica cross in the Giesler vacuum tube in a direction at right angles to the direction of the cathode rays. A well-defined shadow of the cross will be produced on the fluorescent wall at the extreme end of the tube (Fig. 33.5).

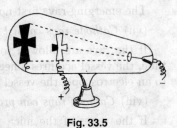

Fig. 33.5

(ii) *Cathode rays are deflected by an electrostatic field.*

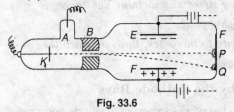

Fig. 33.6

The rays are found to be deflected when they are allowed to pass through two horizontal metal-plates supported within the tube and maintained at a constant potential difference thus creating a vertical electrostatic field (Fig. 33.6).

(iii) *Cathode rays are deflected by a magnetic field.*

In Fig. 33.7, the track of light shown by dotted line produced on fluorescent plate of aluminium placed obliquely in the absence of magnetic field, is found to be bent when a magnetic field is applied.

The beam is deflected by the magnetic field according to *Fleming's Left-hand Rule.* The direction of deflection is perpendicular both to the field and to the rays.

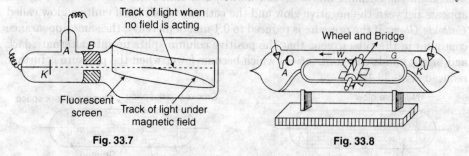

Fig. 33.7   **Fig. 33.8**

(iv) *Cathode rays show heating and mechanical effects.*

If the cathode be concave, a piece of platinum placed at the centre of curvature will be heated to redness. Further, if the mica vanes of a rotating wheel be kept in the path of the rays, the wheel is set in rotation and can move from one side to another by interchanging the potential of the electrodes of the vacuum tube (Fig. 33.8).

(v) *Cathode rays proceed normally from the cathode surface.*

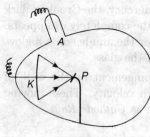

If the cathode be the part of a spherical concave surface, the rays are found to pass along the normals to the surface and converge to the centre of curvature of the surface. Due to their concentration, an aluminium plate placed at the centre of curvature becomes red-hot (Fig. 33.9).

(vi) *Cathode rays can go through thin metal foil or plate without puncturing them and a bluish stream comes out of the foil or the plate.*

Fig. 33.9

The emerging rays first noted by Lenard, are called *Lenard Rays.*

(vii) *Cathode rays consist of negatively charged particles.*

If the rays are allowed to pass into a metal vessel placed within the vacuum tube, the vessel acquires a negative charge. If it be connected to an electrometer or to an electroscope, the vessel is found to be charged negatively.

(viii) *Cathode rays can produce phosphorescence on some bodies.*

If the vanes of the mica wheel be coated with suitable substances, variously coloured phosphorescent light can be observed when the wheel rotates.

(ix) *Cathode rays produce X-rays if they strike any metallic substance.*

(x) *Cathode rays can affect a photographic plate.*

(xi) *Cathode rays can impart conductivity to the gases, through which they pass.*

Therefore, cathode rays can ionize a gas.

33.7.1   Negative Charge Conveyed by the Cathode Rays

The fact that cathode rays carry negative charge was experimentally demonstrated by Thomson using an apparatus as described below. His experiment was a modification of the experiment of Perrin :

In the Fig. 33.10, C is the cathode, the solid brass anode A is earthed and has a slit in it. B and D are two metal vessels insulated from each other. Each vessel is

provided with a narrow transverse slit. The outer vessel B is
earthed and D is connected to
an electrometer or electroscope.
When the metal electrodes are
connected to the terminals of an
induction coil, the cathode rays
are emitted along lines normal to
the surface of the cathode and
pass straight through the slit in
the anode. No charge is acquired

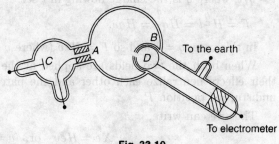

Fig. 33.10

by D when the rays are undeflected. If the rays are deflected by a magnet held in
such a way that the rays strike the slit in B, the vessel D rapidly receives a negative
charge as is shown by the electrometer deflection or electroscope divergence.
However, a limit is soon reached due to the gas in the discharge tube becoming
conducting.

33.8 Determination of Specific Charge (e/m) of Electron

The apparatus used by J.J. Thomson is a highly evacuated discharge tube C as
the cathode, A the anode in a side tube. The wall S of the tube has a coating of
some fluorescent compound (e.g., barium platinocyanide). When the terminals of
an induction coil are connected to C and A, cathode rays are formed in the tube
(Fig. 33.11).

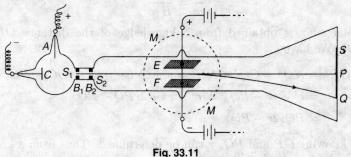

Fig. 33.11

Cathode rays coming out from the cathode pass through the slits S_1 and S_2 in
two metal blocks B_1 and B_2 respectively and then emerge out as a very narrow
beam. The narrow cathode beam then passes through a vertical electric field and a
transverse magnetic field. The electric field is set up by two plates E, F, maintained
at a potential difference connecting to the terminals of a battery, while the magnetic
field restricted to the circular space M, is set up by an electromagnet or by external
coils of wire carrying a current. In the absence of any electric or magnetic field, the
narrow cathode beam proceeds straight to produce a luminous patch at P on the
screen S. As the electric and magnetic fields are mutually perpendicular to each
other, the electric deflection and magnetic deflection occur in the same plane.

Let e be the charge on an electron and X the intensity of the electric field. The
force acting on an electron is equal to Xe. Further, the magnetic force on each
electron is Hev, where H is the intensity of the magnetic field and v, the velocity
of the electrons.

Now, if a wire of length l traversed by a current i be placed in a magnetic field
H acting at right angles to the wire, it moves under a force, $F = Hil$. But we have

$i = q/t$, where q is the charge flowing in t sec.

$$\therefore \quad F = H\frac{q}{t}l = Hq\frac{l}{t} = Hqv. \tag{33.5}$$

In this case, $q = e$ and so $F = Hev$ (where $v =$ velocity of the electron).

When both the two fields are applied at the same time and adjusted to that, their effects neutralize each other and the patch of light remains in the central undisturbed position P.

Thus we can write,

$$Xe = Hev \quad \text{or,} \quad v = \frac{X}{H}. \tag{33.6}$$

The cathode beam is next subjected to magnetic field only. The beam will be deflected and on falling on the fluorescent screen it will produce a patch of light at Q. The path of the beam under magnetic field will be an arc of a circle of radius r, as the direction of the force is perpendicular to the direction of motion of the electron.

Let m be the mass of electron, then the centripetal force acting on it $= \frac{mv^2}{r}$. As this force is equal to Hev, we can write,

$$\frac{mv^2}{r} = Hev \quad \text{or,} \quad \frac{e}{m} = \frac{v}{Hr}. \tag{33.7}$$

Now, putting the value of v from Eq. (33.6), we get

$$\frac{e}{m} = \frac{X}{H^2 r}. \tag{33.8}$$

The value of r is obtained from a knowledge of the distance OP and PQ (Fig. 33.12). We have

$$OP^2 = NQ^2 = CQ^2 - NC^2 = r^2 - NC^2 = r^2 - (OC - NO)^2$$
$$= r^2 - (r - PQ)^2 = r^2 - r^2 + 2rPQ - PQ^2$$
$$= PQ(2r - PQ).$$

Hence, knowing OP and PQ, r can be determined. Thus from a knowledge of X, H and $r, e/m$ can be found out.

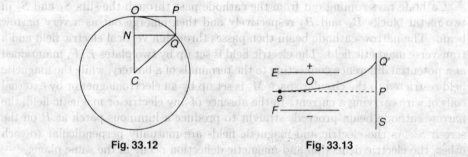

Fig. 33.12   Fig. 33.13

Thomson obtained the value of e/m as 1.77×10^8 coulombs/gm $= 1.77 \times 10^7$ e.m.u. per gram or 5.21×10^{17} e.s.u./gm. The velocity of electron v was found to be of the order of 10^9 cm/sec.

When only the electric field is applied, a force Xe acts on an electron of mass m in a vertical direction (Fig. 33.13). So the acceleration produced $= Xe/m$, acting during the time t spent in traversing the field.

This time t is equal to l/v, where l is the length of the field and v the velocity of the electron. Now the vertical velocity = acceleration × time = $\frac{Xel}{mv}$. After coming out of the field, each electron will possess this vertical velocity and the horizontal velocity v along its original direction of motion. Thus, if L be the distance of the fluorescent screen from the centre of the field O and PQ' be the electric deflection, then we have

$$PQ'/L = \text{vertical velocity/horizontal velocity} = Xel/mv^2$$

or, $$\frac{e}{m} = \frac{v^2}{Xl} \cdot \frac{PQ'}{L} = \frac{X^2}{XH^2} \times \frac{PQ'}{L \cdot l} = \frac{XPQ'}{H^2L \cdot l} \qquad (33.9)$$

$$(\because v = \tfrac{X}{H} \text{ from experiment under combined fields})$$

Hence, knowing X, H, PQ', L and l, the value of e/m can be determined.

33.8.1   Importance of Measurement of e/m of Electron

The value of e/m found to be independent of the material of the cathode, the anode or the nature of the gas within the discharge tube. Besides the discharge tube, electrons may be produced (i) by action of heat on certain bodies (thermions), (ii) by action of light of suitable wavelength on certain metals (photo-electrons). Later experiments revealed that the value of e/m of thermo-electrons and photo-electrons was identical with that of electrons generated inside a discharge tube by ionization. All these led to the conclusion that atoms of all elements contained electrons. In other words, electron is an universal constituent of all elements and hence of all material bodies known.

33.9   Determination of Charge of an Electron by Millikan's Oil-drop Method

The method developed by Millikan is a modification of an earlier experiment done by Wilson who made observation by condensing water drops on charged ions under certain conditions. For eliminating errors due to evaporation, Millikan used drops of oil having low vapour pressure. The experimental arrangement employed by Millikan is shown in Fig. 33.14.

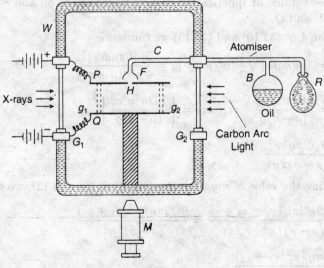

Fig. 33.14

The instrument consists of two optically flat plates of metal P and Q set parallel by glass separators g_1 and g_2 inside an air-tight chamber C. Oil is sprayed into the chamber through the funnel F by using an atomiser. A few drops of oil pass into the space between the plates P and Q through a pin-hole H drilled at the centre of the upper plate P. An electric field is set up between the plates by connecting them with a battery. An intense beam of light from an arc lamp on one side illuminates inside through the glass window G_2. The oil drops and their movements are observed by a microscope M having a scale in its eyepiece. The oil drops within the space between P and Q are charged due to friction in the process of spraying.

Let us consider a single oil drop having negative charge E. In the absence of electric field, the drop moves down under the action of gravity but due to an upward viscous force of air, it falls downward with a uniform terminal velocity. If this velocity be v_1, then from Stokes' Law, we can write,

$$mg = 6\pi\eta a v_1, \tag{33.10}$$

where m = mass of oil drop, a = its radius, η = coefficient of viscosity of air inside P and Q.

If the electric field of intensity X is now applied so that upper plate is positive, the drop rises upwards. The force due to the applied field is XE, and that due to gravity is mg. Therefore, the resultant force $= XE - mg$. If v_2 be the upward steady velocity, then we have

$$XE - mg = 6\pi\eta a v_2 \tag{33.11}$$

Dividing Eq. (33.11) by Eq. (33.10), we get

$$\frac{XE - mg}{mg} = \frac{v_2}{v_1} \quad \text{or,} \quad \frac{XE}{mg} = \frac{v_1 + v_2}{v_1}$$

or, $$XE = mg\frac{v_1 + v_2}{v_1}. \tag{33.12}$$

Further, allowing for buoyancy,

$$mg = \frac{4}{3}\pi a^3(\rho - \sigma)g, \tag{33.13}$$

where $\frac{4}{3}\pi a^3$ = volume of spherical oil drop, ρ = density of oil and σ = density of air between P and Q.

Hence from Eq. (33.10) and (33.13) we can write,

$$\frac{(mg)^3}{mg} = (6\pi\eta a v_1)^3 / \frac{4}{3}\pi a^3(\rho - \sigma)g = \frac{3}{4}\frac{(6\pi\eta a v_1)^3}{\pi a^3(\rho - \sigma)g}$$

or, $$(mg)^2 = \frac{162\pi^2\eta^3 v_1^3}{(\rho - \sigma)g} \quad \text{or,} \quad mg = \left\{\frac{162\pi^2\eta^3 v_1^3}{(\rho - \sigma)g}\right\}^{\frac{1}{2}}.$$

$$\therefore \quad mg = \frac{9\sqrt{2}\pi\eta^{\frac{3}{2}} v_1^{\frac{3}{2}}}{(\rho - \sigma)^{\frac{1}{2}} g^{\frac{1}{2}}}. \tag{33.14}$$

Substituting the value of mg from Eq. (33.14) in Eq. (33.12), we get

$$XE = \frac{9\sqrt{2}\pi\eta^{\frac{3}{2}} v_1^{\frac{3}{2}}}{(\rho - \sigma)^{\frac{1}{2}} g^{\frac{1}{2}}} \cdot \frac{v_1 + v_2}{v_1} = \frac{9\sqrt{2}\pi\eta^{\frac{3}{2}} v_1^{\frac{1}{2}}(v_1 + v_2)}{(\rho - \sigma)^{\frac{1}{2}} g^{\frac{1}{2}}}.$$

$$\therefore \quad E = \frac{18\pi\eta^{\frac{3}{2}} v_1^{\frac{1}{2}}(v_1 + v_2)}{X\sqrt{2}(\rho - \sigma)^{\frac{1}{2}} g^{\frac{1}{2}}}. \tag{33.15}$$

The values of v_1 and v_2 are determined from a knowledge of the times of transit of the oil drop through a fixed distance along the scale of the eyepiece. Thus knowing all quantities of right-hand side of Eq. (33.15), the charge E on the drop can be obtained.

As the oil drop may have captured one, two or more electrons during observation, the charge E does not necessarily correspond to electronic charge itself, but may be twice, thrice or higher multiples of it. For this, the experiment was conducted by Millikan a large number of times using various drops at different intervals of time. It was noted that different values of E obtained were integral multiples of some smallest unit. This smallest unit is, therefore, considered to be equal to the charge of electron e.

Millikan found that the smallest value of the charge of electron as equal to 4.77×10^{-10} electrostatic unit $= 1.59 \times 10^{-19}$ coulomb $= 1.59 \times 10^{-20}$ electromagnetic unit.

33.9.1 Balanced Drop Method for the Determination of Electronic Charge

Applying the identical experimental arrangement as above, the oil drop was allowed to fall under gravity and its steady terminal velocity v_1 was obtained by observation with microscope. Then using Stokes' law, $mg = 6\pi\eta a v_1$, one may proceed as follows :

We have $mg = \dfrac{4}{3}\pi a^3(\rho - \sigma)g$ or, $\dfrac{4}{3}\pi a^3(\rho - \sigma)g = 6\pi\eta a v_1$

or, $\qquad a^2 = \dfrac{9}{2} \cdot \dfrac{\eta v_1}{g(\rho - \sigma)}$ or, $a = \left\{ \dfrac{9}{2} \cdot \dfrac{\eta v_1}{g(\rho - \sigma)} \right\}^{\frac{1}{2}}$. $\qquad$ (33.16)

The plate P was kept positive and the electric field was so adjusted that the drop remained stationary due to equal and opposite forces of gravity and electric field. If X be electric intensity and E be the charge on the oil drop, then force due to electric field is XE.

For equilibrium of oil drop, we can write,

$$XE = mg = \frac{4}{3}\pi a^3(\rho - \sigma)g = \frac{4}{3}\pi \left(\frac{9}{2} \cdot \frac{\eta v_1}{g(\rho - \sigma)} \right)^{\frac{3}{2}} (\rho - \sigma)g$$

or, $\quad XE = \dfrac{9\sqrt{2}\pi\eta^{\frac{3}{2}} v_1^{\frac{3}{2}}}{g^{\frac{1}{2}}(\rho - \sigma)^{\frac{1}{2}}}$.

$\therefore \quad E = \dfrac{9\sqrt{2}\pi\eta^{\frac{3}{2}} v_1^{\frac{3}{2}}}{X g^{\frac{1}{2}}(\rho - \sigma)^{\frac{1}{2}}}$. $\qquad\qquad$ (33.17)

Using Eq. (33.17), E can be determined.

In this method, it has been assumed that the oil drop under observation carried charge of single electron. But in reality, the oil drop could carry one, two or more electronic charges. So the experiments was repeated with same oil drop several times and the values of E were found to be integral multiples of some least amount of charge. The lowest one was considered as the electronic charge e.

In order to get an accurate value of electronic charge e, Millikan applied an important correction. Millikan noted that the value of electronic charge e was not constant being larger for smaller drops than for larger ones. This was attributed to deviation from Stokes' law which when applied to very small drops needs a correction depending on the mean free path λ of gas molecules and the radius of the drop. The formula after correction reduced to a simplified form, $mg = 6\pi\eta av/\{1 + k(\lambda/a)\}$, where k is a constant whose value was determined by Millikan as 0.863.

33.9.2   Importance of Knowledge of Electronic Charge

(i) The smallest quantity of elementary charge associated with all positive or negative ions is the same as that of an electron. It is an atomic unit and is not a statistical average of a quantity which varies. The atomicity of electricity is so established.

(ii) **Mass of Electron and that of Hydrogen Atom :** The value of e/m_h for hydrogen ion in electrolysis is found to be 9645 e.m.u./gm, i.e., $e/m_h = 9645$, where e = charge on hydrogen ion (= electronic charge numerically) and m_h = mass of hydrogen atom. Again, $e/m_e = 1.7 \times 10^7$ e.m.u./gm, where m_e is mass of electron. Hence we get, $m_h/m_e = 9645/(1.7 \times 10) = 1850$. Thus electronic mass $m_e = 1/1850$ of the mass of hydrogen atom.

(iii) Thomson assumed the entire mass of electron as of electrical origin and deduced an expression for its mass which can be written as

$$m = \frac{2}{3} \cdot \frac{\mu e^2}{a}, \qquad (33.18)$$

where e = electronic charge, a = radius of electron sphere, and μ = the permeability of the medium which is unity in air. Hence, from Eq. (33.18), we get

$$a = \frac{2\mu e^2}{3m} = \frac{2 \times 1 \times (1.6 \times 10^{-20})^2}{3 \times 9.06 \times 10^{-28}} = 1.87 \times 10^{-13} \text{ cm.}$$

(iv) From a knowledge of e, we obtain the Avogadro's Number, i.e., the number of molecules in a gram molecule of a substance, or number of atoms in a gram atom of the substance. We have, 1 gm atom of any monoatomic substance is liberated by a charge of 96 500 coulombs.

Thus, the Avogadro's Number $= \dfrac{96\,500}{1.59 \times 10^{-19}} = 6.06 \times 10^{23}$.

(v) One may get the mass of an electron from a knowledge of electronic charge e and specific electronic charge e/m.

Therefore, mass of electron, $m = \dfrac{e}{e/m} = \dfrac{1.59 \times 10^{-19} \text{ coulomb}}{1.76 \times 10^{-8} \text{ coulomb/gm}}$

$$= 9.05 \times 10^{-28} \text{ gm.}$$

33.10   Energy of Moving Electron in *electron-volt*

If an electron of charge e electrostatic unit, falls through a potential difference of v electrostatic unit, then the work done $= ev$ ergs. This work imparts to the electron an equivalent kinetic energy. Again, the energy acquired by an electron in falling through a potential difference of one volt is called an *electron-volt*.

Now we have, charge of an electron $= 4.8 \times 10^{-10}$ electrostatic unit. Also, one volt $= \frac{1}{300}$ electrostatic unit. Thus one electron-volt $= \text{eV} = \frac{1}{300} \times 4.8 \times 10^{-10} = 1.6 \times 10^{-12}$ erg.

33.11   Positive Rays and Particles

We know that electrons (or negatively charged particles) are liberated from electrically neutral atoms of gases under the action of an intense electric field. So, the remainder of the atom will be positively charged particles and will travel towards the cathode. If the cathode is perforated with holes, the positive particles will pass through these holes into the space on the other side to form faintly luminous streams known as *positive* or *canal rays*. These rays are deflected by a magnet in a direction opposite to that of the cathode rays.

Fig. 33.15 shows a discharge tube in which
A is the anode, C a perforated cathode while
P_1 and P_2 are two metal plates attached at two
ends. When the discharge tube is put into action
by an induction coil and the plates are connected
to two quadrant electrometers E_1 and E_2, then

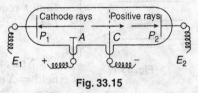

Fig. 33.15

electrometer E_1 indicates a negative charge but the electrometer E_2 indicates a positive charge.

33.12   Properties of Positive Rays

The following are the important properties :

(i)   Positive rays are deflected by both electric and magnetic fields in directions opposite to those of cathode rays indicating that they consist of streams of positively charged particles.

(ii) Positive rays can produce fluorescence.

(iii) The specific charge (e/m) of positive ray particles is smaller than that for cathode ray particles. Its value depends on the nature of the gas in the tube.

(iv) Positive rays can disintegrate metals.

33.13   Thomson's Experiment for the Study of Positive Rays

The apparatus used by Thomson for the study of positive rays is shown in Fig. 33.16. The discharge is produced in a large bulb B so that it can pass readily in a large

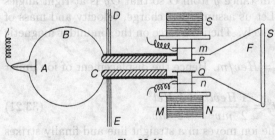

Fig. 33.16

space. In the figure, A is the anode and C is the cathode. The cathode consists of an aluminium rod with rounded end pierced by an axial fine copper tube of fine bore. The copper tube forms a narrow pencil of positive rays to produce a sharp spot on the fluorescent screen or photo-graphic plate S. In order to study positive rays, very low pressure is required in the camera space F, as otherwise due to collisions, velocity of positive rays will vary. The pressure in the discharge bulb should be comparatively high as discharge cannot pass at very low pressures. The fine bore of the cathode tube maintains this pressure difference. An electric field is applied between two soft iron plates P and Q which constitute the pole pieces of an electromagnet N, S, P and Q are electrically insulated from each other by thin mica sheets m, n. The electric and magnetic fields being parallel they produce deflections at right angles to each other which is obtained on a fluorescent screen or on a photographic plate. In absence of any magnetic or electric field, a positive ion goes straight to form a central undeflected bright spot on the screen.

33.13.1   Action of Electric Field

Let an electric field of intensity X be applied between the plates P and Q for a certain path as shown in Fig. 33.17. The positive ion instead of going straight to O

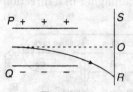

Fig. 33.17

will be deflected by OR in the direction of the field through a distance x from O. If the velocity of the ion be v, then the time t required to pass through the electric field of length l is

$$t = l/v.$$

Now, the force on the ion of charge e due to the electric field $= Xe$.

Hence, acceleration of the ion of mass $m = \alpha_1 = Xe/m$.

Thus the displacement of the ion in traversing the electric field is given by

$$\delta_1 = \frac{1}{2}\alpha_1 t^2 = \frac{1}{2} \cdot \frac{Xe}{m} \cdot \frac{l^2}{v^2}. \qquad (33.19)$$

After emerging from the electric field, the ion moves in a straight line and finally strikes the screen at a distance x from O, where x is proportional to both δ_1 and the distance of screen S from centre of the electric field. Thus we can write,

$$x \propto \frac{1}{2}\frac{Xel^2}{mv^2}$$

or, $$x = K_1 \frac{Xe}{mv^2}, \qquad (33.20)$$

where $K_1 = $ a constant.

33.13.2   Action of Magnetic Field

Let a magnetic field of intensity H be applied between the poles N, S, for the same length of the path l, the positive ion will be deflected by this in a direction perpendicular to that in which it was deflected under the action of electric field. The ion will strike the screen at a distance y from O so that Oy is at right angles to Ox in the plane of the screen. Let us assume that charge, velocity and mass of positive ion to be e, v and m respectively. Then the force on the ion under magnetic field $= Hev$.

The acceleration of the ion, $\alpha_2 = Hev/m$. Hence the displacement of ion under magnetic field,

$$\delta_2 = \frac{1}{2}\alpha_2 t^2 = \frac{1}{2}\frac{Hevl^2}{mv^2} = \frac{1}{2}\frac{Hel^2}{mv}. \qquad (33.21)$$

After emerging from the field the ion moves in a straight line and finally strikes the screen at a distance y from O. As y is proportional to both δ_2 and the distance of the screen from the field, we can write,

$$y \propto \frac{1}{2}\frac{Hel^2}{mv}$$

or, $$y = K_2 \frac{He}{mv}, \qquad (33.22)$$

where $K_2 = $ another constant.

When the electric and magnetic fields are applied simultaneously in directions parallel to each other, the resultant point of impact and so the displacement of the spot will depend upon the magnitudes of x and y.

Squaring Eq. (33.22) and dividing by Eq. (33.21), we get

$$\frac{y^2}{x} = \frac{K_2^2 \cdot H^2 e^2}{m^2 v^2} \Big/ \frac{K_1 \cdot Xe}{mv^2} = \frac{K_2^2 H^2 e^2}{m^2 v^2} \cdot \frac{mv^2}{K_1 Xe}$$

or,
$$\frac{y^2}{x} = \frac{K_2^2}{K_1} \cdot \frac{H^2}{X} \cdot \frac{e}{m} \tag{33.23}$$

$$= K \cdot \frac{e}{m}, \tag{33.24}$$

where K is another constant for given values of H and X.

Utilizing the assigned values of H and X and measuring K, x and y, the value of e/m can be obtained from Eq. (33.24).

33.14 Positive Ray Parabolas

Eq. (33.23) is an equation of a parabola when e/m is constant. This indicates that all the positive ions possessing the same value of e/m, for all values of the velocities will lie along the arc of the same parabola. The positive ions having different values of e/m will lie on different parabolas. Thus the particles for which e/m are different will be sorted out into a series of parabolas.

Let m_1 and m_2 be the masses of two different ions but of same charges. They will be deflected in parabolas ab, cd whose ordinates y_1, y_2 (PN, QN) for the same values of abscissa will be given by

$$\frac{y_1^2}{x} = k \frac{e}{m_1} \cdot \frac{H^2}{X} \quad \text{and} \quad \frac{y_2^2}{x} = k \frac{e}{m_2} \cdot \frac{H^2}{X}.$$

So,
$$\frac{m_2}{m_1} = \frac{y_1^2}{y_2^2} = \frac{PN^2}{QN^2}. \tag{33.25}$$

As the line OX cannot be located accurately, $y_1 (PN)$ and $y_2 (QN)$ cannot be determined correctly. In order to overcome this drawback, the lower curves $a'b'$ and $c'd'$ corresponding to ab and cd respectively are obtained by reversing the direction of the magnetic field, its magnitude being kept constant. Now, from Fig. 33.18, we get

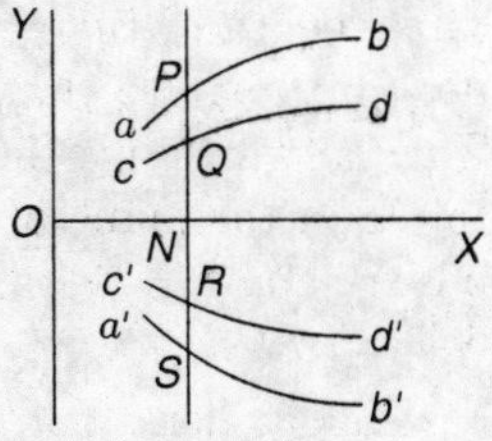

$$y_1 = PN = PS_1/2 \quad \text{and} \quad y_2 = QN = QR_1/2.$$

Fig. 33.18

Therefore,
$$\frac{m_2}{m_1} = \frac{y_1^2}{y_2^2} = \frac{(PS_1/2)^2}{(QR_1/2)^2} = \frac{PS_1^2}{QR_1^2}. \tag{33.26}$$

If m_1 be mass of hydrogen ion, the mass m_2 of the ion of an unknown element can be found out in terms of mass of hydrogen ion. For the most deflected parabola, the value of e/m corresponds to hydrogen atom.

It should be pointed out that the method is not a very accurate one. As the positive rays emerge through a narrow tube as fine beam, its intensity is very small for photograph. As the emerging ions spread into the arc of a parabola, the intensity is further reduced. Since the traces are blurred with no sharp edges, correct measurements are very difficult.

33.14.1 Importance of Thomson's Positive Ray Analysis by Parabola Method

The most significant result derived by Thomson from positive ray analysis was that of neon parabolas. For neon, two distinct parabolas were obtained, one corresponding to an atomic weight 20, and the other much fainter to an atomic weight 22. This showed that ordinary neon is a mixture of two constituents of atomic weights 20 and 22, present in proportion 9 : 1. This gives the average atomic weight 20.20, the conventional chemical atomic weight of neon.

Substances like the constituents of neon possessing identical chemical properties but different atomic weights are called isotopes. It is established that isotopes have same atomic number but different mass numbers. Neon has two isotopes.

33.15 Aston's Mass Spectrograph

To investigate the existence of isotopes in different elements. Aston invented a sensitive mass-identifying device called *mass spectrograph*. In a mass spectrograph, as shown in Fig. 33.19, stream of positive rays in a discharge tube are passed through narrow parallel slits A and B and collimated to a very thin beam to enter the electric field set up between the plates C and D, inclined slightly to the beam. The beam is deflected by θ and a dispersion $\delta\theta$ may occur on reaching the point O where the field is assumed to be concentrated. Now value of θ is given by

$$\theta = k_1 \frac{e}{m} \cdot \frac{1}{v^2}, \tag{33.27}$$

where k_1 is a constant depending on field distribution and is same for all positive particles.

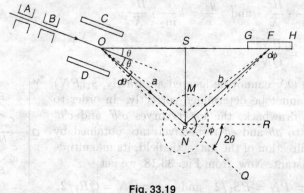

Fig. 33.19

Differentiating Eq. (33.27), we get

$$d\theta = -2k_1 \frac{e}{mv^3} dv. \tag{33.28}$$

From Eqs. (33.27) and (33.28), we have

$$\frac{d\theta}{\theta} = -2\frac{dv}{v}. \tag{33.29}$$

The positive ions after entering magnetic field at P suffer a mean deviation, ϕ, in the opposite direction. Let $d\phi$ be the small angle of convergence within which the ions lie when they are brought to a focus at the point F. Then the deflection due to magnetic field,

$$\phi = k_2 \cdot \frac{e}{mv} \qquad (33.30)$$

where k_2 is a constant depending on the magnetic field intensity H and the geometry of the field.

Differentiating Eq. (33.30), we get

$$d\phi = -k_2 \cdot \frac{e}{mv^2 dv}. \qquad (33.31)$$

Dividing Eq. (33.31) by Eq. (33.30), we have

$$\frac{d\phi}{\phi} = -\frac{dv}{v}. \qquad (33.32)$$

Combining Eq. (33.29) and Eq. (33.32), we get

$$\frac{d\phi}{d\theta} = \frac{\phi}{2\theta}. \qquad (33.33)$$

Now, the width of the limited groups of positive ions at $P = ad\theta$ (where $a = OP$). The points O and P are centres of electric and magnetic fields respectively. If there is no magnetic field the width of the positive ray beam dispersed by electric field after travelling a further distance b becomes $(a + b)d\theta$.

As the magnetic field at P produces a convergence $d\phi$ and brings the ionic beam to a focus at F at a distance $PF = b$, so the divergence $(a + b)d\theta =$ convergence $bd\phi$,

or, $$\frac{a + b}{b} = \frac{d\phi}{d\theta} \qquad (33.34)$$

$$= \frac{\phi}{2\theta} \quad \text{[using Eq. (33.33)]}$$

or, $$\frac{a}{b} = \frac{\phi - 2\theta}{2\theta}. \qquad (33.35)$$

Eq. (33.35) gives a straight line equation drawn from O in a direction inclined to the direction of the beam deflected by the electric field, at an angle 2θ.

When $\phi = 2\theta$, $b = \infty$. Therefore, the image will then be formed at infinity. But when $\phi = 4\theta$, $b = a$.

Thus the ions will be focused at F so that $OP = PF$. The photographic plate is to be kept along a line through O and inclined to the incident beam at an angle θ. When the positive ray beam contains ions of different values of e/m, a number of sharp lines will be formed on the plate GH,

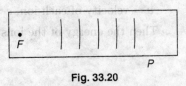

Fig. 33.20

where each line corresponds to a definite value of e/m. The distances of the line traces of ions of known masses are determined from a definite fixed fiducial point F on the photo-plate (Fig. 33.20). Then calibration curve with distances and masses is drawn. The masses of unknown ions corresponding to other line traces can then be ascertained.

33.15.1 Advantages over Thomson's Method

Unlike Thomson's method where ions are spread out into a parabola, here all the ions of same value of e/m are brought to a single point focus. This makes the impressions on photo-plate well defined compared to the parabola method. Also, measurements can be done accurately as the line traces (i.e., the images) are sharp and bright. The intensity of a line in the mass spectrum varies directly as the total number of particles of a given mass. Thus a better idea of relative abundance of various mass components (or isotopes) of an element may be achieved by Aston's method.

33.16 Dempster's Mass Spectrograph

Dempster developed a mass spectrograph for analysis of substances in the solid state. We know that if positive ions are all accelerated by same p.d. and so possessed the same velocity and energy, a magnetic field will suffice to sort out the ions with regard to mass. Dempster's mass spectrograph is based on this principle.

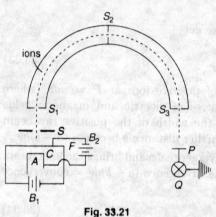

Fig. 33.21

The apparatus is shown in Fig. 33.21. A metal cylinder A with front surface C coated with a salt of the test element and electrically heated serves as the anode. A filament F when heated by the battery B_1 emits electrons. A potential difference of 30 to 60 volts with respect to A is mainted by a second battery B_2. The accelerated electrons bombard the heated salt when positive ions of the element are emitted from the anode A. The emitted ions are collimated into a fine beam by the slit S and then accelerated towards the slit S_1 by a high adjustable p.d. of the order of 800 to 2000 volts maintained between S_1 and S. At S_1, all the ions are accelerated to same velocity to enter a strong uniform magnetic field within two semi-circular pole-pieces of an electromagnet. The magnetic field deflects the ions into a semi-circular path $S_1 S_2 S_3$ (ending at S_3). Passing through S_3 the ions strike a metal plate P which acquires a positive charge at a rate determined by a quadrant electrometer Q.

Principle

Let V = p.d. between S and S_1, B = magnetic field intensity,

   r = radius of the path $S_1 S_2 S_3$, M = mass of an ion,

   v = velocity of each ion, e = charge of an ion,

   Then the energy of the ions as they enter into the magnetic field is given by

$$\frac{1}{2}Mv^2 = eV. \tag{33.36}$$

Again, the circular motion of the ions under the influence of magnetic field is written as

$$Bev = Mv^2/r \tag{33.37}$$

or, $$\frac{e}{M} = v/B \cdot r. \tag{33.38}$$

Using Eqs. (33.36) and (33.37), we get

$$Bev = \frac{mv^2}{r} = \frac{2eV}{r}.$$

$$\therefore \quad v = \frac{2V}{B \cdot r}. \tag{33.39}$$

Substituting the value of v from Eq. (33.39) in Eq. (33.38), we get

$$\frac{e}{M} = \frac{2V}{B^2 r^2}. \tag{33.40}$$

From Eq. (33.40) we find that to bring ions of different masses to the slit S_3, either potential V or the magnetic field B must be altered as r is constant. For all practical purposes, it is convenient to vary V instead of B.

When the ionic current (I) reaching the plate P as measured by the electrometer Q be plotted against different values of V, the curve obtained will be as shown in Fig. 33.22. The curve shows several sharp maxima, each of which corresponds to a particular value of e/M. From the known constants of the apparatus, the maxima could be found out with definite ions. Using the values of V corresponding to different peaks in Eq. (33.40), the masses of the ions can be obtained. In actual experiment, Dempster considered the element potassium. He obtained two peaks

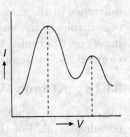

Fig. 33.22

corresponding to masses 39 and 41 as potassium contains two isotopes. In the curve, the heights of the peaks provide the relative abundance of the isotopes present in the element under consideration.

33.17 Isotopes

By using mass spectrograph, Aston found that every ion producing a trace on the photo-plate had a mass which could be represented by a whole number, the mass of oxygen atom being taken as 16.

The mass of chlorine atom, measured by chemical method, is found to be 35.46, while mass spectra method shows that it is essentially a mixture of atomic masses 35 and 37 in the ratio 3 : 1 nearly. Neon consists of atoms of mass 20 and 22 in the ratio 9 : 1, while its chemical atomic weight is 20.2. Like atoms, such as neon and chlorine having different atomic weights but possessing identical chemical properties, are called *isotopes*.

Isotopes of a given element have same atomic number. This means they have same number of units of positive charge on the nucleus of the atom of the element. But as an atom is electrically neutral, the atomic number also denotes the number of units of negative charge on the extranuclear electrons contained in the atom. Though chemical atomic weight of an element is given by a fractional number, the atomic weight of an isotope is always a whole number. About 290 different isotopes, from hydrogen of mass number 1 to uranium of mass number 238 which also include a good number of radio-isotopes, have been known. A large number of unstable isotopes have been isolated by applying method of disintegration. It has been seen that elements of odd atomic numbers do not possess more than two stable isotopes but those of even atomic numbers have larger number, in general.

33.17.1 Isotope of Hydrogen

The existence of a heavy isotope of hydrogen was detected by Uray and his group. Ordinary hydrogen contains a small fraction (about 0.003%) of this isotope having atomic weight 2.0147. Its atomic weight is twice that of ordinary hydrogen and is called *heavy hydrogen* or *deuterium* (or *diplogen*). It has been isolated by fractional electrolysis of water. Heavy water obtained from deuterium (denoted by D) has a formula D_2O and possesses identical chemical properties but somewhat different physical properties from ordinary water. Heavy water is useful in the production of atomic energy to slow down the motion of high velocity neutrons. Neutron is a fundamental particle present in the nucleus of an atom. Neutron has no charge but has a mass same as the mass of fundamental particle called *proton* which is the nucleus of hydrogen atom. In fact, the formation of isotopes may be attributed to the existence of one or more neutrons in the nucleus of the atom of element. The difference in the masses of the isotopes is effected by the difference in the number of neutrons in the atoms of the elements. Though isotopes were separated first by mass spectrographs, but they are more effectively separated by thermal diffusions, electrolysis, low temperature distillation and by other modern techniques.

33.18   Atomic Weight and Atomic Number

In order to designate a given isotope, the notation used is X_Z^A, where X is the chemical symbol of the element to which it belongs; the superscript A represents the atomic weight or the mass number, while the subscript Z indicates the atomic number which stands for the total positive charge on the atom or the total number of electrons in the atom in its normal state. The three isotopes of oxygen are represented as O_8^{16}, O_8^{17} and O_8^{18}. Usually, isotopes are defined as atoms having the same atomic number (Z) but different mass number (A). The ordinary chemical weight of an atom is the average of the masses of its constituent isotopes occurring in the element in different proportions. Chemical methods provide only statistical average weight of atoms of an element on the assumption that all atoms of a given element are similar. However, positive ray method gives the mass of individual atoms of the element.

Examples

1. Calculate the ionization potential of oxygen in volts when the energy required to produce a pair of ions in oxygen is 2.4×10^{-11} erg ($e = 4.8 \times 10^{-10}$ e.s.u.).

   Solution : Let V be the ionization potential in volts, e = charge of ion.

   We have, $Ve = 2.4 \times 10^{-11}$ erg.

   Now, V volts = $\dfrac{V}{300}$ e.s.u. of pot.

   $\therefore$ $Ve = \dfrac{V}{200} \times 4.8 \times 10^{-10}$ erg = 2.4×10^{-11} erg.

   Hence we get

   $$V = \frac{300 \times 2.4 \times 10^{-11}}{4.8 \times 10^{-10}} = \frac{300 \times 2.4}{4.8} \times 10^{-1} = \textbf{15 volts.}$$

2. When the air inside an electroscope of 20 e.s.u. capacitance is ionized by a beam of X-rays, it is observed that the potential of gold leaves changes from 164 volts to 110 volts in one minute. Find the ionization current.

   Solution : In this case, capacity of the electroscope, $C = 20$ e.s.u. $= \frac{20}{9 \times 10^{11}}$ farad; fall of potential per minute = $164 - 110 = 54$ volts.

So the rate of fall of potential, $\dfrac{dv}{dt} = \dfrac{54}{60}$ volts/sec.

Thus, the ionization current, $i = \dfrac{dq}{dt} = \dfrac{d(Cv)}{dt} \quad [\because \; q = Cv]$

$$= C \cdot \dfrac{dv}{dt} = \dfrac{20}{9 \times 100^{11}} \times \dfrac{54}{60} = 2 \times 10^{-11} \text{ A}.$$

3. A water drop of radius 10^{-5} cm is charged with one electron. Calculate the electric field required to keep it stationary; $e = 4.8 \times 10^{-10}$ e.s.u. and $g = 980$ cm/sec^2.

   Solution : In this case, radius of drop, $a = 10^{-5}$ cm; density of water $= 1$ gm/cc; charge on the drop, $e = 4.8 \times 10^{-10}$ e.s.u.; $g = 980$ cm/sec^2.

   Now, let $Xe =$ electric field required to keep the drop stationary.

   Then we have

   $$Xe = mg = \dfrac{4}{3}\pi a^3 \rho g.$$

   $$\therefore \quad X = \dfrac{4\pi a^3 \rho g}{3e} = \dfrac{4 \times 3.14 \times 10^{-15} \times 1 \times 980}{3 \times 4.8 \times 10^{-19}}$$

   $$= 8.56 \times 10^{-3} \text{ e.s.u. per cm.}$$

4. An electron is moving with a velocity of 10^9 cm per second. Calculate its energy in electron-volts. Mass of the electron $= 9.1 \times 10^{-28}$ gm; $e = 4.8 \times 10^{-10}$ electrostatic units.

   Solution : We have the mass of electron, $m = 9.1 \times 10^{-28}$ gm;

   velocity of electron, $v = 10^9$ cm/sec;

   energy of electron $= \dfrac{1}{2}mv^2 = \dfrac{1}{2} \times 9.1 \times 10^{-28} \times 10^{18}$ ergs.

   Now, we have 1 electron-volt $= 1.6 \times 10^{-12}$ erg

   So, the energy in eV (electron-volt) $= \dfrac{9.1 \times 10^{-10}}{2 \times 1.6 \times 10^{-12}} = \dfrac{91 \times 10^2}{32}$ eV.

5. A stream of electrons travelling with a velocity of 3×10^9 cm per second is deflected in passing through an electric field of 0.06 electrostatic unit of potential per cm perpendicular to their path. If the radius of the deflected path is 200 cm, calculate the value of e/m for the electron.

   Solution : In this case, velocity of electron, $v = 3 \times 10^9$ cm/sec;

   $$\text{intensity of electric field, } X = 0.06 \text{ e.s.u.;}$$

   $$\text{radius of the deflected path, } r = 300 \text{ cm.}$$

   Now for deflection under electrostatic field, $Xe = \dfrac{mv^2}{r}$

   or, $\dfrac{e}{m} = \dfrac{v^2}{Xr} = \dfrac{(3 \times 10^9)^2}{0.06 \times 300} = \dfrac{9 \times 10^{18}}{18} = 5 \times 10^{17}$ e.s.u./g.

6. If e/m for cathode rays be 6×10^{17} electrostatic units per gram and v, $1/10$ that of light, find the electrostatic field which will deflect a stream 10 cm long through a distance of 1 mm.

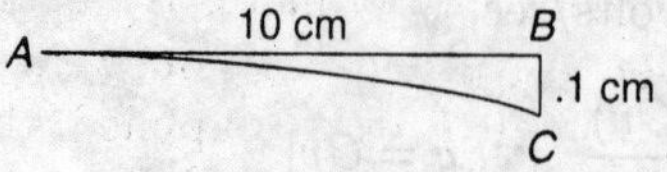

Fig. 33.23

Solution : In Fig. 33.23, $AB = 10$ cm; $BC = 1/10$ cm $= 0.1$ cm.
Now, we have

$$AB^2 = BC(2R - BC).$$

$$\therefore \quad R = \frac{AB^2 + BC^2}{2BC} = \frac{100 + 0.01}{2 \times 0.1} = \frac{10\,001}{20} = 500 \text{ cm (approx.)}$$

$$= \text{radius of curvature.}$$

We can write,

$$Xe = \frac{mv^2}{R}$$

$$\therefore \quad X = \frac{mv^2}{R \times e} = \frac{c^2}{R} \cdot \frac{m}{e}$$

$$\text{or, } X = \frac{(3 \times 10^9)^2}{500} \times \frac{1}{6 \times 10^{17}} = \frac{9 \times 10^{18}}{3 \times 10^{20}} = 3 \times 10^{-2} = 0.03 \text{ e.s.u.}$$

As $X = dv/dx$ (omitting negative sign) and one e.s.u. of potential = 300 volts, a potential gradient of 9 volts per cm will be required.

7. In one of Thomson's experiments, the initial velocity of the cathode rays corresponds to a 100-volt acceleration. The two plates producing the electrostatic field are separated by 5 mm and the p.d. across them is 250 volts. Calculate the value of the magnetic field, limited to the region of the two plates, such that the cathode rays will not suffer any deflection. Assume $e/m = 1.76 \times 10^{11}$ C/kg.

Solution : If electron beam suffers no deflection when both electric and magnetic fields are applied, we have $v = E/B$.
In this case,

$$E = \frac{250 \text{ volts}}{5 \times 10^{-3} \text{ m}} = 5 \times 10^4 \text{ volt/m.}$$

As the electron gets velocity v while passing through a potential diff. of V, we can write,

$$V \cdot e = \frac{1}{2}mv^2 \quad \text{or, } 1000 \times e = \frac{1}{2}m \cdot v^2$$

$$\text{or, } v^2 = 2 \times 1000 \times \frac{e}{m} = 2 \times 10^3 \times 1.76 \times 10^{11} = 3.52 \times 10^{14}.$$

$$\therefore \quad v = 1.87 \times 10^7 \text{ m/sec.}$$

Therefore, $1.87 \times 10^7 = \dfrac{5 \times 10^4}{B}$ or, $B = \dfrac{5 \times 10^4}{1.87 \times 10^7} = \mathbf{2.67 \times 10^{-3}}$ **T.**

8. Calculate the ratio of electric force to the gravitational force acting on all electrons in an electric field of 300 volts/cm; e/m for electrons = 1.76×10^{11} C/kg.

Solution : If E be the intensity of electric field, then the force due to it on the electron, $F_1 = E \cdot e$. Let m be the mass of the electron, then the force due to gravity, $F_2 = mg$. Thus we have

$$\frac{F_1}{F_2} = \frac{E \cdot e}{m} \cdot \frac{1}{g} = \frac{3 \times 10^4 \times 1.76 \times 10^{11}}{9.8} = 5.4 \times 10^{14}.$$

[since $E = 300$ volts/cm $= 300 \times 10^2$ volts/m $= 3 \times 10^4$ volts/m]

9. In a Thomson experiment, the electric field between two plates is 24.0 kV/m, length of each plate is 6.0 cm. Deflection of cathode ray on a screen is 10.9 cm. If the magnetic field of strength 8.0×10^{-4} tesla is applied, there is no deflection. If the distance of the screen from the centre of the plates be 40.0 cm, calculate the value of e/m of electron.

Solution : In this case, electric field, $E = 24$ kV/m $= 24 \times 10^3$ V/m and magnetic field, $B = 8 \times 10^{-4}$ tesla.

For no deflection of the rays, the velocity of electron, $v = \dfrac{E}{B}$.

Therefore, $v = \dfrac{24 \times 10^3}{8 \times 10^{-4}} = 3 \times 10^7$ m/sec.

For electric deflection, $\dfrac{e}{m} = \dfrac{d_e \times v^2}{D_1 \cdot E \cdot l_1}$.

Given, $d_e = 10.9$ cm $= 10.9 \times 10^{-2}$ m; $v^2 = (3 \times 10^7)^2$; $D_1 = 40$ cm $= 40 \times 10^{-2}$ m; $E = 24 \times 10^3$ V/m; $l_1 = 6$ cm $= 6 \times 10^{-2}$ m.

Substituting the values in the above expression, we get

$$\frac{e}{m} = \frac{(10.9 \times 10^{-2}) \times (3 \times 10^7)^2}{40 \times 10^{-2} \times 24 \times 10^3 \times 6 \times 10^{-2}} = \mathbf{1.7 \times 10^{11}} \textbf{ coulombs/kg.}$$

10. A narrow horizontal beam of electrons passes symmetrically between two metal plates mounted one on each side of the beam. The velocity of the electrons is 3×10^7 m/sec, the plates are 3 cm long and 1 cm apart. It is found that when a battery of 568 volts is connected to the plates, the electron beam just strikes the end of them. Calculate the value of e/m. [C.U. 1980]

Solution : The electron beam is deflected between the plates P_1 and P_2 [Fig. 33.24]. It follows the path AB and just strikes the end B of the plate P_2. Therefore, the deflection x is given by

$x = \dfrac{1}{2} \times \text{acceleration} \times (\text{time})^2$

$= \dfrac{1}{2} \times \dfrac{E \cdot e}{m} \times \left(\dfrac{l}{v}\right)^2$

$= \dfrac{1}{2} \times \dfrac{568 \times e}{10^{-2} \times m} \times \left(\dfrac{3 \times 10^{-2}}{3 \times 10^7}\right)^2$.

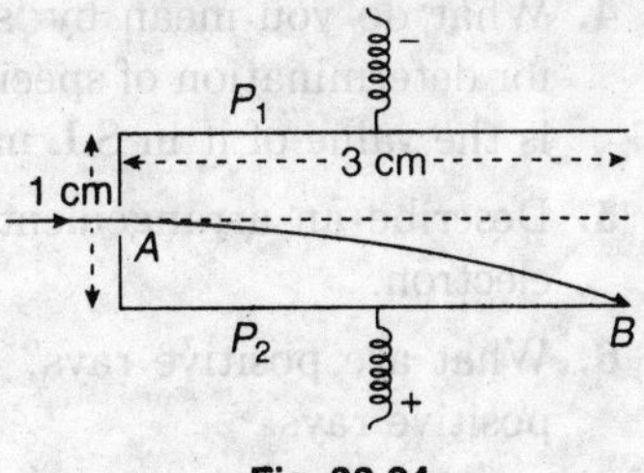

Fig. 33.24

Again, deflection $x = \dfrac{1}{2}$ of the distance between the plates P_1 and P_2

$= 0.5 \times 10^{-2}$ metre

$\therefore \quad 0.5 \times 10^{-2} = \dfrac{1}{2} \times \dfrac{568}{10^{-2}} \times \dfrac{e}{m} \times \dfrac{1}{10^{18}}$

or, $\dfrac{e}{m} = \dfrac{0.5 \times 2 \times 10^{-2} \times 10^{-2} \times 10^{18}}{568} = \mathbf{1.76 \times 10^{11}}$ **coulomb/kg**.

11. What velocity will an electron at rest acquire in moving through a p.d. of 1-volt? Given, $e = 1.6 \times 10^{-19}$ coulomb and $m = 9.108 \times 10^{-31}$ kg.

Solution : We have $v = \sqrt{\dfrac{2eV}{m}}$.

In this case, $e = 1.6 \times 10^{-19}$ C; $V = 1$ volt; $m = 9.108 \times 10^{-31}$ kg.

Hence we get

$$v = \sqrt{\frac{2 \times 1.6 \times 10^{-19}}{9.108 \times 10^{-31}}} \times 1 = \mathbf{6 \times 10^5 \ m \cdot sec^{-1}} \text{ (nearly)}.$$

12. An electron is moving with a velocity of 10^7 metres/sec. Find its energy in electron-volt. Given, $m = 9.1 \times 10^{-31}$ kg; $e = 1.6 \times 10^{-19}$ C. **[B.U. 1992, 2004]**

Solution : We have the kinetic energy of electron $= \dfrac{1}{2} m v^2$

$$= \frac{1}{2} \times 9.1 \times 10^{-31} \times (10^7)^2 \text{ joule} = \frac{1}{2} \times 9.1 \times 10^{-17} \text{ joule}.$$

We know, 1 eV $= 1.6 \times 10^{-19}$ C $\times$ 1 volt $= 1.6 \times 10^{-19}$ J.

Hence, kinetic energy of electron $= \dfrac{9.1 \times 10^{-17}}{2 \times 1.6 \times 10^{-19}} = \mathbf{2.84 \times 10^2 \ eV}.$

Questions

Essay-type

1. What are cathode rays? What are their properties? How do the particles originate?

2. What is ionization current? Describe a method of measuring the ionization current in gases at normal pressure with an ionization chamber. Explain the nature of variation of current with the potential difference between the electrodes.

3. Give an account of the changes that take place in a discharge tube as the pressure inside the tube is gradually diminished. What experimental arrangement would you require for demonstrating the phenomenon?

4. What do you mean by 'specific charge'? Deduce the theoretical expression for determination of specific charge of an electron in Thomson method. What is the value of it in S.I. unit?   **[B.U. 2004]**

5. Describe an arrangement for the determination of the specific charge of an electron.   **[V.U. 2005; C.U. 1982; N.B.U. 2002]**

6. What are positive rays? Describe Thomson's parabola method of studying positive rays.   **[N.B.U. 2005]**

7. A charged particle shoots through a uniform (i) electric field, (ii) magnetic field perpendicular to the lines of force. Describe with necessary theory how it will behave.

8. Describe the construction and working of a Thomson mass spectrograph. Indicate the results obtained with it.   **[C.U. 1966]**

9. In a positive ray, why all the particles do not travel with same speed? Describe the theory behind Thomson's parabola method of positive ray analysis. Explain why in this method the parabolas abruptly end and do not extend to the origin.   **[N.B.U. 2001]**

10. Assuming the formulae for the electric and magnetic deflections of a positively charged particle, how would you show that all particles having same e/m but different v will be spread out along a branch of a parabola and that different e/m values give rise to different parabolas?   **[B.U. 1983]**

11. Describe Aston's mass spectrograph. How is this instrument used for the detection of isotopes? What is its advantage over Thomson's method?

Short Answer-type

12. What is an electron-volt? What is its relation with erg?

13. X-rays are allowed to pass through a gas enclosed between two plates. What are the factors on which (i) the number of ions produced per sec and (ii) the ionization current depend?

14. What led the scientists to believe that the electron is a common constituent of matter? [C.U. 1967]

15. In Thomson's parabola method of analysing positive rays, the parabolas abruptly end at a point and do not extend up to the origin. What is the reason of it? [N.B.U. 2005]

16. What are positive rays? How do they originate? Do all the positive rays originating in a gas have the same mass? If not, why? Do they have same velocity?

17. What are the properties of positive rays?

18. Lithium is produced by the mixture of two types of lithium of atomic weights 6 and 7, their relative abundance being 1 : 10. What should be the chemical atomic weight of lithium? [C.U. 2001]

19. What is an isotope? How was it discovered? [N.B.U. 2001]

20. What is the difference between atomic mass and atomic number of atom? Which particles determine the atomic mass and atomic number?

Numerical Problems

21. In Thomson's method, a magnetic field of 10^{-2} T is used. To make the path of an electron straight through the tube, a p.d. of 600 volts is applied to the deflecting plates which are 0.5 cm apart. Find the velocity of the electron. [**Ans.** 12×10^7 m/sec]

22. A stream of electrons moving with a velocity of 3×10^7 m/sec, enters an electric field of 18 volts/cm perpendicular to their path. If the radius of the deflected path is 3 m, calculate e/m for the electron. [**Ans.** 1.66×10^{11} C/kg]

23. The forces on a cathode particle of velocity 10^8 cm/sec are balanced by crossed electric and magnetic fields. If the magnetic field has an intensity of 100 oersted, what is the intensity of the electric field in volt/cm? What p.d. in volts is required to produce this velocity? $e/m = 1.76 \times 10^7$ e.m.u./g.
[**Ans.** 100 volt/cm; 2.84 volt]

24. A proton entered a magnetic field of 2.0 Wb/m^2, with a velocity 2×10^7 m/sec. If the proton made an angle of 30° with magnetic field, find the force experienced by it. [V.U. 2005]
[**Ans.** 3.2×10^{12} N]

25. An electron is moving with a speed of 10^6 m sec^{-1}. Calculate the kinetic energy of the electron in electron-volts. Given, $m = 9.1 \times 10^{-28}$ gm and $C = 4.8 \times 10^{-10}$ e.s.u. [B.U. 1997]
[**Ans.** 1.5 eV]

26. A narrow beam of electrons, accelerated by a p.d. of 400 volt, passes between two parallel metal plates 4 cm long and 0.6 cm apart in an evacuated tube and then strikes a fluorescent screen 15 cm from the centre of the plates. Calculate the deflection of the spot of light on the screen when a p.d. of 15 volts is established between the plates.   [**Ans.** 1.875 cm]

27. A mixed beam of protons and deuterons which have been accelerated by a potential of 10^4 volts enters a uniform magnetic field of 0.5 tesla in a direction perpendicular to the field. Calculate the separation of the proton beam from the deuteron beam when each has described a semi-circle in the field. Given, $e = 1.6 \times 10^{-19}$ coulomb; mass of proton $= 1.67 \times 10^{-27}$ kg; mass of deuteron $= 3.34 \times 10^{-27}$ kg; $c = 3 \times 10^8$ m/sec.   [**Ans.** 2.4 cm]

28. An electron having 450 eV of energy moves at right angles to a uniform magnetic field of flux density 1.5×10^{-3} Oe. Find the radius of the circular path traced out by the electron. $e/m = 1.76 \times 10^8$ coulombs/gm.

[**Ans.** 472 m]

29. The distance between the traces corresponding to masses 12 and 16 in an Aston's mass spectrograph is 4.8 cm. Calculate the mass of the ion whose trace is at a distance of 8.4 cm from the trace of mass 16.   [**Ans.** 23 or 9]

30. In a parabola method experiment, singly ionized particles of one mass and doubly ionized particles of other, form identical parabolas when the magnetic field are 75×10^2 gauss and 15×10^3 gauss respectively, the electric field being the same. Compare the masses of the particles.   [**Ans.** 1 : 8]

Chapter 34

Atomic Structure of the Matter

34.1 Introduction

Dalton's atomic theory of matter in 1803 was the first approach towards the atomic structure of matter. According to him, all matters were composed of very small particles called *atoms* which retained their individuality in all kinds of chemical combinations. He further pointed out that the atoms of the same substance were all alike and differed from those of all other substances. Also the atoms could not be subdivided, created or destroyed. In 1815, Prout suggested that all the elements are made up of atoms of hydrogen. He suggested this on the basis of the fact that atomic weights of most of the elements were integral multiples of atomic weight of hydrogen atom (e.g., He = 4, C = 12, N = 14, etc.) Subsequently, it was found that atomic weights in many cases were not whole numbers (e.g., Cl = 35.5, Ne = 20.5) and thus Prout's hypothesis was abandoned.

34.2 Thomson's Atom Model

Sir J. J. Thomson, in 1898, discovered the electron and established that electron is a common constituent of all matters. Thomson proposed a physical model of the atom called '*plum pudding atom*'. According to him, the atom was a positive plum pudding in which were embedded negative electrons to distribute in a manner so as to make the entire thing neutral. Thomson's atom model is shown in Fig. 34.1.

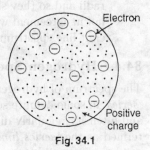

Fig. 34.1

34.3 Rutherford's Nuclear Atom Model

Rutherford, in 1911, proposed a nuclear atom model from the concept of α-scattering experiment. He suggested the following :

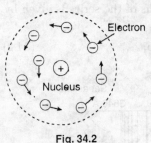

Fig. 34.2

(i) Atom is made up of a central core called *nucleus* of diameter $\sim 10^{-15}$ m in which the entire positive charge and almost all mass of the atom is concentrated.

(ii) The nucleus is surrounded by as many electrons as there are positive charges on the nucleus. As the dimensions of the atom are of the order of 10^{-10} m, most of the space within the atom is empty.

If the electrons were at rest, they will be attracted by the nucleus and neutralized. In order to overcome this difficulty, Rutherford considered that the electrons are revolving round the nucleus in circular orbits, as shown in Fig. 34.2.

Let r be the radius of the electronic orbit and v be the velocity of the electron in its orbit. If Ze be the charge on the nucleus (Z being the atomic number and e the charge of a proton or electron), then we can write

$$\frac{mv^2}{r} = K\frac{Ze \cdot e}{r^2},\tag{34.1}$$

where $K = \dfrac{1}{4\pi\epsilon_0} = 9 \times 10^9$ N-m^2-C^2

and $\epsilon_0 = 8.85 \times 10^{-12}$ F/m.

From Eq. (34.1) we find that it is possible to have an infinite number of orbits in which electrons can revolve round the nucleus.

34.3.1 Drawbacks of Rutherford's Model

Though the model proposed by Rutherford was on the basis of strong experimental support, the model has some serious drawbacks as stated below :

(i) According to electromagnetic theory, a revolving electron should radiate energy continuously. If it be so, the electron will rapidly spiral inwards to fall into the nucleus and the atom would collapse. Calculations show that only about 10^{-16} sec would be required for a stable hydrogen atom to collapse. But atoms do not collapse, rather they are quite stable.

(ii) According to the model, the electrons can revolve in orbits of all possible radii and so they should emit continuous radiation of all frequencies. This is not in agreement with the experimental observations as atoms, like hydrogen, emit line spectrum of certain fixed frequencies only.

34.4 Hydrogen Spectrum

The spectrum of hydrogen atom showed that it consists of a number of lines called '*series*' in some definite sets. The lines in each series are such that their separation and intensity regularly diminish towards shorter wavelengths converging to a limit termed as the '*series limit*'. An element may display several series, each of which can be represented by a similar empirical formula. In 1885, the first spectral series was reported by Balmer and is known as the *Balmer series of hydrogen*. The first line with the longest wavelength (6563 Å) is marked as H_α, the next one is H_β and so on. The Balmer series of hydrogen spectrum is shown in Fig. 34.3. The series limit lies at the wavelength of 3646 Å, beyond which there is a faint continuous spectrum. Balmer's empirical formula for the wavelengths of the series is given by

$$\bar{\nu} = \frac{1}{\lambda} = R\left(\frac{1}{2^2} - \frac{1}{n^2}\right),\ n = 3, 4, 5, \ldots\tag{34.2}$$

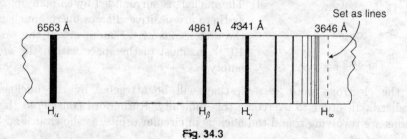

Fig. 34.3

The reciprocal of the wavelength is known as the *wave number* ($\bar{\nu}$). It is the number of waves in unit length. R is a constant called '*Rydberg constant*'. It has the value

$$R = 1.097 \times 10^7 \ \mathrm{m^{-1}}.$$

We may get the wavelength of H_α line by putting $n = 3$ in Eq. (34.2). Similarly, H_β line is obtained by putting $n = 4$. When $n = \infty$, we get the series limit at $\bar{\nu} = R/4$. The Balmer series contains only those spectral lines which are in the visible part of the hydrogen spectrum. This is the reason why the series was the first to be observed. When the ultraviolet and infrared regions of the hydrogen spectrum are examined, they revealed the existence of other series. The lines falling in the ultraviolet region form the 'Lyman series' whose wave numbers and wavelengths are obtained from

$$\bar{\nu} = \frac{1}{\lambda} = R\left(\frac{1}{1^2} - \frac{1}{n^2}\right), \ n = 2, 3, 4, \ldots \ \text{[Lyman series]} \qquad (34.3)$$

In the infrared region, three spectral series have been noted whose wave numbers and wavelengths are obtained from

$$\bar{\nu} = \frac{1}{\lambda} = R\left(\frac{1}{3^2} - \frac{1}{n^2}\right), \ n = 4, 5, 6, \ldots \ \text{[Paschen series]}$$

$$\bar{\nu} = \frac{1}{\lambda} = R\left(\frac{1}{4^2} - \frac{1}{n^2}\right), \ n = 5, 6, 7, \ldots \ \text{[Brackett series]}$$

$$\bar{\nu} = \frac{1}{\lambda} = R\left(\frac{1}{5^2} - \frac{1}{n^2}\right), \ n = 6, 7, 8, \ldots \ \text{[Pfund series]}$$

It should be pointed out that the value of Rydberg constant R is same for all the series. Some of the intense lines of Paschen, Balmer and Lyman series plotted in terms of wavelength are exhibited in Fig. 34.4.

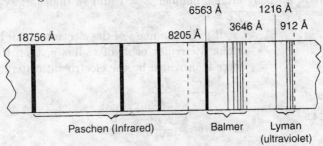

Fig. 34.4

34.5 Bohr's Theory of Atomic Structure

In 1913, Neils Bohr attempted to way out the difficulties in Rutherford Model of the atom and to interpret the emission of spectral lines by hydrogen. He proposed the following postulates :

(i) The electrons revolve around the nucleus in various stationary circular orbits. The required centripetal force to keep the electron in the closed circular orbit is provided by the electrostatic attraction between the electron and the nucleus.

If m be the mass of electron, v its velocity and r the radius of the circular orbit, then the centripetal force is $\frac{mv^2}{r}$. The electrostatic force of attraction between the nucleus of charge Ze and the electron of charge e is KZe^2/r^2, where $K = 1/4\pi\epsilon_0 = 9 \times 10^9$ N-m^2/(coulomb)^2. Hence, according to Bohr's first postulate

$$\frac{mv^2}{r} = K\frac{Ze^2}{r^2}, \tag{34.4}$$

where $K = 1/4\pi\epsilon_0 = 1$ in c.g.s. system.

(ii) The only orbits that are allowed are those in which the angular momentum of the revolving electron is an integral multiple of $h/2\pi = \hbar(= 1.05 \times 10^{-34}$ J-sec). The angular momentum of the only permissible orbits is expressed as

$$L = mvr = \frac{nh}{2\pi}, \quad n = 1, 2, 3, \ldots \tag{34.5}$$

Here $n = 1, 2, 3, \ldots$ is known as the *principal quantum number*. This condition is known as the *Bohr's quantum condition*.

(iii) When an electron is in an allowed orbit, the atom does not radiate energy.

(iv) If the electron jumps from an initial stationary orbit of energy E_i to a final stationary orbit of energy $E_f (E_i > E_f)$, a photon of frequency ν is emitted, where

$$\nu = \frac{(E_i - E_f)}{h}. \tag{34.6}$$

34.6 Bohr's Theory of Hydrogen Atom

Bohr was able to explain the structure and spectrum of hydrogen. According to his atom model, the structure of the hydrogen atom can be represented as shown in Fig. 34.5. For hydrogen, the atomic number $Z = 1$ and so the charge on the nucleus $Ze = e$.

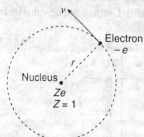

Fig. 34.5

If m be the mass of the electron and v be its velocity along a circular orbit of radius r, then the centripetal force is provided by the electrostatic attraction

$$\frac{mv^2}{r} = \frac{Ke^2}{r^2}$$

or, $\quad mv^2 = \dfrac{Ke^2}{r}$. $\tag{34.7}$

According to Bohr's second postulate, the angular momentum of the electron in a permitted orbit is obtained from

$$mvr = nh/2\pi, \quad n = 1, 2, 3, \ldots$$

or, $\quad v = \dfrac{nh}{2\pi mr},$ $\tag{34.8}$

where v is the velocity of the electron.

Squaring Eq. (34.8) and putting in Eq. (34.7), we get

$$m\frac{n^2h^2}{4\pi^2m^2r^2} = K\frac{e^2}{r} \quad \text{or,} \quad \frac{n^2h^2}{4\pi^2mr} = Ke^2.$$

$\therefore \quad r = \dfrac{n^2h^2}{4\pi^2mKe^2} = \dfrac{\epsilon_0 n^2h^2}{\pi me^2}.$ $\tag{34.9}$

Eq. (34.9) gives the expression of the *radius of the permitted orbit*. It is seen that the radii of the permitted orbits are proportional to n^2 and increase in the ratio of 1, 4, 9, 16,... from one orbit to the next. Putting the values of m, e, h and ϵ_0, the radius of the first hydrogen orbit ($n = 1$) is obtained as

$$r = 5.29 \times 10^{-11} \text{ m} = 0.529 \text{ Å}.$$

This value of the radius is found to be in good agreement with the value of radius of the orbit obtained from other methods. Putting the value of r from Eq. (34.9) in Eq. (34.8), we get

$$\nu = \frac{2\pi Ke^2}{nh}$$

$$= \frac{e^2}{2\epsilon_0 nh}. \tag{34.10}$$

Energy

The energy of electron is partly kinetic and partly potential. The kinetic energy of the electron may be written as

$$T = \frac{1}{2}mv^2$$

$$= \frac{1}{2}\frac{Ke^2}{r} = \frac{e^2}{8\pi\epsilon_0 r}. \tag{34.11}$$

The potential energy at a distance r from the nucleus is same as the work done in removing the electron from r to infinity against the electrostatic attraction $(-e^2/r)$. The P.E. is given by

$$U = \int_r^\infty -\frac{Ke^2}{r^2}\, dr = \left[\frac{Ke^2}{r}\right]_r^\infty = -\frac{Ke^2}{r} = -\frac{e^2}{4\pi\epsilon_0 r}. \tag{34.12}$$

The negative sign in Eq. (34.12) indicates that the charges are unlike. The total energy of the electron is thus given by

$$E = K + U = \frac{Ke^2}{2r} - \frac{Ke^2}{r} = \frac{-Ke^2}{2r} = \frac{-e^2}{8\pi\epsilon_0 r}. \tag{34.13}$$

Putting the value for r from Eq. (34.9), we get

$$E = E_n = -\frac{e^2}{8\pi\epsilon_0} \times \frac{\pi m e^2}{\epsilon_0 n^2 h^2} = -\frac{m e^4}{8\epsilon_0^2 h^2}\left(\frac{1}{n^2}\right). \tag{34.14}$$

Eq. (34.14) provides the energy of the electron revolving in the nth orbit. The negative sign suggests that the electron cannot escape from the orbit. It means that the electron is bound to the nucleus and some work is to be done to pull it away. The equation further shows that the energy of the electron is quantized. Eq. (34.14) indicates that as n increases, E becomes less negative and so its algebraic value increases. The electron gets minimum energy when it is in its innermost orbit or ground state. An electron or an atom must be imparted some energy to jump to an outer orbit. Similarly, energy is emitted by an electron when it jumps from an outer orbit to an inner one. If an electron is forced to revolve in an outer orbit, the state of the atom is called an *excited state*. When an atom is in an excited state, it is not stable and in course of time it jumps to an inner orbit to emit the difference of energy in the form of a quantum of radiation. If E_i and E_f be the energies corresponding to the initial and final orbits, i.e., from higher to lower orbits of an excited atom (for hydrogen $Z = 1$), then we can write,

$$E_i = -\frac{me^4}{8\epsilon_0^2 h^2} \frac{1}{n_i^2} \tag{34.15}$$

and

$$E_f = -\frac{me^4}{8\epsilon_0^2 h^2} \frac{1}{n_f^2}, \tag{34.16}$$

where n_i and n_f are the corresponding quantum numbers. Now, according to Bohr's fourth postulate, the frequency f of the emitted radiation is written as

$$h\nu = E_i - E_f = -\frac{me^4}{8\epsilon_0^2 h^2} \frac{1}{n_i^2} + \frac{me^4}{8\epsilon_0^2 h^2} \frac{1}{n_f^2}$$

$$= \frac{me^4}{8\epsilon_0^2 h^2} \left(\frac{1}{n_f^2} - \frac{1}{n_i^2} \right)$$

or,

$$\nu = \frac{me^4}{8\epsilon_0^2 h^3} \left(\frac{1}{n_f^2} - \frac{1}{n_i^2} \right). \tag{34.17}$$

The corresponding wavelength λ is obtained from

$$\frac{1}{\lambda} = \frac{\nu}{c} = \frac{me^4}{8\epsilon_0^2 c h^3} \left(\frac{1}{n_f^2} - \frac{1}{n_i^2} \right). \tag{34.18}$$

Eq. (34.18) shows that since n_i and n_f can take only integral values, the radiation emitted by excited hydrogen atoms should contain certain discrete wavelengths only. In terms of wave number, we can write Eq. (34.18) as

$$\bar{\nu} = R \left(\frac{1}{n_f^2} - \frac{1}{n_i^2} \right), \tag{34.19}$$

where $R = \frac{me^4}{8\epsilon_0^2 c h^3}$ is a constant whose value becomes equal to the Rydberg constant R in the Balmer's formula. The value of R comes out to be 1.096×10^7 m^{-1} which is in good agreement with the value obtained from the spectroscopic data of the Balmer series.

34.6.1   Spectral Series of Hydrogen Atom

The various series found in the spectrum of hydrogen atom can be explained by using Eq. (34.19) in the following way :

(i) **Lyman series** : Substituting $n_f = 1$ and $n_i = 2, 3, 4, \ldots$ in Eq. (34.19), we get the wave numbers of spectral lines of Lyman series in ultraviolet region. Hence for this series,

$$\bar{\nu} = R \left(\frac{1}{1^2} - \frac{1}{n^2} \right), \quad n_i = 2, 3, 4, \ldots. \tag{34.20}$$

(ii) **Balmer series** : Substituting $n_f = 2$ and $n_i = 3, 4, 5, \ldots$ in Eq. (34.19), we get the wave numbers of spectral lines of Balmer series in the visible region. Hence for this series,

$$\bar{\nu} = R \left(\frac{1}{2^2} - \frac{1}{n_i^2} \right), \quad n_i = 3, 4, 5, \ldots. \tag{34.21}$$

(iii) Paschen series : Substituting $n_f = 3$ and $n_i = 4, 5, 6, \ldots$, we get the wave numbers of spectral lines of Paschen series in the infrared region. Hence for this series,

$$\bar{\nu} = R\left(\frac{1}{3^2} - \frac{1}{n_i^2}\right), \quad n_i = 4, 5, 6, \ldots. \tag{34.22}$$

(iv) Brackett series : Substituting $n_f = 4$ and $n_i = 5, 6, 7, \ldots$, we get the wave numbers of spectral lines of Brackett series in the infrared region. Hence for this series,

$$\bar{\nu} = R\left(\frac{1}{4^2} - \frac{1}{n_i^2}\right), \quad n_i = 5, 6, 7, \ldots. \tag{34.23}$$

(v) Pfund series : Substituting $n_f = 5$ and $n_i = 6, 7, 8, \ldots$, we get the wave numbers of spectral lines of Pfund series in the infrared region. Hence for this series,

$$\bar{\nu} = R\left(\frac{1}{5^2} - \frac{1}{n_i^2}\right), \quad n_i = 6, 7, 8, \ldots. \tag{34.24}$$

The transitions for all the above series are presented in Fig. 34.6.

It may be noted here that the transitions between states with negative energy will give rise to line spectra, while transitions between states with positive energy $E > 0$ and states $E < 0$ will give a continuous spectrum.

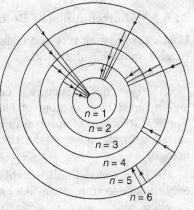

Fig. 34.6

34.6.2 Atomic Energy Levels

We can rewrite Eq. (34.14) as

$$E_n = -\frac{me^4}{8\epsilon_0^2 h^2}\frac{1}{n^2},$$

where $n = 1, 2, 3, \ldots.$

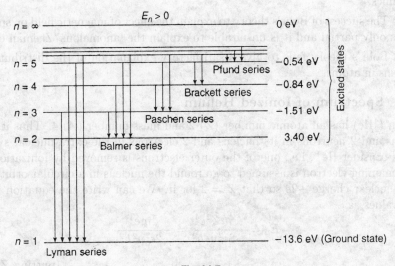

Fig. 34.7

Substituting $m = 9.11 \times 10^{-31}$ kg, $e = 1.6 \times 10^{-19}$ C for the mass and charge of the electron, we get

$$E_n = -\frac{13.6}{n^2} \text{ eV} \quad \text{for } n = 1, 2, 3, \ldots . \tag{34.25}$$

Now, we have

$$1 \text{ eV} = 1.6 \times 10^{-19} \text{ C} \times 1 \text{ volt} = 1.6 \times 10^{-19} \text{ J}.$$

The state of lowest energy (or ground state) corresponds to $n = 1$ and its energy is $E_i = -13.6$ eV.

An energy level diagram is shown in Fig. 34.7 which represents the allowed energies for the hydrogen atom. All the states from $n = 1$ to $n = \infty$ are bound states as they have negative energies. When n increases and approaches to $n = \infty$, the energy states get more closer until the energy difference between two consecutive states becomes so small that the distribution gives a continuous spectrum. Above the line given by $n = \infty$, the energy states have positive energy, $E > 0$ and the spectrum of the states is continuous. Then the system is unbound, meaning that the electron is free.

34.6.3   Shortcomings of Bohr's Atomic Model

Bohr's theory were very successful to explain the spectrum of hydrogen atom and to give valuable information about atomic structure. But it has the following drawbacks :

(a) The 'fine structure', i.e., the individual line of hydrogen spectrum accompanied by a number of faint lines, cannot be explained by Bohr's theory. The fine structure of spectral lines can be explained only when (i) the relativistic variation in the mass of the electron and (ii) the electron 'spin' are taken into account.

(b) Bohr's model fails to explain the spectra of complex atoms. It is applicable only to one-electron atoms like hydrogen, hydrogen isotopes, ionized helium, etc.

(c) Bohr's model fails to explain the variation in intensity of the spectral lines of an element. The intensity of the spectral lines can be explained by using quantum mechanics.

(d) The success of Bohr's theory to explain the effect of magnetic field on spectral lines is only partial and it is unsuitable to explain the 'anomalous' Zeeman effect.

(e) Bohr's theory fails to give a satisfactory explanation of the distribution of electrons in atoms.

34.7   Spectrum of Ionized Helium

Helium ($^4_2$He) has an atomic number (Z) 2 and mass number (A) 4. Thus it has 2 protons and 2 neutrons in its nucleus and 2 electrons in the extra-nuclear system. Let us consider He$^+$, i.e., one of the outer electrons is removed by ionization and the remaining electron is assumed to go round the nucleus in a circular orbit. He$^+$ has a nuclear charge $+2e$ so that $Z = 2$ for it. We can write the equation for its term values as

$$E_n = -\frac{mZ^2e^4}{8\epsilon_0^2 n^2 h^2} = -\frac{me^4}{2\epsilon_0^2 n^2 h^2} \tag{34.26}$$

(putting $Z = 2$).

The term values of He$^+$ are four times larger than the corresponding hydrogen terms. If there is a transition from an initial energy level, n_i to a final level, n_f, then the emitted radiation has the wave number,

$$\overline{\nu} = \frac{1}{\lambda} = \frac{me^4}{2\epsilon_0^2 ch^3}\left(\frac{1}{n_f^2} - \frac{1}{n_i^2}\right)$$

$$= 4R_H\left(\frac{1}{n_f^2} - \frac{1}{n_i^2}\right), \tag{34.27}$$

where R_H is the Rydberg constant for hydrogen.

If we consider transitions from $n_i = 5, 6, 7, 8, \ldots$ levels of He$^+$ to the final level with $n_f = 4$, the series is called *Pickering series*. The ionized helium spectrum is shown in Fig. 34.8. The lines of the Pickering series can be expressed as

$$\overline{\nu} = 4R_H\left(\frac{1}{4^2} - \frac{1}{n_i^2}\right) = R_H\left(\frac{1}{2^2} - \frac{4}{n_i^2}\right). \tag{34.28}$$

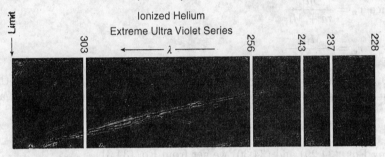

Fig. 34.8

The alternate lines of the Pickering series with n_i even ($n_i = 6, 8, 10, \ldots$) of He$^+$ should have the same wavelengths as the spectral lines of the Balmer series of hydrogen. Thus one can say that the alternate lines of the Pickering series of ionized helium should coincide with the Balmer series of hydrogen. Actual measurements have shown that this coincidence predicted by Bohr's theory is not fully correct. In fact, the lines of the Pickering series of the He$^+$ have slightly higher wave numbers than the corresponding lines of Balmer series. The reason for the above difference is caused by the finite masses of nuclei of hydrogen and helium.

34.8 Finite Mass Correction

It is assumed in the original Bohr's theory that the electron revolves round a nucleus to be at rest. This assumption would be correct when the nucleus is infinitely heavy. But a nucleus of finite mass cannot be at rest and so the combined electron-nucleus system should be considered to revolve round the common centre of mass with the same angular velocity (Fig. 34.9). Let N be the nucleus and E be the electron revolving round the common centre of mass C. We know that the mass of hydrogen nucleus is 1836 times heavier than the

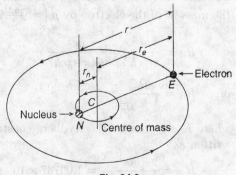

Fig. 34.9

electron mass and the mass of helium nucleus is four times heavier than the mass of the hydrogen nucleus. Though these masses are much higher than the mass of electron but we cannot consider them to be infinitely heavy.

Let r_e and r_n be the radii of the orbits of the electron and the nucleus and M_H and m be the masses of hydrogen nucleus and electron respectively. From the definition of centre of mass, E, C and N are always in a straight line and thus we can write,

$$M_H r_n = m r_e \quad \text{or,} \quad \frac{r_n}{r_e} = \frac{m}{M_H}$$

or,
$$\frac{r_n}{r_e + r_n} = \frac{m}{m + M_H}.$$

If the electron-nucleus distance be r, then we have

$$r = r_e + r_n$$

Hence $r_n = \dfrac{mr}{m + M_H}$ \hfill (34.29)

and $\quad r_e = \dfrac{M_H r}{m + M_H}.$ \hfill (34.30)

If ω be the angular velocity of the system about the centre of mass, then the combined angular momentum of the electron and the nucleus is expressed as

$$m\omega r_e^2 + M_H \omega r_n^2 = L = \frac{nh}{2\pi}.$$ \hfill (34.31)

Using Eqs. (34.29) and (34.30) we get from Eq. (34.31),

$$\left(\frac{mM_H}{m + M_H}\right)\omega r^2 = \frac{nh}{2\pi}.$$ \hfill (34.32)

Let $\quad \mu = \dfrac{mM_H}{m + M_H} = \dfrac{m}{1 + \frac{m}{M_H}},$ \hfill (34.33)

where μ is the reduced mass of the electron.

Then we have

$$\mu\omega r^2 = \frac{nh}{2\pi} = n\hbar.$$ \hfill (34.34)

If we now compare with the simple Bohr theory result, $mvr = m\omega r^2 = n\hbar$, we find that the result of taking into account the finite mass of the nucleus is to replace the mass m of the electron by $\mu \left(= \frac{mM_H}{m+M_H}\right)$. Then Rydberg constant will be

$$R_H = \frac{\mu e^4}{8\epsilon_0^2 ch^3} = \frac{\mu e^4}{64\pi^3 \epsilon_0^2 ch^3}$$ \hfill (34.35)

or, $\quad R_H = \dfrac{R_\infty}{1 + \frac{m}{M_H}},$ \hfill (34.36)

where R_∞ represents the Rydberg constant for an infinitely heavy nucleus and is written as

$$R_\infty = \frac{me^4}{64\pi^3 \epsilon_0^2 ch^3} = 1.09737 \times 10^7 \text{ m}^{-1}.$$ \hfill (34.37)

The transition between two energy levels are responsible for the emission of electromagnetic radiation. The wave number is then obtained from

$$\bar{\nu} = \frac{1}{\lambda} = R_H Z^2 \left(\frac{1}{n_f^2} - \frac{1}{n_i^2} \right)$$

$$= \frac{R_\infty Z^2}{1 + \frac{m}{M_H}} \left(\frac{1}{n_f^2} - \frac{1}{n_i^2} \right). \tag{34.38}$$

We find that the Rydberg constant depends on the nuclear mass M. As $M \gg m$, the difference between R_M and R_∞ is very small. For hydrogen and helium, we have

$$R_H = 1.09677 \times 10^7 \text{ m}^{-1} \quad \text{and} \quad R_{He} = 1.09722 \times 10^7 \text{ m}^{-1}.$$

The value of R_H agrees well with the experimental value as derived from the study of the hydrogen spectrum ($= 1.09678 \times 10^7 \text{ m}^{-1}$). For helium also the agreement between the experimental value and the theoretical value is satisfactory. Again, we find that the reduced mass $\mu < m$ and it increases with increasing nuclear mass M. The reduced mass μ becomes equal to the electronic mass m as $M \to \infty$.

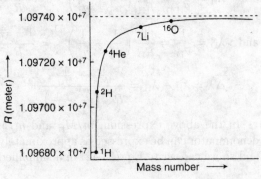

Fig. 34.10

Therefore, R_H increases with the increase of M_H. If $M_H \to \infty$, $R_H \to R_\infty$. As $R_{He} > R_H$ the spectral lines of the Pickering series of He^+ should have slightly higher wave numbers (or shorter wavelengths) than the corresponding lines of the Balmer series of hydrogen. The variation of the Rydberg constant from element to element is presented in Fig. 34.10. The figure shows that the large change occurs between ^1H and ^2H and with increasing mass number the Rydberg constant approaches more and more close to R_∞.

34.9 Discovery of Heavy Hydrogen

We know that the value of the Rydberg constant varies with the mass of the nucleus. This resulted in the discovery of heavy hydrogen called *deuterium*, an isotope of hydrogen. Its nucleus is called *deuteron*. ^1H and ^2H have identical chemical properties. The atoms of both types of hydrogen, viz., ^1H and ^2H have only one electron revolving in their orbits. Their nuclei have same charge but different masses. Mass of the deuteron nucleus $M_D = 2M_H$ and hence the Rydberg constant for the deuterium is slightly higher than that of hydrogen. We have

$$R_H = \frac{R_\infty}{1 + m/M_H}$$

$$\text{and} \quad R_D = \frac{R_\infty}{1 + m/M_D}. \tag{34.39}$$

Calculations show $R_D = 1.09707 \times 10^{+7} \text{ m}^{-1}$ and the lines of the deuterium spectra have slightly higher wave numbers than the corresponding lines of the hydrogen spectra, though the general nature of the two spectra is exactly same.

In 1931, Urey photographed hydrogen spectrum by a large concave grating and found that each hydrogen line was accompanied by a very faint line slightly on the short wavelength side. They obtained the wavelength difference and attributed the faint line to some isotope of hydrogen. This isotope of naturally occurring hydrogen is called 'heavy hydrogen' or 'deuterium'. From the faintness of the lines observed it was clear that its abundance in naturally occurring hydrogen is quite low. Improved techniques have yielded a relative abundance of only about 1 part in $7000[^1_1H - 99.985\%, {}^2_1H(D) - 0.015\%]$ for deuterium.

The wavelength difference between the corresponding spectral lines of ${}^1H$ and ${}^2H$ can be determined in the following way :

We have,

$$\lambda_H = \frac{1}{\bar{\nu}_H} = \frac{1}{R_H}\left(\frac{1}{n_2^2} - \frac{1}{n_1^2}\right)^{-1} = \frac{1 + \frac{m}{M_H}}{R_\infty}\left(\frac{1}{n_2^2} - \frac{1}{n_1^2}\right)^{-1} \qquad (34.40)$$

and
$$\lambda_D = \frac{1}{\bar{\nu}_D} = \frac{1}{R_D}\left(\frac{1}{n_2^2} - \frac{1}{n_1^2}\right)^{-1} = \frac{1 + \frac{m}{M_D}}{R_\infty}\left(\frac{1}{n_2^2} - \frac{1}{n_1^2}\right)^{-1}. \qquad (34.41)$$

$$\therefore \qquad \Delta\lambda = \lambda_H - \lambda_H = \frac{\frac{m}{M_H} - \frac{m}{M_D}}{R_\infty\left(\frac{1}{n_2^2} - \frac{1}{n_1^2}\right)}. \qquad (34.42)$$

In the above expression, m/M_H and m/M_D are very small numbers. So the denominator can be expressed as approximately equal to $1/\lambda_H$. Further, $M_D \approx 2M_H$ and so we can write Eq. (34.42) in a simplified form as

$$\Delta\lambda = \lambda_H \frac{m}{2M_H} = \frac{\lambda_H}{3672}. \qquad (34.43)$$

Now we have $n_1 = 4 \rightarrow n_1 = 2$, a H_β line of the Balmer series of hydrogen and it has wavelength $\lambda_H = 4681$ Å. Using this, we get from Eq. (34.43), $\Delta\lambda = 1.28$ Å for the wavelength difference of the H_β lines of hydrogen and deuterium.

34.10   Bohr's Correspondence Principle

The principle establishes a correlation between the results of classical and quantum theories. The laws of classical mechanics explain the motion of macroscopic bodies, starting from large heavenly bodies to small objects like the atoms and molecules. Kinetic theory of matter is also based on classical mechanics. On the other hand, Planck's quantum theory of radiation, Einstein's light quantum hypothesis to explain photoelectric effect and de Broglie's hypothesis concerning the wave-like behaviour of particles of matter provided a strong ground work for the formulation of quantum mechanics. Bohr suggested that the new laws of quantum mechanics required to describe the motion of the subatomic particles, like the electron inside the atoms, have to be developed in such a way that these laws must go over to the laws of classical mechanics in the limit of larger macroscopic bodies. This is called 'Bohr's Correspondence Principle'.

The frequency f_n of revolution of an electron in the hydrogen atom rotating in its orbit of principal quantum number n is obtained from

$$f_n = \frac{\omega_n}{2\pi} = \frac{V}{2\pi r} = \frac{1}{2\pi}\left(\frac{1}{4\pi\epsilon_0}\frac{Ze^2}{mr_n^3}\right)^{1/2} = \frac{me^4}{32\pi^3\epsilon_0^2 n^3\hbar^3}. \qquad (34.44)$$

The frequency of the radiation emitted due to transition from the $(n+1)$th to the nth orbit of the hydrogen atom is expressed as

$$\nu = \frac{\omega}{2\pi} = \frac{me^4}{64\pi^3\epsilon_0^2\hbar^3}\left[\frac{1}{n^2} - \frac{1}{(n+1)^2}\right]$$

$$= \frac{me^4}{64\pi^3\epsilon_0^2\hbar^3}\frac{2n+1}{n^2(n+1)^2}. \tag{34.45}$$

If $n \gg 1$, then Eq. (34.35) becomes

$$\nu = \frac{me^4}{64\pi^3\epsilon_0^2\hbar^3}\frac{2n}{n^4} = \frac{me^4}{32\pi^3\epsilon_0^2 n^3\hbar^3} = f_n. \tag{34.46}$$

In the limit of very large quantum numbers, the results of Bohr atom model are same as those obtained from classical electromagnetic theory, as required by Bohr's correspondence principle. We have assumed here that the transition takes place from the $(n+1)$th to the nth orbit and the change of quantum number is by 1 unit. If the change of quantum number is $2, 3, \ldots$ units, i.e., if the transition is from $(n+2)$th, $(n+3)$th, $(n+4)$th, etc., orbit to nth orbit, then for large n, we find the frequencies of the emitted radiation to be twice, thrice, four times, etc., of the frequency of radiation. The classical electromagnetic theory also predicts the emission of radiation of these frequencies.

34.10.1 Hydrogen-Like Spectra

The appearance of the spectra of hydrogen and helium are simple. Other hydrogen-like spectra have been found for doubly ionized lithium $Li^{++}(Z=3)$, triply ionized beryllium, $Be^{+++}(Z=4)$ and so on. The spectra of other elements mostly reveal an extremely large number of lines. In such cases it becomes difficult to classify them into series.

We know that the spectra given out by the elements in any particular column of periodic table are similar to each other, e.g., the spectra of the alkali elements and the alkali earth metals bear a resemblance to the hydrogen spectrum. For this reason they are also called *hydrogen-like spectra*. If we examine the Balmer series, we find that each line in this series is a group of very close lines. The lines are said to show a fine structure. We find that the explanation of the complex series found in all hydrogen-like spectra is closely related to the explanation of the fine structure of the Balmer series. Sommerfeld also gave an explanation by postulating that the orbit of the electron is elliptic and not circular as considered by Bohr.

34.10.2 Alkali Atomic Spectra

From the Bohr's model of the atom we find that the wave numbers of various spectral lines can be obtained from the equation,

$$\bar{\nu} = R\left(\frac{1}{m^2} - \frac{1}{n^2}\right), \tag{34.47}$$

where m is fixed for a particular series and is termed as the *fixed term* while n takes running values greater than m and is termed as the *running term*. The atomic spectra of all the elements consisting of atoms having one electron in their outermost orbit are similar and are known as *alkali atomic spectra*. The alkali metals are lithium, sodium, potassium, rubidium and cesium. The other examples showing alkali-like spectra are ionized atoms of beryllium, magnesium, calcium and doubly ionized atoms of boron, aluminium, etc.

Using all the available experimental data and Hartley's law, Rydberg was able to classify the alkali atomic spectra of alkali elements into three series. These are the *sharp*, the *diffuse* and the *principal* series to which were later added the *fundamental* or the *Bergmann* series. We can put his formula for the wave numbers $\bar{\nu}$ of the members of any of these series in the form,

$$\bar{\nu} = R \left[\frac{1}{(m - \alpha)^2} - \frac{1}{(n - \beta)^2} \right], \tag{34.48}$$

where α and β are characteristic constants known as *quantum defects*. The various series found in the alkali atomic spectra are as follows :

(i) **Principal series** : $\bar{\nu}_P = R \left[\dfrac{1}{(1 - \alpha)^2} - \dfrac{1}{(n - \beta_P)^2} \right], n \geq 2$ \hfill (34.49)

(ii) **Sharp series** : $\bar{\nu}_S = R \left[\dfrac{1}{(2 - \alpha)^2} - \dfrac{1}{(n - \beta_S)^2} \right], n \geq 2$ \hfill (34.50)

(iii) **Diffuse series** : $\bar{\nu}_D = R \left[\dfrac{1}{(2 - \alpha)^2} - \dfrac{1}{(n - \beta_D)^2} \right], n \geq 3$ \hfill (34.51)

(iv) **Fundamental or Bergmann series** :

$$\bar{\nu}_F = R \left[\frac{1}{(2 - \alpha)^2} - \frac{1}{(n - \beta_F)^2} \right], n \geq 4, \tag{34.52}$$

where $\beta_P, \beta_S, \beta_D, \beta_F$ are the characteristic constants of principal, sharp, diffuse and fundamental series respectively.

A spectral series in the case of lithium atom can be expressed as

$$\bar{\nu} = R \left[\frac{1}{(2 - 0.040)^2} - \frac{1}{(n - 0.405)^2} \right], \quad n = 3, 4, 5, \ldots \tag{34.53}$$

The other series can be expressed by Ritz combination principle, which states that "*any one of the running terms in one series can be used as the fixed term in another to obtain a new spectral line*".

For lithium atom, we have

$$\bar{\nu} = R \left[\frac{1}{(2 - 0.405)^2} - \frac{1}{(n - 0.040)^2} \right], \quad n = 3, 4, 5, \ldots \tag{34.54}$$

and $\bar{\nu} = R \left[\dfrac{1}{(3 - 0.405)^2} - \dfrac{1}{(n - 0.040)^2} \right], \quad n = 4, 5, 6, \ldots$ \hfill (34.55)

34.11 Sommerfeld's Extension of Bohr Theory

In 1916, Sommerfeld extended the Bohr's theory to include elliptic orbits. In Bohr model the motion of the electron is one-dimensional and so one quantum number (n) was sufficient to specify the state of the atom. But an electron in an elliptic orbit has two degrees of freedom and thus an electron moving in an elliptic orbit needs two quantum numbers (Fig. 34.11). The two degrees of freedom are the radial distance r and the azimuthal angle θ. Sommerfeld and Wilson independently established that Bohr's quantization rule is a particular case of a more generalized quantum condition.

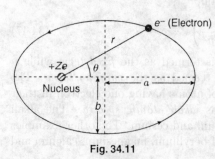

Fig. 34.11

Let p be the momentum and q the corresponding position coordinate. The Sommerfeld and Wilson's general condition of quantization can then be expressed as

$$\int p \cdot dq = nh \tag{34.56}$$

If p_θ and p_r be the angular momenta of the electron, then from Eq. (34.56) we can write,

$$\int_0^{2\pi} p_\theta \cdot d\theta = kh, \quad k = 1, 2, 3, \dots \tag{34.57}$$

and $\oint p_r \cdot dr = n_r h, \quad n_r = 0, 1, 2, \dots . \tag{34.58}$

Here k and n_r are integers, called '*azimuthal*' and '*radial*' quantum number respectively. Using polar equation of the ellipse and integrating over a complete revolution, we can write,

$$\frac{k}{k + n_r} = \frac{b}{a}, \tag{34.59}$$

where a is semi-major axis and b is semi-minor axis of the ellipse. As both k and n_r are integers, we can put,

$$k + n_r = n \quad (n = 1, 2, 3, \dots), \tag{34.60}$$

where n is the 'total or principal quantum number' of the electron. We then have

$$\frac{k}{n} = \frac{b}{a}. \tag{34.61}$$

This is the required condition of quantization for the orbits. Therefore, only those elliptic orbits are permitted for the electron for which the ratio of the major to the minor axis is the ratio of two integers. Sommerfeld determined the total energy E of an electron in a quantized eliptic orbit which is the sum of the kinetic energy (K) and potential energy (U). We can thus write,

$$E = K + U$$

$$= \frac{1}{2}m(\dot{r}^2 + r^2\dot{\theta}^2) - \frac{1}{4\pi\epsilon_0}\frac{Ze^2}{r}. \tag{34.62}$$

As $p_r = m\dot{r}$ and $p_\theta = mr^2\dot{\theta}$, we can rewrite Eq. (34.62) as

$$E = \frac{1}{2m}\left\{ p_r^2 + \frac{p_\theta^2}{r^2} \right\} - \frac{1}{4\pi\epsilon_0}\frac{Ze^2}{r}. \tag{34.63}$$

Now we have

$$p_r = m\dot{r} = m\frac{dr}{dt} = m\frac{dr}{d\theta}\frac{d\theta}{dt} = m\frac{dr}{d\theta}\dot{\theta}$$

$$= (mr^2\dot{\theta})\frac{1}{r^2}\frac{dr}{d\theta} = \frac{p_\theta}{r^2}\frac{dr}{d\theta}. \tag{34.64}$$

Using Eqs. (34.64) and (34.63), we get

$$E = \frac{p_\theta^2}{2mr^2}\left[\left(\frac{1}{r}\frac{dr}{d\theta} \right)^2 + 1 \right] - \frac{1}{4\pi\epsilon_0}\frac{Ze^2}{r}. \tag{34.65}$$

Now we can write the polar equation of the ellipse as

$$\frac{1}{r} = \frac{1}{a}\left(\frac{1 - \epsilon\cos\theta}{1 - \epsilon^2}\right), \tag{34.66}$$

where ϵ is the eccentricity of the ellipse and $1 - \epsilon^2 = \frac{b^2}{a^2}$. Substituting the values of r and $\frac{dr}{d\theta}$ from Eq. (34.66) in Eq. (34.65), we can write,

$$E = -\frac{mZ^2e^4(1 - \epsilon^2)}{(4\pi\epsilon_0)^2 2p_\theta^2}. \tag{34.67}$$

For an isolated system, the angular momentum p_θ remains constant. From Eq. (34.57) we then have

$$p_\theta = \frac{kh}{2\pi}.$$

Further, $1 - \epsilon^2 = \frac{b^2}{a^2} = \frac{k^2}{n^2}.$ \tag{34.68}

By Eqs. (34.67) and (34.68), we get

$$E = -\frac{mZ^2e^4\left(\frac{k^2}{n^2}\right)}{(4\pi\epsilon_0)^2 2\left(\frac{kh}{2\pi}\right)^2}$$

$$= -\frac{mZ^2e^4}{8\epsilon_0^2 h^2}\left(\frac{1}{n^2}\right) \tag{34.69}$$

or, $$E = -\frac{RZ^2hc}{n^2}. \tag{34.70}$$

Therefore, the total energy is independent of the azimuthal quantum number k but depends on the principal quantum number n only. The value of E as expressed in Eq. (34.70) is the same as obtained from Bohr's theory. Thus the principal quantum number n in the Sommerfeld theory is the principal quantum number of the Bohr theory.

34.11.1   Relativistic Correction

It was pointed out by Sommerfeld that the origin of the fine structure of the spectral lines of the hydrogen-like atoms was due to the relativistic variation of mass of the electron revolving in an elliptic orbit. In an elliptic orbit the velocity of the electron changes, when the electron passes close to the nucleus. According to the special theory of relativity, the mass m of a particle moving with velocity v is related to its rest mass m_0 by $m = m_0/\sqrt{1 - v^2/c^2}$. Relativistic effect makes the energy of the electron in a greater eccentricity orbit than that in a non-relativistic elliptic orbit. The path of the electron in an elliptic orbit in the non-relativistic case may be replaced by the following equation when the relativistic variation of mass is taken into consideration :

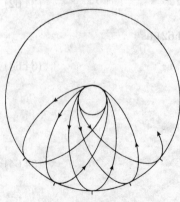

Fig. 34.12

$$r = \frac{a(1 - \epsilon^2)}{1 + \epsilon\cos\gamma\theta}, \tag{34.71}$$

where $\quad \gamma^2 = 1 - \dfrac{Z^2 e^4}{(4\pi\epsilon_0)^2 p^2 c^2}.$ (34.72)

We have written here $p_\theta = p = $ a constant. For non-relativistic case ($c \to \infty$), $\gamma = 1$ and we find that r returns to the same value when θ changes by 2π so that it has the same periodicity as θ. For the variation of the electron mass due to differences in its velocities at different points on its elliptic orbit there is precession of the major axis in the plane of the ellipse about an axis through one of the foci. The trajectory of the electron will be as shown in Fig. 34.12.

According to Sommerfeld the different k-orbits with a given n have slightly different energies. He calculated the total energy to the electron by using the equation,

$$E_{nk} = -\frac{\mu Z^2 e^4}{32\pi^2 \epsilon_0^2 n^2 \hbar^2} \left[1 + \frac{Z^2 \alpha^2}{n^2} \left(\frac{n}{k} - \frac{3}{4} \right) \right],$$ (34.73)

where $\alpha \ll 1 (\simeq 1/137)$ is a pure number. The difference in energy from Bohr's theory as given by the second term with the bracket is very small. In Eq. (34.73), α is called the *fine structure constant*. We can now explain the fine structure of H_α-line which is emitted when the electron jumps from $n = 3$ to $n = 2$ level. The $n = 3$ level consists of 3 sub-levels corresponding to $k = 1, 2, 3$ and $n = 2$ level consists of 2 sub-levels corresponding to $k = 1, 2$.

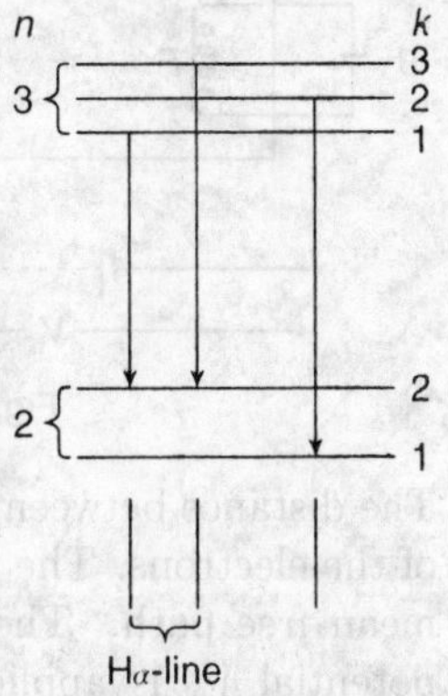

Splitting of the energy levels of hydrogen due to relativistic effect is shown in Fig. 34.13. The splitting shown in the figure have been highly magnified. It should be pointed out that only those electrons jump from the upper sub-levels to the lower sub-levels are permitted for which the k changes by unity, i.e., follows the selection rule :

$$\Delta k = k_f - k_i = \pm 1.$$ (34.74)

The possible transitions consistent with Eq. (34.74) are

$k_i = 1 \quad$ and $\quad k_f = 2 \quad (\Delta k = \pm 1)$
$k_i = 2 \quad$ and $\quad k_f = 1 \quad (\Delta k = -1)$
$k_i = 3 \quad$ and $\quad k_f = 2 \quad (\Delta k = -1).$

Hence there are three possible jumps, indicating that the H_α-line consists of three components. It is seen that the azimuthal quantum number k of the Bohr-Sommerfeld theory has been replaced by the new azimuthal quantum number $l = (k - 1)$ in quantum mechanics. For a given value of n, the possible values of l are $0, 1, 2, 3, \ldots, (n-1)$. The orbital angular momentum of the electron has a value $p_l = \sqrt{l(l+1)}\hbar$. The value of n defines a shell and each value of l determines one sub-shell. A shell corresponding to principal quantum number n has thus n sub-shells. When an electron is in a particular sub-shell, it is designated by a small letter $(s, p, d, f, \ldots)$ to specify the sub-shell. For atoms which have a single optical electron and when this electron is in a particular sub-shell the atom is said to be in a particular state represented by the corresponding capital letter $(S, P, D, F, \ldots)$. These designations are presented in Table 34.1.

At the line of designating an electron, the letter designating it is written after the number that indicates the total quantum number n. Thus by $3p$ electron, we

Fig. 34.13

mean that, 3 is total quantum number and orbital quantum number corresponding to p is 1. For a given value of n the highest possible l value is $(n - 1)$. Thus we have $4d, 5f, 2p$ and $2s$ electrons, while $1p, 2d, 3f$ electrons do not exist.

Table 34.1

Orbital quantum number (l)	0	1	2	3	4	5	6
Optical electron designation	s	p	d	f	g	h	i
State of atom	S	P	D	F	G	H	I

34.12 Franck and Hertz Experiment

Franck and Hertz in 1914 established direct evidence for the existence of discrete energy states within an atom.

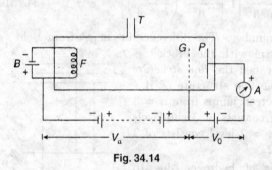

Fig. 34.14

The apparatus used by them is shown in Fig. 34.14. It consists of a glass tube in which a thermionic filament F is mounted. Also there is a grid G and a plate P. The glass tube is evacuated by connecting the side tube T to a pump. The experimental atoms of the element are introduced in the tube in the form of a gas (e.g., mercury vapour) at a pressure of about 1 mm of Hg.

The distance between F and G is made considerably larger than the mean free path of the electrons. The distance between the grid and the plate is made less than the mean free path. The filament F is heated by a battery B, and an accelerating potential V_a is applied between the filament (F) and grid (G). A small fixed retarding potential $V_0(-0.5 \text{ V})$ between grid (G) and plate (P) is maintained.

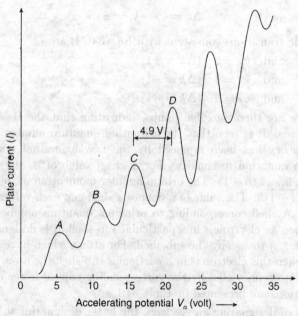

Fig. 34.15

The emitted electrons from the filament (F) are accelerated between F and G by the potential V_a and retarded between G and P by the potential V_0. As a result only those electrons will reach P which have energies higher than eV_0 at G. The plate current is measured by the ammeter A. The current vs. accelerating potential V_α is plotted in Fig. 34.15. The curve reveals a series of regularly spaced peaks. The separation between two consecutive peaks is about 4.9 V. With the increase of V_a the plate current increases as in any electronic tube. However, a significant decrease in the plate current occurs each time when the accelerating potential is increased by approximately 5 V. This is because some electrons with energies slightly greater than 4.88 eV will experience inelastic collisions and will be left with such small energy that they will be unable to reach the plate due to the presence of the retarding voltage. When V_a is increased by an additional 5 V, some electrons that were left with almost no kinetic energy will experience another inelastic collision and will not be able to reach the plate which explains the second dip at a potential of about 5 V greater than the first dip.

34.13 The Pauli Exclusion Principle

In 1925, Pauli enunciated the exclusion principle. According to him, "*no two electrons in an atom can exist in the same quantum state, i.e., no two electrons can have the same set of four quantum numbers, n, l, m_l and m_s*". Also one atomic state corresponds to the assignment of a set of quantum states all of which are different for different electrons to make up the extra-nuclear structure and where there are a sufficient number of such states to account for all the electrons in the atom. It finds no difference which electron is in which quantum state. It is noted that in discussing the spectra of atoms and the splitting of lines in the spectra owing to the superposition of magnetic flux, the quantum numbers n, l, s, m_l, m_s and m_j are all introduced. Out of these, n and l are used to specify the energy and eccentricity of

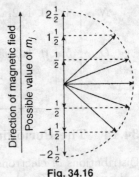

Fig. 34.16

the elliptical orbit. As $j = l + s$, one can determine j if l and s are known. Again, when m_l and m_s are known, s and m_j are predetermined. So only the four quantum numbers n, l, m_l and m_s are required to state.

Let us consider the arrangement of the electrons in atoms. For the nuclear charge Ze the Z electrons are accommodated in the normal atom. Each of these electrons has its own specific set of quantum numbers n, l, m_l and m_s. Electrons with the same principal quantum number n are in the same shell (i.e., K, L, M, etc.). Each shell is divided into sub-shells, where a sub-shell contains electrons which also have the same value of l. The electrons in a given sub-shell must either have different values of m_l, of which there are $2l + 1$ possibilities or different values of m_s, of which there are two possibilities. The maximum possible number of electrons with a given value of l and different values of m_l and m_s is therefore $2(2l + 1)$. Fig. 34.16 shows the possible values of the magnetic quantum number m_j for the case where $j = 2$.

Let us now consider the K, L, M, etc., shells with $n = 1, 2, 3$, etc.

K shell : $n = 1$, l cannot exceed $(n - 1)$, so l must be zero. Hence there can only be 2 $(2l + 1)$, i.e., two $1s$ electrons, one with $m_s = \frac{1}{2}$ and the other with $m_s = -\frac{1}{2}$.

L shell : $n = 2$, l can be 0 or 1. Thus both $2s$ and $2p$ electrons are possible. There can only be two $2s$ electrons and $2(2l + 1) = 6$ electrons with $l = 1$. Thus the maximum possible number of $2p$ electrons is 6, giving 8 electrons in all.

M shell : $n = 3$, l can be 0, 1, or 2. Hence there can be two $3s$ electrons, six $3p$ electrons, and $2(2l + 1) = 10$ electrons with $l = 2$, i.e., $3d$ electrons. In a similar way, the possible electrons in the N and O shells can be decided.

These results are summarised in Table 34.2.

Table 34.2

Shell	n	l	Maximum possible numbers of electrons in sub-shells	Maximum possible number of electrons in shell
K	1	0	Two $1s$	2
L	2	0 or 1	Two $2s$; six $2p$	8
M	3	0, 1, or 2	Two $3s$; six $3p$; ten $3d$	18
N	4	0, 1, 2, or 3	Two $4s$; six $4p$; ten $4d$; fourteen $4f$	32
O	5	0, 1, 2, 3 or 4	Two $5s$; six $5p$; ten $5d$; fourteen $5f$; eighteen $5g$	50

34.14   The Periodic Table

Distributions of electrons in the shells and sub-shells of atoms from the simplest, hydrogen, with $Z = 1$, to the complex one uranium, with $Z = 92$ will take place following the principle that, in normal atom, the electrons are in the lowest possible energy levels. This consideration causes some departures from the predictions of Table 34.2. In Table 34.3, the distributions of the electrons in the first 46 atoms from $Z = 1$ to $Z = 46$ are given. The table reveals that hydrogen has a single $1s$ electron, which may have a spin magnetic quantum number m_s of either $\frac{1}{2}$ or $-\frac{1}{2}$. Helium ($Z = 2$) has two $1s$ electrons, and its K shell is filled. This filled shell corresponds to a stable arrangement of electrons. The element lithium has a filled K shell, but an additional single $2s$ electron. Its K shell is stable with similar elliptical orbits to that of helium, but with different dimensions because Z is now 3. Lithium is monovalent and enters into chemical combinations as its $2s$ electron can be removed by an ionization energy of only 5.39 eV. Neon ($Z = 10$) with filled K and L shells is another inert gas. Sodium ($Z = 11$), with an extra $3s$ electron around a neon-like core, is an alkali metal like lithium with a valency of unity. The third inert gas, argon ($Z = 18$), occurs with filled K and L shells but an incomplete M shell; the full complement of only the $3s$ and $3p$ electrons of the sub-shells of M are filled, the $3d$ sub-shell is still vacant. Potassium ($Z = 19$), the third monovalent element in the group of alkali metals, has an argon-like core but with the additional electron in the $4s$ sub-shell while it would be expected to be in the $3d$ sub-shell.

Table 34.3

Atom	Atomic no. Z	K 1s	L 2s 2p	M 3s 3p 3d	N 4s 4p 4d 4f	O 5s 5p 5d 5f 5g
H	1	1				
He	2	2				
Li	3	2	1			
Be	4	2	2			
B	5	2	2 1			
C	6	2	2 2			
N	7	2	2 3			
O	8	2	2 4			
F	9	2	2 5			
Ne	10	2	2 6			
Na	11			1		
Mg	12			2		
Al	13	Core of		2 1		
Si	14	10 electrons		2 2		
P	15	as in neon		2 3		
S	16			2 4		
Cl	17			2 5		
A	18			2 6		
K	19				1	
Ca	20				2	
Sc	21			1	2	
Ti	22			2	2	
V	23			3	2	
Cr	24			5	1	
Mn	25	Core of		5	2	
Fe	26	18 electrons		6	2	
Co	27	as in argon		7	2	
Ni	28			8	2	
Cu	29			10	1	
Zn	30			10	2	
Ga	31			10	2 1	
Ge	32			10	2 2	
As	33			10	2 3	
Se	34			10	2 4	
Br	35			10	2 5	
Kr	36			10	2 6	
Rb	37					1
Sr	38					2
Y	39				1	2
Zr	40				2	2
Nb	41	Core of			4	1
Mo	42	36 electrons			5	1
Te	43	as in krypton			6	1
Ru	44				7	1
Rh	45				8	1
Pd	46				10	

Elements which have a small number of electrons in the outermost shell or sub-shell in comparison to the maximum number possible in this shell are **electro-positive**. On the other hand, elements which have almost filled outermost shells are known as **electro-negative**.

Examples

1. The Rydberg constant for hydrogen is 10967700 m^{-1}. Determine the short and long wavelength limits of Lyman series.

   Solution : For Lyman series, the wave number is expressed as

   $$\bar{\nu} = \frac{1}{\lambda} = R_H \left(\frac{1}{1^2} - \frac{1}{n^2} \right)$$

   For the short wavelength limit $(\lambda = \lambda_s), n = \infty$

   or, $\quad \bar{\nu} = \frac{1}{\lambda_s} = R_H \left(\frac{1}{1^2} - \frac{1}{\infty^2} \right) = R_H.$

   So we can write,

   $$\lambda_s = \frac{1}{R_H} = \frac{1}{10967700} \text{ m}.$$

   For long wavelength limit $(\lambda = \lambda_L), n = 2$

   $\therefore \quad \bar{\nu}_L = \frac{1}{\lambda_L} = R_H \left(\frac{1}{1^2} - \frac{1}{2^2} \right) = \frac{3}{4} R_H.$

   Therefore, $\lambda_L = \frac{4}{3R_H} = \frac{4}{3} \times 991.6 \text{ Å} = \mathbf{1215 \text{ Å}}.$

2. The wavelength of the first member of the Balmer series in the hydrogen spectrum is 6563 Å. Determine the wavelength of the first member of the Lyman series.

   Solution : For the first member of the Balmer series, we can write,

   $$\frac{1}{\lambda} = R \left[\frac{1}{2^2} - \frac{1}{3^2} \right] = \frac{5R}{36}. \tag{i}$$

   For the first member of the Lymann series,

   $$\frac{1}{\lambda'} = R \left[\frac{1}{1^2} - \frac{1}{2^2} \right] = \frac{3R}{4}. \tag{ii}$$

   Dividing (i) by (ii), we get

   $$\frac{\lambda'}{\lambda} = \frac{5 \times 4}{36 \times 3} = \frac{5}{27} \quad \text{or,} \quad \lambda' = \frac{5}{27}\lambda = \frac{5}{27} \times 6563 = \mathbf{1215 \text{ Å}}.$$

3. In a hydrogen-like atom the ionization energy equals 4 times Rydberg's constant for hydrogen is 2.2×10^{-18} J. Find the wavelength of radiation emitted when a jump takes place from the first excited state to the ground state. Also calculate the radius of first Bohr's orbit.

   Solution : The ionization energy of hydrogen-like Bohr atom of atomic number Z is obtained from

   $$E = -RZ^2 = -\frac{2\pi k^2 Z^2 m e^4}{n^2 h^2}.$$

Hence the Rydberg constant,

$$R = \frac{2\pi^2 kme^4}{n^2 h^2} = 2.2 \times 10^{-18} \text{ J}.$$

As ionization energy, $E = 4\times$ Rydberg constant $= 4R$.

Now we have

$$4R = RZ^2, \quad \therefore \quad Z = 2.$$

Energy of radiation emitted E when the electron jumps from the first excited state to the ground state, is expressed as

$$E = RZ^2 \left(\frac{1}{1^2} - \frac{1}{2^2}\right) = 4R \left(1 - \frac{1}{4}\right)$$

$$= 3R = 3 \times 2.2 \times 10^{-18} = 6.6 \times 10^{-18} \text{ J}.$$

Hence, $\lambda = \dfrac{hc}{E} = \dfrac{6.6 \times 10^{-34} \times 3 \times 10^8}{6.6 \times 10^{-18}} = 3 \times 10^{-8} \text{ m}.$

Again, radius of the first Bohr orbit $= \dfrac{\text{Bohr radius of hydrogen atom}}{Z}$

$$= \frac{5 \times 10^{-11}}{2} \text{ m} = \mathbf{2.5 \times 10^{-11} \text{ m}}.$$

4. Hydrogen atom in its ground state is excited by a monochromatic radiation of wavelength 970.6 Å. How many different wavelengths are possible in the resulting emission spectrum? Obtain the longest wavelength amongst these.

Solution : We can write,

$$E = h\nu = \frac{hc}{\lambda} = \frac{6.6 \times 10^{-34} \times 3 \times 10^8}{970.6 \times 10^{-10} \times 1.6 \times 10^{-19}} = 12.75 \text{ eV}.$$

So the energy of the excited state

$$E_n = -13.6 + 12.75 = -0.85 \text{ eV}.$$

Now, we know,

$$E_n = \frac{-13.6}{n^2}$$

or, $n^2 = \dfrac{-13.6}{E_n} = \dfrac{-13.6}{-0.85} = 16.$

$$\therefore \quad n = 4.$$

The number of possible transitions to the ground state is shown in Fig. 34.17.

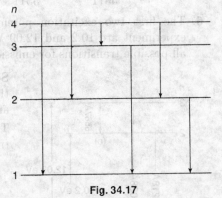

The longest wavelength corresponds to minimum energy difference, i.e., for the transition from $n = 4$ to $n = 3$. We can write,

Fig. 34.17

$$E_3 = \frac{-13.6}{3^2} = -1.51 \text{ eV}.$$

$$\frac{hc}{\lambda_{\text{max}}} = E_4 - E_3,$$

$$\therefore \quad \lambda_{\max} = \frac{6.6 \times 10^{-34} \times 3 \times 10^8}{(1.51 - 0.85) \times 1.6 \times 10^{-19}} = 18.75 \times 10^{-7} \text{ m} = \mathbf{18750 \text{ Å}}.$$

5. The wavelength of the first Balmer line (H_α) of hydrogen is 6562.8 Å. Calculate the wavelength of the same line for tritium ($_1H^3$).

Solution : The wavelengths of H_α-line ($n = 3 \to n = 2$) of hydrogen (^1H) and tritium (^3H) are written as

$$\frac{1}{\lambda_H} = R_H \left(\frac{1}{2^2} - \frac{1}{3^2} \right) = \frac{5}{36} R_H \quad \text{and} \quad \frac{1}{\lambda_T} = R_T \left(\frac{1}{2^2} - \frac{1}{3^2} \right) = \frac{5}{36} R_T$$

where R_H and R_T are Rydberg constants for hydrogen and tritium respectively ($Z = 1$ for both).

From this, we get

$$\frac{\lambda_T}{\lambda_H} = \frac{R_H}{R_T}. \tag{i}$$

The Rydberg constant for an atom of mass M is given by

$$R_m = \frac{R_\infty}{1 + \frac{m}{M}},$$

where R_∞ is the Rydberg constant for any atom of infinitely heavy nucleus.

From (i) we can write,

$$\frac{\lambda_T}{\lambda_H} = \frac{1 + \frac{m}{M_T}}{1 + \frac{m}{M_H}}.$$

Now, we have, $M_T = 3M_H$ and $M_H = 1836 \, m$. Thus,

$$\frac{\lambda_T}{\lambda_H} = \frac{1 + \frac{1}{3 \times 1836}}{1 + \frac{1}{1836}} = \frac{5509}{5511}.$$

$$\therefore \quad \lambda_T = \frac{5509}{5511} \times \lambda_H = \frac{5509}{5511} \times 6562.8 = \mathbf{6560.4 \text{ Å}}.$$

6. The first two excitation potentials of atomic hydrogen in Franck-Hertz experiment are 10.2 and 12.09 V. Draw an energy level diagram and show all possible transitions for emission and absorption along their wavelengths.

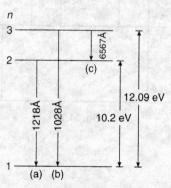

Fig. 34.18

Solution : The energy level diagram and three possible transitions marked by (a), (b) and (c) are presented in Fig. 34.18.

The frequency of radiation resulting from the transitions (a) is obtained as

$$\nu_a = \frac{c}{\lambda_a} = \frac{E_2 - E_1}{h}$$

or, $$\lambda_a = \frac{hc}{E_2 - E_1} \tag{i}$$

or, $$\lambda_a = \frac{6.63 \times 10^{-34} \times 3 \times 10^8}{10.2 \times 1.6 \times 10^{-19}}$$

$$= 1216 \times 10^{-10} \text{ m} = 1219 \text{ Å}$$

In a similar way,

$$\lambda_b = \frac{hc}{E_2 - E_1}$$

$$= \frac{6.63 \times 10^{-34} \times 3 \times 10^8}{12.09 \times 1.6 \times 10^{-19}} = 1.028 \times 10^{-7} \text{ m} = 1028 \text{ Å}$$

Also, $\lambda_c = \dfrac{hc}{E_3 - E_2} = \dfrac{hc}{(E_3 - E_1) - (E_2 - E_1)}$

$$= \frac{hc}{(12.09 - 10.2) \text{ eV}} = \frac{hc}{1.89 \text{ eV}}$$

$$= \frac{6.63 \times 10^{-34} \times 3 \times 10^8}{1.89 \times 1.6 \times 10^{-19}} = 6.577 \times 10^{-7} \text{ m} = \mathbf{6577 \text{ Å}}$$

In absorption, only the transitions starting from $n = 1$ shall be observed, which correspond to 1218 Å and 1028 Å.

7. A doubly ionized lithium atom is hydrogen-like with atomic number $(Z) = 3$.

(i) Find the wavelength of the radiation required to excite the electron in Li^{++} from the first to the third Bohr orbit. (Take ionization energy of the hydrogen atom $=13.6$ eV.)

(ii) How many spectral lines are observed in the emission spectrum of the above excited system?

Solution : (i) The energy difference of electron in Li^{++} between the first and the third orbit is given by

$$E_3 - E_1 = 13.6 \times Z^2 \left(\frac{1}{n_1^2} - \frac{1}{n_2^2} \right) = 13.6 \times (3)^2 \left(\frac{1}{1^2} - \frac{1}{3^2} \right)$$

$$= 13.6 \times 9 \times \frac{8}{9} \times 1.6 \times 10^{-19} \text{ J}.$$

We have, $E_3 - E_1 = \dfrac{hc}{\lambda}$.

So, $\lambda = \dfrac{hc}{E_3 - E_1} = \dfrac{6.6 \times 10^{-34} \times 3 \times 10^8}{13.6 \times 8 \times 1.6 \times 10^{-19}} = \mathbf{113.7 \text{ Å}}$.

(ii) The three spectral lines observed due to the following transitions are shown in Fig. 34.19. They are

3rd to 1st orbit

3rd to 2nd orbit

2nd to 1st orbit.

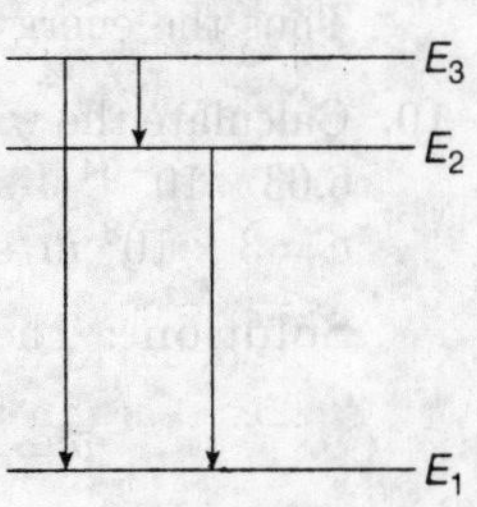

Fig. 34.19

8. The wavelength of the first member of the Balmer series in hydrogen spectrum is 6563 Å. Find the wavelength of the second member of the Lyman series in the same spectrum. [C.U. 2001]

Solution : For Balmer series, $\dfrac{1}{\lambda} = R_\text{H} \left(\dfrac{1}{2^2} - \dfrac{1}{n^2} \right)$, where $n = 3, 4, 5, \ldots$, etc.

Now, for first member, $n = 3$ and $\lambda = 6563$ Å (given).

So, $\dfrac{1}{6563} = R_H \left(\dfrac{1}{4} - \dfrac{1}{9} \right) = R_H \cdot \dfrac{5}{36}$ \hfill (i)

For Lyman series, $\dfrac{1}{\lambda} = R_H \left(\dfrac{1}{1^2} - \dfrac{1}{n^2} \right)$, where $n = 2, 3, 4, 5, \ldots$, etc.

For second member, $n = 3$.

So, $\dfrac{1}{\lambda} = R_H \left(\dfrac{1}{1} - \dfrac{1}{9} \right) = R_H \cdot \dfrac{8}{9}$ \hfill (ii)

Dividing (i) by (ii), we get

$$\dfrac{\lambda}{6563} = \dfrac{5}{36} \times \dfrac{9}{8} = \dfrac{5}{32}.$$

$\therefore \quad \lambda = 6563 \times \dfrac{5}{32} = \mathbf{1025.46\ \text{Å}.}$

9. The energy of electron of the hydrogen atom revolving in the first Bohr orbit is -13.6 eV. Find the energy of the photon emitted when the electron jumps from the second Bohr orbit to the first.

   Solution : The energy of the photon emitted when the electron of the hydrogen atom jumps from n_2 orbit to n_1 orbit is written as

   $$E_{n2} - E_{n1} = \dfrac{2\pi^2 m e^4}{h^2} \left(\dfrac{1}{n_1^2} - \dfrac{1}{n_2^2} \right).$$

   If $n_2 = \infty$, and $n_1 = 1$, then $-E_1 = \dfrac{2\pi^2 m e^4}{h^2}$. $\left[\because E_{n2} = 0 \text{ and } \dfrac{1}{\infty} = 0 \right]$

   Given that, $E_1 = -13.6$ eV.

   $\therefore \quad \dfrac{2\pi^2 m e^4}{h^2} = 13.6$ eV

   We have, $n_2 = 2$ and $n_1 = 1$.

   So, $E_2 - E_1 = 13.6 \left(\dfrac{1}{1} - \dfrac{1}{2^2} \right) = 13.6 \times \dfrac{3}{4} = 10.2$ eV.

   Thus the energy of the emitted photon = **10.2 eV**.

10. Calculate the wave number of the first spectral line of Lyman series, given $h = 6.63 \times 10^{-34}$ J-sec; $m = 9.1 \times 10^{-31}$ kg; $e = 1.6 \times 10^{-19}$ C; $\epsilon_0 = 8.85 \times 10^{-12}$; $c = 3 \times 10^8$ m/sec. \hfill [V.U. 2005]

    Solution : The wave number of the first spectral line of Lyman series is

    $$\bar{\nu} = R_H \left(\dfrac{1}{1^2} - \dfrac{1}{2^2} \right) = \dfrac{3}{4} \cdot R_H.$$

    Now we have, $R_H = \dfrac{m e^4}{8 \epsilon_0^2 c h^3}$

    Therefore, $R_H = \dfrac{9.1 \times 10^{-31} \times (1.6 \times 10^{-19})^4}{8 \times (8.85 \times 10^{-12})^2 \times 3 \times 10^8 \times (6.63 \times 10^{-34})^3}$

    $= 1.09 \times 10^7$

    $\therefore \qquad \bar{\nu} = \dfrac{3}{4} \times 1.09 \times 10^7 = \mathbf{8.175 \times 10^6\ m^{-1}.}$

Questions

Essay-type

1. From Bohr's theory, obtain an expresion for the energy of hydrogen atom. What is the significance of negative sign in the expression.

    [C.U. 2003, '05; B.U. 2003]

2. State and explain Bohr's postulates regarding the structure of hydrogen atom. Derive from Bohr's theory, an expression for the total energy of an atom in its nth stationary state. [N.B.U. 1983, 2005; V. U. 2005]

3. Discuss, with the energy level diagram of a hydrogen atom, the origin of Lyman, Balmer and Paschen spectral series. [B.U. 1984]

4. Give an account of Bohr's theory of hydrogen atom. How can the origin of the spectral lines of hydrogen be explained with the help of this theory?

5. Give an account of Bohr-Sommerfeld model of elliptical electron orbit of hydrogen atom. How does it account for the structure of hydrogen spectrum?

6. Explain (i) Ritz combination principle, (ii) Bohr's correspondence principle and (iii) Reduced mass of an electron.

7. State Bohr's postulates regarding hydrogen atom. Deduce an expression for the energy of the nth Bohr orbit.

8. Explain Pauli's exclusion principle. How is this principle applied in explaining the periodic table of elements? [C.U. 2005]

9. A group of four quantum numbers completely specify the energy state of an electron in an atom. What are these quantum numbers and what is their significance?

10. State the fundamental postulates of Bohr's theory. With the help of them, deduce an expression for total energy of an electron in nth orbit of an atom and show that the wavelength of light emitted due to transition from orbit n_2 to orbit n_1 may be written as $\frac{1}{\lambda} = R \cdot Z^2 \left(\frac{1}{n_1^2} - \frac{1}{n_2^2} \right)$, where R is Rydberg's constant. [B.U. 2004]

11. Find an expression for the energy required to ionize hydrogen atom in the lowest energy level.

12. State the postulates of Bohr's theory and deduce an expression for the energy of the nth orbit of hydrogen atom. What interpretation do you give to the negative sign of the energy value?

13. Explain the effect of nuclear mass on the Rydberg constant and how it led to the discovery of heavy hydrogen.

14. Discuss early views on atomic structure. How did Bohr modify Rutherford's model to make it dynamically stable? In what respects Bohr's model of the atom found to be lacking? How these defects of Bohr's model have been removed in Sommerfeld's model?

15. Why in Bohr's theory of hydrogen atom the quantum number n, cannot take the value zero?

16. State Bohr's postulates. Derive an expression for the frequencies of radiation emitted in hydrogen atom. Hence, explain the various spectral series of this atom.

17. Lyman series can be observed in absorption spectra while the Balmer series cannot be observed. Explain.

18. Can a hydrogen atom absorb a photon of energy greater than the binding energy of the atom?

19. Explain, how Bohr's theory can be applied to a singly-ionized helium atom.

20. Discuss the effect of nuclear motion ('finite' nuclear mass) on the spectra of hydrogen-like atoms.

21. What relationship do you expect between the hydrogen spectrum and the ionized helium spectrum?

22. Give a qualitative discussion of the improvements made by Sommerfeld in Bohr's atomic model. Show how fine structure of Balmer lines was explained on this.

23. Discuss relativistic Sommerfeld theory of hydrogen atom. How does it explain the fine structure of H_α-line.

24. Discuss Bohr's correspondence principle.

25. What do you understand by excitation and ionization potentials of an atom? Describe Franck and Hertz experiment and show that it provides a direct evidence of the existence of discrete energy levels in an atom. State the limitations of the experiment.

Short Answer-type

26. How many quantum numbers are required to define the state of an electron in an atom? What are they?   [B.U. 2003]

27. What are the special features of vector atom model? What are the possible values of l, the orbital quantum number for electrons in M-shell? Why was spin quantum number introduced?

28. What is Rydberg constant? What are the different spectral series produced by hydrogen? Hydrogen atom has only one electron. How does it produce so many spectral lines?

29. Which spectral series of hydrogen spectrum lie in the visible part?

30. Why is an atom neutral in charge? Why is a simple positive-nucleus-and-electron atom unstable both (a) without orbital motion of the electrons and (b) with orbital motion of the electrons?

31. What is the principal quantum number and how does this determine the radii of orbits, the orbital velocity and energy levels of the atom?

32. What led Sommerfeld to introduce new quantum numbers? What is precession?

33. What are the number of electrons in N-shell? How can you get the number of electrons from the principal quantum number of the shell?

Numerical Problems

34. Calculate the ionization potential of hydrogen atom. [C.U. 2005]
[**Ans.** 13 eV]

35. Calculate the value of Rydberg constant for hydrogen if the wavelength of the first Balmer line of hydrogen spectrum be 6553 Å. [**Ans.** 1.09×10^7 m^{-1}]

36. The first member of the Balmer series of H_2 has a wavelength of 6563 A.U. Calculate the wavelength of its second member. [N.B.U. 2002]
[**Ans.** 4861.5 A.U.]

37. Rydberg constant of hydrogen is 109737 cm^{-1}. Find the shortest and the longest wavelengths of Balmer series. [**Ans.** 3646 Å; 6560 Å]

38. Find the radius of the first Bohr orbit for hydrogen atom. Given, $h = 6.63 \times 10^{-34}$ J-sec; $m = 9.1 \times 10^{-31}$ kg; $e = 1.6 \times 10^{-19}$ C. [N.B.U. 1983]
[**Ans.** 0.53×10^{-10}]

39. Calculate the nearest energy required to raise hydrogen atom from the ground state $n = 1$ to the first excited state $n = 2$. [**Ans.** 10.2 eV]

40. Show that the velocity of electron in the first hydrogen atom orbit is $c/137$, where c is the velocity of light.

41. The wavelength of the first member of Balmer series in hydrogen spectrum is 6563 Å. Calculate the wavelength of the first member of the Lyman series in the same spectrum. [**Ans.** 1215 Å]

42. The first member of Balmer series of hydrogen has a wavelength 6563 Å. Calculate the wavelength of the second member. [**Ans.** 4861.5 Å]

43. Calculate the radius of the second Bohr orbit of hydrogen atom and the velocity of electron in this orbit.
[$1/4\pi\epsilon_0 = 9 \times 10^9$ N-m^2/c^2, $m = 9.1 \times 10^{-31}$ kg, $e = 1.6 \times 10^{-19}$ C and $h = 6.63 \times 10^{-34}$ J-sec.] [**Ans.** 2.1 Å, 1.1×10^6 m/s]

44. The Rydberg constant for hydrogen is 10967700 m^{-1}. calculate the short and long wavelength limits of Lyman series.
[**Ans.** (i) $\lambda_s = 911.6$ Å, (ii) $\lambda_L = 1215$ Å]

45. Electrons of energy 12.2 eV are fired at the hydrogen atoms in a gas discharge tube. Determine the wavelength of the lines that can be examined by hydrogen.
[**Ans.** $\lambda_1 = 6563$ Å, $\lambda_2 = 1215$ Å, $\lambda_3 = 1026$ Å corresponding to $n = 3 \rightarrow 2$, $n = 2 \rightarrow 1$ and $n = 3 \rightarrow 1$ transitions respectively]

46. Calculate the wavelength of the photon emitted when the hydrogen atom goes from $n = 10$ state to the ground state ($R_H = 1.097 \times 10^{-3}$ Å). [**Ans.** 921 Å]

47. How many times does the electron go round the first Bohr orbit of hydrogen in 1 sec? [**Ans.** 6.57×10^{15} Hz]

48. Calculate the time taken by the electron to traverse the first orbit in the hydrogen atom. Electron mass and charge are 9.1×10^{-31} kg and 1.6×10^{-19} C and $h = 6.63 \times 10^{-34}$ J-sec. [**Ans.** 1.5×10^{-16} s]

49. In a Franck-Hertz experiment, the first dip in the current-voltage graph for hydrogen was observed at 10.2 V. Calculate the wavelength of light emitted by hydrogen atom when excited to the first excitation level. [**Ans.** 1217 Å]

50. Calculate the wavelength of the eighth line of the Balmer series of the hydrogen atom. Rydberg constant for hydrogen atom is 1.097×10^7 m^{-1}.

[**Hint** : For eighth line, $n = 10$]   [**Ans.** 3798 Å]

51. The series limit of Balmer series is 3646 Å. Calculate the wavelength of the first member of this series.   [**Ans.** 6563 Å]

52. The wavelength of the first line of Balmer series of hydrogen is 6562.8 Å. Calculate (a) the ionization potential and (b) the first excitation potential of the hydrogen atom.   [**Ans.** (a) 13.6 eV, (b) 10.2 eV]

53. An orange photon of wavelength 600 nm is emitted from an atom. Find the difference in energy in the two atomic states involved. Find the same result for the red 6563 Å line of hydrogen.   [**Ans.** 2.07 eV, 1.9 eV]

54. With Franck-Hertz type of experiment on sodium, the first spectral line to appear is the D-line, $\lambda = 5890$ Å. What is the first excitation potential of the sodium?   [**Ans.** 2.1 V]

Chapter 35

X-Rays, Photoelectric Effect and Wave Mechanics

35.1 Introduction

The X-rays, the photoelectric effect and the wave mechanics—these three branches of modern physics have contributed significantly in modern civilization. Many important discoveries are there under these headings. The experiments in these branches of physics and the associated theories emerged thereafter may be considered undoubtedly as very important milestones for future sciences for many decades. We have, truly speaking, just outlined those important experiments and theories in this chapter because of our limitation of presentation in the text herein.

35.2 Production of X-rays by Coolidge Tube

The X-ray tube designed by Coolidge is called *Coolidge Tube* according to his name. It consists of a highly evacuated bulb where the cathode C is a tungsten filament F heated by current from a battery E and rheostat Rh (Fig. 35.1). The filament emits electrons called *thermions* which move towards the tungsten anti-cathode A with a velocity depen-ding on the applied potential diff-

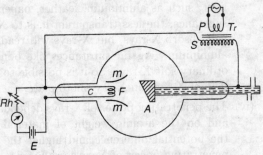

Fig. 35.1

erence between C and A. The cathode filament is surrounded by a molybdenum shield m kept at a negative potential with respect to the filament. As a result the rays can be directed to a fine point on the target A. In the absence of the shield the electrons would diverge in all the directions. No ionization occurs as the tube is evacuated to the no-discharge limit. The target plate is attached to a brass rod surrounded by jacket through which cold water is circulated. The working voltage of the tube is obtained from the secondary of a step-up transformer. The tube acts as its own rectifier and the voltage in a large plant is rectified also by the thermionic valve rectifier. The applied voltage controls the hardness of the emitted X-rays while the temperature of the filament regulated by the battery current controls electron emission and the intensity of the X-rays produced.

The anti-cathode in the Coolidge tube has the following characteristics :

(i) It has high atomic weight for production of hard X-rays.

(ii) It has high melting point to stand the high temperature developed due to most of the energy of the impinging electrons becoming converted into heat.

(iii) It has large thermal conductivity to get rid of the heat developed quickly.

Metals tantalum, platinum and tungsten are used in general; the last one is the best and is used extensively. A heavy block of this metal is mounted on a massive brass rod and the face is inclined at an angle of 45° to the electron beam.

To find the maximum speed of electron striking the anti-cathode, let V (in e.s.u.) be the P.D. applied to the X-ray tube. Then work done on the electron in moving from cathode to anti-cathode will be Ve ergs, where e is the electronic charge in e.s.u.

If v_{max} max be the maximum velocity acquired by the electron, then maximum kinetic energy is given by

$$\frac{1}{2}mv_{max}^2 = Ve \quad \text{or,} \quad v_{max} = \sqrt{\frac{2Ve}{m}}. \tag{35.1}$$

35.3   Properties of X-rays

(i) They travel in straight lines with the velocity of light.

(ii) X-rays, like cathode rays are invisible to our eye.

(iii) They penetrate or pass through many solids which are opaque to ordinary light, such as aluminium, leather, paper, wood, flesh, etc. The denser the substance, the less transparent it is to X-rays. A lead sheet of 1 mm thick will absorb X-rays, but X-rays will readily pass through equal thickness of aluminium. Again, substances like bone and dense metals are opaque to ordinary soft X-rays. So it is possible to get a picture of the bones with the help of X-rays on X-ray photo-plate.

(iv) The penetrating power of X-rays depends on the applied potential difference and on the atomic weight of material of the anti-cathode. The larger the potential difference and higher the atomic weight, the greater is the penetrating power of X-rays produced.

Also it has been found that shorter the wavelength of the X-rays, the greater is their penetrating power. The highly penetrating X-rays are called hard X-rays while those which are readily absorbed by bodies are known as soft X-rays.

(v) X-rays can cause fluorescence in many substances like barium platinocyanide, zinc sulphide, calcium tungstate, etc.

(vi) X-rays are not deflected by electric and magnetic fields. This property shows that X-rays do not consist of charged particles. Also this distinguishes X-rays from cathode rays.

(vii) X-rays passing through air or other gases have the capacity to render it as a conductor of electricity, i.e., they can ionize a gas through which they pass.

(viii) They have a destructive effect on tissues of living beings. Exposure to X-rays causes reddening and surface sores in human body.

(ix) Like ordinary light, X-rays consist of electromagnetic waves of extremely short wavelength. They can show phenomena of reflection, refraction, interference, diffraction and polarization in a similar manner.

(x) They affect a photographic plate having silver salt and this action is stronger than ordinary light.

35.4   Uses of X-rays

(a) In Engineering : On account of high penetrating power, X-rays are used to investigate the structure of metals, for testing of castings for flaws and gas pockets and for detecting cracks and ruptures in metal plates and beams.

(b) In Industry : X-rays are used in industry to detect defects in tennis balls, motor tyres, wood and wireless valves.

(c) In Surgery : X-rays can pass through flesh, but not through bones. Therefore, they are extensively used in surgery for detecting fractures, foreign bodies, diseased organs, etc. The diseased person is made to stand between an X-ray bulb and a fluorescent screen. The illumination of the screen depends on the stopping power of different parts of the body. A light shadow of the flesh and a deep shadow of the bones can thus be obtained. A photograph called radiograph may be obtained and studied for diagnosis.

(d) In Radio-therapy : As diseased tissues of the body are destroyed by X-rays, they can be used to cure skin diseases, malignant growths and tumours.

(e) In Scientific Research : X-rays are used for investigation of the structure of crystals, structure and properties of atoms and arrangements of atoms and molecules inside material bodies.

(f) In Detective Work : X-rays are used for detecting contraband goods like opium, cincona, explosives, etc., concealed in wooden or leather cases. They can detect presence of precious metals such as gold and silver in the body of smugglers.

35.5   Secondary Radiations

If X-rays are allowed to fall on matter, some of the beam passes through it with reduced intensity but in addition the matter becomes source of secondary radiations. These are of following categories :

(1) Electronic radiation : This consists of electrons ejected from matter by the incident beam. It is similar to photoelectric emission set up when ultraviolet light falls on some substances.

(2) Scattered radiations : These are of two types, viz., (a) Scattered X-rays which are same as incident beam. This refers to general scattering without modification of wavelength λ. (b) Scattered X-rays which differ in wavelength from the incident beam. This is scattering with modification of the wavelength λ and is known as Compton effect.

35.6   Spacing between Three-Dimensional Lattice Planes

Let us consider O as the origin and OX, OY, OZ are three rectangular axes as shown in Fig. 35.2. Let a reference plane pass through O. Now we consider a set of parallel planes defined by Millerindices (hkl).

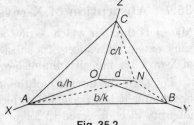

Beside reference plane through O, if we assume that the next plane passes through A, B and C, then the respective intercepts are a/h, b/k and c/l. Let ON be the normal between this plane and the reference plane. Then $ON = d$ be the interplanar spacing. To find the value of d in terms of a, b and c, let the normal make angles α, β and γ with crystal axes, so that

Fig. 35.2

$$\angle NOX = \alpha, \quad \angle NOY = \beta \quad \text{and} \quad \angle NOZ = \gamma.$$

From Fig. 35.2, we have

$$d = \frac{a}{h}\cos\alpha = \frac{b}{k}\cos\beta = \frac{c}{l}\cos\gamma$$

or, $\cos\alpha = \dfrac{d}{(a/h)}, \cos\beta = \dfrac{d}{(b/k)}, \cos\gamma = \dfrac{d}{(c/l)}.$

But $\cos^2\alpha + \cos^2\beta + \cos^2\gamma = 1.$

$\therefore$ $$\left[\frac{d}{(a/h)}\right]^2 + \left[\frac{d}{(b/k)}\right]^2 + \left[\frac{d}{(c/l)}\right]^2 = 1. \tag{35.2}$$

We can write Eq. (35.2) as

$$d^2\left[\frac{h^2}{a^2} + \frac{k^2}{b^2} + \frac{l^2}{c^2}\right] = 1$$

or, $$d = \left[\frac{h^2}{a^2} + \frac{k^2}{b^2} + \frac{l^2}{c^2}\right]^{-\frac{1}{2}}. \tag{35.3}$$

Now for a simple cubic lattice we have

$$a = b = c.$$

So for such a lattice, inter-planar separation is written as

$$d_{hkl} = \frac{a}{\sqrt{(h^2 + k^2 + l^2)}}. \tag{35.4}$$

Hence, $d_{100} = \dfrac{a}{\sqrt{(1^2 + 0^2 + 0^2)}} = a$

$$d_{110} = \frac{a}{\sqrt{(1^2 + 1^2 + 0^2)}} = \frac{a}{\sqrt{2}}$$

and $$d_{111} = \frac{a}{\sqrt{(1^2 + 1^2 + 1^2)}} = \frac{a}{\sqrt{3}}.$$

Therefore, the separations between successive (100), (110) and (111) planes are $a, a/\sqrt{2}$ and $a/\sqrt{3}$ respectively. Thus the ratio of their separation is

$$d_{100} : d_{110} : d_{111} = 1 : \frac{1}{\sqrt{2}} : \frac{1}{\sqrt{3}}.$$

In a similar way, for fcc lattice,

$$d_{100} = a/2; d_{110} = a/2\sqrt{2} \text{ and } d_{111} = a/\sqrt{3}$$

and for bcc lattice,

$$d_{100} = a/2; d_{110} = a/\sqrt{2} \text{ and } d_{111} = a/2\sqrt{3}.$$

35.7   Absorption of X-rays

Materials through which X-rays are allowed to pass are found to absorb them to some extent. If a sheet of a substance is kept in the path of a homogeneous beam of X-rays, its intensity diminishes.

Let I_0 be the intensity of the incident X-ray beam and l be the intensity of the beam after it has traversed a thickness dx of the absorber. Then the decrease in intensity dl is observed to follow the equation $dl = -\mu I dx$, where μ is the linear absorption coefficient and it depends on the wavelength of X-rays used as well as on the nature of the absorbing material.

We can write,

$$\frac{dI}{I} = -\mu dx$$

or, $I = I_0 e^{-\mu x} = I_0 e^{-(\mu/\rho) \times \rho x}$

$$= I_0 e^{-\mu_m m} \qquad (35.5)$$

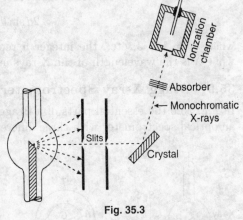

Fig. 35.3

where $\mu/\rho = \mu_m$ is known as the mass absorption coefficient and m is the mass of unit area of the absorbing sheet. The mass absorption coefficient (μ_m) varies as the cube of the incident wavelength (λ) and also the atomic number (Z) of the absorber following, $\mu_m = k\lambda^3 Z^3$. This indicates why materials with high atomic numbers are preferred for shielding against X-rays.

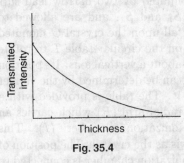

Fig. 35.4

In order to study the penetrating ability of X-rays an ionization chamber can be used. The apparatus is shown in Fig. 35.3. As shown X-rays are collimated by slits, rendered monochromatic by Bragg reflection, and passed through the material under study. The thickness of the absorbing material is altered and the transmitted intensity is plotted against thickness which is an expotential decay curve ($I = I_0 e^{-\mu x}$), as drawn in Fig. 35.4.

35.8   Bragg's Law and Its Derivation

If monochromatic X-rays impinge on the atoms in a crystal lattice, each atom acts as a source of scattering radiation of same wavelength. The crystal then acts as a series of parallel reflecting planes. The intensity of the reflected beam at certain angles will be maximum if the path difference between two reflected waves coming from two different planes is an integral multiple of the wavelength λ.

In order to derive the Bragg's law we consider a set of parallel planes of atom points at a spacing d between two successive planes. As shown in Fig. 35.5 a narrow monochromatic X-ray beam of wavelength λ be incident on the first plane at a glancing angle θ. We consider the ray PQ incident on the first plane at an angle θ. The corresponding reflected ray QR be inclined also at the same angle θ to the plane. As X-rays are more penetrating than ordinary light, there is only partial reflection at each plane. The complete absorption occurs only after penetrating several layers. Let us consider two parallel rays PQR and $P'Q'R'$ in the beam which are reflected by two atoms Q and Q' where Q' is vertically below Q. The ray $P'Q'R'$ has a longer path than the ray PQR.

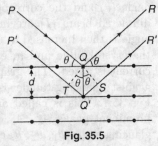

Fig. 35.5

To obtain the path-difference between the two rays from Q, we draw normals QT and QS on $P'Q'$ and $Q'R'$ respectively. Then we have the path-difference

$$= TQ' + Q'S = d\sin\theta + d\sin\theta = 2d\sin\theta.$$

The two rays will reinforce each other to produce maximum intensity when

$$2d\sin\theta = n\lambda, \tag{35.6}$$

where $n = 1, 2, 3$, etc., the integer n represents the order of the scattered beam while λ is the wavelength of the X-rays used. Eq. (35.6) is called the *Bragg's law.*

35.9   Bragg X-ray Spectrometer

In Fig. 35.6 the essential parts of a Bragg spectrometer are shown. It is similar to an optical spectrometer with three different sections.

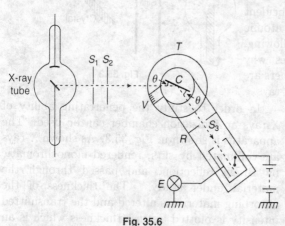

Fig. 35.6

These are : (i) a source of X-rays, (ii) a crystal held on a circular table which is graduated and provided with vernier and (iii) a detector (ionization chamber). X-rays from an X-ray tube are limited by two narrow lead slits S_1 and S_2, and are allowed to fall upon the crystal C mounted on the circular table T to rotate about a vertical axis. Its position can be determined by the vernier V. The table is provided with a radial arm (R) which carries an ionization chamber (I). This arm can also be rotated about the same vertical axis as the crystal. The position of this arm is determined by a second vernier. The ionization chamber is connected to an electrometer (E) for measuring the ionization current. Thus we can measure the intensity of the diffracted beam of the X-rays which are diffracted in the direction of the ionization chamber. S_3 is a lead slit used to limit the width of the diffracted beam. The crystal table is geared to the ionization chamber so that the chamber turns through 2θ when the crystal is turned by an angle θ.

Principle

The glancing angle θ for the incident beam is kept very small and the ionization chamber is adjusted to receive the reflected beam till the rate of deflection becomes maximum. The glancing angle (θ) and the corresponding intensity of the diffracted beam (I) are measured. The glancing angle is then increased in equal steps, by rotating the crystal table and in each case the ionization current is noted. The graph of ionization current against glancing angle is drawn as shown in Fig. 35.7. This is called an X-*ray spectrum.* The

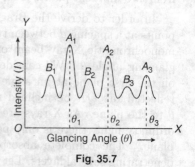

Fig. 35.7

prominent peaks A_1, A_2, A_3 in the figure refer to X-rays of wavelength λ. The glancing angles θ_1, θ_2, θ_3 corresponding to the peaks A_1, A_2, A_3 are found from the graph. It is seen that $\sin\theta_1 : \sin\theta_2 : \sin\theta_3 = 1 : 2 : 3$. This indicates that A_1, A_2, A_3, refer to the first, second and third order reflections of same wavelength. Again, B_1, B_2, B_3 are peaks for the first, second and third order for another wavelength (λ_2). In this way, Bragg experimentally verified the relation $2d\sin\theta = n\lambda$.

35.9.1　Measurement of Wavelength of X-rays

The wavelength of X-rays can be determined using the equation $2d \sin \theta = n\lambda$. The glancing angle θ is experimentally obtained for a known order. If d is known, λ can be found out.

35.9.2　Calculation of d

Rocksalt (NaCl) possesses a cubic structure with sodium and chlorine ions situated alternately at the corners of a cube. Let d be the distance between two neighbouring ions and ρ the density of the crystal, then mass of the unit cube $= \rho d^3$. Each corner ion is shared by 8 neighbouring cubes. This is illustrated by the ion as indicated by an asterisk in Fig. 35.8. Thus each ion contributes only $\frac{1}{8}$th of its mass of the cube. As the unit cube is made up of 4 sodium ions and 4 chlorine ions, the mass of each cube = the mass of $\frac{1}{2}$ NaCl molecule. Let M be the molecular weight of NaCl and N_A the Avogardo's number. Then, we have

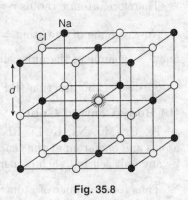

Fig. 35.8

$$\text{mass of } \frac{1}{2} \text{ NaCl molecule} = M/2N_A.$$

Hence we can write,

$$\rho d^3 = \frac{M}{2N_A} \quad \text{or} \quad d = \sqrt[3]{\frac{M}{2N_A\rho}}. \tag{35.7}$$

From a knowledge of M, N_A and ρ, we can determine d using Eq. (35.7).

For NaCl, $M = 58.45$ kg; $\rho = 2170$ kg m^{-3} and $N_A = 6.06 \times 10^{26}$ and, therefore,

$$d = \sqrt[3]{\frac{58.45}{2 \times (6.06 \times 10^{26}) \times 2170}} = 2.81 \times 10^{-10} \text{ m}.$$

35.10　Crystal Structures and Associated Terminology

(i) Coordination number : The number of nearest atoms directly surrounding a given atom is known as *coordination number*. It indicates the closeness of the packing of the atoms.

(ii) Atomic radius : It is equal to half the distance between nearest neighbours in a crystal of a pure element.

(iii) Packing fraction (or packing factor) : It is defined as the ratio of volume of atoms per unit cell to the total volume of the unit cell.

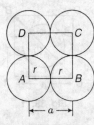

Fig. 35.9

In order to calculate the packing fraction for the three types of cubic crystals, we assume that the atoms are hard spheres and that the nearest neighbours touch each other. The calculations are as follows :

(a) Simple Cube

Polonium is the only element which has this structure. In polonium, there are 8 atoms at 8 corners and each atom is common for 8 cubes. Hence, the number of atoms in a unit cell $= 8 \times \frac{1}{8} = 1$. The atoms touch each other along the lattice as shown in Fig. 35.9.

Let $a =$ lattice constant (side of the unit cell)

and $r =$ radius of the atom.

Then $a = 2r$.

Therefore, atomic radius $r = a/2$.   (35.8)

Now, volume of one atom $= \frac{4}{3}\pi r^3 = \frac{4}{3}\pi \left(\frac{a}{2}\right)^3 = \frac{\pi a^3}{6}$

and   volume of the unit cell $= a^3$.

So the packing fraction (P.F.) $= \dfrac{\pi a^3/6}{a^3} = \dfrac{\pi}{6} = 0.52$.

(b) Body-Centred Cube

Fe, Cr, Mo, Na, K, Li, Rb, Cs, etc., crystallize in this form. It has 8 corner atoms and one atom at the centre of the cube where the central atom is not shared by any unit cell but each corner atom is shared by 8 unit cells.

Thus total number of atoms per unit cell $= 1 + \left(8 \times \dfrac{1}{8}\right) = 2$.

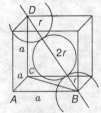

Fig. 35.10

As shown in Fig. 35.10, the corner atoms do not touch each other though each corner atom touches the central atom. Considering the geometry of one unit cell, we can write,

$$BD^2 = BC^2 + CD^2 = AB^2 + AC^2 + CD^2$$

or, $(r + 2r + r)^2 = a^2 + a^2 + a^2$

or, $(4r)^2 = 3a^2$

Therefore, $r = \sqrt{3}a/4$ (35.9)

Hence, the volume of 2 atoms $= 2 \times \frac{4}{3}\pi r^3 = 2 \times \frac{4}{3}\pi \left(\dfrac{\sqrt{3}a}{4}\right)^3 = \dfrac{\pi a^3 \sqrt{3}}{8}$

and volume of unit cell $= a^3$.

∴   P.F. $= \dfrac{\pi a^3 \sqrt{3}/8}{a^3} = \dfrac{\pi \sqrt{3}}{8} = 0.68$.

(c) Face-Centred Cube

There are 8 atoms one at each corner of the cube plus 6 face-centred atoms at 6 planes of the cube. Each corner atom is shared by 8 surrounding cubes and each face-centred atom is shared by 2 surrounding cubes. So the total number of atoms per unit cell

$$= 8 \times \frac{1}{8} + 6 \times \frac{1}{2} = 4.$$

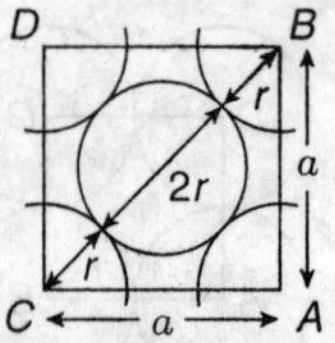

As shown in Fig. 35.11, the corner atoms do not touch, but each corner atom touches the central atom of each face. If r be the atomic radius and a, the lattice parameter, from geometry of the face of the unit cell, we get

$$BC^2 = AB^2 + AC^2$$

or, $(r + 2r + r)^2 = a^2 + a^2$

or, $16r^2 = 2a^2$.

Fig. 35.11

Therefore, $r = a/2\sqrt{2}$ (35.10)

Hence, volume of 4 atoms $= 4 \times \dfrac{4}{3}\pi r^3 = 4 \times \dfrac{4}{3}\pi \left(\dfrac{a}{2\sqrt{2}}\right)^3 = \dfrac{\pi a^3}{3\sqrt{2}}$

and volume of the unit cell $= a^3$.

$\therefore$ P.F. $= \dfrac{\pi a^3/3\sqrt{2}}{a^3} = \dfrac{\pi}{3\sqrt{2}} = 0.74$.

35.11 The Crystal Lattice

Crystal is made by the infinite repetition in space of identical structural units like atoms, molecules or ions. Each unit can be replaced by a geometrical point. The result is a pattern of points having same geometrical properties as the crystal. This geometrical pattern is called the *crystal lattice* or simply the lattice and the points are known as *lattice points*. We may, therefore, define the crystal lattice in the following way :

The regular pattern of points which in a crystal structure describe the three-dimensional arrangement of particles (atoms, molecules or ions) is known as the *crystal lattice* or *space lattice*.

In Fig. 35.12(a), we have shown an array of points in two dimensions where the environment about any two points is same. The figure thus represents a crystal lattice (or space lattice).

A crystal structure is constructed by associating with every lattice point a unit assembly of atoms or molecules which are identical in composition. This unit assembly is known as **basis.** Fig. 35.12(b) represents a particular arrangement of two different ions. The number of atoms in the basis so formed may be as low as one, as for many metals. However, there are structures for which the basis exceeds 1000 atoms.

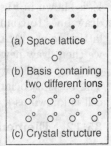

(a) Space lattice

(b) Basis containing two different ions

(c) Crystal structure

Fig. 35.12

A **crystal structure** is formed by the addition of a basis to every lattice point [Fig. 35.12(c)]. Thus we may say Lattice + Basis = Crystal Structure. Fig. 35.12 illustrates the difference between the crystal lattice, the basis, and the crystal structure.

The atoms in a crystal are arranged in a periodic array. Thus it is possible to isolate a representative unit cell in each variety of crystal. This unit cell may be a group of ions, atoms or molecules. We may construct the crystal by repeatedly translating the unit cell in three dimensions. The smallest portion of a space lattice which can generate the complete crystal by repeating its own dimensions in different directions is known as the *unit cell*. A unit cell may be defined by the length of its edges and by the angles between them (Fig. 35.13). Let $OA = a$, $OB = b$ and $OC = c$ are the dimensions of the unit cell. The angles between b, c; c, a and a, b are denoted by α, β and γ respectively. These are called *interfacial angles*. The vectors $\mathbf{a}, \mathbf{b}, \mathbf{c}$ define the axes of the crystal.

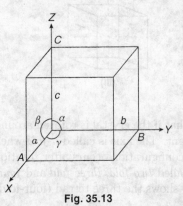

Fig. 35.13

35.11.1 Primitive Lattice Cell

The parallelepiped defined by primitive axes $\mathbf{a}, \mathbf{b}, \mathbf{c}$ is called a *primitive cell*, as

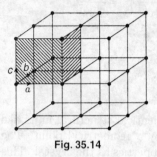

shown in Fig. 35.14. A primitive cell is a type of unit cell which will fill all space under the action of suitable crystal translation operations. A primitive cell is a minimum volume unit cell; there is a density of one lattice point per primitive cell.

Fig. 35.14

There are lattice points at the eight corners of the parallelepiped. Each corner point is shared among the eight cells which touch there. The volume V_c of a primitive cell as defined by primitive axes $\mathbf{a}, \mathbf{b}, \mathbf{c}$ is expressed as

$$V_c = |(\mathbf{a} \times \mathbf{b}) \cdot \mathbf{c}| \tag{35.11}$$

An alternative way of choosing a cell of equal volume V_c is shown in Fig. 35.15. As shown in the figure, let us draw lines to connect a given lattice point to all nearby lattice points. At the midpoint and normal to these lines, we then draw new lines or planes. The smallest volume enclosed in this way is the Wigner-Seitz primitive cell. The basis associated with a lattice point of a primitive cell is known as a *primitive basis*.

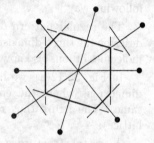

35.12 Elements of Symmetry

Fig. 35.15

A symmetry of a particular kind exists, when a certain operation leaves something unaltered. Thus a candle is symmetric about a vertical axis as it can be rotated about that axis without changing its appearance or any other feature.

Crystals possess different types of symmetries. The symmetry operations of a crystal performed about a point or line are called *point-group symmetry*. The point-group symmetry elements possessed by a crystal are the following :

(1) Plane of symmetry : A crystal is said to have a plane of symmetry, if it is divided by an imaginary plane into two halves, so that one is the mirror image of the other. Thus a cube has nine planes of symmetry. Fig. 35.16(i) represents a plane of symmetry parallel to the faces of a cube while Fig. 35.16(ii) represents one of the six diagonal planes of symmetry.

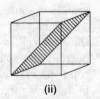
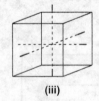

(i)   (ii)   (iii)

Fig. 35.16

(2) Axis of symmetry : This is an axis so that if the crystal is rotated around it through some angle, the crystal remains invariant. The axis is called *n-fold* when the angle of rotation is $360/n$. When equivalent configuration occurs after rotation of 180°, 120° and 90°, the axes of rotation are called *two-fold, three-fold* and *four-fold axes of symmetry* respectively. Fig. 35.16(iii) shows the three tetrad (four-fold) axes of a cube.

(3) Centre of symmetry : It represents a point so that any line drawn through it will meet the surface of the crystal at equal distances on either side. A crystal may possess a number of planes or axes of symmetry but it can have only one centre of symmetry. A cube has a single centre of symmetry at the centre of the cube.

35.12.1   Point Group and Space Group

A lattice **point group** is defined as the collection of symmetry operations which, when applied about a lattice point, leave the lattice invariant. 32 such groups are possible. Every known crystal is assigned to one of these 32 crystal classes.

When identical objects are kept at the lattice points of a space lattice, a regular special array is found, which has symmetry elements over and above those of the point group of the original lattice. Due to some symmetry property of the identical objects, there may exist glide (= reflection + translation) planes and screw (= rotation + translation) axes. There are only 230 different types of symmetry possible for such a system.

35.13   Bravais Lattices

As shown in Fig. 35.17, there are five Bravais lattices in two dimensions. These are listed in Table 35.1.

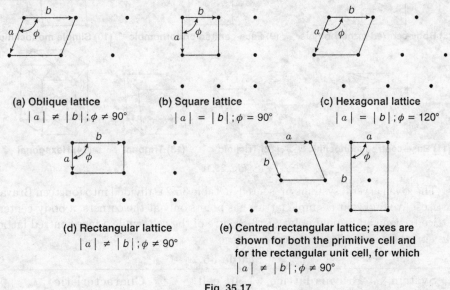

(a) Oblique lattice
$|a| \neq |b|$; $\phi \neq 90°$

(b) Square lattice
$|a| = |b|$; $\phi = 90°$

(c) Hexagonal lattice
$|a| = |b|$; $\phi = 120°$

(d) Rectangular lattice
$|a| \neq |b|$; $\phi \neq 90°$

(e) Centred rectangular lattice; axes are shown for both the primitive cell and for the rectangular unit cell, for which
$|a| \neq |b|$; $\phi \neq 90°$

Fig. 35.17

Table 35.1

Lattice	Conventional unit cell	Axes of conventional unit cell	Point-group symmetry of lattice about lattice points
Oblique	Parallelogram	$a \neq b$ $\phi \neq 90°$	2
Square	Square	$a = b$ $\phi = 90°$	4 *mm*
Hexagonal	60° rhombus	$a = b$ $\phi = 120°$	6 *mm*
Primitive rectangular	Rectangle	$a \neq b$ $\phi = 90°$	2 *mm*
Centered rectangular	Rectangle	$a \neq b$ $\phi = 90°$	2 *mm*

(The notation *mm* means that two mirror lines are present.)

Bravais showed that 14 types of space lattice are only possible. Fig. 35.18 reveals the 14 Bravais lattices. From the figure it is seen that seven sets of axes are sufficient to construct the 14 Bravais lattices which lead to the classification of all crystals into seven crystal systems. These are :

(1) Cubic, (2) Tetragonal, (3) Orthorhombic, (4) Monoclinic, (5). Triclinic, (6) Trigonal (sometimes called rhombohedral) and (7) Hexagonal.

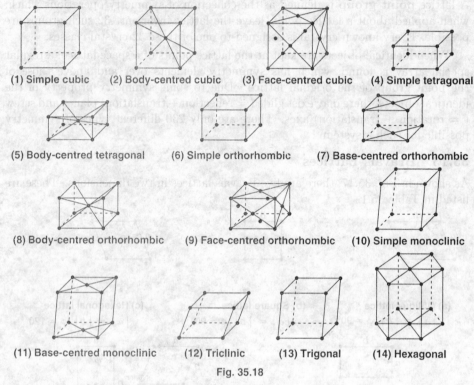

(1) Simple cubic   **(2) Body-centred cubic**   **(3) Face-centred cubic**   **(4) Simple tetragonal**

(5) Body-centred tetragonal   **(6) Simple orthorhombic**   **(7) Base-centred orthorhombic**

(8) Body-centred orthorhombic   **(9) Face-centred orthorhombic**   **(10) Simple monoclinic**

(11) Base-centred monoclinic   **(12) Triclinic**   **(13) Trigonal**   **(14) Hexagonal**

Fig. 35.18

The seven crystal systems presented in Table 35.2 is divided into fourteen Bravais lattices. We find that a simple lattice has points only at the corners, a body-centerd lattice has one additional point at the centre of the cell, while a face-centred lattice has six additional points, one on each face.

Table 35.2

System	Bravais lattice	Unit cell characteristics	Characteristic symmetry elements
Cubic	Simple Body-centred Face-centred	$a = b = c$ $\alpha = \beta = \gamma = 90°$	Four 3-fold rotation axes (along cube diagonal)
Tetragonal	Simple Body-centred	$a = b \neq c$ $\alpha = \beta = \gamma = 90°$	One 4-fold rotation axis
Orthorhombic	Simple Base-centred Body-centred Face-centred	$a \neq b \neq c$ $\alpha = \beta = \gamma = 90°$	Three mutually orthogonal 2-fold rotation axes

Contd.

System	Bravais lattice	Unit cell characteristics	Characteristic symmetry elements
Monoclinic	Simple Base-centred	$a \neq b \neq c$ $\alpha = \beta = 90° \neq \gamma$	One 2-fold rotation axis
Triclinic	Simple	$a \neq b \neq c$ $\alpha \neq \beta \neq \gamma \neq 90°$	None
Trigonal (rhombohedral)	Simple	$a = b = c$ $\alpha = \beta = \gamma \neq 90°$	One 3-fold rotation axis
Hexagonal	Simple	$a = b \neq c$ $\alpha = \beta = 90°$ $\gamma = 120°$	One 3-fold rotation axis

In a simple cubic lattice, each particle is adjoined by six other particles and so the coordination number is six while the coordination number of body-centred and face-centred cubic lattice are 8 and 12 respectively.

35.14 Miller Indices

In order to designate a plane in a crystal, Miller introduced a system wherein he arranged a set of three numbers to specify a plane in a crystal. This set of three numbers is known as Miller indices of the concerned plane.

To find the Miller indices the steps to be followed are :

(1) To determine the intercepts of the plane along the x-, y- and z-axes in terms of the lattice constants a, b and c.

(2) To determine the reciprocals of these numbers.

(3) To find the least common denominator (lcd) and then multiply each by this lcd. The result is written in the form (hkl) and is known as the Miller indices of the plane.

Example : Let us consider a plane having intercepts 4, 1 and 2 on the three axes. The reciprocals are 1/4, 1 and 1/2; lcd is 4. Multiplying each by 4, we get 1, 4 and 2. Thus (142) are the Miller indices of the plane.

Some important points are noted below :

(i) If a plane cuts an axis on the negative side of the origin, corresponding index is negative.

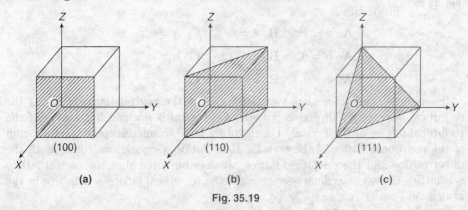

Fig. 35.19

(ii) For an intercept at infinity, the corresponding index is zero.

(iii) It is only the ratio of the indices which is important is this notation. The (622) planes are the same as (311) planes.

(iv) The indices (hkl) do not define a particular plane but a set of parallel planes. Thus the planes whose intercepts are 1, 1, 1; 2, 2, 2; $-3, -3, -3$, etc., are all represented by the same set of Miller indices. Miller indices of a few important planes in a cubic crystal are exhibited in Fig. 35.19.

35.15   Reciprocal Lattice

The reciprocal lattice has important role in the analysis of crystal structures. It is simple to picture a collection of points in reciprocal space than to visualise a complex of interpenetrating planes in a crystal. A two-dimensional plane can be represented by its normal which has only one dimension. The direction of normal represents the orientation of plane. If the length assigned to each normal is directly proportional to the reciprocal of the interplanar spacing of that plane, the points at the end of the normals drawn from a common origin form a lattice known as the *reciprocal lattice*.

To understand the **reciprocal lattice vectors**, we consider a direct space lattice whose basis vectors are $\mathbf{a}, \mathbf{b}$ and $\mathbf{c}$; the real basis vectors $\mathbf{a}$, $\mathbf{ab}$ and $\mathbf{c}$ form a primitive basis. We may define a new set of basis vectors $\mathbf{A}, \mathbf{B}$ and $\mathbf{C}$ according to the relations

$$\mathbf{A} = 2\pi \frac{\mathbf{b} \times \mathbf{c}}{\mathbf{a} \cdot \mathbf{b} \times \mathbf{c}}; \quad \mathbf{B} = 2\pi \frac{\mathbf{c} \times \mathbf{a}}{\mathbf{a} \cdot \mathbf{b} \times \mathbf{c}}; \quad \mathbf{C} = 2\pi \frac{\mathbf{a} \times \mathbf{b}}{\mathbf{a} \cdot \mathbf{b} \times \mathbf{c}}. \tag{35.12}$$

We find that the common denominator in each case is $V = \mathbf{a} \cdot \mathbf{b} \times \mathbf{c}$ which is the volume of the primitive cell of the direct lattice. Let us use the vectors $\mathbf{A} \cdot \mathbf{B}$ and $\mathbf{C}$ as a basis for a new lattice whose vectors are represented as

$$\mathbf{G}_n = n_1 \mathbf{A} + n_2 \mathbf{B} + n_3 \mathbf{C}, \tag{35.13}$$

Fig. 35.20

where n_1, n_2, n_3 are any set of integers. The lattice defined by Eq. (35.13) is called the *reciprocal lattice* while $\mathbf{A}, \mathbf{B}$ and $\mathbf{C}$ are known as the *reciprocal basis vectors*. The relation between the reciprocal basis vectors $\mathbf{A}, \mathbf{B}$ and $\mathbf{C}$ to the direct basis vectors $\mathbf{a}, \mathbf{b}$ and $\mathbf{c}$ is exhibited in Fig. 35.20. The vector $\mathbf{A}$ is normal to the plane defined by the vectors $\mathbf{b}$ and $\mathbf{c}$. This is true for $\mathbf{B}$ and $\mathbf{C}$ also. Thus $\mathbf{A}, \mathbf{B}, \mathbf{C}$ have the following properties :

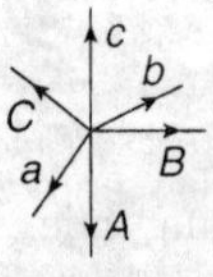

$$\mathbf{A} \cdot \mathbf{a} = 2\pi, \quad \mathbf{B} \cdot \mathbf{a} = 0, \quad \mathbf{C} \cdot \mathbf{a} = 0,$$

$$\mathbf{A} \cdot \mathbf{b} = 0, \quad \mathbf{B} \cdot \mathbf{b} = 2\pi, \quad \mathbf{C} \cdot \mathbf{b} = 0,$$

$$\mathbf{A} \cdot \mathbf{c} = 0, \quad \mathbf{B} \cdot \mathbf{c} = 0, \quad \mathbf{C} \cdot \mathbf{c} = 2\pi.$$

Every cystal structure has two lattices : (i) the crystal lattice and (ii) the reciprocal lattice. A diffraction pattern of a crystal is nothing but a map of the reciprocal lattice of the crystal. On the other hand, a microscope image is a map of the reciprocal lattice of the crystal. If we rotate a crystal, we rotate both the direct lattice and the reciprocal lattice. It may be noted that the crystal lattice is a lattice in real or ordinary space while the reciprocal lattice is a lattice in the associated Fourier space.

35.15.1   Structure of Zinc Blende (ZnS)

The zinc blende structure, shown in Fig. 35.21, consists of two fcc sub-lattices. Zn atoms occupy the lattice points of one sub-lattice while S atoms of the other. In this way, each Zn atom has four S neighbours at the corners of a regular tetrahedron and vice versa. In ZnS, there are double bonds between atoms which are partially covalent and partially ionic. Many semiconductor compounds crystallize in the ZnS structure.

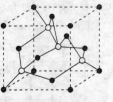

Fig. 35.21

35.16   Determination of Crystal Structure by Bragg's Law

In order to determine the structure of a crystal, the lattice constant d is measured using different planes of the crystal as reflecting surface for the same known wavelength of X-rays. The lattice constants are expressed as ratios with one of those taken as unity. This ratio appears to be different for different crystals. The experimentally found ratio is then compared with the calculated ratio. In this way, a particular structure may be identified.

35.16.1   Structure of KCl Crystal

Let us consider a crystal of simple cubic system wherein an atom lies at each corner of the cube. This is shown in Fig. 35.22. The structure is repeated in all directions and thus constituting a space lattice. As shown there are three sets of planes which are rich in atoms. (i) The first set of planes (such as $ABFE, CDHG, ADHE,$ $BCGF, ABCD$ and $EFGH$) are all alike. They are known as (100) planes. We assume that the distance between the consecutive planes be d_1. (ii) The second set of planes consist of parallel planes [like $ADGF$ or $ABGH$ (110 planes)] inclined at an angle of $45°$ to the cubic faces. If d_2 be the spacing between these planes, then $d_2 = d_1/\sqrt{2}$. (iii) The third set of planes consist of planes like AFH (111 planes) and separation between these planes (d_3) can also be calculated in terms of $d_1 (d_3 = d_1/\sqrt{3})$.

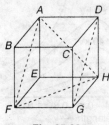

Fig. 35.22

Therefore, for a simple cubic system,

$$d_1 : d_2 : d_3 = 1 : \frac{1}{\sqrt{2}} : \frac{1}{\sqrt{3}}.$$

The first order spectrum from the (100), (110) and (111) planes of KCl was noted at the glancing angles $5.22°$, $7.30°$ and $9.05°$ respectively. Now we have $d \propto \frac{1}{\sin\theta}$.

So, $d_1 : d_2 : d_3 = \dfrac{1}{\sin 5.22°} : \dfrac{1}{\sin 7.30°} : \dfrac{1}{\sin 9.05°} = 1 : 1/\sqrt{2} : 1/\sqrt{3}$.

This value is in agreement with the theoretical result. Thus KCl belongs to the simple cubic system. However, from these studies, no information is available about the nature of the constituents at the lattice corners, i.e., whether they are molecules of KCl or ions of K and Cl alternately. The answer is achieved from observations made on NaCl crystal.

35.16.2   Structure of NaCl Crystal

The results obtained with NaCl crystal for the same three planes are similar to KCl. But, a weak reflection at the (111) face at about $5°$ is also noted. Taking this into consideration we get

$$d_1 : d_2 : d_3 = 1 : 1/\sqrt{2} : 2/\sqrt{3}.$$

This agrees with the calculated values for a face-centred cube. Thus NaCl appears to belong to the face-centred cubic system.

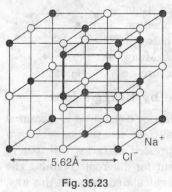

The difference between the KCl and NaCl crystals can be explained by considering the number of electrons in the atom. This determines the amount by which an atom scatters X-rays. The atomic numbers of potassium (19) and chlorine (17) are not very different. If all the atoms are considered identical, then the face-centred arrangement of NaCl becomes a simple cubic arrangement for KCl. In NaCl crystal, three is a difference between the atomic numbers of Na (11) and Cl (17). It means that their scattering powers are different and give rise to a face-centred cubic lattice. From this study we find that both NaCl and KCl have identical structure.

Fig. 35.23

35.17   X-ray Spectra

Urey analysed the X-ray beam by making use of different potential differences but of same target. He used tungsten as target and applied different values of potential differences. The intensities of the ray produced are then plotted against wavelength.

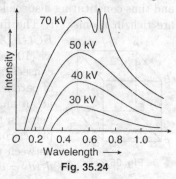

The variation of intensity with wavelength is shown in Fig. 35.24. When the p.d. applied 30 kV, 40 kV and 50 kV, the spectrum becomes white while if the applied p.d. is 70 kV, two sharp peaks are noted. The sharp peaks reveal the line or characteristic radiation. The line spectra are found to be absent until the p.d. exceeds a particular value. The smoothly varying curves in the figure represent the continuous spectrum and the superimposed lines on the continuous background represent the characteristic spectrum.

Fig. 35.24

35.17.1   Features of Continuous X-ray Spectrum

(a) For each anode potential, there is a minimum wavelength (λ_{min}) below which no radiation can be emitted. Above this critical value, the intensity of the radiation rapidly increases with increasing wavelengths but after reaching a maximum it decreases gradually. The intensity never attains zero value showing that the radiation contains all possible wavelengths above the minimum limit.

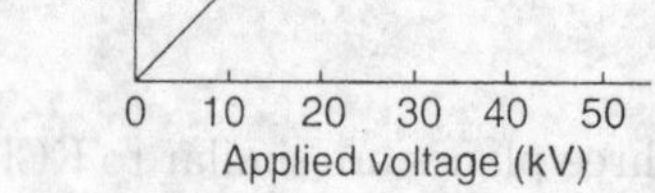

(b) If the voltage across the X-ray tube is increased, λ_{min} is shifted towards the smaller values, it has been observed that λ_{min} is inversely proportional to the applied voltage V. If the limiting frequency (ν_{max}) is plotted against the applied voltages, a straight line graph, passing through the origin is obtained. This is shown in Fig. 35.25. This empirical law as deduced by Duane and Hunt can be expressed as

$$eV = h\nu_{max} = \frac{hc}{\lambda_{min}}, \qquad (35.14)$$

Fig. 35.25

where eV is the kinetic energy of the bombarding electron. If the entire kinetic energy of the electron striking the target is converted into the energy of the X-ray photon, then according to Einstein's theory, the relation (35.14) holds good.

Now, we have

$$\nu_{max} = \frac{c}{\lambda_{min}}. \tag{35.15}$$

So, by Eqs. (35.14) and (35.15), we get

$$eV = \frac{hc}{\lambda_{min}} \quad \text{or,} \quad \lambda_{min} = \frac{hc}{eV} \tag{35.16}$$

i.e., $\lambda_{min} \propto \dfrac{1}{V}$.

Following this relation most of the electrons that generate X-ray photons give up a part of their energy. Thus most of the X-radiation is of longer wavelength than λ_{min} and the continuous spectrum is the result of the inverse photoelectric effect, with electron kinetic energy (eV) being transformed into photon energy ($h\nu$).

35.18   Characteristic X-ray Spectrum

There are two different methods of producing characteristic X-rays. These are :

(i) The characteristic X-rays of an element is excited by using the element as the target in the X-ray tube and in this way subjecting it to direct bombardment by electrons. For each target there is a minimum potential below which the line spectra are not seen. This critical p.d. below which the line spectra do not appear, is different for different targets, e.g., molybdenum shows up the line spectra only if the p.d. is greater than 35 kV.

(ii) Characteristic X-rays of an element can also be excited by permitting primary X-rays from a hard X-ray tube to fall on the element. The primary X-rays should be harder than the characteristic X-rays to be produced. The peaks obtained in the X-ray spectrum provide the line spectrum which is characteristic of the element used in the target. The group of lines of shortest wavelength is known as the K-series. Two lines of this series are detected in general and they are termed as K_α and K_β lines in the order of decreasing wavelengths. The next group is termed as the L-series of longer wavelengths and denoted as $L\alpha, L_\beta, L_\gamma$, etc. For heavier elements a third series, called M-series, has also been noted.

35.18.1   Origin of Characteristic X-rays

This can be explained from Bohr's theory. Let an atom in the target of an X-ray tube be bombarded by a high-speed electron. When a K-electron is removed, a vacancy will be created in the K-shell which can be filled up by an electron from either of L, M or N shells or a free electron. These possible transitions are the cause for K_α, K_β lines and the limiting line. In a similar way, the longer wavelength L-series originates if an L-electron is knocked out of the atom, the M-series if an M-electron is knocked out and so on. This is shown in Fig. 35.26.

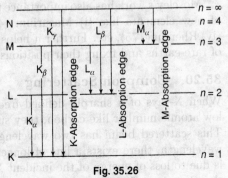

Fig. 35.26

35.19   Moseley's Law

Moseley plotted the square root of the frequencies ($\sqrt{\nu}$) of a given line against the atomic number (Z) of the elements emitting that line and obtained a straight line. Similar linear relation was found to hold good for any line in any series. This is

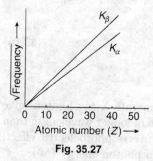

Fig. 35.27

shown in Fig. 35.27. From the study he concluded that atomic number is the fundamental property of elements and not the atomic weight.

Moseley's law can be stated as : *The frequency of a spectral line in X-ray spectrum is proportional to the square of the atomic number of the element emitting it, i.e., $\nu \propto Z^2$.* Alternately the Moseley's law can be expressed as $\sqrt{\nu} = a(Z - b)$, where Z is the atomic number of the element, and a and b are constants depending upon the particular line.

35.19.1   Explanation from the Bohr's Theory

Bohr's theory of hydrogen spectrum provides the frequency of a spectral line. This can be written as

$$\nu = Z^2 Rc \left(\frac{1}{n_1^2} - \frac{1}{n_2^2} \right), \tag{35.17}$$

where R is the Rydberg's constant and c the velocity of light. If the K-line is considered, we can regard it as originating from the transition of electron from the second to the first orbit. Thus putting $n_1 = 1$ and $n_2 = 2$, we get the frequency of K_α-line,

$$\nu = Z^2 Rc \left(\frac{1}{1^2} - \frac{1}{2^2} \right) = \frac{3}{4} cRZ^2. \tag{35.18}$$

Eq. (35.18) corresponds to Moseley's law approximately.

35.19.2   Importance of Moseley's Law

According to this law, it is the atomic number and not the atomic weight of an element which determines its characteristic properties (both physical and chemical). So, the atoms must be arranged in the periodic table according to their atomic numbers and not according to their atomic weights. This removes some discrepancies in the order of certain elements from the point of view of their atomic weights. As for example, argon $_{18}Ar^{40}$ comes before potassium ($_{19}K^{39}$), cobalt ($_{27}Co^{58.9}$) comes before nickel ($_{28}Ni^{58.7}$), etc. Thus the arrangement is correct in the order of atomic number.

Moseley's work has also importance to perfect the periodic table by the discovery of new elements like (i) Masurium (43), (ii) Illinium (61), (iii) Hafnium (72), (iv) Rhenium (75), etc. Further it helps in the determination of the atomic numbers of rare-earths and fixing their positions in the periodic table.

35.20   Compton Scattering

When X-rays of a sharply defined frequency were made to fall on a material of low atomic number like carbon, they suffered a change of frequency on scattering. This scattered beam has two wavelengths. In addition to the expected incident wavelength, there exists a line of longer wavelength. The variation of wavelength is due to loss of energy of the incident X-rays. This elastic interaction is known as the *Compton effect.* For incoherent scattering, a scattered beam undergoes not only deviation in its direction but also a change of wavelength occurs. In Compton effect, there is a change in wavelength of the scattered beam with the change in its direction. Thus Compton effect is an incoherent scattering. This is illustrated in Fig. 35.28.

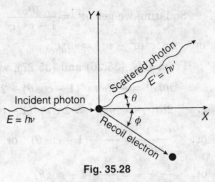

Fig. 35.28

Compton explained this effect on the basis of quantum theory of radiation. The process is treated as a particle collision event between X-ray photon and a loosely bound electron of the scatterer. In photon-electron collision, a portion of the energy of the photon is transferred to the electron and consequently the X-ray proceeds with less than the original energy. It thus gets a lower frequency or a higher wavelength. Let the incident photon with an energy $h\nu$ and momentum $h\nu/c$ strike an electron at rest. The initial momentum of the electron is zero and its initial energy is the rest mass energy m_0c^2. We assume that the scattered photon of energy $h\nu'$ and momentum $h\nu'/c$ moves off in a direction inclined at an angle θ to the original direction where the electron acquires a momentum mv and moves at an angle ϕ to the original direction. The energy of the recoil electron being mc^2, we can write, according to the principle of conservation of energy,

$$h\nu + m_0c^2 = h\nu' + mc^2. \tag{35.19}$$

If we consider the X and Y components of the momentum and apply the principle of conservation of momentum, we get

$$\frac{h\nu}{c} = \frac{h\nu'}{c}\cos\theta + mv\cos\phi \tag{35.20}$$

and $\quad 0 = \dfrac{h\nu'}{c}\sin\theta - mv\sin\phi.$ \hfill (35.21)

Using Eq. (35.20), we get

$$mvc\cos\phi = h(\nu - \nu'\cos\theta). \tag{35.22}$$

Again from (35.21), we have

$$mvc\sin\phi = h\nu'\sin\theta. \tag{35.23}$$

Squaring and adding Eqs. (35.22) and (35.23), we have

$$m^2v^2c^2 = h^2(\nu^2 - 2\nu\nu'\cos\theta + \nu'^2\cos^2\theta) + h^2\nu'^2\sin^2\theta$$
$$= h^2(\nu^2 - 2\nu\nu'\cos\theta) + h^2\nu'^2 = h^2(\nu^2 - 2\nu\nu'\cos\theta + \nu'^2). \tag{35.24}$$

Now from Eq. (35.19),

$$mc^2 = h(\nu - \nu') + m_0c^2.$$

$\therefore \quad m^2c^4 = h^2(\nu^2 - 2\nu\nu' + \nu'^2) + 2h(\nu - \nu')m_0c^2 + m_0^2c^4. \tag{35.25}$

Subtracting (35.24) from (35.25), we get

$$m^2c^2(c^2 - v^2) = -2h^2\nu\nu'(1 - \cos\theta) + 2h(\nu - \nu')m_0c^2 + m_0^2c^4. \tag{35.26}$$

The value of $m^2c^2(c^2 - v^2)$ can be achieved from the relativistic formula. We have

$$m = \frac{m_0}{\sqrt{(1 - v^2/c^2)}}.$$

Squaring we get $m^2 = \dfrac{m_0^2}{1 - v^2/c^2} = \dfrac{m_0^2 c^2}{c^2 - v^2}$

or, $m^2 c^2 (c^2 - v^2) = m_0^2 c^4.$ (35.27)

From Eqs. (35.26) and (35.27), we get

$m_0^2 c^4 = -2h^2 \nu\nu'(1 - \cos\theta) + 2h(\nu - \nu')m_0 c^2 + m_0^2 c^4.$

$\therefore \quad 2h(\nu - \nu')m_0 c^2 = 2h^2 \nu\nu'(1 - \cos\theta)$

or, $\dfrac{\nu - \nu'}{\nu\nu'} = \dfrac{h}{m_0 c^2}(1 - \cos\theta)$ or, $\dfrac{1}{\nu'} - \dfrac{1}{\nu} = \dfrac{h}{m_0 c^2}(1 - \cos\theta)$

or, $\dfrac{c}{\nu'} - \dfrac{c}{\nu} = \dfrac{h}{m_0 c}(1 - \cos\theta)$

or, $\lambda' - \lambda = \dfrac{h}{m_0 c}(1 - \cos\theta).$ (35.28)

Hence, the change in wavelength, $d\lambda = \dfrac{h}{m_0 c}(1 - \cos\theta).$ (35.29)

Eq. (35.29) shows that $d\lambda$ is independent of the wavelength of the incident radiations and the nature of the scattering substance but it depends on the angle of scattering.

(i) If $\theta = 0$, $\cos\theta = 1$ and then $d\lambda = 0$.

(ii) If $\theta = 90°$, $\cos\theta = 0$ and then

$$d\lambda = \frac{h}{m_0 c} = \frac{6.63 \times 10^{-34}}{(9.11 \times 10^{-31}) \times (3 \times 10^8)}\text{m} = 0.0243 \text{ Å}.$$

This is called *Compton wavelength*.

(iii) If $\theta = 180°$, $\cos\theta = -1$ and then $d\lambda = 2h/m_0 c = 0.0485$ Å.

Thus $d\lambda$ has the maximum value at $\theta = 180°$.

35.20.1   Experimental Verification of Compton Scattering

Monochromatic X-rays of wavelength λ are incident on a scattering substance like a carbon block and the scattered X-rays are received by a Bragg spectrometer to find their wavelength. The wavelength of the scattered X-rays is determined for different values of the scattering angle. The experimental arrangement is shown in Fig. 35.29.

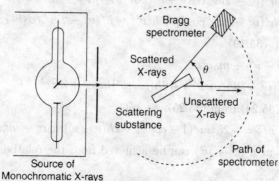

Fig. 35.29

The experimental values obtained by Compton in his study are shown in Fig. 35.30. It is seen that in the scattered radiation in addition to the incident wavelength (λ), a line of longer wavelength (λ') also exits. The Compton shift $d\lambda$ is found to vary with the angle at which the scattered rays are observed.

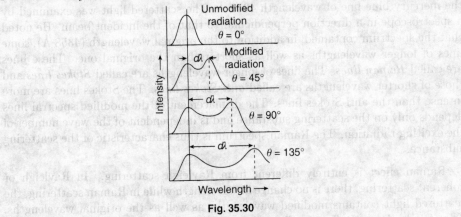

Fig. 35.30

35.20.2 Direction and Kinetic Energy of Recoil Electron

Dividing Eq. (35.23) by Eq. (35.22), we have

$$\tan \phi = \frac{h\nu' \sin \theta}{h(\nu - \nu' \cos \theta)} = \frac{\nu' \sin \theta}{(\nu - \nu' \cos \theta)}. \tag{35.30}$$

Using Eq. (35.28), we get

$$\frac{1}{\nu'} = \frac{1}{\nu} + \frac{h}{m_0 c^2}(1 - \cos \theta) = \frac{1}{\nu} + \frac{h}{m_0 c^2} \cdot 2 \sin^2 \frac{\theta}{2}$$

or,

$$\nu' = \frac{\nu}{1 + \left(\frac{h\nu}{m_0 c^2}\right) 2 \sin^2 \frac{\theta}{2}}$$

$$= \frac{\nu}{1 + 2\beta \sin^2\left(\frac{\theta}{2}\right)}, \quad \text{where } \beta = \frac{h\nu}{m_0 c^2}. \tag{35.31}$$

Putting this value of ν' in Eq. (35.30), we get

$$\tan \phi = \frac{\nu \sin \theta / \left[1 + 2\beta \sin^2\left(\frac{\theta}{2}\right)\right]}{\left[\nu - \left\{\nu \cos \theta / \left(1 + 2\beta \sin^2 \frac{\theta}{2}\right)\right\}\right]} = \frac{\cos\left(\frac{\theta}{2}\right)}{(1 + \beta)}.$$

$$\therefore \quad \tan \phi = \frac{\cot\left(\frac{\theta}{2}\right)}{1 + \left(\frac{h\nu}{m_0 c^2}\right)}. \tag{35.32}$$

The kinetic energy of the recoil electron is the difference between the energies of incident and scattered photons. Thus we have

$$\text{kinetic energy, } E_K = h\nu - h\nu' = h\nu - h\left[\frac{\nu}{1 + 2\beta \sin^2(\theta/2)}\right]$$

$$= h\nu \left[\frac{2\beta \sin^2(\theta/2)}{1 + 2\beta \sin^2(\theta/2)}\right] \tag{35.33}$$

(where $\beta = h\nu/m_0 c^2$).

35.21 Raman Effect

Raman, while studying the scattering of light, found that when a beam of monochromatic light was passed through organic liquids (e.g., benzene, toluene, etc.), the scattered light contained other frequencies in addition to that of the incident light. This is called *Raman effect.*

The arrangement used by Raman was very simple in design. A round-bottomed glass flask was filled with pure dust-free benzene and it was strongly illuminated by the mercury blue line of wavelength 4358 Å. The scattered light was examined by a spectroscope in a direction perpendicular to that of the incident beam. He noted that the spectrum contained, in addition to the original wavelength (4358 Å), some lines of longer wavelengths as well as shorter than the original one. These lines are called *Raman lines.* The lines of longer wavelengths are called *Stokes lines* and those of shorter wavelengths are called *anti-Stokes lines.* The Stokes lines are more intense than the anti-Stokes lines. The displacement of the modified spectral lines depends only on the scattering substance and is independent of the wave number of the exciting radiation. The Raman spectrum is thus characteristic of the scattering substance.

Raman effect is entirely different from Rayleigh scattering. In Rayleigh or coherent scattering, there is no change in wavelength while in Raman scattering, the scattered light contains modified wavelengths as well as the original wavelengths. That is why Raman effect is also called *incoherent scattering* and is taken as the optical analogue of the Compton effect.

35.21.1   Experimental Study of Raman Effect

The arrangement is shown in Fig. 35.31. It consists of a glass tube AB containing pure experimental liquid free from dust and air bubbles. It is closed at one end by an optically plane glass plate W and at the other end it is drawn into a horn (H)

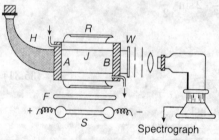

and blackened on the outside. Light from a mercury arc S is allowed to pass through a filter F. This allows only monochromatic radiation of $\lambda = 4358$ Å to pass through it. The tube is surrounded by a water-jacket (J) through which water is circulated for preventing overheating of the liquid. A semi-cylindrical aluminium reflector R is used for increasing the intensity of illumination. The scattered light coming

Fig. 35.31

out of W is condensed on the slit of a spectrograph. The spectrograph has a large light gathering power and the prism has a large resolving power. A camera of short focal length is used to photograph the spectrum.

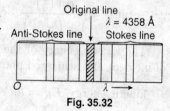

Fig. 35.32

After developing the photographic plate a number of Stokes lines, a few anti-Stokes lines and a strong unmodified line are obtained as shown in Fig. 35.32.

35.21.2   Characteristics of Raman Lines

(i) The Stokes lines are more intense than anti-Stokes lines.

(ii) The Raman lines are symmetrically displaced about the parent line.

(iii) The frequency difference between the modified and parent line represents the frequency of the corresponding infrared absorption line.

35.22 Quantum Theory of Raman Effect

Raman effect is caused by the interaction between a light photon and a molecule of the scatterer. Let a photon of frequency ν_1 be incident on a molecule and there be a collision between them. If m be the mass of the molecule, v_1 and v_2 its velocities before and after impact, E_1 and E_2 the intrinsic energies of the molecule before and after collision then applying the principle of conservation of energy, we can write,

$$E_2 + \frac{1}{2}mv_2^2 + h\nu_2 = E_1 + \frac{1}{2}mv_1^2 + h\nu_1, \tag{35.34}$$

where ν_2 is the frequency of the scattered photon.

We may assume that the K.E. of the molecule remains unaltered during the process and so we have

$$E_2 + h\nu_2 = E_1 + h\nu_1 \quad \text{or,} \quad \nu_2 - \nu_1 = \frac{E_1 - E_2}{h}$$

or, $\quad \nu_2 = \nu_1 + \dfrac{E_1 - E_2}{h}.$ \hfill (35.35)

From Eq. (35.35), three cases may arise as discussed below :

(i) If there is no change in the energy of the molecule, i.e., $E_1 = E_2$, then we have $\nu_1 = \nu_2$. This provides the unmodified line.

(ii) If $E_2 > E_1$, then, $\nu_2 < \nu_1$. This provides the Stokes line. It indicates that the molecule has absorbed some energy from the incident photon. As a result the scattered photon has lower energy or longer wavelength.

(iii) If $E_2 < E_1$, then, $\nu_2 > \nu_1$. This provides the anti-Stokes line. It indicates that the molecule was previously in the excited state and it transferred some of its intrinsic energy to the incident photon. Thus the scattered photon has greater energy or shorter wavelength.

As the molecules possess quantized energy levels, we have

$$E_1 - E_2 = nh\nu_c, \tag{35.36}$$

where $n = 1, 2, 3$, etc., and $\nu_c =$ the characteristic frequency of the molecule. For $n = 1$, Eq. (35.35) becomes

$$\nu_2 = \nu_1 \pm \nu_c. \tag{35.37}$$

Eq. (35.37) reveals that the frequency difference $(\nu_1 - \nu_2)$ between the incident and scattered photon corresponds to the characteristic frequency ν_c of the molecule.

35.23 Raman Effect and Fluorescence

Raman effect and fluorescence resemble each other as the incident light in both the cases suffers a change of wavelength, and lines of new wavelengths appear in the spectrum of either. However, Raman effect is different from fluorescence, a comparison of the two phenomena is made below :

Raman Spectra	Fluorescence Spectra
1. Raman lines are strongly polarized.	1. Fluorescent lines are not polarized.
2. Spectral lines have frequencies greater and smaller than the incident frequency.	2. The frequencies of the lines in the fluorescent spectrum are always smaller than the incident frequency.
3. The frequency shifts of the Raman lines are obtained by the scatterer rather than the frequencies themselves.	3. Frequencies of the fluorescent lines are obtained by the nature of the scatterer.

35.24   Comparison between Raman Effect and Compton Effect

A comparative study between the two effects is done below :

Raman Effect	Compton Effect
1. Incoherent scattering.	1. Incoherent scattering.
2. Elastic and inelastic collision between photon and atom or molecule.	2. Elastic and inelastic collision between photon and free or loosely bound electron.
3. Wavelengths both higher and lower than the incident wavelength are present.	3. Wavelengths only higher than the incident wavelength are present.
4. Frequency shift depends on the scatterer.	4. Frequency shift is independent of the scatterer.
5. Applicable for visible monochromatic light.	5. Applicable for monochromatic X-rays.

35.25   Photoelectricity

The photoelectric effect was first discovered by Hertz in 1887 who observed that air in the spark gap became a better conductor if the negative electrode was illuminated with ultraviolet light from an arc lamp. The effect was later studied by a number of research workers. Hallawachs noticed that the alkali metals give the largest amount of electrons and, therefore, they are best suited for photoemissive effects.

From their experiments it was evident that only negatively charged particles are emitted from a surface irradiated by UV radiations. From the measurement of the specific charge (e/m) of these particles Lenard concluded that they were identical with electrons. The particles thus emitted are generally called photoelectrons and the effect is known as *photoelectricity*.

The following two laws of photoelectric emission are well established :

(i) Electrons emitted per second from a photosensitive surface are directly proportional to the amount of light flux incident on it.

(ii) The maximum kinetic energy of electrons emitted from a photosensitive surface is linearly related with the frequency of light flux but is independent of the amount of light flux.

35.26   Experimental Study

A typical arrangement for the general study of the photoelectric phenomenon is shown in Fig. 35.33. Here K and A are two metallic plates fitted to the evacuated glass cylinder gg which has a window for the passage of incident light. With the help of a battery and a rheostat a potential difference is maintained between K and A, which can be altered as desired. A galvanometer G is connected in the circuit as shown.

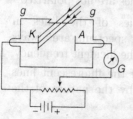

Fig. 35.33

When light from a quartz mercury arc lamp falls on K, the photoelectrons are emitted by it. As a result, current will flow in the circuit showing a deflection in the galvanometer. If monochromatic light of known wavelength be incident on K, the electrons emitted from the surface will be acted upon by the electric field between K and A. In the circuit if A is positive with respect to K the electrons will be accelerated towards A and if A is negative, they will be retarded. The current registered by G will be proportional to the number of electrons reaching at A per second. If this current (i) is plotted against the p.d. (V) applied between K and A, we get a curve as shown in Fig. 35.34(a). The figure shows that for all positive values of V, the current is constant and as A is made negative with respect to K, it decreases rapidly and reduces to zero at a certain value V_0. Only if the intensity of the incident beam is increased from I_1 to I_2 the value of i increases proportionately for all positive values of V, but gradually decreases as V is made negative and reaches the value $i = 0$ for the same value of p.d., i.e., at V_0. This value of V_0 is known as the *stopping potential* for that particular λ.

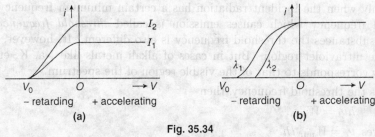

Fig. 35.34

Again, if two beams of identical intensity but different λs are used, then the nature of the curve will be as shown in Fig. 35.34(b). It is found from the figure that the stopping potential is different for different λs.

35.27 Einstein's Photoelectric Equation

A satisfactory explanation of the laws of photoelectric emission was established by Einstein in 1905. The explanation was given on the basis of the quantum theory of light wherein he assumed that a beam of light consists of discrete 'bundles' of energy called 'quanta.' When light is made to fall on a metal surface, some of this energy of a quantum is transferred to one of the unbound electrons within the metal causing to overcome the surface forces. If the applied energy is higher, the electrons are more readily released. According to the quantum theory given by Planck, the energy of each quantum is directly proportional to its frequency. If E is the quantum energy of a radiation of frequency ν, then

$$E = h\nu, \tag{35.38}$$

where h is a constant called *Planck's constant* and is equal to 6.62×10^{-27} second. If this energy is transferred to an electron within the metal, then the absorbing electron will get an energy equal to $h\nu$. Some part of this energy will be utilized in getting out an electron from the surface of the metal. If W_{min} represents the minimum energy necessary to release an electron from the metal, then the maximum kinetic energy that the electron can have, should be

$$\frac{1}{2}m_e v_{max}^2 = h\nu - W_{min}, \tag{35.39}$$

where m_e is the mass of an electron and v_{max} is its maximum velocity.

Eq. (35.39) above is the well-known Einstein's photoelectric equation. W_{min} in the right-hand side of Eq. (35.39) provides important information regarding the origin of the photoelectrons. W_{min} is commonly known as the *photoelectric work function*.

The above equation of Einstein makes some important quantitative predictions :

(i) The maximum energy of emission is entirely determined by the frequency of the exciting radiation and is independent of its intensity.

(ii) The curve connecting the K.E. of the speediest electrons to the frequency of the exciting radiation is a straight line.

(iii) No electron will be able to eject unless the frequency ν of the incident light is sufficiently greater, so that $h\nu$ is greater than or at least equal to W_{min}.

(iv) Lastly, it predicts a definite value for the maximum energy of ejection.

35.27.1   Threshold Frequency

After the discovery of the effect, it was observed that the photoelectric emission occurs only when the incident radiation has a certain minimum frequency. That minimum frequency which causes emission is called *threshold frequency*. For different substances the threshold frequency is also different. It, however, usually lies in the ultraviolet region. But in cases of alkali metals like Na, K, etc., this frequency corresponds to that of the visible region of the spectrum.

If ν_t is the threshold frequency, then

$$h\nu_t = W_{min},$$

which gives $\nu_t = W_{min}/h$. \hfill (35.40)

The wavelength corresponding to the threshold frequency is known as the *threshold wavelength*.

35.28   Experimental Verification of Photoelectric Equation : Millikan's Experiment

Principle

The experiment is based on the concept of stopping potential which is the retarding potential difference required to just halt the most energetic photoelectron emitted.

The K.E. of a photoelectron leaving the surface of a metal irradiated with light $= \frac{1}{2}mv_{max}^2$ which is equal to $h\nu - \phi$.

Let V be the p.d. applied between the emitter and a collecting electrode to prevent the photoelectron from just leaving the emitter. Then we have

$$eV = \frac{1}{2}mv_{max}^2$$

or, $\quad eV = h\nu - \phi \quad$ or, $\quad V = \dfrac{h}{e}\nu - \dfrac{\phi}{e},$ \hfill (35.41)

where ϕ is a constant for a given metal; h and e are also constants.

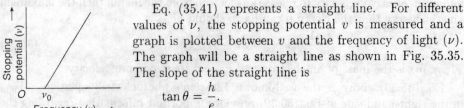

Fig. 35.35

Eq. (35.41) represents a straight line. For different values of ν, the stopping potential v is measured and a graph is plotted between v and the frequency of light (ν). The graph will be a straight line as shown in Fig. 35.35. The slope of the straight line is

$$\tan\theta = \frac{h}{e}.$$

$\therefore \quad h = e\tan\theta.$ \hfill (35.42)

Thus the value of Planck's constant h can be calculated. The intercept on the X-axis gives the threshold frequency ν_0 for the particular emitter. Hence the photoelectric work function, $\phi = h\nu_0$ can be obtained.

Experiment Arrangement

The apparatus is shown in Fig. 35.36. Alkali metals are used as emitters, as they exhibit photoelectric emission even with visible light. Cylindrical blocks (C) of sodium, potassium or lithium are mounted on a spindle S at the centre of the glass flask G which is evacuated to a very high vacuum to free the metals from all absorbed gases and to prevent their oxidation. The spindle rotated from

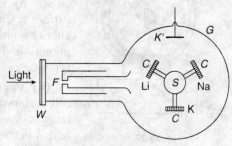

Fig. 35.36

outside by using an electromagnet. As each metal block passes by the adjustable sharp edge K', a thin layer of it is removed to expose a fresh surface of the metal to the irradiating light entering the flask through a quartz window W. Light of monochromatic wavelength provided by a spectroscope illuminates the fresh metal surfaces and the photoelectrons are collected by a Faraday cylinder F by copper oxide which is not photosensitive. The photocurrent is determined by an electrometer connected to the Faraday cylinder.

The stopping potential of the liberated photoelectrons is obtained by raising the emitter surface to a positive potential. The stopping potential (v) is found for different wavelengths of the incident light which is corrected for any contact potential between the metal (C) and Faraday cylinder (F). Then plotting v against ν, a straight line is obtained. Measuring the slope of the straight line, the value of h/e is found out. Substituting the known value of e, the value of h is calculated which agrees fairly well with the value obtained by other methods. The Einstein's equation can thus be experimentally verified.

35.29 Classification of Photoelectric Phenomena

The phenomena may be broadly classified as follows :

(i) **Photoemissive effect :** It consists in the liberation of electrons from metal surface when exposed to light. The metal is then called a *photosensitive metal*.

(ii) **Photovoltaic effect :** If the boundary surface between two substances in close contact is exposed to light, a p.d. is produced across the boundary. This is called photovoltaic effect.

(iii) **Photoconductive effect :** It consists in the change of resistance of semi-conductors according to incident light.

35.30 Photoelectric Cells

Photoelectric cells are devices with the help of which light energy can be converted into electrical energy and wherein the photoelectrons are the main agents for such conversion. Three different types of photoelectric cells are there, viz., (i) Photoemissive cells, (ii) Photovoltaic cells, and (iii) Photoconductive cells.

35.30.1   Photoemissive Cells

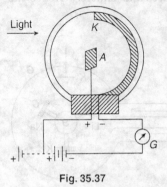

Light →

Fig. 35.37

The cells consist of a photosensitive surface from which electrons are emitted when light is made to fall on it. As a result a current will flow between this surface (called cathode) and a collecting plate (called anode) which is kept at a considerably high positive potential. Photoemissive cells are either of vacuum types or gas-filled types.

(a) **Vacuum cells :** A vacuum type of emission cell is shown in Fig. 35.37. Here, K is the cathode of large surface area coated with photosensitive material and A is the anode or the collecting plate.

Both the cathode and the anode are mounted inside a high vacuum glass bulb and they are then connected with a battery terminals. The anode A is connected to the higher potential point while the cathode K is connected through a galvanometer G to the lower potential point of the battery. When light is allowed to fall on the cathode surface, photoelectrons are liberated and are repelled on to A from the cathode. As a matter of fact, a small current flows through the tube. With

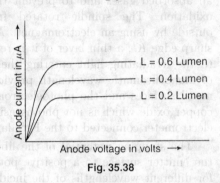

Fig. 35.38

the increase of the p.d. between A and K, current increases at first and then a saturation stage is reached at a certain anode voltage. The current-voltage characteristic of a vacuum photocell is shown in Fig. 35.38.

In this type of photocells emission is found to be strictly proportional to the intensity of the incident light. Obviously these are very quick and accurate in response.

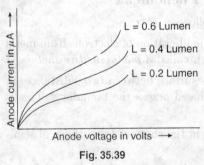

Fig. 35.39

(b) **Gas-filled cells :** The output current of a gas-filled photocell is considerably increased unlike of a vacuum photocell by inserting an inert gas, like argon, etc., at a low pressure. An increase of current and sensitivity are achieved here due to the production of ions by collision process in the neutral gas. The current-voltage characteristic of a gas-filled photocell is shown in Fig. 35.39.

Photocell of this type is usually used for commercial purposes because of high sensitivity. But since there is a fluctuation of current even for a constant intensity beam, the gas-filled cells are seldom used for precision work.

35.30.2   Photovoltaic Cells

Becquerel in 1839 discovered that when a pair of electrodes were immersed in an electrolyte and light was made to fall on one of the electrodes, a potential difference was created between them. This phenomenon is known as photovoltaic effect. Devices which exhibit this effect are called *photovoltaic cells*. Substances like selenium and silicon are mostly used for preparing photovoltaic cells. The recent forms of such cells are commonly known as barrier layer cells. Barrier layer cells are of two different types : (i) front-effect cell and (ii) back-effect cells.

In front-effect cell, a thin metallic film F of silver, gold or platinum is deposited on a semiconducting layer like cuprous oxide or iron selenide. The whole arrangement is then attached to a metal-base plate as shown in Fig. 35.40(a). When light falls on F, it penetrates easily and at the barrier layer between the metallic film and the semiconductor, photoelectric emission occurs. Light further travels and at the barrier layer between the semiconductor and the metal-base causes photoelectric emission which is much less than in the previous case. As a result, the conventional current moves from the base to the metal film in the external circuit which is recognized by a metre M.

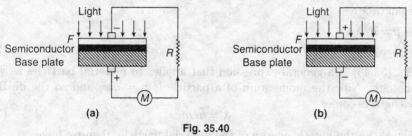

Fig. 35.40

In the back-effect cell, the light passes directly through the semi-conductor as shown in Fig. 35.40(b). Here, electrons flow across the barrier layer from the semiconductor to base plate and so conventional current flows in the opposite direction.

Photovoltaic cells are used in photographic exposure metre and for operation of relays. Silicon cells, because of their better response in the infrared region, are widely used in artificial satellites for conversion of solar energy into electrical energy. No separate battery is required to run photovoltaic cell.

35.30.3 Photoconductive Cells

Substances like selenium, cadmium sulphide, etc., decrease their resistances when light falls on them. The amount of this decrease, of course, depends on the intensity and colour of the incident light. So insertion of such a substance in the circuit and allowing light to fall on it will cause a change of electrical resistance. Hence there will be a variation of current in the circuit in steps with the variation of the intensity of the incident beam of light. This property is utilized in constructing photoconductive cells.

Photoconductive cells have a high sensitivity, low cost and long life. They can be used directly with a power supply of low voltage to operate a relay. These are used extensively in street-lighting controls, door-openers, burglar alarm systems and also in modem television camera tubes.

35.31 Wave Mechanics

According to de Broglie the wavelength λ associated with any moving particle of momentum p for mass m and velocity v is expressed as

$$\lambda = \frac{h}{p} = \frac{h}{mv}, \tag{35.43}$$

where h is Planck's constant. Such waves are called *matter waves* or *de Broglie waves*. Bohr's theory of hydrogen atom led de Broglie to the concept of matter waves. Bohr's theory proposed that the stable states of electrons in the atom are governed by integer rules. de Broglie thought that the electrons might be characterized by a periodicity and he suggested that matter, like radiation, has dual nature.

35.32   The de Broglie Wavelength

If we consider a photon of light of frequency ν, then its momentum p can be written as

$$p = h\nu/c, \tag{35.44}$$

where $\nu = c/\lambda$. Thus the momentum of the photon can be written in terms of wavelength λ as

$$p = h/\lambda$$

or, $\lambda = h/p.$ $\tag{35.45}$

Eq. (35.45) is a general expression that applies to material particles as well as to photons. Now the momentum of a particle is $p = mv$, and so the de Broglie wavelength becomes

$$\lambda = h/mv. \tag{35.46}$$

Let E_k be the kinetic energy of the material particle, then we have

$$p = \sqrt{(2mE_k)} \tag{35.47}$$

Hence by Eq. (35.46), we get

$$\lambda = \frac{h}{\sqrt{2mE_k}}. \tag{35.48}$$

Now, if a charged particle carrying charge q is accelerated through a potential difference V, then the kinetic energy

$$E_k = qV. \tag{35.49}$$

By Eq. (35.48) and (35.49), we get

$$\lambda = \frac{h}{\sqrt{2mqV}}. \tag{35.50}$$

35.33   Phase Velocity of de Broglie Waves

Let a particle of mass m be moving with a velocity v. The wave associated with it has a wavelength λ given by

$$\lambda = \frac{h}{mv}. \tag{35.51}$$

If E be the total energy of the particle and ν be the frequency of the associated wave, then equating the quantum expression $E = h\nu$ with the relativistic formula for total energy $E = mc^2$, we get

$$h\nu = mc^2 \quad \text{or,} \quad \nu = mc^2/h. \tag{35.52}$$

If v_p be the de Broglie wave velocity, then

$$v_p = \nu\lambda = \left(\frac{mc^2}{h}\right)\left(\frac{h}{mv}\right) = \frac{c^2}{v}. \tag{35.53}$$

As the particle velocity v is always less than the velocity of light c, the de Broglie wave velocity v_p must be greater than c.

35.34   Expression for Group Velocity

We consider two waves of same amplitude A but they differ by an amount $\Delta\omega$ in angular frequency and an amount Δk in wave number. They can be represented as

$$y_1 = A\cos(\omega t - kx) \tag{35.54}$$

$$y_2 = A\cos[(\omega + \Delta\omega)t - (k + \Delta k)x]. \tag{35.55}$$

When the two waves are superposed, it will yield a single wave packet or wave group. Now, the resultant displacement y at any instant of time t is given by

$$y = y_1 + y_2$$

$$= A\cos(\omega t - kx) + A\cos[(\omega + \Delta\omega)t - (k + \Delta k)x]$$

$$= 2A\cos\frac{1}{2}[(2\omega + \Delta\omega)t - (2k + \Delta k)x]\cos\frac{1}{2}(\Delta\omega t - \Delta kx), \tag{35.56}$$

where $\Delta\omega$ and Δk are small compared to ω and k respectively. So,

$$2\omega + \Delta\omega \approx 2\omega$$

$$2k + \Delta k \approx 2k.$$

Therefore, $y = 2A\cos\left(\dfrac{\Delta\omega}{2}t - \dfrac{\Delta k}{2}x\right)\cos(\omega t - kx).$ $\tag{35.57}$

Eq. (35.57) gives the resultant wave packet due to superposition of two waves where the second cosine function is the original wave. The coefficient of this cosine is the amplitude that varies with x and t. This variation of amplitude is known as *modulation* of the wave.

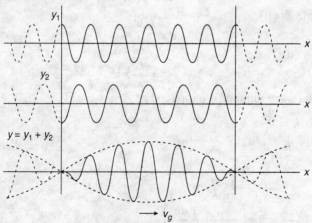

Fig. 35.41

Thus Eq. (35.57) represents a wave of angular frequency ω and wave number k that has superimposed upon it a modulation of angular frequency $\frac{1}{2}\Delta\omega$. This is illustrated in Fig. 35.41. We can now express the group velocity,

$$\nu_g = \frac{\Delta\omega}{\Delta k}. \tag{35.58}$$

If ω and k have continuous spreads, the group velocity is expressed as

$$\nu_g = \frac{d\omega}{dk}. \tag{35.59}$$

35.34.1   Group Velocity of de Broglie Waves

We have the group velocity ν_g as

$$\nu_g = \frac{d\omega}{dk}.$$

The angular frequency (ω) and wave number (k) of the de Broglie waves associated with a particle of rest mass m_0 moving with the velocity v are written as

$$\omega = 2\pi\nu = \frac{2\pi mc^2}{h} = \frac{2\pi m_0 c^2}{h\sqrt{1 - v^2/c^2}} \tag{35.60}$$

and $$k = \frac{2\pi}{\lambda} = \frac{2\pi mv}{h} = \frac{2\pi m_0 v}{h\sqrt{1 - v^2/c^2}}. \tag{35.61}$$

Differentiating Eqs. (35.60) and (35.61), we get

$$\frac{d\omega}{dv} = \frac{2\pi m_0 \nu}{h(1 - v^2/c^2)^{3/2}} \tag{35.62}$$

$$\frac{dk}{dv} = \frac{2\pi m_0}{h(1 - v^2/c^2)^{3/2}}. \tag{35.63}$$

The group velocity v_g of the de Broglie waves associated with the particles is then given by

$$v_g = \frac{d\omega}{dk} = \frac{d\omega/dv}{dk/dv} = v. \tag{35.64}$$

Thus the de Broglie wave group associated with a moving particle travels with the same velocity as the particle.

35.34.2   Relation between Group (ν_g) and Phase Velocity (ν_p)

We have wave velocity,

$$v_p = \frac{\omega}{k} \tag{35.65}$$

and group velocity,

$$\nu_g = \frac{d\omega}{k}. \tag{35.66}$$

Further the wave number is expressed as

$$k = \frac{2\pi}{\lambda} \tag{35.67}$$

or, $$\frac{dk}{d\lambda} = -\frac{2\pi}{2}. \tag{35.68}$$

Also $$\omega = 2v\nu = 2\pi\frac{v_p}{\lambda}.$$

Therefore, $$\frac{d\omega}{d\lambda} = 2\pi\left[-\frac{v_p}{\lambda^2} + \frac{1}{\lambda}\frac{dv_p}{d\lambda}\right]$$

or $$\frac{d\omega}{d\lambda} = -\frac{2\pi}{\lambda^2}\left[v_p - \lambda\frac{dv_p}{d\lambda}\right]. \tag{35.69}$$

Dividing Eq. (35.69) by Eq. (35.68), we have

$$\frac{d\omega}{d\lambda} \cdot \frac{d\lambda}{dk} = \frac{-\frac{2\pi}{\lambda^2}\left[v_p - \lambda\frac{dv_p}{d\lambda}\right]}{-\frac{2\pi}{\lambda^2}}$$

or, $$\frac{d\omega}{dk} = v_p - \lambda\frac{dv_p}{d\lambda}.$$

$$\therefore \qquad \nu_g = v_p - \lambda \frac{dv_p}{d\lambda}. \tag{35.70}$$

Eq. (35.70) shows the relationship between group velocity (v_g) and phase velocity (v_p). From this relation the following two situations arise :

Case 1. For dispersive medium, $v_p = f(\lambda)$. Usually, $dv_p/d\lambda$ is positive (normal dispersion) and so

$$v_g < v_p.$$

This is the case with de Broglie waves.

Case 2. For non-dispersive medium,

$$v_p \neq f(\lambda) \cdot \frac{dv_p}{d\lambda} = 0.$$

$$\therefore \qquad v_g = v_p. \tag{35.71}$$

This result is true for electromagnetic waves in vacuum.

35.35 Davisson and Germer's Experimental Study of Matter Waves

The experimental arrangement is shown in Fig. 35.42. By heating a filament (F) electrons are produced which are restricted to a fine parallel pencil by two thin aluminium diaphragms D_1 and D_2. These electrons are then accelerated by passing them through an aluminium cylinder A where high potential is applied. The electron beam falls on a large single crystal of nickel (N) which is capable of rotation about an axis parallel to the axis of the incident beam by a handle H. In all directions, electrons are scattered by the atoms in the crystal. The scattered electrons are

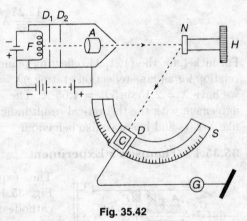

Fig. 35.42

collected by a Faraday cylinder C (called the *collector*) connected to a sensitive galvanometer G and can be moved along a graduated circular scale S, so that it receives the reflected electrons at angles between 20° and 90°. The collector has two insulated walls C and D. A retarding potential is applied between the two walls of collector. As a result, only the electrons with nearly the incident velocity and not the secondary slow electrons may enter the collector. The nickel crystal (belongs to the face centred cubic type) is so cut as to present a smooth reflecting surface parallel to the lattice plane (111). Turning the handle, any azimuth of the crystal can be presented to the plane of the incident beam and the reflected beam entering the collector. In normal incidence, the beam of electrons are allowed to fall on the surface of the crystal to produce a diffraction effect. For each azimuth of the crystal, a beam of electrons is incident normally on the crystal, and the collector is moved to different positions on the scale S. The galvanometer deflection corresponding to each position is noted which gives a measure of the intensity of the diffracted beam of electrons. The galvanometer deflection is then plotted against the angle between the incident beam and the beam entering the collector. The experiment is repeated for different accelerating voltages. Number of curves are then drawn as shown in

Fig. 35.43. The graph remains fairly smooth up to the accelerating voltage of 44 V when a spur appears on the curve. With the increase of the accelerating voltage the length of the spur increases up to 54 V at 50°. When the acceleration voltage is further increased, the spur decreases in length and disappears at 68 V.

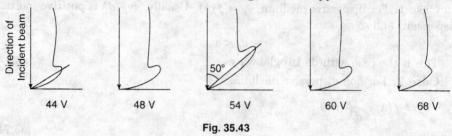

Fig. 35.43

The pronounced spur at 50° with the electrons accelerated through 54 V is due to the constructive interference of the electron waves, from the regularly spaced parallel planes in the crystal. According to de Broglie's relation, the wavelength of 54 V electrons is given by

$$\lambda = \frac{12.25}{\sqrt{54}}\text{Å} = 1.66 \text{ Å}. \tag{35.72}$$

For nickel, for the (1, 1, 1) reflecting plane we get $d = 2.15$ Å. Hence, applying the relation for a plane reflection grating $n\lambda = d\sin\theta$, n referring here to the first order, we have $\lambda = 2.15\sin 50° = 1.65$ Å. The experimental value is, therefore, in close agreement with the theoretical result indicating that the beam of electrons behaves like X-rays and has wavelike behaviour.

35.35.1 Thomson's Experiment

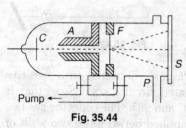

Fig. 35.44

The experimental arrangement is shown in Fig. 35.44. In a discharge tube AC a beam of cathode rays is produced by an induction coil. The electrons are allowed to pass through a fine hole A, to fall on a thin gold foil F of thickness about 10^{-8} m. The emergent beam of electrons is received on the photographic plate P and the pattern is examined by the fluorescent screen S.

After developing the plate a symmetrical pattern consisting of concentric ring about a central spot as revealed in Fig. 35.45 is obtained. The pattern has similarity with the pattern produced by X-rays in the powdered crystal method. If the cathode rays in the discharge tube are deflected by a magnetic field, the pattern on the screen S is found to shift. On removing the film F, the pattern disappears. It is interesting to note that if the electrons behaved as corpuscles, the electrons passing through the foil should have been scattered through a wide angle. The experiment thus demonstrates that the electron beam behaves as waves, as diffraction patterns can be produced by waves only.

Fig. 35.45

Verification of the de Broglie Equation

Thomson applied very high voltages of the order of 50 kV to accelerate the electrons. To calculate λ from the radii of the rings let AB be the incident beam

passing through the film at B while BP is
the direction of the reflected beam (Fig. 35.46).
This reflected beam falls at the point P on the
photographic plate at a distance R from the central
point O and let the distance BO from the film to
the plate be L. As shown, $\angle PBO = 2\theta$, where θ is
the glancing angle given by the Bragg equation,

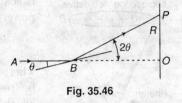

Fig. 35.46

$$n\lambda = 2d\sin\theta.$$

We have

$$R/L = \tan 2\theta = 2\theta \text{ (as } \theta \text{ is small)}$$

or, $\quad \theta = R/2L.$ \hfill (35.73)

But $\quad 2d\sin\theta = 2d \cdot \theta = n\lambda \quad$ or, $\theta = n\lambda/2d.$ \hfill (35.74)

By Eqs. (35.73) and (35.74), we get

$$\frac{n\lambda}{2d} = \frac{R}{2L} \quad \text{or,} \quad \lambda = \frac{Rd}{nL}. \tag{35.75}$$

Using Eq. (35.75), the wavelength is determined which confirms the wave nature
of the electron.

35.36 Heisenberg's Uncertainty Principle

It is impossible to find precisely and simultaneously the values of both the members
of a pair of physical variables to describe the motion of an atomic system. Such
pairs of variables are termed as the canonically conjugate variables.

According to this principle, the position and momentum of a particle cannot be
obtained simultaneously to any desired degree of accuracy. Considering Δx as the
error in finding its position and Δp as the error in finding its momentum at the
same instant, these quantities are related as

$$\Delta x \Delta p = h/2\pi. \tag{35.76}$$

Thus the product of the two errors is approximately of the order of Planck's
constant. When Δx is small, Δp will be large and vice versa. This means that
if one quantity is measured accurately, the other quantity becomes less accurate.
Any instrument, therefore, cannot measure the quantities more accurately than
predicted by Heisenberg's principle of uncertainty or indeterminacy. Relation
(35.73) is also applicable for the energy and time related to any given event. We
can thus write,

$$\Delta E \Delta t = h/2\pi. \tag{35.77}$$

From the classical concept it is possible for a particle to occupy a fixed position
and to have a definite momentum. We may thus predict exactly its position and
momentum at any time later. But according to the uncertainty principle, it is
impossible to find accurately the simultaneous values of position and momentum of a
particle at any time. Heisenberg's principle suggests that in physical measurements
probability takes the place of exactness and finds a small but finite probability of
occurrence.

35.36.1 Determination of Position with a γ-ray Microscope

If we try to measure the position and linear momentum of an electron using a high
resolving power microscope, we may observe the electron if at least one photon

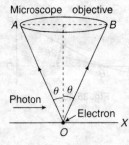

Microscope objective

Fig. 35.47

is scattered by it into the microscope lens. The resolving power of the microscope is expressed as

$$\Delta x = \frac{\lambda}{2\sin\theta}, \qquad (35.78)$$

where Δx is the distance between two points which can be resolved by the microscope. This is the range in which the electron would be visible when disturbed by the photon. Thus Δx is the uncertainty involved in the position measurement of the electron. However, the incoming photon interacts with the electron through the Compton effect. In order to see this electron, the scattered photon should enter the microscope within the angle 2θ. During the impact the momentum imparted by the photon to the electron is of the order of h/λ. Along OA, the component of this momentum $= -\frac{n}{\lambda}\sin\theta$ and along OB, the momentum component $= \frac{n}{\lambda}\sin\theta$. So the uncertainty in the momentum measurement,

$$\Delta p_x = \frac{h}{\lambda}\sin\theta - \left(-\frac{h}{\lambda}\sin\theta\right) = \frac{2h}{\lambda}\sin\theta \quad \text{[in the X-direction]}$$

Hence, $\Delta x \times \Delta p_x = \dfrac{\lambda}{2\sin\theta} \times \dfrac{2h}{\lambda}\sin\theta = h.$ $\qquad (35.79)$

A more sophisticated approach can show that $\Delta x \Delta p_x \geq h/2\pi$.

35.36.2   Diffraction of a Beam of Electrons by a Slit

As shown in Fig. 35.48, let a beam of electrons be transmitted through a slit and received on a photographic plate P kept at a distance from the slit. We can say that the electrons have passed through the slit and we cannot specify its exact location.

Thus the position of any electron recorded on the plate is uncertain by an amount equal to the width Δy of the slit. If λ be the wavelength of the electrons and θ be the angle of deviation corresponding to first minimum, then from the theory of diffraction we have $\Delta y = \frac{\lambda}{\sin\theta}$. This gives the uncertainty in finding the position of the electron along Y-axis.

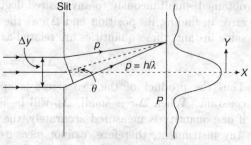

Fig. 35.48

Initially, the electrons are moving along the X-axis and hence they have no component of momentum along Y-axis. Since the electrons are deviated at the slit, they acquire an additional component of momentum along Y-axis. Let p be the momentum of the electron on emerging from the slit. Then the component of momentum of electron along Y-axis is $p\sin\theta$. As the electron may be situated anywhere within the pattern from $-\theta$ to $+\theta$, the Y-component of momentum may be anywhere between $-p\sin\theta$ and $+p\sin\theta$. So, the uncertainty in the Y-component of momentum of the electron is given by

$$\Delta p_y = 2p\sin\theta = \frac{2h}{\lambda}\sin\theta \quad \left(\because \lambda = \frac{h}{p}\right).$$

Hence, $\Delta y \Delta p_y = \dfrac{\lambda}{\sin\theta} \times \dfrac{2h}{\lambda}\sin\theta = 2h.$ $\qquad (35.80)$

i.e., $\Delta y \Delta p_y \geq h/2\pi$, and this is the Heisenberg's uncertainty principle.

35.37 Wave Mechanical Atom Model

According to the wave mechanics developed by Heisenberg, Schrödinger and Dirac, the electrons revolve round the nucleus as wave packets, which are formed similar to standing waves in sound. This atom model has electrons in various orbits and the electrons are similar to matter waves of wavelength $\lambda = h/mv$. The electron exists as a standing wave in each orbit, and the energy level and 'orbits' of Bohr model are retained (Fig. 35.49). We consider the electron in the hydrogen atom as a standing wave extending in a circle round the nucleus. This wave may just occupy the circumference of a circle. The circle must contain an integral number of wavelengths, i.e., $2\pi r = n\lambda$, where r is the radius of the circle and n is an integer.

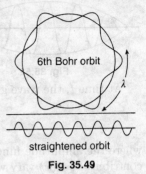

6th Bohr orbit

λ

straightened orbit

Fig. 35.49

But we have $\lambda = \dfrac{h}{mv}$.

$$\therefore \quad 2\pi r = n\frac{h}{mv} \quad \text{or,} \quad mvr = n\frac{h}{2\pi}. \tag{35.81}$$

In Eq. (35.81) mvr is the angular momentum of the electron. Therefore, the angular momentum is equal to an integral multiple of $h/2\pi$.

35.37.1 The Particle in a Box

We consider the possible energy states of a particle in a box on the basis of de Broglie's hypothesis. Let us consider a particle of mass m enclosed in a box of length L. The bound particle is moving back and forth in the X-direction with

Fig. 35.50

constant speed v, making perfectly elastic collisions with the walls of the box. As the walls of the box are impenetrable, the particle cannot move beyond the walls. So the amplitude of the associated wave must drop to zero at the walls. The particle will form a stationary-wave pattern with nodes at the walls. Wave functions of the particle trapped in the box are shown in Fig. 35.50. The formula for the permitted de Broglie wavelengths of the particle is expressed as

$$\lambda_n = \frac{2L}{n}, \quad n = 1, 2, 3, \dots . \tag{35.82}$$

Thus the possible values of the momentum of the particle are

$$p = \frac{h}{\lambda_n} = n\frac{h}{2L}$$

As a result, the possible values of the kinetic energy of the particle are

$$\dot{E}_n = \frac{p^2}{2m} = n^2\frac{h^2}{8mL^2} \tag{35.83}$$

$$n = 1, 2, 3, \dots .$$

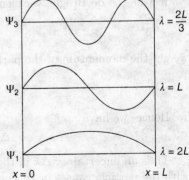

Ψ_3 $\lambda = \dfrac{2L}{3}$

Ψ_2 $\lambda = L$

Ψ_1 $\lambda = 2L$

$x = 0$ $x = L$

Fig. 35.51

Therefore, only certain discrete energy states are possible for the particle bound in a box. Each permitted energy is known as an energy *level*. The integer n that specifies an energy level E_n is known as the *quantum number*.

35.38   Proof of Uncertainty Principle for One-Dimensional Wave Packet

We may derive the position-momentum uncertainty expression by using the theory

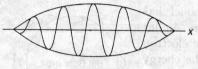

of Fourier analysis. An isolated wave group is the superposition of an infinite number of waves with different angular frequencies ω, continuous range of wave numbers k and amplitudes as shown in Fig. 35.52.

Fig. 35.52

At time t, the wave group $\psi(x)$ can be represented by the Fourier integral,

$$\psi(x) = \int_0^\infty g(k) \cos kx \, dk, \qquad (35.84)$$

where the amplitude function $g(k)$ provides that the amplitudes of the waves that contribute to $\psi(x)$ vary with wave number k. $\psi(x)$ and $g(k)$ are Fourier transforms of each other. Fig. 35.53 reveals gaussian* distributions for the amplitude function $g(k)$ and the wave packet $\psi(x)$. The relation between the distance Δx and the wave number spread Δk depends on the shape of the wave group and also on how Δx and Δk are defined. The widths Δx and Δk follow a reciprocal relation in which the product $\Delta x \, \Delta k$ is a pure number. The minimum value of the product $\Delta x \, \Delta k$ occurs when the envelope of the group has the bell shape of a gaussian function. Hence the gaussian wave packets happen to be minimum uncertainty wave packets. When Δx and Δk are taken as the standard deviations of the respective functions $\psi(x)$ and $g(k)$, then the minimum value is $1/2$. As wave groups do not have gaussian forms in general, we can write,

$$\Delta x \, \Delta k \geq \frac{1}{2}. \qquad (35.85)$$

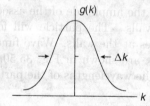
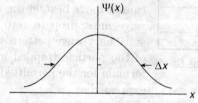

Fig. 35.53

If λ be the de Broglie wavelength of the particle, then from

$$k = \frac{2\pi}{\lambda} = \frac{2\pi p}{h},$$

we get the momentum of the particle in terms of the wave number k as

$$p = \frac{hk}{2\pi}. \qquad (35.86)$$

Hence, we have

$$\Delta p = \frac{h \Delta k}{2\pi} = \hbar \Delta k. \qquad (35.87)$$

Thus an uncertainty Δk in the wave number of the de Broglie waves associated with the particle causes in an uncertainty Δp in the particle's momentum.

---

*As per Royal Society's direction the first letter of Gaussian, Newtonian, etc. should be small letter.

From Eq. (35.85), $\Delta x \Delta k \geq 1/2$ or, $\Delta k \geq 1/2\Delta x$

$$\therefore \quad \Delta x \Delta p \geq \hbar/2. \tag{35.88}$$

This gives the Heisenberg uncertainty relation for position and momentum. Thus the uncertainty Δx in measuring the x coordinate of a particle is related to the uncertainty Δp_x in measuring the x component of the momentum. The product of the uncertainties becomes equal to or greater than $\hbar/2$. The three-dimensional form of the Heisenberg uncertainty relations for position and momentum is written as

$$\Delta x \Delta p_x \geq \frac{\hbar}{2}, \quad \Delta y \Delta p_y \geq \frac{\hbar}{2} \quad \text{and} \quad \Delta z \Delta p_z \geq \frac{\hbar}{2}. \tag{35.89}$$

The Fourier analysis may also be invoked to get a time-energy uncertainty relation. According to Fourier analysis, a wave packet of duration Δt must be composed of plane-wave components whose angular frequencies extend over a range $\Delta \omega$ so that $\Delta t \Delta \omega \geq 1/2$. As $E = \hbar \omega$, we can write,

$$\Delta t \Delta E \geq \hbar/2. \tag{35.90}$$

This gives the Heisenberg uncertainty relation for time and energy. It relates the uncertainty ΔE in the determination of the energy of a system with the time interval Δt available for this energy determination. Therefore, if a system does not stay longer than a time Δt in a given state of motion, its energy in that state will be uncertain by an amount $\Delta E \geq \hbar/2\Delta t$.

35.39 Basic Postulates of Wave Mechanics

In Wave Mechanics, there are certain basic postulates which have fundamental importance. The three fundamental postulates are explained below. Other wave properties are derived from them.

(a) *Each dynamical variable relating to the motion of a particle can be represented by a linear operator.*

In classical Physics, certain functions of suitable variables are associated with each observable quantity. Thus (x, y, z) are associated with position, mv with momentum, $\frac{1}{2}mv^2$ with K.E. and so on. In wave mechanics and quantum mechanics, also certain operators are associated with observable quantities. Thus the X-component of the linear momentum of a particle, $p_x = m\left(\frac{dx}{dt}\right)$ is the classical expression while we have a quantum mechanical operator $-i\left(\frac{\partial}{2\pi}\right)\frac{v}{\partial x}$. In the vector form, this operator is $-i\left(\frac{h}{2\pi}\right)\nabla$. For angular momentum the operator can be written as

$$(\mathbf{r} \times \mathbf{p}) = -i\left(\frac{h}{2\pi}\right)(\mathbf{r} \times \nabla).$$

Similarly, for the observable total energy, the classical representation is $\frac{1}{2m}(p_x^2 + p_y^2 + p_z^2) + V(x, y, z)$ while the quantum mechanical operator is

$$-\frac{(h/2\pi)^2}{2m}\left(\frac{\partial^2}{\partial x^2} + \frac{\partial^2}{\partial y^2} + \frac{\partial^2}{\partial z^2}\right) + V(x, y, z).$$

An operator suggests what operation is to carry out on the quantity that follows it. The operator $i\left(\frac{h}{2\pi}\right)\frac{\partial}{\partial t}$ tells us to take the partial derivative of what comes after it with respect to t and multiply the result by

$$i\left(\frac{h}{2\pi}\right).$$

The quantum operators are summarised in Table 35.3.

Table 35.3

Quantity	Classical Definition	Quantum Operator
Position	$\mathbf{r}$	$\mathbf{r}$
Momentum	$\mathbf{p}$	$-i\dfrac{h}{2\pi}\boldsymbol{\nabla}$
Angular momentum	$\mathbf{r} \times \mathbf{p}$	$-i\dfrac{h}{2\pi}\mathbf{r} \times \boldsymbol{\nabla}$
Kinetic energy	$p^2/2m$	$-(h^2/8\pi^2 m)\nabla^2$
Total energy	$p^2/2m + E_p(\mathbf{r})$	$-(h^2/8\pi^2 m)\nabla^2 + E_p(\mathbf{r})$

(b) *A linear eigenvalue equation can be always linked with each operator.*

We have the total energy operator as $i\left(\frac{h}{2\pi}\right)\frac{\partial}{\partial t}$. Let us consider the eigenvalue equation,

$$i\left(\frac{h}{2\pi}\right)\frac{\partial \psi}{\partial t} = E\psi,$$

where ψ is said to be an eigenfunction of the operator $i\left(\frac{h}{2\pi}\right)\frac{\partial}{\partial t}$ and E is the corresponding energy eigenvalue.

Generally, if a measurement of the dynamical quantity a is made on a particle for which the wave function is ψ, we get different values of a during different trials. This is in conformity with the uncertainty principle. The most probable value of a is written as

$$\langle a \rangle = \int \psi^* \hat{A} \psi \, dV, \tag{35.91}$$

where $\hat{A}$ is the operator associated with the quantity a and ψ^* is the complex conjugate of ψ. The quantity $\langle a \rangle$ is known as the expectation value of $\hat{A}$. The expectation value of momentum and energy are obtained by using the corresponding differential operator. Thus we can express,

$$\langle \mathbf{p} \rangle = \int_{-\infty}^{\infty} \psi^* \left(-\frac{ih}{2\pi}\boldsymbol{\nabla}\right)\psi \, dx\, dy\, dz \tag{35.92}$$

$$\langle E \rangle = \int_{-\infty}^{\infty} \psi^* \left(i\frac{h}{2\pi}\frac{\partial}{\partial t}\right)\psi \, dx\, dy\, dz. \tag{35.93}$$

35.40 Derivation of Time-dependent Form of Schrödinger Equation

The quantity which characterizes the de Broglie waves is known as the *wave function* and is denoted by Ψ. It may be a complex function. Let us assume that Ψ is specified in the X-direction by an equation,

$$\Psi = Ae^{-i\omega(t-x/v)}. \tag{35.94}$$

If ν is the frequency, then $\omega = 2\pi\nu$ and $v = \nu\lambda$.

Hence, $\Psi = Ae^{-2\pi i(\nu t - x/\lambda)}$. $\tag{35.95}$

If E be the total energy and p the momentum of the particle, then $E = h\nu$ and $\lambda = h/p$. Substituting these in Eq. (35.95), we get

$$\Psi = Ae^{-(2\pi i/h)(Et - px)}. \tag{35.96}$$

Eq. (35.95) gives a mathematical description of the wave equivalent of an unrestricted particle of total energy E and momentum p moving in the $+X$-direction.

Differentiating Eq. (35.96) twice with respect to x, we have

$$\frac{\partial^2 \psi}{\partial x^2} = -\frac{4\pi^2 p^2}{h^2}\psi. \tag{35.97}$$

Again, differentiating Eq. (35.96) with respect to t, we have

$$\frac{\partial \psi}{\partial t} = -\frac{2\pi i E}{h}\psi. \tag{35.98}$$

At a speed smaller than that of light, the total energy E of a particle is the sum of its kinetic energy $p^2/2m$ and potential energy V where V is in general a function of position x and time t. We can write,

$$E = \frac{p^2}{2m} + V. \tag{35.99}$$

Multiplying both sides of Eq. (35.99) by ψ, we have

$$E\psi = \frac{p^2\psi}{2m} + V\psi. \tag{35.100}$$

From Eqs. (35.98) and (35.97) we find that,

$$E\psi = -\frac{h}{2\pi i}\frac{\partial \psi}{\partial t} \tag{35.101}$$

and $\quad p^2\psi = -\dfrac{h^2}{4\pi^2}\dfrac{\partial^2 \psi}{\partial x^2}.$ \hfill (35.102)

Substituting these expressions for $E\psi$ and $p^2\psi$ into Eq. (35.100), we get

$$-\frac{h}{2\pi i}\frac{\partial \psi}{\partial t} = -\frac{h^2}{8\pi^2 m}\frac{\partial^2 \psi}{\partial x^2} + V\psi$$

or, $\quad \dfrac{ih}{2\pi}\dfrac{\partial \psi}{\partial t} = -\dfrac{h^2}{8\pi^2 m}\dfrac{\partial^2 \psi}{\partial x^2} + V\psi.$ \hfill (35.103)

Eq. (35.103) is the time-dependent form of Schrödinger's equation.

In three dimensions the time-dependent form of Schrödinger's equation can be expressed as

$$\frac{ih}{2\pi}\frac{\partial \psi}{\partial t} = -\frac{h^2}{8\pi^2 m}\left(\frac{\partial^2 \psi}{\partial x^2} + \frac{\partial^2 \psi}{\partial y^2} + \frac{\partial^2 \psi}{\partial z^2}\right) + V\psi. \tag{35.104}$$

35.40.1 Steady-state Form of Schrödinger's Equation

In some situations the potential energy of a particle does not depend upon time explicitly. The forces that act on it and hence V, change with the position of the particle only. When this is true, Schrödinger's equation may be simplified by removing all references to t. The one-dimensional wave function ψ of an unrestricted particle may then be written in the form

$$\psi = Ae^{-(2\pi i/h)(Et-px)}$$

$$= Ae^{-(2\pi iE/h)t} \cdot e^{+(2\pi ip/h)x}$$

or, $\psi = \psi_0 e^{-(2\pi iE/h)t}$,   (35.105)

where $\psi_0 = Ae^{+(2\pi ip/h)x}$. Thus Ψ is the product of a position-dependent function Ψ_0 and a time-dependent function $e^{-(2\pi iE/h)t}$.

Now, differentiating Eq. (35.105) with respect to t, we have

$$\frac{\partial \psi}{\partial t} = -\frac{2\pi iE}{h}\psi_0 e^{-(2\pi iE/h)t}.$$ (35.106)

Differentiating Eq. (35.105) twice with respect to x, we get

$$\frac{\partial^2 \psi}{\partial x^2} = \frac{\partial^2 \psi_0}{\partial x^2} e^{-(2\pi iE/h)t}.$$ (35.107)

These values can be substituted in the time-dependent form of Schrödinger's equation and we get

$$\frac{ih}{2\pi} \cdot \frac{\partial \psi}{\partial t} = -\frac{h^2}{8\pi^2 m}\frac{\partial^2 \psi}{\partial x^2} + V\psi.$$

$$\therefore \quad E\psi_0 e^{-(2\pi iE/h)t} = -\frac{h^2}{8\pi^2 m}\frac{\partial^2 \psi_0}{\partial x^2}e^{-(2\pi iE/h)t} + V\psi_0 e^{-(2\pi iE/h)t}.$$

Dividing by the common exponential factor, we have

$$\frac{\partial^2 \psi_0}{\partial x^2} + \frac{8\pi^2 m}{h^2}(E - V)\psi_0 = 0.$$ (35.108)

Eq. (35.108) is the steady-state form of Schrödinger's equation.

In three dimensions it may be written as

$$\nabla^2 \psi_0 + \frac{8\pi^2 m}{h^2}(E - V)\psi_0 = 0.$$ (35.109)

Eq. (35.109) can be expressed, in general, as

$$\nabla^2 \psi + \frac{8\pi^2 m}{h^2}(E - V)\psi = 0.$$ (35.110)

35.41 Properties of the Wave Function

(a) Physical significance of Ψ. The probability that a particle will be found at a given place in space at a given instant of time is characterized by the function $\Psi(x, y, z, t)$, called the *wave function*. The wave function can be either real or complex. The only quantity having a physical meaning is the square of its magnitude $P = |\Psi|^2 = \Psi\Psi^*$ where Ψ^* is the complex conjugate of Ψ. The quantity P is called the *probability density*. The probability of finding a particle in a volume $dxdydz$ is $|\Psi|^2 dx\,dy\,dz$. Again, as the particle is found to be somewhere in the space, we can write,

$$\int \int \int |\Psi|^2 dx \cdot dy \cdot dz = 1,$$ (35.111)

where the triple integral extending over all possible values of x, y, z. When a function (Ψ) satisfies this relation, it is called a *normalized wave function*.

(b) Orthogonal and normalized wave functions : Let the product of a function $\Psi_1(x)$ and the complex conjugate $\Psi_2^*(x)$ of a function $\Psi_2(x)$ vanishes when integrated with respect to x over the interval $a \leq x \leq b$. Then we can write,

$$\int_a^b \Psi_2^*(x)\Psi_1(x)dx = 0, \tag{35.112}$$

where $\psi_1(x)$ and $\psi_2(x)$ are said to be orthogonal in the interval (a, b).

Again, the probability of finding a particle in the volume element dV is given by $\Psi\Psi^* dV$. The total probability of finding the particle in the entire space is unity, i.e.,

$$\int |\Psi|^2 dV = 1, \tag{35.113}$$

where the integration extends over all space. Eq. (35.113) can alternately be expressed as

$$\int \Psi\Psi^* dV = 1. \tag{35.114}$$

Any wave function satisfying this equation is said to be normalized to unity or simply called normalized. It is possible to multiply Ψ by a constant A, to give a new wave function, $A\Psi$, which is also a solution of the wave equation. A should be chosen properly so that the new wave function becomes a normalized function. To become a normalized function, it must meet the requirement

$$\int (A\Psi)^* A\Psi \, dx\,dy\,dz = 1$$

or, $$|A|^2 \int \psi\psi^* dx\,dy\,dz = 1$$

or, $$|A|^2 = \frac{1}{\int \Psi\Psi^* dx\,dy\,dz} \tag{35.115}$$

$|A|$ is known as normalizing constant.

In order to arrive at results consistent with the physical observations, several additional requirements are imposed on the wave function $\Psi(x)$. These are :

(i) It must be well behaved, i.e., single-valued and continuous everywhere.

(ii) If $\Psi_1(x), \ldots, \Psi_n(x)$ are solutions of Schrödinger equation, then the linear combination $\psi(x) = a_1\psi_1(x) + a_2\psi_2(x) + \cdots + a_n\psi_n(x)$ must be a solution.

(iii) The wave function $\psi(x)$ must approach zero as $x \to \pm\infty$.

(c) Eigenfunctions and Eigenvalues : Schrödinger's time-independent equation is an example of a type of differential equation known an *eigenvalue equation*. We can write an eigenvalue equation as

$$F_{op}\Psi = f\Psi. \tag{35.116}$$

The differential operator F_{op} operates on a function ψ and this yields a constant f times the function. The function ψ is then called an *eigenfunction of the operator* F_{op}. The corresponding value for f is termed as the *eigenvalue*.

35.42 The Particle in a Box (Infinite Square Well Potential)

This is a simple application of Schrödinger's equation. We consider a particle moving inside a box along the X-direction. The particle is bouncing back-and-forth between the walls of the box. The box has insurmountable potential barriers at $x = 0$ and $x = L$. Thus, as shown in Fig. 35.54, the box is supposed to have

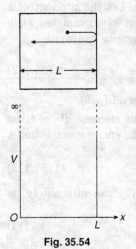

Fig. 35.54

walls of infinite height at $x = 0$ and $x = L$. Let the particle has a mass m and its position x at any instant is given by $0 < x < L$.

The potential energy V of the particle is infinite on both sides of the box. The potential energy V of the particle can then be assumed to be zero between $x = 0$ and $x = L$.

In terms of the boundary conditions as imposed by the problem, the potential function V can be expressed as

$$\left. \begin{array}{l} V = 0 \text{ for } 0 < x < L \\ V = \infty \text{ for } x \le 0 \\ V = \infty \text{ for } x \ge L \end{array} \right\} \tag{35.117}$$

The particle cannot exist outside the box and so its wave function Ψ is 0 for $x \le 0$ and $x \ge L$. Our object is to find what Ψ is within the box, between $x = 0$ and $x = L$.

The Schrödinger's equation within the box can be expressed as

$$\frac{d^2\psi}{dx^2} + \frac{8\pi^2 m}{h^2} E\psi = 0. \tag{35.118}$$

Substituting $\frac{8\pi^2 mE}{h^2} = k^2$, Eq. (35.118) become,

$$\frac{d^2\psi}{dx^2} + k^2\psi = 0 \tag{35.119}$$

The general solution of Eq. (35.119) is

$$\psi = A \sin kx + B \cos kx. \tag{35.120}$$

To evaluate the constants A and B in Eq. (35.120), the boundary conditions can be used. We have

$$\Psi = 0 \text{ at } x = 0 \text{ and hence } B = 0$$

$$\Psi = 0 \text{ at } x = L. \text{ Thus } 0 = A \sin kL.$$

As $A \ne 0$, $kL = n\pi$, where n is an integer or $k = \dfrac{n\pi}{L}$.

Hence, $\psi_n(x) = A \sin \dfrac{n\pi x}{L}$. $\tag{35.121}$

The energy of the particle,

$$E_n = \frac{k^2 h^2}{8\pi^2 m} = \frac{h^2 n^2 \pi^2}{L^2 8\pi^2 m}$$

or, $E_n = \dfrac{n^2 h^2}{8mL^2}$. $\tag{35.122}$

For each value of n, there is an energy level and the corresponding wave function is given by Eq. (35.122). Each value of E_n is known as an eigenvalue and the corresponding Ψ_n is the eigenfunction. Thus inside the box, the particle can only have the discrete energy values specified by Eq. (35.121).

As the particle is somewhere inside the box, so for a normalized wave function, we can write,

$$\int_0^L \psi^*\psi dx = 1, \quad \text{i.e.,} \quad A^2 \int_0^L \sin^2\left(\frac{n\pi x}{L}\right) dx = 1$$

or, $A^2 \int_0^L \left(\frac{1 - \cos 2n\pi x/L}{2}\right) dx = 1$ or, $A^2 \frac{L}{2} = 1$

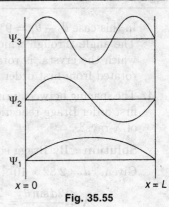

or, $A = \sqrt{\dfrac{2}{L}}.$ (35.123)

Therefore, the normalized wave functions of the particle,

$$\psi_n = \sqrt{\frac{2}{L}} \sin \frac{n\pi x}{L}.$$ (35.124)

Fig. 35.55

The normalized wave functions Ψ_1, Ψ_2 and Ψ_3 are plotted in Fig. 35.55.

Examples

1. In a tetragonal lattice, $a = b = 0.25$ nm and $c = 0.18$ nm. Deduce the lattice spacings between (111) planes.

   Solution : The lattice spacings for a given set of parallel planes (hkl) is expressed as

   $$d = \left[\frac{h^2}{a^2} + \frac{k^2}{b^2} + \frac{l^2}{c^2}\right]^{-1/2}.$$

   Given, $h = 1$, $k = 1$ and $l = 1$.

   Further, $a = b = 0.25$ nm and $c = 0.18$ nm.

   $\therefore \qquad d_{111} = \left[\dfrac{1^2}{(0.25)^2} + \dfrac{1^2}{(0.25)^2} + \dfrac{1^2}{(0.18)^2}\right]^{-1/2} = \textbf{0.126 nm.}$

2. Calculate the interplanar spacing for a (321) plane in a simple cubic lattice whose lattice constant is 4.2×10^{-10} m.

   Solution : $a = b = c = 4.2 \times 10^{-10}$ m

   and $\qquad d_{hkl} = \dfrac{a}{\sqrt{(h^2 + k^2 + l^2)}}$

   For the plane (321), $h = 3$, $k = 2$ and $l = 1$.

   Therefore, $d_{321} = \dfrac{4.2 \times 10^{-10}}{\sqrt{(3^2 + 2^2 + 1^2)}}$ m $= \textbf{1.12} \times \textbf{10}^{-10}$ **m.**

3. Bragg's spectrometer is set for the first order reflection to be received by the detector at glancing angle of $9°18'$. Calculate the angle through which the detector is rotated to receive the second order reflection from the same face of the crystal.

   Solution : Let λ be the wavelength of X-rays. If θ_1 and θ_2 be the glancing angles for the first and the second orders, then we have

   $$2d \sin\theta_1 = 1\lambda \quad \text{and} \quad 2d \sin\theta_2 = 2\lambda.$$

   $\therefore \qquad \sin\theta_2 = 2\sin\theta_1 \quad \text{or,} \quad \sin\theta_2 = 2\sin 9°18' = 0.3232 \quad \text{or,} \quad \theta_2 = 18°48'.$

In this case $\theta_2 - \theta_1 = 9°30'$. So the crystal is rotated through an angle $9°30'$. The angle through which the detector is rotated is twice the angle through which the crystal is rotated. Hence the angle through which the detector is rotated from first order to second order $= 2(\theta_2 - \theta_1) = \mathbf{19°}$.

4. The spacing between principal planes of NaCl crystal is 2.82 Å. It is found that first order Bragg reflection occurs at an angle of 10°. What is the wavelength of X-rays?

Solution : By Bragg equation we can write, $2d\sin\theta = n\lambda$.

Given, $d = 2.82 \times 10^{-10}$ m; $n = 1$ and $\theta = 10°$. $\lambda = ?$

$$\lambda = \frac{2d\sin\theta}{n} = \frac{2 \times (2.28 \times 10^{-10})\sin 10°}{1} = \mathbf{0.98 \times 10^{-10}}\ \mathbf{m}.$$

5. In a crystal, a lattice plane cuts intercepts of $2a$, $3b$ and $6c$ along the axes, where a, b and c are primitive vectors of the unit cell. Determine the Miller indices of the given plane.

Solution : If the given plane cuts intercepts ra, sb, tc along the three axes, we can write,

$$ra : sb : tc = 2a : 3b : 6c,$$

where a, b and c are primitive vectors of the unit cell.

$$\therefore \quad r : s : t = 2 : 3 : 6$$

$$\frac{1}{r} : \frac{1}{s} : \frac{1}{t} = \frac{1}{2} : \frac{1}{3} : \frac{1}{6} = 3 : 2 : 1.$$

Hence, Miller indices of the plane are (321).

6. An X-ray tube with Cu target is operated at 28 kV. The smallest glancing angle for NaCl crystal for the Cu K_α line is 15.8°. Find the wavelength of this line. Also find the glancing angle for photons at the short wavelength limit (d for NaCl = 0.282 nm).

Solution : From Bragg's equation, we have $2d\sin\theta = n\lambda$. Here, $n = 1$.

Therefore, $\lambda = 2d\sin\theta = 2 \times (0.282$ nm$) \times \sin 15.8° = 0.153$ nm.

$$\lambda_{\min} = \frac{hc}{eV} = \frac{6.62 \times 10^{-34} \times 3 \times 10^8}{1.6 \times 10^{-19} \times 28 \times 10^3}\ \text{m} = 0.0443\ \text{nm}.$$

Let θ' be the glancing angle corresponding to $\lambda_{\min}$. Then we have,

$$\theta' = \sin^{-1}\left(\frac{\lambda_{\min}}{2d}\right) = \sin^{-1}\left(\frac{0.0443\ \text{nm}}{2 \times 0.282\ \text{nm}}\right) = \sin^{-1} 0.0785 = \mathbf{4.5°}.$$

7. The wavelength of the L_α X-ray line of plantinum (atomic number 78) is 1.321 Å. An unknown substance emits L_α X-rays of wavelength 4.174 Å. Calculate the atomic number of the unknown substance. Given, $b = 7.4$ for L_α lines.

Solution : Moseley's law can be expressed as

$$\sqrt{\nu} = a(Z - b).$$

Let ν_1 and ν_2 be the frequencies of the L_α line of platinum and the unknown substance respectively, and their atomic numbers be Z_1 and Z_2 respectively. Then we can write,

$$\sqrt{\nu_1} = a(Z_1 - b) \quad \text{and} \quad \sqrt{\nu_2} = a(Z_2 - b)$$

or, $\quad \sqrt{\dfrac{\nu_1}{\nu_2}} = \dfrac{Z_1 - b}{Z_2 - b} \quad$ or $\quad Z_2 - b = (Z_1 - b)\sqrt{\dfrac{\nu_2}{\nu_1}}$

$\because c = \nu\lambda$, we get $\nu_2/\nu_1 = \lambda_1/\lambda_2$.

$\therefore \qquad Z_2 - b = (Z_1 - b)\sqrt{\dfrac{\lambda_1}{\lambda_2}} \quad$ or, $\quad Z_2 = b + (Z_1 - b)\sqrt{\dfrac{\lambda_1}{\lambda_2}}$.

Given, $b = 7.4$; $Z_1 = 78$; $\lambda_1 = 1.321$ Å and $\lambda_2 = 4.174$ Å.

$\therefore \qquad Z_2 = 7.4 + (78 - 7.4)\sqrt{1.321/4.174} = 47.12$.

Thus the atomic number of the unknown substance is **47.12**.

8. X-rays of wavelength 0.7080 Å are scattered from a carbon block through an angle of 90° and are analysed with a calcite crystal, the interplanar distance of whose reflecting planes is 3.13 Å. Determine the angular separation, in the first order between the modified and the unmodified rays.

Solution : We have the wavelength of the modified rays,

$$\lambda' = \lambda + \frac{h}{m_0 c}(1 - \cos\theta)$$

$$= 0.7080 \times 10^{-10}\ \text{m} + \left(\frac{6.63 \times 10^{-34}}{9.11 \times 10^{-31} \times 3 \times 10^8}\right)\ \text{m} = 0.7323\ \text{Å}.$$

Let θ and θ' be the angles of Bragg's reflections corresponding to the wavelengths λ and λ'. Then, for $n = 1$ (first order), we have

$$2d\sin\theta = n\lambda = 0.7080 \times 10^{-10}\ \text{m}$$

and $\quad 2d\sin\theta' = n\lambda' = 0.7323 \times 10^{-10}$ m.

Given, $d = 3.13 \times 10^{-10}$ m.

$\therefore \qquad \theta = 6°30' \quad$ and $\quad \theta' = 6°43'$.

Thus the angular separation, in the first order, between modified and unmodified rays $= \theta' - \theta = $ **13'**.

9. In a discharge tube, the p.d. between the cathode and the anode surfaces is 25000 volts. Express in electron-volts the energy of an electron inside the tube. If this electron is made to strike a target and if the whole energy is emitted as a photon, then calculate its frequency.

Solution : The energy of an electron,

$\quad E = $ p.d. between cathode and anode $\times 1$ electronic charge

$\quad\quad = 25000$ electron-volts.

Again, we have

$\quad E = h\nu$, where $h = $ Planck's constant and $\nu = $ frequency.

$\therefore$ frequency,

$$\nu = (E/h) = \frac{25000 \times 1.6 \times 10^{-12}}{6.62 \times 10^{-27}} \quad (\because\ 1\ \text{electron-volt} = 1.6 \times 10^{-12}\ \text{erg})$$

$$= \mathbf{0.6 \times 10^{-19}}\ \textbf{c/s}.$$

10. When an ultraviolet light of wavelength 3000 Å falls on a metal surface, a retarding potential of 0.5 volt is applied to keep the most energetic electrons from reaching the collector. Calculate the work function.

Solution : We have $\dfrac{1}{2}m_e v_{max}^2 = h\nu - W_{min}$

or, $W_{min} = h\nu - \dfrac{1}{2}m_e v_{max}^2 = h\dfrac{c}{\lambda} - \dfrac{1}{2}m_e v_{max}^2.$

Here, the increase of potential energy of an electron passing through a retarding field of 0.5 volt = loss of its kinetic energy.

$\therefore$ maximum kinetic energy, $\dfrac{1}{2}m_e v_{max}^2 = 0.5$ electron-volt.

Again, $h = 6.62 \times 10^{-27}$ erg-second $= \dfrac{6.62 \times 10^{-27}}{1.6 \times 10^{-12}}$

$= 4.13 \times 10^{-15}$ electron-volt-second;

$c = 3 \times 10^{10}$ cm/sec and $\lambda = 3000$ Å $= 3000 \times 10^{-8}$ cm.

$\therefore \qquad W_{min} = \dfrac{4.13 \times 10^{-15} \times 3 \times 10^{10}}{3000 \times 10^{-8}} - 0.5 = 4.13 - 0.5$

$$= \textbf{3.63 electron-volts}.$$

11. The p.d. between the cathode and anode of a discharge tube is 50000 volts. What is the energy in electron-volt of an electron inside the tube and what is its velocity? If this electron strikes a target and if all the energies were emitted as a photon, what would be its frequency and the corresponding wavelength in Å?

Solution : Energy, $E = 50000$ volts $\times 1$ electronic charge = 50000 electron-volts.

If v be the velocity, then

$$\frac{1}{2}mv^2 = 50000 \text{ electron-volts}$$

or, $v^2 = \dfrac{2 \times 50000 \times 1.6 \times 10^{-12}}{9.1 \times 10^{-28}}$ $(\because m = 9.1 \times 10^{-28} \text{ gm})$

or, $v = 1.324 \times 10^{10}$ cm/second.

Frequency, ν can be written as

$$\nu = \frac{\text{energy}}{h} = \frac{50000 \times 1.6 \times 10^{-12}}{6.62 \times 10^{-27}} = 1.2 \times 10^{19} \text{ c/s}.$$

Now, from the relation, $v\lambda = c$, we get

wavelength, $\lambda = \dfrac{c}{\nu} = \dfrac{3 \times 10^{10}}{1.2 \times 10^{19}} = 2.5 \times 10^{-9} = 0.25 \times 10^{-8}$ cm $= \textbf{0.25 Å}.$

12. An ultraviolet ray of wavelength 3000 Å is made to fall on the surface of a metal which ejects an electron. If the work function of the metal is 2.28 electron-volts, find the velocity of the emitted electron. (Given, $m_e = 9.1 \times 10^{-28}$ gm.)

Solution : We have

$$\frac{1}{2}m_e v_{max}^2 = h\nu - W_{min} = h(c/\lambda) - W_{min},$$

where W_{min} = work function.

Now, $h = 6.62 \times 10^{-27}$ erg-second;

$c = 3 \times 10^{10}$ cm/sec; $\lambda = 3000$ Å $= 3000 \times 10^{-8}$ cm

and $W_{min} = 2.28$ electron-volts $= 2.28 \times 1.6 \times 10^{-12}$ ergs.

Hence, we get

$$\frac{1}{2} m_e v_{max}^2 = \frac{6.62 \times 10^{-27} \times 3 \times 10^{10}}{3000 \times 10^{-8}} - 2.28 \times 1.6 \times 10^{-12}$$

$$= 2.98 \times 10^{-12}$$

$$\therefore \qquad v_{max} = \sqrt{\frac{5.96 \times 10^{-12}}{9.1 \times 10^{-28}}} = \mathbf{8.1 \times 10^7 \ cm/sec.}$$

13. Calculate the energy of an electron so accelerated as to emit a quantum with a frequency of 4.0×10^7 c/s when it strikes a target, supposing the whole energy of the electron to be utilized in the production of the quantum. What p.d. between the electrodes is required to produce this acceleration?

Solution : We have the energy, $E = h\nu$.

Here, the whole energy of the electron is utilized in the production of the quantum.

Now, $h = 6.62 \times 10^{-27}$ erg-second   and $\nu = 4.0 \times 10^{18}$ c/s.

$$\therefore \qquad E = 6.62 \times 10^{-27} \times 4.0 \times 10^{18} \text{ ergs}$$

$$= \frac{26.48 \times 10^{-9}}{1.6 \times 10^{-12}} \text{ electron-volts}$$

$$= 16000 \text{ electron-volts} = 1.6 \times 10^{-2} \text{ meV.}$$

Since an electron has an energy of 16000 electron-volts, the accelerating p.d. $= 16000$ eV/electron = **16000 volts**.

14. An X-ray tube operates at 50 kV. Determine the shortest wavelength of the X-rays produced. Given that, $h = 6.62 \times 10^{-27}$ erg-second and the electronic charge, $Q_e = 4.8 \times 10^{-10}$ e.s.u.

Solution : Let the whole energy of an impinging electron is converted to an X-ray photon of energy $h\nu$. Now, the energy of an impinging electron $= Qe$, where e is the potential.

Thus we can write,

$$h\nu = Q_e e \quad \text{or,} \quad \nu = \frac{Q_e e}{h}.$$

But, $\nu = \dfrac{c}{\lambda}$,

$$\therefore \qquad \frac{c}{\lambda} = \frac{Q_e e}{h} \quad \text{or,} \quad \lambda = \frac{hc}{Q_e e}.$$

Here, $h = 6.62 \times 10^{-27}$ erg-second; $c = 3 \times 10^{10}$ cm/second;

$$e = 50 \text{ kV} = 50 \times 10^3 \text{ volts} = 50 \times 10^3 \times \frac{1}{300} \text{ e.s.u. of p.d.}$$

and $Q_e = 4.8 \times 10^{-10}$ e.s.u.

$$\therefore \qquad \lambda = \frac{6.62 \times 10^{-27} \times 3 \times 10^{10} \times 300}{50 \times 10^3 \times 4.8 \times 10^{-10}} = 2.48 \times 10^{-9} \text{ cm}$$

$$= \mathbf{0.248 \ \text{Å}.}$$

15. Show that the de Broglie wavelength associated with an electron of energy V electron-volts is approximately $(1.227/\sqrt{V})$ nm.

Solution : The de Broglie wavelength λ associated with an electron of mass m and energy E is written as

$$\lambda = \frac{h}{\sqrt{(2mE)}}.$$

In this case kinetic energy, $E_k = V$ eV $= 1.6 \times 10^{-19} V$ J

$$\lambda = \frac{6.62 \times 10^{-34}}{\sqrt{(2 \times 9.1 \times 10^{-31} \times 1.6 \times 10^{-19} V)}}$$

$$= \frac{1.227 \times 10^{-9} \text{m}}{\sqrt{V}} = \frac{1.227}{\sqrt{V}} \text{ nm}.$$

16. Find the de Broglie wavelength associated with

(i) a 46 gm golf ball with velocity 36 m/sec;

(ii) an electron with a velocity 10^7 m/sec.

Which of these two shows wave character and why?

Solution : (i) As $v \ll c$, we may consider $m = m_0$ (the rest mass).

So, $\lambda = \dfrac{h}{mv} = \dfrac{6.63 \times 10^{-34} \text{ J-sec}}{(0.046 \text{ kg})(36 \text{ m/sec})} = 4.0 \times 10^{-34}$ m.

The wavelength associated with golf ball is, therefore, much smaller as compared to its dimensions. So no wave aspect can be expected in its behaviour.

(ii) Since $v \ll c$, hence $m = m_0 = 9.1 \times 10^{-31}$ kg.

Therefore, $\lambda = \dfrac{h}{mv} = \dfrac{6.63 \times 10^{-34}}{(9.1 \times 10^{-31}) \times 10^7} = \mathbf{7.3 \times 10^{-11}}$ **m**.

Thus the wavelength is comparable with the atomic dimensions. So **a moving electron exhibits a wave character**.

17. Find the kinetic energy of a proton whose de Broglie wavelength is 1 fm.

Solution : We have $pc = (mv)c = hc/\lambda$

$$= \frac{(4.136 \times 10^{-15} \text{ eV-sec})(3 \times 10^8 \text{ m-sec}^{-1})}{1 \times 10^{-15} \text{ m}}$$

$$= 1.241 \text{ GeV}.$$

Rest energy of proton $= E_0 = 0.938$ GeV.

$pc > E_0$. So a relativistic calculation is needed.

The total energy of the proton is given by

$$E = \sqrt{E_0^2 + p^2 c^2} = \sqrt{(0.938 \text{ GeV})^2 + (1.241 \text{ GeV})^2} = 1.556 \text{ GeV}.$$

So the kinetic energy of the proton is

K.E. $= E - E_0 = (1.556 - 0.938)$ GeV $= \mathbf{0.618 \text{ GeV}}$.

18. An electron, initially at rest, is accelerated through a p.d. of 5000 V. Compute (i) the momentum and (ii) the de Broglie wavelength of the electron. (iii) Also calculate the Bragg angle for its first order reflection from the (111) planes of nickel which are 2.04 Å apart.

Solution : If v be the velocity of the electron, then its K.E. $= \frac{1}{2}mv^2 = Ve$.

(i) Momentum of the electron $= mv = \sqrt{2mVe}$.

$\therefore \quad mv = \sqrt{2(9.11 \times 10^{-31})5000(1.6 \times 10^{-19})} = 3.818 \times 10^{-23}$ kg-m-sec^{-1}.

(ii) $\lambda = \dfrac{h}{mv} = \dfrac{6.625 \times 10^{-34}}{3.818 \times 10^{-23}} = 1.729 \times 10^{-11}$ m.

(iii) Let θ be the Bragg angle for the first order reflection from (111) planes of nickel. Given $d = 2.04$ Å$= 2.04 \times 10^{-10}$ m, $n = 1$, $\lambda = 1.729 \times 10^{-11}$ m. By Bragg's equation we have $2d\sin\theta = n\lambda$.

or, $2(2.04 \times 10^{-10})\sin\theta = 1 \times (1.729 \times 10^{-11})$

or, $\sin\theta = 0.04237$ or, $\theta = 2°25'$.

19. 10 kV electrons are passed through a thin film of metal for which the atomic spacing is 5.5×10^{-11} m. What is the angle of deviation of the first order diffraction maximum?

Solution : Wavelength of the electron, $\lambda = \dfrac{h}{\sqrt{2mVe}}$.

$\therefore \quad \lambda = \dfrac{6.626 \times 10^{-34}}{\sqrt{2(9.11 \times 10^{-31})10^4(1.602 \times 10^{-19})}} = 1.227 \times 10^{-11}$ m.

Applying Bragg's formula for diffraction at the atomic planes,

$n\lambda = 2d\sin\theta$ or, $1 \times (1.227 \times 10^{-11}) = 2 \times (5.5 \times 10^{-11})\sin\theta$

or, $\sin\theta = 0.1115$. $\therefore$ $\theta = 6°24'$.

Angle through which electron is deviated $= 2\theta = 12°48'$.

20. An electron has a speed of 600 m-sec^{-1} with a accuracy of 0.005%. Calculate the certainty with which we can locate the position of the electron. $h = 6.6 \times 10^{-34}$ J-sec and $m = 9.1 \times 10^{-31}$ kg.

Solution : We have, momentum of the electron

$= mv = 9.1 \times 10^{-31} \times 600$ kg-m-sec^{-1}.

$\Delta p = \left(\dfrac{0.005}{100}\right)mv = (5 \times 10^{-5})(9.1 \times 10^{-31} \times 600)$ kg-m-sec^{-1}.

From uncertainty principle, we have

$\Delta x \Delta p \approx h/2\pi$.

$\therefore \quad \Delta x \approx \dfrac{h}{2\pi\Delta p} = \dfrac{6.6 \times 10^{-34}}{2\pi(5 \times 10^{-5} \times 9.1 \times 10^{-31} \times 600)} = \mathbf{0.003846}$ **m.**

21. A microscope, using photons, is employed to locate an electron in an atom within a distance of 0.2 Å. What is the uncertainty in the momentum of the electron located in this way?

Solution : Given, $\Delta x = 0.2$ Å $= 0.2 \times 10^{-10}$ m. $\Delta p =?$

We can write,

$\Delta x \Delta p \approx \dfrac{h}{2\pi}$ or, $\Delta p = \dfrac{h}{2\pi\Delta x}$

or, $\Delta p = \dfrac{6.626 \times 10^{-34}}{2\pi(0.2 \times 10^{-10})} = \mathbf{5.274 \times 10^{-34}}$ **kg-m-sec^{-1}.**

22. The lifetime of an excited state of an atom is about 10^{-8} sec. Calculate the minimum uncertainty in the determination of the energy of the excited state.

    Solution : We can write, $\Delta E \Delta t \geq h/2\pi$.

    $$\therefore \quad \Delta E \geq \frac{h}{2\pi\Delta t} = \frac{6.6 \times 10^{-34}}{2\pi(10^{-8})}, \quad \therefore \quad \Delta E \geq 1.0 \times 10^{-26} \text{ J} = 6.5 \times 10^{-8} \text{ eV}.$$

    This is known as the *energy width* of an excited state.

23. A particle is moving in a one-dimensional box (of infinite height) of width 10 Å. Calculate the probability of finding the particle within an interval of 1 Å at the centre of the box, when it is in its state of least energy.

    Solution : The wave function of the particle in the ground state ($n = 1$) is given by

    $$\psi_1 = \sqrt{\frac{2}{L}} \sin \frac{\pi x}{L}.$$

    Then the probability of finding the particle in unit interval at the centre of the box ($x = L/2$) is written as

    $$P = \psi_1^2 = \left[\sqrt{\frac{2}{L}} \sin \frac{\pi(L/2)}{L} \right]^2 = \frac{2}{L} \sin^2 \frac{\pi}{2} = \frac{2}{L}$$

    So the probability of finding the particle within an interval of Δx at the centre of the box,

    $$W = |\psi_1|^2 \Delta x = \frac{2}{L} \Delta x.$$

    In this case, $L = 10 \times 10^{-10}$ m   and $\Delta x = 10^{-10}$ m.

    $$\therefore \quad W = \frac{2}{10 \times 10^{-10}} \times 10^{-10} = \mathbf{0.2}.$$

24. Calculate the permitted energy levels of an electron, in a box 1 Å wide.

    Solution : We have the mass of the electron, $m = 9.1 \times 10^{-31}$ kg; $L = 1$ Å $= 10^{-10}$ m.

    So the permitted electron energies,

    $$E_n = \frac{n^2 h^2}{8mL^2} = \frac{n^2(6.626 \times 10^{-34})^2}{8(9.1 \times 10^{-31})(10^{-10})^2}$$

    $$= 6 \times 10^{-18} n^2 \text{ J} = 38n^2 \text{ eV}.$$

    Now, the minimum energy, the electron can have, is $E_1 = \mathbf{38 \ eV}$, corresponding to $n = 1$.

    The other values of energy are $E_2 = 4E_1 = \mathbf{152 \ eV}$, $E_3 = 9E_1 = \mathbf{342 \ eV}$ and so on.

25. Find the expectation value $\langle x \rangle$ of the position of a particle trapped in a box L wide.

    Solution : $\langle x \rangle = \displaystyle\int_{-\infty}^{\infty} x|\psi|^2 dx = \frac{2}{L} \int_0^L x \sin^2 \frac{n\pi x}{L} dx$

    $$= \frac{2}{L} \left[\frac{x^2}{4} - \frac{x \sin(2n\pi x/L)}{4n\pi/L} - \frac{\cos(2n\pi x/L)}{8(n\pi/L)^2} \right]_0^L$$

    $$\therefore \quad \langle x \rangle = \frac{2}{L} \left(\frac{L^2}{4} \right) = \frac{L}{2}.$$

26. Calculate the expectation value $\langle p_x \rangle$ of the momentum of a particle trapped in a one-dimensional box.

Solution : The normalized wave functions of the particle are written as

$$\psi_n^* = \psi_n = \sqrt{\frac{2}{L}} \sin \frac{n\pi x}{L}.$$

$$\frac{d\psi}{dx} = \sqrt{\frac{2}{L}} \left(\frac{n\pi}{L}\right) \cos \frac{n\pi x}{L}.$$

We have, $\langle p_x \rangle = \int_{-\infty}^{\infty} \psi^* \left(-i\frac{h}{2\pi}\frac{d}{dx}\right) \psi dx$

$$= -\frac{ih}{2\pi}\frac{2}{L}\frac{n\pi}{L} \int_0^L \sin\frac{n\pi x}{L} \cos\frac{n\pi x}{L} dx = 0.$$

Therefore, the expectation value $\langle p_x \rangle$ of the particle's momentum is **0**.

27. An X-ray bulb operates at 50 kV. Calculate the shortest wavelength of the X-ray produced. Given, $h = 6.62 \times 10^{-34}$ J-sec; $e = 1.6 \times 10^{-19}$ coulomb.

[V.U. 2005]

Solution : Let all the energy of the electron be converted into X-radiation. The X-ray produced will have the shortest wavelength given by

$$\lambda_{\min} = \frac{c \cdot h}{e \cdot V}.$$

We have, $h = 6.62 \times 10^{-34}$ J-sec; $e = 1.6 \times 10^{-19}$ C; $V = 50 \times 10^3$ volts and $c = 3 \times 10^8$ m/sec.

Hence, $\lambda_{\min} = \dfrac{6.62 \times 10^{-34} \times 3 \times 10^8}{1.6 \times 10^{-19} \times 50 \times 10^3}$ metre

$$= 0.25 \times 10^{-10} \text{ m} = \mathbf{0.25 \ Å}.$$

28. When ultraviolet rays of wavelengths 800 Å and 760 Å are made to incident on hydrogen atom at ground state, it emits electron of energies 1.8 eV and 4.0 eV respectively. Calculate Planck's constant. Using this value, determine the de Broglie wavelength associated with neutron having speed of 1.06×10^5 m-sec^{-1}.

[B.U. 2002]

Solution : We have $E = h\nu - \omega_0 = h \cdot \dfrac{c}{\lambda} - \omega_0$.

For the 1st wavelength, $1.8 \times 1.6 \times 10^{-19} = \dfrac{h \times 3 \times 10^8}{800 \times 10^{-10}} - \omega_0$.

(1 eV = 1.6×10^{-19} J and 1 Å = 10^{-10} metre)

For the 2nd wavelength, $4 \times 1.6 \times 10^{-19} = \dfrac{h \times 3 \times 10^8}{700 \times 10^{-10}} - \omega_0$.

Subtracting we get

$$1.6 \times 10^{-19} \times 2.2 = \frac{h \times 3 \times 10^8}{100 \times 10^{-10}} \cdot \left(\frac{1}{7} - \frac{1}{8}\right) = h \times 3 \times 10^{16} \times \frac{1}{56}.$$

$$\therefore \quad h = \frac{1.6 \times 2.2 \times 56 \times 10^{-19}}{3 \times 10^{16}} = \mathbf{6.57 \times 10^{-34} \ J\text{-}sec.}$$

Further, de Broglie wavelength of a particle moving with velocity v is given by

$$\Delta = \frac{h}{mv}.$$

We have $h = 6.67 \times 10^{-34}$ J-sec, $m = 1.675 \times 10^{-27}$ kg (neutron) and $v = 1.06 \times 10^5$ m-sec^{-1}.

$$\therefore \quad \lambda = \frac{6.57 \times 10^{-34}}{1.675 \times 10^{-27} \times 1.06 \times 10^5} = 3.68 \times 10^{-12} \text{ m} = \mathbf{0.0368 \text{ Å}}.$$

29. An electron has a speed of 200 m-sec^{-1} accurate to 0.01%. With what fundamental accuracy can we locate the position of this electron? Mass of electron $= 9.1 \times 10^{-31}$ kg. **[C.U. 2002]**

Solution : We have the momentum of the electron,

$$p_x = m \cdot v = 9.1 \times 10^{-31} \times 200 = 18.2 \times 10^{-29} \text{ kg-m-sec}^{-1}.$$

As uncertainty in the measurement of velocity is 0.01%, the uncertainty in the measurement of momentum is also 0.01%.

Therefore, the uncertainty in momentum,

$$\Delta p_x = p_x \times \frac{0.01}{100} = 0.0001 \times 18.2 \times 10^{-29} = 18.2 \times 10^{-33} \text{ kg-m-sec}^{-1}$$

We have from Heisenberg's uncertainty principle,

$$\Delta x \cdot \Delta p_x \simeq h \quad \text{or,} \quad \Delta x \simeq \frac{h}{\Delta p_x} = \frac{6.6 \times 10^{-34}}{18.2 \times 10^{-33}} = 0.036 \text{ m}$$

So, the uncertainty in the position $= \mathbf{0.036 \text{ m}}$.

30. A microscope using photon is employed to locate an electron in an atom within a distance of 1 Å. What is the uncertainty in the momentum of the electron located in this way? $h = 6.62 \times 10^{-34}$ J-sec. **[N.B.U. 2005]**

Solution : We have from uncertainty principle, $\Delta x \, \Delta p_x \simeq h$.

In this case, uncertainty in position $\Delta x = 0.1$ Å $= 0.1 \times 10^{-10}$ m and $h = 6.62 \times 10^{-34}$ J-sec.

Therefore, uncertainty in momentum, $\Delta p_x = \dfrac{h}{\Delta x} \simeq \dfrac{6.62 \times 10^{-34}}{0.1 \times 10^{-10}}$

$$\simeq 6.62 \times 10^{-23} \text{ kg-m-sec}^{-1}.$$

Questions

Essay-type

1. Give an account of Moseley's work on X-ray spectra. How would you explain the origin of lines in the X-ray emission spectra of elements? **[V.U. 2002]**

2. Describe modern X-ray tube with a neat diagram and explain how X-rays are produced. Explain what you mean by hard and soft X-rays.

[B.U. 1984]

3. Establish Bragg's law. What are Laue spots?

[V.U. 2002; C.U. 2002; N.B.U. 2005]

4. State Moseley's law. Explain how it helped the discovery of some new elements in the periodic table. **[B.U. 1984; C.U. 1994]**

5. What is Bragg's law for the diffraction of X-rays through a crystal? Explain the application of the law in analysing the structure of simple crystal.

6. Write down Einstein's photoelectric effect? How can this equation explain the principal facts relating to photoelectric effect? Comment on the dual aspect of light.   [B.U. 1983; C.U. 1995]

7. State the principal facts relating to photoelectric emission. How did Einstein explain photoelectric effect?   [N.B.U. 2005]

8. Describe an experiment to demonstrate photoelectric effect. Derive in a simple way Einstein's photoelectric equation.   [C.U. 1980]

9. What is photoelectric effect? How has it been explained on the basis of the quantum nature of light? Describe a photoelectric cell and state some of its applications.

10. Give an account of Millikan's work on photoelectric effect. How did he verify Einstein's equation?   [C.U. 1980; B.U. 1995]

11. Discuss Einstein's photoelectric equation. What do you mean by threshold frequency and stopping potential? Mention their relation with work function.   [C.U. 2003]

13. Describe the experimental evidences for associating a wavelength with material particles.

14. Explain de Broglie concept of matter waves. Describe Davisson and Germer experiment to determine the de Broglie wavelength of a moving particle.

15. Discuss de Broglie's theory of matter waves and obtain an expression for the de Broglie wavelength of an electron.

16. Explain Heisenberg's uncertainty principle.   [B.U. 2004; N.B.U. 2005]

17. Establish the time-independent Schrödinger wave equation for a single particle.   [C.U. 2002]

18. Show that the velocity of de Broglie wave associated with a moving particle is equal to the velocity of the particle.

19. Show that diffraction of electrons through a narrow slit takes place in accordance with Heisenberg's uncertainty principle.

20. What do you mean by a potential well? Show with the help of Schrödinger's wave equation that the energy of electrons in a potential well varies as the square of the natural numbers.

21. Establish the Schrödinger equation for a particle moving in one-dimensional potential box with infinitely high sides. Determine the probable energy levels of the particle.   [N.B.U. 2005; K.U. 2003]

22. (a) What are the maximum and minimum values of $\Delta\lambda$?   [C.U. 2000, '04]

    (b) What is the momentum of a photon of frequency ν?   [C.U. 2003]

23. (a) What is Raman effect?   [C.U. 2000, '01]
       Compare between Raman effect and Compton effect.

    (b) What are Stokes line and anti-Stokes line?   [C.U. 2005]

24. Einstein's photoelectric equation gives $\frac{1}{2}mv^2 = h\nu - \phi$, where m is the electron mass, v is the maximum speed of the electron and ϕ is a constant. (i) What does this equation imply as to the nature of light? (ii) How is the quantity ϕ interpreted? (iii) On what does the quantity ϕ depend?

25. Indicate the main difference between photoelectric cell and photovoltaic cell.

26. (a) What is threshold wavelength? Why is there a threshold wavelength for radiation used for generating photoelectrons from a metal surface?

   (b) What is stopping potential? On what does it depend?

27. Write short notes on : **(a)** Photoelectric effect and its application, **(b)** Photocells and their applications **(c)** Raman effect.   [C.U. 2004]

Short Answer-type

28. What are hard and soft X-rays?   [C.U. 2003]

29. How may **(i)** the intensity and **(ii)** the penetrating power of X-rays be controlled?

30. Explain how the minimum wavelength emitted by an X-ray tube can be controlled and hence deduce an expression from which the wavelength can be calculated.

31. Mention two differences between visible light rays and X-rays.   [C.U. 2004]

32. X-rays and visible light travel at the same speed in vacuum. Do they travel at the same speed in glass?

33. When a Coolidge tube is operated for some time, it becomes hot. Where does the heat come from?

34. Give an explanation of Moseley's law from Bohr's theory.   [V.U. 2002]

35. Deduce Bragg's law for X-ray diffraction.   [B.U. 2004]

36. Why does the ordinary grating fail to produce diffraction in the case of X-rays?   [V.U. 2002]

37. State Moseley's law for the characteristic X-ray spectra and its implication with respect to periodic table.   [C.U. 2003]

38. Explain **(i)** Lattice structure, **(ii)** Laue spots and **(iii)** Cleavage plane.

39. What is Compton effect? Write down the expression of wavelength difference $\Delta\lambda$ between the incident and the scattered X-rays.

40. What is de Broglie wave equation? A particle of mass m is at rest. What is the wavelength of the wave associated with it?   [C.U. 2001, '03]

41. What is meant by de Broglie wavelength of a moving body?   [B.U. 2004]

   Each of seven visible lights has a wavelength and a colour. If an electron has a de Broglie wavelength associated with it, does it also have a colour?

42. The de Broglie wavelength λ associated with a particle of mass m moving with a velocity v is given by

   (i) $\dfrac{mv}{h}$,   **(ii)** $\dfrac{h}{mv}$,   **(iii)** $\dfrac{v}{mh}$,   **(iv)** $\dfrac{m}{vh}$. Which is correct?

43. What is complementary principle?

44. A proton and an electron are accelerated by the same potential difference. Let λ_e and λ_p denote the de Broglie wavelengths of the electron and the proton respectively. Then

   (i) $\lambda_e = \lambda_p$,   **(ii)** $\lambda_p > \lambda_e$,   **(iii)** $\lambda_e > \lambda_p$. Which is correct?

45. Consider the de Broglie wavelengths of an electron and a proton. Which wavelength is smaller if the two particles have **(a)** the same speed, **(b)** the same momentum and **(c)** the same energy?

46. Write down Schrödinger **(i)** time-independent and **(ii)** time-dependent wave equation. Explain the symbols used.

47. When can a wave equation be called normalized?

48. What is the significance of the wave function ψ?

49. de Broglie wavelength of a body of mass m and kinetic energy E is given by

   (i) $\lambda = \dfrac{h}{mE}$,   **(ii)** $\lambda = \dfrac{\sqrt{2mE}}{h}$,   **(iii)** $\lambda = \dfrac{h}{2mE}$,   **(iv)** $\lambda = \dfrac{h}{\sqrt{2mE}}$. Which is correct?

50. Write Schrödinger's wave equation. What do you mean by eigenvalues and eigenfunction?

51. State Heisenberg's uncertainty principle.   [**C.U. 2000, '01, '05**]

   What are its main applications?   Write down the time-independent Schrödinger equation for a particle subjected to a potential V.   [**C.U. 2005**]

Numerical Problems

52. An X-ray tube operating at 20 kV emits a white spectrum with a short wavelength limit of 6.2×10^{-11} metre. Calculate Planck's constant.
   [**Ans. 6.634×10^{-34} J-sec**]

53. The energy of X-ray photon is $h \cdot \nu$ joule where $h = 6.63 \times 10^{-34}$ J-sec and ν is the frequency in hertz. X-rays are emitted from a target bombarded by electrons, which have been accelerated by a p.d. of 10^2 kV. Calculate the minimum possible wavelengths of X-rays. $e = 1.6 \times 10^{-19}$ C; $c = 3 \times 10^8$ m-sec^{-1}.
   [**Ans. 0.124 Å**]

54. The distance between the cathode and the anti-cathode in an X-ray tube is 1.5 metres. If the cut-off wavelength (minimum) is 30×10^{-12} m, find the electric field between the cathode and anti-cathode.   [**C.U. 2004**]
   [**Ans. 27 kV/m**]

55. Calculate the separation of atomic planes in a crystal (calcite), given molecular mass = 100.1 and density = 2.71×10^3 kg-m^{-3}.   [**Ans. 3.13 Å**]

56. The short wavelength limit shifts by 26×10^{-12} m when the operating voltage in an X-ray tube is increased by 1.5 times the original value. Find the original value of the operating voltage.   [**Ans. 15.9 kV**]

57. The first order Bragg reflection is formed when X-rays of wavelength 0.842 AU. is made incident on a crystal at glancing angle 8°35'. What will be the glancing angle for third order reflection?   [Given, $\sin 8°25' = 0.15$ and $\sin^{-1}(0.45) = 2.65$.]   [**B.U. 2004**]
   [**Ans. 26.6°**]

58. Find the minimum wavelength of X-ray produced by a X-ray tube operated upon 1000 kV. Given : $h = 6.625 \times 10^{-34}$ J-sec; $e = 1.602 \times 10^{-19}$ C and $c = 3 \times 10^8$ m/sec.   [**V.U. 2005**]
   [**Ans. 0.012 Å**]

59. Find the constants a and b in Moseley's equation $\sqrt{\nu} = a(Z - b)$ from the following data :

Elements	Z	Wavelength of K_α-line
A	42	71×10^{-12} m
B	27	178.5×10^{-12} m

[**Ans.** $a = 5 \times 10^{-7} (\text{Hz})^{1/2}$, $b = 1.37$]

60. What should be the p.d. through which an electron must be accelerated from rest, so that when it falls on a target the short wavelength limit of its continuous spectrum shall be 10^{-10} m? Also estimate the maximum speed of the electron.   [**Ans.** 12.4 kV; 6.61×10^{-1} m-s^{-1}]

61. The p.d. across an X-ray tube is 10^5 volts. What is the maximum frequency of X-rays emitted? What is the corresponding wavelength?
[**Ans.** 2.4×10^{19} Hz; 1.25×10^{-11} m]

62. An X-ray tube operates at 12 kV. Find the maximum speed of the electrons striking the anticathode. Mass of electron $= 9.1 \times 10^{-31}$ kg; charge of electron $= 1.602 \times 10^{-19}$ C.

63. Calculate the heat generated per minute in the target of an X-ray tube if the voltage applied is 20 kV and the current is 10 mA. How much power is radiated if the efficiency is 0.2%?   [**Ans.** 12000 J; 0.4 W]

64. An X-ray tube is operated at 0.04 megavolt. The radiations from the tube are analysed by a Bragg spectrometer. Calculate (a) the shortest wavelength limit of the spectrum and (b) the glancing angle for the 2nd order of this wavelength. Given, the crystal grating spacing = 3.036 Å.
[**Ans.** 0.309 Å; 2°55′]

65. Find the smallest glancing angle at which K_α radiation of molybdenum of wavelength 0.7 Å, will be reflected from calcite crystal of spacing 3.036 Å. At what angle will be third-order reflection?   [**Ans.** 6°37′; 20°18′]

66. In an X-ray diffraction by the powder method, the radius of the cylindrical photographic film is 8 cm while the radius of a first order spectrum line on the photograph is 5 cm. If the spacing of the reflecting atomic planes is 2.75 Å, calculate the wavelength of the X-rays used.   [**Ans.** 1.52 Å]

67. NaCl has its principal planes spaced at 2.20 Å. The first order of Bragg reflection is located at 10°. Calculate (a) the wavelength of the X-rays and (b) the angle for the second-order Bragg reflection. [**Ans.** 0.9790 Å; 20°19′]

68. Determine the velocity and kinetic energy of a proton having the de Broglie wavelength equal to 2 Å. Given, mass of proton $= 1.67 \times 10^{-27}$ kg.
[**Ans.** 1.98×10^3 m-sec^{-1}; 3.27×10^{-21} joule]

69. If E be the kinetic energy of a particle with rest mass m_0, prove that the de Broglie wavelength is given by $\lambda = \dfrac{h \cdot c}{\sqrt{E(e + 2m_0c^2)}}$.

70. Show that the de Broglie wavelength of an electron moving with a small velocity compared to light and with a kinetic energy of V electron-volt can be written as $\lambda = \frac{12.26}{\sqrt{V}}$ Å.

71. X-rays of wavelength 0.82 Å fall on a metal plate. Find the de Broglie wavelength associated with photo-electrons emitted. Neglect the work function of the metal. [**Ans.** 9.98×10^{-2} Å]

72. In a diode valve, the plate has a potential of 150 volts relative to the filament. Determine the wavelength associated with the electron as it reaches the plate. Given $e = 1.6 \times 10^{-19}$ coulomb. [**Ans.** 4.27 Å]

73. A moving electron has an energy about 2×10^{-5} J and a position uncertainty of 10^{-10} m. Calculate the corresponding uncertainty in its speed Δv. Determine the fractional uncertainty $\Delta v/v$. [**Ans.** 7.3×10^{6} m-sec^{-1}; 11%]

74. An electron of mass m when accelerated through a p.d. V, has de Broglie wavelength λ. Find the de Broglie wavelength associated with a proton of mass M accelerated through the same p.d. [**Ans.** $\lambda\sqrt{\frac{m}{M}}$]

75. Show that if uncertainty in the location of a particle is equal to the de Broglie wavelength associated with the particle, the uncertainty in its velocity is equal to its velocity.

76. A microscope is used to view a·small particle which is illuminated by light of wavelength 5000 Å. If the objective of the microscope subtends an angle of 90° at the particle, find the uncertainty in the position and momentum of the particle. [**Ans.** 3.52×10^{-7} m; 1.873×10^{-27} kg-m^{-1}]

77. The photoelectric threshold for a particular metal is 3000 Å. What will be the energy of an electron ejected by a radiation of wavelength 1000 Å incident on the metal surface? $h = 6.55 \times 10^{-34}$ J-sec. [**Ans.** 8.1 eV]

78. A monochromatic source of light operating at 200 W emits 4×10^{20} photons per second. Find the wavelength of the light. [**Ans.** 3.97×10^{-7} m]

79. The maximum kinetic energy of the electrons emitted from a metallic surface is 1.6×10^{-19} joule when the frequency of radiation falling on the surface is 7.5×10^{14} cycles/sec. Calculate the minimum frequency of radiation for which electron will be just emitted. Given, $h = 6.6 \times 10^{-34}$ joule-sec.
[**Ans.** 5.1×10^{14} cycles/s]

80. The maximum electron energy in an experiment on the photoelectric effect using radiation of wavelength 4×10^{-5} cm was observed to be 1.4×10^{-19} joule. Derive a value for Planck's constant. [**Ans.** 6.64×10^{-34} joule-sec]

81. Find the wavelength of light which liberates electron from potassium whose work function is 2.24 eV. Given, $h = 6.6 \times 10^{-34}$ joule-sec; $e = 1.6 \times 10^{-19}$ coulomb; $c = 3 \times 10^{8}$ m/sec. [**Ans.** 5.5×10^{-5} cm]

82. Light of frequency 5×10^{14} cycles/sec liberates electrons with energy 2.31×10^{-19} joule from a certain metal surface. What is the wavelength of light which liberates electrons of energy 8.93×10^{-19} joule from the same surface? $c = 3 \times 10^{-10}$ cm/sec; $h = 6.62 \times 10^{-34}$ joule-sec. [**Ans.** 2×10^{-5} cm]

83. Calculate Compton wavelength for an electron. Given, $h = 6.62 \times 10^{-34}$ J-sec; mass of electron $= 9.11 \times 10^{-31}$ kg and $c = 3 \times 10^{8}$ m-sec^{-1}. [**Ans.** 0.0242 Å]

84. An X-ray photon of energy 1.02 MeV is scattered through 90° by a free electron. Calculate the energy of the photon and electron after collision.
[**Ans.** Photon = 0.51 MeV; Electron = 0.51 MeV]

Chapter 36
Radioactivity, Structure of Nucleus and Cosmic Rays

36.1 Introduction

This chapter deals with some very important aspects of modern physics, like the natural and artificial radioactivity, structure of the nucleus, detectors of nuclear radiations, particle accelerators, artificial transmutation, nuclear fission and fusion, and finally about the cosmic rays and the universe.

36.2 Natural Radioactivity

The phenomenon of spontaneous emission of radiations of high penetrating power form heavy elements of atomic weights greater than 206 and occurring in nature, is known as *natural radioactivity*. The elements which reveal this property are *radioactive elements*. The atoms of radioactive elements emit radiations of three distinct types. Radioactivity is spontaneous and is unaffected by external agent, like high temperature, high pressure, large electric and magnetic fields, etc.

Artificial transmutation of elements has been able to produce radioactivity in many elements lighter than those occur in nature. Radioactivity induced in an

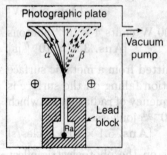
Fig. 36.1

element by bombarding it with α-particles, neutrons, protons, and other particles or radiations is known as *artificial radioactivity*. The artificial radioactive elements usually have short life-times and emit electrons, positrons and other particles, as well as γ-rays in their decomposition.

The existence of three distinct types of radiation can be demonstrated by simple experiment. A small quantity of radium (Ra) is kept at the bottom of a small hole drilled in a lead block as shown in Fig. 36.1. A beam of radiation from Ra will issue through the hole of the lead block placed inside an evacuated chamber to avoid absorption of the rays. The photographic plate (P) is placed above the lead block to receive the rays. A strong magnetic field is applied at right angles to the plane of the figure. After exposure, the photographic plate is developed when three distinct lines will be found on the plate. The α-particles will be deflected towards left, indicating that they are *positively charged*. The β-particles will be deflected towards right, showing that they are negatively charged, while the γ-rays are not deflected and hit the plate P straight. This proves the γ-rays are uncharged (neutral rays). If an electrostatic field is applied, instead of magnetic field, the β-rays are

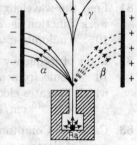
Fig. 36.2

deflected towards the positive plate, the α-rays towards the negative and γ-rays go straight. This is clearly shown in Fig. 36.2.

36.2.1 Properties of Alpha Rays

(i) α-particles shot out from radioactive substances have high velocities from 1.4×10^7 to 1.7×10^7 m/sec. They move along straight lines. Their tracks can be seen in the Wilson's cloud chamber.

(ii) An α-particle is a helium nucleus of two protons and two neutrons, it has two units of positive charge.

(iii) They produce ionization in the gas through which they pass. Their ionizing power is 100 times more than that of β-rays and 10 000 times greater than that of γ-rays.

(iv) They produce fluorescence if they fall on substances like barium platinocyanide or zinc sulphide.

(v) They affect a photographic plate but the effect is feeble.

(vi) They are scattered by nuclei of heavy elements, e.g., gold.

(vii) They are deflected by electric and magnetic fields indicating that they are charged particles.

(viii) They produce a heating effect. The evolution of heat is due to the stoppage of α-, β- and γ-rays by the radioactive substance.

(ix) The value of e/m for α-particles was obtained by Rutherford to be half of that for hydrogen ion. The charge on each α-particle (e) was found to be twice that of a hydrogen ion. The mass of the α-particle was shown to be four times that of hydrogen. Thus an α-particle is the nucleus of the helium atom.

36.2.2 Properties of Beta Rays

(i) All β-particles emitted from a substance do not have same velocity but have a range from $0.3c$ to $0.99c$. At high velocities, e/m decreases indicating an increase in mass of the particles following

$$m = \frac{m_0}{\sqrt{1 - v^2/c^2}}.$$

(ii) β-particles possess negative charge and mass equal to that of an electron.

(iii) They affect a photographic plate.

(iv) Their ionizing power is low and so the range is large.

(v) They are deflected by electric and magnetic fields. Their direction of deflection shows that they are negatively charged particles.

(vi) They produce fluorescence in barium platinocyanide, willemite, etc.

(vii) The value of e/m for β-rays is the same as that of cathode rays. The charge on a β-particle is also same as the charge on an electron. Thus β-rays are identical with electrons.

(viii) They penetrate through thin metal foils and the penetrating power is higher than that of α-rays.

36.2.3 Properties of Gamma Rays

(i) γ-rays are electromagnetic waves of considerably short wavelength having a range from 0.005 Å to 0.5 Å.

(ii) They are not charged particles and travel with the velocity of light.

(iii) They produce fluorescence and affect a photographic plate.

(iv) They ionise the gas through which they pass. The ionisation produced is, however, very small.

(v) They are diffracted by crystals like X-rays.

(vi) They have more penetrating power than even β-rays. They have the capability of even passing through an iron plate of 30 cm thickness.

(vii) They are not affected by electric and magnetic fields.

36.3 Determination of e/m of Alpha Particles

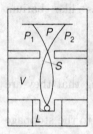

Fig. 36.3

The experiment by Rutherford and Robinson for finding the specific charge of α-rays is described below. In this experiment a beam of α-particles is subjected to electric and magnetic fields. From the deflections produced by the fields, the value of e/m is found out. The arrangement made for the magnetic deflection is shown in Fig. 36.3. A fine wire coated with radium (RaC) which emits α-particles is kept in a cavity L of a lead block. the α-particles emitting from the source are limited by a slit S. They are then incident on a photographic plate P. This arrangement is kept in an evacuated vessel V and a uniform magnetic field of flux density B is applied perpendicular to the plane of the paper. Under the action of the field, the α-particle will describe an arc of a circle of radius r. Reversing the magnetic field, the path of the particle may be reversed. As a result the α-particles reach the points P_1 and P_2 respectively before and after reversing the magnetic field. The velocity v of the α-particles is nearly equal for all the particles in the case of the RaC source. If e and m represent the charge and mass of the α-particle respectively, then we can write,

$$Bev = \frac{mv^2}{r} \quad \text{or,} \quad \frac{e}{mv} = \frac{1}{Br}. \tag{36.1}$$

Knowing B and r, one can determine $\frac{e}{m}$ if v is calculated.

For getting e/mv^2 an apparatus as shown in Fig. 36.4 is used. In this part of the experiment, α-particles from the same source are subjected to the action of an electric field maintained between the two metallic plates E_1 and E_2. The α-particles passing through this electric field are deflected at right angles to their path. After traversing parabolic path in the electric field, the particles are recorded on a photographic plate when the deflection becomes AD_1. Reversing the field, the trace is obtained at D_2 and then the deflection is AD_2. The mean deflection d is then determined.

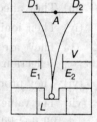

Fig. 36.4

Let l = the length over which the electric field acts, L = distance of photographic plate from the field, X = intensity of the electric field and d = deflection on the photographic plate. We then have

$$d = \frac{Xe}{m}\frac{l}{v}\frac{L}{v} \quad \text{or,} \quad \frac{e}{mv^2} = \frac{d}{XlL}. \tag{36.2}$$

From Eq. (36.1). $\frac{e}{mv}$ and from Eq. (36.2), $\frac{e}{mv^2}$ are determined and hence we can calculate values of both e/m and v. The value for e/m of α-particles is obtained as 4.82×10^7 C/kg which is very close to the value of e/m calculated for doubly ionized helium.

36.3.1 Determination of the Charge of Alpha Particle

In order to determine the charge of α-particle, a known quantity of RaC is placed in a shallow dish R as shown in Fig. 36.5. The dish is covered with a thin aluminium foil. It absorbs the atoms wherefrom α-particles are emitted. After passing through a window (W) of known area covered with a very thin aluminium foil, the α-particles fall upon the collecting plate P which is connected to an electrometer. The charge received by the plate P in a certain time t is obtained from the electrometer reading. A strong magnetic field prevents the β-rays (emitted by the source) from reaching the collecting plate. The number of α-particles falling on the plate is found out using the Geiger counter. The charge carried by each α-particle is thus estimated as :

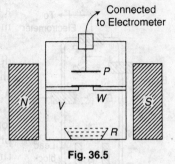

Fig. 36.5

$$e = 3.19 \times 10^{-19} \text{ C.}$$

Identification of α-particles

Charge on the α-particle, $e = 3.19 \times 10^{-19}$ C.

Electronic charge, $e' = 1.6 \times 10^{-19}$ C.

$\therefore \quad e = 2e'$.

Mass of the α-particle, $m = \dfrac{e}{(e/m)} = \dfrac{3.19 \times 10^{-19}}{4.82 \times 10^7} = 6.62 \times 10^{-27}$ kg.

Comparing this mass with the mass of the hydrogen atom we get

$$\frac{m}{m_H} = \frac{6.62 \times 10^{-27}}{1.67 \times 10^{-27}} \approx 4 \quad \text{or,} \quad m = 4m_H.$$

So we find that the α-particle has the mass of a helium atom and carries two positive elementary charges. This further shows that the α-particle is a helium atom that has lost both its electrons.

36.3.2 Velocity of Alpha-Particles

The velocity of emission of α-particles is the characteristic of the isotope wherefrom they emanate. Rutherford's experiments provide the velocity of the alpha-particles from RaC as 2×10^7 m sec^{-1}. In fact, the velocity of α-particles varies from 1.45 to 2.2×10^7 m sec^{-1} for different radioactive sources.

36.4 Range of α-particles : Experimental Determination

When α-particles are passed through a gas, they are slowed down by losing energy in ionizing the gas particles, until its energy falls below the ionization potential of the gas. The α-particle then captures two electrons and becomes a neutral helium atom. The distance, the α-particle travels in the gas, is called the *range*. Beyond that range all the three properties of the α-rays, viz., ionizing power, photographic action and fluorescence effect disappear simultaneously. In general, the range is expressed as so many cm in air at 0.76 m pressure and 15 °C. This range depends on (i) the initial energy of the α-particles, (ii) the ionization potential of the gas and (iii) the chances of collision between the α-particle and the gas particles.

The distance through which an α-particle travels in a substance before coming to rest is known as the '*range*' of the particle in that substance.

36.4.1 Bragg's Experiment

Fig. 36.6 shows Bragg's apparatus for finding the range of α-particles in a gas at different pressures. T is the evacuated glass tube. The radioactive substance R is placed in a lead block on the platform of the adjustable rod C which can be raised up or down. The tube is filled with the gas at desired pressure to be measured by a manometer. The plate P is connected to the electrometer.

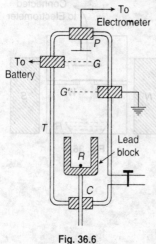

Fig. 36.6

The ionization produced by the particles is determined by an ionization chamber which consists of the plate P and a grid G. Between these electrodes a p.d. is maintained to ensure that an electrometer connected to the chamber measures the saturation ionization current. The second grid G' is used to prevent the diffusion of ions from the chamber. The tube is filled with the gas and the rod C is adjusted. The α-particles reaching the grid G pass into the space between G and P. The particular position of the platform is detected by the electrometer when the ionization current falls to zero. The range of the α-particles is obtained from the distance between the source and the grid G.

It is established that the range is inversely proportional to the density of the gas. Now the specific ionization is the number of ions produced by α-particles per unit length of the path. The curve relating the specific ionization with the distance from the source was obtained by Bragg as shown in Fig. 36.7. The graph shows the so-called "Bragg hump" near the end of the range. "Sight tail" or "straggling effect" is also noted in the figure which arises because all the α-particles are not emitted from the source with the same initial velocity.

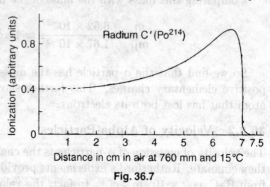

Fig. 36.7

36.4.2 Geiger and Nuttal Experiment

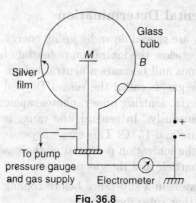

Fig. 36.8

The α-particle source taken was in the form of a thin film on a small metal disc M (Fig. 36.8). It was mounted at the centre of a spherical glass bulb B which is coated inside with silver and a high p was applied between the silver film and the disc M. The saturation ionization current in the bulb produced by the passage of the α-particles was measured by an electrometer.

The gas under study can be admitted at any pressure inside the bulb, and the saturation current for different gas pressures was measured. A graph was then plotted between the ionization current and the corresponding pressure P of the gas. The nature of the curves was as shown in Fig. 36.9. The ionization at first increases with the pressure but at a certain critical pressure P_c, maximum ionization was attained.

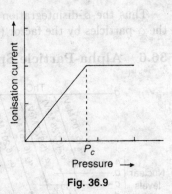

Fig. 36.9

Geiger's Law

Geiger established the relation between the range (R) of an α-particle and its velocity of emission (v). He showed that the range R is proportional to the cube of the velocity, i.e., $R \propto v^3$ or, $R = av^3$, where a is a constant.

Range-Energy Relation

The energy E of the emitted particle is found to be directly proportional to the square of the velocity v. Thus, Geiger's law can be expressed as $R = bE^{3/2}$, where b is a constant.

Geiger-Nuttal Law

The range R of an α-particle and the disintegration constant λ of the radioactive element that emits it are expressed as

$$\log \lambda = A + B \log R. \tag{36.3}$$

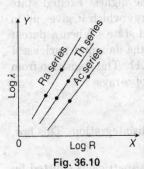

Fig. 36.10

The relation expressed in Eq. (36.3) is called *Geiger-Nuttal* law. When $\log \lambda$ is plotted against $\log R$ for different α-emitters in the three series, three almost parallel straight lines are obtained, one for each series (Fig. 36.10). In Eq. (36.3), $\log \lambda = A + B \log R$, the constant B is same for all the series while A is different for different series. According to this relation, if the disintegration constant is high, the range is also high. As the range also depends on the energy, we may conclude that radioactive substances of large decay constants emit high energy α-particles.

This law is important to find the decay constants of radioactive substances of very short or very long lives. Experimentally determining the ranges of α-particles, the respective decay constants can be found by extrapolation from the curves representing the Geiger-Nuttal relation.

36.5 Alpha Particle Disintegration Energy

If an α-particle is emitted from a nucleus, the nucleus recoils in order to conserve momentum. Let m and v be the mass and velocity of the α-particle while M and V be the mass and velocity of the daughter nucleus. According to conservation of momentum, we have

$$mv = MV. \tag{36.4}$$

The sum of the kinetic energies of the α-particle and the product nucleus is known as the *alpha disintegration energy*, E.

We thus have,

$$E = \frac{1}{2}mv^2 + \frac{1}{2}MV^2 = \frac{1}{2}mv^2 + \frac{1}{2}M\left(\frac{mv}{M}\right)^2$$

or, $$E = \frac{1}{2}mv^2\left(1 + \frac{m}{M}\right). \tag{36.5}$$

Thus the α-disintegration energy can be obtained by multiplying the K.E. of the α-particles by the factor $(1 + m/M)$.

36.6 Alpha-Particle Spectra

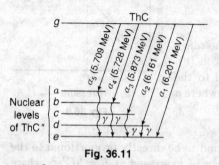

Fig. 36.11

Earlier it was assumed that the nucleus of a radioactive substance emitted alpha particles of some fixed energy. Measuring the energies of α-particles using magnetic spectrograph, it was found that several radioactive nuclei emitted α-particles of different energies falling within a narrow range. As for example, we consider a ThC nucleus which decays into a ThC$''$ ($_{81}$Tl^{208}) nucleus after emitting an α-particle. ThC emits five groups of α-particles with energies 5.709 MeV, 5.728 MeV, 5.873 MeV, 6.161 MeV and 6.201 MeV. The emission of groups of α-particles with different energies indicates that nuclei may exist in a number of discrete, excited energy states above the ground state. The parent nucleus decays from its ground state to several excited states or to the ground state of the daughter nucleus. The daughter nucleus ThC$''$ formed due to disintegration of ThC exists in several excited energy states a, b, c, d, e, where e is the ground state and a is the highest excited state of the daughter nucleus. Each excited state has some energy which it gives up in the form of γ-radiation during its transition to the ground state. When a parent nucleus goes from its ground state to the ground state of the daughter nucleus, it emits an α-particle of maximum energy as shown in Fig. 36.11. The transition from an excited state to the ground state involves the emission of γ-rays.

36.7 Soddy-Fajans' Displacement Law

Soddy and Fajans in 1913 discovered a law of radioactive disintegration. This law, known as the *displacement law*, may be stated as follows :

(i) In all radioactive transformations, either an α- or a β-particle is emitted by the atom.

(ii) If a radioactive atom emits an α-particle, a new atom is formed whose mass number becomes less by four units and atomic number less by two units than those of the parent atom, e.g.,

$$_{92}U^{238} \xrightarrow{\alpha} {}_{90}Th^{234}.$$

(iii) If a radioactive atom emits a β-particle, the new atom formed has the same mass number but the atomic number is increased by one unit. e.g.,

$$_{90}Th^{234} \xrightarrow{\beta} {}_{91}Pa^{234}.$$

36.8 Natural Radioactive Series

By using the displacement law, we can determine the mass and atomic numbers of different elements in successive radioactive changes, provided the mass and atomic numbers of the parent are known. The different atoms so produced at different stages of disintegration form a series. The first member is known as the *parent*, the intermediate members are called *daughters* and the final stable member is called the *end product*. Uranium series, Actinium series, Thorium series and Neptunium series are four such series each of which consists of a succession of daughter elements. An explanation of exactly four series can be given. We know that alpha decay reduces the mass number of a nucleus by 4. Hence the nuclides, whose mass numbers are all given by $A = 4n$, where n is an integer, can decay into one another in descending order of mass number. All radioactive nuclides whose mass numbers follow the equation $A = 4n$ are said to be members of the $4n$ series. Radioactive nuclides whose mass numbers obey an equation $A = 4n + 1$ belong to the $(4n + 1)$ series. Similarly, $A = 4n + 2$ and $A = 4n + 3$ belong to the $(4n + 2)$ series and $(4n + 3)$ series respectively. A list of the names of four important radioactive series, their parent nuclides, the half-lives of these parents, and the stable daughter which are end products of the series are presented in Table 36.1.

Table 36.1 : Four radioactive series

Mass numbers	Series	Parent	Half-life (years)	Stable end product
$4n$	Thorium	$_{90}Th^{232}$	1.39×10^{10}	$_{82}Pb^{208}$
$4n + 1$	Neptunium	$_{93}Np^{237}$	2.25×10^6	$_{82}Bi^{209}$
$4n + 2$	Uranium	$_{92}U^{238}$	4.51×10^9	$_{82}Pb^{206}$
$4n + 3$	Actinium	$_{92}U^{235}$	7.07×10^8	$_{82}Pb^{207}$

We consider the Uranium series with mass number $A = 238$ and $Z = 92$. It is also called *Uranium I* or UI. Table 36.2 shows the sequence of the disintegration which is ended with stable $_{82}Pb^{206}$.

Table 36.2 : Uranium series

No.	Substance	Symbol	Atomic number Z	Mass number A	Particles emitted	Half-life period T
1	Uranium I	UI	92	238	α	4.56×10^9 years
2	Uranium X$_1$	UX$_1$	90	234	β, γ	24.1 days
3	Uranium X$_2$	UX$_2$	91	234	β, γ	1.18 minutes
4	Uranium II	UII	92	234	α	2.56×10^5 years
5	Ionium	Io	90	230	α, γ	8.3×10^4 years
6	Radium	Ra	88	226	α, γ	1622 years
7	Radon	Rn	86	222	α	3.825 days
8	Radium A	RaA	84	218	α, γ	3.05 minutes
9	Radium B	RaB	82	214	β, γ	26.8 minutes
10	Radium C	RaC	83	214	α or β, γ	19.7 minutes
11a	Radium C' or	RaC' or	84	214	α	1.6×10^{-4} second
11b	Radium C''	RaC''	81	210	β	1.32 minutes
12	Radium D	RaD	82	210	β, γ	22 years
13	Radium E	RaE	83	210	β	5 days
14	Radium F (Polonium)	RaF	84	210	α, γ	138.3 days
15	Radium G (Lead)	RaG (Pb)	82	206	Stable	Lead $A = 206$

36.9   Law of Radioactive Disintegration

Rutherford and Soddy found that the number of atoms of radioactive material that break up at any instant is proportional to the number of atoms present at that instant. Let N be the number of atoms of a radio-element at a given instant t. Then the rate of decrease $(-dN/dt)$ is proportional to N.

i.e.,
$$-\frac{dN}{dt} = \lambda N, \tag{36.6}$$

where λ is a constant called *disintegration constant* or *decay constant* of the radioactive element. It is defined as the ratio of the amount of the substance which disintegrates in a unit time to the amount of substance present. Mathematically, we can write,

$$\lambda = \frac{-dN/dt}{N}. \tag{36.7}$$

Now, Eq. (36.6) can be written as

$$\frac{dN}{N} = -\lambda dt.$$

Integrating, $\log_e N = -\lambda t + C,$ (36.8)

where C is the integration constant.

Let us assume that the number of radioactive atoms initially present be N_0.

Thus, when $t = 0, N = N_0$.

$$\therefore \qquad \log_e N_0 = C.$$

Substituting for C in Eq. (36.8), we get

$$\log N = -\lambda t + \log N_0$$

or,
$$\log_e \frac{N}{N_0} = -\lambda t \quad \text{or,} \quad N = N_0 e^{-\lambda t}. \tag{36.9}$$

Eq. (36.9) shows that the number of atoms of a given radioactive substance decreases exponentially with time. This is shown in Fig. 36.12. Theoretically, an

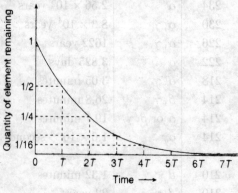

Fig. 36.12

infinite time is required for the radioactivity to disappear completely. To compare one radioactive substance with another, a quantity called *half-life period* is used.

Half-life

The half-life period of a radioactive substance is defined as the time required to disintegrate for one-half of the radioactive substance.

For a given radio-element, at the end of time $T_{1/2}$ only 50% of the radioactive atoms remains unaltered. Similarly, at the end of $2T_{1/2}$ only 25%, after $3T_{1/2}$ 12.5%, after $4T_{1/2}$ 6.25%, etc., remain unchanged.

Value of Half-life Period

We know, $N = N_0 e^{-\lambda t}$. If $T_{1/2}$ be the half-life period, then at $t = T_{1/2}$, $N = N_0/2$.

Putting the values,

$$\frac{N_0}{2} = N_0 e^{-\lambda T_{1/2}} \quad \text{or,} \quad e^{\lambda T_{1/2}} = 2 \quad \text{or,} \quad \lambda T_{1/2} = \log_e 2 \quad \text{or,} \quad T_{1/2} = \frac{\log_e 2}{\lambda}.$$

$$\therefore \quad T_{1/2} = \frac{\log_e 2}{\lambda} = \frac{0.6931}{\lambda}. \tag{36.10}$$

Eq. (36.10) reveals that $T_{1/2}$ is inversely proportional to λ. Half-life period is different for different radioactive substances, e.g., uranium has a half-life period of 4.5×10^9 years. For radium, $T_{1/2}$ is 1622 years while radon has a half-life period of 3.8 days only.

36.10 The Mean Life

The life-time of every atom is different. The actual lives of the various atoms range from zero to infinity. Thus the mean life of a radioactive element may be defined as :

$$\text{The mean life of a radioactive element} = \frac{\text{sum of the lives of all the atoms}}{\text{total number of atoms}}.$$

Hence, the mean life of a radio-element is the ratio of the total life-time of all the radioactive atoms to the total number of such atoms in it.

Value of Mean Life

We assume that N_0 be the total number of radioactive atoms in the beginning. Let N be the number of atoms of that element after time t. Then we have $N = N_0 e^{-\lambda t}$. If dN be the number of atoms disintegrating between time t and $t + \delta t$, then dN atoms have had a life between t and $(t + \delta t)$. As δt is very small, each of these atoms had a life of t. Therefore, the total life of dN atoms $= (dN)t$.

Now, the possible life of any of the total number N_0 radioactive atoms varies from 0 to ∞. Hence,

$$\text{total life-time of all } N_0 \text{ atoms} = \int_0^\infty t \, dN.$$

We have the mean or average life,

$$T_{av} = \frac{\text{total life-time}}{\text{total number of atoms}} = \frac{\int_0^\infty t \, dN}{N_0}$$

$$\because \quad N = N_0 e^{-\lambda t}, \quad \text{we get} \quad \frac{dN}{dt} = -\lambda N_0 e^{-\lambda t}$$

$$\text{or,} \quad dN = -\lambda N_0 e^{-\lambda t} dt. \tag{36.11}$$

We can ignore the negative sign of Eq. (36.11) as it merely indicates the decrease in the number of atoms with time. Hence we can write,

$$dN = \lambda N_0 e^{-\lambda t} dt. \tag{36.12}$$

$$\therefore \quad T_{av} = \frac{\int_0^\infty t \lambda N_0 e^{-\lambda t} dt}{N_0} = \lambda \int_0^\infty t e^{-\lambda t} dt. \tag{36.13}$$

Integrating by parts, we get from Eq. (36.13),

$$T_{av} = \lambda \left[\frac{t e^{-\lambda t}}{-\lambda} - \int \frac{e^{-\lambda t} dt}{-\lambda} \right]_0^\infty$$

$$= \lambda \left[\frac{t e^{-\lambda t}}{-\lambda} - \frac{e^{-\lambda t}}{-\lambda^2} \right]_0^\infty = \lambda \left(\frac{1}{\lambda^2} \right) = \frac{1}{\lambda}.$$

Hence, we get

$$T_{av} = \frac{1}{\lambda}. \tag{36.14}$$

Eq. (36.14) shows that the mean life of a radioactive substance is the reciprocal of the decay constant.

36.11 Measurement of Decay Constants

The three constants λ, $T_{1/2}$ and T_{av} of a radioactive substance are interrelated. We have $T_{1/2} = \frac{0.693}{\lambda}$ and $T_{av} = \frac{1}{\lambda}$. The decay constant λ can be determined by experiment. Different methods are used for finding λ according as λ is large or small. From a knowledge of λ, $T_{1/2}$ and T_{av} can be found out.

36.11.1 Elements of Short Period (Large λ)

The decay curve is drawn from experimentally measured values of intensity and time. The logarithm of intensity is then plotted against time giving a straight line graph representing the equation,

$$\log N = \log N_0 - \lambda t$$

or, $y = a - \lambda t,$ \hfill (36.15)

where $y = \log N$ and $a = \log N_0$ (constant).

$\therefore \quad \dfrac{dy}{dt} = -\lambda$. Hence the slope of the straight line gives λ.

36.11.2 Elements of Long Period (Small λ)

Each disintegrating atom emits only one α-particle. So the number of α-particles counted must be equal to the number of atoms disintegrating. Now, we can write,

$$-\frac{dN}{dt} = \lambda N \quad \text{or,} \quad \lambda = \frac{-dN/dt}{N}. \tag{36.16}$$

From Eq. (36.16) we find that the decay constant λ is equal to the ratio of the atoms disintegrating per unit time to the total number of atoms present.

36.12 Units of Radioactivity

The activity of a radioactive substance is generally expressed in curie whose submultiples are millicurie (mCi) and microcurie (μCi). The curie is defined as the quantity of a radioactive substance which gives 3.70×10^{10} disintegrations/second. This is the number of disintegrations per second per gram of radium.

Another unit rutherford (Rd) is also used. It is defined as the quantity of a radioactive substance which gives 10^6 disintegrations/second. For a substance with very short half-life period, very little of the substance is essential for 1 curie of activity while for the substance with very long half-life period, a very large quantity of the substance is essential for 1 curie of activity.

36.12.1 Activity

By the term *activity* of a sample of any radioactive nuclide we mean the rate at which the nuclei of its constituent atoms decay. Let N be the number of nuclei present in the sample at a certain time. Its activity R is then given by $R = -dN/dt$.

The SI unit of activity is named after Henri Becquerel. Thus we have,

1 becquerel = 1 Bq = 1 event/sec.

1 MBq = 10^6 Bq and 1 GBq = 10^9 Bq.

36.13   Law of Successive Disintegration

By chain disintegration we mean a process in which a radioactive substance disintegrates to form a new substance, which disintegrates to form another new substance and so on. Let us consider a substance A which decays to form a substance B; then the substance B decays to form a substance C and so on. We then have,

$$A \to B \to C \to \ldots X \quad \text{(stable)}.$$

Any two adjacent elements in a radioactive series are considered as *parent* and *daughter*. Thus in a series, the parent of the following element will be daughter of the preceding one. Now let us assume that at time $t = 0$, the number of initial atoms in $A = N_0$ and the number of initial atoms in $B = 0$.

Again, at time t, let the number of atoms in $A = N_1$ and the number of atoms in $B = N_2$.

We assume that λ_1 and λ_2 are the decay constants of A and B respectively. As at every time an atom of A disappears and an atom of B is produced, we have

rate of formation of daughter, $B = \lambda_1 N_1$.

The rate at which B decays $= \lambda_2 N_2$.

Therefore, the net increase in the number of B atoms is

$$\frac{dN_2}{dt} = \lambda_1 N_1 - \lambda_2 N_2. \tag{36.17}$$

Since $N_1 = N_0 e^{-\lambda_1 t}$, we get $\dfrac{dN_2}{dt} = \lambda_1 N_0 e^{-\lambda_1 t} - \lambda_2 N_2$.

$$\therefore \quad \frac{dN_2}{dt} + \lambda_2 N_2 = \lambda_1 N_0 e^{-\lambda_1 t}. \tag{36.18}$$

Multiplying both sides of Eq. (36.18) by the integrating factor $e^{\lambda_2 t}$, we get

$$\frac{dN_2}{dt} e^{\lambda_2 t} + \lambda_2 N_2 e^{\lambda_2 t} = \lambda_1 N_0 e^{(\lambda_2 - \lambda_1)t} \quad \text{or,} \quad \frac{d}{dt}[N_2 e^{\lambda_2 t}] = \lambda_1 N_0 e^{(\lambda_2 - \lambda_1)t}.$$

Integrating, $N_2 e^{\lambda_2 t} = \dfrac{\lambda_1}{\lambda_2 - \lambda_1} N_0 e^{(\lambda_2 - \lambda_1)t} + C$. \hfill (36.19)

The constant of integration C is determined from the initial conditions.

When $t = 0$, $N_2 = 0$.

$$\therefore \quad C = \frac{-\lambda_1 N_0}{\lambda_2 - \lambda_1}. \tag{36.20}$$

Substituting the value of C from Eq. (36.20) in Eq. (36.19), we have

$$N_2 e^{\lambda_2 t} = \frac{\lambda_1 N_0}{\lambda_2 - \lambda_1}[e^{(\lambda_2 - \lambda_1)t} - 1]$$

or, $\quad N_2 = \dfrac{\lambda_1 N_0}{\lambda_2 - \lambda_1}[e^{-\lambda_1 t} - e^{-\lambda_2 t}]$. \hfill (36.21)

36.14   Radioactive Equilibrium

36.14.1   Secular or Permanent Equilibrium

Let $T_1 \gg T_2$ with $T \approx \infty$ and $T_2 = 0$, i.e., the half-life of A is very very large than that of B.

Then, $\lambda_1 \ll \lambda_2$ and $\lambda_1 \approx 0$. In Eq. (36.21) $e^{-\lambda_1 t} \to 1$.

$$\therefore \quad N_2 = \frac{N_0 \lambda_1}{\lambda_2}(1 - e^{-\lambda_2 t}). \tag{36.22}$$

After an appreciably long time, $e^{-\lambda_2 t}$ becomes negligible and then we have

$$N_1 \approx N_0.$$

Then we can write,

$$N_1 \lambda_1 = N_2 \lambda_2. \tag{36.23}$$

Eq. (36.23) shows that at equilibrium, the rate of decay of any radioactive product is equal to its rate of production from the previous member of the chain.

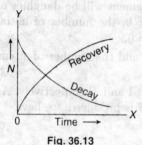

Fig. 36.13

Then the daughter is said to be in secular or permanent equilibrium with the parent. As an example, we can write the equation

$$\text{Ra}^{226} \rightarrow \text{Rn}^{222} + \alpha. \tag{36.24}$$

The half-life period of Ra is 1590 years which is very large compared to Rn (3.8 days). Fig. 36.13 reveals the experimental decay and recovery curves. After a long time, compared to its mean life, Rn is in permanent equilibrium with Ra. Its amount becomes constant as evident by the sum of the ordinates of the two curves.

36.14.2 Transient Equilibrium

Let $\lambda_1 \ll \lambda_2$ but $\lambda_1 \neq 0$, i.e., the decay constant λ_1 is not too small to be ignored. In that case, after a sufficiently long time, $e^{-\lambda_2 t}$ becomes negligible compared to $e^{-\lambda_1 t}$. So we have

$$N_2 = \frac{N_0 \lambda_1}{\lambda_2 - \lambda_1} e^{-\lambda_1 t} = \frac{\lambda_1 N_1}{\lambda_2 - \lambda_1} \quad \text{or,} \quad \frac{N_2}{N_1} = \frac{\lambda_1}{\lambda_2 - \lambda_1}. \tag{36.25}$$

In this case, both A and B decay but the ratio N_2/N_1 remains unaltered.

36.15 The Age of the Earth

The age of the earth may be estimated from the relative abundance of the two isotopes of uranium, U^{238} and U^{235}. The half-periods of U^{238} and U^{235} are 4.5×10^9 years and 7×10^8 years respectively. Let at the beginning when the earth was formed, the proportions of the two isotopes were same. The present relative abundance of U^{238} to U^{235} in natural uranium is 99.3% to 0.7%. Hence we have

$$\frac{N_1}{N_2} = \frac{99.3}{0.7} = \frac{N_0 e^{-\lambda_1 t}}{N_0 e^{-\lambda_2 t}} = e^{(\lambda_2 - \lambda_1)t}, \tag{36.26}$$

where $\lambda_1 = \dfrac{0.6931}{4.5 \times 10^9}$ and $\lambda_2 = \dfrac{0.6931}{7 \times 10^8}$.

Thus, $\log_e \left(\dfrac{99.3}{0.7} \right) = (\lambda_2 - \lambda_1)t$

or, $t = \dfrac{1}{\lambda_2 - \lambda_1} \log_e \left[\dfrac{99.3}{0.7} \right]$

$$= \frac{1}{\left(\frac{0.6931}{7 \times 10^8} \right) - \left(\frac{0.6931}{4.5 \times 10^9} \right)} \log_e \left(\frac{99.3}{0.7} \right) = 5.93 \times 10^9 \text{ years.}$$

The value so obtained agrees approximately with that given by astronomical evidence for the age of the universe.

36.15.1 Radioactive Dating

The decay of radioactive elements does not depend on the physical and chemical conditions imposed on them. Although the decay of an individual particle from a nucleus is a random process, the gross decay of many nuclei in a given sample gives a way of measuring times. Joly and Rutherford in 1913 proposed that if igneous rock, formed due to a prehistoric volcanic eruption, contained a small amount of uranium it would steadily decay, leaving less uranium and so depositing more stable Pb-206. Determining the ratio of uranium to lead in rock samples, a correct time can be obtained for the origin of the geological deposits. Uranium dating calculates times of the order of millions of years.

As all the plants use CO_2 from the atmosphere for growth, a portion of the carbon in plants is radioactive C-14 and hence the plants are radioactive. When a plant dies, no additional C-14 is taken in. The plant body them begins to decay without being replaced. Measurement of the relative amounts of C-14 and C-12 in an organic archeological sample gives a very sensitive method of dating.

36.16 Biological Effects of Nuclear Radiations

Nuclear radiation like α-particles, β-particles, γ-rays and neutrons can cause damage to the human body. The harmful effects of nuclear radiations are owing to the ionization or excitation of atoms in living cells by the Compton effect, photoelectric effect, bremsstrahlung and so on. Some of the cell constituents are destroyed by ionization. Even some of the products formed may act as poisons. Damage may occur in the breaking up of chromosomes, changes in the permeability of cell membranes, swelling of the nucleus of a cell and destruction of cells.

The biological effects are divided into three groups :

(a) The genetic effects;

(b) Short-term recoverable effects; and

(c) Long-term irrecoverable effects.

The effects in group (a) only appear in later generations while groups (a) and (b) are limited to the person who have received the radiations.

The genetic effect appears in the future generations of those irradiated. Experiments on animals reveal that the genetic effects are expected from breeding of the radiation-dosed human individuals. The damages include an increase in mental deficiencies, an increase in the number of monsters born and a general deterioration of the species in quality and population number. If excessive doses are absorbed, a drop in the white blood cell count is noticed which becomes prominent in the first few hours after exposure. This is followed by diarrhoea, vomiting and fever which is termed as *radiation sickness*. Recovery is possible if doses are low but high doses are lethal within a few weeks. Smaller doses produce short-term effects like skin disorders and loss of hair which are usually recoverable. More serious is the damage of the bone marrow and other cells which may even leads to leukaemia and to the production of cancerous cells.

36.16.1 Unit of Radiation Dose

The SI unit of radiation dosage is the *gray*. 1 Gy corresponds to 1 J of energy absorbed per kilogram of target material. The gray being a large unit, a smaller one the rad, equal to 0.01 Gy, is more widely used. One rad is defined as the absorbed dose of any nuclear radiation that results in the absorption of 0.01 J of energy per kilogram of absorbing material. As the absorbed dose required to produce a certain effect which may vary for various types of radiation, this difference is expressed by the relative biological effectiveness (RBE) of the particular nuclear radiation. Again, a dose unit for biological effect is the *rem* (red equivalent man) which is the dose in rads multiplied by the RBE. The RBE of 250 keV X-rays is taken as 1. A dosage of 1 rad of such X-rays to a person is considered as 1 rem. The RBEs of other X-rays and of gamma and beta rays are close to 1 while the RBE of fast neutrons is about 10 and that of 1 MeV alpha particles is about 25; 1 rad absorbed from such alpha particles means a dosage of about 25 rem.

36.16.2 Artificial Radioactivity and Radio-isotopes

Joliot and Curie first observed that a piece of aluminium bombarded by α-particles, gave off positrons which is identical with electron, except that its charge is positive. The unstable positron soon unites with an ordinary electron. In their experiment Curie-Joliot noted that the positron activity did not stop immediately when the stream of α-particles was cut off, but continued like natural beta activity. It was also seen that some of the aluminium atoms had been changed into radioactive isotopes of other elements. This phenomenon was subsequently called as *artificial radioactivity* while the changed aluminium atoms were called radio-isotopes. Later experimenters have revealed ways of producing many artificially radioactive atoms, or radio-isotopes by bombarding different elements with energetic particles.

Radio-isotopes are widely used in medicine, agriculture, industry, higher scientific research and in various other fields.

(i) In Medicine : Radio-isotopes are used to diagnose and cure diseases, particularly when conventional methods of diagnosis are not helpful, like diagnosis of brain tumor, Leukemia (blood cancer) etc.

(ii) In Industry : Radioactive tracers are widely used for quality control of castings and fabricated machine parts. Due to high heat and electrical resistance, it is used as a good insulating coating for wires.

(iii) In Scientific Research : Radio-isotopes are used in higher scientific research, like the determination of age of minerals, rocks, ancient archaeological and anthropological specimens, etc. Meteorologists use radio-isotope to study the air movement. The radio-isotopes are also used to find the life of atomic reactors. In medical research, C^{14} and I^{131} isotopes are used to investigate the efficiency of a newly prepared medicine. Hydrologists use radio-isotopes to study the movement of silt on sea-bed.

(iv) In Agriculture : With the help of radio-phosphorus P^{32} scientists can study the way in which wheat and other cereals utilize phosphorus from artificial fertilizers. Different types of phosphate fertilizers are now available. Out of these which particular variety may be used most effectively by a particular soil can be tested and this facilitates the choice of fertilizer. Again, using radioactive 'tracers' scientists have been able to follow the mechanism of food manufacture by the photo-synthesis. Genetic studies of plants with γ-rays or neutrons have enabled the agricultural scientists to get crops with high yield.

36.17 Classification of Nuclei

In 1911, the atomic nucleus was discovered by Rutherford. α-particle scattering experiments by Rutherford revealed that the atom consists of a very small nucleus of the order of 10^{-14} m in diameter surrounded by orbiting electrons. Atomic nuclei are made by elementary particles called *protons* and *neutrons*. A proton has a positive charge of same magnitude as that of an electron while a neutron is electrically neutral. The proton and the neutron are of two different charge states of the same particle which is called a *nucleon*. A species of nucleus, called *nuclide*, may be represented schematically by $_ZX^A$ where Z, the atomic number, indicates the number of protons and A, the mass number, indicates the total number of protons and neutrons while X is the chemical symbol of the species. If N represents the number of neutrons, then $N = A - Z$. As an example, the chlorine nucleus $_{17}Cl^{35}$ has $Z = 17$ protons, $A = 35$ nucleons and so, $N = 35 - 17 = 18$ neutrons.

Atoms of different elements may now be classified in the following way :

(a) Isotopes are nuclei with the same atomic number Z but different mass numbers A. The nuclei $_{14}Si^{28}$, $_{14}Si^{29}$, $_{14}Si^{30}$ and $_{14}Si^{32}$ are all isotopes of silicon. All the isotopes of an element contain the same number of protons but different number of neutrons. The nuclear charge of all the isotopes of an element have identical chemical behaviour but differ physically in mass only.

(b) Nuclei, with an equal number of neutrons, are known as *isotones*. Some isotones are $_6C^{14}$, $_7N^{15}$ and $_8O^{16}$. They all have same neutrons.

(c) Nuclei, with the same mass number A but different atomic number Z, are known as *isobars*. Examples are $_8O^{16}$ and $_7N^{16}$. Isobars are atoms of different elements and they have different physical and chemical properties.

(d) Some atoms are there which have same Z and same A, but differ in nuclear energy states and exhibit differences in their internal structures. These nuclei have different life-times and are called *isomeric nuclei* or *isomers*.

(e) Nuclei of same mass number A, but with the proton and neutron number interchanged are called *mirror nuclei*.

Example : $_4Be^7$ ($Z = 4$ and $N = 3$) and $_3Li^7$ ($Z = 3$ and $N = 4$).

36.18   Properties of Nucleus

Nuclear size

Rutherford showed that the mean radius of an atomic nucleus is of the order of 10^{-14} to 10^{-15} m while that of the atom is about 10^{-10} m. Therefore, the nucleus is about 10000 times smaller in radius than the atom. The empirical formula for the nuclear radius can be represented as,

$$R = r_0 A^{1/3} \qquad (36.27)$$

where A is the mass number and $r_0 = 1.3 \times 10^{-15}$ m = 1.3 fm. Nuclei are so small that the fermi (fm) is chosen an appropriate unit of length. 1 fm = 10^{-15} m. From Eq. (36.27), we find that the radius of the C^{12} nucleus is $R \approx (1.3)(12)^{1/3} = 3$ fm. Similarly, calculations show that the radius of the $_{47}Ag^{107}$ nucleus is 6.2 fm and that of the $_{92}U^{238}$ nucleus is 8.1 fm. The radius may be estimated from the scattering of neutrons and electrons by the nucleus. This can also be done by analysing the effect of the finite size of the nucleus on nuclear and atomic binding energies.

Nuclear density

The nuclear density ρ_N is calculated by $\rho_N = \dfrac{\text{nuclear mass}}{\text{nuclear volume}}$. We have the nuclear mass = Am_N (where A = mass number, m_N = mass of the nucleon = 1.67×10^{-27} kg) and nuclear volume = $\dfrac{4}{3}\pi R^3 = \dfrac{4}{3}\pi (r_0 A^{1/3})^3 = \dfrac{4}{3}\pi r_0^3 A$.

Hence, $\rho_N = \dfrac{Am_N}{\frac{4}{3}\pi r_0^3 A} = \dfrac{m_N}{\frac{4}{3}\pi r_0^3} = \dfrac{(1.67 \times 10^{-27})}{\frac{4}{3}\pi(1.3 \times 10^{-15})^3}$

$$= 1.816 \times 10^{17} \text{ kg m}^{-3}.$$

This calculation shows that the nuclear matter is in an extremely compressed state. Certain stars (e.g., the "white dwarfs") are composed of atoms whose electron shells have collapsed due to enormous pressure and the densities of such stars approach that of pure nuclear matter.

Nuclear charge

The charge of the nucleus is due to the protons in it; each proton has a positive charge of 1.6×10^{-19} C. The nuclear charge is Ze where Z is the atomic number of the nucleus whose value is known from X-ray scattering experiments, from the nuclear scattering of α-particles, and also from the X-ray spectrum.

Spin angular momentum

Like electron, both the proton and neutron have an intrinsic spin. The spin angular momentum is computed by $L_s = \sqrt{l(l+1)}h/2\pi$ where the quantum number l, called the *spin*, is equal to $1/2$. Then the spin angular momentum has a value $L_s = \frac{\sqrt{3}}{2}\frac{h}{2\pi}$.

Resultant angular momentum

In addition to the spin angular momentum, the protons and neutrons in the nucleus have also an orbital angular momentum. The resultant angular momentum of the nucleus can be obtained by adding the spin and orbital angular momenta of all the nucleons within the nucleus. The total angular momentum of a nucleus can be expressed as $L_N = \sqrt{l_N(l_N + 1)}\frac{h}{2\pi}$. This total angular momentum is called *nuclear spin*.

Nuclear magnetic dipole moments

The spinning electron has an associated magnetic dipole moment of 1 Bohr magneton, which can be expressed as

$$\mu_e = \frac{eh/2\pi}{2m_e}. \tag{36.28}$$

Due to the spin of proton, it should have a magnetic dipole moment. According to Dirac's theory,

$$\mu_N = \frac{eh/2\pi}{2m_p}, \tag{36.29}$$

where m_p is the proton mass. μ_N is called a *nuclear magneton* and is the unit of nuclear magnetic moment. μ_N has a value of 5.050×10^{-27} J/T. Since $m_p = 1836m_e$, the nuclear magneton is only $1/1836$ of a Bohr magneton. For nucleons, measurements give $\mu_p = 2.7925\mu_N$ and $\mu_n = -1.9128\mu_N$.

Electric quadrupole moment

In addition to its magnetic moment, a nucleus has an electric quadrupole moment. It is defined as

$$Q = \left(\frac{1}{e}\right) \int (3z^2 - r^2)\rho d\tau, \tag{36.30}$$

where ρ is the charge density in the nucleus. Q is a measure of the eccentricity of the ellipsoidal nuclear surface. Thus, $Q = 0$ for a spherically symmetric charge distribution. A charge distribution stretched in the prolate will give a positive quadrupole moment, and an oblate distribution will give a negative quadrupole moment as shown in Fig. 36.14. Since the expression is divided by the electronic charge, the dimension of the quadrupole moment is that of an area which is measured in barn (1 barn = 10^{-28} m^2).

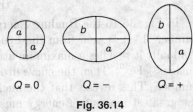

Fig. 36.14

36.19 Mass Defect and Nuclear Binding Energy

An explanation for the mass defect is based on Einstein's equation $E = mc^2$. We know that Z protons and N neutrons are combined to make a nucleus when some of the mass (Δm) disappears as it is converted into an amount of energy $\Delta E = (\Delta m)c^2$. This energy is known as the *binding energy* (B.E.) of the nucleus. In order to disrupt a stable nucleus into its constituent protons and neutrons, the minimum energy required is the binding energy. The magnitude of the B.E. of a nucleus determines its stability against disintegration. When the B.E. is large, the nucleus is stable. A nucleus having the least possible energy (equal to the B.E.) is said to be in the *ground state*. If the nucleus has an energy $E > E_{min}$, it is then in the excited state. If $E = 0$, it corresponds to dissociation of the nucleus into its constituent nucleons.

Let M be the experimentally determined mass of a nuclide having Z protons and N neutrons. Then

$$\text{B.E.} = \{(Zm_p + Nm_n) - M\}c^2 \qquad (36.31)$$

If B.E. > 0, the nucleus is stable. The required energy must be supplied then from outside to disrupt it into its constituents. On the other hand, if B.E. < 0, the nucleus is unstable and it will disintegrate by itself.

We have illustrated the calculation of B.E. by taking the example of the deuteron which is formed by a proton and a neutron.

We have the mass of proton = 1.007276 u and mass of neutron = 1.008665 u.

∴ mass of proton + neutron in free state = 2.015941 u.

Mass of deuteron nucleus = 2.013553 u

Therefore, mass defect = Δm = 0.002388 u and B.E. = 0.002388 ×931 = 2.23 MeV (∵ 1 u = 931 MeV).

Hence, when a deuteron is formed from a free proton and neutron, 2.23 MeV of energy is liberated. On the other hand, 2.23 MeV must be supplied from an external source to break up a deuteron into a proton and a neutron. This may be confirmed by experiments that show that a gamma-ray photon with a minimum energy of 2.23 MeV can split a deuteron into a free neutron and a free proton. This is illustrated in Fig. 36.15.

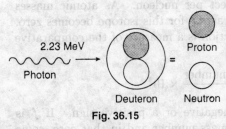

Fig. 36.15

36.19.1 Stability of Nucleus and Binding Energy

We have the B.E. per nucleon = $\dfrac{\text{total B.E. of a nucleus}}{\text{the number of nucleons it contains}}$.

In Fig. 36.16 the Binding Energy per nucleon is plotted as a function of mass number A. It is seen from the figure that the curve rises steeply at first and then gradually it reaches a maximum at 8.79 MeV for $A = 56$, corresponding to the iron nucleus $_{26}\text{Fe}^{56}$. Then the curve drops slowly to about 7.6 MeV at the highest mass number. This reveals that the nuclei of intermediate mass are the most stable, as the greatest amount of energy must be supplied to liberate each of their nucleons and thus indicating that a large amount of energy will be liberated if heavier nuclei be split into lighter ones or if light nuclei can be joined to form heavier ones. The former process is called *nuclear fission* while the latter one is known as *nuclear fusion*.

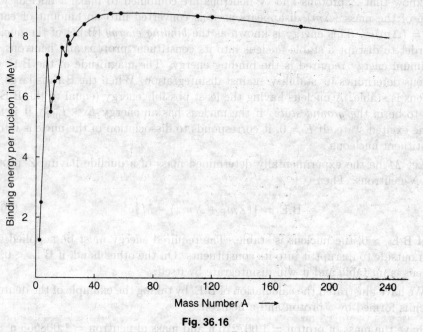

Fig. 36.16

36.19.2 Packing Fraction

The ratio between the mass defect (Δm) and the mass number (A) is termed as the packing fraction (f). We can thus write,

$$f = \Delta m / A. \qquad (36.32)$$

Hence, packing fraction is the mass defect per nucleon. As atomic masses are measured relative to C-12, the packing fraction for this isotope becomes zero. Alternately, we can say that the packing fraction is a measure of the comparative stability of the atom and we can define,

$$\text{Packing fraction} = \frac{\text{Isotopic mass} - \text{Mass number}}{\text{Mass number}} \times 10^4.$$

Packing fraction f may have either a negative or a positive sign. If f is negative, the isotopic mass is less than the mass number and in that case, some mass gets transformed into energy in the formation of that nucleus, in accordance with Einstein's equation $E = mc^2$. Such nuclei become more stable. A positive f, on the other hand, would imply a tendency towards instability.

In Fig. 36.17 we have plotted packing fraction against the corresponding mass numbers of different elements. The figure shows that helium, carbon and oxygen atoms of mass numbers 4, 12 and 16 respectively do not fall on this curve as their packing fractions have small values. These elements are all stable. The transition elements, with mass numbers around 45, have lowest f with a negative sign indicating their high stability. The packing fraction beyond mass number 200 is positive and increases with increase in mass number, thus indicating an increasing instability. Elements with mass numbers more than 230 are radioactive and undergo spontaneous disintegration.

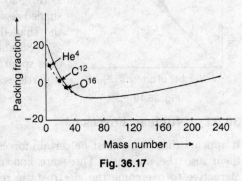

Fig. 36.17

36.20 Nuclear Stability

Table 36.3 reveals how the 272 stable nuclei found in nature. They are classified according to even and odd numbers of protons neutrons.

Table 36.3 : Stable nuclei

Protons	Neutrons	Stable Nuclides
even	even	160
even	odd	56
odd	even	52
odd	odd	4
		272

The table shows that the nucleus formed by combination of an even number of protons and an even number of neutrons is preferred by nature for stable nuclides.

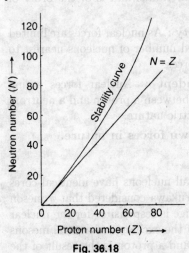

Fig. 36.18

The odd-odd combination of stable nuclides is found only in light elements while the number of even-odd combinations is about the same. A plot of the number of neutrons versus the number of protons for the stable nuclides is exhibited in Fig. 36.18. For $Z < 20$, the stability line is a straight line with $Z = N$. For the heavier nuclides $Z > 20$, $N > 20$ and the stability curve bends in the direction of $N > Z$. As for example, $_{20}\text{Ca}^{48}$ has $N = 28$, $Z = 20$. For larger values of Z, the tendency is more prominent as in the case of $_{91}\text{Pa}^{232}$ which has $N = 141$, $Z = 91$. Thus for large values of Z, the Coulomb electrostatic repulsion has vital role, and then the number of neutrons must be greater to compensate this repulsive effect.

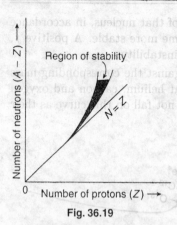

Fig. 36.19

It is seen that the curve departs more and more from the $N = Z$ line as Z increases. For maximum stability, there must be an optimum value of neutron/proton ratio. The number of neutrons $N(= A - Z)$ necessary for maximum stability is plotted as a function of proton number Z (Fig. 36.19). All the stable nuclei fall within the shaded region of the figure. Nuclei above and below the shaded region are unstable. All nuclei with $Z > 83$ and $A > 209$ transform them into lighter ones spontaneously through the emission of α and β particles.

36.21 Nuclear Forces

It appears that there must be certain forces acting between the nucleons that bind them into the nucleus. These are known as *nuclear forces* which are strongly attractive to overcome the electrostatic repulsion between protons. Three kinds of attractive forces can be conceived in the nucleus. These are neutron-neutron (n-n), neutron-proton (n-p) and proton-proton (p-p) interactions. Nuclear forces have the following important characteristics :

(i) **Nuclear forces are effective only at short ranges :** Nuclear forces are appreciable when the distance between nucleons is of the order of 10^{-15} m or less. These distances are known as the *action radii* or *range* of the nuclear forces. It is assumed that interaction between nucleons is accomplished by the exchange of pi-mesons. If m be the rest mass of the pi-meson, then the rest energy of the pi-meson $\Delta E = mc^2$. According to uncertainty principle, the required time for nucleons to exchange π-mesons cannot exceed Δt, for which $\Delta E\,\Delta t \geq h/2\pi$. This distance that a π-meson can move away from a nucleon in the nucleus during the time Δt, is

$$R_0 \approx \frac{h/2\pi}{mc}, \quad \text{where } c \text{ is the velocity}$$
$$\approx 1.2 \times 10^{-15} \text{ m}.$$

This nearly coincides with the value of the nuclear radius and is of the order of magnitude of the nuclear force range.

(ii) **Nuclear forces have saturation property :** As nuclear forces are limited in range, each nucleon interacts with only a limited number of nucleons nearest to it. This effect is called the *saturation* of nuclear forces.

(iii) **Nuclear forces are charge-independent :** Nuclear forces acting between two protons, or between two neutrons, or between a proton and a neutron, are identical. Thus nuclear forces are of a non-electric nature.

(iv) **Nuclear forces are the strongest known forces in nature.**

36.21.1 Meson Theory of Nuclear Forces

According to the meson theory of nuclear forces, all nucleons have identical cores surrounded by a "cloud" of one or more mesons. Yukawa considered that π-meson is exchanged between the nucleons and this exchange is responsible for the nuclear binding forces. The forces that act are the result of the exchange of neutral mesons (π°) between them. The force between a neutron and a proton is the result of the exchange of charged mesons (π^+ and π^-) between them. Thus a neutron emits a π^--meson and is converted into a proton,

$$n \rightarrow p + \pi^-.$$

Again, the absorption of the π^--meson by the proton converts it into a neutron,

$$p + \pi^- \rightarrow n.$$

On the other hand, in the reverse process, a proton emits a π^+-meson becoming a neutron, and π^+-meson which subsequently becomes a proton,

$$p \rightarrow n + \pi^+$$
$$n + \pi^+ \rightarrow p.$$

So we can say that in the nucleus of an atom, attractive forces exist between (i) proton and proton, (ii) proton and neutron, and (iii) neutron and neutron. These forces of attraction are greater than the electrostatic force of repulsion between the protons and so a stability to the nucleus is the result.

Yukawa assumed the equation for particle of mass m as

$$\left(\nabla^2 - \frac{m^2 c^2}{(h/2\pi)^2} - \frac{1}{c^2} \frac{\delta^2}{t^2} \right) \phi = 0. \tag{36.33}$$

Eq. (36.33) is a relativistic equation valid only for spinless particles. If we separate the time-dependent part, the equation for the radial part becomes

$$(\nabla^2 - \mu^2)\phi(r) = 0. \tag{36.34}$$

[where $\mu = mc/(h/2\pi)$].

The solution of Eq (36.34) may be written as

$$\phi(r) = -g \frac{e^{-\mu r}}{r}, \tag{36.35}$$

where g is a constant. The constant g plays the same role as the charge q in electromagnetic theory. In analogy with electromagnetism, the potential between two nucleons can be expressed as

$$V(r) = -g^2 \frac{e^{-\mu r}}{r}, \tag{36.36}$$

where g^2 is the 'coupling constant'. This argument helped Yukawa to predict the existence of pion as a quantum of nuclear force field.

The range of the pion field $= \dfrac{h/2\pi}{m_\pi c} \approx 1.4$ fm.

The form of $V(r)$ as expressed in Eq. (36.36) is known as the *one-pion-exchange potential*.

If Δt be the time interval between the emission of meson from one nucleon and the absorption by the other nucleon, then we can write,

$$\Delta t = R/c$$

or, $$\Delta E = \frac{(h/2\pi)}{\Delta t}. \tag{36.37}$$

Hence, the minimum meson mass can be specified by $m \geq \dfrac{(h/2\pi)}{Rc}$.

Again, in terms of the electronic mass m_e, the mass of the meson is obtained as

$$\frac{m}{m_e} = \frac{h/2\pi}{m_e Rc} = \frac{1.054 \times 10^{-34}}{(9.108 \times 10^{-31})(1.4 \times 10^{-15})(3 \times 10^8)} = 275. \qquad (36.38)$$

So the mass of the meson $\approx 275\times$ mass of electron.

36.22   Interaction between Energetic Particles and Matter

(a) Heavy charged particles : Heavy charged particles like proton, α-particle or fission fragment have a definite range in a solid, liquid, or gas. The particle loses energy mainly by the excitation and ionization of atoms in its path which occurs in a large number of small increments. The primary particle has a large momentum and as a result its direction is usually not changed during the slowing process. The energy loss per unit length $(-dE/dx)$ is known as the *stopping power*. The rate $(-dE/dx)$ at which a heavy particle of charge Ze and speed v loses energy in an absorber of atomic number Z containing N atoms per unit volume whose average ionization energy is I can be expressed as

$$-\frac{dE}{dx} = \frac{z^2 e^4 N Z}{4\pi\varepsilon_0^2 m_0 v^2}\left[\ln\left(\frac{2m_0 v^2}{I}\right) - \ln\left(1 - \frac{v^2}{c^2}\right) - \frac{v^2}{c^2}\right], \qquad (36.39)$$

where m_0 is the electron rest mass.

Integrating Eq. (36.39) the range can be calculated over the energies of the particle as

$$R = \int_T^0 \left(-\frac{dE}{dx}\right)^{-1} dE. \qquad (36.40)$$

(b) Absorption of γ-rays : The interaction of γ-rays with matter is different from that of charged particles like α- or β-particles. γ-rays being extremely penetrating, they are able to pass through considerable thicknesses of matter. γ-rays reveal an exponential absorption in matter. If radiation of intensity, I, is incident on an absorbing layer of thickness, dx, then the amount of radiation absorbed, dI, is proportional to dx and I. So we can write,

$$dI = -\mu I dx$$

or, $I = I_0 e^{-\mu x}$ $[I_0 = \text{initial intensity}]$, $\qquad (36.41)$

where μ is the constant of proportionality and it depends on the property of the medium, μ is known as *linear absorption coefficient*. The mass absorption coefficient, μ_m, is obtained by dividing μ by the density of the medium, i.e., $\mu_m = \pi/\rho$. Eq. (36.41) gives the intensity of the beam after traversing a thickness x of the homogeneous material. At low energies from 0.1 MeV to 25 MeV, three important processes are there through which γ photons are absorbed by matter. These three processes are illustrated in Fig. 36.20.

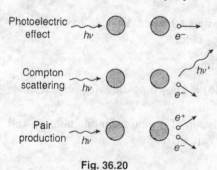

Fig. 36.20

(c) Electrons : Electrons interact through Coulomb scattering from atomic electrons, just like heavy charged particles. There are, however, a number of important differences :

(1) Electrons travel at relativistic speeds.

(2) Electrons will suffer large deflections in collisions with other electrons and, therefore, will follow erratic paths. The range will, therefore, be very different from the length of the path that the electron follows.

(3) Very energetic electrons ($E > 1$ MeV) lose an appreciable fraction of their energies by producing continuous X-rays (also called *Bremsstrahlung*). The cross-section for this process increases with increasing E.

(i) Photoelectric effect : In the process, γ-rays knock out electrons from inside the atoms of the absorbing material, causing ionization of the atoms and the emission of fluorescent radiations. For the photoelectrons the Einstein's equation can be expressed as

$$\frac{1}{2}mv_K^2 = h\nu - W_K, \quad \frac{1}{2}mv_L^2 = h\nu - W_L, \ldots, \text{etc.,}$$

where $h\nu$ is the photon energy, v_K, v_L represent the velocities of the photoelectrons arising in the $K, L, \ldots$ shells, and $W_K, W_L, \ldots$ are the binding energies of $K, L, \ldots$ shells.

(ii) Pair production : In the process, the photon disappears for converting to an electron-positron pair. The process occurs only when the photon energy becomes greater than $2m_0c^2$ and occurs in the presence of a nuclear field. In this process, the nucleus recoils conserving momentum. However, the K.E. carried out by the nucleus is negligible owing to its large mass in comparison to the electron. If photon energy is in excess of $2m_0c^2$, it is shared as K.E. by the product particles.

(iii) Compton effect : The process is elastic scattering where the photon imparts energy to an electron. If a photon of energy $h\nu$ strikes the free electron, the photon with reduced energy $h\nu'$ is scattered at an angle θ with the direction of incident photon and the electron recoils at an angle ϕ. The energy absorbed by these Compton electrons is only a small part of the total energy of the incident γ-rays.

When the photon energies is low, the photoelectric effect is the main mechanism of energy loss which decreases with increasing energy. Compton scattering is dominant at photon energies of a few tens of keV while the pair production is likely when the photon energy exceeds the threshold of 1.02 MeV. Fig. 36.21 is a graph of the linear attenuation coefficient for photons in lead as a function of photon energy is shown in Fig. 36.21. The contributions to μ of the photoelectric effect, Compton scattering and pair production are clearly noticed in the figure.

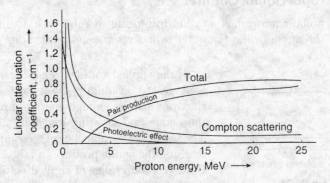

Fig. 36.21

36.23   Ionization Chamber

Charged sub-atomic particles can ionize gases. The number of ion-pairs so produced gives information of the incident particles and also on their energy.

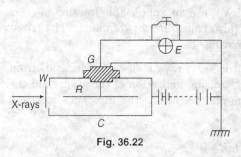

Fig. 36.22

The ionization chamber shown in Fig. 36.22 consists of a hollow metallic cylinder C, closed at both ends, with a window W at an end for the entry of the ionizing particles or radiations. A metal rod R insulated from the cylinder is coaxially mounted within the cylinder and is connected to a quadrant electrometer E where a p.d. of several hundred volts is maintained. An earthed guard ring G opposes leakage of charge from the cylinder to the rod. The chamber contains sulphur dioxide or methyl bromide gas. When a charged particle enters the chamber, it creates a large number of ion pairs in the enclosed gas along its path. All the positive ions move towards R and the negative ions towards C. The electrometer E is used to measure the rate of positive charge deposition on the metal rod R.

The ionization currents produced in the process are of very small value. It is of the order of 10^{-12} to 10^{-15} ampere which can be measured by amplifying devices or by using a very special type of electrometer. If individual particles are counted, then the pulses of current produced are fed to a pulse amplifier joining the ionization chamber by a coupling capacitor (Fig. 36.23).

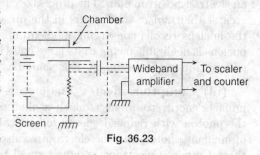

Fig. 36.23

Ionization chambers are used for studying α-particles, β-particles, protons, electrons and nuclei of lighter elements. They are also used in the studies of cosmic-ray phenomena and to measure X-rays and γ-rays.

However, an ionization chamber is less sensitive to β-particles as β-particles produce fewer pairs of ions in their passage through the chamber. In order to detect γ-rays, an ionization chamber of thick wall made of high atomic-number material (Pt, Bi) is used.

36.24   Proportional Counter

The proportional counter has a cylindrical gas-filled tube with a thin central wire to serve as the anode while the outer cylinder serves as a cathode. This is shown in Fig. 36.24.

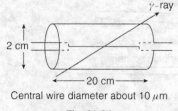

Fig. 36.24

If the applied voltage to an ionization chamber is increased gradually by a certain value, the electrons acquire enough energy in moving toward the anode and creating ion pairs along the way. The resulting avalanche of secondary electrons reaching the anode produces a larger output pulse. Up to a certain range of applied voltages, the pulse size is proportional to the original number of ion pairs, and the device is known as a proportional counter. The variation of applied voltage with the ionization current is shown in Fig. 36.25. As the central wire is very thin and the p.d. fairly large, the electric field $E = dV/dr$ at a distance r from the centre is very high. If b be the radius of the cylinder and a be the radius of the wire, then the radial field E at a distance r from the centre is written as

$$E = \frac{V}{r \log_e(b/a)}, \tag{36.42}$$

where V represents the positive voltage of the central wire relative to the outer cylinder. In a proportional counter thus the field strength near the wire is very high. So the electrons travelling towards the wire are rapidly accelerated, and produce additional electrons in that region due to the phenomena of ionization by collision. This process is known as the *gas multiplication*.

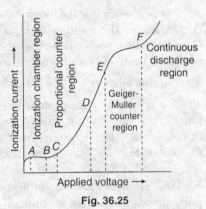

Fig. 36.25

The voltage-pulse characteristics of Fig. 36.25 represent three distinct regions, viz., (i) the ionization chamber region AB, (ii) the proportional counter region CD, and (iii) the Geiger-Muller region EF. After the point F, the tube becomes a simple type of discharge tube. Similar to the ionization chamber, the proportional counter gives single pulses of height proportional to the ionizing power of the radiation.

36.25 Geiger-Muller Counter

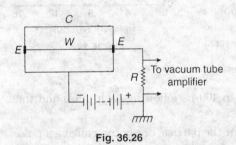

Fig. 36.26

The G-M counter has a metal chamber C containing air or some other gas at a pressure of about 10 cm of Hg. A fine tungsten wire (W) is stretched along the axis of the tube. This is insulated by ebonite plugs E and E as shown in Fig. 36.26. The wire is connected to the positive terminal of a high tension battery of about 1000 to 3000 volts through a high resistance R of about 100 megaohms while the negative terminal is connected to the chamber C. The d.c. voltage is made slightly low than that which will cause a discharge between the electrodes. If an ionizing particle (say an α-particle) enters the counter, ionization occurs and a few ions are produced. When the applied p.d. is sufficiently strong, these ions are multiplied by further collisions. As a result an avalanche of electron moves towards the central wire and flows through the resistance R. The critical potential is suddenly lowered to cause a sudden discharge through the resistance R. The p.d. so developed across R is amplified by vacuum tube circuits and is made to operate a mechanical counter. Thus single particles can be registered. The sudden pulse of discharge sweeps away the ions from the chamber and as a result the counter becomes ready to register the arrival of the next particle.

In Fig. 36.27, the voltage count rate characteristic of a G-M counter is shown. This plot is done by considering the counting rate against the counter potential

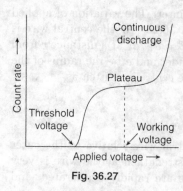

Fig. 36.27

with a radioactive source placed close to the counter. The figure shows that there is a threshold voltage of value few hundred volts below which the tube does not work. With the increase of the applied voltage, the counting starts and rises rapidly to a flat portion of the curve known as *plateau*. At this region, the counting rate is independent of small changes in p.d. across the tube. Beyond the plateau region, the applied voltage becomes so high that a continuous discharge takes place in the tube as evident from the figure when the count rate rapidly increases.

The efficiency of the counter may be defined as the ratio of the observed counts/sec to the number of ionizing particles entering the counter per second. Counting efficiency is thus the ability of its counting, if at least one ion pair is produced in it. We can therefore write,

counting efficiency, $\quad \epsilon = 1 - e^{slp}$, $\qquad\qquad\qquad$ (36.43)

where s = specific ionization at one atmosphere, l = path length of the ionization particle in the counter and p = pressure in atmospheres. The efficiency ϵ of a counter is plotted in Fig. 36.28 as a function of pressure for air and hydrogen.

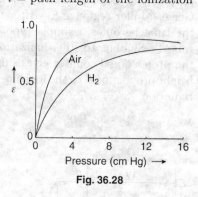

Fig. 36.28

The transistorised counter set-up is a portable one and serves for mineral prospecting, besides its several other applications in cosmic-ray study. As in a G-M counter the pulse height remains constant over a range of applied voltages, the power supply does not have to be precisely regulated. Also, the pulse being several volts in height, no amplifier is required.

Disadvantages of G-M Counter

(1) It is insensitive for a period of 200 to 400 μs following each pulse and thus prevents its use at very high counting rates.

(2) It is unable provide information about the particle or photon causing a pulse.

36.26   Wilson Cloud Chamber

As shown in Fig. 36.29, it consists of a large cylindrical chamber A, with walls and ceiling made of glass. The chamber contains dust-free air saturated with water vapour. When the piston P working inside the chamber moves down rapidly, adiabatic expansion of the air inside the chamber takes place. The piston is then connected to a large evacuated vessel F through a valve V. If the valve is opened, the air under the piston rushes into the evacuated vessel F, causing the piston to drop suddenly. The wooden blocks W and W reduce the air space inside the piston and water at the bottom ensures saturation in the chamber. By altering the height of the piston, the expansion ratio may be adjusted.

When the gas in the expansion chamber is subjected to sudden expansion, the ionizing particles are shot into the chamber through a side window. As a result, a large number of fine droplets are formed on all the ions produced by the ionizing particles. All these droplets produce a track of the moving ionizing particles. The expansion chamber is then illuminated by a powerful beam of light L and two cameras C and C are used to photograph the tracks. The process of expansion, shooting of the ionizing particles into the expansion chamber, illuminating the chamber and clicking the camera must be carried out very fast for getting better results. The ionizing agent can be identified conveniently from its path in the cloud chamber.

It may be pointed out that α-particles, being comparatively massive, go straight and their paths are thick, straight and sharply defined,

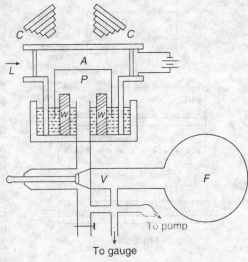

Fig. 36.29

while β-particles, being lighter, are deflected by collision and their paths are thin and crooked. The cloud chamber has led to the discovery of many elementary particles such as meson, positron, etc.

Advantages

(1) Cloud chambers are used for investigating the variation of specific ionization along the track of a charged particle and the range of such particles.

(2) The sign of the electric charge as well as the momentum p of the particle can be obtained if the chamber is placed in a strong magnetic field. Consider a particle of mass m and charge q moving with a velocity v perpendicular to the direction of the magnetic field of flux density B. The particle will be forced by the field to follow a circular path of radius R. The magnetic force Bqv is balanced by the centrifugal force mv^2/R. We can write,

$$Bqv = mv^2/R \quad \text{or} \quad mv = p = BRq. \qquad (36.44)$$

If the rest mass energy m_0c^2 of the particle is known, then we may calculate the kinetic energy of the particle by using the relation,

$$\text{K.E.} = E_k = \sqrt{[p^2c^2 + (m_0c^2)^2]} - m_0c^2. \qquad (36.45)$$

Limitations

(1) We may not always be certain of the sense of track photographed.

(2) There remains some uncertainty always about the nature of the nuclei constituting the arms of the forked tracks.

(3) The range of the particle may exceed the dimensions of the chamber when the whole track is not photographed.

36.27 Diffusion Cloud Chamber

A cloud chamber needs a definite time to recover after an expansion and so it is unsuitable to have a continuous record of events taking place in the chamber. This difficulty was removed in the diffusion cloud chamber. The apparatus is shown in Fig. 36.30. It consists of a chamber containing a heavy gas kept warm at the top

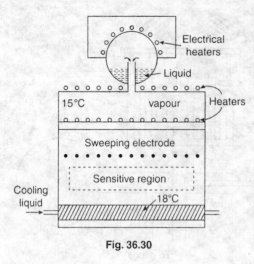

Fig. 36.30

and cold at the bottom. This thermal gradient is maintained between the bottom and top of the chamber by external heating or cooling. The methyl alcohol liquid vaporises in the warm region, where the vapour pressure is high. The vapour diffuses downwards continuously where the vapour pressure is low and thus causes condensation. Near the base, the supersaturation factor is high and condensation occurs around the available ions. The chamber remains sensitive to ionize particles until the supply of the volatile liquid is exhausted. The system is strongly illuminated and by using sensitive camera the track of the particle is photographed.

36.28 Bubble Chamber

Usually, the liquid boils with the evolution of bubbles of vapour at the boiling point. When the liquid is heated under a high pressure to a temperature well above its normal boiling point, a sudden release of pressure will leave the liquid in a superheated state. If then an ionizing particle is allowed to pass through the liquid within a few milliseconds, the ions left in the track of a particle act as condensation centres for the formation of vapour bubbles. The vapour bubbles grow at a rapid rate to attain a visible size in a time of the order of 10 to 100 μsec. In a bubble chamber, a vapour bubble forms in a superheated liquid, while in a cloud chamber, a liquid drop forms in a supersaturated vapour.

In Fig. 36.31, a liquid hydrogen bubble chamber, operating at a temperature of 27 K is shown. A box of thick glass walls is filled with liquid hydrogen. It is connected to the expansion pressure system. For maintaining the chamber at constant temperature, it is surrounded by liquid nitrogen and liquid hydrogen shields. High energy particles are allowed to enter the chamber through the side window W. A sudden release of pressure from the expansion valve is done. It is followed by strong light flash and sensitive camera to take the stereoscopic view of the chamber.

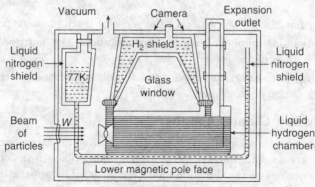

Fig. 36.31

The incoming beam triggers the chamber and the charge of the tracks can be identified by the direction of their curvature in the magnetic field applied over the bubble chamber. Analysing the curvature and length of the track, the momentum and energy of the particle can be determined. The bubble chamber is utilized for investigating particle interaction and also to detect very high energy particles.

Advantages

(1) The density of a liquid is large compared to a gas and so the chances of collision of a high energy particle with a molecule of the liquid are greater. Thus there is a greater chance of their track being recorded. The chances of recording events like cosmic-ray phenomena are significantly improved in comparison to cloud chambers.

(2) The bubble chamber is very sensitive even to particles of low ionizing power.

(3) The bubbles grow rapidly and consequently the tracks are not likely to get distorted due to convection currents in the liquid.

36.29   Spark Chamber

A spark chamber has a set of conducting plates alternately connected to a source of high d.c. voltage. This is shown in Fig. 36.32.

The chamber is first filled with an inert gas. High voltages are suddenly applied to alternate plates (the others are left at ground potential), causing a very high electric fields across the gaps. As a result electrical breakdown occurs along the trails of ions. The trajectory of a given particle through the system is marked by a series of sparks, and the spark-trails are photographed stereoscopically. When the chamber is located in a magnetic field, the charge and momentum of the particle can be determined from the curvature of the track.

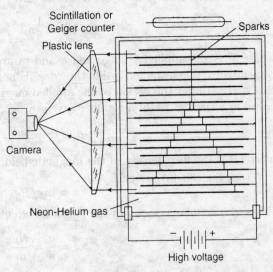

Fig. 36.32

The spark chamber has a very important advantage over the bubble chamber. A bubble chamber can be rendered sensitive for only a very short time and thus rare events can be missed. The spark chamber can be used suitably for that purpose.

36.30   Cyclotron

The cyclotron consists of two hollow semicircular metal boxes, D_1, D_2, called "dees," as shown in Fig. 36.33. A source of ions is located near the mid-point of the gap between the "dees" which are insulated from each other and are enclosed in another vaccum chamber. The "dees" are connected to a powerful radio-frequency oscillator, as shown. The whole arrangement is kept between the pole-pieces of a strong electromagnet in a manner so that the magnetic field is perpendicular to the plane of the "dees."

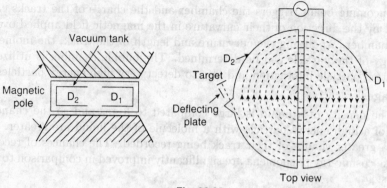

Vacuum tank

Magnetic pole

D_2 D_1

D_2

Target

Deflecting plate

D_1

Top view

Fig. 36.33

Principle

Let a positive ion leave the ion source at the centre of the chamber at the instant when the "dees", D_1 and D_2, are at the maximum negative and positive a.c. potentials respectively. As a result the positive ion will be accelerated towards the negative dee D_1 before entering it. We assume that the ions enter the space inside the dee with a velocity v. Then we have,

$$Ve = \frac{1}{2}mv^2,$$

where V is the applied voltage and e and m are the charge and mass of the ion respectively. When the ion inside the "dee" is not accelerated as there is no field in this space. Under the action of the applied magnetic field, the ions inside the dee, travel in a circular path of radius r given by

$$mv^2/r = Bev, \qquad (36.46)$$

where B is the flux density of the magnetic field.

From Eq. (36.46), we get

$$r = mv/Be. \qquad (36.47)$$

Hence the angular velocity of the ion in its circular path,

$$\omega = \frac{v}{r} = \frac{Be}{m}. \qquad (36.48)$$

Also, the time taken by the ion to travel the semicircular path,

$$t = \frac{\pi}{\omega} = \frac{\pi m}{Be}. \qquad (36.49)$$

Now, let the strength of the field (B) or the frequency of the oscillator (f) be so adjusted that by the time the ion has described a semicircular path to enter just in the space between D_1 and D_2, D_2 has become negative with respect to D_1. The ion is then accelerated towards D_2 to enter the space inside it with a higher velocity. As the ion is moving with higher velocity, it will describe a semicircle of greater radius in the second "dee." But from the equation $t = \pi m/Be$, we find that the time taken by the ion to describe a semicircle is independent of both the radius of the path (r) and the velocity of the ion (v). So the ion describes all semicircles in same time irrespective of their radii. The process will continue until the ion reaches the periphery of the dees. The ion thus spirals round in circles of increasing radii to acquire high energy and will finally come out of the dees through the window in the direction indicated.

Energy of ion

If r_{max} be the radius of the outermost orbit described by the ion and v_{max} be the maximum velocity gained by the ion in its final orbit, then the equation for the motion of the ion in a magnetic field can be expressed as

$$Bev_{max} = \frac{mv_{max}^2}{r_{max}} \quad \text{or,} \quad v_{max} = B\frac{e}{m}r_{max}. \tag{36.50}$$

Hence the energy of the ion,

$$E = \frac{1}{2}mv_{max}^2 = \frac{B^2 r_{max}^2}{2}\left(\frac{e^2}{m}\right). \tag{36.51}$$

Now, the condition for acceleration of the ion in the inter-dee gap is that the time taken by the ion to travel the semicircular path = half the time period of oscillation of the applied high frequency voltage.

We may thus write,

$$\frac{\pi m}{Be} = \frac{T}{2} \quad \text{or,} \quad T = \frac{2\pi m}{Be}. \tag{36.52}$$

Hence the frequency of the oscillator,

$$f = \frac{1}{T} = \frac{Be}{2\pi m}v. \tag{36.53}$$

Thus the energy of the ion is given by

$$E = 2\pi^2 r_{max}^2 \text{ fm.} \tag{36.54}$$

In an actual case the particles are ejected out of the cyclotron as pulsed streams and not continuously.

Limitations of the Cyclotron

The energies to which particles can be accelerated in a cyclotron are limited by the relativistic increase of mass with velocity. The mass m of a particle, when moving with a velocity v is given by

$$m = \frac{m_0}{\sqrt{1 - v^2/c^2}},$$

where m_0 is the rest mass and c the velocity of light.

From Eq. (36.49), we find that the time taken by the ion to travel the semicircular path,

$$t = \frac{\pi m}{Be} = \frac{T}{2}.$$

Therefore, the frequency of the ion,

$$n = \frac{1}{T} = \frac{Be}{2\pi m} \quad \text{or,} \quad n = \frac{Be\sqrt{1 - v^2/c^2}}{2\pi m_0}. \tag{36.55}$$

Hence the frequency of rotation of the ion decreases with increase in velocity. It is seen that the ions take longer time for describing their semi-circular paths than the fixed period of the oscillating electric field. So the ions lag behind the applied potential and finally they are not accelerated. For this reason, the energy of the ions produced by the cyclotron is limited. This limitation can be overcome by two ways :

(a) Field variation : The frequency of the ion is kept constant by increasing the magnetic field (B) at a rate so that the product $B\sqrt{1 - v^2/c^2}$ remains constant. For this, the value of the magnetic field B should be increased as velocity of the ion increases, so that the product $B\sqrt{1 - v^2/c^2}$ remains unaltered. This type of instrument in which the frequency of electric field is maintained constant and magnetic field is changed is called synchrotron.

(b) Frequency modulation : In the second method, the frequency of the applied a.c. is varied so that it becomes equal to the frequency of rotation of the ion. This type of instrument in which magnetic field is maintained constant and the frequency of the applied electric field is altered is called a *frequency modulated cyclotron* or *synchrocyclotron.*

36.31   Synchrocyclotron

It is a modified form of cyclotron. It consists of only one dee placed in a vacuum chamber between the poles of an electromagnet as shown in Fig. 36.34. Instead of the second dee, there is a metal sheet which is earth-connected. Alternating p.d. is applied between the dee and the metal plate (Fig. 36.35). This applied alternating potential to the "dee" is made to rise and fall periodically, instead of remaining constant and the frequency is varied at a rate so that the ion lags a little for increase in mass due to the increase in velocity. The electric field frequency also lags in variation and the particle always enters the dee at the correct moment when it experiences maximum acceleration.

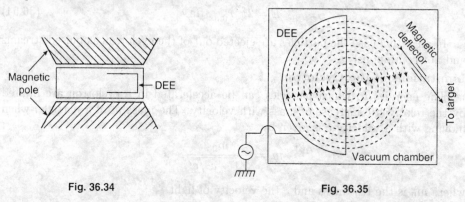

Fig. 36.34   Fig. 36.35

Advantage of using one dee in a synchrocyclotron is that it leaves sufficient space in the vacuum chamber for the ion source and the target. The shape of the pole-pieces of the magnet are to be chosen properly so that the field decreases outwards from the centre.

36.32   Betatron

Betatron is an instrument used to accelerate beta particles to very high energies. Its action depends on the principle of a transformer.

It has a doughnut-shaped vacuum chamber kept between the pole-pieces of an electromagnet which is energized by an alternating current. The magnet produces a very strong magnetic field in the doughnut. The electrons produced by the electron gun (FG) are allowed to move in a circular orbit of constant radius in the vacuum chamber (Fig. 36.36). The magnetic field changes slowly in comparison to the frequency of revolution of the electrons in the equilibrium orbit. The varying

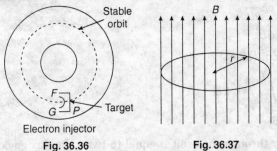

Fig. 36.36   Fig. 36.37

magnetic field which is acting parallel to the axis of the vacuum tube, produces two distinct effects on the electrons. These are, (i) The changing flux owing to the electromagnet produces the induced e.m.f. which is responsible to accelerate the electrons. (ii) The field of the magnet serves to bend the electrons in a circular path in the chamber and thus confine them to the region of the changing flux.

Principle

Let the electron be moving in an orbit of radius r, and ϕ be the flux linked with the orbit (Fig. 36.37). The flux increases at the rate $d\phi/dt$ and the induced e.m.f. in the orbit can be expressed as

$$E = -\frac{d\phi}{dt}. \tag{36.55}$$

Hence the work done on an electron of charge e in one revolution

$$G = Ee = -e\frac{d\phi}{dt}. \tag{36.56}$$

If F be the tangential electric force acting on the orbiting electron, then the work done on the electron in one revolution $= F \times 2\pi r$ [since for one revolution, the path length is $2\pi r$].

So we can write,

$$F \times 2\pi r = -e\frac{d\phi}{dt} \quad \text{or,} \quad F = -\frac{e}{2\pi r}\frac{d\phi}{dt}. \tag{36.57}$$

The velocity of the electron will increase by the above force and will try to move into an orbit of larger radius. Due to the presence of the magnetic flux perpendicular to the plane of the electron orbit, the electron will experience an inward radial force. We can therefore write,

$$Bev = mv^2/r, \tag{36.58}$$

where B is the value of the magnetic field intensity at the electron orbit of constant radius r, m = mass of the electron and v = velocity of the electron. From Eq. (36.58) we have

the momentum of the electron $= mv = Ber$ (36.59)

Now, from Newton's second law of motion, we get

$$F = \frac{d}{dt}(mv) = er\frac{dB}{dt}. \tag{36.60}$$

In order to maintain the constant radius of the orbit, the values of F given in Eqs. (36.57) and (36.60) must be numerically equal. Hence we can write,

$$\frac{e}{2\pi r}\frac{d\phi}{dt} = er\frac{dB}{dt}$$

or, $d\phi = 2\pi r^2 dB$.   (36.61)

Integrating Eq. (36.61),

$$\int_0^\phi d\phi = \int_0^B 2\pi r^2 dB$$

or, $\phi = 2\pi r^2 B$.   (36.62)

Thus the flux through the orbit is equal to twice the flux enclosed by the orbit, if the magnetic field were to be uniform over the area. Eq. (36.62) represents the condition under which a betatron works and is known as *betatron condition*. This distribution of magnetic flux can be obtained by the special pole-pieces where the magnetic field is higher at the centre of the orbit than at its circumference.

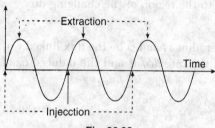

Fig. 36.38

The variation of magnetic field with time is shown in Fig. 36.38. During the time by which the magnetic field attains its peak value, the electrons make several thousand revolutions and get accelerated. If they are permitted to revolve any more, the decreasing magnetic field would retard the electrons. So, the electrons can be extracted at this stage by an auxiliary magnetic field to deflect them from normal course. The high energy electron beam can be used to strike the target, generating X-rays. Also, the electrons can be made to emerge out and may be used suitably for transmutation work.

36.33   Variable Energy Cyclotron

The cyclotron when accelerates a given particle to a fixed energy are known as fixed energy cyclotron. This can be modified by a variable energy cyclotron for getting improved performance. The Bhaba Atomic Research Centre (BARC) situated at Kolkata (Salt Lake area) has set up such a variable energy cyclotron. If protons are accelerated beyond 25 MeV, synchronization between the electric field and the revolution time of the ion in a magnetic field does not hold good. Using auxiliary coils, known as

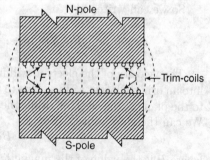

Fig. 36.39

trim-coils, the magnetic field can be increased towards the periphery of the circular pole face. This is shown in Fig. 36.39. The resulting defocusing tendency of the circulating ion beam is then required to correct. This is done by dividing the pole-gap azimuthally into alternate regions of strong and weak fields and then attaching sector-shaped steel piece over the pole faces of the magnet. Machines so constructed are called AVF (Azimuthally Varying Field) cyclotron or sector focused cyclotron.

The 224 cm AVF cyclotron developed at BARC delivers a beam of high energy particles. It delivers protons of energy between 6 to 60 MeV, deuterons between 12 to 65 MeV and α-particles between 25 to 130 MeV. This energy can be changed by changing the magnetic field as well as the radio-frequency of electric field used for acceleration. That is why the cyclotron is called variable energy cyclotron and popularly known as VEC. Its design at BARC Kolkata is based on some improvement of the 88-inch cyclotrons of the Lawrence Barkeley Laboratory. The VEC is suitable for advanced research in the field of nuclear physics and solid state physics. It is also used for gathering important information on radiation biology.

36.34 Discovery of Artificial Transmutation and Rutherford's Experiment

Artificial transmutation is the conversion of an element into another by artificial way. Rutherford first demonstrated artificial transmutation by a simple apparatus shown in Fig. 36.40. It consists of a chamber C; one side of it is a thin sheet of silver foil F. A zinc sulphide screen S is kept close to F and the scintillations on it are seen by a microscope M. The chamber is filled with gas

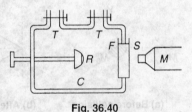

Fig. 36.40

through the side tubes TT. The source of α-particles (RaC$'$) was kept at R on a small disc. The distance of R from the foil F can be varied by a long rod attached to the disc at one end. This is manipulated from outside the chamber. The range of the α-particle used was of about 7 cm, corresponding to an energy of about 8 MeV. The effects produced by the α-particles on different gases can be examined by the scintillations on S.

When the chamber was filled with CO_2 or oxygen no scintillations were noted on the screen when the distance between R and F was greater than the range of the α-particle. But if the chamber was filled with nitrogen, scintillations were noted on the screen even when the distance between R and F was as high as 40 cm. As the α-particles themselves could not penetrate such a distance, one may conclude that scintillations were not caused by the α-particles but by the particles emitted by the nitrogen atoms. From magnetic deflection experiments it was understood that these particles were hydrogen nuclei or protons. From Bohr's theory of the compound nucleus, the reaction can be expressed as

$$_7N^{14} + {_2}He^4 \longrightarrow (_9F^{18}) \longrightarrow {_8}O^{17} + {_1}H^1.$$

$_2He^4 \quad _7N^{14} \qquad _9F^{18}$

$_8O^{17}$ $_1H^1$

Fig. 36.40(a)

In Fig. 36.40(a) the reaction is represented pictorially. The new element so formed was the rare isotope of oxygen with mass number 17. The transmutation of nitrogen into oxygen was thus established first time.

36.35 Bohr's Theory of Nuclear Disintegration

Bohr considered the nucleus as a liquid drop and when a projectile strikes that nucleus, the projectile is captured by the nucleus which is then called a *compound nucleus*. The energy of the projectile is quickly distributed in the compound nucleus and may be considered to exist in a quasi-stationary excitation states. The compound nucleus persists in its excited state until a particular nucleon escapes from the compound nucleus.

A nuclear reaction may be represented as

$$a + X \longrightarrow Y + b.$$

This formula shows that the particle a interacts with the nucleus X to yield the nucleus Y and particle b. The above equation can be abbreviated as

$$X(a, b)Y.$$

We consider an example, $_6\text{C}^{12}(d, n)_7\text{N}^{13}$ which means a reaction between an incident deuteron $(d = _1\text{H}^2)$ and a $_6\text{C}^{12}$ nucleus to produce a $_7\text{N}^{13}$ nucleus with the emission of a neutron.

36.36   The Q-value Equation for a Nuclear Reaction

We assume that a particle of mass M_1 moves with a velocity v_1 to collide with a

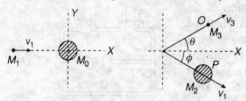

(a) Before collision   **(b) After collision**

Fig. 36.41

target nucleus of mass m_0 at rest [Fig. 36.41(a)]. After collision let the particle O of mass M_3 be emitted with velocity v_3 at an angle θ and the recoiling nucleus P of mass M_2 is emitted with a velocity v_2 at an angle ϕ. From the conservation of linear momentum we can, therefore, write,

$$M_1 v_1 = M_3 v_3 \cos\theta + M_2 v_2 \cos\phi \tag{36.63}$$

$$0 = M_3 v_3 \sin\theta - M_2 v_2 \sin\phi. \tag{36.64}$$

Therefore, $M_2 v_2 \cos\phi = M_1 v_1 - M_3 v_3 \cos\theta \tag{36.65}$

$$M_2 v_2 \sin\phi = M_3 v_3 \sin\theta. \tag{36.66}$$

Squaring and adding Eqs. (36.65) and (36.66), we have

$$M_2^2 v_2^2 = M_1^2 v_1^2 + M_3^2 v_3^2 - 2 M_1 M_3 v_1 v_3 \cos\theta. \tag{36.67}$$

Now, using the kinetic energy relations, we get

$$E_{k_1} = \frac{1}{2} M_1 v_1^2, \quad E_{k_2} = \frac{1}{2} M_2 v_2^2 \quad \text{and} \quad E_{k_3} = \frac{1}{2} M_3 v_3^2$$

Putting these values in Eq. (36.67), we get

$$2 M_2 E_{k_2} = 2 M_1 E_{k_1} + 2 M_3 E_{k_3} - 2(M_1 M_3 E_{k_1} E_{k_3})^{1/2} 2 \cos\theta$$

or, $E_{k_2} = \dfrac{M_1 E_{k_1}}{M_2} + \dfrac{M_3 E_{k_3}}{M_2} - \dfrac{2}{M_2}(M_1 M_3 E_{k_1} E_{k_3})^{1/2} \cos\theta. \tag{36.68}$

We can write,

$$Q = (E_{k_2} + E_{k_3}) - E_{k_1}. \tag{36.69}$$

Putting the value of E_{k_2} from Eq. (36.68) in Eq. (36.69), we get

$$Q = \frac{M_1 E_{k_1}}{M_2} + \frac{M_3}{M_2} E_{k_3} - \frac{2}{M_2}(M_1 M_3 E_{k_1} E_{k_3})^{1/2} \cos\theta + E_{k_3} - E_{k_1}$$

or, $Q = E_{k_3}\left(1 + \dfrac{M_3}{M_2}\right) - E_{k_1}\left(1 - \dfrac{M_1}{M_2}\right) - \dfrac{2}{M_2}(M_1 M_3 E_{k_1} E_{k_3})^{1/2} \cos\theta. \tag{36.70}$

If $\theta = 90°$, $\cos 90° = 0$. So, Eq. (36.70) reduces to

$$Q = E_{k_3}\left(1 + \frac{M_3}{M_2}\right) - E_{k_1}\left(1 - \frac{M_1}{M_2}\right). \tag{36.71}$$

Now, the threshold energy (E_{th}) may be defined as the minimum kinetic energy of the incident particle which will initiate an endoergic reaction. The threshold energy can be calculated using the centre of mass coordinate system. For any collision in centre of mass coordinate system, the linear momentum is always zero before and after the collision. If $E_{k_{1'}}$ be the kinetic energy of the incident particle in centre of mass coordinate system, then an endoergic reaction is possible, if

$$E_{k_{1'}} \geq |Q|. \tag{36.72}$$

Again, if M_{red} be the reduced mass of incident particle and the target nucleus, then we can write,

$$M_{red} = \frac{M_1 M_0}{(M_0 + M_1)}. \tag{36.73}$$

Hence we get,

$$E_{k_{1'}} = \frac{1}{2} M_{red} v_1^2 = \frac{1}{2} \frac{M_1 M_0}{(M_0 + M_1)} v_1^2. \tag{36.74}$$

From Eqs. (36.72) and (36.74), we get

$$\frac{1}{2} \frac{M_1 M_0}{(M_0 + M_1)} v_1^2 \geq |Q| \quad \text{or,} \quad \frac{1}{2} M_1 v_1^2 \geq \left(\frac{M_0 + M_1}{M_0} \right) |Q|.$$

Therefore, the threshold energy,

$$E_{th} = \left(1 + \frac{M_1}{M_0} \right) |Q|. \tag{36.75}$$

36.37 Nuclear Reactions

Some main types of nuclear reaction are discussed below:

(i) **Elastic scattering** : Here the incident particle strikes the target nucleus and leaves without loss of energy. However, its direction may be changed. As an example we may mention the scattering of α-particles from a thin gold foil which follows the reaction

$$_{79}\text{Au}^{197} + {}_2\text{He}^4 \longrightarrow {}_{79}\text{Au}^{197} + {}_2\text{H}^4.$$

(ii) **Inelastic scattering** : Here the incident particle loses a part of its energy to excite the target nucleus to a higher allowed energy level. The excited nucleus subsequently decays to the ground state, radiating the excess energy in the form of a γ-ray photon. As an example we may mention the following reaction:

$$_3\text{Li}^7 + {}_1\text{H}^1 \rightarrow {}_3\text{Li}^{7^*} + {}_1\text{H}^1$$

$$_3\text{Li}^{7^*} \rightarrow {}_3\text{Li}^7 + \gamma.$$

(iii) **Radiative capture** : In this case, the incident particle is captured by the target nucleus to form a new nucleus, which has a considerable excess of energy and decays with the emission on one or more γ-ray photons. An example is given below :

$$_6\text{C}^{12} + {}_1\text{H}^1 \rightarrow {}_7\text{N}^{13^*} \rightarrow {}_7\text{N}^{13} + \gamma.$$

(iv) **Disintegration** : In this case, the incident particle is absorbed by the target nucleus and the ejected particle is a different one. The composition of the resultant nucleus differs from the parent nucleus. An example given below shows the disintegration of beryllium by α-particle producing neutron:

$$_4\text{Be}^9 + _2\text{He}^4 \rightarrow _6\text{C}^{12} + _0n^1.$$

(v) Photodisintegration : If target materials are bombarded with radiations, the resulting compound nuclei are formed in excited states which get rid of the excess excitation energy through neutron emission. An example is given below :

$$_1\text{H}^2 + \gamma \rightarrow _1\text{H}^1 + _0n^1.$$

36.38   Energy Balance in Nuclear Reactions and the Q-value

In nuclear reactions of all types, the total sum of mass and energy is conserved. Let us consider the equation $A + B \rightarrow P + O$, where the target is supposed to be at rest and let its mass be m_1. Also, let the projectile has a mass m_2 and K.E. $= E_2$, the product nucleus has a mass m_3 and K.E. E_3 while the outgoing particle has a mass m_4 and K.E. E_4. The equation representing the conservation of total energy can be expressed as

$$m_1c^2 + m_2c^2 + E_2 = m_3c^2 + E_3 + m_4c^2 + E_4. \tag{36.76}$$

Let us take

$$'Q = E_3 + E_4 - E_2 = (m_1 + m_2 - m_3 - m_4)c^2. \tag{36.77}$$

The quantity Q is known as the *energy balance* or the *Q-value* of the reaction. When Q is positive, the reaction is exothermic or exoergic. As the K.E. of products of transmutation is greater than the K.E. of the reactants, energy is released in the process. When Q is negative, the reaction is endothermic or endoergic. The equation for a nuclear reaction may be written as

$$A + B \rightarrow P + O + Q, \tag{36.78}$$

where Q may be either positive or negative.

36.39   Nuclear Fission

In 1934, Enrico Fermi showed that the bombardment of uranium by neutrons produces β-ray activities with different half-lives. As uranium decays by α-particle emission with a very long half-life, it was considered that transuranic elements $(Z > 92)$ are being formed. In 1938, Hahn and Strassman revealed that one of the radioactive elements produced when uranium is bombarded by neutrons is an isotope of barium, $Z = 56(_{56}\text{Ba}^{141})$. They further noted that barium was accompanied by a radioactive isotope of the gas krypton $(Z = 36)$. The sum of the atomic numbers of these two nuclides is 92, the atomic number of uranium. Meitner and Frisch then suggested that on neutron bombardment, the uranium nucleus splits up into two lighter nuclei Ba and Kr. The process of breaking up of the nucleus of a heavy atom into two fragments with the release of a large amount of energy is known as the *fission*. If uranium is bombarded with neutrons, a uranium nucleus captures a slow neutron thus forming an unstable compound nucleus which splits into two nearly equal parts and some neutrons are released in the process. The equation for the fission process is given by

$$_{92}\text{U}^{235} + _0n^1 \rightarrow _{92}\text{U}^{236*} \rightarrow X + Y + \text{neutrons}. \tag{36.79}$$

Here, $_{92}U^{236*}$ is a highly unstable isotope while X and Y are the fission fragments. Typical fission reactions are given by

$$_{92}U^{235} + _{0}n^{1} \rightarrow _{92}U^{236*} \rightarrow _{56}Ba^{141} + _{36}Kr^{92} + 3_{0}n^{1} + Q \qquad (36.80)$$

$$_{92}U^{235} + _{0}n^{1} \rightarrow _{92}U^{236*} \rightarrow _{54}Xe^{140} + _{38}Sr^{94} + 2_{0}n^{1} + Q. \qquad (36.81)$$

In Eqs. (36.80) and (36.81), Q is the energy released in the reaction. According to Eq. (36.80), when $_{92}U^{235}$ is bombarded by a slow moving neutron, the nucleus becomes unstable $(_{92}U^{236*})$ and splits into $_{56}Ba^{141}$ and $_{36}Kr^{92}$ releasing 3 neutrons and energy Q. This is represented in Fig. 36.42.

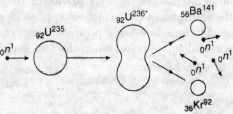

Fig. 36.42

36.39.1 Energy Released in Fission

In nuclear fission, a large amount of energy is released which is produced because the original mass of the nucleus is greater than the sum of the masses of the products produced after fission. The difference of masses before and after fission is converted into energy following to Einstein's equation, $E = mc^2$.

The energy liberated per fission can be calculated in the following way. The fission reaction of $_{92}U^{235}$ is

$$_{92}U^{235} + _{0}n^{1} \rightarrow _{92}U^{236*} \rightarrow _{56}Ba^{141} + _{36}Kr^{92} + 3_{0}n^{1} + Q.$$

We estimate the actual masses before and after the fission reaction.

mass of $_{92}U^{235}$	=	235.045733 u
mass of $_{0}n^{1}$	=	1.008665 u
Hence, total initial mass	=	236.054398 u
Again, mass of $_{56}Ba^{141}$	=	140.9177 u
mass of $_{36}Kr^{92}$	=	91.8854 u
mass of 3 neutrons	=	3.025995 u

Therefore, total final mass = 235.829095 u

$\therefore$ mass decrease = $236.054398 - 235.829095 = 0.2253$ u.

This decrease of mass is converted into energy. Thus,

the energy released = $0.2253 \times 931 = 209.8$ MeV ($\because$ 1 u = 931 MeV).

We find that in the process of fission of one nucleus of uranium, about 200 MeV energy is released.

36.39.2 Bohr and Wheeler's Theory of Nuclear Fission

Bohr and Wheeler explained the nuclear fission considering liquid drop model. A liquid drop is spherical in shape due to internal molecular forces by surface tension (Fig. 36.43). According to Bohr and Wheeler's theory, an excited liquid drop may oscillate in a number of ways. Applying a large external force to the drop, the sphere may change into an ellipsoid. If the external force is sufficiently large, the ellipsoid may again be changed into a dumb-bell shape and ultimately may even break at the narrow end into two portions. One may extend this analogy, to a nucleus which behaves like a liquid drop. If a nucleus absorbs a neutron, it forms a compound nucleus which is highly energetic. The high energy possessed by it comes mainly from the binding energy of the neutron absorbed by it. The extra energy may produce a series of rapid oscillations in the spherical compound nucleus. Due to these oscillations, the shape of the nucleus may change at times from spherical to ellipsoidal, i.e., from shape A to shape B as shown. When the extra energy is large, oscillations may be so violent that stage C and ultimately stage D may be the result when the nucleus is applied like a dumb-bell shaped (stage D). Each bell of the dumb-bell has a positive charge causing a repulsion between them. Stage E is the ultimate result when the fission phenomenon occurs.

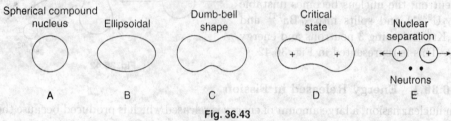

Fig. 36.43

The nuclei that result from fission are called *fission fragments* which are of unequal size. A heavy nucleus undergoes fission when it acquires sufficient excitation energy so that it oscillates violently. Certain nuclei like $_{92}U^{235}$ are excited sufficiently by mere absorption of an individual neutron while other nuclei like $_{92}U^{238}$ require more excitation energy for fission. In facts, $_{92}U^{238}$ undergoes fission only by reaction with fast neutrons whose kinetic energies are greater than 1 MeV.

36.40   Chain Reaction and Natural Uranium

By chain reaction, we mean a self-propagating process in which a number of neutrons goes on rapidly multiplying during fission till whole of fissile material is disintegrated. Two types of chain reactions are possible. In one type, the chain reaction is first accelerated so that the neutrons are built up to a certain level and thereby the number of fission producing neutrons is kept constant. This is called *controlled chain reaction*. A controlled chain reaction is used in nuclear reactors. In other type, the number of neutrons is allowed to multiply indefinitely so that the entire energy is released all at once. This type of reaction takes place in case of atom bombs.

Natural uranium has 99.28% of U^{238} and 0.72% of U^{235}. Since most of the mass of natural uranium consists of U^{238}, the neutrons released during nuclear fission will mostly try to bombard the nuclei of U^{238} and very few will bombard U^{235}. U^{235} undergoes fission by neutrons of low energy like thermal neutrons while U^{238} is fissionable only with fast neutrons of energy more than 1 MeV. Thus very few neutrons can cause fission of U^{238} but neutrons of all possible energies can cause fission of U^{235}. Hence, chain reaction is not possible in natural uranium by simple means.

A chain reaction can be developed in natural uranium, if the fast neutrons from it are quickly reduced to thermal ones before they are lost through non-fission capture in the uranium, as then the chances of the thermal neutron fission of U^{235} go up. Neutrons can be slowed down by distributing among the rods of uranium a material called *moderator*. The purpose of the moderator is to slow down the neutrons produced by fission by elastic collision. Commonly used moderators are heavy water (D_2O), graphite, beryllium oxide, hydrides of metals and organic liquids. The nuclei of these substances absorb very small neutrons.

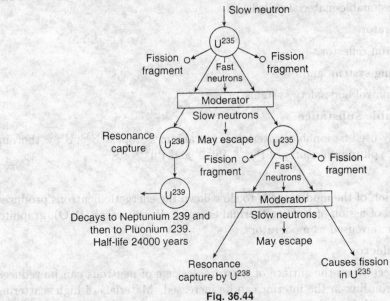

Fig. 36.44

A self-sustaining chain reaction is shown in Fig. 36.44. A slow neutron when bombards a U^{235} nucleus, it breaks into two fragments and in the fission process three fast neutrons are emitted. The neutrons are slowed down by the moderator. One neutron may escape. The second neutron may be captured by U^{238} to form U^{239} which decays to Np^{239} and then to Pu^{239}. The third neutron is still available for carrying on the chain reaction. It bombards U^{235} and the process is continued.

36.41 Atom Bomb

The principle of fission is used in the construction of the atom bomb which consists of two pieces of $_{92}U^{235}$, each smaller than the critical size and a source of neutrons. The two subcritical masses of U^{235} in the form of hemispheres are kept apart by a

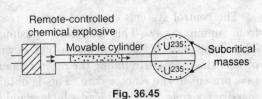

Fig. 36.45

separator aperture as shown in Fig. 36.45. When the bomb has to be exploded, a third cylinder of U^{235} is propelled so that it will fuse together with the other two pieces. As the total quantity of U^{235} is now greater than the critical mass, an uncontrolled chain reaction takes place resulting a terrific explosion in the form of heat, light and radiation. In fact, a temperature of millions of degrees and a pressure of millions of atmospheres are produced. The explosions produce shock waves which spread radioactivity in air and cause loss of life.

36.42 Nuclear Reactors

During the fission of U^{235}, a large amount of energy is released. In a nuclear reactor, the chain reaction is brought about under controlled conditions. When the chain reaction is put under control, then after a lapse of time a steady state is attained when the rate of energy production also attains a constant level. Such a device where energy is released at a given rate is known as a *nuclear reactor*. Nuclear reactor has five main elements. These are :

(i) The fissionable material called *fuel*,

(ii) Moderator,

(iii) Neutron reflector,

(iv) Cooling system, and

(v) The control and safety systems.

The fissionable substance

Commonly used fissionable materials are uranium isotopes U^{233}, U^{235}; thorium isotope Th^{232}; plutonium isotopes Pu^{239}, Pu^{240} and Pu^{241}.

Moderator

The function of the moderator is to slow down the energetic neutrons produced in the process of fission of U^{235} to thermal energies. Heavy water (D_2O), graphite, beryllium, etc. are used as moderators.

Neutron reflector

Using reflectors on the surface of reactors, leakage of neutrons can be reduced and the neutron flux in the interior can be increased. Materials of high scattering cross-section and low absorption cross-section can serve the purpose of good reflectors.

Cooling system

The cooling system removes the heat evolved from the K.E. on the fission fragments in the reactor core. The coolant is pumped through the reactor core and through a heat exchanger, it transfers heat to the secondary thermal system of the reactor.

Control and safety systems

The control systems enable the chain reaction to be controlled and prevent it from running away. This is done by pushing control rods into the reactor core. These rods absorb the neutrons to cut down the reactivity. The safety systems protect the space surrounding the reactor against intensive neutron flux and gamma rays present in the reactor core. This is obtained by surrounding the reactor with massive concrete walls and lead which would absorb neutrons and gamma rays.

36.42.1   Components of a Power Reactor

The heat generated in a nuclear reactor is used to produce power in a nuclear power plant. The components of a power reactor is shown in Fig. 36.46. Uranium in the form of pure metal or solution of a soluble salt in water constitutes the centre of the heat energy source. A huge quantity of heat is produced in the fission process. The cadmium rods regulate the temperature to a pre-determined level. To bring down the temperature, the cadmium rods are pushed down further so as to absorb more neutrons. On the other hand, if the temperature has to be raised, the cadmium rods are pulled up a little. A fluid is circulated through the shielded reactor and heat exchanger to convert water into steam. The steam produced runs turbines to produce electricity.

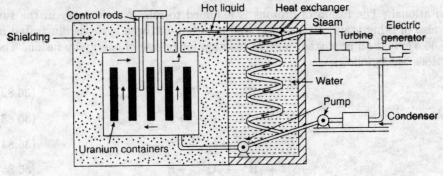

Fig. 36.46

Uses of Nuclear Reactors

(1) **Nuclear power :** Nuclear reactors are utilized in the production of electric energy.

(2) **Production of radioisotopes :** Nuclear reactors can be used in producing a large number of radio-isotopes. For the production of radio-isotope, a suitable compound is drawn into the centre of the reactor core where the flux of neutrons may be more than $10^{16}/m^2/sec$. Sodium-24 is manufactured by this method :

$$_{11}Na^{23} + {}_0n^1 \rightarrow {}_{11}Na^{24*}$$

(3) **Scientific research :** Reactors produce a number of radioactive materials required for research purposes. The reactors may provide a huge source of neutrons which can be used to produce radio-isotopes. The effect of neutrons on biological tissues may also be studied. Reactors may also be used for investigating radiation damage.

36.43   Nuclear Fusion

In the fusion process, two or more light nuclei are combined to form a single heavy nucleus. For example, if four hydrogen nuclei are fused together, a helium nucleus is formed. The mass of the single nucleus so formed is always less than the sum of the masses of the individual light nuclei. The difference in mass is converted into energy following Einstein's equation $E = mc^2$.

We consider a single helium nucleus formed by the fusion of two deuterium nuclei. Mass of $_1H^2 = 2.014102$ u and mass of $_2He^4 = 4.002604$ u.

Now we have
$$_1H^2 + {}_1H^2 \rightarrow {}_2He^4.$$

The initial mass of 2 deuterium atoms $= 2 \times 2.014102 = 4.028204$ u.

Mass of helium atom $= 4.002604$ u.

Hence, decrease in mass $= 4.028204 - 4.002604 = 0.025600$ u.

Therefore, energy released $= 0.025600 \times 931.3$ MeV $= 23.84$ MeV.

So, the energy released in fusion $= 23.84$ MeV.

36.43.1   Source of Stellar Energy

The temperatures of the stars are too high and they radiate a huge amount of energy. The sun is one of the stars. It radiates 3.8×10^{26} joules of energy in each second. The origin of this huge amount of energy is neither chemical nor gravitational. The fusion of protons is assumed to release the energy in the sun and also in other stars. Bethe suggested a carbon-nitrogen cycle as illustrated in Fig. 36.47. It is an important nuclear reaction for release of energy by fusion. The reactions are as follows :

$$_6C^{12} + {}_1H^1 \rightarrow {}_7N^{13*} + \gamma \tag{36.82}$$

$$_7N^{13*} \rightarrow {}_6C^{13} + {}_1e^0 + \nu \tag{36.83}$$

$$_6C^{13} + {}_1H^1 \rightarrow {}_7N^{14} + \gamma \tag{36.84}$$

$$_7N^{14} + {}_1H^1 \rightarrow {}_8O^{15*} + \gamma \tag{36.85}$$

$$_8O^{15*} \rightarrow {}_7N^{15} + {}_1e^0 + \nu \tag{36.86}$$

$$_7N^{15} + {}_1H^1 \rightarrow {}_6C^{12} + {}_2He^4 \tag{36.87}$$

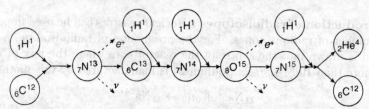

Fig. 36.47

In this cycle C^{12} behaves like a catalyst.

The reaction cycle is :

$$4{}_1H^1 \rightarrow {}_2He^4 + 2{}_1e^0 + 2\nu + Q. \tag{36.88}$$

The loss in mass can be calculated in the following way:

$4{}_1H^1 = 4.031300$; $_2He^4 = 4.002603$ and $2{}_1e^0 = 0.001098$.

Therefore, the loss in mass = 0.02756 u.

∴ energy released = $0.02756 \times 931 = 25.7$ MeV.

It is seen that in one million years the sun loses about 10^{-7} of its mass by the above process. Considering mass of the sun as 2×10^{30} kg and its present age of 10^{10} years, it can be estimated that the C-N cycle may keep going for another 30 billion years.

Proton-proton cycle

Later modification of the estimates of the central temperature of the sun now favours the proton-proton chain. In the *p-p* chain, two protons first fuse to produce a deuterium nucleus. This combines with another proton to yield He^3. Two He^3 nuclei interact to form He^4 and two protons. These reactions can be represented by the equations:

$$_1H^1 + {}_1H^1 \rightarrow ({}_2He^2) \rightarrow {}_1H^2 + {}_1e^0 + \nu + 0.42 \text{ MeV}$$

$$_1H^2 + {}_1H^1 \rightarrow ({}_2He^3) \rightarrow {}_2He^3 + \gamma + 5.5 \text{ MeV}$$

$$\frac{_2He^3 + {}_2He^3 \rightarrow ({}_4Be^6) \rightarrow {}_2He^4 + {}_1H^1 + {}_1H^1 + 12.8 \text{ MeV}}{4{}_1H^1 \rightarrow {}_2He^4 + 2{}_{+1}e^0 + 2\nu + 2\gamma + 26.7 \text{ MeV}} \tag{36.89}$$

36.43.2 Thermonuclear Reactions

We know that the source of stellar energy is fusion. This definitely suggests that a huge amount of energy can be achieved by nuclear fusion. It is of course not too simple to fuse the light nuclei into a single nucleus. The main complexity in the fusion of nuclei is the electric force of repulsion between the positively charged nuclei. Fusion is possible when the K.E. of each of the nuclei is sufficiently large to overcome the repulsion. Fusion reactions occur only at very high temperatures, of the order of 10^7 to 10^9 K. In fact, at a very high temperatures only the nuclei are able to overcome their mutual Coulomb repulsion and enter the zone of nuclear attractive forces. These reactions are known as *thermonuclear reactions.* A star controls thermonuclear fusion in its core due to its strong self-gravity. The thermonuclear reactions in the core of the sun are responsible for the high temperatures which generate strong outward pressures. These act against the sun's own gravity holding it in the equilibrium condition. The equation of stellar structure, established by Eddington, relates the gravitational force in the star to the progressive changes of pressure from its centre outwards. From these equations also stable models of stars emerge and idea of thermonuclear fusion can be extended. Definitely the main role is played by the controlling force of gravity. The large mass of an astronomical system makes the gravity most important to study its behaviour.

Hydrogen bomb

It is a device where the principle of nuclear fusion is used. The very high temperature essential for an uncontrolled thermonuclear reaction may be obtained by the detonation of an atom bomb. In this weapon, the hydrogen is at the core. The fission bomb creates a very high temperature, at which thermonuclear reactions start causing the fusion of hydrogen nuclei to form helium. Sufficiently higher energy per unit mass is achieved from a hydrogen bomb in comparison to a nuclear fission bomb.

36.43.3 Controlled Thermonuclear Reactions

A huge amount of energy can be released in a fraction of a second in a hydrogen bomb. If the thermonuclear reaction could be controlled in a manner so that the process occurs slowly, then the energy released may be used for constructive purposes. We know that the main problem is to produce a high temperature in a nuclear fusion process and to find a container for the gas which can stand this temperature. At this temperature the gas is ionized highly and is called *plasma.* Now, one of the major problems is to design a "container" where a very hot plasma can be contained under high pressure to initiate a fusion reaction. For this purpose a speciality as shown in Fig. 36.48 can be used. By changing the shape of the field and increasing the value the plasma in the "magnetic bottle" can be raised to the required temperature and pressure for fusion reactions.

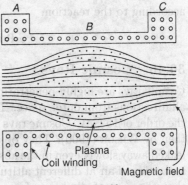

Fig. 36.48

Nuclear fusion as an energy source has high possibilities due to the following causes :

(i) Hydrogen is everywhere available on this planet in various forms.

(ii) A fusion reactor does not leave behind as in fission reactor radioactive waste, the disposal of which poses severe problems.

(iii) Due to the lightness of the reactant nuclei, the energy per unit mass of the reacting material becomes greater than that in nuclear fission process.

36.44   Transuranic Elements

Elements with atomic numbers greater than uranium ($Z = 92$) are known as *transuranic elements*. All these transuranic elements are man-made and radioactive. Some of them are fissionable and thus become very useful. A list of transuranic elements is given below:

$Z =$	93	94	95	96	97	98
	Np	Pu	Am	Cm	Bk	Cf
	Neptunium	Plutonium	Americium	Curium	Berkelium	Californium
$Z =$	99	100	101	102	103	104
	Es	Fm	Md	No	Lw	Xv
	Einsteinium	Fermium	Mendelevium	Nobelium	Lawrencium	Kurchatovium

Transuranic elements may be produced in the laboratory by bombarding certain heavy nuclides with neutrons.

Methods of production, the reactions involved and the radioactive decays of two of these nuclides are given below:

(a) Neptunium ($Z = 93$) : When $_{92}U^{238}$ is bombarded with slow energy neutrons, neptunium is produced following the reaction :

$$_{92}U^{238} + _0n^1 \rightarrow _{92}U^{239}$$

$$_{92}U^{239} \rightarrow _{93}Np^{239} + _{-1}e^0.$$

(b) Plutonium ($Z = 94$) : Neptunium ($_{93}Np^{239}$) is itself radioactive and emits a β-particle to form plutonium following the reaction,

$$_{93}Np^{239} \rightarrow _{94}Pu^{239} + _{-1}e^0.$$

Plutonium emits α-particles to decay into $_{92}U^{235}$ with a half-life of 24000 years according to the reaction,

$$_{94}Pu^{239} \rightarrow _{92}U^{235} + _2He^4.$$

36.45   Cosmic Rays

Cosmic rays are highly penetrating radiations entering in our earth's atmosphere in all directions from outer space. The rays consist of high energy charged particles of the order of 15 GeV. Cosmic rays were first detected by Elster and Geital (1899) and then by Wilson (1900). They observed that the charge of an insulated electroscope leaked away slowly even in the absence of any ionizing agent. In 1911, Hess measured ionization of air at different altitudes by sending electroscopes in balloons and noted that the rate of discharge from electroscope increases as one goes higher above the earth while the ionization of air in the electroscope diminishes as one goes down into mines or the sea. These simple measurements suggested that some kinds of penetrating rays were entering the earth's atmosphere from outer space in all directions. Millikan called these rays as *cosmic rays.*

36.46   Latitude Effect of Cosmic Rays

In Fig. 36.49 we have shown the variation of cosmic ray intensity with latitude. The intensity is maximum at the geomagnetic poles ($\lambda = 90°$) and minimum at the geomagnetic equator ($\lambda = 0$). It remains constant between $42°$ and $90°$. The variation of cosmic ray intensity with geomagnetic latitude is known as the *latitude effect.*

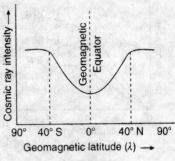

Fig. 36.49

The effect is explained considering the effect of the earth's magnetic field on cosmic rays. The presence of such an effect clearly suggests that the cosmic rays are charged particles. The earth's magnetic field is directed from south to north and the earth's magnetic field at the equator is perpendicular to the direction of travel of charged cosmic ray particles. So it exerts

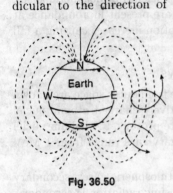

Fig. 36.50

maximum force ($F = av\,B \sin 90°$) upon the particles to suffer maximum deflection. Fig. 36.50 reveals that they are deflected away from the earth. The intensity of cosmic rays is minimum at the equator, and at poles, cosmic ray particles move parallel to the earth's field. Thus the intensity of cosmic rays is maximum at the poles. It has been established mathematically that for a given latitude (λ), there is a minimum momentum (p_{min}) below which no particle can reach the earth. The minimum momentum p_{min} at zenith is obtained from

$$p_{min} = 15 \cos^4 \lambda \, (BeV/c). \tag{36.90}$$

36.47   The East-West Effect of Cosmic Rays

It has been observed that the number of cosmic ray particles coming from the west is greater than those coming from the east. This effect is called *east-west effect*. It is maximum at the equator. It has been noted that at the equator, the number of particles coming from west is 14% more than the particles coming from east. This phenomenon gives an indirect support that cosmic rays are composed mainly by positively charged particles.

The charged particles, when approach towards the earth's atmosphere, are deflected by its magnetic field in a direction perpendicular to the magnetic field and to the direction of their motion. Fleming's left-hand rule suggests that the positively charged particles are deflected towards the east by earth's magnetic field and hence appear to come from the west of the vertical. This is illustrated in Fig. 36.51. Thus at any azimuth, greater number of particles approach the earth from the west than from the east.

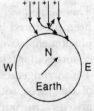

Fig. 36.51

Let I_W and I_E be the intensities of cosmic rays coming from the west and the east respectively. Then the east-west asymmetry may be defined as

$$\frac{I_W - I_E}{[(I_W + I_E)/2]}.$$

36.47.1   Altitude Effect

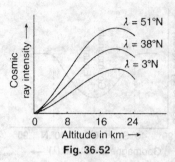

Fig. 36.52

The intensity of cosmic rays was determined by measuring the ionization produced by cosmic rays at different altitudes. The variation of intensity with altitude is represented in Fig. 36.52. It is seen that the intensity increases slowly up to a height of about 8 km. After that height the intensity rises fast up to about 24 km. At a height above 24 km, the intensity gradually decreases. The experiments were performed at 3°, 38° and 51° N. The results are exhibited in the figure. It was noted from a series of experiments that the maximum intensity is not at the top of the atmosphere but well below it. This is because at this height the primary cosmic rays produce a good number of secondary particles due to interaction with nuclei of atmospheric gases. As a matter of fact, both primary and secondary rays are present in abundance at that height. With decrease of altitude a fall the absorption increases causing a fall of intensity.

36.48   Primary and Secondary Cosmic Rays

The cosmic rays just entering in our earth's atmosphere from outer space are known as *primary cosmic rays*. They mainly consist of positively charged atomic nuclei with Z up to about 40. Nearly 90% of the primaries are protons, 9% helium nuclei and the remaining heavy nuclei. The energies of primary rays range from 1 MeV to 10^{14} MeV.

If primary cosmic rays interact with the nuclei of atmospheric gases, secondary cosmic rays are produced. Below 20 km altitude, all cosmic radiation is secondary. After entering into the atmosphere, the primary cosmic rays collide with air nuclei to produce mostly π-mesons (positive, negative and neutral) and also some hyperons. The π-mesons carry sufficient energy and subsequently, decay into lighter particles like μ-mesons, electrons, positrons, neutrinos and photons. All these particles constitute the secondary cosmic rays. The secondary cosmic rays at sea level contain about 70% μ-mesons, 29% electron-positron pairs and 1% heavy particles. The mesons in the secondary cosmic rays constitute the hard component while the electrons, positrons and photons constitute the soft component of cosmic rays.

36.49   Cosmic Ray Showers

This name is given to a grouping of cosmic ray particles which have been produced by some common cause and not by mere chance. The phenomenon was investigated by Rossi by using three coincidence counters in a triangular pattern with a lead plate above the counters. The arrangement is shown in Fig. 36.53. A coincidence discharge of the three counters can be produced by simultaneous passage of at least two particles, including the incident one. Rossi noted that an appreciable number of coincidence counts were registered and the number of coincidences increased with the increase of the thickness

Fig. 36.53

of the lead plate. From this experiment he concluded that the three counters were affected by two or more secondary particles produced simultaneously by a single cosmic ray after penetrating the lead plate. Thus the shower production in the lead plate was detected. The results of Rossi were explained by Bhabha and Heitler.

It was also explained independently by Carlson and Oppenheimer who gave the cascade theory of cosmic ray showers.

36.49.1 Cascade Theory of Showers

There are two distinct processes involved in shower production. These are radiative collision and pair production.

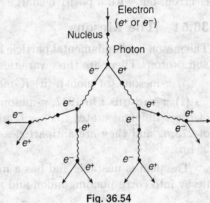

Fig. 36.54

A high energy electron or positron present in cosmic rays, loses some energy when it encounters the atomic nuclei in our earth's atmosphere. The energy in this case appears as high energy photon which interacts with the electric field of an atomic nucleus. As a result it is absorbed completely to produce an electron-positron pair. The energy essential for pair production is more than 1 MeV. The electron and positron so formed have high energy to produce more photons on interaction with nuclei. These photons have further role in pair production, thus causing the generation of a large number of photons, electrons and positrons having a common origin. The multiplication will continue in a manner as shown in Fig. 36.54 until the initial energy is divided between a large number of pairs. In the process the individual energies of the particles fall below the "critical energy" when the emission of photon and pair-production can no longer occur.

Pair production

When the photon traverses the strong electric field surrounding a nucleus, a conversion of a photon into an electron and a positron occurs. This is called *pair production*. The electric charge is conserved as the electron and positron have charges of same magnitude but of opposite sign. The energy of the photon provides the following :

(i) The rest energy of the electron (m_0c^2),

(ii) The rest energy of the positron (m_0c^2),

(iii) The K.E. of the electron (E^-), and

(iv) The K.E. of the positron (E^+).

If $h\nu$ represents the energy content of the radiation, then we can write,

$$h\nu = 2m_0c^2 + E^+ + E^-. \tag{36.91}$$

The equation suggests that a photon cannot create an electron-positron pair unless its energy exceeds $2m_0c^2$. This represents the threshold energy for pair production.

36.50 Discovery of Positron

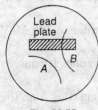

Fig. 36.55

The positron may be taken as the counterpart of the electron, having same mass and one unit of positive charge. In 1932 it was discovered by Anderson at the lime of cosmic ray investigations with a cloud chamber placed in a strong magnetic field. He observed in one photograph, two tracks of the same curvature but in opposite directions in a manner as shown in Fig. 36.55. The curve A was identified as due to electron while the track B was for the positron. At first it was thought to be due to electron moving from above in downward direction. But the energy of the particles on the two sides of the lead plate when measured showed that the energy above the plate was smaller than that below the plate. This indicated that the particle was moving from below upwards, similar to the electron causing the track A. It was thus ascertained that the track B was due to a particle of the same mass as the electron, but with a positive charge e. The particle was named as positron.

36.51   The Mesons

The meson is a fundamental particle having mass intermediate between the electron and proton. There are three varieties of mesons. They are :

(i) π-mesons (or pions), (ii) K-mesons (or kaons) and (iii) η-mesons.

(i) π-mesons : In 1947, π-mesons were discovered in the cosmic rays. They are of three different states : π^+, π^- and π^0. π^+- and π^--mesons have a rest mass of $273m_e$ and they are antiparticles of each other. The rest mass of π^0 meson is $264m_e$.

The pion is unstable and has a mean life of 2.6×10^{-8} sec. The charged pions decay into corresponding muon and a μ-neutrion, according to the reactions :

$$\pi^+ \to \mu^+ + \nu_\mu \tag{36.92}$$

$$\pi^- \to \mu^- + \overline{\nu_\mu}. \tag{36.93}$$

The mean life of neutral pion is 8.7×10^{-17} sec. It decays into two gamma rays :

$$\pi^\circ \to \gamma + \gamma. \tag{36.94}$$

Positive and negative muons ($\mu+$ and μ^-) have the same rest mass of $106 \, \text{MeV}/c^2 (207m_e)$ and the same spin of $1/2$. Both of them decay with a relatively long mean life of 2.2×10^{-6} sec into electrons and neutrino-antineutrino pairs, as shown below :

$$\mu^+ \to e^+ + \nu_e + \overline{\nu_\mu} \tag{36.95}$$

$$\mu^- \to e^- + \nu_\mu + \overline{\nu_e}. \tag{36.96}$$

(ii) K-Mesons : It is a heavier class of mesons. K^+ has a rest mass of $966m_e$ with mean life of 1.2×10^{-8} sec. Two varieties of neutral K-mesons are K_1^0 and K_2^0. Their rest masses are same ($974m_e$), but their mean lives are 9×10^{-11} sec and 5×10^{-8} sec respectively.

(iii) η-Meson : In 1961, the neutral eta-mesons (β^0) was discovered. It has a rest mass of $1073m_e$ and a zero spin value (boson) with a mean life of 6×10^{-19} sec.

36.52   Van Allen Belts

Artificial satellites successfully discovered the presence of two strong radiation belts known as *Van Allen belts*. These belts are formed around the earth except at the magnetic poles, at heights of 3200 km and 16000 km above the equator. Each belt exhibits localized zones :

(a) Inner zone : It consists of high energy protons of the order of 100 MeV and low energy electrons of the order of 1 MeV.

(b) Outer zone : It is less intense in comparison to the inner zone. It consists of only low energy electrons of the order 0.1 MeV.

High energy protons and electrons in the Van Allen belts are originating from the sun and cosmic rays which have been captured by the earth's magnetic field. The existence of the belt proved undoubtedly that high intensity particles are trapped by the earth's magnetic field.

36.53 Origin of Cosmic Rays

Many theories have been established about the origin of primary cosmic rays. These theories have highlighted the mechanism by which they acquire enormous energies.

(a) Explosion theory : Lemaitre, Regener and subsequently many other scientists have suggested that once upon a time the whole mass of the universe was concentrated in a single nucleus. It is assumed that about three billion years ago, this universe was exploded, forming the galaxies which are still running away from each other. During the explosion, a significant amount of radiation was formed. Protons and other nuclei were shot out in directions with enormous amount of energy. The cosmic rays are simply the dust of the explosion. However, this view does not explain the presence of heavy nuclei in primary rays. The tremendous explosion should have broken up the heavy nuclei into their constituent particles— protons and neutrons.

(b) Origin from cosmic ray stars : One of the views is that the cosmic rays come from the so-called cosmic ray stars. The stars are even more active than the sun. Our galaxy consists of about 10^{11} stars including variable stars, double stars, novae and supernovae. These all may be the possible origins of cosmic rays. The reccent opinion of the origin of cosmic rays is that the sun emits low energy cosmic rays; but high energy cosmic rays are emitted by cosmic ray stars within our galaxy while the sun emits low energy cosmic rays. Nowadays most of the scientists working in the field believe that protons acquire acceleration in interstellar magnetic fields causing the tremendous energies of cosmic rays.

(c) Origin from the sun : Another view is that the sun may be the source of some of the cosmic rays. At the times of solar activity, violent eruptions occur causing ionization to the gases shoot out from the sun. Thus in the process some of the protons in the sun acquire high energies and are thrown out into interplanetary space. As a matter of fact, the cosmic ray intensity increases during solar flares and changes slightly with the rotation of the sun. But as because the cosmic ray intensity remains almost the same at all the hours of day and night, the sun cannot be assumed to be responsible for the majority of the primary cosmic ray particles. It may only be the source of the small fraction of the low energy primaries.

36.54 The Big Bang Theory of the Universe

This theory suggests that all matters in the universe was concentrated in a very dense and hot primeval nucleus at the early stage. There is sufficient reason to assume that cosmic explosion occurred some 15 billion years ago when the matter was thrown out in the form of galaxies. The galaxies so formed are continuously moving away from each other, thus increasing the distances between the galaxies and space will grow more and more empty. Hydrogen in each galaxy is gradually used up and as a result, galaxies themselves be fainter and fainter resulting the space more and more empty. Eventually the galaxies will completely fade out and in the end, the universe will be devoid of all matter, energy and life.

Three observations strongly support the Big-Bang cosmology. These are : (a) The uniform expansion of the universe, (b) the relative abundance of hydrogen and helium in the universe and (c) the cosmic microwave background radiation.

36.55 Thermal History of the Universe

Cosmologists are giving efforts to reconstruct the story of Big Bang but yet they cannot do that back to time zero. Nothing can be confirmed about the state of the universe until 10^{-43} sec after the Big Bang in the absence of a quantum-mechanical theory of gravity. We may discuss what the universe must have been like from about 10^{-43} sec after the Big Bang to the current time.

As the initial compact, intensely hot fireball of dense matter and radiation from the Big Bang expanded. Subsequently it cooled and underwent a series of transitions at specific temperatures. The time-temperature variation of the universe is shown in Fig. 36.56. We have plotted the time since the Big Bang in logarithmic scale along the x-axis and the corresponding temperature in eV along the y-axis. Here the unit of kT is in eV. In order to convert the temperature T in kelvin to kT in electron-volts, the formula to be used is given by

$$kT \text{ (eV)} = 8.6 \times 10^{-5} \, T(\text{K}) \tag{36.97}$$

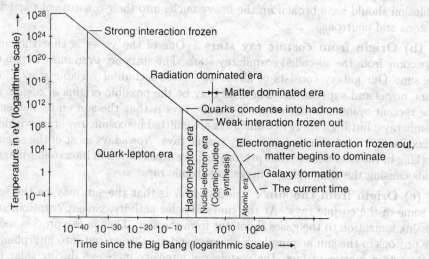

Fig. 36.56

The initial expansion of the universe started about 2×10^{10} years ago. Cosmologists refer to this event as the *initial singularity* as at this time the volume of the universe was zero and the density of mass-energy was infinite[*]. We have summarized the thermal history of the universe below :

(i) From 10^{-43} sec to 10^{-35} sec, there was a cooling of the universe from 10^{28} to 10^{23} eV. At energies like the strong, electromagnetic and weak interactions are merged into a single interaction mediated by superheavy X bosons. At 10^{-35} sec, particle energies became very low for free X bosons to be created any longer. The strong interaction became separated from the electroweak interaction. Then the quarks and leptons became independent.

(ii) From 10^{-35} to 10^{-10} sec, the universe consisted of a very dense soup of quarks and leptons. the behaviours of quarks and leptons were controlled by the strong, electroweak, and gravitational interactions. At 10^{-10} sec, the electroweak interaction became separated into the electromagnetic and weak components.

[*]Interested readers may consult the text entitled '*Astronomy and Astrophysics*' by A.B. Bhattacharya, S. Joardar and R. Bhattacharya (Publisher : Infinity Science Press, Massachusetts, USA).

(iii) If the time since the Big Bang is about 10^{-6} sec, the quarks condensed into hadrons.

(iv) At $t = 1$ sec, neutrino energies sufficiently fell to be unable to interact with the hadron-lepton soup. The neutrinos and anti-neutrinos that existed thus remained in the universe. However, they did not participate any further in its evolution. From then protons could no longer be transformed into neutrons by inverse beta-decay. But interestingly the free neutrons could beta-decay into protons following the reaction :

$$n \rightarrow p + e^- + \bar{\nu}. \tag{36.98}$$

With the fall of temperature, the number of neutrons fell but the number of protons rose. Now initial nucleosynthesis also takes place. Helium-producing nuclear reactions began to occur. Nuclear synthesis stopped at about $t = 5$ min. The small amount of nuclear matter is nearly 76% by mass protons and 24% by α-particles. There are traces of deuterons and of $^3_2$He nuclei.

(v) From 5 min to about 100 000 yr after the Big Bang, the universe consisted of a plasma of hydrogen and helium nuclei and electrons in thermal equilibrium with radiation. When the temperature fell below 13.6 eV, hydrogen atoms could form and not be disrupted. At that time, the matter and radiation were decoupled and the universe became transparent. Further, the electromagnetic interaction was frozen out.

After 2000 years, when hydrogen and helium began to dominate the universe and radiation became a secondary constituent, the matter era started. It may be noted that the neutrinos decoupled at near 1 sec but the decoupling of the photons of the black-body radiation from the surviving electrons, protons and the α-particles did not completely occur until the temperatures fell to about 10^4 K (0.86 eV) at an age of about 10^6 years. Before that Compton scattering and bremsstrahlung kept the photons in equilibrium with the electrons and nuclei. But the time when the temperature fell below the first excitation potentials of hydrogen and helium, the universe became transparent to photons. Afterwards, the black-body radiation was free to cool independently.

(vi) The radiation then left behind continued to spread out with the rest of the universe and undergoing Doppler shifts. The radiation cooled to become the 2.7 K cosmic black-body radiation observed later.

(vii) Before decoupling, radiation pressure kept the matter distribution smooth. After the decoupling of matter and radiation, gravity became the dominant influence on the evolution of the universe. The gaseous matter could now form the first galaxies. Thereafter, small inhomogeneities could grow and condense into the first gravitationally bound systems.

36.56 Hubble's Law

The spectral lines of many elements in galaxies are shifted either towards the high frequency, called *blue shift* or towards the low frequency, called *red shift*. The Doppler shift suggests that the galaxies are either moving towards or away from the earth. It was observed by Hubble that galaxies in all direction are moving away from us. There is a direct proportionality between the distance of a galaxy and its red shift. Hubble's law states that the velocity of recession v of a galaxy is directly proportional to its distance from the earth (R). We can, therefore, write,

$$v = HR, \tag{36.99}$$

where H is known as *Hubble's parameter*. We may thus conclude that the universe is expanding.

36.57   The Future of the Universe

It is now a big question to all of us that, will the universe continue to expand forever and will the material in it become cold. Scientists believe, in general, that it depends on how much matter the universe contains and on how fast it is expanding. The expansion of the universe may stop if it contains sufficient mass for gravity. Because then it can provide an adequate attractive force to slow down and reverse the expansion. If ρ_c be the critical density above which expansion will be arrested, then calculations show that the value of ρ_c is 6×10^{-27} kg m^{-3} which is equivalent to about 3.5 hydrogen atoms per m^3. Let ρ be the average density of the universe. Three possibilities may be there :

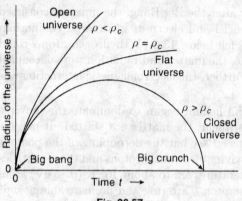

Fig. 36.57

(i) When $\rho < \rho_c$, the universe is open and the expansion will never stop (Fig. 36.57). As a result, in due course, new galaxies and stars will cease to form and existing ones will end up as neutron stars, black dwarfs and black holes.

(ii) When $\rho > \rho_c$, the universe is closed as shown in the figure. Sooner or later gravity will stop the expansion. The universe will then start to contract. The progression of events will be the reverse of those that took place after the Big Bang, with an ultimate Big Crunch, nothing but a fiery death. Perhaps, then the system will rebound in another Big Bang. There is a possibility of a continuing cycle of Big Bang, expansion, contraction and Big Crunch.

(iii) When $\rho = \rho_c$, the expansion will continue at an ever-decreasing rate. Yet the universe will not contract. The universe is then said to be flat due to the geometry of space in such a universe (Fig. 36.58). Under the condition when $\rho < \rho_c$, space is negatively curved and a two-dimensional analogy is a saddle. On the other hand, when $\rho > \rho_c$, space is positively curved. The surface of a spherical ball has positive curvature. In all the cases, however, the space-time is curved.

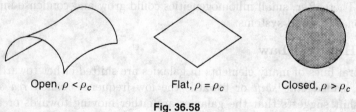

Open, $\rho < \rho_c$ Flat, $\rho = \rho_c$ Closed, $\rho > \rho_c$

Fig. 36.58

The flatness problem relates whether or not the geometry of the universe is open or closed. This problem may be focused with the parameter Ω, where Ω = actual mass-energy density/critical density.

When $\Omega = 1$, the geometry is flat; when $\Omega < 1$, it is hyperbolic, and when $\Omega > 1$, it becomes spherical and closed.

36.57.1   To Find the Value of the Critical Density

Let us consider a spherical volume of the universe of radius R with the earth as the centre. We assume that the distribution of matter in the universe is uniform. If ρ be the density of matter inside this volume, then

mass of the universe, $M = \dfrac{4}{3}\pi R^3 \rho$.

Again, let m be the mass of the galaxy. Then the total energy E of the galaxy is the sum of its kinetic and potential energies. Therefore, we can write,

$$E = \frac{1}{2}mv^2 - mMG/R. \tag{36.100}$$

In order to escape permanently from the universe, the galaxy must have a minimum kinetic energy $\frac{1}{2}mv^2$ so that its total energy E becomes zero. Hence we can write,

$$E = \text{K.E.} + U = \frac{1}{2}mv^2 - \frac{GmM}{R} = 0$$

or, $\dfrac{1}{2}mv^2 = \dfrac{GmM}{R}.$ $\hspace{3cm}$ (36.101)

Now, according to Hubble's law, we have $v = HR$, where H is Hubble's parameter. Hence we can write,

$$\frac{1}{2}m(HR)^2 = \frac{Gm}{R}\left(\frac{4}{3}\pi R^3 \rho_c\right).$$

Thus the critical density,

$$\rho_c = \frac{3H^2}{8\pi G}. \tag{36.102}$$

If the density is higher than the critical value ρ_c, the galaxy is bound in the universe. Then it will eventually fall back. If the density is less than the critical value, the galaxy will move away. It will keep the universe expanding. From astronomical observations, the present mass density has been estimated to be $\sim 5 \times 10^{-28}$ kg/m^3, about ten times less than the critical value. This indicates that the universe will go on expanding for ever.

36.58   Dark Matter

Matter that may be present in the universe but is invisible by being in a luminous state is known as *dark matter*. It may be present in the form of undeveloped stars or of already cold compact stellar objects. It could also be present in the form of (i) neutrinos with mass, (ii) unknown particles with mass.

Examples

1. Polonium-212 emits α-particles whose K.E. is 10.54 MeV. Calculate the α disintegration energy.

    Solution : When polonium-212 emits an α-particle, the mass of the daughter nucleus becomes 208 units. Thus we have

    $M = 208$ units, $m = 4$ units.

    $\therefore$ K.E. of the α-particles $= \dfrac{1}{2}mv^2 = 10.54$ MeV.

Hence, $E = \dfrac{1}{2}mv^2 \left(1 + \dfrac{m}{M}\right)$

$= 10.54 \left(1 + \dfrac{4}{208}\right) = \mathbf{10.74 \ MeV}.$

2. Calculate the time required for 10% of a sample of thorium to disintegrate. Assume the half-life of thorium to be 1.4×10^{10} years.

Solution : We know, $N = N_0 e^{-\lambda t}$. Given, $N = 0.9 N_0$.

$$\lambda = \frac{0.6931}{T_{1/2}} = \frac{0.6931}{1.4 \times 10^{10}} \ \text{sec}^{-1}$$

or, $0.9 N_0 = N_0 e^{-\lambda t}$ or, $\lambda t = \log_e \left(\dfrac{1}{0.9}\right)$

or, $t = \dfrac{1}{\lambda} \log_e \left(\dfrac{1}{0.9}\right)$

or, $t = \dfrac{1.4 \times 10^{10}}{0.6931} \times \log_e 1.111 = 2.1 \times 10^9$ years.

3. One gram of radium is reduced by 2.1 mg in 5 years by α-decay. Find the half-life period of radium.

Solution : Initial mass of radium = 1 gram.

Mass of radium left behind after 5 years = $1 - 0.0021 = 0.9979$ gm.

We know, $N = N_0 e^{-\lambda t}$.

In this case, $\dfrac{N}{N_0} = \dfrac{0.9979}{1}$; $t = 5$ years.

Hence, $0.9979 = e^{-5\lambda}$ or, $e^{5\lambda} = \dfrac{1}{0.9979}$

or, $5\lambda = \log_e \left(\dfrac{1}{0.9979}\right)$

$\therefore \quad \lambda = \dfrac{1}{5} \log_e \left(\dfrac{1}{0.9979}\right) = \dfrac{2.3026}{5} \log_{10} \left(\dfrac{1}{0.9979}\right)$

$= 41.45 \times 10^{-5}$ per year.

Therefore, $T_{1/2} = \dfrac{0.6931}{\lambda} = \dfrac{0.6931}{41.45 \times 10^{-5}} = \mathbf{1672 \ years}.$

4. The disintegration constant λ of a radioactive element is 0.00231 per day. Find its half-life and average life.

Solution : Here, $\lambda = 0.00231$ per day.

Half-life period,

$$T_{1/2} = \frac{0.693}{\lambda} = \frac{0.693}{0.00231} = 300 \ \text{days}.$$

Average life period,

$$T_{av} = \frac{1}{\lambda} = \frac{1}{0.00231} = \mathbf{432.9 \ days}.$$

5. One gram of a radioactive substance disintegrates at the rate of 3.7×10^{10} disintegration per second. The atomic weight of the substance is 226. Determine its mean life.

Solution : Number of atoms disintegrated in one second $= 3.7 \times 10^{10}$.

The mass of the substance disintegrated in one second

$$= \frac{(3.7 \times 10^{10}) \times 226}{6.02 \times 10^{26}} = 1.389 \times 10^{-14} \text{ kg}.$$

In this case, $N = 1 \text{ gm} = 10^{-3} \text{ kg}$; $-dN/dt = 1.389 \times 10^{-14} \text{ kg}$.

We know, $-dN/dt = \lambda N$

or, $\quad \lambda = \dfrac{-dN/dt}{N} = \dfrac{1.389 \times 10^{-14}}{10^{-3}} = 1.389 \times 10^{-11} \text{ sec}^{-1}.$

Hence, mean life, $T_{av} = \dfrac{1}{\lambda} = \dfrac{1}{1.389 \times 10^{-11}}$ sec = **2282 years**.

6. Calculate the weight in kg of one curie of RaB (Pb^{214}) from the half-life of 26.8 minutes.

   Solution : 1 curie $= 3.7 \times 10^{10}$ disintgrations/sec.

   Here, $-dN/dt = \lambda N = 3.7 \times 10^{10}$

   or, $\quad N = \dfrac{3.7 \times 10^{10}}{\lambda} = \dfrac{3.7 \times 10^{10} \times T_{1/2}}{0.693}.$

   $\therefore \qquad N = \dfrac{(3.7 \times 10^{10})(26.8 \times 60)}{0.693} = 8.585 \times 10^{13} \text{ atoms}.$

   From Avogadro's hypothesis, 6.023×10^{26} atoms are contained in 214 kg of RaB.

7. Geiger and Rutherford found by the method of scintillations that thorium emits 4500 α-particles per second per gram. 1 gram of thorium contains 2.61×10^{21} atoms. Determine its half-life.

   Solution : We have $\lambda = \dfrac{4500}{2.61 \times 10^{21}} = 1.72 \times 10^{-18} \text{ sec}^{-1}$

   $$= 5.44 \times 10^{-11} \text{ year}^{-1}.$$

   Hence, $T_{1/2} = \dfrac{0.693}{\lambda} = \dfrac{0.693}{5.44 \times 10^{-11}} = 1.28 \times 10^{10} \text{ years}.$

8. Find the activity of 1 mg (10^{-6} kg) of radon. Half-life of radon is 3.8 days.

   Solution : We have the decay constant of radon,

   $$\lambda = \frac{0.0693}{T_{\frac{1}{2}}} = \frac{0.693}{3.8 \text{ d}} = \frac{0.693}{3.8 \times 86400 \text{ sec}} = 2.1 \times 10^{-6} \text{ s}^{-1}$$

   The no. of atoms in 10^{-6} kg of Rn^{222}

   $$= N = \frac{(6.023 \times 10^{26}) \times 10^{-6}}{222} = 2.7 \times 10^{18}.$$

   Hence, $R = \lambda N = (2.1 \times 10^{-6}) \times (2.7 \times 10^{18})$

   $$= 5.7 \times 10^{12} \text{ events/sec} = 5.7 \times 10^{3} \text{ GBq} = \textbf{153 Ci}$$

   Here, the "events" are alpha decays.

9. A carbon specimen found in a cave contained 1/8 as much C^{14} as an equal amount of carbon in living matter. Calculate the approximate age of the specimen. Half-life period of C^{14} is 5568 years.

Solution : Given, $T_{1/2} = 5568$ years; $T_{1/2} = \dfrac{0.6931}{\lambda}$

or, $\qquad \lambda = \dfrac{0.6931}{T_{1/2}} = \dfrac{0.6931}{5568}$ year^{-1}.

We know, $N = N_0 e^{-\lambda t}$ or, $\dfrac{N}{N_0} = e^{-\lambda t}$ or, $\dfrac{1}{8} = e^{-\lambda t}$ or, $\lambda t = \log_e 8$.

$\therefore \qquad t = \dfrac{\log_e 8}{\lambda} = \dfrac{(2.3026 \log_{10} 8) \times 5568}{0.6931} = \textbf{16710 years}.$

10. The half-life of radon is 4 days. After how many days will only 1/10th of a radon sample be left behind?

Solution : We have $T_{\frac{1}{2}} = \dfrac{0.693}{\lambda}$.

$\therefore \qquad \lambda = \dfrac{0.693}{T_{\frac{1}{2}}} = \dfrac{0.693}{4}$ per day.

We know, $N = N_0 e^{-\lambda t}$. Given that, $N = \dfrac{N_0}{10}$.

$\therefore \qquad \dfrac{N_0}{10} = N_0 e^{\frac{0.693t}{4}}$ or, $e^{\frac{0.693t}{4}} = 10$

or, $\qquad \dfrac{0.693}{4} \times t = \log_e 10 = 2.303 \log_{10} 10 = 2.303.$

Therefore, $t = \dfrac{2.303 \times 4}{0.693} = \textbf{13.3 days (approx.)}.$

11. If a certain radioactive element disintegrates for an interval of time equal to its mean life, (i) what fraction of the original amount remains and (ii) what fraction will have disintegrated?

Solution : We have $N = N_0 e^{-\lambda t}$; given, $t = T_a = \dfrac{1}{\lambda}$.

Putting this we get

$$N = N_0 e^{-\lambda \frac{1}{\lambda}} = N_0 e^{-1} \quad \text{or,} \quad \dfrac{N}{N_0} = \dfrac{1}{e}.$$

Therefore, the fraction of the original amount left $= \dfrac{1}{e}$ and the fraction disintegrated

$$= 1 - \dfrac{N}{N_0} = 1 - \dfrac{1}{e} = \dfrac{e-1}{e}.$$

12. The half-life of radium (at. wt. = 226) is 1600 years and that for radon (at. wt. =222) 3.8 days. Calculate the volume of radon gas that would be in equilibrium with 1 gm of radium.   [C.U. 1982]

Solution : From the half-life of radium and radon we find that there will be secular equilibrium between them. For secular equilibrium,

$$\dfrac{N_1}{N_2} = \dfrac{\lambda_2}{\lambda_1} = \dfrac{(T_{\frac{1}{2}})_{\text{radium}}}{(T_{\frac{1}{2}})_{\text{radon}}}$$

Given, $N_1 = 1$ gm; $(T_{\frac{1}{2}})_{\text{radium}} = 1600 \times 365$ days.

Also, $(T_{\frac{1}{2}})_{\text{radon}} = 3.8$ days. Hence, $N_2 = \dfrac{3.8}{1600 \times 365}$ gm.

We have, 222 gm of radon occupy at N.T.P. 22.4 litres.

$\therefore \dfrac{3.8}{1600 \times 365}$ gm radon occupy at N.T.P. $\dfrac{22.4 \times 3.8}{222 \times 1600 \times 365}$ litre

$$= \dfrac{22.4 \times 3.8 \times 10^3}{222 \times 1600 \times 365} \text{ cm}^3 = \mathbf{0.656 \times 10^{-3} \text{ cm}^3}.$$

13. Calculate the binding energy per nucleon of a helium nucleus ($_2\text{He}^4$), given the mass of a proton = 1.0028 a.m.u., mass of a neutron = 1.00867 a.m.u.; mass of helium nucleus = 4.00276 a.m.u.; and 1 a.m.u. = 931 MeV.[C.U. 1993]

Solution : In a helium nucleus, there are 2 protons and 2 neutrons.

Mass of 2 protons $= 2 \times 1.00728 = 2.01456$ a.m.u.

Mass of 2 neutrons $= 2 \times 1.00867 = 2.01734$ a.m.u.

Hence, total mass of 2 protons and 2 neutrons

$$= 2.01456 + 2.01734 = 4.03190 \text{ a.m.u.}$$

Now, actual mass of helium nucleus = 4.00276 a.m.u.

Mass difference $= 4.03190 - 4.00276 = 0.02914$ a.m.u.

So, the total binding energy $= 0.02914 \times 931 = 27.13$ MeV (approx).

Hence, binding energy per nucleon $= \dfrac{27.13}{4} = \mathbf{6.78 \text{ MeV}}$.

14. The nuclei are approximately spherical and have an average radius r given by $r = r_0 A^{\frac{1}{3}}$ where A is the mass number and r_0 a constant equal to 1.2×10^{-15} m. If the mass of proton and neutron be approximately equal to 1.67×10^{-27} kg, show that the nuclear density is greater than the density of waver by a factor 10^{14}. **[N.B.U. 2002]**

Solution : If A be the mass number, then the total number of protons and neutrons in the nucleus $= A$.

So, the mass of the nucleus $= A \times 1.67 \times 10^{-27}$ kg.

Further, volume of the nucleus

$$= \dfrac{4}{3}\pi r^3 = \dfrac{4}{3}\pi \times r_0^3 A = \dfrac{4}{3}\pi \times (1.2 \times 10^{-15})^3 \times A$$

$$= 7.234 \times 10^{-45} \times A \text{ m}^3.$$

Therefore, the density of the nucleus $= \dfrac{\text{mass}}{\text{volume}} = \dfrac{1.67 \times 10^{-27} \times A}{7.234 \times 10^{-45} \times A}$

$$= 1.38 \times 10^{17} \text{ kg-m}^{-3}.$$

As density of water $= 10^3$ kg-m^{-3}, so

$$\dfrac{\text{density of nucleus}}{\text{density of water}} = \dfrac{1.38 \times 10^{17}}{10^3} = 1.38 \times 10^{14}.$$

This shows that nuclear density is greater than the density of water by a factor 10^{14}.

15. Ra^{226} disintegrates to Ra^{222} with the liberation of an α-particle. Calculate the disintegration energy. Given, $M(\text{Ra}^{226}) = 226.096$ a.m.u., $M(\text{Ra}^{222}) = 222.0869$ a.m.u. and $M(\text{He}^4) = 4.00387$ a.m.u. **[C.U. 2000, '05 V.U. 2002]**

Solution : We can write,

$$Ra^{226} \rightarrow Ra^{222} + {}_2He^4 + Q \quad [Q = \text{disintegration energy}]$$

Hence, $Q = M(Ra^{226}) - [M(Ra^{222}) + M(He^4)]$

$$= 226.096 - [222.0869 + 4.00387]$$

$$= 226.096 - 226.09347 = 0.00253.$$

$\therefore \quad Q = 0.00253 \times 931 = \textbf{2.355 MeV}.$

16. Each atom of U-235 causes a mass defect of 0.2154 a.m.u. due to nuclear fission. Calculate the total energy released in kWh unit when all the atoms in 1 gm of U-235 undergo nuclear fission. 1 a.m.u. = 931 MeV; Avogadro number = 6.025×10^{23}. **[K.U. 2001]**

Solution : We have the number of atoms in 1 gm of

$$U\text{-}235 = \frac{6.025 \times 10^{23}}{235} = 2.56 \times 10^{21}.$$

Total mass defect = $2.56 \times 10^{21} \times 0.2154$ a.m.u.

Now, energy released = $2.56 \times 10^{21} \times 0.2154 \times 931$ MeV = 513.37×10^{21} MeV.

We know, 1 MeV = 1.6×10^{-13} joule.

So, energy released = $513.37 \times 10^{21} \times 1.6 \times 10^{-13}$ J = 821.4×10^8 J.

Further, 1 kWh = 3600×10^3 joules.

So, the energy released = $\dfrac{821.4 \times 10^8}{3600 \times 10^3} = 2.28 \times 10^4$ kWh.

17. Calculate the Q-value of the following nuclear reaction : ${}_7N^{14} + {}_2He^4 = {}_8O^{17} + {}_1H^1$; given, ${}_7N^{14} = 14.00755$ a.m.u.; ${}_2He^4 = 4.00388$ a.m.u.; ${}_8O^{17} = 17.00453$ a.m.u. and ${}_1H^1 = 1.00815$ a.m.u. 1 a.m.u. = 931 MeV.

Solution : We can write the equation as, ${}_7N^{14} + {}_2He^4 = {}_8O^{17} + {}_1H^1 + Q$

Total mass of $({}_7N^{14} + {}_2He^4) = 14.00755 + 4.00388 = 18.01143$ a.m.u.

Total mass of $({}_8O^{17} + {}_1H^1) = 17.00453 + 1.00815 = 18.01268$ a.m.u.

Hence, mass difference = $18.01143 - 18.01268 = -0.00125$ a.m.u.

Therefore, $Q = -0.00125 \times 931 = \textbf{-1.16375 MeV}.$

18. Calculate the energy generated in MeV when 0.1 kg of Li^7 is converted to He^4 by proton bombardment, given masses of Li^7, He^4 and ${}_1H^1$ in a.m.u. are 7.0183, 4.0040 and 1.0081 respectively. (1 a.m.u. = 931 MeV). **[N.B.U. 2005]**

Solution : We can write, ${}_3Li^7 + {}_1H^1$ (proton) $\rightarrow 2\,{}_2He^4$.

$\therefore \quad 7.0183 + 1.0081 \rightarrow 2 \times 4.0040$

$\therefore$ mass difference = $8.0264 - 8.0080 = 0.0184$ a.m.u.

We have, 1 a.m.u. generates 931 MeV.

$\therefore \quad 0.0184$ a.m.u. generates $0.0184 \times 931 = 17.13$ MeV.

Now, 1 a.m.u. = 1.66×10^{-27} kg.

$\therefore \quad 7.0183$ a.m.u. of Li = $7.0183 \times 1.66 \times 10^{-27}$ kg

$$= 11.65 \times 10^{-27} \text{ kg}.$$

$\therefore$ 11.65×10^{-27} kg of Li^7 generates 17.13 MeV.

or, 0.1 kg of Li^7 generates $\dfrac{17.13 \times 0.1}{11.65 \times 10^{-27}} = \mathbf{1.47 \times 10^{26}}$ **MeV**.

19. A radioactive substance contains 5 mg of U^{234}. After 4.96×10^4 years, the amount of U^{234} becomes 4.35 mg. Calculate the activity of it in curie. Given $\lambda = 9 \times 10^{-14}$ second and Avogadro number, $N_a = 6.023 \times 10^{23}$.

[V.U. 2005]

Solution : We have the number of atoms in 4.35 mg of U^{234}

$$= \frac{(4.35 \times 10^{-3}) \times (6.023 \times 10^{23})}{234}.$$

Again, $\dfrac{dN}{dt} = \lambda N$ [ignoring negative sign]

$$= \frac{(9 \times 10^{-14}) \times (4.35 \times 10^{-3})(6.023 \times 10^{23})}{234}$$

$$= 10^6 \text{ disintegrations/sec [approx.]}.$$

Therefore, activity in curie $= \dfrac{10^6}{3.7 \times 10^{10}} = \mathbf{2.7 \times 10^{-5}}$ **curie.**

20. Calculate the minimum energy of a γ-photon in MeV which can produce one electron-positron pair. Rest mass of an electron is 9.11×10^{-31} kg. [C.U. 2005]

Solution : Pair production is given by the reaction,

$$h\nu = {}_{-1}e^0 + {}_{+1}e^0,$$

where ${}_{-1}e^0$ is an electron and ${}_{+1}e^0$ a positron. Positron has the same rest mass as the electron and so the minimum energy required for pair production is

$E = 2m_0 c^2 = 2 \times 9.11 \times 10^{-31} \times (3 \times 10^8)^2$ J

$= 18.22 \times 9 \times 10^{-15}$ J

$= \dfrac{18.22 \times 9 \times 10^{-15}}{1.6 \times 10^{-19}}$ eV [$\because$ 1 eV $= 1.6 \times 10^{-19}$ J]

$= 102.5 \times 10^{-2}$ MeV $= \mathbf{1.02}$ **MeV.**

21. Find the binding energy of an α-particle and express the result both in MeV and joules.

Solution : Mass of 2 protons + 2 neutrons

$= (2 \times 1.007276 + 2 \times 1.008665)$ u $= 4.031882$ u.

Mass of the α-particle $= 4.001506$ u.

$\therefore$ mass defect, $\Delta m = (4.031882 - 4.001506)$ u $= 0.030376$ u

Hence, B.E. $= (0.030376 \times 931.3)$ MeV $= 28.29$ MeV

$$= \mathbf{45.32 \times 10^{-13}} \text{ J.}$$

22. Given the following isotope masses :

$${}_3Li^7 = 7.016004, \ {}_3Li^6 = 6.015125 \text{ and } {}_0n^1 = 1.008665.$$

Find the B.E. of a neutron in the ${}_3Li^7$ nucleus. Express the result in u, MeV and joules.

Solution : We have the B.E. of a neutron in u

$$= M(_3\text{Li}^6 + _0n^1) - M(_3\text{Li}^7) = 6.015125 + 1.008665 - 7.016004$$

$$= \mathbf{0.007786 \ u}.$$

In MeV this becomes 0.007786×931 MeV $= \mathbf{7.35 \ MeV}$.

$$= 7.35 \times 1.6 \times 10^{-13} \text{ J} = \mathbf{1.18 \times 10^{-12} \ J}.$$

23. The linear attenuation coefficient for 2-MeV gamma rays in water is about
    5 m^{-1}. (a) Find the relative intensity of a beam of 2 MeV gamma rays after
    it has passed through 0.1 m of water. (b) How far must such a beam travel
    in water before its intensity is reduced to 1 percent of its original value?

    Solution : We know, $I = I_0 e^{-\mu x}$.

    (a) In this case, $\mu = 5$ m^{-1}; $x = 0.1$ m; $I/I_0 = ?$

    $$\frac{I}{I_0} = e^{-\mu x} = e^{-0.5} = 0.61.$$

    (b) In this case, $I_0/I = 100$, $\mu = 5$ m^{-1}; $x = ?$

    $$x = \frac{\log_e(I_0/I)}{\mu} = \frac{\log_e 100}{5} = \mathbf{0.92 \ m}.$$

24. An ionization chamber is connected to an electrometer of capacitance 0.5 pF
    and voltage sensitivity of 4 divisions per volt. A beam of α-particles causes
    a deflection of 0.8 divisions. Calculate the number of ion pairs required and
    the energy of the α-particles. Given that 1 ion pair requires energy of 35 eV
    and $e = 1.6 \times 10^{-19}$ coulomb.

    Solution : Voltage sensitivity of electrometer = 4 divisions/volt.

    So, the voltage required to produce a deflection of 0.8 division

    $$= \frac{0.8}{4} \text{ volt} = 0.2 \text{ volt}.$$

    $$Q = CV = (0.5 \times 10^{-12}) \times 0.2 \text{ [since } C = 0.5 \text{ pF} = 0.5 \times 10^{-12} \text{ F]}$$

    $$= 10^{-13} \text{ C}.$$

    Hence, number of ion pairs required $= \dfrac{10^{-13}}{1.6 \times 10^{-19}} = 6.25 \times 10^5$.

    1 ion pair requires 35 eV.

    Therefore, the total energy required $= 35 \times (6.25 \times 10^5)$ eV $= \mathbf{21.88 \ MeV}$.

25. α-particles of energy 5 MeV pass through an ionization chamber at the rate
    of 10 per second. Assuming all the energy is used in producing ion pairs,
    calculate the current produced (35 eV is required for producing an ion pair
    and $e = 1.6 \times 10^{-19}$ C).

    Solution : Energy of α-particles $= 5 \times 10^6$ eV.

    Energy required to produce one ion pair = 35 eV.

    No. of ion pairs produced by one α-particle $= \dfrac{5 \times 10^6}{35} = 1.429 \times 10^5$.

    As 10 particles enter the chamber in one second, so the number of ion pairs
    produced per second

    $$= 1.429 \times 10^5 \times 10 = 1.429 \times 10^6.$$

Charge on each ion $= 1.6 \times 10^{-19}$ C.

$\therefore$ current $= (1.429 \times 10^6) \times (1.6 \times 10^{-19})$ C/sec $= 2.287 \times 10^{-13}$ A.

26. It is required to operate a proportional counter with a maximum radial field of 10^7 V m. What is the applied voltage required if the radii of the wire and tube are 0.002 cm and 1 cm respectively?

Solution : We have the radial field $= E = \dfrac{V}{r \log_e(b/a)}$

and radial field at the wire surface, $E = \dfrac{V}{a \log_e(b/a)}$

Therefore, $10^7 = \dfrac{V}{(2 \times 10^{-5})2.302 \log_{10}(10^2/2 \times 10^5)}$ or, $V = \mathbf{1242}$ **volts.**

27. A self-quenched G-M counter operates at 1000 volts and has a wire diameter of 0.2 mm. The radius of the cathode is 2 cm and the tube has a guaranteed lifetime of 10^9 counts. What is the maximum radial field and how long will the counter last if it is used on an average for 30 hours per week at 3000 counts per minute? Consider 50 weeks to a year.

Solution : The radial field at the central wire is given by

$$E_{\max} = \frac{V}{r \log_e(b/a)} = \frac{1000}{0.0001 \times 2.3026 \log_{10}\left(\frac{2 \times 10^{-2}}{10^{-4}}\right)}$$

$$= 1.89 \times 10^6 \text{ volts/metre.}$$

Now, if the lifetime of the tube is N years, then the total number of counts recorded will be

$$N \times 50 \times 30 \times 60 \times 3000 = 2.7 \times 10^8 N$$

or, $2.7 \times 10^8 \times N = 10^9$

$\therefore \quad N = \mathbf{3.7}$ **years.**

28. Deuterons in a cyclotron describe a circle of radius 0.32 m just before emerging from the dees. The frequency of the applied e.m.f. is 10 MHz. Find the flux density of the magnetic field and the velocity of deuterons emerging out of the cyclotron. Mass of deuterium $= 3.32 \times 10^{-27}$ kg; $e = 1.6 \times 10^{-19}$ C.

Solution : We know, $f = \dfrac{Be}{2\pi m}$ or, $B = \dfrac{2\pi m f}{e}$.

Given, $m = 3.32 \times 10^{-27}$ kg; $f = 10$ MHz $= 10^7$ Hz; $e = 1.6 \times 10^{-19}$ C

Therefore, $B = \dfrac{2\pi(3.32 \times 10^{-27})10^7}{1.6 \times 10^{-19}} = 1.303$ weber/m^2.

Again, we know,

$$\frac{mv^2}{r_{\max}} = Bev \text{ or, } v = \frac{Ber_{\max}}{m}.$$

In this case, $B = 1.303$ weber/m^2; $e = 1.6 \times 10^{-19}$ C, $r_{\max} = 0.32$ m and $m = 3.32 \times 10^{-27}$ kg.

Hence, $v = \dfrac{Ber_{\max}}{m} = \dfrac{1.303(1.6 \times 10^{-19})0.32}{3.32 \times 10^{-27}} = 2.009 \times 10^7$ m sec^{-1}.

29. A cyclotron in which the flux density is 1.4 weber/m^2 is employed to accelerate protons. How rapidly should the electric field between the dees be reversed? Mass of the proton $= 1.67 \times 10^{-27}$ kg and charge $= 1.6 \times 10^{-19}$ C.

Solution : Given, $B = 1.4$ weber/m^2; $m = 1.67 \times 10^{-27}$ kg; $e = 1.6 \times 10^{-1}$ C.

Hence, $t = \dfrac{\pi m}{Be} = \dfrac{\pi (1.67 \times 10^{-27})}{1.4 \times (1.6 \times 10^{-19})} = \mathbf{2.342 \times 10^{-8}}$ **sec.**

30. In a certain betatron the maximum magnetic field at orbit was 0.4 Wb/m^2, operating at 50 Hz with a stable orbit diameter of 1.524 m. Calculate the average energy gained per revolution and the final energy of the electrons.

Solution : In the betatron, the electron velocities are approximately c.

Hence, the total distance travelled in the acceleration time

$$= c \times \frac{T}{4} = c \times \frac{\pi}{2\omega} \text{ (as it is one quarter cycle)}.$$

Therefore, the total number of revolutions $= N = \dfrac{c\pi/2\omega}{2\pi r} = \dfrac{c}{4\omega r}$.

Given, frequency $= f = 50$ Hz.

$\therefore \quad \omega = 2\pi f = 2\pi \times 50 = 100\pi$; $r = 0.762$ m and $c = 3 \times 10^8$ m sec^{-1}.

$\therefore \quad N = \dfrac{3 \times 10^8}{4(100\pi)0.762} = 3.132 \times 10^5$.

Let us assume that E be the final energy acquired by the electrons. **As the** electrons must be treated relativistically, we can write,

momentum of the electron $= mv = E/c$.

But $mv^2/r = Bev$ or, $mv = Bev$ or, $E = Berc$

$\therefore \quad E = \dfrac{0.4(1.6 \times 10^{-19})(0.762)(3 \times 10^8)}{1.6 \times 10^{-13}}$ MeV $= 91.45$ MeV.

Average energy gained per revolution $= \dfrac{91.45 \times 10^6}{3.132 \times 10^5} = \mathbf{291.9 \ eV}$.

31. Determine the product nuclei and Q-values in the following reactions : $\text{Al}^{27}(d,\alpha)$ and $\text{Mg}^{25}(\alpha, d)$. Masses of Al^{27}, Mg^{25}, α and d are 26.9901 a.m.u., 24.9936 a.m.u., 4.0039 a.m.u. and 2.0147 a.m.u. respectively. Comment on your results.

Solution : (i) The nuclear reaction is

$$_{13}\text{Al}^{27} + {}_1\text{H}^2 \rightarrow {}_{12}\text{Mg}^{25} + {}_2\text{He}^4 + Q$$

$\therefore \quad Q = 26.9901 + 2.0147 - 24.9936 - 4.0039 = 0.0073$ a.m.u.

i.e., $Q = 0.0073 \times 931.3$ MeV $= 6.797$ MeV.

(ii) $_{12}\text{Mg}^{25} + {}_2\text{He}^4 \rightarrow {}_{13}\text{Al}^{27} + {}_1\text{H}^2 + Q$

$\therefore \quad Q = 24.9936 + 4.0039 - 26.9901 - 2.0147 = -0.0073$ a.m.u.

i.e., $Q = -0.0073 \times 931.3$ MeV $= -6.797$ MeV.

32. A deuterium reaction that occurs in experimental fusion reactor is $\text{H}^2(d,p)\text{H}^3$ followed by $\text{H}^3(d,n)\text{He}^4$. (a) Compute the energy release in each of these.

(b) Compute the total energy release per gram of the deuteron used in the fusion. (c) Compute the percentage of the rest mass of deuteron released as energy. (d) Compare U^{235} fission with deuteron fusion as a source of energy release. Given,

$$H^2 = 2.014102 \text{ u}, \ H^3 = 3.016049 \text{ u}, \ H^1 = 1.007825 \text{ u}, \ _0n^1 = 1.008665 \text{ u},$$

$$He^4 = 4.002604 \text{ u and } \ U^{235} = 235.0439 \text{ u}.$$

Solution : (a) (i) The fusion reaction $H^2(d, p)H^3$ is written as

$$_1H^2 + _1H^2 \rightarrow _1H^3 + _1H^1 + Q.$$

Mass decrease in the reaction,

$$\Delta m = (2.014102 + 2.014102 - 3.016049 - 1.007825) \text{ u} = 0.00433 \text{ u}.$$

So, the energy released $= 0.004330 \times 931.3 \text{ MeV} = \textbf{4.032 MeV}.$

(a) (ii) The reaction $H^3(d, n)He^4$ is given by

$$_1H^3 + _1H^2 \rightarrow _2He^4 + _0n^1 + Q.$$

$\therefore \quad \Delta m = (3.016049 + 2.01402 - 4.002604 - 1.008665) \text{ u} = 0.018842 \text{ u}.$

Energy released $= 0.018842 \times 931.3 = 17.58 \text{ MeV}.$

Hence, total energy release $= 4.032 + 17.58 = \textbf{21.61 MeV}.$

(b) This total energy release is from the fusion of 3 $_1H^2$ nuclei.

So, the energy release per $H^2 = 21.61/3 = 7.203 \text{ MeV}.$

Number of nuclei in 1 gram of $H^2 = \dfrac{6.02 \times 10^{23}}{2.014102}.$

Hence, total release of energy from 1 gram of H^2

$$= \dfrac{6.02 \times 10^{23}}{2.014102} \times 7.203 = \textbf{2.153} \times \textbf{10}^{24} \textbf{ MeV}.$$

(c) Energy equivalent of one H^2 nucleus $= 2.014102 \times 931.3 \text{ MeV}.$

Average release of energy per H^2 nucleus $= 7.203 \text{ MeV}.$

$\therefore$ the percentage of the rest of mass of deuteron released as energy

$$= \dfrac{7.203}{2.014102 \times 931.3} \times 100 = \textbf{0.3840\%}.$$

(d) In U^{235} fission, 200 MeV is released per uranium nucleus.

Hence, percentage of mass energy release in U^{235} fission

$$= \dfrac{200}{235.0439 \times 931.3} \times 100 = 0.09137\%$$

Therefore, $\dfrac{\text{Energy release from } H^2 \text{ fusion}}{\text{Energy release from } U^{235} \text{ fission}} = \dfrac{0.3840}{0.09137} = \textbf{4.202}.$

33. A reactor is developing energy at the rate of 3000 kW. How many atoms of U^{235} undergo fission per second? How many kilograms of U^{235} would be used in 1000 hours of operation assuming that on an average energy of 200 MeV is released per fission?

Solution : Rate of development of energy by the reactor $= 3000 \text{ kW}$ $= 3 \times 10^6 \text{ J sec}^{-1}.$

Energy released per fission $= 200$ MeV $= 200 \times 1.6 \times 10^{-13}$ J

$$= 32 \times 10^{-12} \text{ J}.$$

Hence, number of atoms undergoing fission per second

$$= \frac{3 \times 10^6}{32 \times 10^{-12}} = 9.4 \times 10^{16}.$$

Number of atoms undergoing fission in 1000 hours

$$= (9.4 \times 10^{16}) \times (1000 \times 60 \times 60) = 3.384 \times 10^{23}.$$

According to Avogadro's hypothesis, 6.025×10^{26} atoms of U^{235} weight 235 kg.

So, the weight of 3.384×10^{23} tons of U^{235}

$$= \frac{235 \times (3.384 \times 10^{23})}{6.025 \times 10^{26}} = \mathbf{0.1321 \text{ kg}}.$$

Questions

Essay-type

1. Describe the experiments which have shown that the radiations emitted by radioactive substance are of three distinct types. Give an account of the nature and properties of one of these radiations.

2. What is radioactivity? What radiations are emitted by a radioactive substance? State the principal properties of these radiations.

3. What are the different characteristic properties of α-particles? How would you show experimentally that α-particles are helium nuclei?

   [C.U. 1967 '88 cf. '70]

4. How do the three radiations emitted by a radioactive body compare in their penetrating power in matter, their deflection by electric and magnetic fields and their tracks in cloud chamber?

5. Give an account of the properties of radiations emitted by a radioactive substance. Explain what is meant by the half-life of a radioactive element.

   [C.U. 1967]

6. Describe a cloud chamber used for studying α- or β-particle. Can it be used for studying γ-rays?

7. Calculate the average life of a radioactive substance in terms of disintegration constant. [N.B.U. 1982]

8. Define expressions for 'half-life' and 'mean life' of a radioactive element. What is the relation between them? [C.U. 1989]

9. Give the law of decay of radioactive nuclei. Define mean life and show its relationship with the half-life. [C.U. 1967, V.U. 2005]

10. What is radioactive equilibrium? Distinguish between temporary and secular equilibrium. Which phenomenon led Rutherford to propose nuclear model of atom?

11. A radioactive element P disintegrates to another radioactive element Q with a disintegration constant λ_1. If Q disintegrates with a disintegration constant

λ_2, find the expression for the number of atoms of Q at any time t with respect to the initial number of P. In this context, what do you mean by 'transient equilibrium'? [C.U. 2000]

12. Give a reasoned statement of the changes in atomic weight and atomic number of radioactive nuclei when (i) α-particles, (ii) β-particles and (iii) γ-rays are emitted. [C.U. 1980]

13. Consider a radioactive nucleus P (nucleus 1) to decay into another radioactive nucleus Q (nucleus 2)—the latter again decays into a stable end product R (nucleus 3). If λ_1 and λ_2 be the decay constants of nuclei 1 and 2 respectively and N_1, N_2 and N_3 be the number of atoms of the three kind at any instant t, then show that

(i) $N_1 = N_0 e^{-\lambda_1 t}$; (ii) $N_2 = \dfrac{\lambda_1}{\lambda_2 - \lambda_1} N_{10}(e^{-\lambda_1 t} - e^{-\lambda_2 t})$;

(iii) $N_3 = N_{10}\left(1 + \dfrac{\lambda_1}{\lambda_2 - \lambda_1}e^{-\lambda_2 t} - \dfrac{\lambda_2}{\lambda_2 - \lambda_1}e^{-\lambda_1}\right)$, where $N_{10} \to$ number of N_1 atoms at time $t = 0$. [N.B.U. 2005]

14. How is radioactivity used to measure (a) the age of the earth, (b) the age of the bones of prehistoric animals?

15. What are radio-isotopes? Mention the uses of radio-isotopes in (a) medicine, (b) agriculture, (c) industry and (d) higher scientific research.

16. What is artificial transmutation? How was it first effected?

17. Explain why a nucleus becomes unstable and describe on theoretical basis the phenomenon of radioactive disintegration including successive equilibrium. [Burd. U. 2002]

18. What do you mean by nuclear binding energy of elements? Draw a curve connecting nuclear binding energy versus mass number of elements, and discuss the importance of binding energy on the stability with example. [Burd. U. 2002]

19. Describe, in brief, the structure and properties of a nucleus.

20. What do you mean by nuclear binding energy of an atom? [Burd. U. 2003]

21. What do you mean by controlled chain reaction? How the chain reaction can be controlled in a nuclear reactor? Mention the role of the moderator in a reactor. [N.B.U. 2005]

22. Describe the essential parts of a cyclotron and explain the principle underlying its operation. What is variable energy cyclotron?

23. Explain primary and secondary cosmic rays. Clarify the cascade theory of showers.

Short Answer-type

24. Why does the anode of a G-M counter have to be made of a thin wire?

25. Is ordinary radioactivity a natural phenomenon? Can it be induced artificially? Has it any relation with the o ' ital electrons?

26. The isotope of $_{92}U^{238}$ decays successively to form $_{90}Th^{234}$, $_{91}Pa^{234}$, $_{92}U^{254}$, $_{90}Th^{230}$ and $_{33}Ra^{226}$. What are the radiations emitted in these five steps? [Ans. (i) α, (ii) β, (iii) β, (iv) α, (v) α]

27. Mention the differences between the tracks formed in a cloud chamber by α- and β-particles. What is the reason of this difference?

28. What is radio-carbon dating?

29. Starting from the formula $N = N_0 e^{-\lambda t}$, show that the activity A of a radioactive substance at time t, is related to the initial activity A_0 by the equation $A = A_0 e^{-\lambda t}$. What is the unit of activity?

30. What is binding energy of a nucleus? Wherefrom does this energy come? Explain why nuclear reactions can sometimes be used as a source of energy.

31. Answer the following questions :

   (i) Which particles determine atomic mass and atomic number?

   (ii) Which particle determines the physical and chemical properties of an element?

   (iii) Why is an atom neutral in charge?

   (iv) Between atomic number and atomic weight, which one is more fundamental as regards the arrangement of elements in the the periodic table?

32. What bombarding particles were used to produce artificial transmutation for the first time? Write down the transmutation equation.

33. Write short notes on (i) nuclear fission and (ii) pair production. [C.U. 1983]

34. Can an electron be accelerated in a cyclotron?

35. What are the sources of energy in a fission type and a fusion type bomb?   [C.U. 1984]

36. Write short notes on (i) cloud chamber and (ii) bubble chamber.

37. What is Hubble's law? What is the future of the universe?

38. What is the Big Bang theory of the universe?

39. Put a tick mark against the correct answers in the following cases :

   (i) A nucleus $_Z X^A$ is converted into another nucleus $_{Z+1} Y^A$ by emission of a radioactive radiation. What is that radiation?
       [**Ans.** (a) α-ray, (b) β-ray, (c) γ-ray]

   (ii) A nuclear reaction brought about by neutron is represented in the following way :
       $_3 Li^6 + _0 n^1 \rightarrow _2 He^4 + (\ )$. What is the product in the parenthesis?
       [**Ans.** (a) $_1 H^1$, (b) $_1 H^3$, (c) $_2 H^3$]

   (iii) A neutron strikes $_5 B^{10}$ nucleus with the subsequent emission of an α-particle. What is the mass number of the product nucleus?
       [**Ans.** (a) 4, (b) 10, (c) 6]

   (iv) What is the atomic number of the product nucleus in the above case?   [**Ans.** (a) 5, (b) 3, (c) 2]

   (v) An isotope of uranium has mass number 238 and atomic number 92. What is the number of neutron in its nucleus?
       [**Ans.** (a) 92, (b) 238, (c) 146]

(vi) Find out X, Z and Y of the following :

$$_{13}\text{Al}^{27} + _1\text{H}^1 \rightarrow _{14}\text{Si}^{28} + X$$
$$_{92}\text{U}^{238} + _2\text{He}^4 \rightarrow _{94}\text{Pu}^{241} + Y$$
$$_{15}\text{P}^{30} \rightarrow _{14}\text{Si}^{30} + Z.$$

(vii) Complete the nuclear reaction :

$$_7\text{N}^{14} + (\cdots) \rightarrow (\cdots)^{18} \rightarrow _8\text{O}^{17} + _1\text{H}^1.$$

[B.U. 2002]

Numerical Problems

40. The half-life of radioactive K^{40} is 18.3×10^8 years. Find the number of β-particles emitted per second per gm of K^{40}, assuming the disintegration constant $\lambda = 1.2 \times 10^{-17} \text{ sec}^{-1}$, and Avogadro number $= 6.023 \times 10^{23}$.

[C.U. (Hons.) 1965]
[**Ans.** 1.8×10^5]

41. The half-life of a radioactive element is 4 years. After what time the amount of radioactive element present in a specimen reduces to $\frac{1}{64}$th of its original mass?

[C.U. 1984]
[**Ans.** 24 years]

42. Number of atoms in a radioactive substance decreases to half in 10 years. How much will it reduce in 20 years?

[C.U. 1980]
[**Ans.** $\frac{1}{4}$th]

43. A small volume of a solution which contained a radioactive isotope of sodium had an activity of 12000 disintegrations per minute when it was injected into the blood stream of a patient. After 30 hours, the activity of 1 cc of the blood was found to 0.5 disintegration per minute. If the half-life of sodium isotope is taken as 15 hours, estimate the volume of blood in the patient.

[**Ans.** 6000 cc]

44. A source, of which the half-life is 130 days, contains initially 10^{20} radioactive atoms and the energy released per disintegration is 8×10^{-13} joule. Calculate (a) the activity of the source after 260 days have elapsed and (b) the total energy released during this period.

[**Ans.** (a) 1.54×10^{12} per second, (b) 6×10^7 J]

45. A radioactive substance has decayed to 1/128th of its initial activity after 50 days. What is its half-life?

[**Ans.** 7.5 days]

46. When a deuteron of atomic mass 2.0147 and negligible kinetic energy is absorbed by Li^6 nucleus of mass 6.0169, the intermediate nucleus disintegrates spontaneously into two α-particles, each of mass 4.0039. How much energy is given to each α-particle?

[**Ans.** 11.11 MeV]

47. The half-life of the cobalt radioisotope (Co^{60}) is 5.3 years. What strength will a millicurie source of this isotope have after a period of one year?

[**Ans.** 0.877 millicurie]

48. One gram of radium has an activity of one curie. What activity of radon will accumulate from one milligram of pure radon in 3.825 days, which is the half-life of radon?

[**Ans.** 153.7 curie]

49. The half-life of radon is 3.8 days. After how many days will only 1/20 of a radon sample be left over?

[**Ans.** 16.43 days]

50. How long will it take for a sample of radium D to decrease to 10%, if its half-life is 22 years?   **[Ans. 73.11 years]**

51. Given that the period of radon is 3.82 days and that the volume at normal temperature and pressure of the radon in equilibrium with 1 gm of radium is 0.63 mm^3; deduce the half-life period of radium. (Gram molecular volume = 22.4 litres and atomic weight of radium = 226.)   **[Ans. 1676 years]**

52. The isotope $_6C^{11}$ decays into $_5B^{11}$. What kind of particle is emitted?

                                                       [Ans. a positron]

53. If 20% of a radioactive material decays in 5 days, how much of the original material will be left after 20 days?   **[Ans. 37.07%]**

54. Tritium ($_1H^3$) has a half-life of 12.5 years against β-decay. What fraction of a sample of pure tritium will remain undecayed after 25 years?   **[Ans. $\frac{1}{4}$]**

55. A sample of RaE contains 4.00 mg. If the half-life is 5.0 days and the average energy of the β-particles emitted is 0.34 MeV, at what rate in watts does the sample emit energy?

56. Identify the nuclei that result from the positive β-decay of $_{48}Cd^{107}$, $_{19}K^{38}$, and $_{51}Sb^{120}$.   **[Ans. $_{47}Hg^{107}, _{18}A^{38}, _{50}Sn^{120}$]**

57. If a radioactive material initially contains 3 milligrams of uranium (U^{234}), how much it will contain after 150000 years? What will be its activity at the end of this time? $T_{1/2} = 2.5 \times 10^5$ years; $\lambda = 8.8 \times 10^{-14}$ per second.   **[Ans. 1.98×10^{-6} kg; 4.5×10^5 disintegrations/sec]**

58. Why does $_4Be^7$ invariably decay by electron capture instead of by positron emission? The atomic mass of $_4Be^7$ is 7.0169 u and that of $_3Li^7$ is 7.0160 u. Note that $_4Be^7$ contains one more atomic electron than does $_3Li^7$.

    [Ans. The mass of $_4Be^7$ is not sufficiently larger than that of $_3Li^7$ to permit the creation of a positron.**]**

59. The maximum energy of β-particles from $_{15}P^{32}$ is 1.71 MeV. What magnetic field perpendicular to the beam of β-particles from $_{15}P^{32}$ would bend it to give a radius of 100 mm? Given, $m = m_0(1 - v^2/c^2)^{-1/2}$.

                                        [Ans. 0.072 weber/m^2]

60. The K conversion electrons in Cs^{137} are found to have a momentum corresponding to Br = 2.665×10^{-6} Wb-m^{-1} in a magnetic spectrometer experiment. If the binding energy of the conversion electron is 37.5 keV, find the energy of the γ-photon involved in the process.   **[Ans. 662.2 keV]**

61. The γ-ray emitted by a substance dislodges a photoelectron from lead and these photoelectrons describe circular paths of radius 12.5 cm in a magnetic spectrograph in which the flux density is 0.01 Wb/m^2. The value of e/m for electron is 1.750×10^{11} coulomb/kg; the mass of the electron is 9.11×10^{-31} kg and the binding energy of K-shell electrons in lead is 0.0891 MeV. Calculate the wavelength of the γ-rays.   **[Ans. 0.05481 Å]**

62. Conversion of $_{83}Bi^{210}$ (209.98411 u) to $_{84}Po^{210}$ (209.982886 u) is by emission of β and a neutrino. Calculate the maximum energy of β-ray emitted.

                                        [Ans. 1.14 MeV]

63. Given that the atomic masses of $_{88}Ra^{226}$ and $_{86}Rn^{222}$ are 226.0254 and 222.0175 u respectively, find the disintegration energy in the α-decay of Ra^{226}.

Calculate also the kinetic energy of the α-particles.

[**Ans.** 4.934 MeV; 4.847 MeV]

64. In a Bucherer-type experiment, the plates are 1 mm apart and have a P.D. of 10 kV. A magnetic field of flux density 2 T is applied parallel to the plane of the plates. Calculate the velocity of electrons which are able to escape from between the plates in direction inclined at 30° to the magnetic field.

[**Ans.** 10^7 m sec^{-1}]

65. In a sample of carbon, the ratio of C^{14} nuclei to the number of C^{12} nuclei is 5×10^{-12}. One gram of the sample gives an activity of one disintegration per second. Calculate the mean life of C^{14}.

[**Ans.** 8208 years]

66. Compute the mass of 1.00 Ci of C^{14}. The half-life of C^{14} is 5570 years. Note, Ci is abbreviation of curie.

[**Ans.** 2.18×10^{-7} kg]

67. One gm of a radioactive substance takes 50 sec to lose 1 centigram. Find its half-life period.

[**Ans.** 56.97 minutes]

68. In what way is the neutron/proton ratio changed when a radioactive nucleus emits **(i)** an electron and **(ii)** a positron? [**Ans.** (i) decreases, (ii) increases]

69. The isotope $_{92}U^{238}$ successively undergoes eight α-decays and six β-decays. What is the resulting isotope?

[**Ans.** $_{82}Pb^{206}$]

70. When a nucleus emits a gamma-ray photon, what happens to its atomic number and its actual mass?

[**Ans.** Atomic number and mass number remain unchanged. The actual mass, however, decreases in proportion to the energy lost.]

71. Which of the following refer to the same thing?

(a) α-particles, **(b)** β-particles, **(c)** X-rays, **(d)** Photoelectrons, **(e)** Cathode rays.

[**Ans.** β-particles, Photoelectrons, Cathode rays]

72. Explain why —

(a) the mass of $_2He^3$ is less than that of $_1H^3$,

(b) the mass of $_7N^{14}$ is less than that of $_6C^{14}$,

(c) the mass of $_{19}K^{41}$ is less than that of $_{20}Ca^{41}$, although $_{19}K^{42}$ is more massive than $_{20}Ca^{42}$.

[**Ans.** In each of the above cases, the heavier nucleus undergoes β-decay to the lighter nucleus.]

73. The fission fragments in the thermal neutron fission of U^{235} are found to be $_{42}Mo^{98}$ and $_{54}Xe^{136}$. What are the elementary particles released in the reaction? Estimate the energy liberated in the reaction, given the masses of U^{235}, Xe^{136} and Mo^{98} are 235.044 u, 135.907 u and 97.906 u respectively.

[**Ans.** 2 neutrons and 4 electrons; 205.06 MeV]

74. The fusion reaction $2\,_1H^2 \rightarrow\,_2He^4 +$ energy, is proposed to be used for the production of industrial power. Assuming the efficiency of the process to be 30%, find how many kg of deuterium will be consumed in a day for an output of 50 000 kW. Given : mass of $_1H^2 = 2.014102$ u; mass of $_2He^4 = 4.002604$ u.

[**Ans.** 2.525×10^{-2} kg]

75. What is the energy released when 1 kg of nuclear fuel is consumed if the fusion reaction $_1H^2 + _1H^2 \rightarrow\,_2He^4$ is possible?

[**Ans.** 5.75×10^{14} J]

Review Short Questions on *Modern Physics* (with Answers)

Conduction of Electricity

1. *What is ionization of a gas?*

Ans. The process of breaking up of the neutral atoms into positive and negative ions is called ionization. In this process both types of ions are produced equal in numbers.

2. *Mention different methods of producing ionization in gases.*

Ans. Different methods for producing ionization in gases are the following:

(a) By electromagnetic radiations of X-rays, ultraviolet light, γ-rays and cosmic rays.

(b) By radioactive radiations.

(c) By heat.

3. *Which process has greater ionization power?*

Ans. Electromagnetic radiations have shorter wavelength and they have greater energy. Hence ionization produced by electromagnetic radiations has greater ionization power.

4. *What is ionization current?*

Ans. When a potential is applied between the two electrodes of a tube containing gaseous ions, the positive and negative ions move towards the cathode and anode respectively. The movement of the oppositely charged ions constitutes what is called ionization current.

5. *What will be the nature of the graph connecting the ionization current and applied potential?*

Ans. If the potential difference between cathode and anode be gradually increased, the ionization current is also increased. Up to a certain potential differences, the current increases linearly with the voltage and Ohm's law is obeyed up to this voltage. Then the rate of increase of current with voltage decreases and after a certain voltage it remains constant. This current is called saturation current and when the applied voltage is large, sparking takes place between the plates.

6. *What do you mean by spark potential and on what factors it depends?*

Ans. The potential difference required to start discharge is called the spark potential.

It depends on the distance between the plates and on the pressure of the gas between them.

7. *Mention the factors which control the saturation voltage.*

Ans. The factors which control the saturation voltage are the distance between the plates, the intensity of ionization and the pressure of the gas.

8. *Define the terms 'excitation potential' and 'ionization potential'.*

Ans. **Excitation potential**—In an inelastic collision, the energy which is given to the atom is used in raising an electron in the atom from its normal orbit to a higher orbit for a very short time of the order of 10^{-8} second. The atom is said to be excited. The minimum potential required to excite an atom is called excitation potential.

1028

Ionization potential—When an electron collides with an atom, an electron is removed from its orbit to outside the effect of the nucleus, the atom is said to be ionized. The minimum potential required to ionize an atom is called ionization potential.

9. *What is ionic mobility?*

Ans. The velocity acquired by an ion under an electric field of unit potential gradient is called the mobility of an ion.

10. *Distinguish between Faraday's dark space and Crookes' dark space.*

Ans. At a pressure of 1 mm of mercury of the gas between the cathode and the anode, the positive column is increased in length. A dark space separates the positive column from the cathode. This dark space is called Faraday's dark space.

As the pressure is further reduced, the negative glow is detached from the cathode and a dark space is found to exist between the negative glow and the cathode. This dark space is called Crookes' dark space.

11. *At what pressure the Crookes' dark space fills the whole discharge tube?*

Ans. At a pressure of about 0.01 mm of mercury, the Crookes' dark space fills the whole discharge tube.

12. *What will be the field distribution in normal electrical discharge?*

Ans. The field distributions between the cathode and the anode along the axis of the tube are:

   (i) There is a very intense field in the Crookes' dark space which decreases linearly with distance from the edge of the cathode glow to the negative glow.

  (ii) Electric field then increases slightly in the negative glow.

 (iii) Again the field decreases in the Faraday's dark space.

  (iv) The field increases gradually as the positive column is approached.

   (v) In the positive column the field is almost constant.

  (vi) The field again increases rapidly at the anode.

13. *When the cathode rays are found in the discharge tube?*

Ans. At a pressure of about 0.01 mm of mercury in the discharge tube, a stream of invisible negatively charged particles falls upon the anode and causes fluorescence. These moving charged particles are called cathode rays.

14. *Why cathode rays are called Lenard rays?*

Ans. If cathode rays are allowed to pass through a thin metal foil, a bluish stream comes out of the foil. These rays are first observed by Lenard and are known as Lenard rays.

15. *How can you show that the cathode rays are negatively charged particles?*

Ans. If cathode rays are made to pass into a metal vessel placed within the tube, the vessel acquires a negative charge. The existence of the negative charge can be proved if we connect the vessel to an electrometer.

16. *'The cathode rays always heat the material upon which they fall.' How can you prove it?*

Ans. Suppose the cathode of the discharge tube is made spherical and a platinum wire is placed at the centre of curvature of the cathode. In this case the cathode rays are emitted from cathode and concentrated on the platinum wire. We found that the platinum is heated to redness. This clearly shows that the cathode rays heat the material upon which they fall.

17. *What error is introduced to measure the electronic charge by a cloud chamber?*

Ans. After adiabatic expansion the air becomes cooled. But it again warms up by radiation. So the waterdrops begin to evaporate and their mass decreases gradually during the experiment.

18. *Suppose cathode ray is subjected to a magnetic field of intensity H. What will be its e/m value in terms of H?*

Ans. We know that the path of the beam under magnetic field is an arc of a circle. Suppose the radius of the circle is r. If m and v are respectively the mass and the velocity of the electron, then the centripetal force acting on the electron is $\frac{mv^2}{r}$.

Again, the magnetic force on the electron $= Hev$.

So, $\dfrac{mv^2}{r} = Hev.$

$\therefore$ $\dfrac{e}{m} = \dfrac{v}{Hr}$

19. *If waterdrops of radius r formed in the cloud chamber are fallen with a terminal velocity under gravity, what will be its terminal velocity?*

Ans. The terminal velocity with which the waterdrops fall down under gravity is given by Stokes' law,

$$v = \frac{2}{9} \frac{gr^2}{\eta}(\rho - \sigma),$$

where η = coefficient of viscosity of the medium,

ρ = density of waterdrop,

σ = density of the medium.

20. *Mention the name of an accurate method to determine the electronic charge.*

Ans. Millikan's oildrop method is the most suitable method to determine the charge of an electron.

21. *What was the value of the electronic charge obtained from Millikan's oildrop method?*

Ans. The value of the charge of an electron found by Millikan was 4.77×10^{-10} e.s.u.

22. *How can you find the Avogadro's number from the knowledge of electronic charge?*

Ans. To liberate 1 gm atom of any mono-atomic substance, a charge of 96 500 coulombs is required. The charge of an electron is 1.59×10^{19} coulombs. Now the Avogadro's number is the number of atoms in a gram-atom of the substance.

Here Avogadro's number $= \dfrac{96\,500}{1.59 \times 10^{-19}} = 6.03 \times 10^{23}.$

23. *What will be the value of the energy of an electron subjected to a potential difference of 1 volt?*

Ans. The energy gained by an electron in potential of v volt $= ev$.

Here, $e = 4.8 \times 10^{-10}$ e.s.u.

$$v = 1 \text{ volt} = \frac{1}{300} \text{ e.s.u.}$$

Therefore, the energy of an electron

$$= 1.6 \times 10^{-12} \text{ ergs.}$$

24. *Mention some applications of discharge of electricity through gases and vapours.*

Ans. Discharge phenomena are utilised to construct helium, hydrogen and neon tubes which are used as spectroscopic sources of light and to construct fluorescent lamp.

25. *What are positive rays?*

Ans. In a cathode-ray tube both positive and negative ions are produced due to collision. The negative ions constitute the cathode rays. If we use perforated cathode, these positive ions are seen as a stream of rays, known as positive rays.

26. *Why positive ions are called canal rays?*

Ans. In a cathode-ray tube if we use perforated cathode with holes, the positive ions will pass through these holes or canals and so the positive rays are also called canal rays.

27. *State the properties of positive rays.*

Ans. Properties of positive rays:

(1) Positive rays are deflected by electric and magnetic field.

(2) The specific charge of positive rays depends on the nature of the gas in the tube.

(3) It can produce fluorescence.

(4) It can disintegrate metals.

28. *What will be the nature of the path if positive rays are subjected to a parallel electric and magnetic field?*

Ans. The path of the positive rays will be a parabola.

29. *What information you will get from Thomson's positive ray analysis of neon?*

Ans. For neon two distinct parabolas are obtained. One of which corresponds to atomic number 22 and the other to atomic number 20. From this result one can conclude that neon has two isotopes.

30. *A positively charged particle is subjected to an electric field normal to the direction of motion of the particle. Find the deflection of the particle.*

Ans. Suppose the intensity of the electric field is X and length of the electric field is l.

So the time required to pass through a length l with velocity v is given by

$$t = \frac{l}{v}.$$

The force on the charge particle of charge e due to electric field $= Xe$.

$\therefore$ acceleration of the particle $= \dfrac{Xe}{m}$, where m is the mass of the particle.

So the displacement of the positively charged particle emerging from the electric field is

$$d = \frac{1}{2} \left(\frac{Xe}{m} \right) t^2 = \frac{1}{2} \left(\frac{Xe}{m} \right) \frac{l^2}{v^2}.$$

31. *What are the advantages of Aston's mass spectrograph method over Thomson's parabola method to detect isotopes?*

Ans. In Thomson's method the ions are spread out into a parabola whereas in Aston's method all ions having same value of e/m are focused into a single point. So the impressions on photo-plate will be well defined compared to impressions in the parabola method. The measurements can be done accurately in Aston's method. Moreover, correct idea of relative abundance of isotopes of an element may be made by Aston's spectograph method.

X-rays : Photo-electric Effect

32. *How are X-rays produced?*

Ans. X-rays are produced when fast-moving electrons are made to strike a solid target.

33. *Mention the names of the metals which are generally used as a target to produce X-rays.*

Ans. Tantalum, platinum and tungsten are usually used as a target.

34. *State the properties of X-rays.*

Ans. Properties of X-rays:

 (i) They are invisible.

 (ii) They travel with the velocity of light.

 (iii) They can penetrate many substances like aluminium, leather, paper, wood, flesh, etc.

 (iv) X-rays are not effected by electric and magnetic field.

 (v) They can ionize a gas.

 (vi) They affect photographic plate.

 (vii) X-rays can show phenomena of reflection, refraction, interference, polarization, etc.

 (viii) They destroy the tissues of living beings.

35. *For what purposes the X-rays are used?*

Ans. X-rays are used in surgery, radio-therapy, in studying structure of metals, for detection of cracks in metal plates, in detective work, to investigate structure of crystals, etc.

36. *Distinguish between soft X-rays and hard X-rays.*

Ans. X-rays of short wavelength are called hard X-rays whereas X-rays of longer wavelength are said to be soft X-rays. The penetrating power of hard X-rays is greater than that of soft X-rays.

37. *What are advantages of Coolidge tube over gas-filled tube?*

Ans. The applied voltage in gas-filled tube depends on the pressure of the gas which does not remain constant. So the intensity of X-rays cannot be kept constant. In Coolidge tube the intensity and the quality of X-rays can be controlled independently. The applied voltage controls the quality, and the temperature of the filament controls the intensity of the X-rays.

38. *Find the expression for maximum speed of the electron striking the anticathode?*

Ans. Let the applied voltage be V. So the energy gained by an electron of charge e is eV.

If v be the maximum velocity acquired by the electron, then

$$\frac{1}{2}mv_{max}^2 = eV,$$ where m is the mass of the electron.

$$\therefore \quad v_{max} = \sqrt{\frac{2eV}{m}}.$$

39. *What is the characteristic X-ray?*

Ans. If powerful X-rays are allowed to fall on a metallic target, secondary X-rays are emitted. The wavelengths of these X-rays are characteristic of the element used as a target known as characteristic X-ray.

40. *How can you explain the origin of characteristic X-ray spectra?*

Ans. We know that the electrons in an atom revolve round the nucleus in a number of shells. When X-rays are made to fall on the target, the loosely bound electrons acquire energy and jump into the outer shell and then come back to their original positions. The excess energy is given out in the form of X-rays.

41. *State Moseley's law.*

Ans. The frequency of a X-ray spectral line varies as the square of the atomic number of the element emitting it.

$$v = K(Z - a)^2,$$

where v = frequency of X-ray,

Z = atomic number of the element,

a and K are constants.

42. *Write the expression which is used to obtain X-ray spectra by diffraction.*

Ans. If d be the distance of separation of successive atomic layers and θ be the angle between the incident beam and crystal surface, then

$$2d\sin\theta = n\lambda,$$

where λ is the wavelength of X-rays and n is the order of the spectrum.

43. *Discuss the importance of Moseley's law.*

Ans. According to Moseley's law the characteristic properties of an element depend on the atomic number. The atoms should arrange in the periodic table according to their increasing atomic numbers. The position of argon, cobalt and tellurium in the periodic table was corrected by Moseley. Moseley further showed that in some cases the atomic numbers did not increase in the same order as the atomic weights of the elements. Thus the atomic weights of iron, nickel and cobalt are 55.84, 58.69 and 58.94 respectively. The atomic numbers assigned by Moseley were 26, 27 and 28.

44. *What is photoelectric effect?*

Ans. The emission of electrons from a metal surface when light radiation of suitable frequency is incident on it, is known as photoelectric effect.

45. *What is photoelectric current?*

Ans. The current produced by photoelectrons under the application of an applied potential difference is called photoelectric current.

46. *On what factors do the emission of photoelectrons and the strength of photoelectric current depend?*

Ans. The emission of photoelectrons depends on the frequency of the incident beam. For a given metal if the frequency of incident beam is less than a certain value, called threshold frequency, emission of photoelectron is not possible. The emission does not depend on the intensity of the incident beam. The strength of photoelectric current, however, depends on the intensity of the incident light.

47. *Write down Einstein's photoelectric equation.*

Ans. If W_{min} represents the minimum energy necessary to release an electron from the metal, then the maximum kinetic energy that the electron can have, should be

$$\frac{1}{2} m_e v_{max}^2 = hv - W_{min},$$

where m_e is the mass of an electron and v_{max} is its maximum velocity.

The above equation is known as Einstein's photoelectric equation.

48. *What predictions can be drawn from Einstein's photoelectric equation?*

Ans. The photo-electric equation of Einstein makes some important quantitative predictions:

(i) The maximum energy of emission is entirely determined by the frequency of the exciting radiation and is independent of its intensity.

(ii) The curve connecting the K.E. of the speediest electrons to the frequency of the exciting radiation is a straight line.

(iii) No electron will be able to eject unless the frequency v of the incident light is sufficiently greater so that hv is greater than or at least equal to W_{min}.

(iv) It predicts a definite value for the maximum energy of ejection.

49. *What is threshold frequency?*

Ans. The emission of photoelectrons occurs only when the incident radiation has a certain minimum frequency. That minimum frequency which causes emission is called threshold frequency.

If v_t is the threshold frequency, then

$$hv_t = W_{min},$$

which gives $v_t = \dfrac{W_{min}}{h}$.

50. *Give the names of three different types of photo-cells.*

Ans. Three different types of photocells are:

(i) Photo-emissive cells,

(ii) Photo-voltaic cells,

(iii) Photo-conductive cells.

51. *What are the uses of (i) photo-emissive cells, (ii) photo-voltaic cells, and (iii) photo-conductive cells?*

Ans. **(i) Photo-emissive cells**—This type of photocells is usually used for commercial purposes because of high sensitivity. But since there is a fluctuation of current even for a constant intensity beam, the gas-filled cells are seldom used for precision work.

(ii) Photo-voltaic cells—Photo-voltaic cells are used in photographic exposure meter and for operation of relays. Silicon cells, because of their better response in the infrared region, are widely used in artificial satellites for conversion of solar energy into electrical energy.

(iii) Photo-conductive cells—Photo-conductive cells can be used directly with a power supply of low voltage to operate a relay. These are used extensively in street lighting controls, door-openers, burglar alarm systems and also in modern television camera tubes.

Radioactivity

52. *What is radioactivity? What radiations are emitted by a radioactive substance?*

Ans. Radioactivity is the property of certain elements of emitting rays spontaneously. These rays affect the photographic plates, ionize gases and cause phosphorescence on certain compounds.

Radioactive substances give out radiations known as (i) α-rays, (ii) β-rays and (iii) γ-rays.

53. *How are different types of radiations identified?*

Ans. The three radiations, viz., α-rays, β-rays and γ-rays are identified by observing their behaviours with electric and magnetic fields, and their different penetrating powers.

54. *What are α-rays?*

Ans. α-rays are positively charged helium nucleus.

55. *State the properties of α-rays.*

Ans. Properties of α-rays:

(i) α-rays are positively charged particles.

(ii) α-particles have velocities in the range 10^7 to 10^9 cm/second.

(iii) They affect photographic plates.

(iv) They have very small penetrating power.

(v) The α-rays are deflected by magnetic and electric fields.

(vi) They can produce fluorescence.

(vii) They can produce ionization.

56. *For what reasons α-particles are said to be a helium nucleus?*

Ans. From Rutherford and Geiger experiment they obtained the charge of alpha particle $e_\alpha = 9.3 \times 10^{-10}$ e.s.u. and mass of α-particle is $m_\alpha = 6.62 \times 10^{-24}$ gm which is four times that of a hydrogen atom. Since an α-particle carries two-positive electronic charge and mass equal to that of the helium atom, so the α-particle is nothing but a doubly charged helium nucleus.

57. *State the properties of β-rays and γ-rays.*

Ans. Properties of β-rays:

(i) β-rays are negatively charged particles.

(ii) They have velocity in the range 10^8 to 10^{10} cm/second.

(iii) They can ionize the gases. But the ionization power is less than that of α-particles.

(iv) They affect photographic plate.

(v) They can penetrate large thickness of matter.

(vi) They are deflected by electric and magnetic fields.

(vii) They can produce fluorescence.

Properties of γ-rays:

(i) γ-rays are neutral particles.

(ii) They are neither deflected by electric nor magnetic fields.

(iii) They affect photographic plates strongly.

(iv) They have high penetration power.

(v) Ionization power is very poor.

(vi) They travel with the velocity same as that of light.

58. *What do you understand by radioactive disintegration?*

Ans. The radioactive elements after the ejection of a positively charged α-ray or the ejection of a negatively charged β-ray from the parent atom produce fresh radioactive elements. This process continues until the stable element lead is reached. This phenomenon is called radioactive disintegration.

59. *What is Soddy's displacement law?*

Ans. Soddy's displacement law states that the emission of a β-particle is always associated with an increase in the atomic number by unity and the emission of an α-particle always decreases the atomic number by two.

60. *Give an account of the law of disintegration of radioactive substance.*

Ans. The number of atoms that disintegrate in unit time is directly proportional to the number of uncharged atoms remaining.

If N is the number of atoms that have not disintegrated at time t and $\frac{dN}{dt}$ is the rate at which disintegration occurs, then

$$\frac{dN}{dt} = -\lambda N.$$

The constant λ is called decay constant.

If original number of atoms be N_0, i.e., $N = N_0$ at time $t = 0$, the law can be expressed as

$$N = N_0 e^{-\lambda t}.$$

61. *Define the terms: (i) half-life and (ii) mean life of a radioactive element.*

Ans. (i) Half-life—The half-life of a radioactive element is defined as the time taken for half of the number of atoms of the radioactive element to disintegrate.

The statement said that $\frac{N}{N_0} = \frac{1}{2}$ at $t = T_{1/2}$.

So, $T_{1/2} = \dfrac{0.693}{\lambda}$.

(ii) Mean life—It is the mean or average life time of the atoms, i.e.,

Mean life, $T_{av} = \dfrac{\text{total life time of all atoms}}{\text{total number of atoms}}$

$$= \frac{\int_0^\infty t\, dN}{N_0}$$

$$= \int_0^\infty t\lambda e^{-\lambda t}\, dt = \frac{1}{\lambda}.$$

Thus the mean life T_{av} is the reciprocal of decay constant λ.

62. *What is successive disintegration and secular equilibrium of a radioactive element?*

Ans. If a radioactive element disintegrates giving a daughter element which is also radioactive, the latter will also disintegrate at its own characteristic rate and, therefore, does not accumulate without limit. This is known as successive disintegration.

If the parent element has a longer life time than that of daughter, then after some time the rate of disintegration of both of them becomes identical and an equilibrium between the parent and the daughter is established. This equilibrium is called secular equilibrium.

When the members of a radioactive series are in secular equilibrium, then the relative amount of each is given by

$$\lambda_1 N_1 = \lambda_2 N_2 = \lambda_3 N_3 = \cdots = \lambda_n N_n = \cdots$$

63. *What is meant by curie and rutherford?*

Ans. curie is the unit of radioactive disintegration and it is equal to 3.7×10^{10} disintegrations per second. rutherford is also a unit to measure disintegration rate, defined as 10^6 disintegrations per second.

64. *How can you measure the age of rocks?*

Ans. During the formative period, a rock was formed with uranium and no lead. Lead was generated after successive disintegrations of uranium.

We know the decay constant of uranium and so the amount of lead formed per year can be estimated. So knowing the percentage of lead present, the age of the rock can be determined.

65. *Why radioactive rays are called Becquerel rays?*

Ans. Becquerel first discovered that compounds of uranium, and other radioactive substances emit spontaneously invisible rays which can pass through black paper and thin glass sheet. So these rays are called Becquerel rays.

66. *Give some examples of transformations using (i) α-particles, (ii) neutrons, (iii) γ-rays and (iv) deuteron as projectiles.*

Ans. (i) α-particles as projectiles :

$$_3\text{Li}^7 + {}_2\text{He}^4 \to {}_5\text{B}^{11} \to {}_5\text{B}^{10} + n.$$

$$_{13}\text{Al}^{27} + {}_2\text{He}^4 \to {}_{15}\text{P}^{31} \to {}_{15}\text{P}^{30} + n.$$

(ii) Neutrons as projectiles :

$$_7\text{N}^{14} + n \to {}_7\text{N}^{15} \to {}_3\text{Li}^7 + {}_2\text{He}^4 + {}_2\text{He}^4$$

$$_5\text{B}^{10} + n \to {}_5\text{B}^{11} \to {}_3\text{Li}^7 + {}_2\text{He}^4.$$

(iii) γ-rays as projectiles :

$$_1H^2 + hv \rightarrow {}_1H^1 + {}_0n^1$$
$$_{15}P^{31} + hv \rightarrow {}_{15}P^{30} + {}_0n^1.$$

(iv) Deuteron as projectiles :

$$_1H^2 + {}_1H^2 \rightarrow {}_2He^4 \rightarrow {}_1H^3 + p$$
$$_3Li^7 + {}_1H^2 \rightarrow {}_4Be^9 \rightarrow {}_2He^4 + {}_2He^4 + n.$$

67. *What do you mean by Induced Radioactivity?*

Ans. The radioactivity produced by the bombardment of high energy articles, like α-particle, proton, neutron, etc., with certain substances is called induced radioactivity. For example, when α-particle strikes a boron atom, the latter is transformed into a nitrogen isotope. This nitrogen isotope is radioactive which reduces to carbon with the emission of positron,

$$_5B^{10} + {}_2He^4 \rightarrow {}_7N^{13} + {}_0n^1$$
$$_7N^{13} \rightarrow {}_6C^{12} + e^+.$$

68. *What is an electron?*

Ans. The electrons are negatively charged particle having mass equal to $\frac{1}{1836}$th of that of a hydrogen atom. The charge of each particle is 1.6×10^{20} e.m.u.

69. *Enumerate the different sources from which the electrons are obtained.*

Ans. The various sources from which electrons are obtained:

(i) Cathode rays.

(ii) X-rays, striking on a metal target.

(iii) Radioactive substance emitting β-rays.

(iv) Photoelectric cells.

(v) Thermoionic tube.

70. *Give the nature of the following particles: (a) Proton, (b) Positron, (c) Neutron, (d) Meson, (e) Neutrino, (f) Deuteron.*

Ans. (a) Proton: The protons are positively charged particles having mass 1836 times that of an electron and charge 1.6×20^{-20} e.m.u. The mass of proton is 1.67×10^{-24} gm.

(b) Positron: It is the positive counterpart of an electron having charge equal to that of an electron but of opposite sign.

(c) Neutron: Neutrons are neutral particles having zero charge, and mass is almost equal to that of proton. When beryllium is struck by α-particles, neutrons are produced.

(d) Meson: Mesons are unstable particle having mass equal to 200 times that of electron. They may be either positively or negatively charged.

(e) Neutrino: These particles are assumed to have no charge and to have mass smaller than that of an electron.

(f) Deuteron: It is the isotope of hydrogen and it consists of one proton, one neutron and one electron. Mass of deuteron is 2.0136 a.m.u.

71. *What are Cosmic Rays?*

Ans. Cosmic rays are very penetrating electromagnetic radiations. The source of cosmic rays is beyond our galaxy. It consists largely protons before they come into the earth's atmosphere. After the interaction with nuclei of the atmosphere mesons are produced. But mesons are very unstable particles which easily convert into electrons. Cosmic rays reaching the earth consisted of two main components of considerable different penetrating powers; one is the soft component (consists of electron, positrons and photons) and the other is the hard component (consists of mesons). Soft components are absorbed by 10 cm of lead. The linear absorption coefficient of soft component is about 0.55 per metre of water at sea level ; for the hard component the coefficient is about 0.1.

72. *From which instrument the charged particles are accelerated?*

Ans. The charged particles are accelerated by using cyclotron. The energy associated with the accelerated particle is about 100 MeV.

73. *Write the names of some experimental techniques which are used to detect charged particles.*

Ans. To detect charged particles the following experimental techniques are used:

1. Geiger-Müler counter.

2. Scintillation counter.

3. Ionization chamber.

4. Cloud chamber.

74. *What do you know about Calcutta Fixed Energy Cyclotron and Calcutta Variable Energy Cyclotron?*

Ans. Calcutta Fixed Energy Cyclotron: This cyclotron is situated at the Saha Institute of Nuclear Physics. It is a fixed 4 MeV proton cyclotron. With this cyclotron proton beam of strength 50 μA is accelerated to a proton beam of strength 10 mA. The strength of magnetic field is 7 kilogauss and frequency of the oscillator used is 10 MHz. The order of vacuum is $\lambda \times 10^{-5}$ mm of Hg.

Calcutta Variable Energy Cyclotron: This cyclotron is situated at Salt Lake. It will deliver a beam of high energy particles—protons of energies between 6 MeV and 60 MeV, alpha particles between 25 MeV and 130 MeV and deuterons between 12 MeV and 65 MeV. The energy of the particle can be varied by varying magnetic field and electric field.

Atomic Structure

75. *What do you know about the Rutherford-Bohr model of atom?*

Ans. According to Rutherford-Bohr model of atom, the atom consists of two parts : a positively charged core called the nucleus and extranuclear electrons which revolve round the nucleus in definite orbits. In a neutral atom, number of electrons and positive charges are equal. The size of an atom is of the order of 10^{-8} cm, whereas the nuclear size is of the order of 10^{-13} cm.

76. *From what experiment, Rutherford gave the atom model?*

Ans. On the basis of the experiment on α-scattering Rutherford proposed the model for an atom.

77. *State Bohr's first and second postulate.*

Ans. First postulate—The electron can only rotate in certain orbits obeying specified conditions. Corresponding to these allowed orbits, stationary state exists in the atom. The atom can remain indefinitely in one of these stationary states, i.e., the electron can rotate in one of the allowed orbits, without radiating energy.

Second postulate—If an electron is rotating in an orbit for which the energy of the stationary state of the atom is En_2, then it can make a quantum jump to another allowed orbit for which the energy of the stationary state of the atom is En_1. Furthermore, in doing so, it will radiate energy of frequency v given by

$En_1 - En_2 = hv$, where h is Planck's constant and $En_2 > En_1$.

78. *Write the expression and the value of Rydberg's constant.*

Ans. Rydberg's constant is expressed as

$$R = \frac{2\pi^2 e^4 m}{ch^3},$$

where e = electronic charge = 4.8×10^{-10} e.s.u.,

m = mass of an electron = 9.11×10^{-28} gm,

c = velocity of light = 3×10^{10} cm/second,

h = Planck's constant = 6.62×10^{-27} erg-second.

Therefore, the value of the Rydberg's constant

$$R = \frac{2 \times (3.14)^2 \times (4.8 \times 10^{-10})^4 \times 9.11 \times 10^{-28}}{3 \times 10^{10} \times (6.62 \times 10^{-27})^3} = 10.99 \times 10^5 \text{ cm}^{-1}.$$

79. *Give the value of orbital radius for the ground state of hydrogen atom.*

Ans. The orbital radius is given by

$$r = \frac{n^2 h^2}{4\pi^2 m Z e^2}.$$

For ground state $n = 1$, and $Z = 1$ in case of hydrogen atom.

So, $r = \dfrac{h^2}{4\pi^2 m e^2} = \dfrac{(6.62 \times 10^{-27})^2}{4(3.14)^2 \times 9.11 \times 10^{-28} \times (4.8 \times 10^{-10})^2}$

$= 0.527 \text{ Å}.$

80. *'Ionization potential for the hydrogen atom is 13.64 eV.' Justify the statement.'*

Ans. The ionization potential is the energy necessary to remove the electron from the ground state.

So the ionization energy E_i is given by

$$E_i = \frac{2\pi^2 e^4 m}{h^2} = \frac{2 \times (3.14)^2 \times (4.8 \times 10^{-10})^4 \times 9.11 \times 10^{-28}}{(6.62 \times 10^{-27})^2} \text{ erg}$$

$$= \frac{2 \times (3.14)^2 \times (4.8 \times 10^{-10})^4 \times 9.11 \times 10^{-28}}{(6.62 \times 10^{-27})^2 \times 1.6 \times 10^{-12}} \text{ eV}$$

$= 13.64 \text{ eV}.$

81. *State Pauli's Exclusion Principle.*

Ans. Pauli's Exclusion Principle states that no two electrons in an atom can exist in the same quantum state, i.e., no two electrons can have the same set of four quantum numbers n, l, m_l and σ.

82. *What are the functions of different quantum numbers?*

Ans. (i) Principal quantum number $n(1, 2, \ldots)$ gives the energy and orbital radius of the electron.

(ii) Azimuthal quantum number l $(0, 1, 2, \ldots, n-1)$ gives the shape of the orbit.

(iii) Magnetic quantum number $m_e (l, l-1, -0, \ldots, -l)$ gives the possible space orientations of the orbital angular momentum.

83. *Write the ground state configurations of (i) Sodium $(Z = 11)$, (ii) Neon $(Z = 10)$, (iii) Potassium $(Z = 19)$ and (iv) Helium $(Z = 2)$.*

Ans.

(i) In case of Sodium, $Z = 11$.

∴ the configuration will be $1s^2 2s^2 2p^6 3s^1$.

(ii) For Neon, $Z = 10$.

∴ the configuration will be $1s^2 2s^2 2p^6$.

(iii) For Potassium, $Z = 19$.

∴ the configuration will be $1s^2 2s^2 2p^6 3s^2 3p^6 4s^1$.

(iv) For Helium, $Z = 2$.

∴ the configuration will be $1s^2$.

84. *What will be the wavelength of H_α line of hydrogen in the Balmer series, if the value of Rydberg Constant is 1.099×10^5 cm^{-1}.*

Ans. The wave number of a line is given by

$$\bar{v} = \frac{1}{\lambda} = R \left(\frac{1}{n_1^2} - \frac{1}{n_2^2} \right).$$

For H_α line of Balmer series $n_1 = 2$, $n_2 = 3$.

$$\therefore \quad \bar{v} = 1.099 \times 10^5 \left(\frac{1}{4} - \frac{1}{9} \right) = \frac{1.099 \times 10^5 \times 5}{36}$$

$$= \frac{5.495}{36} \times 10^5 \text{ cm}^{-1}.$$

So the wavelength of H_α line will be

$$\lambda = \frac{36}{5.495} \times 10^{-5} \text{ cm}$$

$$= 6549 \text{ Å}.$$

85. *Define Atomic Weight and Atomic Number of an element.*

Ans. Atomic Weight—It is the weight of the total number of protons and neutrons in an atom.

Atomic Number—Atomic number is the total number of protons.

86. *What is mass defect?*

Ans. The atomic nucleus consists of protons and neutrons. From the knowledge of masses of protons and neutrons, mass of the nucleus can be determined. Then this value is compared with the experimental value. It is found that the experimental value is less than that of predicted value. This discrepancy is known as mass defect and mathematically expressed as

$$\Delta m = M - A,$$

where M is the total mass of protons and neutrons constituting the nucleus and A is the nuclear mass.

87. *Define nuclear binding energy.*

Ans. When a number of protons and neutrons are combined to form a nucleus, a loss of mass Δm results, i.e., the mass of the resultant nucleus is less than that of its constituents. This mass loss is equivalent to an energy loss of E given by $E = \Delta m \cdot c^2$, where c is the velocity of light. E is called the binding energy of the nucleus.

88. *What is the expression for nuclear spin?*

Ans. If Ze is the nuclear charge and m is the nuclear mass, then

$$\text{spin} = \frac{Zeh}{4\pi mc},$$

where h is the Planck's constant.

89. *Write the value of nuclear radius.*

Ans. From neutro-scattering experiment, the nuclear radius is found to be $1.45 \times 10^{-13} A^{1/3}$ cm and from electron scattering the value comes out to be $1.1 \times 10^{-13} A^{1/3}$ cm.

90. *The atomic weight of lithium is 7 and its atomic number is 3. What is the constitution of lithium atom?*

Ans. In the nucleus of lithium, there are 3 protons and 4 neutrons. Further, there are 3 orbital electrons.

91. *In what respect are the cathode-ray particles the same and in what respect do they differ?*

Ans. Charge to mass ratio of these particles are found to be same but the velocity is different for different particles.

92. *'X-rays possess dual character'—explain.*

Ans. X-rays have a dual nature. In a class of phenomena like reflection, refraction, interference, diffraction and polarization, they behave as waves. In another class involving emission and absorption of X-rays, they behave as particles.

93. *What do you mean by 'hard X-rays', 'soft X-rays' and 'characteristic X-rays'.*

Ans. If the applied p.d. between the anode and the cathode is very high, X-rays produced are called hard X-rays. If the applied p.d. is low, then the X-rays are called soft X-rays.

If powerful X-rays are allowed to fall on a metallic target, secondary X-rays are emitted, the wavelength of which are characteristic of the element used as a target called characteristic X-rays.

94. *Establish the relation $\lambda = \frac{h}{p}$, where the symbols have usual significance.*

Ans. If a photon is equivalent to a wave of frequency ν, then its energy

$$E = h\nu \ (h = \text{Planck's constant}).$$

On the other hand, if a photon is treated as a particle of mass m, then

$$E = mc^2.$$

$\therefore \qquad E = h\nu = mc^2. \tag{1}$

Again, the momentum of a photon,

$$p = mc. \tag{2}$$

From equations (1) and (2), we get

$$p = mc = \frac{h\nu}{c} = \frac{h}{\lambda}.$$

$$\therefore \quad \lambda = \frac{h}{p}.$$

95. *'In a hydrogen atom we have only one electron but its emission spectrum shows many lines.' Explain.*

Ans. A hydrogen atom contains one electron only which may occupy any one of the permitted stationary orbits. When hydrogen atom is excited by the absorption of energy from outside, then this electron is promoted to any higher energy orbit.

According to Bohr's theory, the higher energy state being unstable, the electron jumps to the lower energy orbit emitting radiation of certain frequency. In the excited state, electron may occupy many higher energy orbits and may jump to any lower energy orbit; corresponding to each orbit change, there will be emission of spectral lines. Thus emission spectrum of hydrogen atom shows many lines.

96. *Electrons are readily liberated from lithium when it is irradiated with ultraviolet light than from fluorine. Why?*

Ans. In the outermost shell of lithium atom, there is only one electron while to complete the outermost shell of fluorine one more electron is only required. Electron in lithium is loosely bounded in one hand and electron in fluorine is tightly bounded on the other hand. That is why electrons are readily liberated from lithium.

97. *Can a hydrogen atom absorb a photon whose energy exceeds its binding energy 13.6 eV?*

Ans. By absorbing an energy more than 13.6 eV, hydrogen atom no longer remains as hydrogen atom. It will split into proton and electron.

98. *Chlorine has a proton number 17 and as occurring in nature, a relative atomic mass 35.5. There are two isotopes of it with nuclear numbers 35 and 37. What further information can be obtained from the data given? Calculate the relative abundance of the two isotopes in naturally occurring chlorine.*

Ans. One isotope of chlorine contains $(37 - 17) = 20$ neutrons and the other isotope contains $(35 - 17) = 18$ neutrons.

Let us assume that the naturally occurring chlorine have x fraction isotope of nuclear number 37 and $(1 - x)$ fraction isotope of nuclear number 35.

$$\therefore \quad 37x + (1 - x)35 = 35.5$$

or, $$\frac{x}{1 - x} = \frac{0.25}{0.75} = \frac{1}{3}.$$

This gives the required ratio.

99. *The charge of an electron is 4.8×10^{-10} e.s.u. Calculate the value of its charge in e.m.u. and coulomb.*

Ans. We have

the charge of an electron, $Q_e = 4.8 \times 10^{-10}$ e.s.u.

$$= \frac{4.8 \times 10^{-10}}{3 \times 10^{10}} \text{ e.m.u.}$$

$$[\because \ 1 \text{ e.m.u.} = 3 \times 10^{10} \text{ e.s.u.}]$$

$$= 1.6 \times 10^{20} \text{ e.m.u.}$$

Again,   1 coulomb = $\frac{1}{10}$ e.m.u. of charge.

$\therefore$ $Q_e = 1.6 \times 10^{-20}$ e.m.u.

                = 1.6×10^{-19} coulomb.

100. *The specific charge of an electron is 1.76×10^7 e.m.u./gm. What is its mass? (Given that the charge of an electron is 4.8×10^{-10} e.s.u.)*

Ans. Specific charge of an electron, $\dfrac{Q_e}{m_e} = 1.76 \times 10^7$ e.m.u./gm

and its charge, $Q_e = 4.8 \times 10^{-10}$ e.s.u.

$$= \frac{4.8 \times 10^{-10}}{3 \times 10^{10}} \text{ e.m.u.}$$

$$= 1.6 \times 10^{-20} \text{ e.m.u.}$$

$\therefore$ mass of an electron, $m_e = \dfrac{Q_e}{Q_e/m_e}$

$$= \frac{1.6 \times 10^{-20}}{1.76 \times 10^7}$$

$$= 9.1 \times 10^{-28} \text{ gm.}$$

101. *Of α-rays, β-rays, γ-rays, cathode rays, positive rays and X-rays indicate which are the streams of charged particles or electromagnetic radiations.*

Ans. Cathode rays, positive rays, α-rays and β-rays are streams of charged particles while X-rays and γ-rays are electromagnetic radiations of high penetrating power.

102. *Write down the nature of cathode rays, positive rays, α-rays and β-rays.*

Ans. Cathode rays are streams of negatively charged particles, i.e., electrons. Positive rays are streams of positive ions.

α-rays are streams of positively charged helium nuclei and β-rays are negatively charged high speed electrons.

103. *Is there any similarity between positive rays and α-rays?*

Ans. Yes, both the rays are streams of positively charged ions.

104. *What are the basic differences between the α-rays and positive rays?*

Ans.

α-rays	Positive rays
(i) α-rays are spontaneously emitted in all directions from the nuclei of radioactive material. This emission cannot be influenced by any external process.	(i) Positive rays are produced by the movement of positive ions in an electric field from anode towards cathode in the cathode-ray tube.
(ii) Velocity of α-particle is equal to $\frac{1}{10}$th the velocity of light. Also its energy lies in the range of 1 to 9 MeV.	(ii) Velocity and energy of the positive ray particles are small in comparison to α-particles.

105. *Compare the properties of cathode rays and β-rays.*

Ans.

Cathode rays	β-rays
(i) Cathode rays are streams of negatively charged particles, i.e., electrons.	(i) β-rays are also streams of negatively charged particles.
(ii) Cathode rays are produced when they move in the direction from cathode to anode.	(ii) β-rays are spontaneously emitted in all directions from nuclei of suitable radioactive substances and this cannot be influenced by any external process.
(iii) By increasing the p.d. across the electrodes of the cathode-ray tube, the velocity and hence the energy of the the cathode rays can be increased.	(iii) The energy of β-particle emitted from nucleus is much higher ($\sim$ 1 MeV) compared to the cathode rays.

106. *Examine the similarity and dissimilarity of nature of X-rays and γ-rays.*

Ans.

X-rays	γ-rays
(i) X-rays are invisible electromagnetic waves of velocity equal to that of light.	(i) γ-rays are also invisible electromagnetic waves with a velocity equal to that of light.
(ii) X-rays have a penetrating power.	(ii) Compared to X-rays, the penetrating power of γ-rays is extremely high.
(iii) Its wavelength is high.	(iii) It has a very small wavelength, which is $\frac{1}{100}$th the wavelength of X-rays.
(iv) If electrons with high speed are made to strike a target, its energy is converted to X-ray photon. So X-rays have to be produced.	(iv) γ-rays are emitted spontaneously from the nuclei of radioactive substances.

107. *'In the nucleus there is no free existence of electron.' How then the emission of β-particles from the nucleus of radioactive material be explained?*

Ans. In the nucleus, there exists neutron which may be considered as the combination of proton ($_1H^1$) and electron ($_{-1}e^0$). Thus we have

$$_0n^1 \rightarrow {_1H^1} + {_{-1}e^0}.$$

In the case of a radioactive material also a neutron breaks into a proton and an electron. The electron as β-particle comes out of the nucleus.

108. *'α-rays may be considered as the stream of nuclei of helium gas.' Explain.*

Ans. We know that the α-rays are stream of positively charged particles. Experimental determination shows that the charge and mass of α-particle are the same as the helium nucleus (He^{++}). In fact, Rutherford and Royd's experiment established that α-particles are identical with helium nuclei. Thus we may conclude that the α-rays are streams of helium nuclei.

109. *What is the velocity acquired by a charged particle when it moves across a potential difference V ?*

Ans. If m, e and v are respectively the mass, charge and velocity acquired by a charged particle, then its kinetic energy is expressed as

$$\frac{1}{2}mv^2 = Ve.$$

So the velocity, $v = \sqrt{\dfrac{2Ve}{m}}$.

110. *Do the positive rays originating in a gas have the same mass? If not, why?*

Ans. Positive rays when originate from a particular gas, being its ionized atoms in motion, should have the same mass. If, on the other hand, the mass be not same, it will indicate that the ionized atoms are of different masses.

Atoms of same gas with different masses indicate more than one isotope of the gas. When positive rays originate from a mixture of the gas they have their masses different.

111. *'At the time of production of cathode rays in a discharge tube positive rays are also produced.' Explain how.*

Ans. When moving with a high speed towards the anode, cathode-ray particles collide with atoms of the gases and dislodge one electron or more from each of them when they become positive ions. The positively charged ions move towards cathode in the direction of the electric field and constitute the positive rays. Thus at the time of production of cathode rays in a discharge tube, positive rays are also produced.

112. *Will the specific charge of all (a) cathode-ray particles, (b) positive-ray particles be the same? Give reasons against your answer.*

Ans. (a) Cathode-ray particles are electrons with their fixed mass and charge. So its specific charge is fixed.

(b) Positive rays are stream of positively ionized atoms which have different masses and their charges also may not be same. So the specific charges of all positive-ray particles are not same.

113. *Will the specific charge of He^{++} ions and α-particles be the same?— Explain.*

Ans. The specific charge of an α-particle is slightly less than that of the He^{++} ions.

α-particle emitted from a radioactive substance is helium nucleus (He^{++}) in motion. α-particles have a velocity of about 10% of the velocity of light and so its relativistic mass increases slightly. As this is slightly greater than the rest mass of He^{++}, the specific charge of α-particle is little less.

114. *Is the specific charge of a positive-ray particle greater or less than that of a cathode-ray particle? Explain.*

Ans. The specific charge of positive-ray particle is less. Since the mass of a positive ion is much greater than that of an electron, so its specific charge is less than that of a cathode-ray particle.

115. *How is it ascertained whether a ray is a stream of charged particles or an electromagnetic wave?*

Ans. If an electric field or a magnetic field is applied at right angle to the ray and if there is a deflection on a fluorescent screen, then one may conclude that it is a stream of charged particles. On the other hand, if it shows no deflection, then it is an electromagnetic wave.

116. *Do positive rays and cathode rays deflect in the same direction?*

Ans. We know that the cathode rays are the stream of negatively charged particles. Hence, for the same magnetic field positive rays and cathode rays are deflected in the opposite directions.

117. *Why are the cathode rays or the positive rays deflected by a magnetic field?*

Ans. Either the cathode rays or the positive rays are stream of charged particle and so they indicate electric current. If a magnetic field is applied at right angle to that current, a deflection occurs.

118. *When the path of motion of the charged particle is deflected by a magnetic field, on what factors does the magnitude of the deflecting force act? Find also the magnitude of force when a magnetic field is applied along the direction of velocity of the charged particle.*

Ans. If v is the velocity of a particle of charge e, H is the strength of the magnetic field and θ is the angle between the direction of velocity and that of the field, then the deflecting force F can be written as

$$F = Hev \sin \theta.$$

Thus F depends on H, e, v and $\sin \theta$.

If H is applied along the direction of v, we have $\theta = 0$.

$\therefore \quad F = 0.$

Hence no deflection occurs in that case.

119. *If a H^+ ion and a He^{++} ion move with the same velocity normally through a particular magnetic field, which ion will be deflected more?*

Ans. The deflection of H^+ ion will be more. Its deflection will be twice the deflection of He^{++} ion.

120. *'When a magnetic field is applied perpendicular to a ray, it bends like a circle.' Show on what factors and how the radius of curvature of the ray depends.*

Ans. With the application of a magnetic field if a ray bends, it represents a stream of charged particles. If e, m and v are respectively the charge, mass and velocity of the particle, then the force due to the magnetic field is

$$Hev = \frac{mv^2}{r},$$

where r is the radius of curvature. Its value is given by

$$r = \frac{v}{H(e/m)}.$$

Thus we find that the radius of curvature r depends on v, H and e/m.

121. *How do X-rays differ from ordinary light rays?*

Ans. (i) X-rays have high penetrating power than the ordinary light rays. Substances which are opaque to ordinary light are transparent to X-rays.

(ii) The wavelength of X-rays is much smaller than the wavelength of any ordinary light. The wavelength of any ordinary light is 6000 Å (say) while that of X-rays may be 1 Å.

122. *What minimum wavelength of X-rays are produced when a voltage of 1 million volt is applied?*

Ans. The minimum wavelength of X-rays produced λ_{min} is given by

$$\lambda_{min} = \frac{12412}{V} \text{ Å}.$$

Here, $V = 1$ million volts $= 10^5$ volts.

$$\therefore \qquad \lambda_{min} = \frac{12412}{10^5} \text{ Å} = 0.12412 \text{ Å}.$$

123. *How is the penetrating power of X-rays related to the applied voltage?*

Ans. If λ is the wavelength and V the voltage applied, then

$$\text{penetrating power} \propto \frac{1}{\lambda} \propto V.$$

So greater is the voltage applied the less is the wavelength of X-rays produced and greater is the penetrating power.

124. *How are soft X-rays converted to hard X-rays?*

Ans. Soft X-rays are those which have small penetrating power and operated with comparatively small voltage, V. If the voltage V is increased sufficiently, hard X-rays of high penetrating power are obtained.

UNIVERSITY QUESTION PAPERS

Calcutta University Question Papers

2003

Physics (General)

Second Paper

Full Marks 100

The figures in the margin indicate full marks.

Group A

1. Answer *any ten* questions : 2×10

   (a) Compare the spectra produced by a prism and diffraction grating.

   (b) What do you mean by optical activity?

   (c) How does polarized light differ from unpolarized light?

   (d) The e.m.f. of a cell can be determined accurately with the help of a potentiometer—explain.

   (e) Mention main differences between an Ammeter and a Voltmeter.

   (f) What is Wattless Current?

   (g) Find the expression for the energy of a charged condenser.

   (h) State Pauli's exclusion principle.

   (i) What is meant by Raman effect?

   (j) Why soft iron is used as the core of an electromagnet?

   (k) What is a non-inductive resistance coil?

   (l) What are hard and soft X-rays?

   (m) What are the differences between Joule's Effect and Peltier Effect?

   (n) Draw an AND gate and write its Truth Table.

   (o) What is Zener potential?

Group B

Answer *any one* question.

2. (a) Explain with a diagram how and where a Fresnel bi-prism froms an interference pattern of light. 6

   (b) Obtain an expression for the separation of fringes in the above pattern. 6

   (c) A glass plate of thickness 3 mm is placed between a point source of light and a screen 3 cm apart.

   (i) What is the optical path between the source and the screen?

   (ii) What is the number of waves between them? (Given, μ (glass) = 1.5 and $\mu = 6000$ Å.) 4

3. (a) What are the essential differences between interference and diffraction of light? 2

   (b) Describe and explain the Fraunhofer diffraction pattern obtained with a narrow single slit illuminated by a parallel beam of monochromatic light incident normally on the plane of the slit. Indicate the variation of intensity in the diffraction pattern. 7

(c) Define specific rotation for both solids and solutions.   4

(d) How many lines per cm are there in a grating which gives a deflection of 30° in the first order at wavelength 6×10^{-5} cm?   3

Group C

Answer *any two* questions.

4. (a) What is meant by total normal induction over a surface? State and prove Gauss's theorem on total normal induction.   4

(b) Find the resultant capacity of combination of condensers when three condensers of capacities C_1, C_2 and C_3 are connected (i) in series and (ii) in parallel.   7

(c) A metal ball of radius 5 cm is given a charge of 100 e.s.u. Find the force acting on it per unit area.   5

5. (a) Applying Kirchhoff's laws obtain an expression for the current through the galvanometer in an unbalanced Wheatstone bridge. Hence indicate the relation amongst its resistances in the balanced condition of the bridge.   5 + 2

(b) State and explain Norton's theorem for a simple two terminal network.   2 + 4

(c) Find the neutral and inversion temperatures of a thermocouple of which the constants are : $a = 10.3\,\mu V/°C$ and $b = 0.018\,\mu V/°C^2$ the cold junction being at $0\,°C$.   3

6. (a) Discuss the theory of Helmholtz double coil galvanometer, assuming the expression for the magnetic field at a point on the axis of a circular coil carrying current. Find its reduction factor.   6 + 2

(b) What is Lorentz force? Write its expression.   2

(c) Define coefficient of self-induction of a circuit. Calculate its value for two long parallel wires.   2 + 4

7. (a) A steady e.m.f. E is applied to a circuit consisting a resistance R and an inductance L. Discuss the growth of current. What do you mean by time-constant of the circuit?   4 + 2

(b) Illustrate the nature of the hysteresis loop of a small piece of steel and that of a soft iron piece. Indicate from these how the two materials differ in their magnetic behaviour.   3 + 3

(c) A circuit has its resistance 20 ohms and inductance 0.1 henry. If the current through the circuit at any instant be 1 ampere and the same is growing at the rate of 20 A/sec. What is the e.m.f. applied in the circuit?   4

8. (a) Obtain an expression for the instantaneous value of current in an a.c. circuit containing a resistance R and a capacitance C in series when a sinusoidal e.m.f. $E = E_0 \sin pt$ is applied in the circuit.   9

(b) Find the phase angle of the current relative to e.m.f. Does the current lag or lead with respect to e.m.f.?   2 + 1

(c) Calculate the power factor of a 50 cycles/sec a.c. circuit in which an inductance of 0.1 henry and a resistance of 20 ohms are connected in series.   4

Group D

Answer *any one* question.

9. (a) Define α and β of a transistor, and find the relation between them.
$$2+2+2$$

(b) Current amplification factor of common base configuration transistor is 0.88. Find the value of the base current when the emitter current is 1 mA. 4

(c) Explain with a diagram the function of a bridge rectifier. 6

10. (a) Perform the following addition and subtraction of binary members :
$$2+2$$

(i) $111 + 11 + 111$ (ii) $11010 - 1101$

(b) Show how you can form an AND gate and all OR gate from NAND gates. Verify with appropriate truth tables. $4+4$

(c) State De Morgan's theorems. 4

Group E

Answer *any one* question.

11. (a) What is known as matter wave? What is its wavelength? $2+1$

(b) Write down Heisenberg's uncertainty Principle and explain it. 4

(c) Discuss Einstein's photoelectric equation. What do you mean by threshold frequency and stopping potential? Mention their relations with work function. $3+4+2$

12. (a) From Bohr's theory, obtain an expression for the energy of hydrogen atom. 8

(b) State Moseley's law for the characteristic X-ray spectra and its implication with respect to periodic table. $2+4$

(c) State the basic postulates of the special theory of relativity. 2

13. Write short notes on *any two* of the following : 8×2

(a) Nuclear reactor (b) Zone plate

(c) Transformer-principle of action (d) NOR gate as universal gate

(e) Raman effect.

2004

The figures in the margin indicate full marks.

Group A

1. Answer *any ten* questions : 2×10

(a) What is a wavefront?

(b) Why the centre of Newton's rings is dark?

(c) Compare between a zone plate and a convex lens.

(d) State two differences between interference and diffraction.

(e) 'The capacitance of a capacitor is 1 μF'—explain the statement.

(f) Why a meter bridge is not suitable for measurement of a high resistance?

(g) State and explain Fleming's left-hand rule.

(h) What is thermoelectric power? Draw a graph to show the variation of thermoelectric power with temperature difference between hot and cold junctions of a thermocouple.

(i) Define one tesla. How are tesla and gauss related?

(j) Name the unit of coefficient of self-induction in S.I. system and define it.

(k) What is meant by Q-factor of an a.c. series resonant circuit?

(l) What is meant by a logic gate?

(m) Mention two differences between visible light rays and X-rays.

(n) How does a free neutron decay?

(o) What is meant by Compton effect?

Group B

Answer *any one* question.

2. (a) Write down the conditions for interference of light.   2

(b) Explain the theory of formation of Newton's ring and from it deduce the working formula for determination of wavelength of monochromatic light.   2 + 5

(c) The diameter of the 3rd bright Newton's ring is 0.00181 m and that of the 23rd bright ring is 0.00501 m. If the radius of curvature of the lower surface of the lens be of 0.50 m, calculate the wavelength of the light used.   4

(d) Distinguish between Fresnel type and Fraunhofer type of diffraction.   3

3. (a) What is meant by resolving power of a plane diffraction grating? Obtain an expression for it.   3 + 5

(b) Describe briefly the construction of a Nicol prism. Explain how polarization of light takes place by this prism.   5 + 3

Group C

Answer *any two* questions.

4. (a) Calculate the electric potential and intensity at any point in free space produced by an electric dipole.   8

(b) Calculate the capacity of an air-filled parallel plate capacitor.   3

(c) A sphere of radius 5 cm charged with 50 e.s.u. of charge, is connected by a conducting wire with another sphere having radius twice the former one and charged with the same amount of charge. Calculate the loss of energy.   5

5. (a) State and explain Thevenin's theorem for a simple two terminal network.   2 + 4

(b) State Laplace's law regarding the magnetic intensity due to a current carrying conductor. Use this law to calculate the magnetic intensity at a point on the axis of a circular coil carrying current.   2 + 6

(c) The radius of a circular loop of wire is 25 mm and it carries a current 750 mA. Calculate the magnetic intensity produced at the centre of circular loop.   2

6. **(a)** Illustrate the law of intermediate metal and the law of intermediate temperature in connection with thermoelectricity. $2 + 2$

(b) What is Peltier effect? What is the difference between Peltier effect and Joule heating effect? $1 + 2$

(c) The thermo e.m.f. of a thermocouple is e (in μV) $= 16.34t - 0.021t^2$ when one junction of the thermocouple is at $0\,°C$. Determine **(i)** the neutral temperature and **(ii)** Peltier coefficient at $100\,°C$. 4

(d) What do you mean by coefficient of self-inductance? How is a non-inductive coil constructed? What do you mean by mutual induction? $1 + 2 + 2$

7. **(a)** Derive the expression for the growth of charge on a condenser connected in series to a resistor, and the circuit is fed by a steady d.c. e.m.f. 6

(b) A 40 μF capacitor in series with a 2000 Ω resistor is connected across a 200 V d.c. source. Calculate **(i)** the initial current and **(ii)** the time constant. 4

(c) Define intensity of magnetization, magnetic induction and magnetic susceptibility. Obtain a relation among them. $3 + 3$

8. **(a)** An alternating current is represented by $i = i_0 \sin \omega t$. Find the mean and the r.m.s. values of the current in terms of the peak value. 4

(b) Derive an expression for the instantaneous value of current in a circuit containing an inductance L in series with a resistance R when an e.m.f. $E = E_0 \sin \omega t$ is applied to the circuit. 8

(c) An inductor (0.5 H) and a resistance (10 ohms) are connected in series in an a.c. circuit of frequency 20 Hz. What is the value of power factor of the circuit? 4

Group D

Answer *any one* question.

9. **(a)** What is a Zener voltage? Explain the use of a Zener diode in the stabilisation of voltage. $2 + 6$

(b) Draw and explain the output characteristic curves for a transistor in CE configuration. $2 + 6$

10. **(a)** Convert the following decimal numbers to binary equivalent : 4
   (i) 923; **(ii)** 4.9.

(b) Perform the following binary operations : 6
   (i) $11001 + 01111$; **(ii)** $11001 - 10011$; **(iii)** 1010×111.

(c) Draw an OR gate for positive logic having two diodes and explain its operation. $2 + 4$

Group E

Answer *any one* question.

11. **(a)** Write down the special Lorentz transformation equations. With the help of these, establish the length contraction and time dilation formulae. $3 + 4 + 4$

(b) State Pauli's exclusion principle and explain briefly its significance. $2 + 3$

12. **(a)** Starting from the relation of variation of mass with velocity, establish the equivalence relation between mass and energy.   4

   (b) Deduce expression for half-life and mean-life of a radioactive element. What is the relation between them?   2 + 3 + 1

   (c) How the method of radio-carbon dating can be used for age determination?   3

   (d) The distance between the cathode and the anticathode in an X-ray tube is 1.5 m. If the cut-off wavelength is 30×10^{-12} m, find the electric field between the cathode and the anticathode. (Given, $h = 6.62 \times 10^{-34}$ J·sec, $e = 1.6 \times 10^{-19}$ C)   3

13. Write short notes on (**any two**) :   8 × 2

   (a) Moseley's law   **(b)** Nuclear fission   **(c)** Photoelectirc effect

   (d) Artificial radioactivity   **(e)** Bohr's theory of hydrogen spectra

2005

The figures in the margin indicate full marks.

(Compulsory Questions)

1. Answer **any ten** questions :   2 × 10

   (a) Distinguish between Fresnel and Fraunhofer class of diffraction.

   (b) What is the relation between path difference and phase difference.

   (c) Distinguish between prism spectrum and grating spectrum.

   (d) How can you measure a current of 5 amperes with the help of a milliammeter of range 50 mA? The resistance of the milliammeter is 5 ohms.

   (e) What is Curie point?

   (f) Why is soft iron used in transformer core?

   (g) What is an electric dipole? Define dipole moment.

   (h) State Norton's theorem.

   (i) Define Peltier coefficient. What is its unit?

   (j) What is a non-inductive coil?

   (k) What is 'Choke'? Why is it used in a.c. circuits?

   (l) State Pauli's exclusion principle.

   (m) Write down the relation between the rest mass of a body and its moving mass.

   (n) Draw the output characteristics of a *P-N-P* transistor in common emitter configuration.

   (o) (i) Convert the decimal number 23 into binary number; (ii) 10010 − 1001 =? (Numbers are binary.)

Group A

Answer **any two** questions.

2. **(a)** What is interference of light? Deduce an expression for the intensity of light at a point due to superposition of waves coming from two light sources. Hence find the conditions of constructive and destructive interference.   1 + 4 + 2

(b) In Young's experiment for interference of light, the slits being 0.2 cm apart, are illuminated by yellow light ($\lambda = 589$ Å) Calculate the fringe which is observed on a screen placed 1 m from the plane of the slits.   3

3. (a) Explain the rectilinear propagation of light with the help of wave theory.

3

(b) What is a Zone plate? Find an expression for its primary focal length.

$2 + 5$

4. (a) State Brewster's law.   2

(b) Light reflected from a smooth ice surface is found to be completely polarized. Find the angle of incidence of light if the refractive index for ice is 1.309.   4

(c) What are double refraction and optical activity? $2 + 2$

Group B

Answer *any three* questions.

5. (a) State and prove Gauss's theorem in electrostatics. $1 + 3$

(b) Two condensers of capacitances C_1 and C_2 are charged to potentials V_1 and $V_2 (V_2 > V_1)$ respectively. Calculate the loss in energy when the condensers are connected by a wire. Does it violate the principle of conservation of energy? Explain. $4 + 2$

6. (a) State and explain Kirchhoff's laws for electrical circuit.   4

(b) State and explain Norton's theorem for a simple two terminal network.

$2 + 4$

7. (a) Find an expression for the magnetic field at a point on the axis of a circular coil carrying current.   5

(b) Define coefficient of self-induction of a circuit. Calculate its value for two long parallel wires. $1 + 4$

8. (a) A circuit containing an inductor and a resistor is connected with a battery. Find the rate of growth of current in the circuit. What is the significance of the 'time-constant' of the circuit? $5 + 2$

(b) What do you mean by positive and negative Thomson coefficients? Give examples. $2 + 1$

9. (a) Find an expression for the average power consumed in a series L-R circuit connected to a sinusoidal source of e.m.f. What is power factor? Under which condition the power in the above circuit vanishes? $4 + 1 + 1$

(b) A resistance of 20 ohms is joined in series with an inductance of 1 henry. What capacitance should be put in series with the combination to obtain the maximum current? What will be the potential difference across the resistance, inductance and capacitance respectively? The current is being supplied by 200 volts, 50 c.p.s. a.c. mains.   4

Group C

Answer *any one* question.

10. (a) Explain with diagram the working principle of a bridge rectifier.   4

(b) Define α and β of a transistor. Find a relation between the two. $1 + 1 + 2$

    (c) What is load line?   2

11. (a) State De Morgan's theorems.   2

    (b) What are NOR and NAND gates? Give their truth tables.   2 + 2

    (c) Is it possible to get AND gate by using a few NOR gates? How? 1 + 3

Group D
Answer *any two* questions.

12. (a) Write down the postulates of Einstein's special theory of relativity.   2

    (b) Derive relativistic velocity addition theorem.   5

    (c) Calculate the minimum energy of a γ-photon in MeV which can produce one electron-positron pair. Rest mass of an electron is 911×10^{-31} kg.   3

13. (a) Find an expression for the energy of electron in hydrogen atom according to Bohr model. What is the significance of negative sign in the expression?   4 + 1

    (b) Calculate the ionization potential of hydrogen atom.   3

    (c) What are Stokes line and anti-Stokes line?   2

14. (a) State Heisenberg's uncertainty principle.   2

    (b) Write down the time-independent Schrödinger equation for a particle subjected to a potential V.   2

    (c) Ra^{226} disintegrates to Rn^{222} with the liberation of α-particle. Calculate the disintegration energy. Given, M (Ra^{226}) = 226.096 a.m.u., $M(Rn^{222})$ = 222.0869 a.m.u. and $M(He^{4})$ = 4.00387 a.m.u.   6

2006
The figures in the margin indicate full marks.

(Compulsory Questions)

1. Answer *any ten* questions :   2 × 10

    (a) Why two independent light sources cannot produce observable interference pattern on a screen?

    (b) "Only transverse waves can be polarized but not longitudinal waves."— Why?

    (c) Why the electrostatic field is said to be conservative field?

    (d) What is the capacitance in Farad of a spherical conductor of radius 1 m placed in air medium?

    (e) State Ampere's circuital law.

    (f) What are neutral temperature and inversion temperature? Do they depend upon the temperature of the cold junction of the thermocouple?

    (g) Define Q-factor in L-C-R series combination.

    (h) What is time constant of a L-R circuit? What is its significance?

    (i) What is Wattless Current?

    (j) What is the practical utility of hysteresis loop?

    (k) Express 1 eV energy into erg unit.

(l) What do you mean by work function of a metal?

(m) Why electrons cannot stay inside nucleus?

(n) Give examples for the production of photon by electron and electron by photon.

(o) Convert 17.35 to binary number.

Group A

Answer *any two* questions.

2. (a) What is Huygens' principle of wave propagation? Establish Snell's law of refraction using this principle.   1 + 4

   (b) Describe the construction of a Nicol prism and explain its working principle.   5

3. (a) What are Newton's rings? Describe an experiment to find wavelength of monochromatic light using these rings.   2 + 4

   (b) Show that in interference phenomenon, energy is neither created nor destroyed but is conserved.   4

4. (a) Discuss Fraunhofer diffraction by a single slit. Find the conditions of maxima and minima of intensity distribution of the same.   2 + 6

   (b) What is plane diffraction grating?   2

Group B

Answer *any three* questions.

5. (a) Calculate the electric potential and intensity at any point (r, θ) in free space produced by an electric dipole.   5

   (b) Calculate the equivalent capacitance between points P and Q in the following circuit :   5

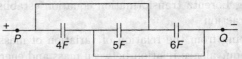

6. (a) Calculate the current through the galvanometer in an unbalanced Wheatstone bridge.   5

   (b) Use Thevenin's theorem to calculate the current through the 100 ohms resistance in the following circuit :

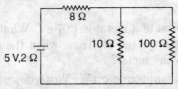

7. (a) Use Biot-Savart law to calculate the intensity of magnetic field at a point due to a straight current.   5

   (b) Define magnetic permeability and magnetic susceptibility. Find a relation between them.   3 + 2

8. (a) Prove that $\pi = T \frac{de}{dt}$, the symbols being usual.   4

(b) A 40 μF capacitor in series with a 2000 Ω resistor is connected across a 200 V d.c. source. Determine (i) the value of current when the time is equal to the time constant of the circuit and (ii) energy stored in the capacitor at time 0.04 sec.   3 + 3

9. (a) An alternating current is represented by $i = i_0 \sin \omega t$. Find the mean and r.m.s. values of the current.   2 + 2

(b) A circuit contains a resistance R, an inductance L and a capacitance C in series. A supply $E = E_0 \sin \omega t$ is connected across the combination. Find, (i) current at any instant in the circuit, (ii) impedance of the circuit and (iii) condition of resonance of the circuit.   4 + 1 + 1

Group C

Answer *any one* question.

10. (a) What is Zener diode? Explain its working as a voltage regulator. 1 + 3

(b) Draw the circuit diagram of a C.E. amplifier with a *N-P-N* transistor and hence find the voltage gain of the amplifier using load line.   6

11. (a) Draw the circuit diagram of an OR gate using discrete components and write down the truth table.   2 + 2

(b) Draw the circuit diagram to prove $\overline{A \cdot B} = \overline{A} + \overline{B}$.   2 + 2

(c) Convert -23_{10} to binary number.   2

Group D

Answer *any two* questions.

12. (a) Establish Bragg's equation of X-ray diffraction.   5

(b) Discuss Moseley's law of characteristic X-ray spectrum. How does Bohr theory explain the law?   2 + 3

13. (a) Using Lorentz transformation equation establish the formula of length contraction.   3

(b) Starting from the relation of variation of mass with velocity, establish the equivalence relation between mass and energy.   4

(c) The half-life of radon is 3.8 days. After how many days will only $\frac{1}{10}$th part of some quantity of radon be left behind?   3

14. (a) Write down Einstein's photoelectric equation. Discuss how Einstein's photoelectric equation explains the essential features of the photoelectric emission.   1 + 3

(b) Work function of a metal is 1.07 eV. What will be the maximum kinetic energy of the ejected electrons when the light of wavelength 6000 Å is incident on the metal?   3

(c) What is "Compton effect"? Write down the expression of wavelength difference "$\Delta\lambda$" between the incident and scattered X-rays from a scatterer and angle of scattering.   3

2007

(New and Old Syllabi)

Candidates are required to give their answers in their own words as far as practicable.

[New Syllabus]

(Under 1 + 1 + 1 System)

The figures in the margin indicate full marks.

(Compulsory Questions)

1. Answer *any ten* questions : 2 × 10

   (a) A convex lens of focal length 50 cm is in contact with a concave lens of focal length 25 cm. Will the combination act as a convex lens?

   (b) What do you mean by 'optical path'?

   (c) Why the centre of Newton's rings is dark?

   (d) Compare the spectra produced by a prism and plane diffraction grating.

   (e) What is optical activity?

   (f) You are given a small rod, how will you identify whether it is paramagnetic, diamagnetic or ferromagnetic?

   (g) What is meant by hysteresis?

   (h) What is the name of unit of coefficient of self-inductance in S.I. system? Define it.

   (i) What are the power factors in case of a purely inductive or purely resistive loads?

   (j) What do you mean by time constant of C-R circuit?

   (k) What is meant by Q-factor of an a.c. series resonant circuit?

   (l) Draw an AND gate and write its truth table.

   (m) State Pauli's exclusion principle.

   (n) Write down the postulates of Einstein's special theory of relativity.

   (o) Mention two differences between visible light rays and X-rays.

Group A

Answer *any one* question.

2. (a) State Fermat's principle and establish Snell's law of refraction from it for a plane surface separating two media. 2 + 4

   (b) Define dispersive power of a transperent medium. 2

   (c) State two main defects of an image formed by a lens. 2

3. (a) Deduce the condition of achromatism of two thin lenses in contact. 5

   (b) Show that the longitudinal magnification of the image of an object formed by a convex lens is equal to the square of the linear magnification of the image. 3

   (c) A very small piece of paper sticks on a glass sphere of radius 5×10^{-2} metre. Where would the image be formed when looked from the other side? (Refractive index of glass = 1.5) 2

Group B

Answer *any two* questions.

4. (a) Explain with a diagram how a Fresnel bi-prism forms an inference pattern of light.   3

   (b) Obtain an expression for the separation of fringes in the above pattern. 4

   (c) In Newton's ring experiment the radii of fifth and twenty-fifth dark rings are 1.8 mm and 5 mm respectively and the radius of curvature of the lower surface of planoconvex lens used is 50 cm. Calculate the wavelength of light used.   3

5. (a) Explain the rectilinear propagation of light with the help of wave theory. 3

   (b) What is a zone plate? Find an expression for its primary focal length.
                                                                          2 + 5

6. (a) Define specific rotation for both solids and solutions.   2 + 2

   (b) State Brewster's law in polarization of light.   2

   (c) What is the thickness of a doubly refracting crystal which is required to introduce a path difference of $\lambda/2$ between the O-ray and E-ray when $\lambda = 600$ nm, $\mu_O = 1.65$ and $\mu_E = 1.48$?   4

Group C

Answer *any two* questions.

7. (a) Find an expression for the magnetic field at a point on the axis of a circular coil carrying current.   4

   (b) A steady e.m.f. E is applied to a circuit consisting of a resistance R and an inductance L. Discuss the growth of current.   4

   (c) A circuit consists of a 50 Ω resistor and a 100 mH inductance in series with a cell. Find the time taken to reach half of its maximum current. 2

8. (a) What is Lorentz force? Write its expression.   2

   (b) Calculate the coefficient of mutual inductance of two coaxial solenoids. 4

   (c) Define magnetic susceptibility and permeability. Write down the relation between them.   4

9. (a) Obtain an expression for the instantaneous value of current in an a.c. circuit containing a resistance R and a capacitance C in series, when a sinusoidal e.m.f. $E = E_0 \sin pt$ is applied to the circuit. Find the phase angle of the current relative to e.m.f.   5 + 1

   (b) Calculate the power factor of a 50 cycles/sec a.c. circuit in which an inductance of 0.1 henry and a resistance of 20 ohms are connected in series.   4

Group D

Answer *any one* question.

10. (a) Define α and β of a transistor and find the relation between them.
                                                                       1 + 1 + 2

    (b) Explain with diagram the working principle of a bridge rectifier.   4

(c) The Zener diode used in the adjacent circuit, has breakdown voltage of 6.0 V and a maximum allowable current = 80 mA. What should be the minimum value of R in order to protect the Zener diode? 2

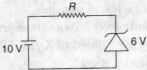

11. (a) Perform the following addition and subtraction of binary numbers :
     (i) 111.11 + 101.10, (ii) 11001 − 10101 2 + 2
    (b) State De Morgan's theorems. 2
    (c) Show how you can form an AND gate and an OR gate from NAND gates. 4

Group E

Answer *any two* questions.

12. (a) Write down Lorentz transformation equations. 3
    (b) Derive relativistic velocity addition theorem. 4
    (c) A clock keeps correct time. What should be the relative velocity between the clock and the observer so that the clock runs 5 minutes slow per day? 3

13. (a) Find an expression for the energy of electron in a hydrogen atom. What is the significance of the negative sign in the expression? 4 + 1
    (b) State Heisenberg's uncertainty principle and explain it. 3
    (c) What are Stokes line and anti-Stokes line? 2

14. (a) What are mass defect and binding energy? 1 + 1
    (b) Write down one dimensional Schrödinger's time-independent equation for a particle subjected to a potential V. 2
    (c) Find expressions for half-life and mean life of a radioactive element. 2 + 2
    (d) Calculate the minimum energy of a γ-photon in MeV which can produce one electron-positron pair. Rest mass of an electron is 9.11×10^{-31} kg. 2

[Old Syllabus]

The figures in the margin indicate full marks.

Question No. 1 is compulsory.

1. Answer *any ten* questions : 2 × 10
   (a) Compare the spectra produced by a prism and a diffraction grating.
   (b) Why are the colours observed in thin films of liquid when exposed to white light?
   (c) How does polarized light differ from unpolarized light?
   (d) How can you measure a current of 5 amp. with the help of a milliammeter of range 100 mA? The resistance of the milliammeter is 5 ohms.
   (e) A capacitor of capacitance 5 μF is connected to an a.c. source of frequency 2 kHz. Find the capacitive reactance.

(f) What is Curie point?

(g) What is an electric dipole? Define dipole moment.

(h) Why a meter bridge is not suitable for measurement of high resistance?

(i) State Pauli's exclusion principle.

(j) What is Lorentz force? Write its expression.

(k) State Bragg's law related to X-ray diffraction.

(l) What is Compton effect?

(m) Distinguish between Peltier effect and Joule heating effect.

(n) Convert the binary number $(11001.101)_2$ into decimal number.

(o) What is Zener potential?

Group A

Answer *any two* questions.

2. (a) What do you mean by interference of light?   1

(b) Derive the necessary formula to be used to determine the wavelength of monochromatic light with the help of Fresnel's bi-prism.   5

(c) A Fresnel bi-prism with acute angle $1°30'$ and of a material whose $\mu = 1.5$ is used to form interference fringes of a narrow slit with light of wavelength 6563 Å. The distance between the slit and the prism is 20 cm and that between the prism and the screen is 80 cm. Find the width of the fringes.   4

3. (a) Difference between interference and diffraction of light.   2

(b) What is a zone plate? Find an expression for its primary focal length.

$1 + 5$

(c) Functionally how a zone plate differs from a lens?   2

4. (a) State Brewster's law.   2

(b) What are double refraction and optical activity of light? $2 + 2$

(c) What is a half-wave plate? Calculate the thickness of a quartz half-wave plate for the fine 6563 Å for which the extra ordinary and ordinary refractive indices of light are $\mu_e = 1.55$ and $\mu_0 = 1.53$. $2 + 2$

Group B

Answer *any three* questions.

5. (a) State and prove Gauss's theorem in electrostatics. $1 + 3$

(b) A sphere or radius 5 cm is charged to 50 e.s.u. and is connected by a wire to another sphere with the same charge but double the radius. Calculate the loss of energy. Does it violate the principle of conservation of energy? Explain.

$4 + 2$

6. (a) State and explain Kirchhoff's law for electrical circuit.   4

(b) Calculate the currents I_1 and I_2 in the given circuit. Given, $R_i = 2\,\Omega$, $R_2 = 1\,\Omega$, $R_3 = 10\,\Omega$ $V_1 = 6$ volts, $V_2 = 5$ volts.   4

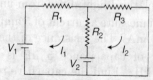

(c) State Norton's theorem. 2

7. (a) Find an expression for the magnetic field at a point on the axis of a circular coil carrying current. 5

(b) Define coefficient of mutual induction. Calculate the mutual inductance between two similar, parallel coaxial circular coils. 1 + 4

8. (a) A circuit containing an inductor (L) and a resistor (R) in series is connected with a battery of e.m.f. E. Find the rate of growth of current in the circuit. What is the significance of the time constant of the circuit? 5 + 2.

(b) A circuit has its resistance 20 Ω and inductance 0.1 henry. If the current through the circuit at any instant be 1 ampere and the same is growing at the rate of 20 amperes/sec, determine the e.m.f. applied in the circuit. 3

9. (a) Find an expression for the average power consumed in a series L-R circuit connected to a sinusoidal source of e.mf. What is power factor? Under which condition the power in the above circuit vanishes? 4 + 1 + 1

(b) A resistance of 20 Ω is joined in series with an inductance of 1 henry. What capacitance should be put in series with the combination to obtain the maximum current? What will be the potential difference across the resistance, inductance and capacitance respectively? The current is being supplied by 200 volts, 50 c.(Hz)p.s. a.c. mains. 4

Group C

Answer *any one* question.

10. (a) Explain with diagram the working principles of a bridge rectifier. 4

(b) Define 'α' and 'β' of a transistor and find the relation between them. 2 + 2 + 2

11. (a) State De Morgan's theorem. 2

(b) Show that NAND gate is an universal gate. 2 + 2 + 1

(c) Convert $(14.75)_{10}$ and $(9.50)_{10}$ to binary numbers and find the sum of the two binary numbers. 1 + 1 + 1

Group D

Answer *any two* questions.

12. (a) Write down the postulates of Einstein's special theory of relativity. 2

(b) Derive relativistic velocity addition theorem. 5

(c) A rod of length 1 metre is in a satellite moving with respect to the earth with a velocity $0.99c$. What is the length of the rod with respect to an observer on the earth? 3

13. (a) What is known as matter wave? What is its wavelength. 1 + 1

(b) What is the de Broglie wavelength of an electron when it moves in an electric field with a p.d. of 500 volts. Given, $e = 1.6 \times 10^{-19}$ coulomb, $m = 9.11 \times 10^{-31}$ kg, $h = 6.63 \times 10^{-34}$ J-sec. 4

(c) State Heisenberg's uncertainty principle. 2

(d) What are Stokes line and anti-Stokes line? 2

14. (a) Explain the terms 'binding energy' and 'packing fraction' of a nucleus. Show graphically the change of packing function with mass number. What idea about the stability of the nucleus is obtained from this graph?

$$1 + 1 + 1 + 1$$

(b) Write down the time independent Schrödinger equation for a particle subjected to a potential V.   2

(c) Calculate the Q-value of the following nuclear reaction

$$_7N^{14} + _2He^4 \rightarrow _8O^{17} + _1H^1$$

Given,   M $(_7N^{14})$ = 14.00755 a.m.u.

M $(_2He^4)$ = 4.00388 a.m.u.

M $(_8O^{17})$ = 17.00453 a.m.u.

M $(_1H^1)$ = 1.00815 a.m.u.

Justify the answer.   3 + 1

Kalyani University Question Papers

2003

Physics (General)

Second Paper

Full Marks : 100   Time : Three Hours

The figures in the right-hand margin indicate full marks.
Candidates are required to give their answers
in their own words as far as practicable.

Illustrate the answer wherever necessary.

Answer *any six* questions, taking *two* from each group.

Group A

1. (a) State Fermat's principle and hence find the laws of reflection of light at a plane surface. $2 + 5$

   (b) A thin converging lens of focal length 20 cm, and made of a material of refractive index 1.6, has one radius of curvature 12 cm. Find the other radius of curvature of the lens and comment on your result. 3

   (c) Find an expression for the axial chromatic aberration of a single lens and interpret your result $3 + 1$

   (d) Find the condition of achromatism of two thin coaxial lenses separated by a distance.

   A concave lens of focal length 8 cm is placed behind a convex lens, made of the same material of focal length 20 cm to form an achromatic combination. Find the position of the concave lens relative to the convex one. $4 + 2$

2. (a) Explain the propagation of a light wave from Huygens' principle. 3

   (b) Find the laws of reflection of a light wave at a plane surface. 7

   (c) Give a sketch how interference pattern of a monochromatic light wave is produced by Fresnel's bi-prism, and hence show how the wavelength of the light is determined.

   Calculate the wavelength of the light if the separation between the virtual images of the slit is 0.05 cm and the fringe-width measured at 100 cm from the slit is 0.118 cm. $(3 + 5) + 2$

3. (a) What is a zone plate? How is it constructed? Give the necessary theory for its primary focal length and explain its action. $2 + 2 + 6$

   (b) Define :

       (i) Angle of polarization,
       (ii) Plane of polarization,
       (iii) Optic axis. $2 + 2 + 2$

   State Brewster's law.

   Find the refractive index of a glass plate, if the angle of refraction of a ray of light through it is 32.5° for an incident light ray at the polarizing angle. $2 + 2$

Group B

4. (a) Write down Maxwell's equations for electromagnetic waves in a medium mentioning the unit used. What are the basic laws that form the equations?   4 + 3

(b) What are the postulates of special theory of relativity?

Write down the expression for kinetic energy of a particle of rest mass m_0 moving with a velocity v.

Find the ratio of the total energy to its rest energy of the particle moving with a velocity 0.6 times that of light.   4 + 2 + 2

5. (a) State Mosley's law in X-rays. How did Mosley prove that atomic number is a more fundamental property of an atom than its atomic weight? How did the law help to discover new elements in the periodic table?

        2 + 3 + 2

(b) Write down Einstein's equation for photoelectric effect. How did this equation explain the characteristics of photoelectric emission?   1 + 4

(c) Calculate the maximum kinetic energy of the electrons emitted from Cesium of work-function 2 eV when light of wave length 4.5×10^{-5} cm falls on the metal.

[1 eV = 1.6×10^{-12} ergs; velocity of light, $c = 3 \times 10^8$ m/sec; Planck's constant, $h = 6.625 \times 10^{-27}$ erg-sec]   3

6. (a) Mention the quantum numbers required to describe the state of an electron in an atom.

State Pauli's exclusion principle. Apply the principle to explain the arrangement of electrons in the first shells around a nucleus. 2 + 2 + 4

(b) Calculate the wavelength of an electron-wave, when an electron is accelerated through a potential difference of 1 volt. [Mass and charge of the electron, $m_e = 9.1 \times 10^{-28}$ gm and $e = 4.8 \times 10^{-10}$ e.s.u.; Planck's constant, $h = 6.625 \times 10^{-27}$ erg-sec]

(c) Solve Schrödinger's equation for a particle confined in an infinitely high-walled potential box of one dimension. Find the possible energy states of the particle.   3 + 1

Group C

7. (a) Describe in details Millikan's oil-drop experiment for determination of charge of an electron.   8

(b) Describe an experiment to prove that alpha particles are identical with helium nuclei.   4

(c) State the main characteristics of natural radioactivity.   3

8. (a) What is the binding energy of a nucleus and that of a nucleon of it? Find expressions for each of them.

The binding energy per nucleon of a $_2\text{He}^4$-nucleus is 7.07 MeV. Calculate the mass-defect in amu to form a helium nucleus from its constituents. [1 amu = 931 MeV]   3 + 2 + 3

(b) Write down the proper equations to the nuclear reactions when a proton particle strikes a $_5\text{B}^{11}$-target to form a compound nucleus that ejects an alpha particle. The product Be-nucleus then breaks into two more alpha particles.

(c) Describe the action of Wilson's cloud chamber for detection of nuclear radiations. 4

9. (a) Sketch the potential distribution at the P-N junction of a semiconductor diode. If the other ends of the P-type and N-type materials of the diode be joined by a conducting wire, should there be a current flow? Give reasons to your answer. 2 + 2

(b) Draw the output characteristic curves of a transistor in CE-configuration. Show how the output resistance and the current amplification factor of the transistor can be estimated from the curves. 5 + 2

(c) Convert

   (i) the binary number 1010.101 into its decimal equivalent, and
   (ii) the decimal number 14.125 into its binary equivalent. 2 + 2

2004

Group A

1. (a) What is optical path? Explain rectilinear propagation of light on the basis of Fermat's principle. 1 + 2

(b) Establish the relation $\frac{n_2}{v} - \frac{n_1}{u} = \frac{n_2 - n_1}{R}$ for refraction at a convex surface separating two media of refractive indices n_1 and n_2 respectively. Hence obtain two principal foci. 4 + 2

(c) What is equivalent lens? Explain the action of a Huygens eyepiece and find its equivalent focal length. 1 + 3 + 2

(d) Explain spherical aberration. Two lenses of same material have focal lengths $3f$ and f respectively and are kept separated by a distance 'a'. Find the value of 'a' for a minimum spherical and chromatic aberration. 2 + 3

2. (a) What is wavefront? Mention three types of wavefronts produced by light sources. 1 + 2

(b) What do you mean by coherent sources? Why two similar lamps are unable to produce permanent interference? A stable interference pattern is formed with a monochromatic light ($\lambda = 5.6 \times 10^{-7}$ m). A thin glass plate of refractive index 1.5 is introduced in the path and the central fringe shifts to next 4th bright fringe. What is the thickness of the plate? 1 + 2 + 3

(c) Explain how Newton's rings are formed by monochromatic light using a plano convex lens and a glass plate. Find the expression for its diameter of the nth order dark ring. The diameters of the nth and $(n + 10)$th bright rings are 2.18 mm and 4.61 mm respectively, when a liquid is placed between the lens and the plate. The radius of curvature of the lens is 100 cm and wavelength, $\lambda = 5890$ Å of light used. Find the refractive index of the liquid. 3 + 5 + 3

3. (a) How wavelength of light can be determined using plane transmission grating? Discuss the experimental arrangement in brief. How does grating spectra differ from a prism spectra? 2 + 4 + 2

(b) Explain the construction and the action of a Nicol prism. 5 + 3

(c) Write notes on any *one* :
   (i) optical activity
   (ii) emission and absorption spectra
   (iii) Zeeman effect.   4

Group B

4. (a) Starting from Maxwell's field equations deduce the electromagnetic wave equation in vacuum. Write its plane wave solution in one dimension. Show that electromagnetic wave is transverse in nature. $4 + 2 + 3$

   (b) Write down the expressions for Lorentz transformation. How can Fitzgerald-Lorentz Contraction be explained? $2 + 4$

5. (a) What is meant by dual nature of a material particle? State the properties of matter waves. Calculate de Broglie wavelength when an electron is passed through a p.d. of 150 V. Given, $e = 1.6 \times 1^{-19}$ C, $m_e = 9.1 \times 10^{-31}$ kg and $h = 6.6 \times 10^{-34}$ J-sec. $2 + 3 + 3$

   (b) Deduce Schrödinger wave equation. What are eigenfunctions and eigenvalues? $4 + 2 + 1$

6. (a) What is Bragg spacing? Deduce Bragg's equation.

   In some X-ray tube, the applied p.d. is 5 kV and the corresponding current is 2 mA. Calculate the number of electrons incident per second and the minimum wavelength of X-ray produced? $2 + 3 + 3$

   (b) Calculate the energy of nth orbital electron of hydrogen atom and hence explain the origin of different spectral series emitted. What is Bohr radius? $3 + 2 + 2$

Group C

7. (a) What is the half-life of a radioactive element? The half-life of radium is 1620 years. In how many years 1 gm of pure element will loose 10 mg? $1 + 3$

   (b) How Thomson's experiment on positive ray led to the discovery of isotopes?

   (c) State giving equations what happens when

      (i) a neutron bombards a magnesium nucleus, and
      (ii) an alpha particle bombards an aluminium nucleus. $2 + 2$

8. (a) What are mass defect and packing fraction? $2 + 2$

   (b) Discuss the shell model of an atomic nucleus. What is magic number? $3 + 2$

   (c) $_{17}Cl^{35}$ has atomic mass 34.98 a.m.u. What is its binding energy per nucleon?

      Given, mass of $_0n^1 = 1.008665$ a.m.u. and that of $_1H^1 = 1.007825$ a.m.u.3

   (d) Write a note on fission.   3

9. (a) Draw the circuit diagram of a triode amplifier. Calculate the voltage gain for a purely resistive load. $3 + 3$

   (b) For positive logic 'OR' gate, draw the circuit diagram using two diodes. Write its symbol and also its truth table. $2 + 1 + 2$

   (c) Convert 12.25 and 11.75 into digital numbers and find the sum. $2 + 2$

2005

(New Syllabus)

Group A

1. (a) State and prove Gauss's theorem of electrostatics.   2

   (b) Define dipole moment of an electric dipole and the electric polarization of a dielectric medium. What is dielectric breakdown? Determine the potential energy of an electric dipole placed in a uniform electric field. $(1 + 1) + 1 + 3$

   (c) Deduce an expression for the capacitance of a parallel plate capacitor with a dielectric medium.   4

2. (a) State and explain Kirchhoff's laws for steady current. A battery of e.m.f. 8 V and of internal resistance 2 Ω is connected in parallel to another battery and of e.m.f. 12 V and of internal resistance 3 Ω. The terminals of the composite so formed are joined by a wire of resistance 2 Ω. Calculate the currents through the wire and the batteries. $3 + 3$

   (b) Using Ampere's circuital theorem determine the magnetic field at an external point due to a long straight wire arrying a current.   3

   (c) Determine the expression for the torque acting on a rectangular current carrying loop placed in a uniform magnetic field.   4

   (d) What is Hall effect? Show that a magnetic force acting on a moving charged particle does no work. $2 + 2$

3. (a) Define the following terms :

       (i) Intensity of magnetization.
       (ii) Magnetic induction.
       (iii) Magnetic permeability.
       (iv) Magnetic susceptibility.

   Compare the hysteresis loops of a soft iron and steel. Draw the curves and indicate the retentivity and coercivity. $4 + 1 + 1$

   (b) State Faraday's laws of electromagnetic induction. Determine the induced e.m.f. at the ends of a conducting wire rotating perpendicular to a uniform magnetic field and about an axis passing through one end of the wire. $2 + 3$

   (c) A steady d.c. voltage is suddenly applied to a capacitor in series with a resistance. Show that current in the circuit decreases exponentially with time. Define the time constant of the circuit. $5 + 1$

4. (a) Obtain expressions for the mean value and the r.m.s. value of a sinusoidal alternating current. What is a transformer? $(2 + 2) + 1$

   (b) Explain Seebeck effect and Peltier effect. Show the variation of e.m.f. of a thermocouple with changing temperature at one junction graphically when the other junction is kept at 0 °C. Indicate the inversion temperature and neutral temperature in the graph. $(2 + 2) + 1 + 1$

   (c) Show that the differential form of Ampere's circuital theorem is not valid for nonsteady current. Write down the correct expression of the above theorem. What is displacement current? Write down the Maxwell's equation which indicates the non-existence of magnetic monopoles. $3 + 1 + 1 + 1$

Group B

5. (a) Using Fermat's 'Principle deduce the laws of refraction of light at a plane surface.   6

(b) Derive the lens formula with the help of refraction at curved surfaces. 4

(c) List the different types of defects of image formed by a lens. An achromatic converging doublet of focal length 15 cm is constructed with two lenses. If the dispersive power of one lens is three times that of the other, find the focal lengths of the two lenses.   3 + 3

6. (a) Explain the propagation of light wave from Huygens's Principle.

The optical path of a monochromatic light is the same if it goes through 2.66 cm of glass or 3 cm of water. If the refractive index of glass is 1.5, what is the refractive index of water?   3 + 2

(b) What do you mean by interference of light? How do we achieve coherent sources in practice? Show diagrammatically the formation of interference pattern obtained in Fresnel's bi-prism experiment. Derive the expression for the wavelength of a monochromatic light in terms of the fringe width in the above experiment.   2 + 2 + 2 + 5

7. (a) What do you mean by Fresnel's half-period zone? Show that the intensity at a point in front of a plane wavefront due to first half-period zone is about for times as great as that produced by the whole wavefront. 2 + 6

(b) What do you mean by Fraunhofer diffraction? Describe with necessary theory the diffraction pattern produced by a narrow slit illuminated by a parallel beam, of monochromatic light incident normally on the slit.
     1 + 7

8. (a) Define :

     (i) Plane of polarization.
     (ii) Optic axis of a doubly refracting crystal.
     (iii) Circularly polarized light.   2 + 2 + 2

(b) Mention one method of obtaining plane polarized light.   2

(c) Calculate the angle of polarization for light travelling from water of refractive index 1.33 to glass of refractive index 1.58.

What do you mean by quarter wave plate?   2 + 2

(d) Determine the magnification of the image formed at the least distance of distinct vision by a magnifying glass.   4

Group C

9. (a) What are the postulates of special theory of relativity? How can the result of the Michelson-Morley experiment be explained on the basis of special relativity?

How does the mass of a particle vary with its Velocity? What is rest energy?

A particle has a rest mass 1.6×10^{-27} kg. Find its energy in MeV when it moves with velocity $0.9c$. (1 MeV $= 1.6 \times 10^{-13}$ J) 2 + 1 + 2 + 2 + 2

(b) What is work function of a metal? Write down Einstein's equation of photoelectric effect. How does it explain the characteristics of photoelectric effect?   1 + 1 + 4

(c) What is Raman effect? 2

10. (a) State and explain Heisenberg's uncertainty principle. 4

(b) Obtain the energy eigenvalues of a particle in a beam. 4

(c) Using the vector atom model identify the quantum numbers of L-shell electrons of an atom. 4

(d) Describe the theory of Millikan's oil-drop experiment for determination of the charge of an electron. 5

11. (a) State the features of natural radioactivity. Write down the atomic numbers and mass numbers of produce nuclei if a parent nucleus with atomic number Z, mass number A emits an alpha-particle and then a beta-particle. When are γ-rays emitted from nucleus? $3 + 1 + 1$

(b) Derive the mean-life of a radioactive nucleus. What do do you mean by 1 curie? $4 + 1$

(c) Explain how Rutherford's experiment led to the discovery of the nucleus. What are the constitute of a nucleus? $3 + 1$

(d) How was the neutron discovered? 3

12. (a) In a cyclotron the strength of the magnetic field 10000 Oe and the accelerated particles emerge tangentially at a distance of 10 cm from centre of the dees. Find the energy of the emerging particle.

Given, charge of the particle $= 1.6 \times 10^{-20}$ gm,

mass of the particle $= 1.66 \times 10^{-24}$ gm. 5

(b) Discuss qualitatively the formation of energy in a solid. Draw the energy band diagram for semiconductors and insulators. $4 + 1$

(c) What do you mean by N-type and P-type semiconductors? Draw the 1-V characteristics of a P-N junction diode for both forward and reverse bias.

Draw the necessary circuit diagrams. $(2 + 2) + 2 + 1$

2006

(Old Syllabus)

Group A

Answer *any two* questions. 2×20

1. (a) What is meant by angle of deviation of light? For refraction through a prism of refracting angle A, prove that $\mu = \frac{\sin \frac{A+D_m}{2}}{\sin A/2}$ [μ = refractive index, D_m = angle of minimum deviation]. $2 + 4 = 6$

(b) Describe a simple microscope. What is its magnification? $2 + 2 = 4$

(c) Find out the conjugate foci relationship of a transparent sphere. 6

(d) Find out the position of the image formed by a transparent glass sphere of diameter 10 cm, when the object is placed at a distance of 40 cm from its surface ($\mu = 1.5$). 4

2. (a) Discuss Huygens's principle about light waves. Hence establish the laws of reflection of light. $4 + 4 = 8$

(b) Light of wavelength 6000 Å is falling from air on glass surface. Determine the wavelength, velocity and frequency of reflected, refracted beams. (Velocity of light in air $= 3 \times 10^{10}$ cm/sec, R.I. of glass $= 1.5$)

$$2 + 2 + 2 = 6$$

(c) How can the refractive index of the material of double convex lens and liquid be determined with the help of pin, holding stand and a plane mirror? 6

3. (a) What is meant by diffraction of light? Make comparative discussion on Fresnel and Fraunhofer types of diffraction. $2 + 4 = 6$

(b) Find a relation between the radii of different Newton's dark interferences rings and the wavelength of the sources of light. Explain whether the central ring is bright or dark. $6 + 2 = 8$

(c) In a Newton's ring experiment the 20th bright ring is of diameter 0.53 cm. If sodium vapour lamp ($\lambda = 5890$ Å) has been used as a source, find out the radius of the lower surface. If water ($\mu = 1.33$) is used in place of air, what will be the radius of the 25th dark ring? $4 + 2 = 6$

4. (a) What is meant by polarization of light? What are differences between ordinary light and polarized light? What is Brewster's law?

$$2 + 2 + 2 = 6$$

(b) What is double refraction? 2

(c) Find out the thickness of a half-wave plate for a light of wavelength 5890 Å ($\mu_o = 1.544, \mu_e = 1.553$). Deduce the necessary working formula.

$$3 + 4$$

(d) 50 cc of sugar water contains 10 gm of sugar. 20 cm long polarimeter tube is filled up with this solution and kept in the path of polarized light. The incident polarized light rotates through an angle of 20°. Find out specific rotation of this solution. 5

Group B

Answer *any two* questions. $2 \times 15 = 30$

5. (a) Write down the postulates of special theory of relativity. Find out an expression of apparent length of a rod as would be observed from a frame of reference moving along a line parallel to the axis of the rod with a velocity v. $3 + 4 = 7$

(b) How long a 7 metre long rod would appear while observing from a frame moving with half the velocity of light in vacuum and making an angle 30° with the axis of the rod? What would have been the percentage variation of a rod if observed from the frame of reference moving parallel to the rod with velocity equal to the velocity of sound in air? $3 + 2 = 5$

(c) State the time dialation principle and explain it. 3

6. (a) Establish Einstein's photoelectric equation. What is meant by threshold frequency? $4 + 2$

(b) Write down Bohr's postulates related to hydrogen atoms spectra. Find out an expression of radius of the n-th orbit of hydrogen atom. Determine the radius of the first orbit of hydrogen. $3 + 4 + 2 = 9$

7. (a) Describe the production of X-rays by Coolidge tube with suitable diagram. Write down the characteristic properties of X-rays. $6 + 3 = 9$

(b) Discuss a method of producing diffraction of X-rays in crystals. Establish Bragg's equation. $2 + 2 = 4$

(c) State Moslay's law in connection with X-ray spectra. 2

8. Write short notes on (any *three*) : $3 \times 5 = 15$

    (a) Matter waves

    (b) Compton effect

    (c) Stern-Gerlach experiment

    (d) Equivalence of mass and energy.

Group C

Answer *any two* questions. $2 \times 15 = 30$

9. (a) What is radioactivity? Write down the characteristics of different rays emitted from radioactive substance. How can you experimentally prove that α-particle is nothing but helium nucleus? $1 + 5 + 3 = 9$

    (b) What amount of radioactive material is disintegrated during time equal to the average life of that radio element? 2

    (c) 1 milligram of radioactive Radon is taken. What amount of it is retained after 15 days? (half-life of 2 radon is 3.5 days) 2

    (d) What force acts on an electron due to electric field of 20 volts/cm? 2

10. (a) Describe with a diagram how $\frac{e}{m}$ of electron is determined by Thomson's method. 7

    (b) Define atomic number, atomic wight and isotope of an element. 3

    (c) An electron after being energised by a potential difference of 5000 volts enters a magnetic field of magnitude 2×10^{-2} weber/metre^2 (acting perpendicularly to its velocity). Find out the radius of the path of the electron. 5

11. (a) Describe the working of a cyclotron with a neat diagram. 5

    (b) Give the construction of a diode valve. Draw the characteristics of a diode for three different filament temperatures and discuss. $2 + 3 = 5$

    (c) How is a triode valve used to amplify an input signal? 5

12. Write short notes on any *three* of the following : $3 \times 5 = 15$

    (a) *N-P-N* transistor

    (b) Modulation and demodulation of radiowaves

    (c) Chain reaction

    (d) G-M counter

    (e) OR, AND and NOT logic gates.

2007

(New Syllabus)

Group A

1. (a) Deduce Gauss's theorem in electrostatics. Write down Coulomb's law. Establish the Coulomb's law from Gauss's theorem. $3 + 2 + 2$

(b) Three concentric shells of radii a, b and c respectively are placed in air. The middle sphere is connected to the earth while the innermost shell is connected by a thin wire to the outermost one and charged. Calculate the capacitance of the combination. 5

(c) Calculate the energy stored in a charged conductor. 5

2. (a) State Kirchhoff's law. 12 equal wires each of resistance R are joined to form a cube. The current enters at one end corner and leaves at the diagonally opposite corner. Find the total resistance between these corners. 3 + 4

(b) Explain the method of measuring the current flowing in a wire with the help of a potentiometer. 5

(c) The e.m.f. of two cells are 1.5 volt and 1.1 volt and their internal resistance are 0.1 ohm and 0.2 ohm respectively. These two cells are now connected with two wires of resistances 0.3 ohm and 0.4 ohm in same polarity. Calculate the e.m.f. of the combination. 5

3. (a) State Laplace's law for the magnetic fields at a point due to a current element. Obtain an expression for the magnetic field at the centre of a circular current loop. 2 + 4

(b) Explain (i) Seebeck effect and (ii) Thomson effect.
How do you determine the Peltier coefficient experimentally. 4 + 4

(c) If the cold junction temperature of a thermocouple be $20\,°C$ and the neutral temperature be $285\,°C$, find the temperature of inversion. 3

4. (a) Show that in a circuit with a steady e.m.f. and an inductive resistance, the current decays exponentially with time when the e.m.f. is suddenly withdrawn. 6

(b) Determine the magnetic moment of a freely suspended magnet in uniform magnetic field. 5

(c) How does the hysteresis curve for a sample of iron determine its suitability for making (a) a permanent magnet and (b) an electromagnet? 6.

Group B

5. (a) State and explain Fermat's principle and prove it in the case of refraction through a plane surface. 2 + 5

(b) Obtain an expression for the refractive index of the material of a prism in terms of the angle of the prism and angle of minimum deviation of a ray of light passing through it. 6

(c) A prism of $5°$ angle is made of crown glass. What must be the angle of a flint glass prism which in combination with the former prism would give no deviation. Given, $\mu_c = 1.518$ and $\mu_f = 1.678$. 3

6. (a) The two surfaces of a lens are of radii r_1 and r_2, and the absolute refraction index of the material is μ. Deduce an expression for its focal length. 6

(b) What is chromatic abberration? Find out the condition of achromatism of two thin lenses in contact with each other. 6

(c) Write down the advantage of Ramsden's eyepiece. 4

7. (a) Explain the total internal reflection by the wave theory. 5

(b) A glass plate 0.5 cm thick with a refractive index 1.5 is placed between a point source and a screen 5 cm away. The source emits light of wavelength 6000° Å in vacuum. What is the length of the optical path between the source and the screen? How many waves are there between the source and the screen? 3

(c) What do you understand by interference of light? Mention the condition necessary for sustained interference. Why light from two different candles does not produce interference? $2 + 4 + 2 = 8$.

8. (a) Light from a luminous point source casts a shadow of a straight edge. State the nature of the light intensity near the edge of the shadow and explain the reason. 8

(b) What is meant by polarized light? Why can we polarize light waves but not sound waves? $2 + 2$

(c) In case of quartz for sodium light of $\lambda = 3.9 \times 10^{-5}$ cm, $\mu_e = 1.553$, $\mu_o = 1.544$. Calculate the thickness of the quartz quarter-wave plate for sodium light. 4

Group C

9. (a) Write down the relationship between total energy and momentum of a body. Hence show that the relativistic expression of K.E. of a moving body reduces to the classical expression when the velocity of the body is extremely small compared to the velocity of light. $3 + 4$

(b) What is meant by photoelectric emission? State the important characteristic of photoelectricity. Discuss Einstein's photoelectric equation to explain these characteristic properties of photoelectrics. $2 + 3 + 2$

(c) 1/1000 part of a substance is converted into energy in a nuclear reaction. If 1 gm of the substance takes part in the above-mentioned reaction, calculate the energy developed in kilowatt. 3

10. (a) Discuss Bohr's theory of H-atom. How does it determine the radii of orbit, the orbital velocity and energy level of the atom? What are the limitation of Bohr theory? $2 + 3 + 3$

(b) What is de Broglie hypothesis? Write down the equation indicating wave-particle dualism. Discuss Davisson-Germer's experiment and indicate how it justified the wave aspect of particle. $2 + 2 + 5$

11. (a) Describe with necessary theory to determine the charge of an electron by Millikan's oil-drop experiment. 7

(b) Explain (any *two*) : $5 + 5$

    (i) Nuclear Fusion,

    (ii) Nuclear Fission,

    (iii) Binding energy,

    (iv) Miller indices.

12. (a) What is Soddy's displacement law of radioactive transformation? Show that in case of radioactive disintegration the number of atoms decreases exponentially. $1 + 3$

(b) What is meant by the average life of a radioactive element? Establish the relation between the half-life and average life of a radioactive element.

$$3 + 2$$

(c) What do you mean by doping of a semiconductor crystals? How do you prepare N-type and P-type semiconductors. $2 + (3 + 3)$

(Old Syllabus)

Group A

Answer *any two* questions. 2×20

1. (a) State Fermat's principle. What is an optical path? How is it related with the actual path traversed by light? $2 + 1 + 1$

   (b) Deduce the relation, $\frac{\mu}{v} - \frac{1}{u} = (\mu - 1)R$, for refraction at a spherical surface and hence deduce the formula, $\frac{1}{v} - \frac{1}{u} = \frac{1}{f}$, for a lens, where the symbols have usual meaning. $4 + 4$

   (c) What is an achromatic doublet? Find the condition of achromatism of two thin lenses in contact with each other. What happens if the two lenses be of the same material?

   (d) The focal lengths for red and violet rays of a thin convex lens are respectively 100 cm and 96.8 cm. Calculate the dispersive power of the lens.   2

2. (a) What is a compound eyepiece? What are the advantages of using a compound eyepiece? Point out the respective merits of Ramsden's and Huygens's eyepieces. $1 + 1 + 2$

   (b) Prove that the least distance between an object and its real image formed by a convex lens is four times its focal length.   4

   (c) What do you mean by coherent sources? Why two similar lamps are unable to produce permanent interference? Find the relation between fringe width and the wavelength of the source light in the interference fringes formed by Fresnel's bi-prism. $1 + 2 + 5$

   (d) Fringes are produced by a bi-prism at the focal plane of a reading microscope, which is 1 m from the slit. A convex lens inserted between the bi-prism and the microscope produces two images of the slit in its two positions. In one case, the two images of the slit are 4.05 mm and in the other are 2.9 mm apart. If sodium light ($\lambda = 589.3$ nm) be used, find the distance between two consecutive bright bands.   4

3. (a) Explain the rectilinear propagation of light on the basis of wave theory.

                                                                           3

   (b) What is Fresnel's half-period zone? Why is it so called? Point out the differences between convex lens and a zone plate. $2 + 1 + 3$

   (c) How wavelength of light can be determined using plane transmission grating? Discuss the experimental arrangement in brief. How does grating spectra differ from a prism spectra? $2+4+2$

   (d) The radius of the 8th circular zone in a zone plate is 4.5 mm. Find its focal length for light of wavelength 650 nm. Also find the position of image for a point source 7.788 m from the plate.   3

4. **(a)** What is optical activity? Define specific rotation. $2 + 2$

(b) What is a quarter-wave plate? Explain how it can be used to produce circularly polarized light? $2 + 2$

(c) Prove that the angle of incidence and refraction are complementary when maximum polarization is obtained by reflection on a plane glass surface. 3

(d) If refractive index of glass be 1.55, find the polarizing angle for glass and angle of refraction at this polarizing angle? 3

(e) Write notes on any *two* of the following : $3 + 3$

    (i) Zeeman effect,

    (ii) Emission and absorption spectra,

    (iii) Nicol prism,

    (iv) Faraday effect.

Group B

Answer any *two* questions. 2×15

5. **(a)** With the help of Maxwell's field equations deduce the electromagnetic wave equation in vacuum. Write its plane wave solution in one dimension. Show that electromagnetic waves are transverse in nature. $4 + 2 + 2$

(b) What do you mean by the dual nature of a material particle? State the properties of matter waves. $2 + 2$

(c) Find the de Broglie wavelength of a proton of energy 10^5 eV. Given, mass of proton $= 1.67 \times 10^{-27}$ kg. 3

6. **(a)** State and explain Heisenberg's uncertainty principle. 3

(b) Write down the time independent Schrödinger wave equation. What are eigenfunctions and eigenvalues. $2 + 1 + 1$

(c) Prove Bohr quantum condition from de Broglie wave equation. 2

(d) How do you explain Mosley's law from Bohr's theory? 3

(e) If the work function of a photometal is 1.9 eV, calculate the threshold wavelength. Given, $h = 6.63 \times 10^{-34}$ J-sec and $e = 1.6 \times 10^{-19}$ C. 2

7. **(a)** Write down the expressions for Lorentz transformation. 2

(b) What was the aim of Michelson-Morly experiment? What do you conclude from this experiment? $2 + 2$

(c) Derive Einstein's theorem of addition of velocities. Hence prove that no material particle can move with a velocity greater than that of light. $3 + 2$

(d) Kinetic energy of a particle is 3 times its rest mass energy. What is its velocity? 4

8. Write short notes on (any *three*) : 5×3

    (a) Pauli's exclusion principle,

    (b) Davison and Germer experiment for study of matter waves,

    (c) Millikan's experiment on photoelectricity,

    (d) Compton effect.

Group C

Answer *any two* questions.   2 × 15

9. (a) What are positive rays? How Thomson's experiment on positive rays led to the discovery of isotopes?   2 + 7

   (b) What do you mean by 'half-life' and 'mean life' of a radioactive substance? Deduce the expression for them.   1 + 1 + 2 + 2

10. (a) Describe Millikan's oil-drop experiment for measuring the charge of electron. What was the value of the charge of electron obtained by Millikan?   9 + 1

   (b) What are mass defects? Calculate the binding energy per nucleon of helium nucleus. Given, mass of a proton = 1.00728 a.m.u., mass of neutron = 1.00867 a.m.u., mass of helium nucleus = 4.00276 a.m.u. and 1 a.m.u = 931 MeV.   2 + 3

11. (a) What is an intrinsic semiconductor? How does P-N junction diode work as a full-wave rectifier?   2 + 5

   (b) Draw the current-voltage characteristic of an ordinary PN junction diode for both forward and reverse bias condition.   3

   (c) Give the Boolean expressions for OR, AND and NOT Gates. Convert 12.25 and 14.75 into binary number and find out their binary sum.

                                                              1 + 2 + 2

12. Write short notes on (any *three*) :   3 × 5

   (a) Nuclear fission and fusion,

   (b) TV transmission and reception,

   (c) Feedback amplifier,

   (d) Modulation and demodulation of radio waves.